The Chemical Constitution
of Natural Fats

The Chemical Constitution of Natural Fats

T. P. HILDITCH

C.B.E., D.Sc. (Lond.), F.R.I.C., F.R.S.
Professor Emeritus in the University of Liverpool

P. N. WILLIAMS

M.Sc. (Liv.), F.R.I.C.
Formerly Divisional Research Manager, Unilever Ltd.

FOURTH EDITION

CHAPMAN & HALL

LONDON · 1964

First published in 1940, reprinted 1941
Second edition 1947, reprinted 1949
Third edition 1956
Fourth edition 1964
© 1964 by T. P. Hilditch and P. N. Williams
Printed in Great Britain by
Spottiswoode, Ballantyne & Co. Ltd
London & Colchester
Catalogue No. 4/225

Preface to the Fourth Edition

Since the first appearance of this book in 1940, revised editions have been published in 1947 and in 1956. At the time of this last (Third) Edition, determination of component fatty acids by gas–liquid chromatography was in its infancy but in the following years it has become of great value and abundant use; in study of component glycerides in natural fats, partial (selective) hydrolysis of triglycerides by pancreatic lipase has similarly proved a most important technique, leading already to considerable fresh understanding of their structure; whilst knowledge of the mechanisms operative in the biosynthesis of (saturated) higher fatty acids has been much enlarged. These three topics, with the discovery of a number of natural fatty acids, especially conjugated unsaturated acids which had not previously been characterised, have again necessitated a major revision during the preparation of the present Fourth Edition.

Meanwhile the main objective of this volume remains as outlined in the Preface to the First Edition: "a monograph on the natural fats in such a form that their inter-relationships as a group of naturally occurring organic compounds should be developed as completely as possible, and without primary reference either to their physiological functions or to their technical applications". Whilst much discussion of the biological relationships of natural fats is included as a matter of course, and whilst specific references are also made to the particular uses, edible or technical, of not a few of the fats usually employed in either of these respects, attention is predominantly focussed upon their specific *chemical constitution.*

The number and variety of natural fats from both vegetable and animal sources becomes increasingly bewildering, and the reader is strongly recommended to study carefully the general outline given in the "Introductory Survey of the Natural Fats" (Chapter I) in order to obtain a true idea of the scope of the subject.

Many fresh records of the component acids of fats have been added to the tables of data in Chapters II, III and IV. The advance of knowledge in this fundamentally important branch of the subject since this book first appeared in 1940 is illustrated by the following approximate figures:

COMPONENT ACIDS OF FATS FROM	1st EDITION 1940	3rd EDITION 1956	PRESENT EDITION 1964
Plant species	400	600	900
Land animal species	80	200	300
Aquatic animal species	100	200	250
	580	1000	1450

It was pointed out in the Preface to the Third Edition that "many authors persist in publishing fat component acid figures as percentages of fatty acids in

v

the original *fat*, or as percentages of 'glycerides' in the original fat, instead of as a percentage of the total fatty acids present, which is the only rational basis of comparison". This bad practice has continued to be followed by many (but not all) of the contributors of results which have appeared since the last edition was published. These results, when not ignored, have been too numerous to warrant the time and trouble needed to convert them (as was done in the earlier editions of the book) to the correctly comparative *percentages of each acid in the total component acids*; to this extent, therefore, some of the recent results now added are not fully comparable with the rest.

The arrangement of the large main tables of component acids of vegetable fats in Chapter IV has been improved by placing each of these tables at the end of the text of the sub-section of fats which it covers. To facilitate reference, the bibliographical references to the items in these tables now immediately follow each table (instead of being placed at the end of the chapter).

Major revisions have been required in several of the later chapters, some of which have been largely rewritten. Recent developments in the experimental study and in the understanding of the structure of natural glycerides have been fully considered in the general survey of this subject (Chapter V). The important recent advances in study of some of the biosynthetic processes whereby carbohydrates are transformed *in vivo* into fats *via* the intermediaries of C_2 (or C_3) units, and the intervention of acetyl- (or malonyl-) co-enzyme A, have led to major alterations in Chapter VIII. The section in Chapter X on synthetic glycerides has been much abbreviated and is now confined to the bearing of synthetical work on glycerides upon the configuration of the more important naturally-occurring members of this group. Finally, Chapter XI, dealing with experimental techniques used in quantitative studies of fats, has been completely rewritten. The very detailed treatment in previous editions of the older "ester-fractionation" procedure (now largely superseded by gas–liquid chromatography) has been much curtailed, and this chapter is now devoted very largely to accounts (necessarily somewhat brief) of the various chromatographic methods which are finding increasing use and value in the investigation of natural fats.

There is still abundant scope for much additional factual information on the detailed composition of individual component acids and component glycerides in natural fats. Some suggestions of the chief lacunae in our knowledge of these are given at the end of the introductory Chapter I (p. 24).

A detailed list of the contents of the book follows this preface, while attention should be drawn to the five indexes at the conclusion of the book. The first of these is a general subject index from which individual fats, fatty acids and glycerides are excluded. Individual fats (and waxes) are indexed alphabetically in a separate index, which is followed by an index of botanical families mentioned in the text. There remain two more separate indexes, one of individual fatty acids and one of individual glycerides. Cursory and incidental references to individual fats, fatty acids or glycerides, which are very unlikely to be sought in the indexes, are for the most part not included therein; this applies especially to the almost continuous mention of the more common fatty acids. "Selective" indexing of this kind has its dangers, but we believe it is preferable to overloading the indexes with page numbers which will probably never be required.

Furthermore, the pages in which a topic or individual fat or fatty acid or glyceride is mainly discussed are indicated by numbers in **heavy type**; and pages where details of component acid* or of component glyceride† compositions will be found are distinguished respectively by asterisks or daggers (as indicated).

Our thanks are offered to Dr F. D. Gunstone and to Mr D. N. Grindley for allowing us to reproduce Figs. 9*a*, 9*b* and Fig. 13 respectively from their original papers; to the governing bodies and Editors of a number of Journals for permission to reproduce the following Figures: *Proceedings of the Royal Society* (Figs. 11, 12), *Journal of the Chemical Society* (Fig. 17), *Biochemical Journal* (Figs. 4, 14, 15), and *Journal of the Science of Food and Agriculture* (Figs. 13, 16); and to Dr R. V. Crawford, who prepared the drawings for the blocks of Figs. 5–8. We are much indebted to the Information Section of the Unilever Research Department, Port Sunlight, for access to some items of published information and to Messrs. Prices (Bromborough) Ltd., for permission to quote some information from their "Analysis of Fatty Acids and Fatty Alcohols" (1960) in connection with gas-liquid chromatographic analysis of fatty acids.

We are greatly indebted to Mrs T. P. Hilditch and Mrs P. N. Williams for much help in the preparation of the typescript and of the indexes, and in checking the proofs (especially the many tables and bibliographical references) of this fourth edition.

January 1964
                                                                T.P.H.
                                                                P.N.W.

Contents

I Introductory Survey of the Natural Fats *page* 1

GENERAL CONSIDERATIONS ON THE STUDY OF NATURAL
DERIVATIVES OF THE HIGHER FATTY ACIDS 2
THE COMPONENT ACIDS OF NATURAL FATS 6
THE COMPONENT GLYCERIDES OF NATURAL FATS 16
SCOPE FOR FURTHER RESEARCH IN THIS FIELD 24

II The Component Acids of Fats of Aquatic Flora and Fauna 26

FATS OF AQUATIC FLORA AND MICRO-FAUNA 27
FATS OF LARGER AQUATIC INVERTEBRATES 31
FATS OF FISH:
    Marine Elasmobranch fish (liver fats) 35
    Marine Teleostid fish (liver fats) 41
    Marine Teleostid fish (body fats) 45
    Freshwater fish 50
    Salmon 54
    Eel 56
    Sturgeon 58
    Tunny 59
    Groper 59
    South African marine fish 61
FATS OF MARINE MAMMALIA:
    Seal family 62
    Whale family 68
    Sperm whale family 72
    Dolphin and porpoise family 74
    Platypus 75

III The Component Acids of Fats of Land Animals 80

DEPOT FATS (GLYCERIDES) OF LAND ANIMALS:
    Invertebrata 81
    Insects 81
    Amphibia and reptiles 84
    Birds 86

Sea birds *page* 89
Bird eggs 90
Rodents 93
Herbivora 99
  Horse 102
  Ruminant animals 104
    Cause of high stearic acid content, etc., in ruminant fats 112
  Sheep, oxen, pigs (bone and hoof fats) 113
  Pigs 116
    Influence of dietary fats on pig depot fats 122
    Influence of dietary fats on depot fats of other animals 125
Carnivora and Omnivora 126
  Animal depot fats 127
  Human depot fats 128
Animal depot fats (Summary) 130
LIPIDS OF ANIMAL ORGANS: 132
  Liver glycerides 133
  Liver phosphatides 134
  Other animal organs 137
  Ox blood lipids 138
  Human blood lipids 140
MILK FATS: 143
  Cow milk fats 145
  Cow milk phosphatides 157
  Milk fats of other animals 158
  Human milk fat 162

IV   The Component Acids of Vegetable Fats 172
CRYPTOGAM FATS: 172
  Bacteria 172
  Yeasts 174
  Moulds and fungi 174
  Clubmoss 177
  Ferns 177
PHANEROGAM FATS: 177
  Leaf fats 180
  Bark and stem fats 183
  Root fats 185
  Lipids of petals and stamens 186
  Short-chain unsaturated acids in flowers and leaves 186
  Fruit fats: 187
    Fruit-coat fats (Table 57, p. 190) 189
    Palm oil (Table 57A, p. 194) 200

Olive oil (Table 57B, p. 196)   *page* 201
Seed fats   202
Seed fats major components linolenic, linoleic, oleic acids   206
Seed fats mainly linolenic-rich (Table 59, p. 213)   208
    Linseed oil (Table 59A, p. 210)   209
Seed fats mainly linoleic-rich (Table 60, p. 229)   218
    Safflower, sunflower, tobacco and niger seed oils (Tables 60A, 60B, pp. 222, 224)   221
Seed fats of the families Rosaceae, Euphorbiaceae and Cucurbitaceae (Table 61, p. 253)   243
    Candlenut and rubber seed oil (Table 61A, p. 246)   246
    Tung (China wood) oil (Table 61B, p. 247)   247
    Castor oil (Table 61C, p. 249)   248
    Stillingia oil (Table 61D, p. 251)   250
Seed fats major components palmitic, oleic, linoleic acids (Table 62, p. 268).   264
Seed fats of Gramineae (Table 63, p. 282)   280
Seed fats major components petroselinic, oleic, linoleic acids (Table 64, p. 287)   286
Seed fats major components tariric, isanic, ximenynic (ethynoid) acids   289
Seed fats major components chaulmoogric and/or hydnocarpic acids (Table 65, p. 293)   292
Seed fats major components erucic, oleic, linoleic acids (Table 66, p. 298)   295
Seed fats major components oleic, linoleic, arachidic, lignoceric acids (Table 67, p. 312)   304
Groundnut oil (Table 67A, p. 306)   305
Soya bean oil (Table 67B, p. 309)   309
Seed fats major components oleic, stearic, palmitic acids (Table 68, p. 324)   319
Seed fats major components lauric, myristic, (capric) acids (Table 69A, p. 335)   332
Seed fats of palm family (Table 69B, p. 341)   339
Seed fats, phosphatides   344
GENERAL CONCLUSIONS (VEGETABLE FATS)   348

V   The Component Glycerides of Natural Fats: General Survey   358

EARLY ATTEMPTS TO ISOLATE NATURAL GLYCERIDES BY CRYSTALLISATION   359
ISOLATION OF CHEMICALLY MODIFIED NATURAL GLYCERIDES   361
MODERN QUANTITATIVE STUDIES OF GLYCERIDE STRUCTURE   362

CONTENTS

I. Determination of fully saturated glycerides *page* 363
    Trisaturated glyceride contents of seed and fruit-coat fats 365
    Trisaturated glyceride contents of land animal depot and milk fats 368
II. Partial resolution of mixed glycerides of natural fats by crystallisation from solvents 372
III. Separation of glycerides by counter-current distribution between two immiscible solvents 383
IV. Separation of glycerides by chromatographic adsorption 385
V. Selective hydrolysis of triglycerides by pancreatic lipase 385

PRESENT KNOWLEDGE OF GLYCERIDE STRUCTURE OF NATURAL FATS 389

Glyceride structure of vegetable fats 390
    Seed fats with high proportions of simple trisaturated glycerides 393
    Seed fats with high proportions of simple triglycerides of polyethenoid C_{18} acids 394
    Selective attachment of oleo- and linoleo-groups in vegetable fats to the central glycerol hydroxyl group 396
    Configuration of seed and fruit-coat glycerides 402
    Optical rotatory power in natural fats 403
    Component acids of trisaturated glycerides present in small quantities in vegetable fats 403
Glyceride structure of animal fats 403
    Land animal depot fats 405
    Marine animal depot fats 409
    Land animal milk fats 410
    Marine animal milk fats 415

AN ALTERNATIVE VIEW OF GLYCERIDE STRUCTURE OF NATURAL FATS (KARTHA) 417

COMPUTATION OF COMPONENT GLYCERIDES IN A FAT FROM ITS COMPONENT ACIDS 419

VI   The Component Glycerides of Individual Vegetable Fats 424

SEED FATS OF THE PALMAE 424
SEED FATS OF THE LAURACEAE, MYRISTICACEAE AND SIMARU-BACEAE 425
SEED FATS CONTAINING 30–65 PER CENT. SATURATED ACIDS IN THEIR COMPONENT ACIDS 430
SEED FATS IN WHICH UNSATURATED ACIDS PREDOMINATE 446
    (i) Oleic-rich seed fats 447
    (ii) Seed fats rich in both oleic and linoleic acids 451
    (iii) Linoleic-rich seed fats 455
    (iv) Seed fats rich in linolenic acid 462

(v) Seed fats rich in conjugated tri- or tetra-ene acids *page* 468

FRUIT-COAT FATS 471

VII The Component Glycerides of Individual Animal Fats 481

MARINE ANIMAL FATS 481

LAND ANIMAL FATS 491

Depot fats:

Birds, rodents 491

Herbivora 493

Carnivora and Omnivora 495

"Stearic-rich" depot fats 497

Pig 498, 502

Ox, sheep, goat 500, 505

Neat's foot oil 505

Progressive alteration in glyceride structure of "stearic-rich"
animal fats 506

Computation of glycerides in "stearic-rich" depot fats 508

Milk fats:

Cow 510

Sheep, goat, camel, buffalo 514

Cow, buffalo (more detailed studies) 515

Human 524

VIII Some Aspects of the Biosynthesis of Fats 528

THE BIOSYNTHESIS OF FATS IN PLANTS 529

THE BIOSYNTHESIS OF FATS IN ANIMALS 541

Marine animal fats 544

Land animal fats 546

Liver fats 546

Reserve (depot) fats 546

Body temperature and composition of reserve fats 548

Milk fats 549

POSSIBLE MECHANISMS OF THE CONVERSION OF CARBOHY-
DRATES INTO FATS 552

Summary of older views 553

Biosynthesis of higher fatty acids from C_2 units 554

Coenzyme A, acetyl-Coenzyme A, malonyl-Coenzyme A 555

Biosynthesis of saturated fatty acids 557

Biosynthesis of unsaturated fatty acids 558

Biosynthesis of glycerol 562

ASSIMILATION OF PREFORMED FATS BY ANIMALS 564

Digestibility of ingested fats *page* 569
Fatty acids essential to growth or health 571

IX Constitution of Individual Natural Fatty Acids 578

NATURALLY OCCURRING SATURATED FATTY ACIDS 578
Syntheses of saturated acids 580
Properties of individual saturated acids 582
Natural odd-numbered and branched-chain saturated acids 585
NATURALLY OCCURRING UNSATURATED FATTY ACIDS 587
Oleic acid 589
*iso*Oleic acids 599
Syntheses of unsaturated fatty acids 600
  Oleic acid 600
  General methods of synthesis 602
Monoethenoid acids $CH_3.[CH_2]_7.CH:CH.[CH_2]_n.COOH$ 609
  Erucic acid 610
Cyclopropenyl derivatives of oleic acid 611
Monoethenoid acids $CH_3.[CH_2]_m.CH:CH.[CH_2]_7.COOH$ 612
  Hexadec-9-enoic (palmitoleic) acid 613
Hydroxy-unsaturated acids (including ricinoleic) 615
  Epoxy-oleic acids 617
Acids containing the structure$=C(H).[CH_2]_4.COOH$ 620
  Petroselinic, tariric acids 620
Chaulmoogric, hydnocarpic, gorlic acids 621
Other monoethenoid acids (including vaccenic) 623
Polyethenoid acids 625
  Linoleic and other octadecadienoic acids 626
  Linolenic and other octadecatrienoic acids 632
  Conjugated unsaturated seed fatty acids 634
    Elaeostearic acid 634
    Licanic acid 635
    Parinaric acid 636
    Isanic and ximenynic acids (containing ethynoid and ethenoid groups) 637
  Tri-, tetra-, penta-, hexa-ethenoid acids (Table 145, p. 640) 637
    Arachidonic acid 638
  Polyethenoid (and polyethynoid) acids not falling within the above groups 643
    Deca-2,4-dienoic acid 643

X Synthetic Glycerides: Naturally Occurring Fatty Alcohols: Acyl Ethers of Glycerol 658

SYNTHETIC GLYCERIDES 658

Monoglycerides *page* 661
Diglycerides 662
Triglycerides 663
SYNTHESES OF OPTICALLY ACTIVE GLYCEROL DERIVATIVES 665
NATURALLY OCCURRING HIGHER ALIPHATIC ALCOHOLS 666
Saturated alcohols (cetyl, etc.) 667
Unsaturated alcohols (oleyl, etc.) 669
GLYCERYL ETHERS (CHIMYL, BATYL AND SELACHYL ALCOHOLS) 670

XI **Notes on Experimental Techniques Employed in the Quantitative Investigation of Fats** 676

I. QUANTITATIVE INVESTIGATION OF COMPONENT FATTY ACIDS 678
Preliminary separation of mixed fatty acids 678
Separation of volatile and non-volatile acids 679
Separation of mixed acids by low temperature crystallisation from solvents 680
Separation of mixed acids as complexes with urea 683
Separation of mixed acids by chromatographic methods 684
Quantitative determination of component fatty acids 688
Fractional distillation of higher fatty acid esters in a vacuum 688
Calculation of composition of ester-fractions 694
Determination of certain polyethenoid acids by spectrophotometric methods 695
Determination of fatty acid composition by gas-liquid chromatography 697
II. QUANTITATIVE INVESTIGATION OF COMPONENT GLYCERIDES 700
Determination of fully-saturated glycerides 700
Preliminary resolution of fats by systematic crystallisation from solvents 701
Preliminary resolution of fats by partition between two immiscible solvents 705
Selective hydrolysis of triglycerides by pancreatic lipase 706
Determination of glyceride constitution by thin-layer chromatography 707

Indexes

GENERAL INDEX OF SUBJECTS 715
INDEX OF INDIVIDUAL FATS AND WAXES 723
INDEX OF PLANT FAMILIES 737
INDEX OF INDIVIDUAL FATTY ACIDS 739
INDEX OF INDIVIDUAL GLYCERIDES 743

CHAPTER I

Introductory Survey of the Natural Fats

This book is planned to give as complete an account as possible of the constitution of the lipids, more especially the glycerides, which are produced
naturally in plant and animal life. It is intended to treat the natural fats as
a group of organic chemical compounds, in exactly the same way as it has
been found helpful to have separate monographs dealing with other natural
groups such as, for example, carbohydrates, terpenes, or alkaloids. It follows
that the fats are considered, primarily, neither from the standpoint of their
utility as raw materials for any industrial purpose nor with regard to their
biochemical functions in the organisms in which they are produced. References
will, it is true, be found to these and other aspects in the course of the work; but
its first objective is the descriptive presentation of the organic chemistry of the
natural fats, so far as our present knowledge takes us.

It is probable that many readers will be already familiar with the subject
from the biochemical or the technological side; this circumstance warrants
some further explanations. First of all, it will be found that much less reference
than usual is made to the many "characteristics" of fats (whether physical,
such as density or refractivity, or chemical, such as saponification, acid, iodine
or acetyl values, etc.) which have been so widely elaborated and which are
indispensable in the routine or rapid characterisation, and even determination,
of fatty materials in technical practice. This is because these "characteristics",
applied to an entire fat, give in general merely average figures which by no
means serve to indicate its detailed composition (although saponification
equivalents, iodine values, and occasionally other analytical characteristics,
are indispensable in collecting the detailed experimental data upon which
knowledge of the chemical structure of fats is ultimately based). The individual
fats discussed in this book, with few exceptions, have been investigated so far
that the proportions of the separate component acids, and frequently the chief
component glycerides, can be stated with some degree of accuracy; and for the
most part the compositions of the fats are given in these forms alone. Many
tables illustrating the component acids present in natural fats have been
included in the book, and it might have been interesting to have incorporated
some of the more important physical and chemical analytical "characteristics"
of each fat mentioned. To do so would, however, have greatly increased the
size and complexity of these tables (already cumbersome enough). To add
separate compilations of the customary analytical characteristics would also
have involved considerable increase in the size of the volume and, since full
details of the analytical characteristics of individual fats have been collected in

1   1

a number of excellent technological or general treatises on fats, it seemed unnecessary to repeat them in a work which is primarily a guide to the chemical structure of natural fats and is concerned only with the data relevant thereto.

In the next place, the arrangement of this volume may be found unusual. Logically, perhaps, the individual fatty acids, their properties and constitutions, should be discussed before proceeding to their combined forms, the glycerides, etc., whilst the experimental and analytical methods employed in the elucidation of their composition should also precede the essential part of the work. It is a great advantage, on the other hand, to come to the main business of the book as soon as possible; and since most readers are doubtless familiar with the fundamental chemistry of the fatty acids, it has been thought feasible to attempt this. The chapters immediately following therefore deal at once with the component acids and glycerides which have been found to occur throughout the vegetable and animal kingdoms, without undue detail as to the evidence upon which, for example, the constitution of any particular fatty acid is based. Later in the book, however, chapters will be found in which the constitution and specific features of individual fatty acids are considered, and in which accounts are given of the chief experimental and analytical methods referred to in the more general portion of the work.

SOME GENERAL CONSIDERATIONS ON THE STUDY OF NATURAL DERIVATIVES OF THE HIGHER FATTY ACIDS

Unanimity has not yet been reached in the terminology to be adopted in classifying the various types of naturally occurring compounds in which higher fatty acids are present. Even a collective title for the whole group is not completely settled. These types are broadly as follows:

(I) *Compounds containing only carbon, hydrogen, and oxygen:*

  (i) Esters of higher fatty acids with glycerol (triglycerides).

  (ii) Esters of higher fatty acids with alcohols other than glycerol (higher aliphatic alcohols, sterols, etc.).

(II) *Compounds containing other elements (phosphorus, nitrogen) in addition to carbon, hydrogen and oxygen:*

  (i) Compounds containing glycerophosphoric acid coupled with a nitrogen base or with inositol (phospholipids).

  (ii) Compounds derived from the long-chain hydroxy-amino alcohol sphingosine (sphingolipids):

   (*a*) phosphoric acid derivatives (sphingomyelin);

   (*b*) not containing phosphorus (cerebrosides).

In the present book the terms used have the following significance:

Lipids. The collective title for the whole group of natural products in which the higher fatty acids are present as essential components.

Fats. Natural triglycerides, solid or liquid.

Waxes (type I (ii)). These will be most frequently referred to as ester-waxes or, more specifically, as sterol, higher aliphatic alcohol, etc., esters.

Phospholipids or Phosphatides. Derivatives of α-glycerophosphoric acid in which the two

2

remaining hydroxyl groups of the glycerol are combined with higher fatty acids (as in glycerides), whilst the phosphoryl group is united as an ester with:

(a) a nitrogen base which may be choline (*phosphatidyl choline*, lecithin), ethanolamine (*phosphatidyl ethanolamine*), or serine (*phosphatidyl serine*):

$$CH_2.(O.CO.R').CH(O.CO.R'').CH_2.O.PO(OH).O—B,$$

where R' and R'' are higher fatty acid groups and B is the nitrogenous base;

(b) the cyclic hexose inositol (*phosphoinositides*).

Phosphatidic acids. Glycerophosphoric acid derivatives of the structure

$$CH_2(O.CO.R').CH(O.CO.R'').CH_2.O.PO(OH)_2,$$

or their metallic (calcium, magnesium) salts.

Plasmalogens. Glycerophosphoric acid derivatives of the structure

$$CH_2(O.CH:CH.R').CH(O.CO.R'').CH_2.O.PO(OH).O—B,$$

where the group R'.CH:CH.O— is a vinyl ether derivative of a higher fatty acid (with R'' and B as in the phosphatides above).

Sphingolipids. In these lipids the fatty acids are present as amido-derivatives of the unsaturated C_{18} alcohol *sphingosine*, 1,3-dihydroxy-2-amino-octadec-4-ene:

$$CH_3.[CH_2]_{12}.CH:CH.CH(OH).CH(NH.CO.R).CH_2OH.$$

In *sphingomyelins* the terminal, primary alcoholic group is combined with a phosphoryl choline ester (as in glycerophosphatides):

$$CH_3.[CH_2]_{12}.CH:CH.CH(OH).CH(NH.CO.R).$$
$$CH_2.O.PO(OH).O.CH_2.CH_2.N(CH_3)_3.OH.$$

In the *cerebrosides* the sphingosine is present in the form of a glycoside of a hexose (usually galactose but sometimes also glucose):

$$CH_3.[CH_2]_{12}.CH:CH.CH(OH).CH(NH.CO.R).CH_2.O.(C_6H_{11}O_5).$$

In this book attention is focussed on the natural fats (triglycerides) and some ester-waxes (higher fatty acid esters of higher fatty alcohols), but in addition some notice is given to the component acids present in phospholipids when the latter accompany the glycerides in specific tissues and organs. The complete chemistry of the phospholipids and the sphingolipids, however, falls beyond the scope of this volume, and for a full account of lipids which include phosphorus and/or nitrogen or carbohydrate groups in their molecules the reader is recommended to consult works on the general biochemistry of lipids (such as those of Deuel[1] or Lovern[2]), or monographs on specific lipid groups such as the phospholipids (Wittcoff,[3] Desnuelle[4]), the sterols (Bergmann[5]), etc.

The constitution of the fats (triglycerides), or for that matter of the ester-waxes or of the phosphatides, may be considered in two distinct ways, namely: (i) with respect to the amounts of the various individual esters present, or (ii) with reference to the proportions of the various *fatty acids* which are present in combination in the natural product as a whole. We may with advantage here confine the discussion to the fats or triglycerides themselves. Very few natural fats have been found to contain only two or even three different acids united with glycerol; more usually five, six, or seven such acids are present and this number may often be much exceeded. Many common fats, notably milk fats and the fats of fishes, contain a dozen or more component acids. If it were the invariable rule that each natural triglyceride molecule contained only one species of fatty acid (e.g. triolein, tripalmitin), there would be no need for the distinction just mentioned. Expressed on a molar (not weight) percentage basis,* the proportions of component fatty acids and of component glycerides would be the same. Most unfortunately, this is exactly what does *not* happen in nature. As will be seen later, the overwhelming tendency is towards the production of mixed triglycerides,† in which at least two, and often three, species of fatty acids are combined; simple triglycerides (i.e., triglycerides containing three identical acyl groups) are the exception, and are only produced, apparently, when no other course is open. It therefore follows that the proportions of the component acids in a natural fat, and those of its component glycerides, are by no means the same thing; and accordingly we have to differentiate at the outset between the *component fatty acids* and the *component glycerides* present in a fat.

Here and there (especially in vegetable seed fats), some natural fats, or fats from a group of biologically related organisms, are found to contain in combination some particular fatty acid which is rarely or never found elsewhere in nature; but this is on the whole decidedly exceptional. The general case is that a few higher fatty acids occur continually throughout nature. The consequence is that the differences between one fat and another depend very largely on the varying proportions of the fatty acids in combination in the different fats, as well as upon the particular acids which happen to be components. The study of the natural fats is therefore somewhat differently placed from that of many other groups of naturally occurring organic compounds in that it must be conducted on a quantitative, rather than solely upon a qualitative, basis. Accepting the necessity for quantitative treatment of the subject, we may therefore consider, as has already been said, either the proportions of the *component triglycerides* in a fat, or of the *component acids* in the total fatty acids present in combination with glycerol.

A practical difficulty next presents itself: whilst the component acids of a fat or other natural lipid can be determined quantitatively with a considerable degree of accuracy (frequently to within, at all events, one unit per cent. of the

---

* The molar composition is frequently more informative than composition by weight in discussing the fats, because it expresses the relative number of molecules of each type of acid, or component glyceride, present in a fat. The difference in the two modes of expression becomes especially significant when fatty acids of widely different molecular weight are present in the same fat. Thus, for instance, the presence of 3 per cent. by weight of butyric acid in the mixed acids of butter fat really means that, out of every 100 mols. of fatty acids, about 10 mols. are butyric acid.

The composition of natural fatty acids being so familiar in the form of weight-percentages, this mode is used to a considerable extent in this book. In many cases, however, it is desirable (as in the milk fats mentioned) to present the facts on a molecular basis of comparison; and in quantitative work on component glycerides this is indeed the only rational course.

† It is unfortunate, from this point of view, to express the composition of a fat (from its detailed fatty acid analysis) as "glycerides of oleic acid", "glycerides of palmitic acid", etc., etc. The only logical and comparable method is to give, in the first place, the component acids as a *percentage* (*wt. or mol.*) *of the total fatty acids present*.

total fatty acids), the quantitative determination of the individual component glycerides in a fat is a matter of much greater difficulty. At present, indeed, fats in which the component glycerides have been determined in anything approaching full detail form only a very small proportion of those for which we have accurate measures of their component fatty acids. Our knowledge of the individual glycerides present in many natural fats is therefore still far from complete. A good deal of knowledge of the general build of the mixed glycerides in the more important groups of natural fats is becoming available, but we cannot yet (except in a very few cases) define the nature and proportion of each individual mixed glyceride present with anything approaching the accuracy with which it is possible to state the total proportions of each fatty acid present in combination in the whole fat.

Nevertheless it has so far become evident that the mode of union – or interweaving, as it were – of the fatty acids in a natural triglyceride is fundamentally similar in wide sectors of both vegetable and animal kingdoms. In other words, the kinds and proportions of the individual fatty acids combined in a fat often seem to have little influence upon the general mode of construction or assembly of the acids into triglycerides; the latter are assembled on principles which operate, to a considerable degree, independently of the particular fatty acids which happen to be present.

On the other hand, the amounts and kinds of the component fatty acids in natural fats vary extremely widely, whilst, as we shall see, these variations run strikingly parallel in most cases with the biological sources of the materials. A great amount of information becomes available, therefore, by consideration of the composition of the total fatty acids, as distinct from the component glycerides. For the reasons which have already been given, the natural fats are considered in detail in this book, first of all, with reference to their *component fatty acids* (Chapters II–IV) and, subsequently, in terms of what is known of their *component glycerides* (Chapters V–VII). Similarly, in endeavouring to present a preliminary survey of the whole field in the present chapter, we shall consider the subject first with reference to the component acids and then with reference to glyceride structure.

The rather impressive rate at which new studies of the *component acids* of natural fats have been made since this book was first published in 1940 is well indicated by tabulating the approximate numbers of species of which the component acids were recorded in the first (1940), third (1956) and present (1964) editions:

	1940	1956	1964
Vegetable fats	400	600	900
Land animal fats	80	200	300
Aquatic animal fats	100	200	250

These figures also illustrate how much less attention has been given to collecting comprehensive data for fats from different animal species than to those from vegetable sources, whilst the latter are of course only an exceedingly small fraction of the total number of plant species.

Studies of *component glycerides* have so far been made on the fats of a very much smaller number of species – probably about 80–100 vegetable fats and only about 20 animal fats.

THE COMPONENT ACIDS OF NATURAL FATS

Before discussing the fatty acids as found in combination in different groups of organisms, vegetable and animal, a few introductory remarks of a general character on the individual naturally occurring fatty acids may be useful. To maintain a correct perspective, it is essential to recognise that **oleic acid** (*cis*-octadec-9-enoic acid, $CH_3.[CH_2]_7.CH:CH.[CH_2]_7.COOH$) is undoubtedly the most widespread of all natural fatty acids; in very many fats it forms more than 30 per cent. of the total fatty acids, and up to the present it has been found absent from no natural fat or phosphatide. The most common constituent of all natural fats is thus an unsaturated (mono-ethenoid), normal aliphatic acid with a content of eighteen carbon atoms and the unsaturated linking between the ninth and tenth carbon atoms of the chain. It has lately been demonstrated that in vegetable fats oleic acid (in so far as its proportion of the total fatty acids permits) is selectively present in combination with the central (2- or β-) hydroxyl group of the glycerol molecule – a feature which has important implications in regard to their glyceride structure, and may also prove informative in connection with the biosynthesis of seed fat glycerides.

Many other unsaturated acids, mono- or poly-ethenoid, are also found in fats, and of these quite a number have features of chemical structure which bear similarity, close or remote, to that of oleic acid. Other unsaturated acids, however, seem to be quite different from oleic acid and its structurally related acids in the arrangement of their unsaturated linkings. None of the other unsaturated acids is so uniformly distributed, or so prominent as a whole, in natural fats as oleic acid; but two at least appear to be nearly as ubiquitous, namely, octadeca-9,12-dienoic acid (**linoleic acid** or related forms), $CH_3.[CH_2]_4.CH:CH.CH_2.CH:CH.[CH_2]_7.COOH$, and hexadec-9-enoic (palmitoleic, zoomaric) acid, $CH_3.[CH_2]_5.CH:CH.[CH_2]_7.COOH$.

The corresponding saturated normal aliphatic acids are, of course, also widely distributed in natural fats. Here the characteristic member of the group is undoubtedly **palmitic acid**, $CH_3.[CH_2]_{14}.COOH$; this acid occurs prominently in very many fats, to which it may contribute from 15 to 50 per cent. of the total fatty acids whilst, like oleic acid, it is completely absent from extremely few, if any, of the natural fats. Whilst a number of other natural saturated higher fatty acids are found in nature, probably only myristic and stearic acids, $C_{13}H_{27}.COOH$ and $C_{17}H_{35}.COOH$, approach palmitic acid in ubiquity of distribution; of neither of these, however, can it be said that they are invariably present in natural fats. Stearic acid, of course, is a very familiar acid, and is often erroneously stated to be typical of the natural saturated acids (as oleic undoubtedly is of the unsaturated group). Actually, it is only found in high proportions (25 per cent. or more of the total fatty acids) in the seed fats of a few tropical families of plants and in the depot fats of some specific families of land animals; its prominence in ox and sheep depot fats doubtless caused the impression that it was as abundant in nature as oleic acid.*

It should be added here that with the exception of *iso*valeric acid (found only in the depot fats of the dolphin and porpoise), and sterculic and malvalic acids (present in only a few seed fats), all natural glyceridic fatty acids, saturated or unsaturated, and present in more than trace proportions, contain even numbers and unbranched (normal) chains of carbon atoms in their molecules.† It may also be mentioned that, when one saturated acid is present in fairly large amount, subsidiary proportions of the natural saturated acids next higher and lower in the homologous series are often also observed. Thus, just as myristic and stearic acids are usually present in subsidiary amounts when palmitic is a major component acid, so, in those tropical seed fats in which, as mentioned, stearic acid is prominent there is also almost always a small amount of arachidic acid, $C_{19}H_{39}.COOH$, as well as palmitic acid.

The chief acids found, as major or minor components, in natural fats are listed on pp. 8, 9 to facilitate reference in the remainder of this chapter. This list of naturally occurring fatty acids is not complete; other unsaturated acids, sometimes with markedly unusual constitutive features, have been and are being steadily added to those already recognised in natural fats. All the acids mentioned in this introductory survey are, however, included, and details of all the known natural fatty acids will be given in Chapter IX (pp. 578–644).

Having cleared the ground by the explanatory matter in the preceding pages, we can now proceed to consider, from a broad point of view, the distribution of fatty acids in the numerous varieties of natural fats. As will be already evident, the proportion of any single acid in the total acids of a fat is widely variable, sometimes very great, in other cases quite small. It is convenient to group the acids of any fat into two rough categories: *major component acids* and *minor component acids*. As employed by the authors, these terms are not interpreted by any means rigidly; a "major component acid" is defined as one which may form anything from about 10 per cent. upwards of the total fatty acids combined in a fat. At first glance, of course, a constituent contributing only 10 per cent. of the whole may appear misnamed as a "major" component; but when it is remembered that many fats include ten or more different acids in their glycerides it will be seen that the presence of one acid to the extent of more than about 10 per cent. frequently means that it may be one of several chief components.

The chief utility of roughly sorting out the component acids of fats into these two groups is that we then perceive at once that, in very many instances, fats

---

* Boekenoogen[6] has statistically surveyed the distribution of fatty acids in world-wide commercial vegetable fats. From his calculations it would appear that the percentage distribution of each fatty acid is as follows: oleic 34, linoleic 29, palmitic 11, lauric 7, linolenic 6, myristic 3, erucic 3, stearic 3, and all others 4 per cent. Whilst these data are not valid for the complete range and output of seed and fruit coat fats, and do not take into account the fats produced in aquatic and land animals, they are of interest as an illustration of the general trend of specific fatty acid production in a sector of the vegetable kingdom.

† Traces of a number of odd-numbered and of branched-chain acids have, however, been observed in many animal fats, especially those of ruminants and related genera.

SATURATED ACIDS, $C_nH_{2n}O_2$ or $C_mH_{2m+1}.COOH$

MOLECULAR FORMULA	COMMON NAME	SYSTEMATIC NAME	STRUCTURAL FORMULA
$C_4H_8O_2$	Butyric	n-Butanoic	$CH_3.[CH_2]_2.COOH$
$C_5H_{10}O_2$	iso-Valeric	3-Methyl-n-butanoic	$(CH_3)_2.CH.CH_2.COOH$
$C_6H_{12}O_2$	Caproic	n-Hexanoic	$CH_3.[CH_2]_4.COOH$
$C_8H_{16}O_2$	Caprylic	n-Octanoic	$CH_3.[CH_2]_6.COOH$
$C_{10}H_{20}O_2$	Capric	n-Decanoic	$CH_3.[CH_2]_8.COOH$
$C_{12}H_{24}O_2$	Lauric	n-Dodecanoic	$CH_3.[CH_2]_{10}.COOH$
$C_{14}H_{28}O_2$	Myristic	n-Tetradecanoic	$CH_3.[CH_2]_{12}.COOH$
$C_{16}H_{32}O_2$	Palmitic	n-Hexadecanoic	$CH_3.[CH_2]_{14}.COOH$
$C_{18}H_{36}O_2$	Stearic	n-Octadecanoic	$CH_3.[CH_2]_{16}.COOH$
$C_{20}H_{40}O_2$	Arachidic	n-Eicosanoic	$CH_3.[CH_2]_{18}.COOH$
$C_{22}H_{44}O_2$	Behenic	n-Docosanoic	$CH_3.[CH_2]_{20}.COOH$
$C_{24}H_{48}O_2$	Lignoceric	n-Tetracosanoic	$CH_3.[CH_2]_{22}.COOH$
$C_{26}H_{52}O_2$	"Cerotic"	n-Hexacosanoic	$CH_3.[CH_2]_{24}.COOH$

UNSATURATED ACIDS

Mono-ethenoid acids, $C_nH_{2n-2}O_2$ or $C_mH_{2m-1}.COOH$

MOLECULAR FORMULA	COMMON NAME	SYSTEMATIC NAME	STRUCTURAL FORMULA
$C_{10}H_{18}O_2$		Dec-9-enoic	$CH_2{:}CH.[CH_2]_7.COOH†$
$C_{12}H_{22}O_2$		Dodec-9-enoic	$CH_3.CH_2.CH{:}CH.[CH_2]_7.COOH†$
$C_{14}H_{26}O_2$		Tetradec-5-enoic	$CH_3.[CH_2]_7.CH{:}CH.[CH_2]_3.COOH†$
$C_{14}H_{26}O_2$		Tetradec-9-enoic	$CH_3.[CH_2]_3.CH{:}CH.[CH_2]_7.COOH†$
$C_{16}H_{30}O_2$	Palmitoleic, zoomaric	Hexadec-9-enoic	$CH_3.[CH_2]_5.CH{:}CH.[CH_2]_7.COOH$
$C_{18}H_{34}O_2$	Oleic	Octadec-9-enoic	$CH_3.[CH_2]_7.CH{:}CH.[CH_2]_7.COOH$
$C_{18}H_{34}O_2$	Petroselinic	Octadec-6-enoic	$CH_3.[CH_2]_{10}.CH{:}CH.[CH_2]_4.COOH$
$C_{18}H_{34}O_3$	Ricinoleic	12-Hydroxy-octadec-9-enoic	$CH_3.[CH_2]_5.CH(OH).CH_2.CH{:}CH.[CH_2]_7.COOH†$
$C_{18}H_{34}O_3$		9-Hydroxy-octadec-12-enoic	$CH_3.[CH_2]_4.CH{:}CH.[CH_2]_2.CH(OH).[CH_2]_7.COOH†$
$C_{18}H_{32}O_3$	Vernolic	12,13-Epoxy-octadec-9-enoic	$CH_3.[CH_2]_4.CH{:}CH.CH{-}CH.[CH_2]_7.COOH†$ (epoxide, O bridge)
$C_{19}H_{34}O_2$	Sterculic	8-(2-n-octylcycloprop-1-enyl)octanoic	$CH_3.[CH_2]_7.C{:}C.[CH_2]_7.COOH†$ (CH_2 bridge)
$C_{20}H_{38}O_2$	Gadoleic	Eicos-9-enoic	$CH_3.[CH_2]_9.CH{:}CH.[CH_2]_7.COOH†$
$C_{20}H_{38}O_2$		Eicos-11-enoic	$CH_3.[CH_2]_7.CH{:}CH.[CH_2]_9.COOH†$
$C_{22}H_{42}O_2$	Cetoleic	Docos-11-enoic	$CH_3.[CH_2]_9.CH{:}CH.[CH_2]_9.COOH$
$C_{22}H_{42}O_2$	Erucic	Docos-13-enoic	$CH_3.[CH_2]_7.CH{:}CH.[CH_2]_{11}.COOH†$
$C_{24}H_{46}O_2$	Selacholeic, nervonic	Tetracos-15-enoic	$CH_3.[CH_2]_7.CH{:}CH.[CH_2]_{13}.COOH†$
$C_{26}H_{50}O_2$	Ximenic	Hexacos-17-enoic	$CH_3.[CH_2]_7.CH{:}CH.[CH_2]_{15}.COOH†$
$C_{30}H_{58}O_2$	Lumequic	Triacont-21-enoic	$CH_3.[CH_2]_7.CH{:}CH.[CH_2]_{19}.COOH†$

Mono-ethynoid acid, $C_nH_{2n-4}O_2$ or $C_mH_{2m-3}.COOH$

	Tariric	Octadec-6-ynoic	$CH_3.[CH_2]_{10}.C{:}C.[CH_2]_4.COOH$

8

Mono-ethenoid-ethynyloid acid, $C_nH_{2n-10}O_2$ or C_mH_{2m-9}.COOH

Formula	Name	Systematic name	Structure
$C_{18}H_{26}O_2$	Isanic, erythrogenic	Octadec-17-en-9,11-di-ynoic	$CH_2:CH.[CH_2]_4.C\vdots C.C\vdots C.[CH_2]_7.COOH†$

Cyclic unsaturated acids, $C_nH_{2n-4}O_2$ or C_mH_{2m-3}.COOH

Formula	Name	Systematic name	Structure
$C_{16}H_{28}O_2$	Hydnocarpic	11-cycloPent-2-enyl-n-undecanoic	(ring: CH=CH / CH$_2$–CH$_2$) >CH.[CH$_2$]$_{10}$.COOH
$C_{18}H_{32}O_2$	Chaulmoogric	13-cycloPent-2-enyl-n-tridecanoic	(ring: CH=CH / CH$_2$–CH$_2$) >CH.[CH$_2$]$_{12}$.COOH
$C_{18}H_{30}O_2$	Gorlic	13-cycloPent-2-enyl-n-tridec-6-enoic	(ring: CH=CH / CH$_2$–CH$_2$) >CH.[CH$_2$]$_6$.CH:CH.[CH$_2$]$_4$.COOH

Di-ethenoid acids, $C_nH_{2n-4}O_2$ or C_mH_{2m-3}.COOH

Formula	Name	Systematic name	Structure
$C_{18}H_{32}O_2$	Linoleic	Octadeca-9,12-dienoic	$CH_3.[CH_2]_4.CH:CH.CH_2.CH:CH.[CH_2]_7.COOH†$

Tri-ethenoid acids, $C_nH_{2n-6}O_2$ or C_mH_{2m-5}.COOH

Formula	Name	Systematic name	Structure
$C_{16}H_{26}O_2$	Hiragonic	Hexadeca-6,10,14-trienoic	$CH_3.CH:CH.CH_2.CH_2.CH:CH.[CH_2]_2.CH:CH.[CH_2]_4COOH$
$C_{18}H_{30}O_2$	Linolenic	Octadeca-9,12,15-trienoic	$CH_3.CH_2.CH:CH.CH_2.CH:CH.CH_2.CH:CH.[CH_2]_7.COOH†$
$C_{18}H_{30}O_2$	Eleeostearic	Octadeca-6,9,12,-trienoic	$CH_3.[CH_2]_4.CH:CH.CH_2.CH:CH.CH_2.CH:CH.[CH_2]_4.COOH$
$C_{18}H_{30}O_2$	Licanic	Octadeca-9,11,13-trienoic	$CH_3.[CH_2]_3.CH:CH.CH:CH.CH:CH.[CH_2]_7.COOH†$
$C_{18}H_{28}O_3$		4-Keto-octadeca-9,11,13-trienoic	$CH_3.[CH_2]_3.CH:CH.CH:CH.CH:CH.[CH_2]_4.CO.[CH_2]_2.COOH†$

Poly-ethenoid acids

(i) TETRA-ETHENOID

Formula	Name	Systematic name	Structure
$C_{16}H_{24}O_2$		Hexadecatetraenoic	
$C_{18}H_{28}O_2$	Parinaric	Octadeca-9,11,13,15-tetraenoic	$CH_3.CH_2.[CH:CH]_4.[CH_2]_7.COOH†$
$C_{18}H_{28}O_2$	Stearidonic	Octadecatetraenoic	
$C_{20}H_{32}O_2$	Arachidonic	Eicosa-5,8,11,14-tetraenoic	$CH_3.[CH_2]_4.CH:CH.CH_2.CH:CH.CH_2.CH:CH.CH_2.CH:CH.[CH_2]_3.COOH$
(?) $C_{22}H_{36}O_2$		Docosatetraenoic	

(ii) PENTA-ETHENOID

Formula	Name	Systematic name
$C_{20}H_{30}O_2$	"Clupanodonic"	Eicosapentaenoic
$C_{22}H_{34}O_2$	Shibic	Docosapentaenoic
$C_{26}H_{42}O_2$		Hexacosapentaenoic

(iii) HEXA-ETHENOID

Formula	Name	Systematic name
$C_{22}H_{32}O_2$	Nisinic	Docosahexaenoic
$C_{24}H_{36}O_2$	Thynnic	Tetracosahexaenoic
$C_{26}H_{40}O_2$		Hexacosahexaenoic

The structural formulæ of the unsaturated acids to which a † is attached indicate that such acids possess one or more points of constitutive resemblance to oleic acid.

9

from organisms which have been classed together from morphological and anatomical considerations by biologists share the same fatty acids as major components; so that we reach the important conclusions that natural fats may to a large extent be classified according to their major component acids, and that such a grouping follows fairly closely that already developed from biological considerations for the parent organisms. Although such classification of natural fats rests chiefly on their major component acids, there are quite a number of cases wherein a minor component acid is as characteristic as the major components for a particular group of fats. This is not so general as the relationships observed in the major component acids of most fats, but is occasionally of importance in defining the similarities in one or other group. The minor component acids which are thus, as it were, as definitely characteristic of a natural fat-group as some of the major components are, for the most part, those acids which (either as major or minor components) pervade the whole range of natural fats. Two simple instances may be given. In seed fats of the families Cruciferæ, Umbelliferæ, and some others palmitic acid (which is in most fats a "major component" forming 10 per cent. or more of the total fatty acids) only amounts to 2–3 per cent. of the total fatty acids, but it is found quite regularly in this proportion in different seed fats of these families and is clearly a characteristic, although a minor, component of the fats in question. Similarly, hexadecenoic acid, which is relatively abundant in fats of aquatic origin, is present as a definitely minor, but quite characteristic, component of the depot and the milk fats of the higher land mammals, where it amounts to only about 3 per cent. of the total fatty acids.

It has been the custom, in treatises on this subject, to commence the descriptive account of natural fats with those produced in the seeds of vegetable plants – probably because of frequent relative simplicity in the component fatty acid mixtures encountered in this group. The detailed data which have been gathered in steadily increasing numbers during the past three or four decades have emphasised the fact, already mentioned, that natural fats tend to align themselves, by their component acids, in groups according to their biological origin, and have also revealed that, to put the matter in a few words, the fats of the simplest and most primitive organisms are usually made up from a very complex mixture of fatty acids whilst, as biological development has proceeded, the chief component acids of the fats of the higher organisms have become fewer in number. In the animal kingdom this change in type is remarkably progressive and culminates, in the depot fats of the higher land mammals, in fats in which oleic, palmitic and stearic acids are the major components. In vegetable seed fats, as a rule, similar simplicity is seen in the major component acids but here, in a number of families, fatty acids are found which apparently occur nowhere else in nature.

It was suggested by one of the present authors in 1934–1935 (in a Jubilee Memorial Lecture to the Society of Chemical Industry[7]) that "perhaps, when in the course of time sufficiently wide and detailed data have been collected, systematic description of the natural fats will commence with those of the minute aquatic flora and fauna, will proceed to those of the larger aquatic denizens, and then to the two respective branches of land flora and land fauna." Since then many further data have been published, all of which add to the force of the argument that the logical sequence of a descriptive account of the natural fats is to take them, as nearly as may be, in the order of evolutionary development of their parent organisms.

The chapters which immediately follow are therefore devoted, in that order, to detailed accounts of the component acids of the fats of aquatic flora and fauna, of land animals, and of land plants. In the next few paragraphs we proceed to give, from this standpoint, a brief general survey of natural fats. **Component acids of fats of aquatic origin.** All fats of aquatic origin contain a typically wide range of combined fatty acids, mainly of the unsaturated series. The unsaturated acids include those containing 16, 18, 20, and 22 carbon atoms in the molecule (conveniently referred to as unsaturated C_{16}, C_{18}, C_{20}, and C_{22} acids) in varying, but major proportions and in different states of unsaturation; the only major component saturated acid is palmitic acid (usually 10–18 per cent. of the total acids). Myristic and stearic acid (the latter rarely exceeding 1–2 per cent.) are often present in minor proportions, as also may be unsaturated C_{14} and even C_{24} acids. The proportions of the major component unsaturated acids vary considerably, however, in the fats of different kinds of marine organisms.

Perhaps the most prominent differences are in the component fatty acids of fats from sea-water life on the one hand and freshwater life on the other. In fats from all freshwater life, plant or animal, small or large, the type appears to be much the same, the component acids being relatively rich in unsaturated C_{16} and C_{18} acids, with low contents of those of the C_{20} and C_{22} series (the latter often being minimal); the unsaturated C_{16} acids frequently form 30 per cent. or more of the total fatty acids. Whilst the relative proportions of the four groups of unsaturated acids are of the same order throughout all fats from freshwater flora or fauna so far studied, minor differences are noticeable in the degree of unsaturation, and also in the extent to which the acids are combined with higher fatty alcohols or glycerol–alcohol ethers (selachyl, chimyl, or batyl alcohols, *cf.* p. 35) in the form of wax esters, in addition to the glycerides (which usually predominate).

In the marine world, on the other hand, definite differences from the freshwater type are often to be observed. The fats of marine diatoms and of green marine algæ are of the freshwater type in instances so far studied, but those of red and brown marine algæ show differences in the relative proportions of the various homologous unsaturated members. Also, the fats of marine plankton Crustacea (which feed on the diatoms) are considerably different from that of their food – unsaturated C_{16} and C_{18} acids are reduced in amount and C_{20}, and especially C_{22}, acids are correspondingly increased. This crustacean fat type persists as a general background throughout almost the whole range of marine fish and mammalia, although it is modified in certain families in various ways. In Elasmobranch fish, for example, the triglycerides are often accompanied by abnormal proportions of non-fatty compounds, including especially the hydrocarbon squalene and sometimes the glycerol ether-esters already

11

mentioned. When these substances are also produced in quantity it has invariably been found that the unsaturation of the acids in the triglycerides is almost wholly mono-ethenoid, while in addition definite proportions (up to 10 per cent.) of a mono-ethenoid C_{24} acid, selacholeic acid, have been observed frequently in these cases. In other families of Elasmobranchs another type of fat is found, characterised by very low proportions of non-glyceridic esters and extremely high unsaturation in the C_{22} and C_{20} acids, which may be present in larger quantities than in the previous type.

Similar specific variations in the component acids of fats of the more developed marine fish and mammalia include the elaboration of esters of higher alcohols as well as triglycerides in depot fats of the Physeteridæ (sperm whales) (here, again, the unsaturation of the acids present is abnormally low), and that of mixed glycerides of the quite exceptional *iso*valeric acid in those of the Delphinidæ (porpoise, etc.); such differences are as definitely characteristic as those in the anatomical features of the respective groups. Other interesting marine animal fats include those of the sturgeon, which are of the freshwater type; while salmon body fats alter progressively as the fish develop from purely freshwater to marine animals.

Component acids of fats of land animals. As we pass from depot fats of aquatic to those of land animals we find marked simplification in the mixed fatty acids, and in the higher land animals the important component acids are almost always the (mono-ethenoid) oleic, $C_{18}H_{34}O_2$, and the (saturated) palmitic, $C_{16}H_{32}O_2$, the latter occurring in much larger proportions than in aquatic animal fats, namely, about 25–30 per cent. of the total fatty acids – a figure which is roughly the same for the depot fats of widely different animals such as the rat, rabbit, kangaroo, cat, pig, sheep, ox, reindeer, horse, bear, lion, man, and also, usually, birds. Nevertheless, the disappearance of the characteristic "aquatic" unsaturated acids of the C_{16} (mainly mono-ethenoid, hexadecenoic), C_{18}, C_{20}, and C_{22} (mono- and poly-ethenoid) series is by no means abrupt.

In depot fats of amphibians and reptiles, unsaturated C_{16}, C_{20}, and C_{22} acids are present, but in less amount than in fish depot fats: frog depot fat contains 15 per cent. of hexadecenoic and the same amount of unsaturated C_{20-22} acids, that of the lizard 10 per cent. of the C_{16}, and 5 per cent. of the C_{20-22} acids; the unsaturation of the C_{20} and C_{22} acids, though still high, is not so pronounced as in the fish oils. In these fats the proportion of saturated acids is not very different from that in "aquatic" fats, and the drop in un-saturated C_{16}, C_{20}, and C_{22} acids is balanced chiefly by increase in unsaturated C_{18} (mainly oleic) acid. In the depot fats of rats and other rodents, and of the domestic fowl and some other birds, there occur small quantities (3–6 per cent.) of hexadecenoic acid and minor amounts (0·5–2 per cent.) of unsaturated C_{20} and C_{22} acids. The latter acids were already known, from the work of J. B. Brown and his colleagues, to be present in very small proportions in other animal depot fats (for example, pig) and in cow body and milk fats. In rats, rabbits, and hens, in contrast to the frog, lizard, and tortoise, the saturated acids of the depot fats form 30–35 per cent. of the total acids (palmitic, 25–28 per cent.).

This progressive alteration in the kinds of fatty acid present in the glycerides of different types of animals is more clearly seen if a table is drawn up giving the general range of values so far observed for the main component acids in some of the groups of the larger animals.

Component acids (percentage wt.) in animal depot fats

	SATURATED	UNSATURATED			
	PALMITIC	C_{16} (Hexadecenoic)	C_{18}	C_{20}	C_{22}
Fish, freshwater	13–15	ca. 20	40–45	ca. 12	0–5
„ marine	12–15	15–18	27–30	20–25	8–12
Whales	12–15	15–18	35–40	15–20	5–10
Frog	11	15	52	15	
Tortoise	14	9	65	7	
Lizard	18	10	56	5	
Domestic fowl	25–26	6–7	ca. 60	0·5–1	
Rat	24–28	7–8	ca. 60	0·3–0·5	
Kangaroo	26	3	49	3	
Cat	29	4	43	Trace	
Pig	25–29	2–3	50–65	0·3–1	
Ox	27–30	2–3	40–50	0·2–0·5	
Sheep	23–28	1–2	40–50	0·6	
Bear (sloth)	29	11	52	2	
Lion	29	2	40	3	
Baboon	19	4	67	0·5	
Human	24–25	5–7	53–57	2–2·5	

Almost all the acids other than palmitic (that is, about 70 per cent. of the component fatty acids) in the depot fats of the land animals belong to the C_{18} series. In many cases, apparently (detailed analyses are still scanty in this group), these acids are largely unsaturated (oleic, sometimes with polyethenoid acids); but in ruminant animals, at all events, stearic acid occurs in the mixed glycerides, often to a marked degree, in place of oleic acid. Specific characteristics in the constitution of the mixed triglycerides in these depot fats, which place them apart from most other natural fats, suggest that the stearic compounds result from hydrogenation of oleic glycerides (cf. below, p. 22).

In the depot fats of the land animals there occurs frequently (usually in not very large amounts) the linoleic acid, $C_{18}H_{32}O_2$, which is a component of many seed fats; but there is reason for thinking that this is derived by assimilation from the latter. At this point it should, perhaps, also be said that the data quoted above refer to animals which have received their natural diet; it is well known, of course, that higher animals, at all events, are able to ingest fats from vegetable seeds, leaves or roots (or, in carnivora, from the fats of other animals), and to lay down some of the specific acids of the latter in their depot fats, but this aspect of fat deposition has been excluded, so far as possible, in the observations on which this survey is based.

Component acids of mammalian milk fats. These have been studied in detail in the cases of comparatively few species (mostly ruminants). The component acids of whale and seal milk fats are almost the same as those of their depot fats (blubber), and there is reason to believe that the same holds good for the milk fats of other marine mammalia and probably also for those of many land

13

animals. In some higher land animals the C_{18} acids may form less of the total acids than in the corresponding depot fats, the differences being approximately balanced by the appearance of lower saturated fatty acids (C_{12}, C_{10}, C_8, C_6 and C_4). In many animals this phenomenon does not proceed as far as the production of butyric, hexanoic and octanoic glycerides, but amongst ruminants it is especially in evidence. Thus cow milk fat contains about 10 mols. per cent. of butyric acid and subsidiary amounts of C_6, C_8, C_{10} and C_{12} acids; sheep and goat milk fats contain less butyric and hexanoic acids, but more octanoic and about 10 mols. per cent. of decanoic acid. Similar differences to those which set apart the glyceride structure of the corresponding depot fats from that of other natural fats are apparent in the component glycerides of cow and similar milk fats (*cf.* below, p. 22).

The parallelisms to be observed between fat types and evolution in the animal world, as outlined above, are clearly apparent and remarkable. It remains now to consider the corresponding sequence in the vegetable kingdom. **Component acids of vegetable fats.** In the land flora, as in the fauna, the data are most abundant for depot (seed) fats of the more developed land plants; there is still a great lack of detailed information on the characteristic fats of the lower forms of land flora and also on those present in the growing parts of the larger plants. Nevertheless, it is interesting that the unsaturated hexadecenoic (C_{16}) acid, so characteristic of aquatic and lower land animal life, has been observed in quantity in the fats of a bacillus (diphtheria), of yeast (*Saccharomyces cerevisiæ*), and of the spores of a cryptogam (*Lycopodium*); whilst it is present in very small proportions (not exceeding 1 per cent.) in several of the more common seed and fruit-coat fats (groundnut, cottonseed, soya bean, teaseed oils, and olive and palm oils). Hexadec-9-enoic acid has been observed in major proportions (*ca.* 20 per cent.) in the seed fats of three species of the primitive family Proteaceæ, of *Anogeissus schimperi* (Combretaceæ), and in one fruit-coat fat, avocado (*Persea gratissima*, Lauraceæ). (The homologous tetradec-9-enoic acid is a major component of *Pycnanthus kombo*, (Myristicaceæ) seed fat, and in another species from the Proteaceæ the seed fat (which also contains some eicos-11-enoic acid) contains *ca.* 20 per cent. of hexadec-11-enoic acid).

The component acids of the glycerides of seeds (and, when present, of the pericarp or other fruit coat) of members of many plant families have, on the other hand, been widely studied in detail in recent years. The first thing which is apparent, in contrast to fats of aquatic flora, is considerable simplification in the component fatty acids. As in the land animals, palmitic and oleic become consistently prominent features; but a third acid, linoleic, must be added to these as a component which is of most frequent occurrence. The latter acid is either absent, or only present in small quantities, in most fats of aquatic origin, but it, and the related, still more unsaturated, linolenic acid, are amongst the most familiar constituents of the widely distributed class of "drying" seed oils.

Fruit-coat fats so far examined include (with at present only one or two exceptions) palmitic and oleic acids as sole major components, irrespective of the plant family in which they occur; linoleic acid is also frequently present, although usually not in major quantities. In many *seed fats*, also, the bulk of the component acids is palmitic, oleic, and linoleic in varying proportions; and, in general, seed fats of the same family have a certain resemblance in the relative proportions of these component acids. Malvaceæ and Bombacaceæ seed fats, for example, are usually high in their content of palmitic acid (20–25 per cent.) and also contain up to about 50 per cent. of linoleic acid. The latter acid is prominent in many seed fats of the conifers, of the larger dicotyledonous trees and shrubs, and in Rosaceæ, Compositæ, Labiatæ, Linaceæ, and other families, and also in those of Gramineæ, the component acids of most of which include about 10–15 per cent. of palmitic, 30–60 per cent. of oleic, and 60–30 per cent. of linoleic.

Land plants differ, however, from all other natural sources of fats in that, in many other families, their seed fats include as major components a fatty acid (or acids) different from any of those previously mentioned; in such cases the occurrence of the specific acid is almost wholly confined to one, or at the most to only a few, of the natural plant families. Thus the unsaturated erucic acid, $C_{22}H_{42}O_2$, is present in quantity in most Cruciferous seed fats; a structural isomer of oleic acid, petroselinic acid, is similarly found in seeds of the Umbelliferæ and the closely related ivy; and the cyclic unsaturated chaulmoogric and hydnocarpic acids in many of the Flacourtiaceæ. Of saturated acids, arachidic (C_{20}) and lignoceric (C_{24}), which occur in minute amounts in many seed fats, only attain major proportions in members of the Sapindaceæ and some of the Leguminosæ, whilst stearic acid is present in quantity only in the seed fats of a few tropical families. Saturated acids of lower molecular weight (lauric, C_{12}; myristic, C_{14}) are similarly characteristic of other, mainly tropical, families; the composition of all Palmæ seed fats yet studied is remarkable for close quantitative similarity, with lauric (45–48 per cent.) and myristic (16–20 per cent.) as main component acids. *n*-Decanoic (capric) acid is present in large proportions in the seed fats of *Ulmus* (elm) and *Zelkova serrata* (Ulmaceæ) but not in those of some other members of this family; it is similarly present in *Cuphea* seed fat (Lythrarieæ).

Sometimes, but relatively rarely, seed fats of one (or at most a few) species of a genus elaborate quite unusual unsaturated fatty acids, entirely different in constitution from those mentioned in the preceding paragraphs. Some of the more outstanding of these include:

ACID	SEED FATS
12,13-Epoxyoleic (Vernolic)	Some *Vernonia* sp. (Compositæ), *Cephalocroton* (Euphorbiaceæ), etc.
Cyclopropene-C_{18}-acids (Sterculic, Malvalic)	*Sterculia fœtida* (Sterculiaceæ), *Hibiscus*, *Gossypium* and some other Malvaceæ.
Octadeca-6,9,12-trienoic	*Œnothera biennis* (Onagraceæ).
Eicos-5-enoic	*Limnanthes douglassii* (Limnanthaceæ).
Eicos-11-enoic	*Delphinium* (Ranunculaceæ), *Cardiospermum* (Sapindaceæ) and some Cruciferæ species.
Conjugated ethenoid acids :	
Octadeca-*cis*-9-*trans*-11-*trans*-13-trienoic (Elæostearic)	*Aleurites fordii*, *A. montana* (Euphorbiaceæ) and some other species.

ACID	SEED FATS
Octadeca-*cis*-9-*cis*-11-*trans*-13-trienoic (Trichosanic, Punicic)	*Tricosanthes* sp. (Cucurbitaceæ), *Punica* sp. (pomegranate, Lythrarieæ).
4-Ketoelæostearic (Licanic)	*Licania rigida* (oiticica, Rosaceæ).
Octadeca-9,11,13,15-tetraenoic (Parinaric)	*Parinarium laurinum* (Rosaceæ).
Acetylenic acids :	
Octadeca-6-ynoic (Tariric)	*Picramnia* sp. (Simarubaceæ).
Octadeca-11-en-9-ynoic (Ximenynic, Santalbic)	*Ximenia* sp. (Olacaceæ), *Santalum* sp. (Santalaceæ).
Octadeca-17-en-9,11-diynoic (Isanic)	*Onguekoa gore* (Olacaceæ).
Hydroxy-unsaturated acids :	
12-Hydroxy-octadec-9-enoic (Ricinoleic)	*Ricinus communis* (Euphorbiaceæ).
9-Hydroxy-octadec-12-enoic	*Strophanthus* sp. (Apocynaceæ).
9-Hydroxy-octadec-10,12-dienoic (Dimorphecolic)	*Dimorpheca aurantiaca* (Compositæ).
18-Hydroxy-elæostearic (Kamlolenic)	*Mallotus philippinensis* (Euphorbiaceæ).
8-Hydroxy-isanic (Isanolic)	*Onguekoa gore* (Olacaceæ).

Probably the most unusual of all these rare fatty acids is the ω-fluoro-oleic acid which is present in the seed fat of *Dichapetalum toxicarium*.

Although the biosynthesis of these specific fatty components places many of the higher land plant families apart from the rest of nature as regards their fat types, we are left with the circumstance that the occurrence of these unusual features runs on the whole remarkably parallel with the groups into which morphologists have placed them. Apart from the widespread occurrence of specific component acids in certain plant families, there is observed a (probably gradual) simplification in fatty acid composition, commencing from the aquatic flora and proceeding in the direction of the fruit fats of the more highly developed land plants, similar to that which may be traced in the animal world.

Ivanov and others have pointed to climatic temperature as the factor mainly operative in determining the relative saturation of seed fats. Production, in plants of cooler latitudes, of fats solid at the prevailing temperatures of the atmosphere is in any case not very probable; but this is not evidence that the tropical temperature *per se* causes or favours development of the more saturated fats. Actually, many of the most unsaturated fats (those of *Aleurites*, *Hevea*, *Perilla*, *Licania* species, to quote only a few) are synthesised in the fruits of plants which can only live in tropical or sub-tropical conditions. On the other hand, in those plants which thrive in either hot or cold climates, the studies of several independent investigators have now clearly demonstrated greater production of the characteristic unsaturated acids in seeds from plants grown in the cooler regions.

THE COMPONENT GLYCERIDES OF NATURAL FATS

The very striking and characteristic differences in the fatty acid mixtures combined as triglycerides in fats from different regions of the vegetable and animal kingdoms are not reflected in the manner in which the triglycerides themselves are put together; for, very broadly speaking, the fatty acids seem to be woven into molecules of triglycerides on much the same general principle, whatever their place of origin may be – vegetable or animal, "depot" (reserve) or "tissue" (organ) fat – and whatever may be the particular mixture of acids present as component fatty acids. This simple principle (which has already been mentioned) is that nature strongly favours the elaboration of "mixed", and not "simple", triglycerides (i.e. glycerides containing three identical acyl groups). **Natural fats should be defined, in fact, as mixtures of mixed triglycerides.** *

Consequently any individual triglyceride molecule tends towards maximum heterogeneity in its composition; but, simultaneously if paradoxically, this may lead in some cases towards closer homogeneity, or fundamental similarity, in the triglycerides considered as a whole. This will be seen if we consider a hypothetical case of a fat containing three different acids, A, B, C, combined in equimolecular proportions with the trihydric glyceryl radical C_3H_5: (which may be written as G). The following combinations of three glycerol and nine fatty acid molecules are possible:

(i) "*Simple*"	$G(A_3)$	$G(B_3)$	$G(C_3)$
(ii) "*Mixed*"	$\begin{cases} G(A_2B) \\ G(A_2C) \end{cases}$	$\begin{cases} G(B_2C) \\ G(B_2A) \end{cases}$	$\begin{cases} G(C_2A) \\ G(C_2B) \end{cases}$
(iii) "*Mixed*"	$G(ABC)$	$G(ABC)$	$G(ABC)$

Thus the exclusive presence of simple triglycerides $G(A_3)$, etc., would, of course, result in a fat which was a mixture of three compounds, while that produced by the exclusive occurrence of triglycerides each containing only two different acids might lead to a still more heterogeneous mixture of twelve components. On the other hand, complete formation of a heterogeneous triglyceride molecule $G(ABC)$ would result in an individual compound (or, at most, of three possible configurational isomers).

If we take another hypothetical case, of a fat containing only two fatty acids, with one of the latter (Y) in much greater amount than the other (y), the possibilities are as follows:

(i)	$G(Y_3)$	$G(y_3)$
(ii)	$G(Y_2y)$	$G(y_2Y)$

If, in natural fats, the component fatty acids were strictly distributed, according to their relative proportions, as evenly or widely as possible amongst all the glycerol or glyceride molecules, the presence of an equimolecular mixture of *three* acids would result in the corresponding fat being an individual compound $G(ABC)$, whilst in the other imaginary example we have considered (with only *two* fatty acids) we should expect the corresponding fat to contain a very large proportion of the mixed triglyceride $G(Y_2y)$.

This is, in fact, the main principle which seems to be operative in the structure of natural fats. Since the number of even the major component acids in a fat often exceeds three, and their relative proportions vary widely, as we have seen, in different cases, it is not often that we encounter instances which approach in simplicity the hypothetical combinations which have just been discussed. Furthermore, fats, as products of a series of complex changes in a living organism, need not be expected to conform rigidly – and indeed rarely do so – to the exact demands of a numerical formula. Thus, where it has been possible

---

* As first suggested, apparently, by F. Guth[8] (1902).

to study seed fats containing, for example, twice or more than twice as much saturated as unsaturated acids, it is found that the triglycerides which contain saturated and unsaturated acyl groups are not wholly made up of disaturated-mono-unsaturated glycerides $G(S_2U)$, but contain a mixture of about 75–80 per cent. of this form with 25–20 per cent. of monosaturated-di-unsaturated glycerides $G(SU_2)$. Any excess of saturated acids above that demanded by this mixture appears as fully saturated triglycerides, $G(S_3)$.

In contrast, the proportion of any simple triglyceride $G(X_3)$ so far observed in a natural fat is in all but a few instances very much less than that calculated on the basis of completely random or indiscriminate distribution amongst the hydroxyl groups of glycerol. In the latter case the amount of $G(X_3)$ would be proportional to the cube of the percentage of the fatty acid X in the total fatty acids of a fat (e.g., if X formed half of the fatty acids the glyceride $G(X_3)$ would form 12·5 per cent. of the fat; with 65 per cent. of X in the total acids the percentage of $G(X_3)$ would be 27·5, and so on).

The development of knowledge (still rather fragmentary) of the glyceride structure of natural fats is best described in relation to the accompanying developments in experimental procedures for the quantitative study of the problem. The earliest quantitative work* (1927) was based on the chemical determination of the amounts of fully saturated (trisaturated) glycerides in various fats, and for about thirty years this remained the only chemical approach. From about 1930–1950 preliminary segregation of a natural fat into simpler mixtures of mixed glycerides was developed by means of systematic crystallisation of the fat from a suitable solvent (usually acetone or ether) over a wide range of temperatures (from room temperature down to as low as $-60°$, depending on the nature of the fat), followed by determination of the fatty acids and trisaturated glycerides in the segregated and simplified groups of glycerides†. This low-temperature systematic crystallisation technique (L.T.C.) provided much useful information on the glycerides present in fats in which polyethenoid acids do not predominate, but later work showed that it is not capable of adequate resolution of the mixtures of glycerides (e.g., oleolinolenins, linoleolinolenins, trilinolein, trilinolenin) present in the more unsaturated types of fatty oils such as the "drying oils". The application of a further physical means of segregation (counter-current distribution of fatty oils between two immiscible organic solvents‡, from 1956 onwards) gave different results from those obtained by low-temperature crystallisation for the predominantly unsaturated (polyethenoid) fatty acids, and here the results obtained by the counter-current distribution (C.C.D.) method must be considered the more reliable.

In 1956 and subsequent years, a new chemical tool (the first since the method for isolation and determination of trisaturated glycerides in 1927) was applied to the investigation of natural glycerides.§ It had been demonstrated that pancreatic lipase hydrolyses acyl groups attached to the primary alcoholic groups (1-, 3-, or α-, α'-) of glycerol, leaving those attached to the 2- or β-

---

* See Chapter V, p. 363.   † See Chapter V, p. 372.
‡ See Chapter V, p. 383.   § See Chapter V, p. 385.

hydroxyl groups substantially intact; determination of the fatty acids in combination respectively with the primary (1-, 3-) or the secondary (2-) alcoholic groups of the glycerol molecule revealed very pronounced differences in their composition.

At the time of writing, relatively few detailed investigations have been reported by either the counter-current distribution method of segregation, or the application of selective pancreatic lipase hydrolysis, but it is much to be hoped that both procedures will be intensively pursued and developed in the near future.

The detailed study of glyceride structure is so far, as indicated on p. 5, much more limited than that of the component acids in natural fats, and moreover has been largely directed to vegetable (seed and fruit-coat) fats. It is therefore most convenient to consider the latter in the first place.

Component glycerides of vegetable (seed and fruit-coat) fats. Following the early studies of many (solid or semi-solid) seed fats in which saturated acids formed from about 45 per cent. upwards of the total component acids it was concluded (Collin and Hilditch[9]) that there is a "pronounced tendency to even distribution of the fatty acids throughout the glycerides of seed fats". This tendency towards even or widest distribution was later defined, somewhat more explicitly, in the following manner:

(i) When a given fatty acid A forms about 35 per cent. (mol.) or more of the total fatty acids $(A+X)$ in a fat, it will occur at least once, $G(AX_2)$, in practically all the triglyceride molecules of the fat in question.

(ii) If it forms from about 35 to about 65 per cent. (mol.) of the total fatty acids $(A+X)$, it will occur twice, $G(A_2X)$, in any given triglyceride molecule in some instances, and of course more frequently the higher the proportion of this acid in the total fatty acids.

(iii) If it forms 70 per cent. or more of the total fatty acids, the remaining fatty acids (X) can at most only form mixed glycerides $G(A_2X)$, and the excess of A then, and broadly speaking then only, appears as a simple triglyceride, $G(A_3)$.

(iv) A minor component acid which forms much less than about a third of the total fatty acids (e.g. 15 per cent. or less), will not occur more than once in any triglyceride molecule (and, of course, not at all in many of the triglyceride molecules).

Whilst this general statement holds for most natural fats, animal as well as vegetable, it was noticed that in a few seed fats the proportions of a simple triglyceride are much greater than it indicates. Instances of this include the respective contents of trilaurin, trimyristin, tripalmitin, triparinarin and trivernolin in the seed fats of *Laurus nobilis*, *Pycnanthus kombo*, *Platonia insignis*, *Parinarium laurinum* and *Vernonia anthelmintica* (examined by low-temperature crystallisation) and also the more recent results (by counter-current distribution) for the trilinolenin content of linseed oil and the trilinolein contents of safflower, soya bean and maize oils.*

A major advance in our knowledge of the glyceride structure of seed fats

* See Chapter V, pp. 394, 395.

19

has resulted from the examination of the fatty acids in combination respectively with the primary (1-, 3-) and the secondary (2-) alcoholic groups of the glycerol molecule, made possible by selective hydrolysis of the fats by pancreatic lipase.* In eleven seed fats and one fruit-coat fat (olive oil) thus studied it has been demonstrated that oleic (or oleic and linoleic in some instances) form 95 per cent. or more of the acids attached to the central (2-) hydroxyl group of the glycerol molecule — so that extremely marked preferential attachment of oleic (linoleic) groups in this position appears to be the general rule. *Per contra*, any saturated acids, and also unsaturated acids other than oleic (linoleic) are sited at the 1- or 3- groups of the glycerol molecule. Further, whilst the oleic (linoleic) groups are almost wholly (in so far as the proportion of this acid present permits) in the central or 2-position, the remaining acids (including any surplus oleic or linoleic) appear to be distributed at the 1- and 3-positions on a random basis. Calculations of the mixed glycerides in a number of seed and fruit-coat fats, made in accordance with these findings, have been shown by Vander Wal and by Gunstone to agree well with the experimental results[10]; Gunstone holds that these recent results " bring together into a single distribution pattern the complicating views of widest distribution and of random distribution and its variants. Fats containing high proportions of C_{18} unsaturated acids will appear to follow the random distribution pattern – the principles of even distribution elaborated by Hilditch *et al.* are also incorporated, for fully saturated glycerides are not expected until the content of unsaturated C_{18} acids falls below about 35 per cent. In many other aspects also, but not in all, many fats will approximate to the widest distribution pattern."

The new evidence provided by selective partial hydrolysis of seed fats has thus already led to considerable clarification of our knowledge of their glyceride structure: extreme selectivity in the union of oleic (or linoleic) groups at the central (2-) hydroxyl group of glycerol is accompanied by apparently random distribution of all other acids at the external (1- and 3-) positions. At the present juncture, however, these statements are still by way of being broad generalisations, although with clearer definition than the earlier "tendency to even distribution". There is scope for much more intensive study of seed fat glyceride structure, whilst similarly detailed investigation of a comparable wide range of animal fats (except perhaps those of some ruminants) has hardly been taken up in real earnest.

Meantime the selective formation in seed fats of 2-oleoglycerides presents several interesting features, including the explanation of the invariable presence, in those seed fats which contain high proportions of palmitic and/or stearic acids (e.g., cocoa butter, *Allanblackia* or *Garcinia* fats, borneo tallow, etc.) of 2-oleo-1,3-disaturated glycerides such as 2-oleodistearin or 2-oleopalmitostearin. Further, this selectivity may be intimately connected with specific features which would seem to be involved in the biosynthesis of the oleic and linoleic glycerides of seed fats (*cf.* Chapter VIII, p. 540). It is also interesting to recall that, in various methods which have been proposed for

---

* See Chapter V, pp. 385–388.

computing the proportions of component glycerides, it was noticed (much earlier than the actual proof afforded by selective hydrolysis) that oleic acid seemed to differ from the rest of the natural fatty acids.[11]

Very recently (1964) Kartha[12] has reported that, in the ripening coconut, the fat consists exclusively of triglycerides (unaccompanied by any mono- or di-glycerides) from the earliest stage of fat development to full maturity; this suggests that, when a glycerol molecule is once absorbed on to a lipase molecule, it is not desorbed until all three glycerol hydroxyl groups have been esterified, the completely esterified molecule alone being desorbed. If this were proved to hold for all seed fats it would clearly be an important addition to our understanding of seed glyceride biosynthesis.

Component glycerides of land animal fats. A much smaller number of land animal depot fats, covering a relatively small range of species, has so far received detailed study in regard to glyceride structure than has been the case in the vegetable (seed and fruit-coat) fats. This is unfortunate, the more so as the fats of one specific section, the ruminant animals, have been examined in much more detail than the wider range of all other land animals; and, as indicated below, ruminant fats display exceptional features which are now known to be the result of the special metabolism of this class of animal. Consequently it is not at the present time possible to discuss the glyceride structure of land animal fats in due perspective, but the main general features, so far as the present inadequate knowledge permits, may be outlined somewhat as follows.

It has been mentioned that the fats of higher land animals contain considerable and approximately constant proportions of palmitic acid (25–30 per cent.). Nevertheless, so long as only minor proportions of other saturated acids are present, only very small proportions (2–3 per cent.) of fully saturated glycerides have been detected in these fats. The absence of any appreciable amount of fully saturated glycerides (e.g. tripalmitin) from animal depot fats in which 30 per cent. of palmitic acid is present shows that the latter is present almost wholly in the form of mixed palmito-unsaturated triglycerides and, thus far, that the usual tendency towards maximum mixed-glyceride formation is in evidence.

More recently the earlier studies were supplemented in a few instances by the systematic crystallisation procedure, leading to more detailed information and, in many cases, approximate figures for the proportions of the chief individual mixed glycerides present.

In the depot fats of the ox, sheep, and other ruminant herbivorous animals in which stearic acid attains more important proportions (in addition to the usual 25–30 per cent. of palmitic acid), the proportion of fully saturated glycerides becomes considerable even when the total amount of saturated acids is still below 60 per cent. of the total fatty acids present. The same feature is observed in the milk fats of this group of animals and, although it does not connote any closer approach to a simpler type of glyceride structure, it indicates an important general characteristic in the component glycerides of these fats. They are therefore considered below as a distinctive group.

21

Selective enzyme hydrolysis of animal fats has so far only been applied to three bird fats, two rodent fats, dog, horse, pig, human, ox and sheep depot fats. In all these except the pig, the proportion of oleic acid in the fatty acids attached at the central (2-) hydroxyl group of the glycerol molecule ranged between 61 and 88 per cent., i.e., definitely lower than in seed fats. In other words, saturated (palmitic and stearic) acids were also united with the 2-hydroxyl group to the extent of 12–39 per cent. of the total fatty acids in that position. In six pig depot fats the acids at the 2-position consisted of 70–80 per cent. saturated (66–77 per cent. palmitic) with only 30–20 per cent. of oleic acid. Whether this is a peculiarity of pig fats, or, as seems more likely, a possibly more general feature of the fats of the higher (non-ruminant) land animals remains to be determined by similar studies of fats from as wide a range as possible of species.

Depot and milk fats of ruminants (*ox, sheep, buffalo, etc.*). In the depot fats of this group, in which stearic acid is an important component, the structure of the mixed glycerides is also distinctive: the amount of fully saturated glycerides (mixed palmito-stearins in these cases) is much greater, for a given ratio of saturated to unsaturated acids in the whole fat, than in "evenly distributed" seed fats of corresponding composition. For example, we have seen that seed fats, whose mixed fatty acids contain 60 per cent. of saturated acids, still contain almost negligible quantities of fully saturated glycerides; but a tallow of similar general composition (i.e. with about 30 per cent. of palmitic and 25 per cent. of stearic acid in the mixed acids) contains about 26 per cent. of palmitostearins. (In the other direction, pig back fats, for example, may contain as little as 7 per cent. of stearic acid with the usual 25 per cent. of palmitic acid (thus far resembling rat or bird fats); in such cases the amount of fully saturated glycerides is very small (about 2–5 per cent.) and the fat conforms more nearly to the usual "evenly distributed" type.) Between these extremes, tallows and lards contain stearic and oleic acids in proportions which vary more or less inversely, the sum of the two being fairly constant in any one specimen of depot fat; and the greater the amount of stearic acid (with correspondingly less oleic acid) the greater is the proportion of fully saturated glycerides.

The corresponding milk fats (the component acids of which, in addition to about 25 per cent. of palmitic and somewhat varying amounts (35–45 per cent.) of oleic acid, include important proportions of butyric and other saturated acids of low molecular weight as well as some stearic and myristic acids) are exactly similar to the depot fats in their unusually high proportions of fully saturated glycerides. Indeed, when the content of fully saturated glycerides is plotted graphically against the total amount of saturated acids in the mixed fatty acids, the whole series, for both depot and milk fats, lies on a smooth curve.

The increase of stearic at the expense of oleic acid in the more saturated depot fats is in conformity with "random" saturation or hydrogenation of an initially more unsaturated fatty acid mixture; the parallel increase in fully saturated glyceride contents suggests that it is preformed oleic *glycerides*, not acids, which are undergoing hydrogenation. The closely similar features in the glycerides of milk fats containing significant proportions of butyric and other saturated acids of shorter chain length than C_{16} and C_{18} likewise suggests that preformed oleic *glycerides* have been modified to give the milk fat. It is known, however, that the short-chain saturated acids are synthesised in the lactating gland,[13] and it has been suggested that the synthesised acids undergo "random" acyl interchange with oleic (or other acyl) groups in the blood glycerides. Butyric-rich milk fats also always contain very small proportions of mono-ethenoid C_{10}, C_{12}, C_{14} and C_{16} acids with the double bond in the same (9:10) position as in oleic acid, which may be thought to arise from shortening of oleo-glyceride chains by simultaneous oxidation and reduction processes.

The hypothesis that stearic-rich depot glycerides in ruminant fats result from a bio-hydrogenation process is strongly supported by experimental evidence[14] (*cf.* Chapter III, p. 112) that the specific bacteria and protozoa of the rumen can convert oleic, linoleic or linolenic esters to stearic esters with concurrent production of geometric isomers of oleic (and linoleic) esters (as in catalytic hydrogenation of fats in presence of nickel).

Fuller discussion of the glycerides in ruminant depot and milk fats will be found in later chapters (III, pp. 109, 110, 112, 113, 153; V, pp. 368, 405, 410; VII, pp. 497, 510; VIII, pp. 546, 550).

Component glycerides of marine animal fats. The large number of component acids in these fats, and their highly unsaturated nature, causes the mixture of component glycerides to be very complex, and their study to be almost beyond the reach of the methods available. Nevertheless a few members of this group, notably whale oil, cod liver oil and a few other fish oils, were investigated by converting the mixed glycerides into bromo-additive products,* many of which are crystalline at room temperature or somewhat lower; the brominated glycerides were separated by fractional crystallisation from appropriate solvents and in a number of cases individual mixed brominated glycerides were identified. The results suggested that, in this group of fats, most of the tri-glyceride molecules contain at least two, and frequently three, different acids in combination.

Later, the glycerides of whale, herring, seal, and a few other marine animal oils were resolved by crystallisation from acetone at low temperatures into fractions sufficiently simple in character for their constitution to be deduced in general terms from the component fatty acids in each separated group of glycerides. The results fully confirmed the wide distribution of all the component acids in these marine oil glycerides.

Even the unusual *iso*valeric acid of the depot fats of the dolphin and porpoise has been shown[15] to be present therein not to any notable extent as "tri-*iso*valerin" but almost wholly in the form of mixed triglycerides in which one or two acyl radicals are those of the typical higher fatty acids of the marine oils.

So far as experimental evidence goes at present, therefore, it is wholly in favour of the view that the triglyceride molecules of marine animal fats are

* See Chapter V, p. 361; VII, p. 482.

extremely heterogeneous in character. The fatty acids are distributed evenly amongst the triglyceride molecules, so that (because of the large number of different fatty acids present) very many of these contain three different acyl groups.

It is intended that this introductory chapter shall serve to outline the method of treatment to be adopted in the remainder of the volume, and to indicate the chief aspects of the field which are treated in fuller detail in the latter.

It may be appropriate at this point, therefore, to consider the chief directions in which further investigation seems at the time of writing to be most urgently desirable.

Component fatty acids have been recorded for a fairly wide range of seed fats and also for depot and milk fats of ruminant animals and the fats of numerous fish and also marine mammals. There is still a relative lack of detailed information of the component acids of fats of land animals, small and large, other than the ruminants, and efforts should be made to obtain as comprehensive a picture here as that already available for seed fats. Even in the latter, further data are welcome both in order further to define the close relations between seed fatty acids and the botanical families where they are found, and to search for fresh instances of the intriguing occurrence of a quite unusual acid in more or less isolated species. Quantitative data for the fatty acids in fats present in growing parts of vegetation other than fruits is also badly lacking at present.

Facts about the *component glycerides* of natural fats are at present (as will be gathered from what has already been said) in a much less satisfactory state. Detailed knowledge of the glyceride structure of many more fats is urgently needed, especially as regards those in the fat depots of a wide range of animal species of all kinds, land and aquatic, small and large; whilst more extended study of seed fat glycerides is still desirable.

All work of this kind, when not actually tedious, may be felt to be humdrum and not very exciting, but much more is needed before anything approaching complete knowledge and understanding of the structure of natural fats will be attained. Hitherto, with a few well-known exceptions, research on fat composition has been much influenced primarily by industrial or, sometimes, biochemical or even medical considerations. This approach is not sufficient; the matter, like any other field of study, must be dealt with in terms of search for knowledge without any particular ulterior interest in one or other fat, or group of fats.

Naturally, much useful information has accumulated as the result of work in industrial or medical research laboratories inspired primarily by specific interests; but disinterested and systematic attacks on these problems may well be more appropriately undertaken in academic centres (unfortunately these, with a very few isolated exceptions, have not been conspicuously attracted to the organic chemistry of natural fats).

Investigations of the kind suggested are much less time-consuming than formerly. *Component acid* determinations can now be carried out in a small fraction of the time, and with a small fraction of the material, necessary in the older method of ester-fractionation. The quantitative study of *component glycerides* is about to be much assisted by the use of the selective lipase hydrolysis technique, but further search for other new experimental procedures in this field is a pressing need; and the alternative segregation methods of systematic crystallisation from solvents and of counter-current distribution between two immiscible solvents, together with new methods of chromatographic (e.g. "thin-layer") separation, afford scope for much further scrutiny.

The chemical constitution of natural fats is much better understood than in the early years of the century: but very much remains to be done before our knowledge can be considered satisfactory, or anywhere near comprehensive.

References to Chapter I

1. H. J. Deuel, Jr, "The Lipids", Vol. I, 1951; Vol. II, 1955; Vol. III, 1957. (Interscience Publishers, London.)
2. J. A. Lovern, "The Chemistry of Lipids of Biochemical Significance." (Methuen & Co. Ltd., London, 2nd Edition, 1957.)
3. H. Wittcoff, "The Phosphatides." (Reinhold Publishing Corporation, New York, 1951.)
4. H. Desnuelle, "Structure and Properties of Phosphatides." ("The Chemistry of Fats and Other Lipids", Vol. I, Pergamon Press Ltd., London, 1952, pp. 70–103.)
5. W. Bergmann, "Sterols." ("The Chemistry of Fats and Other Lipids", Vol. I, Pergamon Press Ltd., London, 1952, pp. 18–69.)
6. H. A. Boekenoogen, *Oliën Vetten Oliezandan*, 1941, **26**, 143.
7. T. P. Hilditch, *Chemistry & Industry*, 1935, **54**, 139, 163, 184.
8. F. Guth, *Z. Biol. Chem.*, 1902, **44**, 78.
9. G. Collin and T. P. Hilditch, *Biochem. J.*, 1929, **23**, 1273.
10. R. J. Vander Wal, *J. Amer. Oil Chem. Soc.*, 1960, **37**, 18; F. D. Gunstone, *Chem. and Ind.*, 1962, 1214.
11. T. P. Hilditch and M. L. Meara, *J. Soc. Chem. Ind.*, 1942, **61**, 117; A. R. S. Kartha, "Studies on the Natural Fats", Thesis, University of Madras, 1951.
12. A. R. S. Kartha, *J. Sci. Food Agric.*, 1964, **15**, 299.
13. S. J. Folley and G. Popják, see Chapter V, pp. 550, 575.
14. R. Reiser *et al.*, *Fed. Proc.*, 1951, **10**, 236; *J. Anim. Sci.*, 1952, **11**, 705; *J. Amer. Oil Chem. Soc.*, 1956, **33**, 155; 1959, **36**, 129; F. B. Shorland, R. O. Weenink *et al.*, *Nature*, 1955 **175**, 1129; *Biochem. J.*, 1957, **67**, 328; G. A. Garton *et al.*, *Nature*, 1958, **182**, 1511; *J. Gen. Microbiol.*, 1961, **25**, 215.
15. J. A. Lovern, *Biochem. J.*, 1934, **28**, 394.

CHAPTER II

The Component Acids of Fats of Aquatic Flora and Fauna

It was pointed out in the previous chapter that the general analytical characteristics of fats are usually insufficient to define their specific composition –
detailed data for at least the major component acids are required for this
purpose. Attention must, therefore, be concentrated upon the results of
analyses made by means of the fractional distillation of esters of fatty acids
which have been given a preliminary separation of the mixed fatty acids (or
their methyl esters) into groups – mainly saturated, mainly mono-ethenoid,
mainly polyethenoid – by crystallisation from acetone or other suitable solvent
at temperatures from $-60°$ C. upwards,* or, more recently, of analyses of the
mixed methyl esters of the fatty acids by gas–liquid chromatography† or by
reversed-phase partition chromatography.‡ Such analyses, although now
fairly numerous, cover only a small fraction of the natural fats of which the
average analytical characteristics have been determined, and, of course, a still
smaller proportion of the fats which exist in all the diverse organisms of plant
and animal life. The detailed data, on which we must depend for the present
purpose, therefore represent at the moment, as it were, a very rough sampling
of the total material – a sampling which, moreover, is very uneven, the data
being much more abundant, for example, for seed fats than for fats of aquatic
flora, and so on. A cautionary word is thus advisable, to warn the reader that
the subject, as about to be described, is in a state of very active development.
The broad outlines have been defined, and in many groups details of specific
differences have been filled in equally definitely; but, in other groups which
have so far received less thorough investigation, we may anticipate that further
research will lead to fresh developments and, it may well be, some modification of the descriptions and classifications given in this and the next few
chapters.

The general analytical characteristics of an exceedingly large number of
fish oils have been recorded, and in nearly all cases it has been found that the
mixed fatty acids yield fairly large proportions of ether-insoluble octa- and
deca-bromo addition products (usually amounting to 30–50 per cent. of the
total weight of the mixed fatty acids). In most cases, also, the percentage of
saturated acids has been determined by the lead salt method, and in a number
of instances (more especially in the hands of Japanese workers) the proportion
of highly unsaturated acids with acetone-soluble lithium salts has also been

---

* See Chapter XI, pp. 680–682, 688–693.   † See Chapter XI, pp. 697–699.
‡ See Chapter XI, pp. 685, 686.

26

given. Such data are at best, however, only partial when dealing with the complex mixture of component acids characteristic of marine animal fats.

The modern methods of analysis lead to figures for the percentages of each saturated acid and of each group of unsaturated acids of the same carbon content, with a value for the mean state of unsaturation of the latter. The mean unsaturation is conveniently expressed by the number of hydrogen atoms necessary to restore a molecule of the acid to the saturated state: thus $(-4 \cdot 0H)$ indicates an average unsaturation corresponding with two double bonds, but does not necessarily imply only the presence of a diethylenic acid.

In the complex mixtures of acids encountered in fats from aquatic sources, the order of accuracy of these detailed analyses is probably less than in those of simpler fatty acid mixtures, but the divergence from the truth is unlikely to exceed 2 or 3 units per cent. in extreme cases. This degree of uncertainty does not have a serious effect for the present purpose, because the type differences which are discernible may involve differences of 5–10 units per cent., or even more, in the proportions of one or other of the component acids.

So far as it is possible to determine at present, it would appear from the general characteristics already referred to that most fats of aquatic origin possess compositions of the same type as those of their respective classes for which detailed data are available. The detailed analyses, at the same time, demonstrate clearly that different groups of aquatic organisms display certain subordinate type differences in the proportions of the various major component acids. It is curious, nevertheless, that in very many cases throughout the whole series of marine animal oils the total proportion of saturated acids is relatively constant and in the neighbourhood of about 20 per cent., whilst, similarly, palmitic acid most frequently forms from 12 to 15 per cent. or thereabouts of the mixed fatty acids.

Fats from the various forms of aquatic life will now be discussed, commencing with those of vegetable and lower animal organisms.

COMPONENT ACIDS OF FATS OF AQUATIC FLORA
AND MICRO-FAUNA

The presence of the characteristic highly unsaturated C_{20-22} acids of fish fats in a large number of algæ was observed in 1925 by Tsujimoto,[1] who isolated them in the form of ether-insoluble polybromo-additive products, but noticed that the yield of the latter was much less than in the case of the majority of fish-liver oil acids. Later, Collin[2] made partial analyses of small quantities of fats from plankton collected by Dr E. R. Gunther and Prof. J. C. Drummond, with the following approximate results:

	ZOOPLANKTON FAT (Per cent.)	PHYTOPLANKTON FAT (Per cent.)
Saturated acids	17·3	15·5
Highly unsaturated acids (from ether-insoluble polybromides)	9·6	2·1
Highly unsaturated acids (from acetone-soluble lithium salts)	43·6 (iod. val. 311)	?

27

Detailed analyses of fats from several species of algæ, both marine and freshwater, were given by Lovern[3a] in 1936 (Table 1A, p. 29); the analyses of *Chlorella* fatty acids are by Paschke and Wheeler[3b] (1954) and Schlenk, Holman *et al.*[3c] (1960).

We shall shortly see that the fats of aquatic animals, large and small, differ typically in their proportions of certain component acids according to whether the habitat of the animal is salt- or fresh water. From the information so far available in Table 1A, however, it seems that this distinction does not hold in the case of aquatic plants. Lovern (*loc. cit.*) makes the following comments on his results:

"In the algæ the properties seem to follow the colour grouping. Of the green algæ three were freshwater species and one marine.

"The saturated acid percentages show great irregularities throughout, but for the unsaturated acids some interesting correlations occur. For the green algæ (Chlorophyceæ) the predominating unsaturated acids are those of 16 and 18 carbon atoms, with little C_{20} and little or no C_{22} acids. The degrees of average unsaturation of the C_{16} and C_{18} acids are unusually high. In the brown algæ (Phæophyceæ), C_{16} unsaturated acids have not the same importance, C_{18} acids are outstanding, and C_{20} acids are present in somewhat greater proportions than for most green algæ. The C_{16} acid is mono-ethylenic only, and the C_{18} acids are not on the whole of an unusually high degree of unsaturation. For the one red alga (Rhodophyceæ) examined C_{20} acids are the major constituent and appreciable quantities of C_{22} acids are present. C_{16} unsaturated acids, whilst not present in large amounts, are again of a relatively high degree of average unsaturation.

"Turning to the higher plant *Anacharis alsinastrum*, we find a fatty acid mixture very similar to that of green algæ.

"The marine diatom *Nitzschia closterium* has a fatty acid mixture also closely resembling that of green algæ, although this diatom is brown in colour.

"Taking these fats as a whole it may be said that the fats of all the green algæ, the pondweed and the diatom are of a type very similar in many respects to freshwater animal fats. The brown algal fats are really of a class by themselves, but more like a freshwater than a marine animal fat. The red algal fat is the only one approximating in composition to a marine animal fat."

Paschke and Wheeler[3b] state that all the polyene acids in the freshwater *Chlorella* fat appear to be of the "all-*cis* singly methylene interrupted" type.

Further analyses by Harper[4] of the pondweed (*A. alsinastrum*) glycerides from the same source, but collected at different times, have given the following results:

	DATE OF COLLECTION		
Component acids (weights per cent.)	November 1934 (Lovern,[3a] cf. Table 1)	July 1935 (Harper[4])	July and October 1935 (composite)* (Harper[4])
Saturated			
C_{14}	2	2	—
C_{16}	15	21	16
C_{18}	5	2	3
C_{20}	—	—	1
Unsaturated			
C_{12}	—	3	3
C_{14}	2	6	2
C_{16}	25	20	6
C_{18}	39	39	64
C_{20}	12	7	5

* About one-third of this material was collected in July and was probably the same as that analysed under "July 1935".

TABLE 1A. Component Acids (per cent. wt.) of Fats of Algæ, etc.

CLASS	SPECIES	SATURATED				UNSATURATED				
		$C<14$	C_{14}	C_{16}	C_{18}	C_{14}	C_{16}	C_{18}	C_{20}	C_{22}
Chlorophyceæ	Nitella opaca*	—	6	18	3	3 ($>-2\cdot0$H)	34 ($-2\cdot5$H)	23 ($-4\cdot5$H)	13 ($-5\cdot8$H)	—
	Oedogonium sp.*	—	2	20	1	—	32 ($-3\cdot1$H)	35 ($-4\cdot6$H)	9 ($-$?H)	1 ($-$?H)
	Cladophora sauteri*	Trace	12	10	2	Trace	19 ($-4\cdot7$H)	49 ($-3\cdot8$H)	8 ($-7\cdot1$H)	—
	Chlorella pyrenoidosa*	Trace	Trace	14	3 ↗	<2	25 (a) ($-$?H)	53 (b)	<4	Trace
	" "		⎧——17——⎫			Trace	15 (c)	67 (d)	1	4 ($-$?H)
	Mixed†	—	4	10	2	3 ($>-2\cdot0$H)	39 ($-3\cdot4$H)	30 ($-5\cdot1$H)	8 ($-6\cdot5$H)	3 ($-$?H)
Phæophyceæ	Fucus vesiculosus (1)†	Trace	8	9	1	Trace	6 ($-2\cdot0$H)	57 ($-3\cdot2$H)	16 ($-7\cdot3$H)	—
	Fucus vesiculosus (2)†	Trace	9	7	2	1	5 ($-2\cdot0$H)	63 ($-3\cdot0$H)	13 ($-7\cdot3$H)	—
	Laminaria digitata†	—	6	14	1	2	11 ($-2\cdot0$H)	42 ($-4\cdot2$H)	24 ($-8\cdot1$H)	—
Rhodophyceæ	Rhodymenia palmata†	1	4	19	1	Trace	6 ($-2\cdot9$H)	20 ($-4\cdot5$H)	36 ($-9\cdot2$H)	13 ($-$?H)
Higher plant	Anacharis alsinastrum*	1	1	15	5	2	25 ($-3\cdot0$H)	39 ($-4\cdot9$H)	12 ($-6\cdot0$H)	—
Diatom	Nitzschia closterium†	—	8	17	2	1	36 ($-3\cdot4$H)	20 ($-5\cdot3$H)	16 ($-7\cdot0$H)	—

* Fresh-water species. † Marine species.
(a) C_{16} monoene 4, diene 6, triene 12, tetraene 3. (b) C_{18} monoene 7, diene 11, triene 34, tetraene 1. (c) C_{16} monoene 3, diene 7, triene 5.
(d) C_{18} monoene 35, diene 18, triene 14.

29

TABLE 1B. Component Acids (per cent. wt.) of Fats of Zooplankton Crustacea

	SATURATED				UNSATURATED				
	$C < 14$	C_{14}	C_{16}	C_{18}	C_{14}	C_{16}	C_{18}	C_{20}	C_{22}
*Daphnia galeata[6a]	1	3	13	2	3 ($>$ −2·0H)	21 ($>$ −2·0H)	45 (−5·0H)	12 (−8·0H)	—
*Diaptomus gracilis[6a]	—	3	20	2	—	16 ($>$ −2·0H)	34 (−4·5H)	25 (−7·1H)	—
*Cyclops strenuus[6a]	—	6	16	1	3 ($>$ −2·7H)	30 (−3·0H)	25 (−5·2H)	16 (−8·6H)	3 (−?H)
†Calanus finmarchicus[6a]	—	8	11	1	1	12 (−2·4H)	17 (−5·1H)	25 (−7·8H)	25 (−8·1H)
†Calanus cristatus[6c] (taken from whale's stomach)	—	9	7	Trace	3 (−2·0H)	10 (−2·2H)	14 (−4·7H)	29 (−4·2H)	28 (−4·2H)

* Fresh-water species. † Marine species.

30

It is evident that two essentially different types of fatty acid mixture have here been encountered; both belong to Lovern's general "freshwater" and not to his "marine" type, but the specimen with a very high unsaturated C_{18} acid content (the component acids of which somewhat resemble those of the marine alga *Fucus vesiculosus*, Table 1A) shows therein a transition towards the typical fats of the higher land plants.

Perhaps the most interesting feature of Table 1A is the clear indication that in the algæ fats (as in the seed fats of the higher plants) the compositions fall into groups agreeing with their botanical relationships, irrespective of their habitat (freshwater or marine).

The component acids of the fat of the marine alga *Cystophyllum hakodatense*, Yendo, were found by Takahashi and co-workers[5] to include myristic 4·5, palmitic 18·5, unsaturated C_{16} 16 ($-2·0H$) and 7 ($-8·0H$), unsaturated C_{18} 39 ($-2·0H$), 3 ($-4·0H$), 1 ($-6·0H$) and 7 ($-4·0H$), and unsaturated C_{22} 1 ($-4·0H$) and 3 ($-6·0H$) per cent. (wt.).

Only a few fats of minute aquatic animal organisms have so far been examined (Table 1B, p. 30), but here the typical distinction between fresh- and salt-water fats is at once seen. So far as this evidence goes, the freshwater micro-fauna exhibit fats with typically high contents of unsaturated C_{16} and C_{18} acids, and almost complete absence of unsaturated C_{22} acids, whereas the marine copepod fat is rich in unsaturated C_{22} acids and low in its content of unsaturated C_{16} and C_{18} acids. *D. gracilis* fat is the "least typically freshwater fat" of the three, but even here the entire lack of C_{22} acids and the high content of unsaturated C_{18} acids would put this fat into the "freshwater" group.

In all the fats enumerated in Tables 1A and 1B, a point of interest is the extremely high average unsaturation of the C_{18} and C_{20} acids, together with the presence of polyethenoid C_{16} acids in nearly all cases. In the fats of more developed aquatic animals, almost all the unsaturated C_{16} acid is made up of hexadecenoic acid, and only very minor amounts of polyethenoid C_{16} acids are present. It is also to be noted that all the fats in question contain large amounts of "unsaponifiable matter", and that the presence of higher fatty alcohols is strongly suggested, although not definitely proved; the latter were also noticed in the zooplankton fats examined by Collin.[2]

COMPONENT ACIDS OF FATS OF LARGER AQUATIC INVERTEBRATES

Lovern[6b] separated the fatty matter of mussels (*Mytilus edulis*) into mainly glyceride (59–68 per cent.) and mainly phosphatide (41–32 per cent.) fractions, and records the following amounts of the usual fatty acids for each fraction (see Table at top of page 32).

The glyceride acids belong to the typical "marine fat" class, and resemble those of the lower marine animals (Table 2) more closely than those of the larger fish. The phosphatide acid figures are interesting because they show divergences from the glyceride acids, some, but not all, of which resemble those observed between the phosphatide and glyceride fatty acids of the liver fats of some of the larger land mammals (*cf.* Chapter III, pp. 133–137).

COMPONENT FATTY ACIDS GLYCERIDES PHOSPHATIDES*
(per cent. wt.)

	GLYCERIDES	PHOSPHATIDES*
Saturated		
C_{14}	2	—
C_{16}	17	27
C_{18}	2	6
Unsaturated		
C_{14}	Trace	—
C_{16}	11 ($-2 \cdot 5$H)	5 ($-3 \cdot 2$H)
C_{18}	21 ($-4 \cdot 1$H)	17 ($-4 \cdot 0$H)
C_{20}	30 ($-7 \cdot 3$H)	32 ($-6 \cdot 0$H)
C_{22}	14 ($-9 \cdot 3$H)	13 ($-8 \cdot 5$H)
C_{24}	3 ($-$?H)	?

* These acids formed about 80 per cent. of the total acidic matter recovered from the phosphatides; of the remainder, about half were highly unsaturated acids of higher molecular weight (mean *ca.* C_{28}) and about half acids of a non-fatty nature, not esterified by methyl alcohol in presence of sulphuric acid.

Klem[7] obtained figures of a somewhat similar order for the total fatty matter of the prawn (*Leander serratis*). The prawn oil, which amounted to about 1·5 per cent. of the (wet) weight of the prawns and contained 6·6 per cent. of unsaponifiable matter, contained acids of the following approximate composition: saturated series – C_{14} 1·5, C_{16} 9·5, C_{18} 2 per cent., C_{20} traces; unsaturated series – C_{14} 0·5, C_{16} 13 (-2H), C_{18} 32 ($-3 \cdot 3$H), C_{20} 34 (-6H) and C_{22} 7 per cent. (-10H).

Toyama and other Japanese workers[8] have recorded the component acids of fatty oils from other aquatic invertebrates, including cuttlefish, sea-anemones, and crabs (Table 2).

TABLE 2. *Component Acids (per cent. wt.) of some Pacific Marine Invertebrates*

	SATURATED			UNSATURATED				
	C_{14}	C_{16}	C_{18}	C_{16}	C_{18}	C_{20}	C_{22}	C_{24}
Ommastrephis solani pacificus[8a] (cuttlefish, squid)	4	14	5	6 ($-2 \cdot 0$H)	14 ($-2 \cdot 0$H)	30 ($-6 \cdot 0$H)	14 ($-10 \cdot 0$H)	2 (-10H)
Spisula sachalinensis[8b]	1	12	4	15 ($-2 \cdot 4$H)	34 ($-4 \cdot 0$H)	23 ($-6 \cdot 8$H)	10 ($-8 \cdot 7$H)	—
Gorgonocephalus caryi[8c]	2	13	4	11 ($-2 \cdot 0$H)	30 ($-3 \cdot 9$H)	22 ($-5 \cdot 8$H)	18 ($-7 \cdot 4$H)	—
Anthopleura japonica[8d] (sea-anemone)	1	11	4	11 ($-2 \cdot 7$H)	23 ($-3 \cdot 5$H)	29 ($-6 \cdot 5$H)	21 ($-8 \cdot 4$H)	—

Bergmann *et al.*[9] state that lipids in the tropical sea-anemone *Condylactis gigantea* include substantial amounts of myristyl myristate and palmitate and of 2-palmityldimyristin, whilst those in sea-anemones from temperate seas (*Bolocera iuediæ, Actinostola collosa*) are mainly esters of unsaturated C_{20} and C_{22} alcohols with unsaturated C_{20} and C_{22} acids, with triglycerides of the same acids; 11-eicosenol and 11-docosenol were identified.

Early observations[10a] on the body fat of the land crab, *Birgus latro*, which is common in the islands of the East Indies and the Indian Ocean, suggested the presence of considerable proportions of lauric acid and minor proportions of lower, steam-volatile saturated acids in the fat of this species. An analysis of the fat of land crabs from the Seychelles Islands by Hilditch and Murti[10b] showed the component acids to include octanoic 1·5, decanoic 5·3, lauric 47·5, myristic 19·0, palmitic 13·1, stearic 1·7, with unsaturated C_{14} 0·7, C_{16} 2·2, C_{18} 6·8, and C_{20-22} 2·2 per cent. (mol.). These figures suggest a combination of about 75–80 per cent. of coconut oil acids with about 25–20 per cent. of more or less typical marine fat acids; this land crab fat (*cf*. Chapter VII, p. 489) contained about 66 per cent. of fully saturated glycerides almost identical in fatty acid composition with the corresponding glycerides of coconut oil. *Birgus latro* is peculiar in that it feeds extensively on coconuts and this circumstance almost certainly leads to much of its depot fat being derived by assimilation of coconut fat. It thus represents a special case and cannot be regarded as a typical crustacean or marine invertebrate fat in this respect.

The lipids of the rock lobster (*Jasus lalandii*) were investigated by Ligthelm *et al*.[11] The component acids of the hepatopancreas oil (the main fat depot) were saturated: C_{14} 1·1, C_{16} 10·3, C_{18} 8·1, C_{20} 4·2, C_{22} 0·5 per cent.; unsaturated: C_{14} 2·4 ($-2·0H$), C_{16} 7·3 ($-2·1H$), C_{18} 14·3 ($-2·9H$), C_{20} 28·4 ($-6·5H$), C_{22} 19·0 ($-8·3H$), C_{24} 2·6 ($-2·1H$) and C_{26} 1·8 ($-2H$) per cent.

Cardin and Meara[12] found that semen of the common Echinoderm sea-urchin (*Echinus esculentus*) contained about 1 per cent. of fat, the component acids of which were (approximately) saturated: 10; unsaturated: C_{16} 2 ($-3H$), C_{18} 30 ($-5H$), C_{20} 45 ($-7H$) and C_{22} 12 ($-6·5H$). The fat, which contained 26 per cent. of phosphatides, is notable for a very high content of C_{20} acids and very low hexadecenoic acid, with somewhat less of saturated acids than is usually found in a marine animal fat.

Lipids of sponges. The fatty acids in the total lipids of two species of sponge, *Spheciospongia vesparia* and *Suberites compacta*, were examined by Bergmann and Swift.[13] Each contained twenty or more different fatty acids with unsaturated members ranging from C_{14} to C_{28}. The most abundant compounds were unsaturated acids containing 26 and 28 carbon atoms in the molecule:

FATTY ACIDS (per cent. wt.)	Spheciospongia vesparia	Suberites compacta
Saturated		
C_{14}	1·7	0·3
C_{16}	9·1	6·6
C_{18}	0·7	1·0
C_{20}	—	1·1
C_{22}	—	0·6
Unsaturated		
C_{14}	0·4 ($-2·0H$)	0·2 ($-2·0H$)
C_{16}	3·1 ($-2·0H$)	3·1 ($-2·0H$)
C_{18}	15·9 ($-2·0H$)	11·1 ($-2·3H$)
C_{20}	6·5 ($> -2·0H$)	7·8 ($-2·3H$)
C_{22}	4·4 ($> -2·0H$)	17·8 ($-6·3H$)
C_{24}	4·5 ($> -2·0H$)	11·6 ($-7·3H$)
C_{26}	38·8 ($> -2·0H$)	$\begin{cases} 9·4 \ (-2·9H) \\ 12·2 \ (-?H) \end{cases}$
C_{28}	14·9 ($> -2·0H$)	17·0 ($-4·5H$)

The authors point out the likelihood that the higher molecular weight acids may be present as cerebroside or as phosphatide-like derivatives (*cf*. the mussel phosphatides above). A hexacos-9-enoic acid and a hexacosa-17,20-dienoic acid, m.p. 58–59·5°, were isolated from *S. vesparia* lipids, and an octacosenoic acid, m.p. 57·3–57·8°, from those of *S. compacta*.

Although the individual instances of fats from lower aquatic organisms so far studied are few in number, the relationships disclosed in their component fatty acids are of definite interest when compared with those disclosed by the corresponding and more abundant investigations which have been made of the component acids of fats from fish and marine mammalia.

COMPONENT ACIDS OF FISH FATS

The compositions of the fatty acids of many fish oils – either flesh oils or, more often, liver oils* – are now known with reasonable certainty, but even here, of course, those which have been investigated in detail are a very small fraction of the whole of the group. It was recognised many years ago, naturally, that the properties of the marine animal oils differed from those of most other then known fats, especially in their very unsaturated character and the avidity with which they absorb oxygen from the air and become partially converted into viscous and gum-like materials. A few historical notes on the recognition of some of the qualitative features of the group may be of interest before we discuss more fully the fish oil fatty acids as known at the present time.

One of the most prominent specific component acids of marine animal oils, hexadecenoic acid, $C_{16}H_{30}O_2$, was recognised as a constituent of the head oil of the sperm whale by Hofstädter,[14] who therefore called it "physetoleic acid", as far back as 1854, and in 1898 Ljubarsky[15] noticed the same acid in seal oil. It seems to have been first recorded in a fish (as distinct from a marine mammal) in 1906 by Bull,[16] who isolated it in a fairly pure condition from cod liver oil, confirmed its formula as $C_{16}H_{30}O_2$, and converted it into a dihydroxypalmitic acid; Lewkowitsch[17] suggested the name *palmitoleic acid* by which it is usually known in Europe and America. Toyama[18] and other Japanese chemists, from about 1924 onwards, isolated the same acid from a large number of Pacific fish and whale oils under the name *zoomaric acid*; its chemical constitution having been shown in all cases to be that of *hexadec-9-enoic acid*, it seems preferable, perhaps, to refer to it by its systematic name and to allow the use of the older specific names to lapse.

Of other characteristic mono-ethenoid acids of fish oils, gadoleic acid, $C_{20}H_{38}O_2$, was also discovered in cod liver oil by Bull[16] in 1906, and shown later by Toyama *et al.*[19] to be eicos-9-enoic acid; the corresponding acid $C_{22}H_{42}O_2$, termed cetoleic acid by Toyama,[20] was shown by this worker to have the constitution of docos-11-enoic acid. Tsujimoto[21] drew attention in 1927 to a tetracos-15-enoic acid, $C_{24}H_{46}O_2$, in shark oil which he named selacholeic acid; this acid frequently occurs in the oils of Elasmobranch (cartilaginous) fish, but has not yet been detected with certainty in those of any of the Teleostid group. It is identical with the nervonic acid obtained by Klenk[22] from brain cerebrosides.

* It should be noted that the livers of many fish, in contrast to those of land animals, are often rich in fat and frequently serve as the main fat depot of the fish.

The components to which the ready autoxidation of fish oils is mainly due are polyethenoid acids of the C_{18}, C_{20}, C_{22}, C_{24}, and even, perhaps, C_{26} series, those of the C_{20} and C_{22} groups being by far the most abundant. Clupanodonic acid, belonging to this series, was isolated by Tsujimoto[23] in 1906 from Japanese sardine oil and at first believed to be a C_{18} acid; but in 1920 he stated that its formula was $C_{22}H_{34}O_2$ (a docosapentaenoic acid). Subsequently a number of other individual polyethenoid acids were reported by Japanese workers, including stearidonic,[24] $C_{18}H_{28}O_4$ (octadecatetraenoic), arachidonic, $C_{20}H_{32}O_2$ (eicosatetraenoic, also present in small amounts in many land animal liver and depot fats); and, in very small quantities in certain fish oils, hiragonic acid,[25] $C_{16}H_{26}O_2$ (hexadecatrienoic), nisinic,[26] $C_{24}H_{36}O_2$ (tetracosahexaenoic), shibic,[27] $C_{26}H_{42}O_2$ (hexacosapentaenoic), and thynnic,[27] $C_{26}H_{40}O_2$ (hexacosahexaenoic) acids. The constitution of these polyethenoid acids has continued to be the subject of much investigation, of which further details will be found in Chapter IX (pp. 637–643).

The detailed description of the component acids of fish oils (in which, it should be noted, the unsaturated acids are placed in their homologous groups with a general statement of their mean unsaturation) will be dealt with in several categories, following where possible the zoological classification of the fish.

Liver fats of (marine) Elasmobranch fish. Tables 3 and 3A (pp. 38, 39) show the quantitative data which have been recorded for some liver oils of this subdivision of fish. (The figures have in most cases been rounded off to the nearest unit or half-unit.)

The component acids of the Elasmobranch fish liver oils shown in Table 3 exhibit considerable variation in type, but those which contain very small proportions of unsaponifiable matter (1–2 per cent.) are typically "marine" in type, with large proportions (*ca.* 50 per cent.) of unsaturated C_{20} and C_{22} acids, of which the mean unsaturation is very high. Tsujimoto[28] classified liver fats of the Elasmobranchii in four groups according to their content of "unsaponifiable matter" and the nature of the latter:

(a) Those with very small unsaponifiable content (1–2 per cent., mainly sterols) and very large proportions of highly unsaturated acids.

(b) Those with moderately large amounts of unsaponifiable matter (10–35 per cent., cholesterol with considerable proportions of the glyceryl ethers known as selachyl, chimyl, and batyl alcohols*) and with mainly monoethenoid fatty acids.

---

* Selachyl alcohol, α-octadec-9-enylglyceryl ether,

$$CH_3 . [CH_2]_7 . CH:CH . [CH_2]_7 . CH_2 . O . CH_2 . CH(OH) . CH_2(OH).$$

Chimyl alcohol, α-hexadecylglyceryl ether,

$$CH_3 . [CH_2]_{14} . CH_2 . O . CH_2 . CH(OH) . CH_2(OH).$$

Batyl alcohol, α-octadecylglyceryl ether,

$$CH_3 . [CH_2]_{16} . CH_2 . O . CH_2 . CH(OH) . CH_2(OH).$$

(*Cf.* Chapter X, pp. 670–672.)

(c) Those with very large amounts of unsaponifiable matter (usually rich in the terpenoid hydrocarbon squalene*) and fatty acids similar to those of group (b).

(d) An exceptional group in which, with unsaponifiable matter usually below 10 per cent. and often only 1–2 per cent., the fatty acids contain an exceptionally high proportion (up to 50 per cent.) of saturated acids.

Swain[29] has shown that, after adsorption of the unsaponifiable matter of marine animal oils on a column of activated alumina, light petroleum elutes hydrocarbons (squalene, etc.), benzene or methylene dichloride then elutes monohydric alcohols (cholesterol, vitamin A), and final elution with ethyl ether removes dihydric alcohols (selachyl, etc., alcohol-ethers).

The liver fats in Table 3 are given in roughly increasing order of their contents of "unsaponifiable matter", the nature of which is as follows:

LIVER FAT FROM	UNSAPONIFIABLE MATTER	
	PER CENT.	APPROXIMATE COMPOSITION
Skate	0·3	Mainly cholesterol
Angel fish	1·5	,, ,,
Thresher shark	1·8	,, ,,
Spotted dogfish	2	,, ,,
Grey dogfish	10	Mainly selachyl, with some chimyl and batyl alcohols.
Ratfish	37	Almost wholly selachyl, with some chimyl and batyl alcohols.
Shark species	50–80	Large amounts of squalene with some selachyl, etc., alcohols.

* The hydrocarbon squalene, $C_{30}H_{50}$ (2,6,10,15,19,23-Hexamethyltetracosa-2,6,10, 14,18,22-hexaene), was first isolated from a shark liver oil by Tsujimoto[30a] in 1906; later (1916–1920) he ascertained its molecular formula[30b] and reported[30c] its presence in the livers of 16 out of 36 species of Elasmobranch fish examined from Japanese waters. It was present chiefly in the liver oils of some members of the family Squalidæ, and also in certain members of the Cetorhinidæ, Chlamydoselachidæ, Dalatiidæ, and Scylliorhinidæ, and in the eggs of two of the species in which it was present in the livers. In 1917 A. Chaston Chapman[31a] had also isolated the hydrocarbon (which he termed spinacene) from a Portuguese shark liver oil. Heilbron, Kamm and Owens[31b] also observed it in comparatively undeveloped eggs of *Etmopterus spinax* (Squalidæ), but not in the more developed ova. Channon[32] found squalene present in the livers of 3 members of the Squalidæ (*Spinax niger, Scymnorhinus lichia,* and *Lepidorhinus iguanosus*) but absent from those of 2 other members of the family and of 11 members of other Elasmobranch families; it was also absent from 14 species of Teleostid fish examined and from various phyto- and zoo-plankton. Hata and Kunisaki[33] reported that the liver oil of a small species of deep sea Formosan shark contains 87·5 per cent. of unsaponifiable matter, of which 84 per cent. was hydrocarbons, chiefly squalene.

The occurrence of squalene thus appears to be comparatively limited, even in the Elasmobranchii, and to be somewhat erratic within individual families in this group. It is frequently accompanied by much smaller proportions of a saturated hydrocarbon $C_{19}H_{40}$ (pristane,[34a] probably 2,6,10,14-tetramethylpentadecane[34b]), and still smaller amounts of a nonadecene $C_{19}H_{38}$ (zamene,[34c] possibly 2,6,10,14-tetramethyl-pentadec-1-ene[34b]).

Squalene has also been found in very small amounts in a few vegetable fats, notably olive oil,[35a] some cereal seed oils[35b] and yeasts.[35c]

The structure of squalene was finally settled in 1929–1931 by the studies of Heilbron *et al.*,[36a] and of Karrer and Helfenstein.[36b]

The change in the character of Elasmobranch fish liver oil component acids (which consists in marked diminution of the polyethenoid unsaturation together with some diminution in the total amounts of C_{20} and C_{22} acids and the appearance of a certain amount of unsaturated C_{24} (selacholeic) acid) sets in almost exactly parallel with the appearance of unusually large proportions of selachyl and the related alcohol-ethers. Lovern[37] has suggested that disappearance of polyethenoid unsaturation in the higher fatty acids, and concurrent appearance of alcohol-ethers of the selachyl type, are both to be regarded as evidence of an unusual tendency towards saturation or hydrogenation in this group of fish liver oils.

It was shown by André and Bloch[38] that the glyceryl ethers almost certainly are not present in the free condition, but occur in the liver oils as fatty acid esters. A very large proportion of ratfish liver oil, containing over 30 per cent. of these ethers, will therefore consist of di-acyl esters of selachyl, chimyl, and batyl alcohols, a possible instance of which would be, for example:

$$CH_2.O.CH_2.[CH_2]_7.CH:CH.[CH_2]_7.CH_3 \qquad \text{Octadecenyl alcohol}$$
$$|$$
$$CH.O.CO.[CH_2]_7.CH:CH.[CH_2]_7.CH_3 \qquad \text{Oleic acid}$$
$$|$$
$$CH_2.O.CO.[CH_2]_7.CH:CH.[CH_2]_9.CH_3 \qquad \text{Gadoleic acid}$$

It remains to be seen, of course, how far these generalisations (based on what are, after all, a very few instances) will be modified as more data are collected for fish of other Elasmobranch species; so far as they go, however, they form a steadily progressive series in the sense which has been indicated.

Many of the analyses in Table 3 are by Dr Lovern of the Torry Research Station, Aberdeen, who is also responsible for a considerable proportion of the data in the rest of this chapter. Reference may be made here to his monograph on "The Composition of the Depot Fats of Aquatic Animals."[39]

The component acids of the basking, spiny, seven-gilled, and soupfin shark liver oils in Table 3 are taken from work,[44, 46, 47] published in 1948 by Karnovsky, Rapson and their co-workers on South African fish products, whilst the figures for the New Zealand school or snapper sharks were published in the same year by Oliver and Shorland.[45]

Holmberg and Sellman (1955)[49a] found the liver oil of the Greenland shark (*Somniosus*) contained both glycerides and esters of glyceryl ethers. The glyceryl ethers included chimyl 5, batyl 43, and selachyl alcohols 52 per cent. (wt.). The fatty acids in the glycerides and the glyceryl-ether esters were respectively: saturated, C_{14} 0·6, 0·4; C_{16} 5·8, 5·3; C_{18} 2·0, 2·1; C_{20} 0·5, 0·5; unsaturated C_{14} ($-2H$) 1·4, 1·5; C_{16} ($-2H$) 5·5, 3·7; C_{18} 30·6 ($-2·1H$), 28·2 ($-2·3H$); C_{20} 24·2 ($-2·9H$), 25·8 ($-3·8H$); C_{22} 14·5 ($-3·2H$), 18·7 ($-5·1H$); C_{24} 14·6 ($-4·2H$), 13·4 ($-2·4H$) per cent. (wt.). In this shark oil the mean unsaturation of the C_{20}, C_{22} and C_{24} acids is somewhat greater than in those similarly rich in glyceryl ethers quoted in Table 3.

Fensch[49b] has described the component acids in the liver oil of the six-gilled shark (*Hexanchus griseus*). Malins and Houle[49c] give a precise statement of

TABLE 3. Component Acids (per cent. wt.) of Liver Fats of (Marine) Elasmobranch Fish

FAMILY	SPECIES	"UNSAPONIFIABLE MATTER" IN OIL (Per cent.)	SATURATED				UNSATURATED					
			C_{14}	C_{16}	C_{18}	C_{20}	C_{14}	C_{16}	C_{18}	C_{20}	C_{22}	C_{24}
Rajidæ	Skate Raia maculata[40]	0·3	4·0	14·0	—	—	Trace	10·5 (—2·0H)	20·5 (—3·3H)	32·5 (—7·3H)	18·5 (—9·5H)	—
Squatinidæ	Angel fish Squatina angelus[41]	1·5	1·4	17·0	2·0	—	—	6·5 (—2·0H)	20·7 (—3·0H)	21·9 (—6·0H)	30·5 (—10·2H)	—
Alopiidæ	Thresher shark Alopœcia vulpes[42]	1·8	7·4	11·3	0·2	—	1·6	12·0 (—2·0H)	19·2 (—3·4H)	31·0 (—6·6H)	17·3 (—10·5H)	Trace?
Scyllidæ	Small spotted dogfish Scyllium canicula[41]	2	1·7	15·7	3·3	—	—	4·0 (—2·2H)	25·3 (—3·0H)	24·4 (—6·4H)	24·8 (—9·2H)	Trace?
	Smooth dogfish Mustelus canis[43]	?	3·2	15·7	2·0	—	1·7	12·6 (—2·0H)	40·3 (—3·0H)	10·7 (—6·0H)	13·8 (—10·4H)	—
Squalidæ	Grey dogfish Squalus acanthias[40]	10	6·0	10·5	3·0	—	—	9 (—2·0H)	24·5 (—2·8H)	29 (—3·3H)	12 (—4·0H)	6 (—2·0H)
Galeidæ	*Soupfin shark (Galeorhinus canis)[44] Female (fat) (South Africa)	3	3·3	17·7	1·6	0·7	0·5 (—2·0H)	9·4 (—3·1H)	25·3 (—3·7H)	24·4 (—8·0H)	15·9 (—10·3H)	1·2 (—10H)
	Female (thin) (South Africa)	7	3·5	17·3	3·6	1·2(a)	1·0 (—2·0H)	8·6 (—2·0H)	23·1 (—2·6H)	17·2 (—6·5H)	17·5 (—9·8H)	6·4 (—10H)
	†School shark (Galeorhinus australis)[45] (NewZealand)	3-8	2·3	16·1	4·7	0·7(b)	0·9 (—2·0H)	5·7 (—2·0H)	27·6 (—2·3 to —2·6H)	19·0 (—4·5 to —5·8H)	22·3 (—6·5 to —9·6H)	0·5
Hexanchidæ	*Seven-gilled shark (Heptranchias pectorosus)[46]	20	1·6	16·6	6·9	1·3(c)	0·7 (—2·0H)	11·0 (—2·0H)	30·3 (—2·5H)	15·6 (—5·4H)	13·0 (—8·7H)	1·4 (—10H)
Chimæridæ	Ratfish Chimæra monstrosa[41]	37	—	8·4	7·2	1·3(d)	—	2·5 (—2·0H)	50·6 (—2·2H)	19·6 (—2·9H)	7·9 (—3·5H)	2·1 (—?H)
Squalidæ	*Basking shark (Cetorhinus maximus)[47]	33-49	2·1	13·6	3·2	3·6(e)	0·5 (—2·0H)	11·9 (—2·0H)	12·8 (—2·2H)	23·2 (—2·9H)	20·0 (—3·6H)	5·6 (—5·9H)
Squalidæ	*Spiny shark (Echinorhinus spinosus)[47]	46-50	3·9	20·4	6·9	0·3(f)	1·6 (—2·0H)	11·9 (—2·0H)	25·6 (—3·0H)	15·4 (—6·6H)	13·9 (—8·1H)	—
Squalidæ	Shark sp. Centrophorus, etc., sp.[48]	50-80	1·0	13·2	1·3	1·2	0·2 (—2·0H)	3·5 (—2·0H)	35·4 (—2·1H)	16·4 (—2·2H)	15·8 (—2·3H)	12·0 (—3·0H)
Squalidæ	Shark sp. Scymnorhinus lichia[48]	70-80	1·2	14·6	3·6	0·8(g)	0·4 (—2·0H)	3·7 (—2·0H)	29·1 (—2·0H)	10·6 (—2·0H)	25·9 (—2·1H)	10·0 (—2·0H)

(a) Also 0·4 per cent. C22. (b) Also 0·2 per cent. C22. (c) Also 1·6 per cent. C22. (d) Also 0·4 per cent. C22. (e) Also 3·2 per cent. C22 and 0·4 per cent. C24. (f) Also 0·2 per cent. C22. (g) Also 0·1 per cent. C22.

* Oils from South African coasts.
† Mean of analyses of four specimens of New Zealand school shark liver oils.

TABLE 3A. *Component Acids (per cent. wt.) of Elasmobranch Liver Fats Rich in Saturated Acids*

SPECIES	SATURATED				UNSATURATED					
	C_{14}	C_{16}	C_{18}	C_{20}	C_{14}	C_{16}	C_{18}	C_{20}	C_{22}	C_{24}
Fanfish *Dasyatis akajei*[50a]	—	19	46	—	—	—	30 (−3·6H)	{ 5 }		—
Indian shark *Galeocerda rayneri*[50b] from Arabian Sea	3·3	24·9	11·1	1·2(a)	1·1 (−2·0H)	11·2 (−2·6H)	19·6 (−3·9H)	22·3 (−7·0H)	4·8 (−10·6H)	—
from Bay of Bengal	1·5	23·6	14·5	0·3	0·2 (−2·0H)	10·9 (−2·0H)	23·3 (−2·6H)	11·6 (−5·8H)	12·3 (−8·4H)	1·9 (−11·0H)
Galeocerda tigrinus[50b] from Bay of Bengal Mature Female	3·0	25·1	13·8	1·3	0·4 (−2·0H)	7·8 (−2·1H)	23·6 (−2·6H)	15·5 (−5·6H)	9·3 (−10·5H)	—
Embryo	8·6	25·1	5·1	—	0·2 (−2·0H)	18·0 (−2·0H)	38·2 (−2·1H)	3·9 (−4·4H)	—	—
Indian Shark *Carcharias melanopterus*[50b] from Arabian Sea	4·4	18·5	9·0	1·8(b)	2·9 (−2·0H)	12·7 (−2·1H)	20·0 (−4·0H)	19·0 (−6·8H)	7·3 (−9·9H)	4·4 (−11·0H)
from Bay of Bengal[50b]	3·1	18·4	9·5	0·1	0·8 (−2·0H)	10·8 (−2·1H)	19·7 (−3·6H)	15·2 (−6·1H)	17·1 (−8·8H)	5·3 (−11·0H)
Carcharias limbatus[50d] from W. Coast of India	2·6	19·1	15·2	0·7	0·5 (−2·0H)	8·4 (−2·0H)	22·7 (−2·6H)	13·4 (−2·9H)	13·9 (−3·9H)	3·5 (−4·5H)
Indian Sawfish *Pristis cuspidatus* from Bay of Bengal[50b]	1·2	22·9	12·7	0·1	0·2 (−2·0H)	8·2 (−2·0H)	28·5 (−2·2H)	16·4 (−5·3H)	5·2 (−7·4H)	4·6 (−11·0H)
from W. Coast of India[50d]	1·8	24·8	14·6	1·0	0·3 (−2·0H)	6·4 (−2·2H)	23·7 (−2·4H)	18·1 (−3·6H)	7·4 (−8·0H)	1·9 (−11·0H)

(*a*) Also 0·4 per cent. lauric acid. (*b*) Also trace of lauric acid.

39

the (all *cis*-) monoethenoid fatty acids in grey dogfish (*Squalus acanthias*) liver oil:

	Per cent. (wt.)		Per cent. (wt.)
Hexadec-9-enoic	6·1	Eicosa-9-enoic	4·0
Octadec-9-enoic	24·7	Eicosa-11-enoic	5·1
Octadec-11-enoic	9·8	Docosa-11-enoic	6·7
		Docosa-13-enoic	1·8

These acids comprised 58 per cent. of the total fatty acids, and 87 per cent. of the unsaturated acids in the oil.

These oils and all the oils in Table 3 fall in one or other of the first three of Tsujimoto's main Elasmobranch groups (p. 35). Until recently few instances of his fourth group – characterised by low-content of unsaponifiable matter and a very high proportion of saturated acids in the total liver oil component acids – had been reported, but detailed analyses of a number of these have now been published.

Tsujimoto[28] found that the liver oil of a white shark (*Carcharias gangeticus*) which contained 12–35 per cent. of "unsaponifiable matter" (mainly alcohols of the selachyl group) was remarkably low in unsaturation. Its component acids included approximately 50 per cent. of saturated (mainly palmitic) with 50 per cent. of unsaturated (almost wholly hexadecenoic and oleic); the total amount of C_{16} (palmitic and hexadecenoic) acids is thus extraordinarily large in this case. (In the cases recorded in Table 3, it will be noticed that the saturated acid contents are relatively constant, the hexadecenoic figure usually low, whilst the amount of unsaturated C_{18} acids, which is 20–25 per cent. of the whole in the oils of most typically "marine" type, rises in one instance to as much as 50 per cent.)

In 1936 Wang and Kan[50a] observed that the liver fat of the fan fish belongs to this group, and since 1952 other fats of the same type have been studied in detail by Pathak *et al.*[50b–d] and by Kamath and Magar.[51a–c] Some detailed analyses are quoted in Table 3A.

In addition to the data in Table 3A, the proportions of total saturated acids in the component acids of some of these Indian shark and sawfish oils have been separately recorded by Kamath and Magar as follows:

	Per cent. Saturated acids
Galeocerda rayneri[51a]	35·6
Carcharias limbatus[51b]	33·8
Cestracion blochii[51b]	25·5
Pristis sp.[51c]	26·9

Saturated acids in these liver oils amount to 25–40 per cent. of the total acids, the palmitic and stearic acid contents being reminiscent of those of land animal depot fats; but the unsaturated acids are typically those of a marine animal fat, with quite high mean unsaturation in the C_{20} and C_{22} acids which are present in varying, but often fairly high amounts.

Morice and Shorland[51d] isolated small amounts (0·2–0·3 per cent.) of *iso*- and *anteiso*-pentadecanoic and -heptadecanoic acids, and of the corresponding *n*-acids, from the liver oil of the New Zealand school shark (*Galeorhinus australis*).

Liver fats of marine Teleostid fish. In some families of this division of fish, the livers contain large amounts of fat and act as the main fat store of the fish, but in others, especially Clupeidæ, the livers are small and/or have only small fat contents whilst the flesh may contain considerable amounts of depot fat. In fish livers which contain much fatty matter, the latter is almost wholly glycerides: the content of phosphatides in these liver oils is usually very low, and the amount of non-fatty or unsaponifiable matter (mainly cholesterol) is also small, usually not exceeding 1 per cent. of the oil.

Table 4 (pp. 42, 43) gives a summary of data which have been published for the quantitative composition of the mixed fatty acids of fats from the livers of various marine Teleostid fish; but a few examples (e.g. liver fats of eels, salmon, and sturgeon) are reserved for special notice after some of the fresh-water Teleostid fish liver oils have been discussed. (Where the figures are from recent work, they are given as published, i.e. to the first decimal place; this does not, of course, mean that they are necessarily accurate to within more than 1 unit per cent., while in certain circumstances the experimental error may be somewhat greater than this.)

Cod liver oil is the most widely used of the liver oils in Table 4, in consequence of its medicinal value due to its content of vitamin A and vitamin D. The component fatty acids of cod liver oils from fish taken in the Arctic White Sea by Hull trawlers were determined[54] by gas–liquid chromatography on seven samples taken at intervals from May 1960 to November 1961. The average composition was:

Saturated acids C_{14} 2·8, C_{16} 11·7, C_{18} 2·7;

Unsaturated acids C_{14}-enoic, mono- 0·2, di- 0·2; C_{16}-enoic, mono- 8·6, di- 0·8; C_{18}-enoic, mono- 25·2, tri- 0·7, tetra- 2·2; C_{20}-enoic, mono- 13·1, tri- 0·9, penta- 9·3; C_{22}-enoic, mono- 6·3, tri- 0·4, penta- 1·0, hexa- 8·7 per cent.

Odd-numbered saturated acids: C_{15} 1·1, C_{17} 1·6 per cent.

Over the whole period there was no marked difference in the oil compositions except that in March the overall unsaturation fell noticeably, but was gradually restored by about August; this coincides with the period when the cod are spawning. The alteration was chiefly caused by some reduction in the proportions of C_{20} and C_{22} polyethenoid acids and some increase in the corresponding mono-ethenoid acids (e.g., C_{20} pentaenoic, from 12 to 8, C_{22} hexaenoic from 9 to 7 per cent.; C_{20} monoenoic from 10 to 14, C_{22} monoenoic from 5 to 7 per cent.). The proportions of saturated acids and of C_{18} unsaturated acids, on the other hand, exhibited little variation throughout.

The recorded percentages of myristic (2·8), palmitic (11·7), unsaturated C_{18} (30·6), C_{20} (23·3) and C_{22} acids (16·4) fall within the limits in the ester-fractionation analyses of the five cod liver oils in Table 4.

The figures in Table 4 suggest that in many cases the following represent the proportions of the major component acids in marine Teleostid fish liver oils: palmitic, 10–15; hexadecenoic, 12–18; unsaturated C_{18} (mean unsaturation *ca.* −3H), 25–30; unsaturated C_{20} (mean unsaturation *ca.* −6H), 25–30;

41

TABLE 4. *Component Acids (per cent. wt.)*

FAMILY	SPECIES	HABITAT	OIL IN LIVER (Per cent.)	"UNSAPONIFI-ABLE MATTER" IN OIL (Per cent.)
Gadidæ	Cod (Gadus morrhua)	Newfoundland[40]	40–65	0·8–1
		Norwegian[40]	,,	,,
		North Sea[40]	,,	,,
		,, ,, [53a]	,,	,,
		,, ,, [53b]	,,	,,
	Coalfish, saith[40] (G. virens)	,, ,,	40–60	0·7–1
		,, ,,	,,	,,
	*Pollack[41] (G. pollachius)	,, ,,	ca. 70	
	Haddock[55] (G. æglefinus)	,, ,,	ca. 70	0·7
	Red cod[56] (Physiculus bachus)	New Zealand, Cook Strait	23	2·7
	Ling[40] (Molva molva)	North Sea	ca. 70	1·1
	Hake[40] (Merluccius merluccius)	,, ,,	ca. 50	1·3
	(Merluccius hubbsi)[60b]	S. Atlantic Argentine coast		
	New Zealand hake[56] (Merluccius gayi)	New Zealand, Cook Strait	23	3·3
	Stockfish[52] (Merluccius Capensis)	S. Atlantic, South African coast	25–35	2·5–3·0
Serranidæ	Groper† (liver glycerides)[56] (Polyprion oxygeneios)	New Zealand, (a) Cook Strait		3·3
	,, ,, (b)		9	5·8
	,, ,, (c)		8	12·3
Scorpænidæ	Jacopever[52] (Sebastichthys Capensis)	S. Atlantic, South African coast	2·5–40	7–11
Zeidæ	Cape John Dory[52] (Zeus Capensis)	S. African coast November, 1944	16	5·8
		June, 1945	29	3·4
Blenniidæ	Catfish[41] (Anarrhichas lupus)	North Sea	ca. 30	4–5
Ophidiidæ	New Zealand Ling[58] (Genypterus blacodes)	New Zealand, Cook Strait	35–40	
		,, ,,		,,
Scombridæ	Tunny[59] (Thynnus thynnus)	North Sea	20–25	1–8 (?)
Pluronectidæ	Halibut[55] (Hippoglossus vulgarus)	,, ,,	ca. 20	6·6
	Turbot[41] (Rhombus maximus)	,, ,,	ca. 20	8·0
Lophidæ	Angler (Monk) fish[55] (Lophius piscatorius)	,, ,,	30–50	1

* Ueno and Matsuda[60a] found that the completely hydrogenated acids of an Alaskan pollack liver oil consisted of C_{14} 1, C_{16} 13–14, C_{18} 37–38, C_{20} 18–19, C_{22} 25–26, and C_{24} 1 per cent.
(a) Also 0·2 per cent. arachidic acid.
(b) Also 1·7 per cent. arachidic and 1·1 per cent. behenic acid.

and unsaturated C_{22} (mean unsaturation *ca.* −7H), 10–15 per cent. A statistical survey by Lovern[41] of the data for the component acids of liver and body oils of marine and freshwater fish bears out the broad differences in the component acids of fish fats of respective marine and freshwater origin (typical *of Liver Fats of Marine Teleostid Fish*

SATURATED			UNSATURATED					
C$_{14}$	C$_{16}$	C$_{18}$	C$_{14}$	C$_{16}$	C$_{18}$	C$_{20}$	C$_{22}$	C$_{24}$
6	8·5	0·5	Trace	20 (−2H)	29 (−3H)	26 (−6H)	10 (−7H)	—
5	6·5	Trace	0·5	16 (−2H)	31 (−3H)	30·5 (−5H)	10·5 (−?H)	—
3·5	10	—	0·5	15·5 (−2H)	25 (−3H)	31·5 (−6H)	14 (−7H)	—
4	11	1	Trace	11 (−2H)	27 (−2·5H)	27 (−5H)	19 (−7H)	—
2	14	1	2	10 (−2H)	26 (−3·3H)	25 (−5·5H)	20 (−7·4H)	Trace
6·5	13	0·5	—	14·5 (−2H)	31 (−3H)	24·5 (−?H)	10 (−?H)	—
6	12	Trace	Trace	9·5 (−2H)	29·5 (−3H)	26·5 (−5H)	16·5 (−7H)	—
2·1	13·0	1·4	—	10·9 (−2H)	34·2 (−2·7H)	25·4 (−5·4H)	13·0 (−6·5H)	—
4·3	14·1	0·3	0·5	12·4 (−2H)	30·5 (−2·6H)	29·3 (−6H)	8·6 (−7·3H)	—
1·6	14·4	3·1	—	7·7 (−2H)	30·7 (−3·0H)	28·2 (−6·6H)	14·3 (−10·3H)	—
5	13	1	Trace	13 (−2H)	32·5 (−3H)	24 (−6H)	11·5 (−7H)	—
7	13	—	Trace	17 (−2H)	18 (−3H)	31 (−5H)	14 (−?H)	—
3·6	15·5	2·3	0·5	7·5 (−2H)	23·4 (−3H)	19·1 (−5H)	25·0 (−8H)	3·1 (−6H)
2·1	18·4	1·2	—	9·3 (−2H)	37·3 (−2·6H)	21·0 (−5·7H)	10·7 (−8·0H)	—
1·4	17·9	1·9§	0·4	11·8 (−2H)	32·6 (−3·3H)	19·3 (−7·1H)	12·0 (−9·0H)	2·3 (−?H)
2·4	23·0	3·4	1·6	23·3 (−2H)	39·3 (−2·5H)	7·0 (−5·9H)	Trace	—
1·9	19·3	3·3	0·1	17·3 (−2H)	45·2 (−2·3H)	9·1 (−6·3H)	3·8 (−6·3H)	—
2·0	22·7	3·3	0·2	18·2 (−2H)	40·8 (−2·4H)	8·8 (−6·0H)	4·0 (−6·0H)	—
1·2	11·6	3·9‡	0·6	13·5 (−2H)	46·3 (−2·3H)	12·7 (−6·3H)	7·5 (−8·7H)	2·4 (−?H)
3·9	15·2	3·9 (a)	1·0 (−2H)	9·5 (−2·0H)	34·9 (−2·8H)	15·0 (−6·9H)	12·8 (−10·5H)	3·6 (−10H)
3·4	15·2	3·7 (b)	0·9 (−2H)	8·5 (−2·0H)	32·8 (−2·6H)	20·2 (−5·7H)	12·5 (−10H)	—
1·5	17·9	2·3	—	11·7 (−2·2H)	46·8 (−2·6H)	12·0 (−6·4H)	5·9 (−8·2H)	1·9 (−?H)
1·1	16·4	2·6	0·1	6·3 (−2H)	37·4 (−2·2H)	21·9 (−5·3H)	14·2 (−9·0H)	—
1·9	16·1	2·7	1·1	6·1 (−2H)	34·5 (−2·1H)	24·2 (−5·3H)	13·4 (−8·5H)	—
—	17·9	8·9	—	3·4 (−2·5H)	23·5 (−2·8H)	28·2 (−5·5H)	18·1 (−7·4H)	—
3·9	15·1	0·5	—	18·7 (−2·0H)	34·4 (−2·0H)	13·8 (−5·5H)	13·6 (−7·6H)	—
7·6	14·9	0·8	1·5	21·4 (−2·1H)	27·1 (−2·5H)	14·0 (−6·1H)	12·7 (−6·7H)	—
4·9	9·6	1·3	0·4	12·1 (−2H)	30·9 (−3·5H)	24·9 (−6H)	15·9 (−8·6H)	—

† Liver glycerides of groper taken in *(a)* spring 1934 (October), *(b)* early winter 1935 (June), and *(c)* late winter, 1935 (August). See also below, p. 60.
§ Also 0·4 per cent. arachidic acid.
‡ Also 0·3 per cent. arachidic and 0·1 per cent. behenic acid.

analyses of freshwater fish fatty acids are given in Table 6, p. 52); the general percentages of unsaturated acids revealed by the statistical analysis of results for fats of marine origin were C$_{16}$, 10; C$_{18}$, 25; C$_{20}$, 25; and C$_{22}$, 15. Whilst these proportions are on the whole typical, and are indeed closely adhered to in quite a number of instances, it is clear from inspection of Table 4 that there are many subordinate variations. The possible incidence of various factors – food, salinity, species characteristics, etc. – has been discussed in some detail by Lovern in the papers cited in Table 4, and we shall return to the subject later (pp. 51, 58). For the present we shall merely draw attention to the chief instances in Table 4 which seem to depart from the typical compositions.

Perhaps the most marked differences are to be seen, so far, in the fatty acid compositions of liver oils of fish inhabiting the seas respectively surrounding New Zealand and Great Britain; for some reason at present unknown, it would appear that some of the New Zealand liver oils tend rather towards the typical composition of a freshwater fish liver oil (cf. Table 6, p. 52), and diverge somewhat from that most frequently encountered in the marine fish liver oils of the North Atlantic. This is not wholly the case, and the liver oils of the New Zealand red cod and hake, for example, belong definitely to what, following Lovern, we may term the "marine" type. Moreover, the differences referred to are mainly increase in unsaturated C_{18} acids at the expense of the C_{22} (and sometimes the C_{20}) group; hexadecenoic acid is usually subnormal in amount, whereas in freshwater fish fats its proportion is generally notably increased.

Studies by Rapson, Schwartz and van Rensburg[52] on fish (stockfish and jacopever) from the South Atlantic and Southern Indian oceans bordering the western and eastern coasts of South Africa have revealed resemblances in the component acids of their liver fats to those of New Zealand fish. It would thus appear that liver oils of marine fish from the Southern Hemisphere as a whole differ slightly in their component acids from those of fish inhabiting the Northern Hemisphere, the main difference being enhanced contents of unsaturated C_{18} acids in the first-named class. It may be added that these authors have observed that fish from the Western coasts of South Africa reach maximum fat content in winter (June–July), whilst those from the Eastern coasts attain maximum fat content in the summer (December) and have correlated this with characteristic differences in mean temperature, relative abundance of phyto- and zoo-plankton, and other factors which differ respectively for the South Atlantic and the southern Indian oceans.

Seasonal variations in the visceral oil of the yellowtails fish (from Japanese waters) have been recorded[60c]:

	COMPONENT ACIDS								
	Saturated				Unsaturated				
	C_{14}	C_{16}	C_{18}	C_{20}	C_{16}	C_{18}	C_{20}	C_{22}	C_{24}
January (a)	1·6	10·2	6·6	1·7	8·6 (−3·6H)	12·5 (−2·8H)	27·0 (−4·1H)	23·4 (−6·9H)	8·0 (−9·7H)
April (b)	3·7	15·2	6·0	1·2	9·3 (−2·4H)	24·5 (−3·0H)	24·7 (−4·8H)	13·7 (−8·1H)	1·0 (−10·7H)

(a) Also 0·3 behenic and 0·1 tetradecenoic acids.
(b) Also 0·1 behenic and 0·7 tetradecenoic acids.

Amongst other irregularities in Table 4 we may note the very low content of hexadecenoic acid in tunny liver oil, and the unusually low proportions of C_{20} acids in halibut and turbot liver oils, together with the almost complete absence of acids more unsaturated than mono-ethenoid in the unsaturated C_{18} acids of halibut liver oil. There is, however, one feature which differentiates halibut and turbot liver oils from the remainder of the oils in Table 4; in these two fish the liver is not the main storage depot of fat, which is chiefly laid down in their body tissues. As will be seen in Table 5, the body fats of halibut and turbot conform to the typical "marine" type.

One of the northern fish so far examined, the catfish, shows very similar divergences from what is, perhaps, the normal type of liver fat to those displayed in some of the New Zealand liver oils (cf. for example, the New Zealand ling liver oil); it also has some points in common with certain Elasmobranch liver oils.

Perhaps all that can usefully be said, with the relatively few detailed analyses yet available, is that a normal or typical composition of the mixed fatty acids seems certainly to characterise many liver oils of marine Teleostid fish, but that many subordinate deviations from this type may occur. The chief utility of the information so far obtained will reside in the encouragement it may offer to other workers to develop further this interesting, although very difficult and tedious, branch of the natural fats; the accumulated data from many similar investigations on different fish species cannot fail to lead to useful and, quite probably, unusually interesting results.

Body fats of marine Teleostid fish. The occurrence of depot fats in the flesh of fish is on the whole less common than in the livers.

The data in Table 5, although comparatively few in number, include those for fishes of widely differing kinds and families; but on the whole the composition of the flesh fats appears to be more regular than in the case of the Teleostid liver fats – species differences are less pronounced. The major component acids in most cases fall within the following limits: palmitic, 15–18; unsaturated C_{16} (mean unsaturation ca. $-2 \cdot 5H$), not exceeding 10; unsaturated C_{18} (mean unsaturation ca. $-3H$), 20–25; unsaturated C_{20} (mean unsaturation ca. $-5H$), 22–26; and unsaturated C_{22} (mean unsaturation ca. -5 to $-7H$), 18–22 per cent. Thus the hexadecenoic acid percentage is distinctly lower, whilst the amount of unsaturated C_{22} acids is higher than is usual in typical marine fish liver fats. The proportions of unsaturated C_{18} and C_{20} acids, and also the degree of average unsaturation of the C_{20} acids, is rather lower than in most of the liver fats.

Lovern[62a] examined (1938) the composition of the body fats of herrings, both during the period (May–July) when the fish are feeding vigorously and largely increasing the amount of flesh fat, and subsequently. The results (quoted in Table 5) show no very great alteration in the percentages of the various homologous groups of acids as the fat content increases; but there is a very marked rise, during the period of intensive deposition of fat, in the degree of average unsaturation of the C_{18} and C_{20} acids, and some increase in that of the unsaturated C_{16} acids. The mean unsaturation of the C_{20} and C_{22} groups is distinctly lower than in most fish oils. Swain[62b] (1953) made a similar study of the body fats, at different seasons, of herring taken in northern and southern waters of British Columbia.

45

TABLE 5. *Component Acids (per cent. wt.)*

FAMILY	SPECIES	HABITAT	OIL IN FLESH (Per cent.)	"UNSAPONIFI-ABLE MATTER" IN OIL (Per cent.)
Clupeidæ	Herring (*Clupea harengus*)	North Sea[62a]		
		April 1937	8·2	2·3
		June 1937	10·7	?
		June 1937	15·7	1·2
		July 1937	20·7	?
		October 1937*	12·0	1·2
		Iceland[63] 1942		1·4
	Herring[64] Visceral Fat	Irish Sea	—	0·75
"	Sprat[55] (*Clupea sprattus*)	North Sea	12	1
"	Pilchard[61] (*Sardinops cærulea*)	Pacific		
"	Pilchard[57b] (*Sardina ocellata*)	S. Atlantic (S. Africa)	15·7	1·7
	" "	"	10·5	2·6
"	Japanese sardine[65] (*Clupanodon melanostica*)	Japan Seas	10–18	0·5–1·5
"	Menhaden (*Brevoortia tyrannus*)	N. Atlantic[65]	10–16	0·6–1·6
		N. Atlantic[66]		
		N. Atlantic[67]		
Salmonidæ	†Salmon[70] (*Salmo salar*) (male)	Scotland	13·9	0·8
	(female)	"	13·2	0·9
"	†Sea trout[41] (*Salmo trutta*)	"	5–10	1·2
"	†Brown trout[41] (*Salmo trutta*)	"	7	3·3
Serranidæ	Sea-bass (Grouper)[43] (*Epinephelus æneus*)	N.W. African coast (visceral fat)	?	0·7
Scorpænidæ	Jacopever[52] (*Sebastichthys Capensis*)	S. Atlantic (S. Africa)	3–5	3–4
Nototheniidæ	South Georgia Cod[99a] (*Notothenia rossii mamorata*)	Antarctic	ca. 10	0·5–1·6
Zeidæ	Cape John Dory[52] (*Zeus Capensis*)	S. African coast November 1944	3·9	4·4
		June 1945	6·2	2·3
Scombridæ	Horse mackerel[57] (*Trachurus trachurus*)	S. Atlantic (St. Helena)	6·1	4·0
"	Tunny[59] (*Thynnus thynnus*)	North Sea	23	0·7
Pluronectidæ	Halibut[41] (*Hippoglossus vulgarus*)	" "	4–7	1·3
"	Turbot[41] (*Rhombus maximus*)	" "	4	2·1
Petromyzonidæ (Cyclostomata)	†Lampern[41] (*Petromyzon fluviatilis*)	R. Severn (tidal)	8·5	2·3

* This specimen had recently spawned.
† See also below, p. 54.
§ Also 3·6 per cent C_{26} and higher unsaturated acids.

of Body Fats of Marine Teleostid Fish

SATURATED			UNSATURATED					
C_{14}	C_{16}	C_{18}	C_{14}	C_{16}	C_{18}	C_{20}	C_{22}	C_{24}
8·0	15·7	0·2	—	4·6 (−2·6H)	22·2 (−2·9H)	22·0 (−3·9H)	27·3 (−4·2H)	—
7·3	16·7	Trace	0·6 (−2·2H)	7·5 (−2·7H)	21·1 (−3·3H)	27·3 (−4·8H)	19·5 (−5·7H)	—
7·5	12·8	0·1	0·3	7·0 (−3·0H)	21·1 (−4·8H)	30·0 (−5·2H)	21·2 (−4·8H)	—
8·3	12·1	0·3	0·5	6·4 (−3·4H)	21·0 (−4·5H)	28·3 (−5·5H)	23·1 (−4·6H)	—
6·6	13·7	0·5	0·2	4·9 (−2·8H)	16·3 (−3·6H)	28·7 (−4·4H)	29·1 (−4·1H)	—
7·0	11·7	0·8 (a)	1·2 (−2·0H)	11·8 (−2·4H)	19·6 (−3·5H)	25·9 (−5·2H)	21·6 (−4·3H)	0·1 (−3·8H)
5·8	15·7	2·8 (b)	1·4 (−2·0H)	10·5 (−2·5H)	31·8 (−2·6H)	22·4 (−7·1H)	9·3 (−10·5H)	—
6·0	18·7	0·9	0·1	16·2 (−3H)	29·0	18·2 (−5·5H)	10·9 (−7H)	—
5·1	14·4	3·2	0·1 (−2H)	11·8 (−2H)	17·7 (−3·3H)	17·9 (−4·1H)	13·8 (−8·5H)	15·2 (−10·9H)
6·7	17·4	2·1 (c)	1·9 (−2·0H)	15·0 (−3·5H)	19·8 (−4·1H)	25·8 (−9·4H)	10·6 (−9·2H)	—
6·9	17·3	2·1 (d)	1·9 (−2·0H)	14·6 (−3·2H)	19·3 (−3·9H)	26·3 (−8·8H)	11·0 (−9·0H)	—
6	10	2	—	13 (−2H)	24 (−5H)	26 (−5H)	19	—
6	16	1·5	—	15·5 (−4H)	30 (−10H)	19 (−10H)	12	—
8·3	14·9	4·7	5·8	23·4 (−2·0H)	31·1 (−3·9H)	8·4 (−5·6H)	3·4 (−6·4H)	—
6·8	15·5	3·1	0·1	14·9 (−2·2H)	23·7 (−3·3H)	17·5 (−?H)	10·8 (−?H)	4·0§ (−?H)
3·8	15·0	2·0	0·1	10·6 (−2·8H)	28·8 (−5·5H)	23·5 (−6·9H)	16·2	—
5·0	11·3	1·1	0·5	9·1	25·7 (−2·7H)	26·5 (−4·7H)	20·8 (−6·4H)	—
2·2	17·0	4·0 (e)	0·1	8·8 (−2·4H)	26·3 (−3·0H)	19·7 (−6·6H)	19·0 (−9·2H)	2·4 (−?H)
3·1	19·0	4·5	0·4	11·5 (−2·6H)	38·3 (−3·9H)	15·0 (−7·8H)	8·2 (−10·1H)	—
5·2	11·3	—	2·6	16·4 (−2·0H)	41·1 (−3·7H)	14·3 (−5·7H)	9·0 (−8·6H)	—
2·6	13·8	1·8 (f)	2·3	12·4 (−2·0H)	28·5 (−2·4H)	21·6 (−7·0H)	16·8 (−9·5H)	—
10·0	13·8	4·5 (g)	0·6 (−2·0H)	15·1 (−2·6H)	28·4 (−3·0H)	17·1 (−8·0H)	10·3 (−9·2H)	—
5·6	19·6	2·0 (h)	2·1	7·4 (−2·0H)	23·2 (−3·6H)	20·5 (−7·3H)	14·7 (−9·8H)	1·9 (−10·0H)
3·1	15·7	4·0 (i)	0·9	9·4 (−2·0H)	23·4 (−2·5H)	19·0 (−7·0H)	21·9 (−10·5H)	0·3 (−10·0H)
7·3	13·1	2·0 (j)	2·8 (−2·0H)	14·1 (−3·0H)	19·0 (−3·8H)	19·4 (−7·9H)	20·7 (−5·3H)	0·2 (−4H)
4·2	18·6	3·5	—	6·2 (−2·7H)	26·0 (−3·2H)	23·5 (−5·5H)	18·0 (−6·8H)	—
4·0	14·8	0·7	Trace	6·5 (−2·6H)	23·8 (−3·0H)	26·9 (−5·2H)	23·3 (−6·5H)	—
3·4	15·1	2·1	0·3	8·9 (−2·6H)	21·7 (−3·4H)	26·6 (−6·0H)	21·9 (−7·7H)	—
9·5	17·6	0·7	—	10·9 (−2·1H)	35·3 (−2·6H)	15·3 (−6·5H)	10·7 (−10·3H)	—

Other minor saturated acids recorded as follows:

	C_{12}	C_{20}	C_{22}		C_{12}	C_{20}	C_{22}		C_{12}	C_{20}	C_{22}
(a)	0·1	0·1	—	(e)	—	0·4	—	(h)	0·5	1·8	0·6
(b)	—	0·3	—	(f)	—	0·2	—	(i)	—	1·8	0·5
(c)	—	0·4	0·3	(g)	0·2	—	—	(j)	0·4	0·4	0·6
(d)	—	0·5	0·1								

The herring visceral oil examined by Hilditch and Pathak[64] differs from the general composition of the herring flesh fats in Table 5 in its higher content of unsaturated C_{18} acids, its lower content of C_{22} acids and, especially, in the higher mean unsaturation of the C_{20} and C_{22} acids. It resembles many marine fish liver fats more closely than herring body fats in the proportions and nature of its component acids. This is the more curious, perhaps, when it is recalled that there is much closer similarity between herring flesh fat and that of the chief food of the herring, the copepod *Calanus finmarchicus* (*cf*. Table 1B, p. 30), than between either and the herring intestinal fat.

By fractionation of the fatty acids from about a ton of Japanese herring oil, Nobori[68a] showed that, in addition to myristic acid, the acids contained very small proportions of lauric, decanoic and octanoic acids; he also found traces of these lower saturated acids in Japanese sardine oil. Much work has been done of late years on the consitution of the highly unsaturated acids present in the body fats of the Clupeidæ family, including those of herring,[68b] pilchard,[68c] sardine[68d] and menhaden[68e]. (*cf*. Chapter IX, pp. 639–643).

Component acid analyses of menhaden oil have been carried out by gas–liquid chromatography by Ahrens *et al.*[69a] and by Keppler *et al.*[69b]. The G.L.C. technique revealed the presence of traces of many straight and branched chain saturated acids and of minor proportions of di-, tri- and tetra-ene C_{16} and C_{18} acids. The figures (per cent. wt.) may be summarised as follows:

Major component acids:

	SATURATED			UNSATURATED			
	C_{14}	C_{16}	C_{18}	C_{16} ($-2H$)	C_{18} ($-2H$)	C_{20} (-4 to $-10H$)	C_{22} (-10 and $-12H$)
Ahrens[69a]	7·2	17·0	3·1	9·8	14·5	9·2	10·9
Keppler[69b]	8·4	20·7	3·8	11·9	15·6	15·4	9·7

Minor component unsaturated acids:

	C_{16}			C_{18}		C_{20}	
	($-4H$)	($-6H$)	($-8H$)	($-4H$)	($-6H$)	($-8H$)	($-2H$)
Ahrens[69a]	2·0	1·3	2·0	2·7	1·3	3·2	2·1
Keppler[69b]	1·8	1·3	0·3	2·0	0·9	2·5	2·8

Trace acids: These included tetradecenoic, saturated n-C_{12}, n-C_{13}, *iso*-C_{13}, *iso*-C_{14}, n- and *iso*-C_{15}, n- and *iso*-C_{17}, n- and *iso*-C_{19}, and n-C_{24} acids.

The body fats of South Atlantic fish such as the Jacopever[52] and the Cape John Dory[52] appear to contain very similar fatty acids to those of the tunny or halibut, and this is also true of the Antarctic *Notothenia* body fat examined by Pedersen.[99a] It is interesting to note that the latter fish (popularly called "South Georgia cod", but not gadoid and more closely related to the European gurnard) feeds, like the Antarctic whales, almost entirely on krill (*Euphausia superba*): nevertheless the respective flesh fats differ materially in several respects. Antarctic whale blubber fats (*cf*. Table 20, p. 69) contain more unsaturated C_{18} acids and, correspondingly, less unsaturated C_{20} and (especially) C_{22} acids than the *Notothenia* body fat, and the general level of unsaturation is distinctly higher in the latter.

The body fat of white pomfret (*Stromateus cinerus*), black pomfret (*S. niger*) and pala (*Hilsa ilsha*), fish taken from the Indian Ocean off Bombay, were found by Karkhanis and Magar[81] to contain the following component acids (per cent. wt.):

		S. cinerus	*S. niger*	*Hilsa ilsha*
Saturated	C_{14}	4·7	4·4	5·3
,,	C_{16}	20·6	13·3	23·5
,,	C_{18}	11·1	7·3	8·9
,,	C_{20}	—	0·5	Trace
Unsaturated	$C_{14}(-2H)$	1·4	2·4	1·3
,,	$C_{16}(-2H)$	9·2	18·8	6·8
,,	$C_{18}(-2H)$	33·2	33·2	32·9
,,	$C_{18}(-4H)$	3·6	0·4	1·7
,,	$C_{18}(-6H)$	3·6	1·7	9·6
,,	$C_{20}(-2H)$	7·5	4·5	9·0
,,	$C_{20}(-8H)$	5·1	6·7	0·5
,,	$C_{22}(-2H)$	—	3·4	—
,,	$C_{22}(-10H)$	—	3·4	0·5

These tropical Teleostid fish body fats differ from those in Table 5 and more nearly resemble the Elasmobranch fats of Tsujimoto's "fourth class" (p. 36) and some tropical Teleostid freshwater fats (p. 51), in their relatively high content of palmitic and stearic acids, and in the low degree of unsaturation in the C_{18}, C_{20} and C_{22} acids and the relatively small proportions of the two last-named groups.

The body fats of the mature salmon and sea trout conform to the same general type as the other marine fish body fats in Table 5, but in the corresponding fats of a freshwater fish (brown trout), or of the lampern which frequents both fresh and salt water, a change in composition is at once apparent, the percentages of C_{20} and, especially, C_{22} acids falling, whilst that of the unsaturated C_{18} acids increases considerably, as also does the degree of average unsaturation of the C_{22} acids. We shall refer to this alteration again (pp. 54–56) after discussing typical freshwater fish fats.

An outstanding exception in the flesh fats of marine Teleostids appears to exist in the castor oil fish, *Ruvettus pretiosus*. This is a large deep-sea fish belonging to the family Gempylidæ, which resembles a perch in appearance but grows to a length of 6 feet and a weight of about 100 lb. It is found in warm seas in the Atlantic and Mediterranean regions, and its flesh has a high fatty content. Cox and Reid[71a] found that the oil contained only traces of glycerides and was substantially a liquid wax, the fatty acids being combined with a mixture of alcohols (cetyl 50 per cent., octadecyl 6 per cent., oleyl 44 per cent.). The composition of the acids was also peculiar, no unsaturation higher than mono-ethenoid being observed. The occurrence of a wax-ester type of oil in the flesh of a marine Teleostid is at present almost unique, but Komori and Agawa[71b] state that the body fat of the North Pacific deep-water fish *Læmonema morosum* contains over 30 per cent. of "unsaponifiable matter", about half of which is docos-11-enol, $CH_3[CH_2]_9.CH:CH.[CH_2]_9.CH_2OH$.

It will be noticed that the amount of fat in the flesh of fish listed in Table 5 is usually more than 10 per cent., although in some instances it is as low as 4 or 5 per cent. In all these cases, however, the fat is mainly glyceridic in nature and is "free", i.e., it can be removed readily by light petroleum or ether and, often, "rendered" by steaming: the flesh of the fish acts as a depot for the storage of the fat of the animal. In many species, of course, there is practically no glyceride fat stored in the flesh tissues. In all fish, however, lipid material is present in a form which is more firmly attached to other substances, mainly of protein nature – the so-called "lipo-proteins". This "bound" lipid cannot be directly removed except by the action of solvents which denature the protein as well as remove the liberated lipids.

The "bound" lipids have only recently commenced to receive detailed study. The work of Lovern and Olley[72a] on the lipids of haddock and cod flesh may be mentioned in this connection. The total lipids extracted amounted to less than 1 per cent. of the haddock flesh and consisted of a complex mixture of which over 40 per cent. was lecithin, 10 per cent. phosphatidyl ethanolamine and inositol lipids, with about 15 per cent. unidentified lipid; free cholesterol, waxes, and free fatty acids each amounted to about 6 per cent. of the total material; cholesterol esters and triglycerides each formed only 3 per cent. or less, with about 2 per cent. each of hydrocarbons and plasmalogens. The component acids of some of the lecithin and unidentified lipid fractions isolated were determined: they differed very much from those of the glyceridic fats which form the main topic of this chapter. Unsaturated C_{20} and C_{22} acids usually formed 60–70 per cent. of the total acids, and the mean unsaturation of these acids was greater than that of typical fish glycerides, e.g. C_{20}, -7 to $-8H$, and C_{22}, -10 to $-12H$. The proportion of unsaturated C_{18} acids was low, never above 20 per cent., and sometimes only 5 per cent., whilst hexadecenoic acid was absent or present only in very minor amounts. Fatty acids present as sterol esters also had unusually high unsaturation, but the glycerides more nearly resembled the "free" depot fats of the fish.

Cardin et al.[72b] state that the phospholipids in fresh cod flesh contained the following acids: saturated C_{16} 15, C_{18} 8·5, C_{20} 1; unsaturated C_{16} ($-2·1H$) 4·5, C_{18} ($-2·5H$) 13·5, C_{20} ($-7·1H$) 22, C_{22} ($-11·4H$) 35, C_{24} ($-11·8H$) 1 per cent. (wt.). The phospholipids of the brain tissues of sperm whale and of pollack, of rorqual hearts, and of pollack ova have been studied by Igarashi et al.[72c].

The composition of the extremely complex lipids linked to protein or other material in living tissues is a field of study which is at present limited, but which is attracting the increasing attention of biochemists.

Fats of freshwater fish. The component acids of fats in various tissues of a number of British, Indian and South American freshwater fish have been determined. These are collected in Table 6 (pp. 52, 53) and it is interesting, to compare the general features of Table 6 with those of Tables 4 and 5 (marine Teleostid fish fats) and Tables 1 and 2 (fats of aquatic flora and micro-fauna).

Generally speaking, it may be said that the distinctive points in the freshwater fish flesh fats in Table 6 are the small proportions of unsaturated C_{22} acids, the reduced proportions (as compared with many marine fish fats) of unsaturated C_{20} acids, often with (especially in tropical freshwater fish fats) increased proportions of palmitic and stearic acids, and the predominance of unsaturated C_{18} acids (which range from about 30 per cent. upwards). In the C_{20} and C_{22} groups the average unsaturation varies considerably, being greater in the fats of freshwater fish from temperate waters than from tropical; in some of the latter unsaturated C_{22} acids are absent or only present to the extent of 1–2 per cent. of the total acids. Similarly, in these fats from warm climates oleic acid frequently forms the greater part of the unsaturated C_{18} acids, and the proportions of palmitic and stearic acids may concurrently rise respectively to as much as 25–28 and 10–12 per cent. It is impossible to say at present how far the typical differences between marine and freshwater fish fats are conditioned by biological species factors or by differences in food or in environmental (e.g., salinity, climatic or seasonal) conditions; moreover, it is clearly inadmissible to compare fats from other than the same parts (liver, mesentery, muscle, etc.) of the fish.

Reiser et al.[75a] studied the fats of five species of freshwater fish which had been kept on a low-fat diet or on the latter supplemented with cottonseed oil or menhaden oil. Neither the low-fat nor the cottonseed oil diet had any effect on the "natural" fat of the fish, but this came to resemble menhaden oil after fish fed on the latter. The authors infer that marine and freshwater fish can synthesise polyethenoid acids from non-fatty sources and that differences between marine and freshwater fish fats may largely result from differences in their dietary fats. (See also Eel fats, p. 56.)

Bottino and Brenner[75b] similarly fed a fat-free diet for 10 weeks to a freshwater species (Pimelodus maculatus), and then injected radioactive acetate for one day before the fish were killed. The intestinal lipids were radioactive, proving that fat synthesis must have taken place. The triglycerides of the liver and muscles, and the total intestinal lipids were analysed for component acids by gas–liquid chromatography. The fatty acids were similar to each other in all three lipids, and also generally similar in composition to that of P. albitans mesenteric fat recorded in Table 6, except that the proportions of unsaturated C_{20} and C_{22} acids (2·3 and 0·5 per cent.) were even smaller than in the latter.

The muscle glyceride fatty acids included ca. 3 per cent. of odd-numbered normal and branched-chain acids, but these amounted to nearly 20 per cent. of the intestinal lipid acids (which may have been produced at this site by the action of intestinal bacteria).

The component acids of Astrakhan whitefish (Coregonus sp., Salmonidæ) are given by Williams and Onischtschenko[75c] as palmitic and stearic 24·9, oleic 49·2, "linoleic" 4·4, "linolenic" 14·0, and "clupanodonic" 7·5 per cent. (wt.).

Some further examples of Specific Fish Fats

The fats of a few fishes have been studied more intensively than the majority of those enumerated in Tables 3, 4, 5, and 6. In one interesting group, that of certain fish which have both fresh and salt-water relationships, the fats of salmon at all stages of the life-cycle have been studied by Lovern[70]; whilst in

TABLE 6. Component Acids (per cent. wt.) of Fats of Freshwater Fish

FAMILY	SPECIES	HABITAT	FAT (Per cent.)	SATURATED			UNSATURATED				
				C14	C16	C18	C14	C16	C18	C20	C22
Salmonidæ	Salmon[70] (Salmo salar)	Scotland (see below, Table 7, p. 55)		3·1	19·0	4·5	0·4	11·5 (−2·6H)	38·3 (−3·9H)	15·0 (−7·8H)	8·2 (−10·1H)
,,	Brown trout[41] (Salmo trutta)	,,		2·9	14·3	1·9	1·5	19·8 (−2·0H)	40·0 (−3·2H)	13·5 (−7·4H)	6·1 (−9·1H)
,,	Pollan[55] (Coregonus pollan)	Ireland (Muscle)		4·7	13·2	0·5	0·8	20·8 (−2·0H)	38·4 (−2·8H)	15·3 (−7·5H)	6·3 (−7·5H)
Esocidæ	Pike[55] (Esox lucius)	Scotland (Muscle)		2·9	15·0	Trace	0·5	20·2 (−2·0H)	42·4 (−3·4H)	15·1 (−6·7H)	3·9 (−8·0H)
		(Mesentery)		3·5	12·5	2·0	1·1	19·4 (−2·0H)	40·5 (−3·2H)	13·8 (−6·8H)	7·1 (−9·2H)
Percidæ	Perch[55] (Perca fluviatilis)	(?Muscle)		3·7	14·6	1·9	1·0	17·8 (−2·0H)	45·8 (−3·2H)	15·2 (−6·9H)	—
Cyprinidæ	Carp[55] (Cyprinus carpio)	(?Muscle)	3·7	1·5	13·6	2·5	1·5	6·7 (−2·0H)	64·0 (−4·3H)	10·2 (−6·4H)	—
,,	Grass-feeding carp[73] (Ctenopharyngodon idellus)	Singapore (Muscle)	ca. 2	2·6	18·0	1·9	0·7	22·9 (−2·1H)	45·7 (−3·0H)	8·2 (−6·5H)	—
		(Mesentery)		1·9	14·7	2·5	0·2	8·0 (−2·0H)	64·6 (−3·7H)	7·6 (−6·0H)	0·5
,,	Mud-feeding carp[73] (Hypophthalmichthys nobilis)	,,	ca. 2	—	17	6	—	9·5 (−2·0H)	54 (−3·6H)	13·5 (−6·8H)	—
,,	Mud-feeding carp[73] (H. molitrix)	(Flesh)	6·3	0·8	21·3	1·1	0·6	17·1 (−2·0H)	49·5 (−3·0H)	9·6 (−6·7H)	Trace
	Bhakur[74a] (Catla buchanani)	India R. Ganges (Viscera)	44·8	2·9	29·0	6·5	0·2	25·3 (−2·7H)	17·9 (−2·5H)	7·5 (−5·7H)	10·1 (−9·0H)
		(Liver)	8·5	2·8	25·3	7·9	1·4	10·0 (−2·7H)	37·2 (−2·5H)	11·9 (−5·7H)	2·1 (−9·0H)
Siluridæ	Pahuna[74a] (Wallago attu)	India R. Ganges (Liver)		0·6	19·0	6·4(a)	Trace	7·0 (−2·7H)	25·4 (−4·8H)	26·5 (−6·5H)	9·4(a) (−8·0H)
		(Liver)	5·1	1·5	14·2	4·0	0·4	8·4 (−2·0H)	32·6 (−2·4H)	19·8 (−5·3H)	19·1 (−8·0H)

Family	Species	Location	Part										Saturated C$_{20}$
Cirrhitidæ	Nain[74b] (Cirrhina mrigala)	India R. Ganges	(Body)	?	1·9	21·4	3·1	3·7	32·6 (−2·2H)	29·5 (−3·6H)	5·0 (−4·9H)	2·8 (−6·0H)	
			(Viscera)	45	5·7	20·1	5·7 (b)	4·2	26·5 (−2·2H)	32·3 (−2·9H)	5·0 (−4·6H)	—	
"	Rohu[74b] (Labeo rohita)	India R. Ganges	(Body)	?	3·4	21·2	11·5 (c)	3·7	8·1 (−2·2H)	32·2 (−3·3H)	12·4 (−5·2H)	6·7 (−6·9H)	
			(Viscera)	45	1·6	26·0	14·6 (d)	0·7	8·6 (−2·7H)	30·3 (−3·6H)	9·6 (−6·3H)	5·5 (−9·0H)	
Clupeidæ	Hilsa (shad)[74c] (Clupanodon ilisha)	India	(Body)	?	5·7	25·3	9·4 (e)	2·0 (−2·0H)	13·0 (−2·4H)	29·2 (−2·7H)	5·8 (−5·7H)	4·3 (−10·2H)	
Diplomystidæ	Belgagra[74] (Rita buchanani)	India R. Ganges	(Body)	?	4·2	20·8	9·3	1·4 (−2·0H)	13·2 (−2·0H)	36·0 (−2·7H)	8·9 (−5·6H)	6·2 (−6·5H)	
			(Viscera)	?	2·9	21·1	12·0	0·5 (−2·0H)	9·1 (−2·4H)	34·3 (−2·4H)	20·1 (−4·3H)	—	
Bagridæ	Mystus seenghala[74h]	India R. Ganges	(Viscera)	?	4·0	26·1	8·1 (l)	1·3 (−2·0H)	14·5 (−2·0H)	29·9 (−2·8H)	11·3 (−5·3H)	4·1 (−9·7H)	
Diplomystidæ	Sabalo[74d] (Prochilotus lineatus)	S. America R. Plate	(Muscle)	5–25	3·1	18·6	7·6	0·9 (−2·0H)	15·2 (−2·2H)	43·7 (−2·6H)	9·9 (−6·3H)	1·0 (−9·7H)	0·7
			(Dorsal panicle)	2–8	4·0	22·9	6·2 (f)	1·4 (−2·0H)	16·0 (−2·1H)	38·8 (−2·7H)	10·0 (−6·6H)	—	0·9
Doradidæ	Armado[74e] (Pterodoras granulos)	S. America R. Plate	(Mesentery)	1–3	2·6	27·8	10·4 (g)	0·6 (−2·0H)	7·9 (−2·0H)	40·0 (−2·3H)	9·8 (−3·6H)	—	0·6
Anostomidæ	Boga[74f] (Leporinus affinis)	S. America R. Plate	(Mesentery)	2–5	2·6	23·6	7·8 (h)	0·6 (−2·0H)	10·7 (−2·1H)	34·1 (−2·6H)	14·3 (−5·6H)	5·7 (−8·1H)	0·6
Pimelodidæ	White bagre[74g] (Pimelodus albicans)	S. America R. Plate	(Mesentery)	2–3	3·2	22·6	8·4 (i)	0·4 (−2·0H)	7·3 (−2·0H)	50·4 (−2·4H)	5·9 (−5·5H)	1·2 (−9·7H)	0·7

Minor component acids recorded as follows (per cent. wt.):

	Saturated C$_{20}$	Unsaturated C$_{24}$	
(a) Bhakur (liver)	3·1	2·6	(f) Sabalo (dorsal panicle)
(b) Nain (viscera)	0·5	—	(g) Armado (mesentery)
(c) Rohu (body)	0·5	0·3	(h) Boga (mesentery)
(d) " (viscera)	3·1	—	(i) White bagre (mesentery)
(e) Hilsa (body)	2·0	3·3	(l) Mystus seenghala (viscera)

53

eels and in some of the larger fish, including sturgeon, tunny, halibut, turbot, and groper, it has been possible to investigate fats from several parts of the animal instead of from only one depot (flesh or liver, as the case may be). These results are of sufficient interest to receive separate consideration at this point.

Salmon fats. It has already been shown, in Table 5, that the flesh fats of the sea trout and the brown trout conform respectively to Lovern's "marine" and "freshwater" types of component fatty acid mixtures; these fish are now regarded as merely the migratory and non-migratory forms of the same species, *Salmo trutta*. Similarly, the lampern, a denizen of tidal estuaries known to visit both salt and fresh water, possesses a body fat more akin to the "freshwater" than to the "marine" type. In the case of the trout, the adult fish may proceed to the sea or may remain in freshwater streams (brown trout); the analyses given in Table 6 refer to the flesh fats of such adult fish.

The Atlantic salmon, *Salmo salar*, differs from the brown trout in that its adult life is spent in the sea until it returns to fresh water for spawning purposes. The eggs hatch out in fresh water, and for the first 1–4 years of their life the young salmon live like any other freshwater fish. During this stage they are known as salmon parr. Each year, at an average age of 2 or 3 years, some of these fish change colour and become silvery like the adult salmon. Now called smolts, they swim downstream and right out to sea, becoming a marine species. The maturing and adult fish feed intensively in the sea, and then, as the spawning time approaches, migrate to the rivers and commence to ascend them. It is certain that from the moment of entering the rivers, if not earlier, the salmon cease feeding entirely. The journey upstream to the spawning grounds demands the expenditure of much energy, which has to be supplied mainly by reserve fat. Moreover, considerable quantities of fat accumulate in the gonads, and this fat is probably transferred from the depots (*vide infra*). Continuous depletion of the latter thus takes place. The fish after spawning are known as kelts, and some of these have been found with as little as 0·3 per cent. of fat in the muscles, contrasted with 13–14 per cent. of fat in a fish fresh from the sea.

Lovern[70] made detailed analyses of the flesh fats from the young fish (parr and smolts), and from adult fish which had returned to spawn at various stages of emaciation; he also examined the ova fats at various stages of development of the eggs. The data for the different component fatty acids are collected in Table 7. The fat from the parr obviously belongs to the freshwater fish class, whilst that of the smolt more nearly resembles that of the mature salmon which has spent its adult life in sea water. The mature salmon body fat conforms fairly closely to the average composition of marine Teleostid fats mentioned on p. 41; in contrast to the parr fat, the content of C_{22} acids is high and that of unsaturated C_{16} acids low, whilst the average unsaturation of all the acid groups is definitely lower in the mature fat. The smolt fatty acids are intermediate in the latter respect.

The changes in the fatty acids during the (fasting) period in which the depot fat is being drawn upon are of great interest, although not very obvious, perhaps, at first sight. The average unsaturation is not greatly altered during

FAT	FAT (Per cent.)	UNSAPONIFIABLE (Per cent.)	SATURATED			UNSATURATED				
			C_{14}	C_{16}	C_{18}	C_{14}	C_{16}	C_{18}	C_{20}	C_{22}
Body fat of parr (Ettrick water)[70]	3·9	5·0	2·7†	17·7	3·3	3·1 (> −2·0H)	21·7 (−2·3H)	30·0 (−3·8H)	12·9 (−8·3H)	9·9 (−10·2H)
" " smolt (Aberdeen harbour)[70]	1·2	18·0	2·7	14·3	5·0	0·7 (−2·0H)	7·9 (−2·0H)	32·2 (−3·2H)	19·4 (−6·7H)	17·8 (−9·4H)
Body fats of male and female salmon returning to spawn (increasing emaciation):[70]										
1 Male	13·9	0·8	3·8	15·0	2·0	0·1	10·6 (−2·0H)	28·8 (−2·8H)	23·5 (−5·5H)	16·2 (−6·9H)
2 "	6·5	1·3	2·0	14·1	0·7	—	6·2 (−2·0H)	27·3 (−2·7H)	26·9 (−4·7H)	22·8 (−7·1H)
3 "	1·1	8·6	2·3	13·2	1·0	—	4·3 (−2·0H)	27·3 (−2·7H)	25·8 (−5·3H)	26·1 (−7·8H)
4 Female	13·2	0·9	5·0	11·3	1·1	0·5 (−2·0H)	9·1 (−2·0H)	25·7 (−2·7H)	26·5 (−4·7H)	20·8 (−6·4H)
5 "	7·3	1·3	2·2	12·5	1·6	—	7·7 (−2·0H)	27·1 (−2·8H)	28·4 (−4·7H)	20·5 (−6·8H)
6 "	3·5	2·2	1·9	10·0	1·8	—	7·8 (−2·0H)	28·5 (−2·6H)	33·2 (−4·3H)	16·8 (−6·4H)
Mature Salmon: Liver[41]	?	?	2·7	10·9	1·6	0·7	12·3 (−2·0H)	32·8 (−2·9H)	25·8 (−5·7H)	13·2 (−7·8H)
Mesentery[41]	?	?	3·6	14·4	2·3	0·1	7·1 (−2·4H)	25·3 (−2·9H)	28·4 (−4·6H)	18·8 (−6·1H)
Salmon ova fats (in increasing order of maturity):[70]										
No. 1 (from River Dee)	‡	8·8	3·1	16·0	0·5	0·1	12·6 (−2·0H)	23·7 (−4·0H)	27·2 (−8·0H)	16·8 (−10·4H)
No. 2 (from River Dee)	‡	7·4	2·9	13·4	0·7	0·4	10·4 (−2·0H)	25·3 (−3·2H)	28·7 (−7·2H)	18·1 (−11·4H)
No. 4 (from River Dee)	‡	6·3	1·8	13·0	2·0	—	9·9 (−2·0H)	36·7 (−2·9H)	21·3 (−7·6H)	15·3 (−11·1H)
No. 5 (from River Tweed)	‡	7·2	2·3	12·9	2·2	—	9·6 (−2·0H)	34·8 (−2·7H)	23·2 (−7·6H)	15·0 (−11·2H)
Ova fat of Alaskan Salmon[69c] (Oncorhynchus gorbuscha)	?	?	1·8	8·3	1·9	0·1	5·1 (−2·0H)	31·3 (−3·6H)	31·1 (−7·3H)	14·7 (−11·8H)
"Baggot"* (from River North Esk)	3–6	8·0	2·3	11·2	1·9	—	12·3 (−2·0H)	34·4 (−2·7H)	21·7 (−7·2H)	16·2 (−9·5H)

55

* "Baggots" is a term applied to ripe female fish which for some reason have not spawned.
† 0·7 per cent. Lauric acid also present.
‡ Irregular, but varying from 7 to 15 per cent.

fasting in fish of either sex. As regards group percentage proportions, it is fairly obvious that, as emaciation proceeds, myristic and unsaturated C_{16} acids show a decrease, balanced by increase in C_{22} acids (in the males) and in C_{18} and C_{20} acids (in the females). These differences become more apparent if the total proportions (in mols. per cent.) of each group of acids containing the same number of carbon atoms are considered (Table 8):

TABLE 8. *Molar Proportions of Total Acids with the same number of Carbon Atoms*

FISH (in Table 7)	C_{14}	C_{16}	C_{18}	C_{20}	C_{22}
1 Male	4·7	28·5	31·2	21·8	13·8
2 ,,	2·6	23·1	28·9	25·5	19·9
3 ,,	2·9	20·1	29·4	24·6	23·0
4 Female	6·9	23·0	27·4	24·8	17·9
5 ,,	2·8	23·0	29·6	26·8	17·8
6 ,,	2·4	20·2	31·2	31·5	14·7

From Table 8 it appears that the constituents preferentially mobilised in the male series are those of low molecular weight, but in the female series this effect is much less in evidence, if indeed it exists at all.

The mesenteric fat examined is very similar to that of the mature flesh fats, whilst the salmon liver fat has somewhat increased amounts of unsaturated C_{16} and C_{18} acids, and somewhat less C_{22} acids.

In the egg fats, at early stages the percentages of the various acid groups are not significantly different from those of a salmon body fat, but the average unsaturation is increased in all cases. As development proceeds, the high degree of average unsaturation of the C_{20} and C_{22} acids is maintained, and there is a definite rise in the proportion of C_{18} acids together with a fall in their mean unsaturation. The final result of the progressive changes in the ova fat during ripening is that it takes on some of the characteristics of a freshwater fish fat, but nevertheless still retains the specific nature of a salmon fat (e.g. low C_{16} and high C_{22} acid contents, in spite of increased proportions (*ca.* 35 per cent.) of unsaturated C_{18} acids). There is as yet little if any evidence to indicate the mechanism by which these changes are brought about, but various possibilities have been discussed by Lovern.[70]

Eel fats. Eels are in some respects opposite in behaviour to salmon, in that many species spend the greater part of their existence in fresh water, but migrate, sometimes many thousands of miles, to marine spawning grounds (e.g. the Sargasso Sea). Analyses of eel fats are available for New Zealand and Scottish freshwater eels, and for the liver and peritoneal fats of the conger, which lives in sea-water (Table 9).

The eel fats* do not fit very closely into either the general fresh- or salt-water types of fat. They are somewhat akin to the freshwater fish fats in Table 6 (p. 52) as regards their high proportions of unsaturated C_{18} acids and their comparatively low contents of C_{22} acids, but the amount of hexadecenoic acid is variable and in any case not high, whilst the average unsaturation in the C_{18} groups is lower than in the case of most fats from freshwater fish. The content

---

* The Scottish eels were taken from tidal waters, and cannot therefore be considered as denizens exclusively of fresh water.

TABLE 9. Component Acids (per cent. wt.) of Eel Fats

FAMILY	SPECIES	HABITAT	OIL (Per cent.)	UNSAPONI-FIABLE (Per cent.)	SATURATED			UNSATURATED				
					C_{14}	C_{16}	C_{18}	C_{14}	C_{16}	C_{18}	C_{20}	C_{22}
Anguillidæ	Anguilla aucklandii[76] (Freshwater eel)	New Zealand	Body	7	0·8	2·0	14·9	0·8	—	19·7 (−2·0H)	47·6 (−2·6H)	14·4 (−6·2H)	0·6 (−?H)
,,	A. vulgaris[6b] (Freshwater eel)	Scotland*	Body	9–30	1·2–2·0	4·3	16·8	2·5	0·1	8·8 (−2·2H)	39·4 (−2·5H)	20·8 (−5·6H)	7·3 (−10·2H)
						4·3	17·8	1·7	Trace	9·2 (−2·2H)	38·4 (−2·7H)	20·1 (−6·0H)	8·5 (−9·3H)
Congridæ	Conger vulgaris[77] (Conger eel)	North Sea	Liver	ca. 20	2·5	5·2	19·2	0·4	0·4	18·0	37·5 (−2·0H)	12·4 (−5·6H)	6·9 (−8·1H)
			Peritoneum	ca. 80	0·7	1·8	18·8	0·9	—	6·2	40·6 (−2·1H)	18·3 (−5·4H)	13·4 (−8·4H)

* The Scottish eels were taken from tidal waters, and cannot therefore be considered as denizens exclusively of fresh water.

of unsaturated C_{18} acids in the New Zealand eel is extremely large. In the conger, the peritoneum is a principal fat depot and the liver only a subsidiary one.

Lovern [6b] studied the composition of fats from eels reared mainly on diets of mussels or herrings. The mussel diet caused a loss of weight in the fish but appeared to have little influence on the composition of the eel fats; the herring diet caused both increase in weight and modification of the eel fat acids to a mixture intermediate in composition between that of the "control" eel fat and herring fat. Lovern [78] also fed eels on individual esters such as ethyl myristate or palmitate with somewhat indefinite results, except that ingestion of ethyl palmitate led to marked increase in palmitic acid content of the eel fats. The possible inferences to be drawn from these experiments, including evidence that both dehydrogenation and hydrogenation readily take place during the biosynthesis of fish depot fatty acids, are fully discussed in Lovern's communications. [6b, 78] (See also Reiser et al. [75a], p. 51.)

In the New Zealand freshwater eels, *Anguilla australis schmidtii* and *A. dieffenbachii*, Shorland and Russell [79] found that in the adult migrant fish the distribution of fat was fairly uniform between the head, trunk, and tail, but that in immature eels the tail (which is 42–43 per cent. of the total body weight) contained about 70 per cent. of the total oil in the fish.

Fats from Different Depots of some Large Fishes

When the size of the fish permits, it has been possible in some instances to determine the component acids from several of the main depots. Some of the resulting data are considered below.

Sturgeon fats. [80] The sturgeon (*Acipenser sturio*) examined had been caught in the North Sea, but all sturgeon ascend the large continental rivers to spawn and, it is believed, do most of their feeding in fresh water. It is not surprising, therefore, to find that its fats conform in general with the freshwater fish type (Table 6), subject as usual to minor specific differences. Fat deposited in the peritoneal cavity is the chief store in the sturgeon, whilst the pancreas is also very rich in fat; the liver is not exceptionally rich in fat. The component acids of fats from these parts of the animal are tabulated in Table 10.

TABLE 10. *Component Acids (per cent. wt.) of Fats from a Sturgeon*

FAT FROM	IODINE VALUE	SATURATED			UNSATURATED				
		C_{14}	C_{16}	C_{18}	C_{14}	C_{16}	C_{18}	C_{20}	C_{22}
Peritoneal cavity	126·5	7·1	14·0	0·8	0·6	23·8	35·8 (−2·9H)	12·1 (−7·4H)	5·8 (−8·6H)
Pancreas*	119·6	4·5	16·4	1·1	—	21·4	36·7 (−2·9H)	14·5 (−6·8H)	5·4 (−9·1H)
Liver	125	3·0	19·2	—	—	19·5	39·6 (−2·7H)	11·8 (−7·1H)	6·9 (−10·0H)

* There is some uncertainty as to whether the organ examined was the pancreas or the pyloric cæca. – (Private communication by Dr. Lovern.)

These form a specially interesting group in several respects. In the first place, it was one of the first instances – several others may be noticed in the course of the preceding and following tables – in which it was shown that the liver

glycerides were no more unsaturated than the main depot fat of the same fish. Although the total content of saturated acids is constant (22 per cent. wt.), the individual acids vary widely; at the same time, however, the percentages of the total C_{16} acids (palmitic and hexadecenoic) are closely constant in the three fats; Lovern [80] suggests that it would appear that all sturgeon fats develop an approximately constant proportion of saturated to unsaturated acids, which may be secured by alteration in the proportions of saturated and mono-ethenoid C_{16} acids.

Tunny fats. The examination of fats from various organs and the flesh of a large tunny (*Thynnus thynnus*) taken in the North Sea (off Scarborough) yielded interesting and suggestive results (Table 11).[59]

TABLE 11. *Component Fatty Acids (per cent. wt.) of Tunny Fats (Glycerides)*

DEPOT	FAT (Per cent.)	SATURATED			UNSATURATED				
		C_{14}	C_{16}	C_{18}	C_{14}	C_{16}	C_{18}	C_{20}	C_{22}
Flesh	23	4·2	18·6	3·5†	—	6·2	26·0	23·5	18·0
						(−2·7H)	(−3·2H)	(−5·5H)	(−6·8H)
Liver	20–25	—	17·9	8·9†	—	3·4	23·5	28·2	18·1
						(−2·5H)	(−2·8H)	(−5·5H)	(−7·4H)
Pyloric cæca	28·5	3·4	18·4	2·7	—	6·3	21·9	25·5	21·8
						(−2·7H)	(−3·7H)	(−5·5H)	(−6·2H)
Spleen	2·6	—	21	7	—	7	27	22	16
						(> −2·0H)	(−3·1H)	(−5·4H)	(− ?H)
Heart	2·4	—	25	3	—	4	26	25	17
						(> −2·0H)	(−3·4H)	(−5·4H)	(−7·5H)

† Traces of arachidic acid also present.

Compared with other marine fish fats, the tunny fats in Table 11 exhibit the following well marked species peculiarities: absence of myristic and tetra-decenoic acids in several cases, somewhat high palmitic acid, unusual amounts of stearic acid in the liver and flesh fats, low hexadecenoic acid contents and lower unsaturation than usual in the C_{18}, C_{20}, and C_{22} acids. The tunny normally spends considerable periods in relatively warm water and moreover is notable for having a body temperature some 3° higher than that of the water; Lovern [59] suggests that this may have some bearing on the specific acid composition.

In all the fats, except that in the pyloric cæca, the total saturated acids (27–28 per cent.) are much above the usual value for marine fish (15–20 per cent.) and this is made up mainly by a higher palmitic acid (18–25 per cent.) than the usual (8–16 per cent.); but the total C_{16} acid percentage (21–29) is much as in most fish fats, and Lovern has pointed out that saturation (hydrogenation) processes seem to be operative in both the C_{16} and C_{18} acids of the tunny fats. He has also drawn attention to the fact that the tunny provides another example in which liver fat is definitely less unsaturated than body fat. (The liver and body fats of the conger eel, Table 9, and those of halibut and turbot, Tables 4 and 5, are other examples in which the degree of average unsaturation and/or the actual contents of unsaturated C_{20} and C_{22} acids are markedly lower in the respective liver fats than in the body fats.)

Groper liver and head oils. The New Zealand groper, *Polyprion oxygeneios*, contains fat deposits in the liver, head, and body of the fish; according to

Johnson[82] a considerable proportion of the total fat is concentrated in the body, whilst Shorland and Hilditch[56] state that the amount in the head is about four times that in the liver, which is therefore in this case a secondary depot for fat. Seasonal variations in the size of groper livers, in the fat contents of the liver and the pyloric cæca, and in the amounts of vitamin A and of total unsaponifiable matter in these fats have been discussed by Shorland.[83]

Groper liver oils (Table 12) seem to have definite species peculiarities, but that from the head is quite similar to many of the fats in Tables 4 and 5 which represent main depots in many other marine fish. The groper liver glycerides are characterised by low proportions of unsaturated C_{20} and (especially) C_{22} acids, with high palmitic, hexadecenoic, and unsaturated C_{18} acids (the mean unsaturation of the latter being comparatively low). The total content of C_{16} acids in the liver glycerides is remarkably high, 36–46 per cent., as is also the total percentage (24–29) of saturated acids. In some respects, these liver glycerides resemble typical freshwater, rather than marine, fish liver fats; but they are sharply differentiated from the former by the high proportions of palmitic acid and the lower contents of unsaturated C_{20} acids.

The liver phosphatides, on the other hand, show the usual features in fatty acid composition as compared with the corresponding glycerides, notably, greater amounts of unsaturated C_{20} and C_{22} acids and correspondingly less unsaturated C_{16} and C_{18} acids. Similar comparative differences in the component acids have been observed by Shorland[58] in the roe glycerides and phosphatides of the New Zealand ling (*Genypterus blacodes*). These appear to be general features in nearly all animal liver phosphatides, and we shall encounter other instances which have been examined in more detail in the case of land animal fats (Chapter III, pp. 132–137).

TABLE 12. *General Composition of Groper Fats*[56]

SOURCE	FATTY CONTENT OF ORGAN (Per cent.)	FATTY EXTRACT			
		IODINE VALUE	UNSAPONI-FIABLE (Per cent.)	GLYCER-IDES* (Per cent.)	PHOSPHA-TIDES (Per cent.)
Liver (spring)	?	88·6	3·3	100	Trace
,, (early winter)	9·2	87·0	5·8	98	2
,, (late winter)	8·0	112·2	12·3	82	18
Head	8·0	145·9	0·7	100	Trace

* i.e. glycerides + unsaponifiable matter, but excluding phosphatides.

Component Acids (per cent. wt.) of Groper Liver and Head Fats[56]

	SATURATED			UNSATURATED				
	C_{14}	C_{16}	C_{18}	C_{14}	C_{16}	C_{18}	C_{20}	C_{22}
Liver glycerides: Spring	2·4	23·0	3·4	1·6	23·3 (−2·0H)	39·3 (−2·5H)	7·0 (−5·9H)	Trace
Early winter	1·9	19·3	3·3	0·1	17·3 (−2·0H)	45·2 (−2·3H)	9·1 (−6·3H)	3·8 (−6·3H)
Late winter	2·0	22·7	3·3	0·2	18·2 (−2·0H)	40·8 (−2·4H)	8·8 (−6·0H)	4·0 (−6·0H)
Liver phosphatides (late winter)	←——18·5——→			—	16·9 (−2·0H)	19·6 (−2·4H)	31·1 (−6·6H)	13·9 (−?H)
Head glycerides	3·0	16·0	3·1	1·1 (−2·0H)	13·8 (−2·0H)	30·8 (−2·6H)	18·5 (−6·2H)	13·7 (−9·2H)

TABLE 13. *General Composition of South African Fish Fats*

FAMILY	SPECIES	HABITAT (Ocean)	HEAD			BODY			VISCERA			LIVER		
			Wt. (Per cent.)	Fat (Per cent.)	I.V.	Wt. (Per cent.)	Fat (Per cent.)	I.V.	Wt. (Per cent.)	Fat (Per cent.)	I.V.	Wt. (Per cent.)	Fat (Per cent.)	I.V.
Scorpænidæ	Jacopever (*Sebastichthys Capensis*)	S. Atlantic	22–25	9–13	150–160	67–70	3–5	150–160	2·0–2·5	20–30	145–160	1·5–3·0	25–40	110–135
Serranidæ	Stonebass (*Polyprion americanus*)	S. Atlantic	27·5	7–18	120–160	65–70	10	120–150	2·8	3–9	155–160	1·6	13–24	110–140
Scombridæ	Snoek (*Thyrsites atun*)	S. Atlantic	12	14–19	160–180	81	12	165–175	1·6	8–13	160–170	1·5	8–19	120–160
Gadidæ	Stockfish (*Merluccius Capensis*)	S. Atlantic	16–17	0·3	?	75	0·8	?	1·0	2·0–3·5	170–195	3	40–50	140–160
Ophidiidæ	Kingklip, Cape Ling (*Genypterus Capensis*)	S. Atlantic	18–21	0·2–0·3	?	69–77	0·1	?	2·0	0·7–1·1	?	2–3	30–40	140–160
Triglidæ	Gurnard (*Chelidonichthys Capensis*)	S. Indian	20–25	2–4	?	68–71	1–2	?	2·0–2·5	1–4	140–160	1·0–2·0	8–12	110–140
Sciænidæ	Kabeljou (*Sciæna hololepidota*)	S. Indian	16–21	2·2–8·8	160–180	70–78	1–4	147–171	1·2–1·5	up to 1	127–167	1·1–1·5	3–20	100–145
Sciænidæ	Geelbek (*Atractoscion æquidens*)	S. Indian	14–18	10–15	165–174	75–77	1–5	168–170	ca. 1	1–2	160–165	1–3	5–30	125–170
Zeidæ	Cape John Dory (*Zeus Capensis*)	S. Atlantic	19–24	0·8–1	160–174	60–66	5–6	153–173	11–18	10–25	140–150	4–5	14–23	140–150

61

Head, body, liver, and viscera oils of some South African marine fish.* Rapson and colleagues[52,57] have published interesting observations on a number of fish from the South Atlantic and southern Indian oceans, in which (as in the groper) head and body tissues appear to be the chief fat depots rather than the liver or mesenterium, the former frequently containing about four times as much fat as the latter. Nevertheless, in these fish, as in others, the liver and body fat stores are more freely metabolised – laid down or withdrawn – than head or visceral fats. In general, as in the groper, the liver fats of this group of fish are almost always less unsaturated than the fats in the main stores (head and body).

Examples illustrating the distribution of fat in these fish, and the mean unsaturation (iodine value) of the various fat deposits are given in Table 13 (p. 61), and detailed component acid figures as observed by van Rensburg[52] for the various fats from the jacopever are reproduced in Table 14. It will be seen from the latter table that the component acids of the head, body, and intestinal fats are much alike, and that their unsaturated acids are uniformly more unsaturated than the corresponding liver fatty acids; moreover, the general composition of these fats is quite similar to marine fish body fats from the Northern Hemisphere. The liver fat, like those of the stockfish, groper, New Zealand ling, etc., shows lower general unsaturation and the enhanced content of unsaturated C_{18} acids which is evidently characteristic for liver oils of marine fish in the Southern Hemisphere.

TABLE 14. *Component Acids (per cent. wt.) of Jacopever Fats*

	SATURATED				UNSATURATED					
	C_{14}	C_{16}	C_{18}	C_{20-22}	C_{14}	C_{16}	C_{18}	C_{20}	C_{22}	C_{24}
Head	2·6	16·3	2·1	0·8	0·9	11·8	30·3	18·8	15·5	1·0
					(−2·0H)	(−2·0H)	(−3·0H)	(−6·8H)	(−9·6H)	(−?H)
Body	2·6	13·8	1·8	0·2	2·3	12·4	28·5	21·6	16·8	—
					(−2·0H)	(−2·0H)	(−2·4H)	(−7·0H)	(−9·5H)	—
Viscera (intestinal)	3·0	14·4	2·2	0·1	1·9	13·1	30·6	19·7	12·3	2·6
					(−2·0H)	(−2·0H)	(−2·5H)	(−6·9H)	(−9·2H)	(−?H)
Liver	1·2	11·6	3·9	0·4	0·6	13·5	46·3	12·7	7·5	2·4
					(−2·0H)	(−2·0H)	(−2·3H)	(−6·3H)	(−8·7H)	(−?H)

COMPONENT ACIDS OF FATS OF MARINE MAMMALIA

Marine mammals such as the seal, whale, or porpoise possess a layer of fatty tissue beneath the skin, known as blubber, which is the source of considerable quantities of useful technical fatty oils. Certain species such as the sperm whale, dolphin, porpoise, etc., also have deposits of fat in the head cavity, and occasionally in the jaw. Such detailed analyses as are available have usually reference to one or other of these fat deposits; detailed information on the fats of the liver or other organs is for the most part still lacking.

The Seal family (Phocidæ). Seal blubber oil has been used for various purposes for at least as long as whale oil, but no statement of its component acids was

* Data on a number of these South African fish fats are also detailed in Tables 3, 4 and 5 (pp. 38, 42, 46).

made until some partial data were given in 1935 by Williams and Makhrov.[84] Semi-quantitative analytical data by Tsujimoto[85] and Bauer and Neth[86] supported the view that seal oil and ordinary whale oil are similar in fatty acid composition. Since 1944 full component acid analyses have been carried out

TABLE 15. *Component Acids (per cent. wt.) of North Atlantic Seal Blubber Oils*

SPECIES	(NEWFOUND-LAND[87])	[88a]	GREY ATLANTIC SEAL			
				NEW-BORN[89] FEMALE	MALE[89] (2 WEEKS OLD)*	MALE[89] (4 WEEKS OLD)†
REMARKS:	(COMMER-CIAL)		MOTHER[89] OF:			
Iodine value	135·8	162·2	157·9	130·0	137·1	136·7
Component acids:						
Myristic	5·1	3·7	3·4	3·5	3·0	3·0
Palmitic	10·7	10·5	8·9	17·1	14·1	13·7
Stearic	1·3	2·0	1·8	2·4	1·9	2·6
Arachidic	0·6	—	0·2	0·1	0·1	—
Unsaturated C_{14}	1·8	1·6	2·0	2·3	2·7	2·2
,, C_{16}	10·5	15·5	15·6	19·0	19·6	16·4
,, C_{18}	39·6	30·8	33·4	32·9	34·4	37·1
,, C_{20}	17·6	16·5	18·7	10·9	12·5	11·8
,, C_{22}	10·6	18·1	16·0	11·8	11·7	13·2
,, C_{24}	2·1	1·3	—	—	—	—
Mean unsaturation of:						
Unsaturated C_{14}	−2·0	−2·0	−2·0	−2·0	−2·0	−2·0
,, C_{16}	−2·1	−2·2	−2·2	−2·1	−2·1	−2·1
,, C_{18}	−2·4	−2·7	−2·5	−2·4	−2·4	−2·3
,, C_{20}	−5·6	−5·7	−6·2	−6·5	−6·7	−6·6
,, C_{22}	−9·3	−10·6	−10·1	−10·4	−11·1	−10·7
,, C_{24}	−10·9	−11·0	—	—	—	—

* Middle of suckling period. † After weaning.

SPECIES	COMMON SEAL[88b]		COMMON SEAL[90b]				
REMARKS:	I	II	NEWBORN FEMALE	MALE PUP 3 DAYS OLD	MALE PUP 6 DAYS OLD	YEARLING FEMALE	ADULT FEMALE
Iodine value	140·0	145·4	108·5	109·4	121·4	149·2	170·4
Component acids:							
Lauric	—	—	0·2	0·2	0·2	—	—
Myristic	2·4	2·2	4·4	3·8	3·8	5·5	3·2
Palmitic	10·3	10·6	12·0	12·8	13·3	11·5	10·7
Stearic	2·5	4·4	0·6	1·4	1·1	1·2	1·5
Arachidic	0·3	0·3	—	0·1	—	0·2	0·4
Unsaturated C_{12}	—	—	0·5	0·6	0·4	—	—
,, C_{14}	2·9	2·2	6·1	5·1	4·3	2·0	2·1
,, C_{16}	25·7	20·8	47·6	43·9	36·6	20·1	16·9
,, C_{18}	32·6	33·7	16·4	18·7	22·9	25·0	29·1
,, C_{20}	12·1	13·6	7·7	7·0	10·3	16·9	18·0
,, C_{22}	11·2	12·2	4·5	6·4	7·1	17·6	18·1
Mean unsaturation of:							
Unsaturated C_{12}	—	—	−2·0	−2·0	−2·0	—	—
,, C_{14}	−2·0	−2·0	−2·0	−2·0	−2·0	−2·0	−2·0
,, C_{16}	−2·1	−2·1	−2·0	−2·0	−2·1	−2·2	−2·2
,, C_{18}	−2·7	−2·4	−2·6	−2·5	−2·7	−3·1	−2·7
,, C_{20}	−5·9	−7·2	−6·3	−7·1	−6·4	−6·0	−6·4
,, C_{22}	−11·0	−11·0	−9·8	−10·6	−10·5	−8·5	−9·8

TABLE 16. Component Acids (per cent. wt.) of Antarctic Elephant Seal Blubber Fats[91]

(i) Seals from Macquarie Island

ANIMAL:	MATURE MALE	MATURE FEMALE	MATURE MALE	PREGNANT FEMALE	FEMALE PUP (a)	MALE PUP (b)
Length (ft.)	9·1	7·7	15·3	9·1	5·0	5·1
Iodine value	Belly 136·4	Belly 152·9	Neck 105·0	Belly 117·6	Belly 98·6	Belly 126·9
Component acids:						
Myristic	5·2	4·4	1·7	1·7	0·9	1·9
Palmitic	11·4	11·5	7·2	9·7	7·2	10·5
Stearic	2·4	2·4	3·8	3·4	4·5	3·4
Arachidic	—	—	0·6	0·2	0·6	0·3
Unsaturated C_{14}	1·7	1·3	0·5	0·6	0·5	1·0
C_{16}	14·5	13·0	7·2	9·6	7·9	9·0
C_{18}	35·1	33·0	38·4	34·4	37·1	40·1
C_{20}	18·8	20·6	27·0	25·7	23·5	22·3
C_{22}	10·6	13·7	12·7	14·1	13·9	11·5
C_{24}	—	—	0·9	0·6	3·9	—
Mean unsaturation of:						
Unsaturated C_{14}	-2·0	-2·0	-2·0	-2·0	-2·0	-2·0
C_{16}	-2·1	-2·1	-2·0	-2·0	-2·0	-2·1
C_{18}	-2·7	-2·4	-2·1	-2·3	-2·1	-2·2
C_{20}	-5·4	-5·9	-3·3	-4·0	-2·8	-4·4
C_{22}	-10·0	-10·8	-5·7	-6·5	-4·9	-9·0
C_{24}	—	—	-2·0	-2·0	-3·9	—

(ii) Seals from Heard Island

	MATURE MALE			MATURE MALE	MATURE FEMALE	MATURE MALE	MATURE FEMALE	MALE PUP (c)	MALE PUP (d)	FEMALE PUP (c)
Length (ft.)			14·0	12·1	7·7	14·1	7·8	3·5	4·3	4·0
Iodine value	Belly 114·8	Neck 114·4	Back 115·5	Belly 145·8	Belly 128·1	Belly 142·6	Belly 120·1	Belly 124·2	Belly 123·0	Belly 115·3
Component acids:										
Myristic	3·4	3·3	3·9	2·5	2·6	4·8	4·7	5·1	4·2	3·8
Palmitic	9·7	9·7	9·6	10·1	8·8	10·0	11·7	11·6	12·6	12·9
Stearic	2·5	2·6	2·6	4·5	4·2	2·3	2·9	2·2	2·9	2·5
Arachidic	0·3	0·2	0·2	0·8	0·6	0·3	0·4	0·3	—	0·2
Unsaturated C_{14}	1·2	1·2	1·5	0·9	1·2	1·5	1·3	1·9	1·9	1·1
C_{16}	10·6	11·4	10·7	12·6	11·2	13·7	10·4	12·8	17·3	12·1
C_{18}	39·9	41·6	39·9	35·0	38·4	33·4	38·3	41·3	43·9	45·0
C_{20}	17·9	17·3	17·4	21·9	22·7	18·4	19·8	14·0	9·7	12·9
C_{22}	14·5	12·7	14·2	11·7	10·3	15·6	10·5	10·8	7·5	9·5
Mean unsaturation of:										
Unsaturated C_{14}	-2·0	-2·0	-2·0	-2·0	-2·0	-2·0	-2·0	-2·0	-2·0	-2·0
C_{16}	-2·1	-2·1	-2·0	-2·1	-2·2	-2·2	-2·1	-2·1	-2·1	-2·1
C_{18}	-2·2	-2·2	-2·2	-2·4	-2·5	-2·6	-2·3	-2·3	-2·3	-2·2
C_{20}	-4·0	-4·0	-4·0	-6·1	-4·4	-5·5	-5·1	-5·5	-6·7	-4·8
C_{22}	-7·4	-7·8	-7·5	-10·0	-8·3	-8·8	-8·3	-9·9	-10·5	-9·1

TABLE 17. *Component Acids (per cent. wt.) of Blubber Oils of other Seals and Related Species*

SPECIES: FAMILY:	LEOPARD[92a] SEAL PHOCIDAE	CRABEATER[92b] SEAL PHOCIDAE	NORTHERN[92c] ELEPHANT SEAL PHOCIDAE	SEA-LION[93a] OTARIIDAE	SEA-LION[93b] OTARIIDAE
Iodine value	130·2	165·3	?	173·1	136·4
Component acids:					
Myristic	4·0	4·7	3·5	4·0	3·3
Palmitic	7·4	10·1	12·8	12·6	5·8
Stearic	1·6	2·1	3·6	2·7	2·3
Arachidic	0·2	—	0·4	—	0·5
Unsaturated C_{14}	1·1	3·2	1·0	2·0	0·7
,, C_{16}	12·7	19·8	10·0	12·1	7·3
,, C_{18}	42·3	30·3	33·2	30·9	26·1
,, C_{20}	17·3	19·2	24·6	23·5	28·8
,, C_{22}	12·4	10·6	10·3	12·2	25·2
Mean unsaturation of:					
Unsaturated C_{14}	−2·0	−2·0	−2·0	−2·0	−2·0
,, C_{16}	−2·1	−2·3	−2·5	−2·4	−2·1
,, C_{18}	−2·2	−3·0	−3·0	−2·6	−2·4
,, C_{20}	−4·6	−7·9	−4·4	−7·5	−3·3
,, C_{22}	−9·4	−10·8	−7·1	−10·7	−6·8

TABLE 18. *Component Acids (per cent. wt.) of North Atlantic Seal Liver Oils*

SPECIES:	COMMON SEAL[88b]	GREY ATLANTIC SEAL[89]		
REMARKS:		FEMALE NEWLY BORN	MALE SUCKLING	PUP WEANED
Oil content of liver:	10·7	5·3	2·9	3·1
Glycerides, per cent., in oil	86	78	80	83
Phosphatides, per cent., in oil	5	19	20	17
Iodine value of glycerides	175	160	134	142
Component acids (glycerides):				
Myristic	0·2	2·2	0·2	0·3
Palmitic	11·4	16·0	16·2	13·5
Stearic	7·8	4·2	13·3	12·7
Arachidic	0·1	0·2	1·2	0·4
Unsaturated C_{14}	—	1·8	—	—
,, C_{16}	8·6	9·9	7·6	9·1
,, C_{18}	27·9	28·3	28·5	27·0
,, C_{20}	23·7	21·9	28·1	27·8
,, C_{22}	20·3	15·5	4·9	9·2
Mean unsaturation of:				
Unsaturated C_{14}	—	− 2·0	—	—
,, C_{16}	− 2·0	− 2·0	− 2·3	− 2·1
,, C_{18}	− 2·4	− 2·4	− 2·7	− 2·4
,, C_{20}	− 6·2	− 7·2	− 7·2	− 6·8
,, C_{22}	− 11·0	− 11·1	− 10·3	− 10·2

TABLE 19. *Component Acids (per cent. wt.) of Seal Milk Fats*

	GREY ATLANTIC		COMMON SEAL
MILK TAKEN FROM:	LACTATING[90a] FEMALE	STOMACH OF[89] NEWBORN SEAL	ADULT FEMALE MAMMARY GLAND[90b]
Fat content:	50 per cent.	45 per cent.	
Iodine value of fat:	146·2	151·8	135·7
Component acids:			
Myristic	2·8	1·7	3·0
Palmitic	16·4	15·5	15·7
Stearic	2·8	3·7	3·2
Arachidic	—	—	0·3
Unsaturated C_{14}	1·7	1·6	1·2
,, C_{16}	12·7	13·7	10·4
,, C_{18}	36·6	33·0	31·5
,, C_{20}	13·6	13·6	16·1
,, C_{22}	13·4	17·2	16·7
,, C_{24}	—	—	1·9
Mean unsaturation of:			
Unsaturated C_{14}	− 2·0	− 2·0	− 2·0
,, C_{16}	− 2·2	− 2·1	− 2·3
,, C_{18}	− 2·3	− 2·3	− 2·6
,, C_{20}	− 6·6	− 7·0	− 5·1
,, C_{22}	− 11·2	− 10·6	− 8·0
,, C_{24}	—	—	− 10·0

on oils from seals of different species and from some other members of the seal family. The oils studied include: a commercial Newfoundland seal oil (Burke and Jasperson[87]); blubber and liver fats of Grey Atlantic (*Halichœrus grypus*) and common (*Phoca vitulina*) seals (Hilditch and Pathak,[88] Cardin and Meara,[89] Meara[90b]); milk fats of Grey Atlantic and common seals (Meara,[90a] Cardin and Meara[89]); blubber fats from a wide range of specimens of the elephant seal (*Mirounga leonina*) from Macquarie and Heard Islands in the Antarctic (Winter and Nunn[91]); and blubber fats of leopard seal (*Hydrurga leptonyx*) and crabeater seal (*Lobodon carcinophagus*) by Winter and Nunn [92a, b] and of the sea-lion (*Zalophus Californianus*) by Gunstone[93a] and Cardin.[93b]

It may be mentioned that Burke and Jasperson's analysis [87] was based on lithium and lead salt separations of the mixed fatty acids, whilst in those of Hilditch and Pathak [88] and Cardin and Meara,[89, 90, 93b] the mixed acids were resolved into groups by crystallisation from acetone at low temperatures; Winter and Nunn [91, 92] converted the oils directly into methyl esters by methanolysis and resolved the esters by similar low-temperature crystallisation.

These results are summarised in Tables 15 (blubber fats of North Atlantic seals), 16 (blubber fats of Antarctic elephant seals), 17 (blubber fats of Californian sea-lion, Antarctic leopard, and crabeater seals), 18 (liver fats of North Atlantic seals), and 19 (milk fats of North Atlantic seals).

Seal blubber fats. The chief component acids belong to the unsaturated C_{18} series (mainly oleic with some polyethenoid), the next most prominent are those of the unsaturated C_{20} and C_{16} series, whilst unsaturated C_{22} acids are usually present in somewhat lower proportions. The composition of seal oils is on the whole somewhat similar to that of Antarctic whale oil (*v. infra*), but frequently in seal oils there are somewhat less saturated and unsaturated C_{16} acids, and somewhat more of the C_{20} and C_{22} unsaturated acids. The proportions of the various groups of acids in oils from different specimens of the same species of seal exhibit rather marked variations. The percentages (wt.) of the main groups in the North Atlantic and Antarctic (elephant) seal oils in Tables 15 and 16 show the following ranges:

	NORTH ATLANTIC SEALS (COMMON AND GREY ATLANTIC)	ANTARCTIC SEALS (ELEPHANT)
Total saturated	16–23	13–20
Palmitic	9–17	7–12
Unsaturated C_{16}	15–47 (-2.1 to -2.2H)	8–16 (-2.0 to -2.2H)
,, C_{18}	16–37 (-2.3 to -2.7H)	33–45 (-2.1 to -2.7H)
,, C_{20}	11–19 (-5.7 to -7.2H)	13–28 (-2.8 to -6.7H)
,, C_{22}	5–18 (-10.1 to -11.1H)	7–15 (-4.9 to -10.5H)

The causes of these variations are not yet evident: the data (including the very detailed study of many individuals of known origin by Winter and Nunn) have so far failed to indicate any correlation between the sex, age, or size of the animals or their probable diets or conditions of living and the changes noted in the composition of the fats. Winter and Nunn (*cf.* Table 16) have, however, observed that the fats from the belly, back, and neck of the same elephant seal were identical in composition. Meara's figures of newly-born common seals (Table 15) indicate that their blubber fat differs markedly from either the blubber fat of mature seals or the milk fat of the mother: the blubber fats of very young seals contain much less unsaturated acids of the C_{22}, C_{20}, and C_{18} series, with very high contents of hexadecenoic acid, traces of lauric and dodecenoic acids, and more palmitic, myristic, and tetradecenoic acids than those of the adult seals of the same species. These variations, so far as they go, contrast with the comparatively constant composition of (Antarctic) whale oils; a possible factor is that individual specimens of seals have been studied, whereas the available data on whale oils are in most instances based on commercial oils, i.e. they represent an average composition of a bulked sample of oil drawn from a probably very large number of individual whales.

Sea-lion blubber fat. Sea-lions are placed by zoologists in a different family, Otariidæ, from the seals (Phocidæ). The two blubber fats which have been studied differ somewhat in composition. One of them,[93a] from a male specimen (*Otaria gillespii*) from the Glasgow zoo, had component acids very similar to those of many of the mature male seals quoted in Tables 15 and 16. The other,[93b] from a male specimen (*Zalophus Californianus*) from the Pacific Ocean but kept in captivity in the London Zoo, had a distinctly different mixture of acids in its blubber fat: palmitic and other saturated acids, and hexadecenoic acid, were present in unusually small proportions, and about 80 per cent. of the total fatty acids consisted of unsaturated C_{18}, C_{20} and C_{22} acids in approximately equal proportions, with more mono-ethenoid C_{20} and C_{22} acids than are common in most marine animal oils.

Seal liver fats. The few detailed analyses of seal liver glycerides show that these (which usually form only about 3–5 per cent. of the livers) differ in composition from the blubber fats: they contain more palmitic and stearic acid, less hexadecenoic and unsaturated C_{18} acids, and higher proportions of unsaturated C_{20} acids. Judged by iodine values, the corresponding liver phosphatides appear to be generally much lower in unsaturation than the liver glycerides.

Seal milk fats. With very minor differences, seal milk fat is quantitatively of much the same composition as the blubber fat. The fatty acid mixture is qualitatively the same in both types of seal fat, and no acids of lower molecular weight than those in the body fats were detected in the milk fats; the mean unsaturation of each homologous group of acids is almost exactly the same in both milk and blubber fats.

The Whale family (Balænidæ). In view of the technical importance which whale oil has attained during the present century, much study has been given to the general characteristics of the blubber oil. Systematic studies of the effect of various factors on the composition of whale fats have been undertaken by several Scandinavian workers. Lund[94] summarised the results of records extending over twenty-five years on whale oil from different species, different localities, different parts of the animal, and from fat and lean whales. The latter yield oils of lower iodine values than those from fat whales. The saponification and iodine values of the blubber oils from different species of whales show consistent, if not very large, variations and suggest the influence of variation in the food. Lund's paper contains a very large number of interesting statistics of the analytical characteristics of whale oils from both northern and southern hemispheres, and should be read by all interested in this subject. A similar review of many samples of oil from different parts and different specimens of the blue whale, together with detailed component acid analyses in certain cases, was made by Tveraaen,[95] whilst corresponding data for the principal food (*Euphausia superba*) of the whale and for the composition of whale milk fat were given by Klem,[7] who also discussed the influence of pregnancy and lactation on the composition of the oil from various parts of the body of the whale.

Detailed component acid analyses of whale oils include three carried out many years ago in the earliest days of the ester-fractionation procedure and six comparatively recent investigations (Table 20). Of the latter, Tveraaen[95] used a bromination procedure to effect partial separation of the saturated, less and more unsaturated acids, followed by ester-fractionation of the de-brominated groups of acids. Terleski[97] and Maddison[98a] first resolved the mixed acids by lithium and lead salt preparations whilst Maddison[98b] used low-temperature crystallisation of the mixed acids on the same specimen of oil as that which he had previously analysed.[98a] Pedersen[99b] fractionally distilled the esters of the mixed fatty acids, saturated esters being separately determined in each ester-fraction.

It is possible that the figures for the C_{20} and C_{22} acids in the older analyses are not very accurate – the complete absence of C_{20} acids from the Newfound-land oil is of course very unlikely, in the light of all recent analyses of marine animal fats. Apart from this, however, there can be little doubt that the Arctic whale oils usually contain considerably more highly unsaturated C_{20} or C_{22} acids than the oils from Antarctic regions. The iodine values of the latter are invariably lower than those of the former (110–120 for Antarctic as compared with 140–150 for Arctic and Greenland oils). The general characteristics of whale oils from different regions as given by Lund[94] (*loc. cit.*) also illustrate these differences in composition. How far such variations are due to differences in food, in temperature, or in salinity of the sea-water, etc., or to species differences, is not yet clear. No detailed analyses of a comprehensive nature have yet been carried out on the component acids of oils from the various species

TABLE 20. *Component Acids (per cent. wt.) of Whale Blubber Fats (Balænidæ)*

WHALE OIL	SATURATED			UNSATURATED				
	C_{14}	C_{16}	C_{18}	C_{14}	C_{16}	C_{18}	C_{20}	C_{22}
Arctic[96]	4·1	10·6	3·5	—	18·4 (−2·5H)	32·8 (−3H)	19·3 (−7H)	11·3 (−8H)
Newfoundland[96]	7·6	9·7	2·8	1·4 (−2H)	18·3 (−2H)	43·9 (−2·4H)	—	16·0 (−8H)
South Sea[96]	8·0	12·1	2·3	1·5 (−2H)	15·0 (−2H)	42·4 (−2·4H)	8·2 (−7·5H)	10·5 (−9H)
Antarctic[95]	7·5	22·2	—	1·0 (−2H)	11·8 (−2H)	45·3 (−2·2H)	10·7 (−4·8H)	1·4 (−11H)
Antarctic[95]	7·6	19·6	—	1·4 (−2H)	11·6 (−2H)	39·1 (−2·9H)	14·7 (−6·8H)	6·0 (−9·6H)
Antarctic[97]	6·3	18·2	2·4	3·7 (−2H)	13·3 (−2H)	38·4 (−2·6H)	11·4 (−5·6H)	6·3 (−9·0H)
Antarctic[98a]	9·3*	15·6	2·8	2·5 (−2·0H)	14·4 (−2·1H)	35·2 (−2·5H)	13·6 (−7·2H)	5·9 (−10·1H)
Antarctic[98b]	9·2†	15·6	1·9	2·5 (−2·0H)	13·9 (−2·1H)	37·2 (−2·4H)	12·0 (−7·1H)	7·1 (−9·4H)
Antarctic[99b]	9·0‡	14·7	4·1	1·1 (−2·0H)	14·4 (−2·1H)	36·7 (−2·4H)	11·7 (−7·0H)	7·7 (−9·0H)

* Also 0·2 per cent. lauric, 0·3 per cent. arachidic, and 0·2 per cent. unsaturated (−10·4H) C_{24} acids.
† Also traces of lauric and 0·6 per cent. arachidic acids.
‡ Also 0·2 per cent. lauric, 0·2 per cent. arachidic, and 0·1 per cent. dodecenoic acids.

of whale, but many records have been given by Japanese and other workers of the general analytical characteristics of whale blubber oil from the more common species, such as the Greenland, right, finner, sei, humpbacked, and other whales.

The Antarctic blubber oils have a range of component acids which is, on the one hand, somewhat similar to that of some New Zealand fish liver oils (*cf.* Table 4, pp. 42, 43) in the slightly low content of hexadecenoic acid and the high content of unsaturated C_{18} acids (approaching 40 per cent.); on the other hand, there are resemblances to typical English freshwater fish liver fats in the unsaturated C_{18} acid content and also in the relatively low content of C_{22} acids with a high degree of average unsaturation. Antarctic whale blubber acids must be considered, however, as a fairly distinct type of mixture; thus the content of saturated acids is high (over 25 per cent.) and the proportion of myristic acid is definitely larger than in the great majority of fish oils. Oleic acid accounts for nearly 90 per cent. of the unsaturated C_{18} acids, the rest being made up of small amounts of octadecatetraenoic acids and octadecadienoic acids, but the ordinary linoleic acid of seed fats is not present in detectable quantities amongst the latter.

We are fortunate to be able to include here some component acid figures for fats from different parts of whales given by L. V. Cocks and B. C. Christian in 1931 in an internal report to the Unilever Research Laboratories. The oils were from two sources: one set was prepared at the South Georgia whaling station (A), the other on a factory ship in the Antarctic (B). The results are summarised in Table 21A.

TABLE 21A. *Component Acids (per cent. wt.) of Fats from Different Parts of Whales*

FAT FROM WHALE	SATURATED			UNSATURATED				
	C_{14}	C_{16}	C_{18}	C_{14}	C_{16}	Oleic	C_{18} diene	C_{20} and C_{22}
Blubber (A)	10·6	13·3	0·5	3·9	13·5	10·7	20·4	28·0 (−6·0H)
Flesh (back) (A)	6·1	16·9	2·0	2·4	6·2	14·9	10·7	38·1 (−5·7H)
Intestinal (A)	6·5	16·6	0·6	0·2	16·5	14·4	23·2	19·8 (−9·0H)
Internal organs (A)	7·5	18·9	1·3	1·8	10·7	18·4	16·5	22·2 (−8·0H)
Blubber (B)	7·7	13·6	1·2	1·7	14·2	24·1	16·4	20·0 (−5·3H)
Bone (B)	7·4	15·2	1·3	4·1	18·9	20·7	17·0	13·5 (−6·8H)
Tongue (B)	8·0	6·3	1·4	4·5	27·9	20·8	20·5	9·2 (−6·0H)

The iodine value of the blubber oil (A) was 137·8, unusually high for an Antarctic whale oil; that (118·8) of the oil (B) is more representative of most Antarctic whale oils. Except for the tongue fat, there is no great difference in composition between the various fats. In the intestine, internal organ and bone fats the proportion of unsaturated C_{20} and C_{22} acids is lower than in the corresponding blubber fats, but their average unsaturation is higher; the oils with the highest contents of C_{20} and C_{22} acids are lowest in unsaturated C_{18} acids. The tongue fat is peculiar in its very high content of hexadecenoic acid and its unusually small proportion of palmitic acid and of unsaturated C_{20} and C_{22} acids. Hexadecenoic acid is also relatively high in the bone fat and very low in the (back) flesh fat (which is, however, exceptionally rich in unsaturated C_{20} and C_{22} acids).

Apart from the differences to which attention has been drawn, the values for individual acids in nearly all the whale fats in Table 21A fall within the range of those in the Antarctic blubber oils shown in Table 20.

The component acids of *whale liver oil* are of biochemical interest. Klem[7] has given the following figures for the liver oil of a blue Antarctic whale: fatty content of liver, 3·5 per cent.; liver oil, iodine value 166, unsaponifiable matter 9·3 per cent.; fatty acids, mean molecular weight 303, "solid" acids 24 per cent., highly unsaturated acids 18·1 per cent. The fatty acid characteristics suggest similarity between the component acids of the liver and blubber fats.

It is even more interesting to find that the component acids of *whale milk fat* are also very similar in type to those of the liver and of the main depot fats. Detailed ester-fractionation analyses of whale milk fats by Klem[7] (1935) and by Cama and Meara[101] (1953) respectively for the blue Antarctic whale (*Balænoptera musculus*) and the finner whale (*B. physalus*) are quoted in Table 21B.

TABLE 21B. *Component Acids (per cent. wt.) of Whale Milk Fats*

	BLUE WHALE[7]	FINNER WHALES[101]		
Oil in milk (per cent.)	35–45	54·5	40·4	37·1
Iodine value of oil:	171·8	170·3	177·3	149·0
Component acids:				
Lauric	—	0·7	—	—
Myristic	8·4	7·1	7·3	10·0
Palmitic	16·8	15·8	16·6	17·6
Stearic	1·8	3·7	2·9	0·3
Arachidic	—	—	0·8	0·3
Unsaturated C_{14}	1·2	1·0	2·4	1·4
„ C_{16}	6·2	7·9	6·2	8·1
„ C_{18}	26·8	29·7	29·7	26·6
„ C_{20}	25·9	18·2	19·1	17·6
„ C_{22}	12·9	15·9	15·0	15·0
Mean unsaturation of:				
Unsaturated C_{14}	−2·0	−2·0	−2·0	−2·0
„ C_{16}	−2·0	−2·2	−2·7	−2·8
„ C_{18}	−3·3	−2·8	−3·3	−2·4
„ C_{20}	−8·5	−7·9	−8·2	−7·6
„ C_{22}	−11·0	−11·0	−10·8	−10·1

As in seal milk fats (Table 19, p. 66), whale milk fats contain the same mixture of fatty acids as their body fats; quantitatively there is some difference in the proportions of the various groups of acids. There is less unsaturated C_{18} and hexadecenoic acids than in the whale blubber fats, and more unsaturated C_{20} and (especially) C_{22} acids; the unsaturated milk fatty acids have on the whole a higher degree of unsaturation than the corresponding groups in the body fats. In neither of these marine mammals is there any production in the milk of fatty acids of lower molecular weight than those in the liver and the adipose tissues.

The Sperm Whale family (Physeteridæ). The oils from the blubber and the head cavity of the sperm whale (*Physeter macrocephalus*) differ from those of other whales in that they consist mainly of esters (waxes) of higher aliphatic alcohols and acids, with only subordinate amounts of glycerides. Further, their component fatty acids are quite distinct in type from those of ordinary whale oil or of other marine animal oils. Unsaturation is almost wholly confined to the mono-ethenoid state, and the average molecular weight of the acids is lower in both head and blubber oils than in ordinary whale oil. This is illustrated by the detailed analyses of Antarctic sperm whale oils in Table 22 (Hilditch and Lovern).[102]

TABLE 22. *Component Fatty Acids (per cent. wt.) of Sperm Whale Head and Blubber Oils*

SATURATED ACIDS	HEAD OIL	BLUBBER OIL
Decanoic	3·5	—
Lauric	16	1
Myristic	14	5
Palmitic	8	6·5
Stearic	2	—

UNSATURATED ACIDS		
C_{12} series	4 (−2H)	—
C_{14} ,,	14 (−2H)	4 (−2H)
C_{16} ,,	15 (−2H)	26·5 (−2H)
C_{18} ,,	17 (−2H)	37 (−2H)
C_{20} ,,	6·5 (−2H)	19 (−2·5H)
C_{22} ,,	—	1 (−4H)

The blubber oil acids resemble blubber acids of other whales more than those of the head oil; but unusually large proportions of hexadecenoic and C_{14} acids, with minor amounts of lauric acid, are present even here, whilst oleic is practically the only unsaturated C_{18} acid and the amount of polyethenoid C_{20} or C_{22} acids is extremely small. The head oil is almost unique (for an animal oil) in its content of decanoic, lauric, and myristic acids; the proportion of oleic acid in the head oil is remarkably small and, although a small percentage of gadoleic acid was observed, C_{22} acids are absent.

The hexadecenoic and oleic acids of both oils have the usual structure. The unsaturated C_{14} acid of the head oil is tetradec-5-enoic acid (Tsujimoto,[103] Hilditch and Lovern,[102] Toyama and Tsuchiya[104]), and according to the Japanese workers the same acid is present in the blubber oil; Hilditch and Lovern, however, identified a tetradec-9-enoic acid in the latter. Toyama and Tsuchiya[104] also state that the mono-ethenoid C_{12} acid of the head oil is dodec-5-enoic acid and that it is present in traces in the blubber oil; whilst they found traces of a dec-9-enoic acid in the head oil.

The sperm head oil studied by Hilditch and Lovern[102] consisted of a mixture of about 74 per cent. of wax esters with 26 per cent. of triglycerides, whilst the blubber oil contained about 66 per cent. of wax esters and 34 per cent. of triglycerides. The proportions of the chief component alcohols were approximately as follows:

SATURATED ALCOHOLS:	HEAD OIL	BLUBBER OIL
C_{14} Tetradecyl	8	—
C_{16} Hexadecyl (cetyl)	44	25
C_{18} Octadecyl	6	1
UNSATURATED ALCOHOLS:		
C_{16} Hexadecenyl	4	—
C_{18} Octadecenyl (oleyl)	28	66
C_{20} Eicosenyl	10	8

The manner in which the wax-esters and glycerides of these sperm oils are assembled is discussed later (Chapter VII, p. 488).

Weitkamp and Brunstrum[105] have also determined the components of "sperm oil alcohols" – apparently from sperm blubber oil – by ester fractionation and record the following data: saturated alcohols, C_{14} 2·1, C_{16} 21·1, C_{18} 5·0; mono-ethenoid unsaturated alcohols, C_{14} trace, C_{16} 7·4, C_{18} 49·7, C_{20} 6·1; and di-ethenoid unsaturated C_{20} alcohols 2·1 per cent. (weight).

The segregation of the acids and alcohols of lowest molecular weight in the head oil, and also of these components into the fully saturated portions of the latter, is a phenomenon similar to that observed subsequently in a number of other instances. It is an example of the behaviour which Lovern[77] has correlated with a possible "filtration" or "absorption" mechanism in which molecular size is considered to operate as a controlling factor in the type of fat deposited.

It is of the greatest interest to note that the *liver oil* of the sperm whale is apparently largely glyceridic and that its component acids align themselves with other marine animal liver oils. Tsujimoto and Kimura[106] have given a partial analysis of the mixed acids of sperm whale liver oil as follows: saturated acids (chiefly palmitic) 25, mono-ethenoid acids 42, and poly-ethenoid (C_{20} and C_{22}) acids 23 per cent. This composition is clearly similar to that of the majority of marine fish liver acids. The characteristic alcohols, and lower fatty acids, of the sperm whale depot fats are therefore substantially absent from the liver fat. The same circumstances occur also in the case of dolphin and porpoise fats (*cf.* below).

Berardius bairdii, belonging to the family Ziphiidæ (beaked whales) which is closely related to the Physeteridæ, is a North Pacific whale, the blubber of which contains 40 per cent. of fatty alcohols combined as wax esters. The alcohols include saturated C_{16} 9, C_{18} 27, C_{20} 2, and unsaturated C_{16} 7, C_{18} 53 and C_{20} 2 per cent. (wt.).[100]

Although the most familiar instance of the occurrence in large amounts of wax esters in an animal fat, the sperm head and body oils must not be supposed to be unique in this respect. There may well be other examples so far unobserved. Thus, Tsujimoto[107] has stated that the fat of the ovary of the grey mullet (*Mugil Japonicus*) contains 40 per cent. of "unsaponifiable matter", which is made up (apart from about 9 per cent. of cholesterol) of a mixture of cetyl, octadecyl, hexadecenyl, and oleyl alcohols; the original "fat", so far as can be judged from the merely qualitative data given, certainly contained a

73

high proportion of wax esters and was apparently not very dissimilar from sperm blubber oil.

The Dolphin and Porpoise family (Delphinidæ). In this group we encounter the most extreme case of an anomalous depot fatty acid, namely, the occurrence in quantity of the branched-chain, "odd-number", *iso*valeric acid, $C_5H_{10}O_2$, in the jaw, head, and blubber fats of this family of marine mammals. The acid was actually first observed in dolphin oil by Chevreul,[108] although it was not until comparatively recently that its identity was definitely confirmed as *iso*valeric acid, $(CH_3)_2CH.CH_2.COOH$, (Gill and Tucker[109]; Klein and Stigol[110]). Gill and Tucker[109] found in the jaw oil of a species of dolphin (*Tursiops truncatus*) 86·7 per cent. *iso*valeric, 8·4 per cent. palmitic, and 4·9 per cent. oleic acid; the oil contained about 19 per cent. of higher fatty alcohols in addition to glycerides.

The most complete information yet available for these fats is, however, the detailed analysis by Lovern[77] of the body and head oils of a dolphin (of unknown species), together with similar studies of the body, head, jaw, and various organ fats of an adult female porpoise (*Phocœna communis*) with a well-developed fœtus. Some particulars of these different fats are given in Table 23.

TABLE 23. *Particulars of Dolphin and Porpoise Fats (Lovern[77])*

SPECIES	FAT FROM	FAT IN TISSUE (Per cent.)	IODINE VALUE	SAP. EQUIV.	UNSAPONIFIABLE	
					(Per cent.)	Type
Dolphin	Body blubber	80–90	136·0	263·4	2·2	Mainly higher alcohols
,,	Head blubber	80–90	82·3	228·4	7·5	,, ,, ,,
Phocœna communis	Body blubber	80–90	88·8	225·7	2·4	,, ,, ,,
,, ,,	Head blubber	80–90	64·7	204·7	2·1	,, ,, ,,
,, ,,	Jaw	80–90	44·9	196·3	3·6	,, ,, ,,
,, ,,	Fœtal body blubber	80–90	108·9	267·8	2·4	Largely cholesterol
,, ,,	Heart	ca. 2	121·3	—	9·7	Mainly cholesterol
,, ,,	Lungs	ca. 2	119·5	—	15·0	,, ,,
,, ,,	Liver	ca. 5	175·0	—	32·1	,, ,,

The weight and molar percentages of the component acids in each fat in Table 23 are given in Table 24; owing to the extreme difference in molecular size between *iso*valeric and, for example, C_{22} acids, it becomes urgent here to make comparisons on a molar, and not merely a weight, percentage basis.

Perhaps the most remarkable feature of the figures in Table 24 is that the porpoise organ fats, without exception, contain no *iso*valeric and lauric acids, and do not contain unusually large proportions of C_{14} and C_{16} acids. High proportions of the acids of low molecular weight, and the presence of *iso*valeric acid, are confined to the depot fats of the body, head, and jaw of the animal. The fœtal fat had only a minute amount of *iso*valeric acid, but contained large quantities of C_{14} and C_{16} acids, whilst the degree of unsaturation of the C_{18} and C_{20} acids was the highest in the whole series, considerably higher even than that of the maternal liver. Further, four-fifths of the *iso*valeric acid present in the porpoise body fat was in combination with higher fatty acids in the form of mixed saturated-unsaturated glycerides, whilst the remaining fifth was present in mixed fully saturated glycerides, but no tri-*iso*valerin was detected. Hence, although *iso*valeric acid is absent from the liver or other organ fats, its mode of association in the depot fat glycerides with the higher fatty acids

TABLE 24. *Component Acids of Dolphin and Porpoise Fats (Lovern[77])*

(i) *Weight Percentages*

SPECIES	DEPOT	SATURATED					UNSATURATED				
		C_5	C_{12}	C_{14}	C_{16}	C_{18}	C_{14}†	C_{16}†	C_{18}	C_{20}	C_{22}
Dolphin	Body	3·2	1·0	7·2	8·6	0·8	4·7	25·9	24·1	18·6	5·9
									(−3·3H)	(−6·5H)	(−7·6H)
,,	Head	13·9	2·4	12·5	11·6	0·4	2·7	25·4	15·8	12·7	2·6
									(−2·8H)	(−5·5H)	(−7·2H)
Phocœna communis	Body	13·6	3·5*	12·1	4·7	—	4·7	27·2	16·7	10·5	7·0
									(−2·8H)	(−4·8H)	(−4·9H)
,,	,, Head	20·8	4·1	15·8	7·5	0·2	4·6	20·8	15·2	9·4	1·6
									(−2·6H)	(−4·5H)	(−4·7H)
,,	,, Jaw	25·3	4·6*	28·3	4·1	—	3·2	20·3	9·3	4·9	—
									(−2·6H)	(−4·9H)	
,,	,, Fœtus	1·2	—	14·9	0·6	—	12·3	48·1	15·4	7·5	—
									(−4·0H)	(−7·4H)	
,,	,, Liver	—	—	—	7·6	5·5	—	6·1	42·5	27·3	11·0
									(−2·8H)	(−5·4H)	(−6·5H)
,,	,, Lungs	—	—	4·6	9·0	1·2	0·1	16·5	27·0	31·0	10·6
									(−2·4H)	(−3·3H)	(−5·4H)
,,	,, Heart	—	—	8·1	8·2	4·4	4·4	16·8	50·4	7·6	—
									(−3·6H)	(−5·4H)	

(ii) *Molar Percentages*

SPECIES	DEPOT	SATURATED					UNSATURATED				
		C_5	C_{12}	C_{14}	C_{16}	C_{18}	C_{14}†	C_{16}†	C_{18}	C_{20}	C_{22}
Dolphin	Body	8·0	1·3	8·1	8·6	0·7	5·3	26·1	21·9	15·5	4·5
,,	Head	29·2	2·6	11·7	9·7	0·3	2·5	21·4	12·0	8·9	1·7
Phocœna communis	Body	28·7	3·8	11·4	3·9	—	4·5	23·0	12·8	7·4	4·5
,,	,, Head	39·6	4·0	13·4	5·7	0·1	3·9	16·0	10·5	5·9	0·9
,,	,, Jaw	44·7	4·1	22·4	2·9	—	2·6	14·4	6·0	2·9	—
,,	,, Fœtus	2·9	—	16·2	0·6	—	13·5	47·0	13·7	6·1	—
,,	,, Liver	—	—	—	8·6	5·6	—	6·9	43·7	25·7	9·5
,,	,, Lungs	—	—	5·7	10·0	1·2	0·1	18·4	27·2	28·4	9·0
,,	,, Heart	—	—	9·5	8·6	4·2	5·2	17·7	48·2	6·6	—

* Trace of dodecenoic acid present.
† The unsaturated C_{14} and C_{16} acids were substantially mono-ethenoid.

is exactly similar to the manner in which the latter are themselves assembled as mixed glycerides.

Williams and Maslov[111] recorded that *iso*valeric acid forms respectively 4·0, 25·1, and 20·0 per cent. (wt.) of the total acids of the body, head, and jaw fats of the white whale (*Delphinapterus leucas*), a member of another family, Delphinapteridæ, of marine mammals closely related to the Delphinidæ.

Another family, Platanistidæ, includes a number of dolphin species which inhabit freshwater or estuarine waters. The blubber fat of the Susu or Ganges dolphin (*Platanista gangetica*), recorded by Pathak *et al.*[112], resembles Indian freshwater fish fats rather than those of the Delphinidæ and allied mammals in its general composition (large proportions of unsaturated C_{16} and C_{18} acids and absence of any acids with fewer than 12 carbon atoms):

Fats of Platanista gangetica *(per cent. wt.)*

	SATURATED				UNSATURATED				
	C_{12}	C_{14}	C_{16}	C_{18}	C_{14}	C_{16}	C_{18}	C_{20}	C_{22}
Blubber	0·3	4·0	14·0	7·3	4·2	22·1	39·5	5·4	3·1
					(−2·0H)	(−2·1H)	(−2·7H)	(−5·7H)	(−8·5H)
Liver	—	7·8	7·5	4·5	5·8	13·4	30·6	26·3	4·1
					(−2·0H)	(−2·0H)	(−2·6H)	(−7·8H)	(−10H)

Platypus fat. The duck-billed platypus (*Ornithorhynchus anatinus*) is a quadruped found in South Eastern Australia and Tasmania which is remarkable as an egg-laying mammal. It is an aquatic animal, living in deep pools in rivers and creeks and feeding chiefly on aquatic flora. Its body fat, examined by Meara and Weerakoon,[113] was found to contain the following component acids: myristic 1·7, palmitic 9·7, stearic 9·8, arachidic 0·8; unsaturated C_{14} 3·4, C_{16} 14·8 ($-2·3H$), C_{18} 37·5 ($-2·9H$), C_{20} 21·7 ($-6·5H$), and C_{22} 0·6 ($-6·8H$) per cent. (wt.). The fat broadly resembles in composition that of freshwater fish (Table 6), notably in its contents of unsaturated C_{18} and C_{16} acids; unsaturated C_{20} acids form a rather higher proportion of the total acids than in most freshwater fish fats, and the saturated acids contain about equal proportions of stearic and palmitic acids. Platypus fat, however, although mammalian, is wholly "aquatic" in type and contrasts with those of amphibian animals such as the frog, turtle, or crocodile (Chapter III, Table 26, p. 85).

References to Chapter II

1. M. Tsujimoto, *Chem. Umschau*, 1925, **32**, 125.
2. G. Collin, J. C. Drummond, E. R. Gunther and T. P. Hilditch, *J. Exp. Biol.*, 1934, **11**, 198.
3. (a) J. A. Lovern, *Biochem. J.*, 1936, **30**, 387; (b) R. F. Paschke and D. H. Wheeler, *J. Amer. Oil Chem. Soc.*, 1954, **31**, 81; (c) H. Schlenk, R. T. Holman *et al.*, *ibid.*, 1960, **37**, 547.
4. D. A. Harper, private communication.
5. E. Takahashi, K. Shirahama and N. Ito, *J. Chem. Soc. Japan*, 1938, **59**, 662.
6. J. A. Lovern, (a) *Biochem. J.*, 1935, **29**, 847; (b) *ibid.*, 1938, **32**, 1214; (c) M. Saiki and T. Mori, *Bull. Japan Soc. Sci. Fisheries*, 1956, **21**, 1041.
7. A. Klem, *Hvalradets Skr.*, 1935, No. 11, 49–96.
8. (a) M. Takao and S. Tomiyama, *J. Agric. Chem. Soc. Japan*, 1953, **27**, 737; (b) Y. Toyama and T. Takagi, *J. Chem. Soc. Japan*, 1954, **75**, 1238; (c) *ibid.*, 1955, **76**, 237; (d) *ibid.*, 1956, **77**, 105.
9. W. Bergmann, S. S. Creighton and W. M. Stokes, *J. Org. Chem.*, 1956, **21**, 721; 1958, **23**, 1241; etc.
10. (a) E. Gérard, *J. Pharm.*, 1893, (v), **28**, 443; R. Jungkunz, *Chem. Umschau*, 1920, **27**, 89; (b) T. P. Hilditch and K. S. Murti, *J. Soc. Chem. Ind.*, 1939, **58**, 351.
11. S. P. Ligthelm, L. Novellie, (Miss) H. M. Schwartz and M. M. von Holdt, *J. Sci. Food Agric.*, 1953, **4**, 21.
12. A. Cardin and M. L. Meara, *J. Exp. Biol.*, 1953, **30**, 561.
13. W. Bergmann and A. N. Swift, *J. Org. Chem.*, 1951, **16**, 1206; 1961, **26**, 1257; etc.
14. P. G. Hofstädter, *Annalen*, 1854, **91**, 177.
15. E. Ljubarsky, *J. pr. Chem.*, 1898, (2), **57**, 19.
16. H. Bull, *Ber.*, 1906, **39**, 3570.
17. J. Lewkowitsch, *cf.* Lewkowitsch, "Chemistry and Technology of Oils, Fats, and Waxes", 6th Edition, 1922.
18. Y. Toyama *et al.*; *cf.* for example, *Chem. Umschau*, 1924, **31**, 221; *J. Soc. Chem. Ind. Japan*, 1927, **30**, 116, 207, 519, 597, 603.
19. Y. Toyama and T. Tsuchiya, *J. Soc. Chem. Ind. Japan*, 1934, **37**, 14B, 17B; Y. Toyama and T. Ishikawa, *ibid.*, 1934, **37**, 534B, 536B.
20. Y. Toyama, *J. Soc. Chem. Ind. Japan*, 1927, **30**, 597.
21. M. Tsujimoto, *J. Soc. Chem. Ind. Japan*, 1927, **30**, 868.
22. E. Klenk, *Z. physiol. Chem.*, 1927, **166**, 287.
23. M. Tsujimoto, *J. Coll. Eng. Tokyo*, 1906, **4**, 1; *J. Soc. Chem. Ind. Japan*, 1920, **23**, 1007.
24. Y. Toyama and T. Tsuchiya, *Bull. Chem. Soc. Japan*, 1929, **4**, 83; B. Suzuki and Y. Yokoyama, *Proc. Imp. Acad. Tokyo*, 1929, **5**, 272.

25. Y. Toyama and T. Tsuchiya, *Bull. Chem. Soc. Japan*, 1929, **4**, 83.
26. Y. Toyama and T. Tsuchiya, *J. Soc. Chem. Ind. Japan*, 1934, **37**, 530B.
27. S. Ueno and C. Yonese, *Bull. Chem. Soc. Japan*, 1936, **11**, 437.
28. M. Tsujimoto, *Chem. Umschau*, 1932, **39**, 50; *J. Soc. Chem. Ind.*, 1932, **51**, 317T.
29. L. A. Swain, *Canad. Chem.*, 1948, **32**, 553; *J. Fish. Res. Bd. Canada*, 1948, **7**, 389.
30. M. Tsujimoto, (*a*) *J. Soc. Chem. Ind. Japan*, 1906, **9**, 953; (*b*) *J. Ind. Eng. Chem.*, 1916, **8**, 889; (*c*) *ibid.*, 1920, **12**, 63.
31. (*a*) A. Chaston Chapman, *J. Chem. Soc.*, 1917, **111**, 56; 1918, **113**, 458; (*b*) I. M. Heilbron, E. D. Kamm and W. M. Owens, *ibid.*, 1926, 1630.
32. H. J. Channon, *Biochem. J.*, 1928, **22**, 51.
33. H. Hata and T. Kunisaki, *J. Chem. Soc. Japan*, 1940, **61**, 1292.
34. (*a*) M. Tsujimoto, *J. Ind. Eng. Chem.*, 1917, **9**, 1098; Y. Toyama, *Chem. Umschau*, 1923, **30**, 181; (*b*) N. A. Sörensen and J. Mehlum, *Acta Chem. Scand.*, 1948, **2**, 140; J. S. and N. A. Sörensen, *ibid.*, 1948, **2**, 166; 1949, **3**, 939; E. Lederer and J. Pliva, *Bull. Soc. Chim.*, 1951, (v), **18**, 72; (*c*) M. Tsujimoto, *Bull. Chem. Soc. Japan*, 1935, **10**, 149.
35. (*a*) T. Thorbjarnarson and J. C. Drummond, *Analyst*, 1935, **60**, 23; J. Fitelson, *J. Assoc. Offic. Agric. Chem.*, 1936, **19**, 496; 1937, **20**, 418; 1945, **28**, 282; 1946, **29**, 247; (*b*) K. Täufel, H. Heinisch and W. Heimann, *Biochem. Z.*, 1940, **303**, 324; J. Fitelson, *J. Assoc. Offic. Agric. Chem.*, 1943, **26**, 499, 506; (*c*) K. Täufel, H. Thaler and H. Shreyegg, *Z. Unters. Lebensm.*, 1936, **72**, 394.
36. (*a*) I. M. Heilbron (with W. M. Owens and I. A. Simpson), *J. Chem. Soc.*, 1929, 873; (with A. Thompson), *ibid.*, 1929, 883; (*b*) P. Karrer and A. Helfenstein, *Helv. Chim. Acta*, 1931, **14**, 78.
37. J. A. Lovern, *Biochem. J.*, 1937, **31**, 755 (p. 759).
38. E. André and A. Bloch, *Compt. rend.*, 1932, **195**, 627; *Bull. Soc. Chim.*, 1935, (v), **2**, 789.
39. J. A. Lovern, "The Composition of the Depot Fats of Aquatic Animals", *D.S.I.R. Food Investigation Spec. Report*, No. 51, 1942.
40. K. D. Guha, T. P. Hilditch and J. A. Lovern, *Biochem. J.*, 1930, **24**, 266.
41. J. A. Lovern, *Biochem. J.*, 1937, **31**, 755.
42. J. A. Lovern, *Biochem. J.*, 1930, **24**, 866.
43. E. Otero Aenlle, *Ion*, 1944, **4**, 161.
44. M. L. Karnovsky, A. W. Lategan, W. S. Rapson and (Miss) A. M. Schwartz, *J. Soc. Chem. Ind.*, 1948, **67**, 193.
45. A. P. Oliver and F. B. Shorland, *Biochem. J.*, 1948, **43**, 18.
46. M. L. Karnovsky, W. S. Rapson, and (Miss) H. M. Schwartz, *J. Soc. Chem. Ind.*, 1948, **67**, 144.
47. M. L. Karnovsky, W. S. Rapson, (Miss) H. M. Schwartz, (Miss) M. M. Black and N. J. van Rensberg, *J. Soc. Chem. Ind.*, 1948, **67**, 104.
48. T. P. Hilditch and A. Houlbrooke, *Analyst*, 1928, **53**, 246.
49. (*a*) J. Holmberg and G. Sellman, Personal communication (1955); (*b*) G. Fensch, *Atti. Soc. pelor. sci. fis. mat. e nat.*, 1955, **1**, 27; (*c*) D. C. Malins and C. R. Houle, *Proc. Soc. Exp. Biol. Med.*, 1961, **108**, 126.
50. (*a*) T. H. Wang and G. H. Kan, *J. Chinese Chem. Soc.*, 1936, **4**, 393; (*b*) S. P. Pathak, C. V. Agarwal and S. S. Mathur, *J. Amer. Oil Chem. Soc.*, 1952, **29**, 593; S. P. Pathak and P. N. Suwal, *ibid.*, 1954, **31**, 332; S. P. Pathak and G. D. Pande, *ibid.*, 1955, **32**, 7; (*c*) S. P. Pathak and P. N. Suwal, *ibid.*, 1955, **32**, 229; (*d*) S. P. Pathak and L. M. Dey, *ibid.*, 1957, **34**, 425.
51. (*a*) G. G. Kamath and N. G. Magar, *J. Indian Chem. Soc., Ind. News. Edition*, 1956, **19**, 201; (*b*) *ibid.*, 1955, **18**, 241; (*c*) *ibid.*, 1956, **19**, 171; (*d*) I. M. Morice and F. B. Shorland, *Biochem. J.*, 1955, **61**, 453; 1956, **64**, 461.
52. W. S. Rapson and (Miss) H. M. Schwartz (with N. J. van Rensberg and C. J. Molteno), *J. Soc. Chem. Ind.*, 1943, **62**, 211; 1944, **63**, 18, 21, 314, 340, 367, 371; 1945, **64**, 5, 7, 44, 47, 61, 114, 139, 140, 172, 326; 1946, **65**, 13.

53. (a) J. A. Lovern (privately communicated); (b) D. A. Harper and T. P. Hilditch, *J. Soc. Chem. Ind.*, 1937, **56**, 322T.

54. K. W. DeWitt, *J. Sci. Food Agric.*, 1963, **14**, 92.

55. J. A. Lovern, *Biochem. J.*, 1932, **26**, 1978.

56. F. B. Shorland and T. P. Hilditch, *Biochem. J.*, 1938, **32**, 792.

57. (a) M. H. Silk and H. H. Hahn, *Biochem. J.*, 1954, **57**, 582; (b) (Miss) M. M. Black and (Miss) H. M. Schwartz, *J. Sci. Food Agric.*, 1950, **1**, 248; *see also* M. H. Silk and H. H. Hahn, *Biochem. J.*, 1954, **57**, 574, 577.

58. F. B. Shorland, *Biochem. J.*, 1939, **33**, 1935.

59. J. A. Lovern, *Biochem. J.*, 1936, **30**, 2023; *see also* W. T. Roubal, *J. Amer. Oil Chem. Soc.*, 1963, **40**, 213, 215.

60. (a) S. Ueno and S. Matsuda, *J. Soc. Chem. Ind. Japan*, 1935, **38**, 691B; (b) I. S. del Frade, R. R. Brenner and P. Cattaneo, *Anal. Asoc. Quim. Argentina*, 1955, **43**, 126; (c) H. Tsuyuki, A. Shionoya and T. Matsumoto, *J. Japan Oil Chem. Soc.*, 1959, **8**, 31.

61. H. N. Brocklesby, *Biol. Bd. Canada, Progress Reports*, 1936, No. 30, 19; H. N. Brocklesby and K. F. Harding, *J. Fish Res. Bd. Canada*, 1938, **4**, 55, 59.

62. (a) J. A. Lovern, *Biochem. J.*, 1938, **32**, 676; (b) L. A. Swain, *Fish. Res. Bd. Canada*, 1953, No. 94, 24.

63. O. B. Bjarnason and M. L. Meara, *J. Soc. Chem. Ind.*, 1944, **63**, 61.

64. T. P. Hilditch and S. P. Pathak, *Biochem. J.*, 1948, **42**, 316.

65. E. F. Armstrong and J. Allan, *J. Soc. Chem. Ind.*, 1924, **43**, 216T.

66. W. H. Baldwin and W. B. Lanham, *Ind. Eng. Chem. (Anal.)*, 1941, **13**, 615.

67. F. A. Smith and J. B. Brown, *Oil and Soap*, 1945, **22**, 277, 321; 1946, **23**, 9.

68. (a) H. Nobori, *J. Soc. Chem. Ind., Japan*, 1940, **43**, 59B, 110B; (b) E. Klenk and H. Brockerhoff, *Z. Physiol. Chem.*, 1957, **307**, 272; 1958, **310**, 153; E. Klenk and H. Steinboch, *ibid.*, 1959, **316**, 31; E. Klenk and L. Brucker-Voigt, *ibid.*, 1961, **324**, 1; (c) M. H. Silk and H. H. Hahn, *Biochem. J.*, 1954, **57**, 582; R. I. Cheftel, J. Moretti and J. Polonovoski, *Bull. Soc. Chim. Biol.*, 1955, **37**, 709; J. M. Whitcutt and D. A. Sutton, *Biochem. J.*, 1956, **63**, 469; J. M. Whitcutt, *ibid.*, 1957, **67**, 60; M. Matic *ibid.*, 1958, **68**, 692; (d) Y. Toyama, T. Shimooka, Y. Iwata and K. Fujimura, *Fette Seif. Anstrichm.*, 1959, **61**, 461, 846; (e) W. Stoffel and E. H. Ahrens, Jr, *J. Amer. Chem. Soc.*, 1958, **80**, 6604; *J. Lipid Research*, 1960, **1**, 139; O. S. Privett, *Ann. Rept. Hormel Inst.*, 1955–6, 59.

69. (a) E. H. Ahrens, Jr, W. Insull, Jr, W. Stoffel, H. J. Thomasson *et al.*, *Lancet*, 1959, (i), 115; (b) R. K. Beerthuis, G. Dijkstra, J. G. Keppler and J. H. Recourt, *Ann. N.Y. Acad. Sci.*, 1959, **72**, 616; (c) R. M. Kyte, *J. Amer. Oil Chem. Soc.*, 1956, **33**, 146.

70. J. A. Lovern, *Biochem. J.*, 1934, **28**, 1955 (adult salmon body fats), 1961 (parr and smolt fats); 1936, **30**, 20 (salmon ova fat).

71. (a) W. M. Cox and E. E. Reid, *J. Amer. Chem. Soc.*, 1932, **54**, 220; (b) S. Komori and T. Agawa, *J. Amer. Oil Chem. Soc.*, 1955, **32**, 525.

72. (a) J. A. Lovern, *Biochem. J.*, 1953, **54**, 126; J. A. Lovern and (Miss) J. Olley, *ibid.*, 1953, **54**, 128; 1953, **55**, 686; (Miss) J. Olley and J. A. Lovern, *ibid.*, 1953, **54**, 569; 1954, **57**, 610; 1955, **62**, 99, 107; J. A. Lovern, *ibid.*, 1956, **63**, 373; *J. Sci. Food Agric.*, 1956, **7**, 729; (Miss) J. Olley, *Biochem. J.*, 1961, **81**, 29P; (b) A. Cardin, M. A. Bordeleau and A. Laframboise, *J. Fish. Res. Bd. Canada*, 1958, **15**, 555; (c) H. Igarashi, K. Zama and K. Matada, *J. Agric. Chem. Soc. Japan*, 1956, **30**, 111, 116, 433, 435, 566, 568.

73. J. A. Lovern, *Biochem. J.*, 1935, **29**, 1894.

74. (a) S. P. Pathak and C. V. Agarwal, *Biochem. J.*, 1952, **51**, 264; (b) S. P. Pathak, G. D. Pande and S. S. Mathur, *ibid.*, 1954, **57**, 449; (c) S. P. Pathak and V. N. Ojha, *ibid.*, 1957, **66**, 193; (d) R. R. Brenner, *Anal. Asoc. Quim. Argentina*, 1953, **41**, 61, 177; (e) R. R. Brenner, A. R. San Martin and P. Cattaneo, *ibid.*, 1954, **42**, 95; (f) R. R. Brenner, S. A. Quaglia and P. Cattaneo, *ibid.*, 1954, **42**, 192; (g) R. R. Brenner, W. H. E. Reinke and P. Cattaneo, *ibid.*, 1955, **43**, 67; *cf. also*, *ibid.*, 1960, **48**, 204, 236; (h) S. P. Pathak and B. R. Reddy, *J. Sci. Food Agric.*, 1963, **14**, 395.

75. (a) P. B. Kelly, R. Reiser and D. W. Hood, *J. Amer. Oil Chem. Soc.*, 1958, **35**, 503; R. Reiser *et al.*, *ibid.*, 1963, **40**, 507; (b) N. R. Bottino and R. R. Brenner, *ibid.*, 1962, **39**, 519; (c) N. V. Williams and A. S. Onischtschenko, *Schrift. Zentr. Forsch. Lebensm.*, (*U.S.S.R.*), 1935, **4**, 145.

76. F. B. Shorland and I. G. McIntosh, *Biochem. J.*, 1936, **30**, 1775.

77. J. A. Lovern, *Biochem. J.*, 1934, **28**, 394.

78. J. A. Lovern, *Biochem. J.*, 1940, **34**, 704.

79. F. B. Shorland and J. Russell, *Biochem. J.*, 1948, **42**, 429.

80. J. A. Lovern, *Biochem. J.*, 1932, **26**, 1985.

81. Y. D. Karkhanis and N. G. Magar, *J. Amer. Oil Chem. Soc.*, 1955, **32**, 492.

82. D. E. Johnson, *Trans. New Zealand Inst.*, 1920, **52**, 20.

83. F. B. Shorland, *Biochem. J.*, 1953, **54**, 673.

84. N. V. Williams and G. A. Makhrov, *Schrift. Zentr. Forsch. Lebensm.* (*U.S.S.R.*), 1935, **4**, 157.

85. M. Tsujimoto, *J. Soc. Chem. Ind. Japan*, 1916, **19**, 715.

86. K. H. Bauer and W. Neth, *Chem. Umschau*, 1924, **31**, 5.

87. F. Burke and H. Jasperson, *J. Soc. Chem. Ind.*, 1944, **63**, 245.

88. T. P. Hilditch and S. P. Pathak, (a) *J. Soc. Chem. Ind.*, 1947, **66**, 421; (b) *Biochem. J.*, 1949, **44**, 218.

89. A. Cardin and M. L. Meara, *Intern. Conference on Biochemical Problems of Lipids*, 1953, pp. 49–58.

90. M. L. Meara, (a) *Biochem. J.*, 1952, **51**, 190; (b) privately communicated.

91. G. Winter and W. J. Nunn, (a) *J. Sci. Food Agric.*, 1950, **1**, 18, 311; (b) *ibid.*, 1953, **4**, 442.

92. G. Winter and W. J. Nunn, (a) *J. Sci. Food Agric.*, 1950, **1**, 311; (b) *ibid.*, 1953, **4**, 439; (c) H. Tsuyuki, *Sci. Rpts. Whale Res. Inst.* (*Tokyo*), 1958, **13**, 323.

93. (a) F. D. Gunstone and W. C. Russell, privately communicated; (b) A. Cardin, *Thesis, University of Liverpool*, 1952, p. 53.

94. J. Lund, *Oil and Soap*, 1936, **13**, 148.

95. I. Tveraaen, *Hvalradets Skr.*, 1935, No. 11, 5–48.

96. C. W. Moore and C. H. Clarke, *cf.* E. F. Armstrong and J. Allan, *J. Soc. Chem. Ind.*, 1924, **43**, 216T.

97. T. P. Hilditch and J. T. Terleski, *J. Soc. Chem. Ind.*, 1937, **56**, 315T.

98. T. P. Hilditch and L. Maddison, (a) *J. Soc. Chem. Ind.*, 1942, **61**, 169; (b) *ibid.*, 1948, **67**, 253.

99. (a) T. Pedersen, *Tidskr. Kjemi*, 1952, **5**, 83; (b) *Hvalradets Skr.*, 1950, No. **34**, p. 24.

100. M. Saiki, S. C. Fang and T. Mori, *Bull. Japan Soc. Sci. Fisheries*, 1958–1959, **24**, 578.

101. J. S. Cama and M. L. Meara, *Biochem. J.*, 1953, **55**, 365.

102. T. P. Hilditch and J. A. Lovern, *J. Soc. Chem. Ind.*, 1928, **47**, 105T; 1929, **48**, 359T, 365T.

103. M. Tsujimoto, *Chem. Umschau*, 1923, **30**, 33; 1925, **32**, 127; *J. Soc. Chem. Ind. Japan*, 1926, **29**, 102.

104. Y. Toyama and T. Tsuchiya, *Bull. Chem. Soc. Japan*, 1935, **10**, 563, 570; *J. Chem. Soc. Japan*, 1935, **56**, 1050, 1055.

105. A. W. Weitkamp and L. C. Brunstrum, *Oil and Soap*, 1941, **18**, 47.

106. M. Tsujimoto and K. Kimura, *Chem. Umschau*, 1928, **35**, 317.

107. M. Tsujimoto, *J. Soc. Chem. Ind. Japan*, 1933, **36**, 676B.

108. M. E. Chevreul, "Récherches chimiques sur les corps gras", 1823, p. 115.

109. A. H. Gill and C. M. Tucker, *Oil & Fat Ind.*, 1930, **7**, 101.

110. A. Klein and M. Stigol, *Pharm. Zentr.*, 1930, **71**, 497.

111. N. V. Williams and N. Y. Maslov, *Schrift. Zent. Forsch. Lebensm.* (*U.S.S.R.*), 1935, **4**, 150.

112. S. P. Pathak, P. N. Suwal and C. V. Aggarwal, *Biochem. J.*, 1956, **62**, 634.

113. M. L. Meara and A. H. Weerakoon (*see* A. H. Weerakoon, *Thesis, University of Liverpool*, 1952, p. 189).

CHAPTER III

The Component Acids of Fats of Land Animals

FATS occur in many different parts of animals, as they do in plants (*cf.* Chapter IV). In each division, vegetable or animal, they are found both in the organs and tissues concerned with the growth and maintenance of life, and in special locations or depots (fruits in the vegetable world and adipose tissues in the animal kingdom) where they are stored as reserve material. Further, a special type of fat may be present in the milk secreted by mammals as food for their young.

Discussion of the ultimate composition of these various groups of animal fats is subject to the usual limitations, namely, paucity of detailed fatty acid analyses in spite of abundant data on saponification values, iodine values, etc., of individual fats or of their corresponding "mixed fatty acids". As has happened in the vegetable fats, the land animal depot fats hitherto studied in detail are those which are most common, most readily obtained in quantity in a pure state, and, incidentally, most in demand for edible or other industrial purposes. There is a consequent lack of perspective in any detailed description of the fatty acids of land animals as a whole, because attention has hitherto been focussed far too much on relatively few species. Thus it is only possible to give an account of the animal depot fats of which the component acids have been adequately studied, to supplement this to some extent, and with discretion, from the general or average data on record in some other instances, and to indicate the lacunæ which remain to be filled by future experimental work.

The constitution of the fats (glyceridic and phosphatidic) of animal organs has been investigated in still less detail than that of the depot fats, owing to the smaller proportions of fatty matter usually present in most organs as compared with adipose tissue, and to the difficulties of separating organ fats in a pure condition in sufficient quantity for full examination. There have, however, been great advances in the past few years in the separation of the various classes of lipids by improved chromatographic techniques, whilst by means of gas–liquid chromatography component acid determinations can now be rapidly made on extremely small samples (1 mgm. or less) of lipid fatty acids, or better, their methyl esters. It should follow that information will now be gathered much more rapidly on the various fatty acid mixtures present not only in depot, milk and liver fats, but also in other organs and tissues. A good deal is already being done, especially, on the various classes of lipids – glycerides, phospholipids, free and esterified sterols, etc. – present in the blood streams of animal species; such studies have been prompted by the urge to define the extent of possible connection of the blood content of specific lipids with the development of arterial disease, thrombosis, etc.

80

In this chapter we shall consider in succession, and subject to the limitations already mentioned, the chief features of the component acids of land animal depot, organ (mainly liver), and milk fats.

Component Acids of Depot Fats (Glycerides) of Land Animals

In discussing the available data for the depot fats of the different categories of land animals, attention will be directed primarily to fats from animals whose diet has not contained more than two or three per cent. of fat, such fat being, as it were, that present in the normal food of the species (grass, grain, etc., as the case may be). When animals are fed on rations containing relatively large proportions of fat, much of the dietary fat may be more or less directly assimilated and the composition of the resulting depot fats is affected to a considerable extent according to the nature and amount of the fat ingested by the animal. This will be illustrated subsequently by examples in which animals have been fed on a high fat ration of known composition, and their depot fats submitted to detailed examination.

It should be pointed out here that animal adipose tissue fats consist, as a rule, almost wholly of glycerides. In liver and other organ fats, in contrast, it is usual to find that the fatty matter also contains fairly large proportions of phosphatides, and also cholesterol and/or cholesterol fatty esters, in addition to mixed triglycerides.

Invertebrata

Before proceeding to discuss the depot fats of vertebrate land animals, the existing information on fats of invertebrate land animals (very slight in amount, and nearly all concerning insects) may receive brief notice.

Although the components of a few fats of marine invertebrates have been determined (Chapter II, pp. 27–34), the only studies of fats of land invertebrates (other than insects) appear to be by Lovern[1a] of the fatty matter which is present to the amount of 1·2–1·3 per cent. in the common earthworm (Lumbricidæ), and by Cmelik and Bartl[1b] of the lipids of tapeworm (*Tænia saginata*). Of the total lipids of the earthworm, 56–67 per cent. were glyceridic, and 44–33 per cent. phosphatidic, in character; but each group contained over 50 per cent. of unsaponifiable or non-fatty matter. Both groups contained unknown acids in addition to fatty acids of the C_{10}–C_{26} series; very low hexadecenoic acid contents and a preponderance of stearic over palmitic acid were observed.

INSECT FATS

"Chrysalis oil", which forms about 25 per cent. of the cocoon of the silkworm, *Bombyx mori*, has received most attention. Kimura[2] gave the fatty acid composition as about 25 per cent. of saturated (mainly palmitic) acids with about 22 per cent. oleic, about 38 per cent. linoleic, and about 15 per cent. linolenic acids, whilst a later communication by Bergmann[3] stated that the average composition is: palmitic 20, stearic 4, arachidic, etc., less than 1; hexadecenoic 2, oleic 35, linoleic 12, linolenic 25, and higher unsaturated acids 1–2 per cent. Bergmann[3] adds that the chrysalis fat of the tent moth, *Malacosoma americana*, has a similar composition. Bachstez and Aragon[4] determined the component acids of the fat of the caterpillar of *Acentrocneme hesperiaris* which feeds on the leaves of the Mexican agave, the sap of which contains cane sugar and invert sugar. The fat, which in this instance is almost certainly synthesised by the insect from sugar, contained as component acids palmitic 30·6, stearic 3·7, oleic 61·3, and linoleic 4·4 per cent. (wt.). Hastings and Pepper[5] recorded that the larval fat of the diapausing codlin moth (*Carpocapsa pomonella*) contains as component acids saturated 3·6, oleic 75·3, and linoleic 21·1 per cent. (wt.). The body of a Brazilian butterfly, *Myelobia smerintha*, is stated by Thoms[6] to contain 22 per cent. of fat, the acids of which consist of about one-third saturated (palmitic and stearic) and two-thirds unsaturated (oleic).

A few analyses of body fats of insects of the Orthoptera (locusts, grasshoppers, etc.) have been given in more or less detail, as will be seen from Table 25.

TABLE 25. *Component Acids (per cent. wt.) of Body Fats of Orthoptera*

Species:	Oxya japonica[7]	Locusta migratoria[8]	Tæniopoda auricornis[9a]		Melanoplus atlantis[9a]	Sphenarium purpurascens[9b]	Hemideina thoracica[10]
Common name:	Locust	Locust			Locust		Weta
Location:	Japan	Africa	Mexico		Mexico	Mexico	New Zealand
Oil in body (per cent.)	3	8			3	8	6
Component acids:			(Male)	(Female)			
Myristic	—	1·0	—	—	—	2·9	—
Palmitic	}25{	24·5	}15·5	35·0{	7·3	14·8	}21·3
Stearic		7·3			12·2	11·4	
Arachidic	—	—	—	—	2·8	—	—
Hexadecenoic	—	2·1	—	—	4·1	9·6	18·0
Oleic	}75{	12·4	24·0	6·5	29·9	35·5	60·7
Linoleic		35·1	60·5	58·5	(−2·8H)	(−2·9H)	(−2·2H)
Linolenic		17·3	—	—			
Unsaturated C_{20}	—	0·3	—	—	38·4 (−3·8H)	25·8 (−4·7H)	—
„ C_{22}	—	—	—	—	5·3 (−3·7H)	—	—

Tsujimoto[7] stated that the 2·4 per cent. of fat in Japanese crickets (*Aceta mitrata*) contains mainly oleic with some polyethenoid C_{18} acids and some unsaturated acids. The occurrence of unsaturated C_{20} or higher acids in this group of fats appears to be sporadic: these were definitely absent from the Weta body fat and, apparently, from that of *Tæniopoda*. The major components in all these fats are evidently linoleic and oleic, whilst saturated acids (mainly palmitic and stearic) are also prominent – 15 to 35 per cent. of the total acids. It is to be noticed that the saturated acid contents of grass or leaf fats (Chapter IV, pp. 180–183), the probable main diet of these Orthopterous insects, are much smaller. Records of similar high saturated acid contents were seen above in fats of the silkworm, and of some of the moths of which the fats have been examined. The data are, however, at present too fragmentary for any useful discussion of their implication.

The body fat of the cantharides beetle has received some attention. Iyer and Ayyar[11] stated that fat (including 5 per cent. of unsaponifiable matter) amounts to 12·5 per cent. of the dry weight of the Indian species *Myalabris pustulata*, the component acids being palmitic 13, stearic 32, arachidic 1, and oleic acid 54 per cent. Janot and Faudemay[12] found the proportions of fatty acids in lipids of the species *Lytta vesicatoria* to be somewhat variable, the major components being palmitic and oleic acids, with minor amounts of stearic, linoleic, and linolenic acids.

The general characteristics of a few other fats of insects belonging to the Coleoptera, Diptera, and Orthoptera have been reported, from which it appears that the major components are oleic and linoleic acids and that, although palmitic acid is probably also present, acids of lower molecular weight are absent. An exception to this statement is, however, found in the fat of *Pemphigus* species (Aphidæ), the acids of which were reported by Schultz[13] to have a mean molecular weight of 218 and to include butyric, caprylic, and lauric as well as palmitic acids.

The larvæ of a beetle (*Pachymerus dactris*) which had fed on the endosperm of the nuts of *Manicaria saccifera* (Palmæ) were found by Collin[14a] to contain nearly 50 per cent. of fat, the component acids of which were made up approximately as follows: lauric 24, myristic 21, palmitic 8, oleic 32, linoleic 3, and a further 12 per cent. of stearic, oleic, or linoleic acids. Comparing these figures with those for the kernel fat of *Manicaria saccifera* (Chapter IV, p. 342), it appears that the acids of lower molecular weight (of which lauric acid is the chief) are present in the larva fat in only about half the amount in which they occur in the kernel fat, while oleic and linoleic acids probably form about 40 per cent. of the mixed acids in the larva fat, as compared with only 11 per cent. in the kernel fat. This suggests that the insect derives its fat partly by direct assimilation of the preformed vegetable fat, and partly by synthesis from carbohydrate (or other non-fatty) components of the kernel. If this be the case, it would appear that the development of fat in insects may follow a course not very different from that which takes place in the larger land vertebrates.

Another interesting instance of the same nature is that of green Chironomids, minute midges (*Tanytarsus lewisi*) which deposit eggs in the Nile and other tropical rivers. The insects do all their feeding on the bed of the river while in the larval stage, and Grindley[14b] found that the body fats of the fully developed insects closely resemble those of algæ and plankton (Chapter II, pp. 27–31); their component acids included hexadecenoic acid and higher polyethenoid (tetra- and penta-ene) acids in addition to palmitic, stearic, oleic, and linoleic acids. Here also, therefore, the composition of the insect body fat is conditioned by the fats present in the larval diet.

On the whole, it seems likely that insects, in the larval as well as mature state, lay down fats very similar in type to those produced by mammals, and that, like the latter, they can assimilate fats present in their diet and also synthesise fat from other constituents of the food. More complete study of insect fats than has hitherto been made might well be of interest from a biochemical standpoint.

It will be noted, of course, that here we are considering the glyceridic fat present in insects or their larvæ, and not the waxes elaborated by some species such as, for example, bees or the cochineal insect. Insect waxes consist almost wholly of ester-waxes derived from aliphatic acids and alcohols of higher molecular weight (e.g. C_{26} and upwards) than those present in natural fats. Bees wax, however, is reputed to contain, amongst its acidic components, a certain amount of palmitic acid and small proportions of oleic acid.

Vertebrata

DEPOT FATS OF AMPHIBIA AND REPTILES

A few, very significant, detailed investigations have been made of depot fats of the frog, lizard, and turtle family, and of some large snakes and of the crocodile.* Their significance lies in the circumstance that in most cases the component fatty acids form a link intermediate in almost all respects between those of depot fats of aquatic and of land animals. The data in question are collected in Table 26.

Despite marked differences in quantitative (and in one species qualitative) composition, it will be seen that the unsaturated C_{16} and C_{20-22} acids of the fats in Table 26 are usually present in smaller proportions than in fish depot fats, whilst the unsaturated C_{18} acids (in which oleic predominates) become the most prominent individual group. We shall find (*vide infra*) that in depot fats of the larger animals the hexadecenoic and C_{20-22} acid contents are reduced to very small proportions. The saturated acids of the fats in Table 26 are more reminiscent of typical fish, etc., fats than the unsaturated components, but in some of the larger snakes and lizards the proportion of palmitic acid rises towards the amount characteristic of the larger land animal depot fats.

The data for the fats of the frog, Greek tortoise, and one of the lizards (1) were given in 1933 and 1935 by Klenk,[16] who commented on the circumstance that the fatty acid compositions were intermediate in character between those of corresponding fats from land mammals and fishes. Actually, the frog fat and the toad fat (Cattaneo,[15b] 1951) are nearer in type to aquatic than to land animal fats, whilst the Greek tortoise and lizard (1) fats are more definitely intermediate in composition. Of the two *lizards*, the specimen (1) examined by Klenk was a mature animal which had been kept in captivity for some years, whilst lizard (2), of the same species, was a very young wild animal killed in Ceylon. Differences in diet and other factors may have contributed to the differences (mainly in palmitic and unsaturated C_{18} acid contents) observed in the depot fat component acids.

Two of the Mexican *turtle fats* studied by Giral[20b,c] are fairly typical amphibian fats, but palmitic acid rises above 20 per cent. and stearic acid is

* Previous to these detailed analyses Tsujimoto[15a] had noted in 1920 that the fatty acids of many amphibians and reptiles yielded varying proportions of ether-insoluble bromo-additive products which indicated the presence of highly unsaturated acids of the C_{20} and C_{22} series and thus pointed to resemblance to the oils of aquatic fauna.

also prominent in one of the fats; but the fats of the *green turtle*[18, 19, 20a] stand apart in that lauric is present in approximately equimolecular proportions to palmitic acid, whilst, with myristic acid, these acids amount to nearly

TABLE 26. *Component Fatty Acids (per cent. wt.) of Amphibian and Reptile Depot Fats*

	SATURATED				UNSATURATED			
	C_{12}	C_{14}	C_{16}	C_{18}	C_{14}	C_{16}	C_{18}	C_{20-22}
Frog (*Rana temporaria*)[16a]	—	4	11	3	—	15 (−2H)	52 (ca. −2·5H)	15 (ca. −6H)
Toad (*Bufo arenarum*)[15b]	0·5	3·4	18·2	3·8 (a)	1·2	13·1 (−2H)	57·9 (−?H)	1·4 (−?H)
Lizard (1) (*Varanus salvator*)[16b]	—	4	18	7	—	10 (−2H)	56 (−2·4H)	5 (ca. −5H)
Lizard (2) (*Varanus salvator*)[17]	—	4	29	10	—	12 (−2H)	40 (−2·7H)	5 (−5·5H)
Greek tortoise (*Testudo græca*)[16b]	—	1	14	4	—	9 (−2H)	65 (−2·4H)	7 (ca. −4H)
Green turtle (*Chelone mydas*)[18]	13·3	10·6	17·0	4·1 (b)	1·3 (−2H)	7·8 (−2H)	39·6 (−2·2H)	6·1 (−6·3H)
,, ,, (Japan)[19]	14·2	7·2	15·2	6·8 (c)	2·6 (−2H)	10·9 (−2H)	39·4 (−2H)	Small (−?H)
,, ,, (Mexico)[20a] Summer	10·2	9·4	17·2	7·0 (d)	0·9 (−2H)	9·9 (−2H)	32·4 (−2·6H)	10·8 (−6·2H)
,, ,, Winter	—	8·2	16·7	5·6 (e)	4·4 (−2H)	13·6 (−2H)	38·0 (−3·1H)	10·0 (−6·5H)
Dull Sea Turtle (Mexico)[20b] (*Caretta caretta*)	—	6·6	21·8	15·5 (f)	3·5 (−2H)	18·0 (−2H)	31·4 (−3·7H)	1·3 (−8·6H)
Dark Sea Turtle (Mexico)[20c] (*Lepidochelis olivacea*)	—	1·8	26·1	5·5	—	11·7 (−2H)	40·1 (−3·1H)	14·8 (−5·0H)
Indian Sea Turtle[20d] (*Erthmochelies imbrocata*)	0·1	10·2	15·1	7·2 (g)	1·3 (−2H)	12·9 (−2H)	23·9 (−2·4H)	25·3 (−4·5H)
Moccasin Snake[21a] (mesenteric) (*Agkistrodon piscivorus*)	—	1·9	16·8	8·8	—	6·9 (−2H)	53·8 (−2·6H)	11·8 (−?H)
Python, Indian (*Python molurus*)[21b]	—	—	16·1	10·1 (h)	—	4·8 (−2H)	51·8 (−2·5H)	14·9 (−2H)
(*Python stinotis*)[21b]	1	1·6	15·7	13·3 (i)	0·2 (−2H)	5·2 (−2H)	49·4 (−2·7H)	13·6 (−2·4H)
Python (mesenteric)[22a] (*Python reticulatus*)	—	1·3	19·7	10·8 (j)	0·5 (−2H)	3·9 (−2H)	58·5 (−2·4H)	4·1 (−4·1H)
Crocodile[22b] (*Crocodylus porosus*)	0·4	2·9	26·6	4·8 (k)	1·3 (−2H)	6·5 (−2·1H)	53·1 (−2·8H)	3·8 (−3·5H)
(*C. niloticus*) (Tanganyika)[22b]	—	3·9	24·0	3·4 (l)	1·0 (−2H)	15·0 (−2·1H)	40·4 (−2·6H)	11·0 (−6·7H)
Crocodile, Indian[23] (*Gavialis gangeticus*)	0·2	4·2	25·8	8·7	2·0 (−2H)	11·6 (−2H)	35·5 (−3·0H)	12·0 (−5·3H)

(a) Also 0·5 per cent. arachidic acid. (b) Also 0·2 per cent. decanoic acid. (c) Also 3·5 per cent. hexanoic acid; C_{20-22} acids highly unsaturated. (d) Also 0·8 per cent. decanoic and 1·4 per cent. arachidic acid. (e) Also 3·5 per cent. arachidic acid. (f) Also 1·9 per cent. arachidic acid. (g) Also 1·1 per cent. arachidic and 2·9 per cent. unsaturated C_{24} (−10H) acids. (h) Also 2·3 per cent. arachidic acid. (i) Also 1·0 per cent. arachidic acid. (j) Also 1·2 per cent. arachidic acid. (k) Also 0·6 per cent. arachidic acid. (l) Also 1·3 per cent. arachidic acid.

half of the total fatty acids. The unsaturated acids, however, conform with those of the other turtle fats and most of the other fats in Table 26. The origin of the lauric acid is obscure: it is probably a dietary rather than a species difference, since the Girals[20a] observed that in winter the green turtle fat (only a tenth of that stored in summer by the animal) was free from lauric acid and was very similar to that of the dull and dark sea turtles in composition. It is possibly significant that all the lauric-rich turtle fats were from animals taken on the shores of the Pacific or Indian oceans – locations of the coconut palm, although any dietary connection between the green turtle and the coconut must seem remote.

Shortly before the figures[18] in Table 26 were given by Green and Hilditch, Tsujimoto[24] reported the presence of unusually large amounts of myristic acid in Japanese green turtle fat and the probable presence of lauric and hexadecenoic acids; Hata[25] identified a range of unsaturated acids similar to those in Table 26 in the body fat which forms 1·6 per cent. of another species of green turtle (*Chelone japonica*) and stated that the chief components of the body, liver, and ovary fats of the Chinese turtle (*Ocadia sinensis*) are myristic, palmitic, stearic, hexadecenoic, and oleic acids.

The moccasin and python *snake fats* in Table 26 all contain 50 per cent. or more of unsaturated C_{18} acids as their main component acids, with subordinate proportions of hexadecenoic and unsaturated C_{20} acids; palmitic acid is fairly prominent (17–20 per cent.) accompanied by about 10 per cent. of stearic acid. In the *crocodile* fats (Gunstone,[22b] Pathak[23]) the palmitic acid contents (24–27 per cent.) approach the figure of 30 per cent. characteristic of depot fats of the larger land animals, but the unsaturated C_{18} acids are in similar proportions to those of most of the other amphibia, accompanied by subordinate amounts of hexadecenoic and unsaturated C_{20} acids.

Individual unsaturated C_{18} acids were recorded as follows by the respective investigators in fats of the mocassin snake, python, and crocodile:

PER CENT. (WT.)	MOCCASIN SNAKE[21a]	PYTHON[22a]	CROCODILES[22b]	
Oleic	37·2	47·0	33·5	30·8
Octadecadienoic	16·6	10·7	17·0	6·5
Octadecatrienoic	—	0·8	2·6	3·0

BIRD DEPOT FATS

Birds deposit fat chiefly in the region of the gizzard, which contains an adherent layer of fat, close to the mesenteric membrane. Fat is also present in the mesenteric membrane, and around the kidneys; whilst there is a fair quantity of adipose tissue in the superficial layers of the abdomen, with other minor deposits of subcutaneous fat in the neck and other parts of the skin.

Goose and hen fats were partially examined by means of lead salt (Twitchell) or oxidation (Bertram) processes by Bömer and Merten,[26] and by Grossfeld;[27] Hilditch, Jones and Rhead[28] investigated, by the ester-fractionation procedure, the abdominal, gizzard, and neck fats from two groups of Light Sussex hens which had been reared on controlled diets. They showed that saturated acids of lower molecular weight than palmitic were not present, but that an anomaly noted by Grossfeld was caused by the presence of about 7 per cent. of hexadec-9-enoic acid.

TABLE 27. *Component Fatty Acids (per cent. wt.) of Body Fats from Light Sussex Hens*[28]

	BIRDS AGED 7 MONTHS			BIRDS AGED 2 YEARS		
	ABDOM-INAL	GIZZARD	NECK	ABDOM-INAL	GIZZARD	NECK
Myristic	0·1	0·1	0·3	1·2	0·6	1·2
Palmitic	25·6	25·2	26·7	24·0	25·4	24·5
Stearic	7·0	7·1	5·9	4·1	4·2	4·2
Hexadecenoic	7·0	7·6	6·6	6·7	7·1	6·9
Oleic	38·4	36·9	39·0	42·5	43·0	42·8
Linoleic	21·3	22·8	21·2	20·8	18·4	20·4
Unsaturated C_{20-22}	0·6	0·3	0·3	0·7	1·3	Trace

The resemblance between the fats from different parts of the birds (*cf.* also, Cruickshank[29]) presents a marked contrast to the differences found in fats from different depots of some of the larger animals (*cf.* pp. 105–107, 114, 117, 119). The following features may be emphasised:

(*a*) Palmitic (with myristic) acid forms 27–28 per cent. (molar) of the total fatty acids; oleic and linoleic acids account for 58–60 per cent. (molar) of the whole. The amount of stearic acid is small (4–6 mols. per cent.).

(*b*) The occurrence of about 7 per cent. of hexadec-9-enoic acid.

(*c*) There are small but definite amounts of highly unsaturated acids of the C_{20} and C_{22} series present, as in the fats of the land mammals.

(*d*) The component acids of the hen fats are more closely related to fats such as those of the rodents than to those of aquatic fauna, or of the amphibia or reptiles.

The depot fatty acids of females of four breeds of chickens and of turkeys (*Meleagris gallopavo*) fed on standard rations were analysed by Nutter *et al.*[30] by means of iodine and thiocyanogen values. In all instances the component acids were not dissimilar to those of the (preceding) hen fats, the ranges of saturated, oleic and linoleic acids being respectively 25–33, 38–50, and 23–32 per cent. (wt.).

Detailed analyses of the component acids of the abdominal fat of the grey lag goose (*Anser anser*, the reputed wild ancestor of the domestic goose) and of the subcutaneous fat of an Australian emu (*Dromalus novæ-hollandiæ*) were recorded by Hilditch and Sime,[31a] and those of the body fats of an adult male ostrich (*Struthia camelus*) of a West African species and of a flamingo (*Phænicopterus chilensis*) by Gunstone and Russell[31b]:

ACID (PER CENT. WT.)	GREY GOOSE	AUSTRALIAN EMU	WEST AFRICAN OSTRICH	FLAMINGO
Lauric	12·3	—	—	—
Myristic	8·2	0·9	0·9	—
Palmitic	20·3	17·5	24·8	24·8
Stearic	5·6	10·1	5·9	7·7
Arachidic	—	0·6	0·4	—
Tetradecenoic	0·6	0·9	0·9	—
Hexadecenoic	2·5	2·1	5·6	4·4
Hexadecadienoic	—	—	0·5	0·5
Oleic	41·6	62·2	39·8	53·4
Octadecadienoic	6·6	5·2	17·1	7·1
Octadecatrienoic	—	—	3·8	0·2
Unsaturated C_{20-22}	2·3	0·5	0·3	1·9

87

These four fats were all taken from animals which had been kept in captivity in various zoological gardens.

The ostrich and flamingo fats are very similar to those of domestic fowls (p. 87), but this may be merely a coincidence, for the emu body fat has a relatively lower palmitic acid content and a very high content of oleic acid, with but little hexadecenoic and diene C_{18} acids; the bird had been fed on various grains and concentrates, its natural diet is roots and herbage. The small contents of hexadecenoic acid in the emu and grey goose fats resemble those in land mammalian fats rather than those in the hen fats (p. 87). The grey goose had been reared in captivity in Colombo and the lauric and myristic acids in its depot fat may possibly have been derived from coconuts or coconut oil cake in its diet. A further analysis of domestic goose fat is necessary to decide whether this is the case or whether lower saturated acids are specific in goose fat.

Shorland and Gass[32] have examined the lipids of the flightless New Zealand kiwi (*Apteryx* sp.), in which the flesh beneath the skin contained 29 per cent. of fat, with component acids: saturated C_{14} 0·9, C_{16} 18·1, C_{18} 3·6, C_{20} 1·5, and myristoleic 0·8, palmitoleic 3·2, oleic 45·9, linoleic 10·8, linolenic 5·4, unsaturated C_{20} 9·3 ($-5·3H$) per cent. (wt.). Traces of lauric and dodecenoic acids were also observed. The kiwi fat, also, is thus broadly similar to the grey goose and ostrich fats.

How far the composition of avian body fats in general is adequately portrayed by these few detailed studies remains to be shown by the collection of a much wider range of data.

Effect of ingested dietary fats on the depot fats of birds. It is apparent that birds, like land mammals, are capable of utilising ingested fat for reserve purposes, as well as of synthesising their own characteristic type of fat when reared on a diet which is normally not over-rich in fat. Miss Cruickshank[29] published data in 1934 which, although based on observations of mean unsaturation (iodine value) alone, amply prove this in the case of the domestic hen. Having shown that, on controlled low-fat diets, hen body fats from various depots had very similar unsaturation (as shown by iodine values), groups of the birds were then fed on diets containing 28 per cent. of palm kernel oil, mutton tallow, or hempseed oil (respective iodine values 15, 45, and 160). In the case of the two relatively saturated fats, feeding caused a diminution of the iodine value of the depot mixed fatty acids from 81–83 to 51–55 in two months (palm kernel oil diet), and to 59–66 in four to five months (mutton tallow diet). The response to the hempseed diet was more rapid, the iodine value of the depot mixed fatty acids rising to 139–145 within six weeks. Conversely, resumption of the control (low-fat) ration caused a relatively rapid increase to normal iodine values for the depot fatty acids in the course of about a month in the case of hens which had received the palm kernel oil or mutton tallow, whilst about six months elapsed after return to the control diet before the high unsaturation of the depot fatty acids, resulting from the hempseed diet, fell to the normal figure of below 90.

Depot Fats of Sea-birds

Sea-birds, which feed mainly on fish, are probably an instance in which it must be considered that the nature of the depot fat is affected considerably by the circumstance that relatively large amounts of fat are assimilated directly from the diet. Koyama[33a] determined the percentage of ether-insoluble bromo-additive products obtained from the "liquid" fatty acids of the depot fats of a number of Japanese land and aquatic birds. The former yielded very small amounts (not exceeding 1 per cent.) of ether-insoluble "polybromides", whereas the sea-bird fats gave much higher yields – up to 10–15 per cent. of products containing about 69 per cent. of bromine.

Lovern[33b] carried out detailed analyses of the component acids of some sea-bird depot fats (Table 28), and pointed out that all four fats are of the "aquatic" type, and are closely similar in their component acids to the average marine fish fat. The sea-bird fats differ from the latter, however, in unsaturation. The stearic acid content is higher than in fish fats, and the degrees of average unsaturation of the C_{20} and C_{22} acids are reduced below the average for fish fats.

TABLE 28. Component Fatty Acids (per cent. wt.) of some Sea-Bird Fats

	FAT CONTENT (Per cent.)	SATURATED				UNSATURATED				
		C_{14}	C_{16}	C_{18}	C_{20}	C_{14}	C_{16}	C_{18}	C_{20}	C_{22}
Gannet (Sula bassana)	6·7	3·2	17·1	3·6	—	1·0 (−2·0H)	5·2 (−2·0H)	28·3 (−2·8H)	24·2 (−4·0H)	17·4 (−6·0H)
Fulmar petrel (Fulmarus glacialis)	15·2	2·0*	13·9	3·2	—	0·9 (−2·0H)	3·9 (−2·0H)	26·9 (−2·8H)	26·8 (−4·0H)	22·1 (−6·6H)
Skua gull (Megalestris catarrhactes)	7·0	1·9	16·4	5·7	0·2	0·4 (−2·0H)	4·6 (−2·1H)	32·6 (−2·6H)	19·7 (−3·3H)	18·5 (−3·8H)
Herring gull (Larus argentatus)	9·7	3·3	18·5	6·2	0·2	0·5 (−2·0H)	4·0 (−2·3H)	30·5 (−2·8H)	20·3 (−4·1H)	16·5 (−4·9H)

* 0·3 per cent. of saturated acids (capric) lower than C_{14}.

The body fat of a penguin was partly studied by Ueno and Aoki,[34] who stated that the fatty acids included 4 per cent. myristic, 14 per cent. palmitic and 5 per cent. stearic acids, with oleic and "clupanodonic" acids, but hexadecenoic acid was not detected. This partial analysis, and the recorded iodine value (134·2) of the penguin fat, suggest that the fat, like those of the smaller sea-birds examined by Lovern,[33b] is similar to that of marine fish on which it feeds.

The sea-birds thus form an apparent exception to the broad rule that fat types can be correlated with phylogenetic relationships. Lovern suggests two possible explanations for this: (a) that they have no specific requirements and any type of depot fat will serve equally well, or (b) that in the course of evolution their specific requirements have been produced or modified to suit the normal diet; but since the food (fish) of sea-birds contains little or no carbohydrate it seems equally likely that they have little opportunity to synthesize fat, and consequently the source of their depot fats is almost wholly exogenous.

Bird Egg Fats

Apart from a few general characteristics which have been reported for the fatty matter present in the eggs of pigeons,[35a] ducks and geese,[35b] attention has been confined to the egg of the domestic fowl, and even here there are at present relatively few detailed analyses. Phosphatides (egg yolk lecithin) are of course prominent in egg lipids, but for the most part the recorded analyses do not differentiate between glyceridic and phosphatidic lipids, giving only the mixed fatty acids present in the total fatty matter. The ether-soluble lipids amount to about 30–35 per cent. of the fresh egg yolk (equivalent to about 60–70 per cent. on a moisture-free basis). The amount of phosphatides in the fresh yolk is variously given as from 4 to 12 per cent., the differences being due possibly both to varying technique in the separation of the phosphatides and to genuine differences due to dietary or other variable factors.

The component acids of egg phosphatides (lecithin) have only been studied in two instances[36a, b] by the ester-fractionation method, although various estimates based on simpler processes of analysis have been given. (For a more complete summary of the older work, the reader is referred to the monograph of MacLean.[37]) All that can be deduced from the older observations is that the egg phosphatide fatty acids seem to be similar qualitatively to those of animal livers (*cf.* p. 135) and that, apart from possibly low proportions of unsaturated C_{20} and C_{22} acids, they may have considerable quantitative resemblance to the latter.

Analyses of the fatty acids of both glycerides and phosphatides of egg yolk were carried out by the modern methods by Riemenschneider, Ellis and Titus[36a] in 1938, and by Shorland[36b] in 1951, with the following results:

	COMPONENT ACIDS[36a] (Per Cent. Wt.)		COMPONENT ACIDS[36b] (Per Cent. Wt.)	
	GLYCERIDES	PHOS-PHATIDES	GLYCERIDES	PHOS-PHATIDES
Myristic	0·7	—	0·1	0·3
Palmitic	25·2	31·8	25·4	27·9
Stearic	7·5	4·1	4·8	16·1
Arachidic	—	—	—	1·8
Hexadecenoic	3·3	—	8·2	0·8
Oleic	52·4	42·6	} 58·4 (−2·3H)	39·8 (−2·4H)
Linoleic	8·6	8·2		8·2
Unsaturated C_{20}	—	—	} 3·1 (−6·0H) {	7·1 (−6·8H)
,, C_{22}	2·3	13·3		6·2 (−8·4H)

The evidence indicated the presence of "clupanodonic" (C_{22}) acid rather than of "arachidonic" (C_{20}) acid, and it will be seen that, as usual, there is more of this acid in the phosphatides than the glycerides. The component acids of the egg yolk glycerides are on the whole similar to those of the hen depot fat glycerides in Table 27, but the oleic acid content is greater (mainly at the expense of linoleic and hexadecenoic acids). Rhodes and Lea[36c] found that hen's egg phospholipids were made up mainly of phosphatidylcholine (73 per cent.) and phosphatidylethanolamine (15 per cent.) with minor amounts (2–6 per cent.) of the respective lyso-derivatives and sphingomyelin.

Hawke[36d] selectively hydrolysed egg phosphatidylcholine by snake venom phospholipase A (which removes the fatty acids from the β-position – not, as formerly supposed, from the α-position), and analysed by gas–liquid chromatography the acids before and after hydrolysis with the following results for the major components:

Per Cent. (Wt.)	Total	ATTACHED TO	
		α	β
Palmitic	28·8	54·6	3·0
Stearic	19·2	36·3	2·0
Oleic	35·1	6·3	63·9
Octadecadienoic	7·9	0·5	15·3
C_{20-22}-polyene	6·3	0·3	12·3

The component acids of guinea fowl egg total lipids were given by Airan and Kalyankar[36e] as myristic 5·5, palmitic 20·0, stearic 12·4, oleic 49·8, linoleic 6·7 and docosapentaenoic 5·6 per cent.

Effect of ingested dietary fat of hen on egg lipids. The effect of added fat in the diet of the hens has been observed materially to alter the composition of the egg lipids. Henriques and Hansen[38] found that the iodine value of the egg phosphatides was unchanged when linseed or hempseed was fed to the hen, but the iodine values of the egg glycerides increased as follows:

FEEDING	IODINE VALUE OF EGG GLYCERIDES
Carbohydrate diet	79
Linseed	97
Hempseed	119–123

In 1934 Miss Cruickshank,[29] using the determination of saturated acids combined with the iodine and thiocyanogen values of the unsaturated fatty acids, examined the mixed fatty acids from the total lipids of eggs from hens fed on rations consisting of a control (mainly cereal) ration (*a*) alone, or (*b*) with 28 per cent. of various fatty oils added.

The component acids of the dietary fats were approximately as follows*:

COMPONENT ACIDS, (Per Cent. Wt.)	PALM KERNEL OIL	PALM OIL	MUTTON FAT	LINSEED OIL	HEMPSEED OIL
Saturated	81	46·3	51·0	9·2	6·1
Oleic	18	46·4	46·8	26·6	12·0
Linoleic	Trace	7·3	2·2	13·4	68·5
Linolenic	—	—	—	50·8	13·4

The data recorded for the egg yolk mixed fatty acids (per cent. wt.) were:

	CON-TROL MASH	MASH + PALM KERNEL OIL	MASH + PALM OIL	MASH + MUTTON FAT	MASH + LIN-SEED OIL	MASH + HEMP OIL	HEMP-SEED ALONE
Saturated acids	31·4	30·3	27·8	29·5	23·9	24·3	21·4
Oleic acid	47·4	51·4	48·6	51·4	37·9	23·5	25·3
Linoleic acid	19·0	17·6	23·6	17·0	17·4	49·6	44·1
Linolenic acid	2·2	0·7	—	2·1	20·8	2·6	9·2

* Unsaturated acids calculated according to the empirically determined thiocyanogen values for linoleic and linolenic acids ("T", Chapter IV, p. 179).

These figures, in spite of some lack of detail, are of great comparative interest, especially in conjunction with the corresponding data for hen depot fats (pp. 87, 88). In the first place it was established by independent tests that the alteration in the egg lipids, due to added dietary fat, is complete in sixteen days. As regards the various fats fed to the fowls, it is evident that, in contrast to the hen depot fats, only the constituents of the more unsaturated dietary fats passed readily into the ova fatty acids; the more saturated fats had comparatively little influence on the composition of the egg fatty acids, apart from a slight *diminution* in the percentage of saturated acids and an increase in linoleic acid content when palm oil (with 7 per cent. of that acid) was present in the diet. On the other hand ingestion of linseed or hempseed oil or of hempseed alone led to very marked increases in the linoleic and/or linolenic acid contents of the egg lipids.

The ease with which the unsaturated acids of these seed oils pass into the egg lipids of hens has been "rediscovered" in recent years[39] when the same result was observed to follow the inclusion of sunflower seeds in the diet of the hen. Similarly, the daily ingestion of 10 gm. of cod-liver oil in a hen's diet was observed by Rhodes[40a] to increase the unsaturation of the egg glycerides, and still more that of the egg phospholipids (in which the increased unsaturation was wholly in the α-acyl groups, the β-acyl groups remaining mainly saturated). Murty and Reiser[40b] state that the levels of linoleic or linolenic acid incorporated into hen's egg lipids reach a maximum when 5 per cent. of either acid is added to the diet of the hen, linoleic reaching a higher level than linolenic acid. Coppock[40c] described experiments in which battery hens received standard diets supplemented by 4 per cent. of either groundnut oil or tallow. The latter made little or no difference to the saturated acids in the egg lipids, but the groundnut oil supplementary diet led to a 2 per cent. increase in the polyunsaturated acids; in both groups, however, a parallel rise and fall of 4 per cent. between maximum and minimum contents of polyene acids was observed, indicating that the age of the hen (perhaps also other factors) was a relevant feature possibly outweighing alterations due to the nature of the ingested fat.

The evidence given by the above analyses suggests that more analyses by the modern methods of the egg lipids of other species of birds, after resolution as far as possible into glyceridic and phosphatidic fractions, would yield interesting and fruitful results.

In recent years the isolation of lipoprotein complexes present in living organisms, and their study, has commenced to make progress. Lea and Hawke[41] have contributed work on the lipovitellin which forms up to 40 per cent. of egg yolk. Whereas the total lipids in egg yolk are made up of about 60 per cent. of glycerides (with small proportions of cholesterol) and 40 per cent. of phosphatides, those of the lipovitellin preparations isolated by Lea and Hawke contained only about 15 per cent. of glycerides with about 85–90 per cent. of phosphatides, these consisting of about 87 per cent. of phosphatidyl choline ("lecithin") and 13 per cent. of phosphatidyl ethanolamine ("kephalin"). The component fatty acids of the phosphatides were considerably more unsaturated than those of the corresponding glycerides (judged by iodine values), and spectrophotometric evidence showed that this difference was essentially due to the presence of several times as much polyethenoid (C_{20} and/or C_{22}) acids in the phospholipids as in the glycerides.

DEPOT FATS OF RODENTS

The detailed study of component acids of rodent depot fats is most abundant for one species – the white rat which has been employed so largely in the biological evaluation of vitamins A and D; this circumstance accounts for the comparatively large amount of work which has been carried out on the fats of this animal. If we may take the white rat as typical, it is clear that rodents share with birds a kind of depot fat which, in its reduced but still appreciable content of hexadecenoic acid, is definitely intermediate in type between the reserve fats of amphibia and reptiles and those of the higher land mammals, whilst its content of palmitic acid already approximates to the 30 per cent. characteristic of fats of the latter category of animals. The data available for rat depot fats render possible an interesting outline of, in the first place, the typical component acids of such fats from animals on diets low in fat and, secondly, of the effect of added dietary fat upon the composition of the depot fat.

Rat depot fats (from animals on low fat diets). The component acids of the rat fats in Table 29A are from figures published by Banks et al.[42] (1933), Klenk et al.[16b] (1935), Spadola and Ellis[43] (1936), and Longenecker and Hilditch[44] (1938); those in Table 29B are from a detailed scheme of feeding and fasting trials on groups of male and female white rats by Longenecker[45] (1939).

The component acids of body fats of rats fed on low fat diets exhibit several points of interest.

(i) As in the hen depot fats, the palmitic acid content is approximately 30 per cent. (molar) – the figure which, as we shall see, is characteristic for nearly all land animal depot fats so far studied.

(ii) The type of "synthetic" fat laid down by the rat from a completely carbohydrate or protein (probably *via* carbohydrate) diet is remarkable not only for the close approximation to 30 per cent. (mol.) of palmitic acid, but still more for the high proportion of hexadecenoic acid (13–15 per cent.). Moreover, this high figure for hexadecenoic acid is only attained when the diet contains 1 per cent. or less of fat – in other low fat diets in which the fat content may have approached 5 per cent. of the whole diet, the hexadecenoic acid content of the body fat was reduced to about 5–8 per cent.

(iii) The utilisation of fat reserves during fasting (*cf.* Table 29B) seems on the whole to involve most of the component acids more or less indiscriminately, although some slight but indefinite evidence of selective mobilisation appears here and there.

(iv) The proportions of polyethenoid C_{18} and C_{20} acids in the rat body fats are also of much interest. Those of the C_{20} and C_{22} series vary only from almost *nil* to about 2 per cent., but the most striking feature, possibly peculiar to the rat, is its inability to synthesise linoleic or other diethenoid C_{18} acids.

93

When linoleic glycerides are present in the dietary fat, however, they appear to pass readily into the fat depots of the rat; probably the moderate proportion of octadecadienoic acid in the body fat of rats fed on cows' milk (Table 29A), and the comparatively high proportion of this acid in the body fats of the rats (Table 29B) fed on Longenecker's stock diet (which included 5 per cent. of fat), arise from direct assimilation. Similarly, in the fats of some wild rodents (*v. infra*) linoleic or other polyethenoid C_{18} acids are present in quantity. Fat synthesised by the rat from carbohydrate, however, appears to be deficient in octadecadienoic acid, which then occurs only to the extent of 1–2 per cent. of the total fatty acids.

TABLE 29A. *Component Acids (per cent. wt.) of Depot Fats of Rats on Low Fat Diets*

	BANKS, HILDITCH, and JONES[42]			KLENK *et al.*[16b]	SPADOLA and ELLIS[43]	LONGE-NECKER and HIL-DITCH[44]
	GROUP A	GROUP B	GROUP C			
Decanoic	—	—	—	—	—	0·3
Lauric	—	—	—	—	—	0·7
Myristic	5	4·5	4	2	5·6	6·9
Palmitic	24	28	30	25	29·3	24·3
Stearic	3	2	2·5	3·5	2·5	5·3
Arachidic	—	—	—	—	—	1·2
Tetradecenoic	—	—	—	—	—	1·2
Hexadecenoic	8	7	8·5	13	14·0	5·6
Oleic	58	58·5	53	} 55 {	48·6	49·1
Octadecadienoic	2	—	2		—	4·9
Unsaturated C_{20-22}	—	—	—	1·5	—	0·5

TABLE 29B. *Component Acids (per cent. mol.) of Depot Fats of Rats on Low Fat Diets*

(LONGENECKER,[45] 1939)

	MALE GROUP		FEMALE GROUP			
Diet, etc.	1 Stock diet (5 per cent. fat)	2 Stock diet then high sucrose diet	1 Stock diet (5 per cent. fat)	2 1, fasted to 30 per cent. loss	3 High carbo-hydrate (no fat)	4 3, fasted to 22 per cent. loss
Myristic	1·6	2·7	1·8	3·1	2·9	4·0
Palmitic	21·6	28·2	24·4	23·0	30·4	28·8
Stearic	3·6	4·3	3·6	7·2	4·9	4·6
Arachidic	2·0	1·2	0·8	0·7	—	0·3
Tetradecenoic	—	1·2	0·3	1·7	1·3	1·9
Hexadecenoic	4·1	12·2	4·8	10·0	13·1	7·2
Oleic	51·9	42·0	44·3	39·9	46·0	51·0
Octadecadienoic	13·0	8·0	18·6	13·3	1·4	2·2
Unsaturated C_{20-22}	2·2	0·2	1·4	1·1	—	—

It was established by Burr and Burr[46] in 1930 that a supply of linoleic or similar diethenoid acid is essential to the health of the rat, and this observation has led to many other biochemical studies as to the function of linoleic acid in the lipids of the animal. The idiosyncrasy of the rat as regards ability to synthesise and store linoleic acid is, however, not by any means clearly understood. In 1938 Nunn and Smedley-MacLean[47] found that rats on a fat-free diet yielded liver fats with no tetra- or penta-ethenoid acids, but that on the same diet with the addition of a little methyl linoleate, the liver fats contained some arachidonic acid ($C_{20}H_{32}O_2$), whilst with the addition of methyl linolenate, both arachidonic and docosapentaenoic ($C_{22}H_{34}O_2$) acids appeared in the liver fats. This is supported by Longenecker's results (Table 29B), in which the arachidonic acid contents of the body fats were negligible when exclusively carbohydrate or protein diets had been given, whereas the stock diet which included 5 per cent. of fat led to the appearance of a fairly high proportion of octadecadienoic acid and also to the presence of appreciable amounts (1·4–2·2 per cent.) of arachidonic acid. Later, Smedley-MacLean et al.[47] put forward evidence which suggests that the highly unsaturated C_{20} or C_{22} acids are more efficient promoters of growth in the rat than linoleic acid.

Since about 1950 much further work on the conversion in vivo of linoleate to arachidonate has been undertaken by Reiser[48a] and by Mead[48b] and their respective co-workers, who have used chickens and mice as well as rats in their studies. The employment of linoleic acid with a radioactive (C^{14}) carboxyl group has given helpful results in some of these investigations and the details of the probable path of this conversion have been made fairly clear in the case of linoleic acid; the corresponding transformation in vivo of linolenates is still the subject of discussion at the time of writing (see also Chapter VIII, p. 571–573).

Thomasson[49] (1953) established that, out of many unsaturated acids tested by biological assay, only those (e.g., linoleic, linolenic, arachidonic, octadeca-6,9,12-trienoic) which contained the terminal structure

$$CH_3.[CH_2]_4.CH:CH.CH_2.CH:CH-$$

or its triene analogue, were active in the promotion of growth in animals. **Rat depot fats (from animals on diets which included various fats).** The following data may be considered here:

(i) Banks, Hilditch and Jones[42] (1933). Adipose tissue fats from a group of rats which had received diets containing from 2 to 15 per cent. (usually 5 per cent.) of cod liver oil for 10 weeks.

(ii) Spadola and Ellis[43] (1936). Adipose tissue fats from rats fed for 10 weeks on a basal diet in which 8 per cent. of dextrin was replaced by 8 per cent. of cottonseed oil, non-hydrogenated or hydrogenated to two different stages.

The component acids of the cottonseed oils employed were as follows (per cent. wt.):

	SATURATED	OLEIC WITH (*iso*-OLEIC)	LINOLEIC
Non-hydrogenated (B)	28·8	22·7	48·5
Hydrogenated (C)	35·5	52·5	12·0
,, (D)	35·4	62·3	2·3

(iii) Longenecker and Hilditch[44] (1938). Total carcass fats of rats fed wholly on cow milk diet (data already given in Table 29A).

(iv) Longenecker[45] (1939). Rats reared on a balanced stock diet and then fasted until they had lost nearly 30 per cent. of their body weight were fed on diets very high in, respectively, maize oil and coconut oil. Some of the animals were killed and the body fats analysed, whilst others were fasted to varying degrees before their depleted body fats were examined (Table 30B).

TABLE 30A. *Component Acids (per cent. wt.) of Depot Fats of Rats on Specific Fatty Diets*

INGESTED FAT	BANKS et al.[42] COD LIVER OIL	SPADOLA AND ELLIS[43]		
		COTTONSEED OIL B	HYDROGENATED COTTON-SEED OIL	
			C	D
Per cent. fat in diet	2–15	8	8	8
Component acids—				
Myristic	5	3·4	4·6	4·3
Palmitic	23	32·8	25·8	26·4
Stearic	2·5	3·4	1·6	2·0
Arachidic	—	—	0·2	0·2
Hexadecenoic	5·5	2·0	6·8	8·8
Oleic	51·5	30·2	52·3	54·4
Octadecadienoic	4	27·3	8·3	3·3
Unsaturated C_{20-22}	8·5	0·9	0·4	0·6

TABLE 30B. *Component Acids (per cent. mol.) of Depot Fats of Rats on Specific Fatty Diets*

INGESTED FAT	(LONGENECKER[45] 1939)					
	MAIZE OIL			COCONUT OIL		
	1	2	3	1	2	3
	High fat diet	1, fasted to 14 per cent. loss	1, fasted to 24 per cent. loss	High fat diet	1, fasted to 15 per cent. loss	1, fasted to 30 per cent. loss
Decanoic	—	—	—	0·7	0·7	1·0
Lauric	—	—	—	31·8	24·5	23·0
Myristic	0·7	0·7	0·7	18·1	19·6	15·4
Palmitic	12·2	14·1	11·8	18·6	19·4	15·8
Stearic	2·9	1·5	2·0	2·7	1·7	5·2
Arachidic	0·2	1·4	1·5	0·6	0·5	0·9
Dodecenoic	—	—	—	0·6	0·4	0·5
Tetradecenoic	—	0·4	—	1·5	0·9	1·1
Hexadecenoic	6·9	4·2	5·4	4·1	3·8	4·3
Oleic	44·8	46·5	48·8	20·1	26·9	30·7
Octadecadienoic	32·3	31·2	29·8	1·2	1·6	2·1

It is possible to draw certain general conclusions from the rather complicated data quoted in Tables 30A and 30B.

(i) Polyethenoid C_{18} acids are readily assimilated from diets (as with cod liver, maize, cottonseed, palm, and olive oils); the amount of linoleic glycerides deposited, in relation to the proportion in the ingested fats, was especially high in the case of Spadola and Ellis's cottonseed oil experiments.

(ii) The highly unsaturated C_{20} and C_{22} acids of cod liver oil are evidently also assimilated and deposited to a marked extent.

(iii) Lauric glycerides formed only about 30 per cent. of the depot fat when coconut oil formed almost the entire diet (Longenecker). Lauric acid is thus definitely less laid down in depot fats than the higher fatty acids, whilst the C_{10} and lower saturated acids of coconut oil or cow milk fat are to all intents and purposes not stored by animals in their reserve fats.

(iv) In view of the ready influx of ingested unsaturated acids to the depots, it is natural that, when feeding the more unsaturated oils (e.g. olive or cod liver oil), the percentage of palmitic acid is often substantially reduced. This suggests that the "normal" content of about 30 per cent. of palmitic acid in animal depot fats is conditioned mainly by the fat actually synthesized by an animal; that this figure is attained only when the diet is "balanced" in so far that it does not contain more than a certain proportion of preformed fat; and that feeding of rations with a high fat content (irrespective of the capacity of the animal to store considerable proportions of the ingested fat) causes interference with the normal production of fat in the animal, and must therefore be regarded as definitely abnormal, if not almost pathological.

Several more recent communications confirm the above conclusions that ingestion of relatively saturated fats[50a] produces relatively little alteration in rat body glycerides, whereas feeding sunflower seed oil[50a] or maize oil[50b] notably increased the linoleic contents of the body glycerides. Similarly, Hopkins et al.[50b] showed that eicosenoic, erucic or oleic acids were readily incorporated into the body fats of rats whose diet included these respective acids in the form of methyl esters.

(v) Further interesting evidence on the utilization of the different constituents of reserve fats by the rat during fasting will be found in Table 30B.

Other rodent depot fats. Baldwin and Longenecker[51a] examined the body fat of healthy *guinea-pigs* reared on a normal diet, whilst Clément and Meara[51b] analysed the fatty acids in the perinephric and interscapular fats of a healthy Chinchilla *rabbit* which had received a low fat diet of greenstuff and rat control food cake. Table 31 shows the component acids of the body fats of the guinea-pig[51a] and of a mouse (from an animal breeding station) and a porcupine (from a zoo) (Gunstone and Russell[51c]).

TABLE 31. *Component Acids (per cent. wt.) of other Rodent Fats*

ACID	GUINEA PIG[51a] Caria cutleri	RABBIT Lepus cuniculus Perinephric[51b]	Interscapular[51b]	Body[51c]	MOUSE[51c] Mus musculus	PORCUPINE[51c] Hystrix cristata	SPERMOPHILE[51d] Citellus citellus
Lauric	1·1	0·4	2·4	—	—	—	—
Myristic	5·3	5·5	3·8	2·6	0·2	5·2	—
Palmitic	19·4	30·5	29·0	25·1	26·7	36·3	24·0
Stearic	5·7	5·0	4·0	5·6	2·6	11·7	—
Arachidic	—	—	—	0·4	—	—	—
Tetradecenoic	0·8	—	1·4	2·2	—	1·5	—
Hexadecenoic	2·1	5·9	6·9	6·0	5·6	3·6 (a)	?
Oleic	36·2	31·9	36·7	26·6	35·8	27·1	70·9
Octadecadienoic	18·8	16·3	11·8	25·9	26·2	13·6	5·1
Octadecatrienoic	1·2	3·1	2·0	5·6	1·9	0·5	—
Unsaturated C_{20-22}	9·4	1·4	1·9	—	1·0	—	—

(a) Also 0·5 per cent. hexadecadienoic acid.

All the fats contain comparable amounts of oleic and polyethenoid C_{18} acids, the latter being mainly ordinary linoleic acid. The guinea-pig fat has less palmitic acid than other rodent fats, and an unusual proportion of polyethenoid C_{20} and C_{22} acids. Mouse, porcupine and rabbit fats showed much closer resemblance to the body fats of rats, notably in their contents of palmitic, hexadecenoic, oleic, and unsaturated C_{20-22} acids. Traces of di- and tri-ethenoid C_{16} acids accompany the hexadecenoic acid in some rabbit fats[51b]. The octadecadienoic (mainly linoleic) acid contents of the rodent fats in Table 31 are fairly substantial, reaching about 26 per cent. in the mouse and in one of the rabbits. The fats of *wild* rabbits tend to be rich in linoleic (and to a less extent linolenic) glycerides (total C_{18} di- and tri-ene acids 50–65 per cent.), as shown in detail by Futter and Shorland[52b]. Much earlier, in 1928, Vickery[52a] had observed the very unsaturated nature of wild rabbit fat (68·5 per cent. of unsaturated acids, largely linoleic and linolenic, with a mean iodine value of 189).

It is not yet clear how far the unsaturation of animal body fats is conditioned by their habit of life (wild or domesticated): the iodine values of the body fats of two other wild rodents, the hare (102–119)[53a] and the marmot (93–111)[53b] seem to support the view that wild animals develop relatively unsaturated fats.

The sebum lipids of some rodents (guinea-pig, mouse, rabbit and rat) have been studied by Wheatley and James.[54] They are largely saturated with only about 10 per cent. or less of oleic acid. The saturated acids are somewhat variable, with from 6–24 per cent. of palmitic and also of stearic acid, and sometimes little, sometimes up to 14 per cent. of arachidic acid. Odd-numbered saturated acids ($C_{15}, C_{17}, C_{19}, C_{21}$) are also present in lesser but still prominent amounts, individual acids varying from about 3 to as much as 12 per cent. in some instances. Sebum lipids belong to the class of ester-waxes rather than to the glycerides of most fatty tissues.

The component acids of the scent gland fat of the Louisiana *musk rat* (*Andatra zibethicus rivaticus*) were found by Erickson and Hix[55] to contain (in addition to 22·5 per cent. of acids non-volatile at about 200°C./2 mm.) myristic 6·8, palmitic 23·1, hexadecenoic 8·1, oleic 24·2, linoleic 5·4, unsaturated C_{24} and C_{26} acids 8·5 per cent. (wt.), with 0·2–0·3 per cent. each of decanoic, lauric, stearic, lignoceric, do- and tetra-decenoic acids.

DEPOT FATS OF THE LARGER LAND ANIMALS

The patchiness of the existing data on the depot fats of land animals will be appreciated when it is pointed out that there are detailed analyses extant for the depot fatty acids of less than a dozen carnivorous animals, whilst in the herbivorous group there are detailed records for fats from the horse, camel, reindeer, and some other animals, together with a very large number of full component acid analyses of the depot fats of oxen, sheep, and pigs. It is much to be desired that adequate data for a wide range of depot fats of the carnivora, and for a wider range of the corresponding fats of the herbivora, should be collected – an aim which should not be very difficult to attain in co-operation with zoological authorities.

Many detailed records of animal depot fats (including those of oxen, sheep, and pigs) refer only to palmitic, stearic, oleic, linoleic, and myristic acids as the component acids; but it was subsequently found that small proportions of hexadecenoic and of unsaturated C_{20} acids are also present. The detailed analyses must accordingly be regarded as belonging to two categories: (a) the full statements which take account of all the minor components at present detected, and (b) other analyses, which refer chiefly to the major components and which must, in the light of more recent work, be considered only as a first approximation to the more complete statement of the whole of the component acids. The latter group are serviceable in so far as they indicate, within reasonably narrow limits, the quantitative proportions of the major component acids.

Depot Fats of the Herbivora

The recorded figures for the fatty acid compositions in this group may be considered conveniently as follows: (a) the data for fats from a number of animals, other than those of oxen, sheep, and pigs; (b) the more numerous analyses of the body fats of oxen, sheep, and pigs (followed, in the case of the last-named, by consideration of the influence of various fatty diets upon the composition of pig depot fats).

Depot fats of various herbivorous animals (other than horse, oxen, sheep, and pigs). The component acids of the few body fats of herbivorous animals which have been examined by modern methods are shown in Table 32; in this table analyses made by earlier forms of the ester-fractionation procedure wherein no account was taken of hexadecenoic or unsaturated C_{20-22} acids, or of some other minor component acids, are given in terms of the *nearest unit per cent.* only.

The goat, deer, camel, and hippopotamus depot fats, and to some degree the kangaroo fat, in Table 32 belong to the group of "stearic-rich" animal depot fats. These are specially characteristic of ruminant animals, but are also encountered in a number of other species. In contrast, many other animal body fats contain less than 10 per cent. of stearic acid, and in such fats it must be looked upon as a minor component acid: the panda, bear, antelope, and elephant fats in Table 32 are examples of this class.

In nearly all the fats in Table 32 *palmitic acid* forms about 25 to 30 per cent. of the total fatty acids by weight, equivalent to from 27 to 32 mols. of palmitic in every 100 mols. of total fatty acids. This approximate constant proportion of palmitic acid in nearly all fats of the larger land animals is their outstanding characteristic.

The *goat*, *deer*, and *camel* fats closely resemble sheep depot fats (p. 107) in their component acids: stearic acid approaches palmitic acid in proportion and the only other major component, oleic acid, is correspondingly low. The minor component acids are similar in kind and amount to those in ox and sheep fats, except that the octadecadienoic and octadecatrienoic acids of the Scottish deer and the camel were observed by Gunstone and Paton[58a] to contain in quantity ordinary seed-fat linoleic and linolenic acids (in ox or sheep body fats these are largely replaced by isomeric forms, *cf.* p. 110).

The characteristics of fats from various tissues of another species of *deer*, the Virginia white-tailed deer (*Odocoileus virginianus borealis*) have been

99

TABLE 32. *Component Acids (per cent. wt.) of Body Fats of Herbivorous Animals*

	SATURATED				UNSATURATED					
	C_{14}	C_{16}	C_{18}	C_{20}	C_{14}	C_{16}	Oleic	Lino-leic	Lino-lenic	C_{20-22}
Bovidæ—										
Goat (*Capra domestica*)										
Back fat[56] (a)	2	26	28	2	—	?	38	—	—	—
Cervidæ—										
Reindeer (*Cervus tarandus*) Loin[57]	7	35	20	1	—	?	37	—	—	—
Scottish stag[58a] (*C. elaphus*)	4·4	25·1	35·4	1·5	0·5	2·8	25·2	2·6	2·5	—
Camelidæ—										
Camel (*Camelus bactrianus*) Mesentery[58a]	6·3	28·8	27·4	1·6	0·5	3·2	26·4	1·9	0·9	3·0
Camel (*C. indicus*) Body[58b]	4·9	33·9	29·0	—	0·7	5·3	26·2	—	—	—
Tragelaphinæ—										
Antelope (*Tragelaphus scriptus*) Abdominal[31b]	2·8	20·6	3·8	0·4	0·4	8·6	40·5	19·2	3·7	—
Hippopotamidæ—										
Hippopotamus (*Hippopotamus amphibius*) Body[58c]	2·3	27·1	22·2	1·1	0·4	2·2	39·3	3·5	1·5	0·4
Macropodidæ—										
Kangaroo (*Macropus major*) Body[31a] (b)	4·7	25·5	14·1	1·5	0·4	2·7	45·5	2·6	—	2·8
Procyonidæ—										
Giant panda (*Ailuropoda melanoleuca*) Abdominal[31a] (c)	5·0	26·4	6·7	—	0·9	3·6	45·1	11·9	—	—
Ursidæ—										
Ceylon sloth bear (*Melursus ursinus*) Body[31a]	2·6	28·7	3·4	—	1·4	10·6	50·5	1·0	—	1·8
Indian bear (*Ursus*) Body[59a]	1·8	25·0	10·7	—	1·3	18·0	34·5	8·7	—	—
Proboscidæ—										
Elephant, Indian (*Elephas maximus*) Body[59c] (d)	6·6	44·1	6·5	—	1·0	4·5	26·5	6·4	0·5	2·9

(a) Also 3·5 per cent. lauric acid. (b) Also 0·2 per cent. lauric acid. (c) Also 0·4 per cent. lauric acid. (d) Also 0·8 per cent. lauric and 0·2 per cent. unsaturated C_{12} acids.

recorded by Treadwell and Eckstein,[60] from which the proportions of saturated, oleic, and linoleic acids appear to be approximately as below:

	IODINE VALUE	THIO-CYANOGEN VALUE	COMPONENT ACIDS		
			SATURATED	OLEIC	LINOLEIC
Pericardial fat	29·1	26·2	70	27	3
Perirenal fat	30·3	27·0	69	27	4
Omental fat	33·6	29·4	66	29	5
Mesenteric fat	33·1	30·1	65	31	4

The chief present value of the figures in Table 32 is the hint which they afford of further interesting data awaiting collection in this field. The body fat of the *hippopotamus*, the largest amphibious mammal, has the typical

100

composition of the fat of a land animal, with little or no resemblance to the fats of the Amphibia. It contains minimal amounts of unsaturated C_{16} and C_{20-22} acids, has a typical "land animal depot fat" content (27 per cent.) of palmitic acid and, moreover, belongs to the "stearic-rich" group (with 22 per cent. of stearic acid). The hippopotamus is reputed to feed mainly on water vegetation, although also resorting to dry land where it is liable to ravage herbage and growing grain. The observed composition of the body fat suggests that it may be derived mainly from a carbohydrate diet, since the proportions of the major component acids and the molar ratio (1:2·05) of palmitic to total C_{18} acids are those which have been shown to be characteristic of fat synthesised by an animal from carbohydrate (cf. this chapter, pp. 111, 121; Chapter VIII, p. 544).

The kangaroo fat examined by Maddison[31a] is almost indistinguishable from those of our common herbivorous cattle (v. infra), although it comes from a marsupial widely removed from the latter both by evolutionary development and by environmental conditions. But it is significant that the quokka (Sentonix brachyurus), and probably therefore other marsupials, has been found[58d] to possess a ruminant-like digestive system, the contents containing a microbial flora similar to that of sheep. Again, the hippopotamus family is placed by biologists between the true ruminants and the pig family. The specific similarity between the depot fats of the ruminants, the marsupials and the hippopotamus may well be due to the similar special features of their digestive systems.

On the other hand, the panda and antelope fats seem to be characterised by higher contents of octadecadienoic acids, much of which is the linoleic acid of seed fats; the panda is remarkable as an ancestrally carnivorous animal which has become wholly herbivorous, its food being almost exclusively the bamboo.

The natural diet of members of the bear family is largely herbivorous – fruits, honey and sometimes insects, young birds and eggs. The Ceylon sloth bear had been fed in captivity on rice and sugar with occasional meat. The body fats of this animal and of the Indian bear are similar in composition to most of the low-stearic fats of the other non-ruminant animals in Table 32, except for unusually large proportions of hexadecenoic acid. Whether this is characteristic of the fats of Ursus species is a point which must await the collection of a wider range of data (as in so many other cases of non-ruminant animal fats). Analyses[59b] of body, intestinal and kidney fats of a brown bear (Ursus arctus) fed on a vegetable diet showed contents of 29–33 per cent. palmitic, 1–7 per cent. of stearic, 43–50 per cent. of oleic and 13–15 per cent. of linoleic acid, but allowance was apparently not made for any hexadecenoic acid.

The elephant body fat differs from other depot fats of the herbivora in its extremely high content of palmitic acid. The fat, which was taken from the body tissues of an Indian elephant "Raja" which had been in captivity for some years at the Zoological Gardens, London, was also peculiar in that it was dispersed amongst layers of connective tissue, and did not consist of a separate adipose deposit; it formed 76 per cent. of the body material in which it was present. Palmitic acid contents of over 33 per cent. (wt.) have only been observed (apart from the goat back and reindeer loin fats, in which hexadecenoic acid was not determined) in the body fats of some Indian oxen (in one instance 41 per cent.) and in this elephant fat in which it forms 44 per cent. of the total fatty acids, or nearly half as much again as that normally found in animal depot fats. Whether this is a species difference, or whether it is due to dietary factors or a pathological idiosyncrasy of the particular animal concerned, can only be decided by further evidence on the composition of the fats of other Asiatic and African elephants. The rest of the elephant depot fatty acids are similar to those of bovine and many other animals. The component acids of the glycerides and phosphatides in the liver of this elephant are discussed with those of other animal liver lipids later in this Chapter (pp. 133–136).

Depot fats of the horse. The body fats of the horse are exceptional because this animal stores glycerides containing comparatively large quantities of the natural (vegetable) triene linolenic acid. A number of detailed studies of the internal body fats, and also of the liver, bone (marrow), and milk fats of the horse are now available.

Body fats. The results of analyses of the component acids of horse offal fat (Brooker and Shorland[61]) and perinephric and mesenteric fat (Holmberg et al.,[62a,b] Gupta and Hilditch[63]) are given, together with subsequent figures by Dahl[64a] in Table 33.

TABLE 33. *Component Acids (per cent. wt.) of Horse Body Fats*

	SATURATED					UNSATURATED					
	C_{12}	C_{14}	C_{16}	C_{18}	C_{20}	C_{14}	C_{16}	Oleic	Lino-leic	Lino-lenic	C_{20-22}
Sweden, Perinephric[62a] (Stall-fed, oats)	0·6	2·8	20·3	7·2	—	0·6	3·7	38·8	22·1	2·2	1·5
Mesenteric[62b] (Pasture)	—	2·1	26·7	3·9	—	1·8	4·3	37·5	5·4	17·4	0·9
New Zealand, Offal[61] (Pasture)	—	1·1	27·4	1·7	—	0·8	10·5	34·7	5·1	17·0	1·7
England, Mesenteric[63] (Pasture)	0·4	4·5	25·9	4·7	0·2	—	6·8	33·7	5·2	16·3	2·3
Sweden, Abdominal[64a] (Spring)	0·4	5·9	27·2	4·3	—	1·4	7·2	39·5	8·2	5·4	0·5
(Autumn)	0·5	4·9	26·6	5·3	—	1·0	9·0	31·5	8·5	12·4	0·3
Sweden, Withers[64a]	—	4·4	26·0	2·1	—	1·7	14·2	35·2	6·4	9·6	0·4

The fatty acids in the horse body fats in Table 33 are the same as those found in most other herbivores and the contents of palmitic acid generally approach the characteristic figure of 30 per cent. (mol.). The proportions of stearic acid are low but hexadecenoic acid is present in somewhat larger amounts than usual. The most significant feature is the presence of up to 16–17 per cent. of linolenic acid in the body fats of pasture-fed horses: similar amounts have been observed in the bone and hoof fats of these animals (Table 34) and in the milk fat of a pasture-fed mare (this Chapter, p. 160). On the other hand the horse fed in stall on oats had little linolenic acid, but much linoleic acid, in its perinephric and bone fats.[62a] It may be concluded that (like the pig, *cf.* pp. 122–125) the horse is capable of directly assimilating the natural fats present in herbage or seeds which form major parts of its food: pasture grass fats are rich in linolenic acid (*cf.* Chapter IV, p. 180) whereas the fatty oil in oats contains much linoleic and little linolenic acid (*cf.* Chapter IV, p. 281). At the same time the proportions of these polyethenoid C_{18} acids in horse fats do not correspond with those of the dietary vegetable fats, and oleic acid is the most abundant (35–40 per cent.) of the total horse fatty acids. This typical composition of horse body fats is in sharp contrast to those of ruminants (pp. 105–111), for in the latter polyethenoid C_{18} acids occur in very small quantities and are mainly isomeric forms of the seed fat acids, whilst stearic acid is produced in them in very large amounts. In other words, different species of animals feeding on the same pasture elaborate entirely different kinds of reserve fats.

Horse bone and hoof fats. Some data obtained by Brooker and Shorland[61] and by Holmberg and Rosenqvist[62a] are shown in Table 34.

TABLE 34. *Component Acids (per cent. wt.) of Horse Bone and Hoof Fats*

ORIGIN:	NEW ZEALAND[61]		SWEDEN[62a]	
DIET:	PASTURE		STALL-FED	
DEPOT:	HOOF	BONE	MARROW FROM POROUS BONE	GELATINOUS MARROW
Component acids:				
Lauric	—	0·2	—	—
Myristic	0·8	3·1	4·4	2·7
Palmitic	17·9	25·3	20·0	22·0
Stearic	2·5	4·1	2·2	1·6
Arachidic	0·7	0·1	0·3	—
Tetradecenoic	0·6	0·6	1·2	1·1
Hexadecenoic	18·8	8·3	9·7	10·8
Oleic	34·3	35·1	42·0	36·3
Linoleic	5·1	5·2	14·6	14·6
Linolenic	16·9	17·3	3·6	2·4
Unsaturated C_{20-22}	2·4	0·7	1·9	8·4

The figures in Table 34 for the *bone* fats are very similar to those for corresponding body fats (Table 33). The bone fats of the Swedish stall-fed horse differ from its perinephric fat significantly only in lowered proportions of linolenic acid and increased proportions of linoleic acid, whilst that of the New Zealand pasture-fed animals is almost identical in composition with the intestinal fat, the contents of linolenic (17 per cent.), as well as of all the other component acids, being extremely similar in both cases.

The component acids of the New Zealand *hoof* fat differ, however, from the rest of the horse fats in a lower proportion (18 per cent.) of palmitic acid and an increased amount (19 per cent.) of hexadecenoic acid: the combined percentage (37) of C_{16} acids is at the same time similar to that in the corresponding offal (38) and bone (34) oils. Linolenic acid, as in the body and bone fats of the New Zealand pasture-fed animals, forms 17 per cent. of the total fatty acids.

The composition of the horse hoof fat should be compared with that of cattle hoof fat (neat's foot oil, pp. 114, 115). It would appear that the lowered palmitic and increased hexadecenoic acid proportions are typical of animal hoof fats and differentiate them from other body fats.

The composition of glycerides and phosphatides present in the *liver* of the horse will be dealt with later in conjunction with other animal liver lipids (pp. 133–136).

Depot fats of ruminant animals (oxen and sheep). The older analyses of these products, quoted in Table 35, are based upon materials from industrial sources, i.e. on marketed specimens of authentic sheep or ox tallows and not on fats taken from specific parts of a single animal or group of animals. They represent bulked samples of depot fats from many animals and may have been derived from back, abdominal, or perinephric (suet) fats, or a mixture of all of these. Analyses (performed wholly or in part by the ester-fractionation procedure, but in which hexadecenoic and other minor components were not allowed for) are included in Table 35; more recent figures, in which account has been taken of the minor components, hexadecenoic and unsaturated C_{20} acids, are given in Table 36.

TABLE 35. *Component Acids (per cent. wt.) of Depot Fats of Sheep, Oxen and Buffalo*
(*analyses not including hexadecenoic acid or unsaturated C_{20} acids*)

	SATURATED			UNSATURATED	
	C_{14}	C_{16}	C_{18}	Oleic	"Lino-leic"*
Sheep (*Ovis aries*)—					
South American[65]	1	21	30	43	5
Australian[65]	2	25	23	47	3
Australian[66]	4	25	31	36	4
Ox (*Bos taurus*)—					
North American[65]	2	32	15	48	3
North American[67]	6	27	14	50	3
South American[65]	2	25	20	48	5
South American[67]	4	31	19	43	3
South American[67]	8	28	24	39	1
South American[67]	6	24	28	42	—
Australian[65]	2	27	22	49	—
Buffalo (*Bubalis buffelus*)[72b]					
Perinephric					
Indian, male	1	37	32	28	2
Indian, female	1	33	22	43	1

* The "linoleic" acid of these depot fats is better termed octadecadienoic acid (or acids), since it differs from that of vegetable fats in failing to yield a tetrabromo-adduct of m.p. 114°, and only yields traces of the tetrahydroxystearic acids, m.p. 155° and m.p. 173°, on oxidation with alkaline permanganate (*vide infra*, p. 110).

Table 36 includes the following figures:

(*a*) Full fatty acid compositions of four English ox perinephric fats (Hilditch and Longenecker,[68] Hilditch and Paul[69]);

(*b*) Figures for total saturated and unsaturated C_{18} and C_{20-22} acids for American ox brisket (breast) fats (Dugan *et al*[70]);

(*c*) Detailed figures for perinephric and subcutaneous (brisket) fats of Swedish cattle (Dahl[64a]);

(d) Fully detailed data for some Indian ox[71b] and buffalo[72a] depot fats;

(e) Data for perinephric and external tissue fats of ewes[73] grown on a standard (low fat) diet to different live weights, and of fat ewes after fasting for different periods;

(f) Figures for loin fats (adipose and muscle) of two New Zealand sheep (Hartman and Shorland[74b]);

(g) Data for fats from New Zealand, Indian, and Somali sheep.

At this point it is desirable to consider in some detail the very specific character of the fatty acids which compose the depot fats of ruminants. These may be usefully considered in three groups:

(a) *Major component acids* each of which is present to more (usually much more) than 10 per cent. of the total acids;

(b) *Minor component acids* which may each be present to the extent of 1–10 per cent. of the total acids;

(c) *Trace component acids* each forming less than 1 per cent. (usually less than 0·5 per cent.) of the total acids.

TABLE 36. *Component Acids (per cent. wt.) of Ox and Sheep Depot Fats (including minor Component Acids)*

(a) *English Ox Depot Fats (Perinephric)*

	I[68]	II[68]	III[68]	IV[69]
Lauric	—	0·2	0·1	0·5
Myristic	3·0	3·1	2·0	2·7
Palmitic	29·2	24·9	26·9	30·4
Stearic	21·0	24·1	26·5	23·7
Arachidic	0·4	0·8	1·3	—
Tetradecenoic	0·6	0·4	0·4	0·4
Hexadecenoic	2·7	2·4	1·9	1·7
Oleic	41·1	41·8	39·1	38·6
Octadecadienoic	1·8	1·8	1·7	2·0
Unsaturated C_{20-22}	0·2	0·5	0·1	—

(b) *American Ox Depot Fats (Brisket, i.e. Breast)[70]*

	COW	STEER		YEARLING
FAT LAYER:	UNKNOWN	OUTER	INNER	UNKNOWN
Component acids:				
Saturated	27·6	36·8	47·3	39·5
"Oleic" (with hexadecenoic)	67·6	59·9	49·1	57·2
"Linoleic"	3·4	2·4	2·8	2·4
"Linolenic"	0·6	0·5	0·5	0·4
"Arachidonic"	0·8	0·4	0·3	0·5

(c) (i) *Perinephric and subcutaneous fats of Swedish cows[64a]*

Fat:	COW Perinephric		HEIFER Perinephric		COW Subcutaneous	COW Brisket
Feed:	Spring	Autumn	Spring	Autumn	Autumn	Autumn
Lauric	—	—	0·3	0·2	—	—
Myristic	3·9	3·5	3·8	5·1	4·1	3·2
Palmitic	32·4	31·2	31·4	31·8	28·2	31·3
Stearic	22·3	22·7	26·4	24·1	5·9	5·4
Arachidic	—	0·3	0·3	0·5	—	—
Tetradecenoic	0·5	0·5	0·6	0·6	2·8	1·9
Hexadecenoic	5·1	2·9	3·7	2·8	12·4	16·9
Oleic	34·9	37·0	31·4	32·0	41·1	38·9
Octadecadienoic	0·6	0·9	1·9	1·6	4·3	2·4
Octadecatrienoic	0·3	0·8	—	1·2	1·1	—
Unsaturated C_{20}	—	0·2	0·2	0·1	0·1	—

TABLE 36—*continued.*

(c) (ii) *Depot fats of bullocks*[64b]
(Analyses by gas–liquid chromatography)

	PERI-NEPHRIC	MESENTERIC	BRISKET	SUBCU-TANEOUS
Lauric	0·3	—	0·4	0·4
Myristic	3·6	3·5	2·2	3·2
As C_{15}	1·3	1·2	0·7	0·5
Palmitic	29·3	29·9	19·9	31·8
As C_{17}	2·0	2·1	1·4	2·0
Stearic	33·6	34·9	14·5	12·5
Tetradecenoic	0·9	0·8	1·1	1·6
Hexadecenoic	4·4	3·6	7·2	8·4
Hexadecadienoic	0·8	1·5	1·5	2·5
Oleic	21·5	20·0	47·8	35·1
Octadecadienoic	1·2	2·0	2·6	2·0
Octadecatrienoic	0·5	0·5	0·2	—
Eicosenoic	0·6	—	0·5	—

(d) Indian Ox and Buffalo Depot Fats *(mainly perinephric)*

	CALICUT[71b] (COW)	CAL-CUTTA[71b]	BOMBAY[71b] (BULLOCK)	BOMBAY[71b] (COW)	BUFFALO[72a]
Lauric	0·3	0·2	0·2	0·1	—
Myristic	3·1	2·4	3·7	4·5	3·3
Palmitic	32·9	36·9	37·1	41·4	31·5
Stearic	29·3	26·8	29·4	24·3	33·2
Arachidic	—	0·4	1·2	0·5	0·6
Tetradecenoic	0·4	0·3	0·4	0·4	0·3
Hexadecenoic	1·5	2·1	1·0	1·3	1·9
Oleic	30·7	29·2	25·9	26·4	28·9
Octadecadienoic	1·3	0·9	0·9	1·0	—
Unsaturated C_{20-22}	0·5	0·9	0·2	0·1	0·3

(e) *Sheep (ewes) on controlled diets*[73]

	PERINEPHRIC FATS			EXTERNAL TISSUE FATS		
	(i) Feeding on "supermaintenance" ration					
Days on ration:	22	58	81	22	58	81
Live weight (lb.):	91	127	151	91	127	151
Lauric	—	—	—	0·4	0·6	0·9
Myristic	2·9	2·7	2·3	3·4	3·0	3·1
Palmitic	24·0	24·7	26·2	27·8	28·0	28·3
Stearic	24·9	28·3	27·1	14·7	16·2	13·5
Tetradecenoic	0·7	0·3	0·3	0·4	0·3	0·2
Hexadecenoic	2·4	0·9	1·0	1·6	0·8	0·6
Oleic	39·2	36·8	38·7	46·3	46·6	50·8
Octadecadienoic	5·2	5·7	3·3	4·8	3·9	1·9
Unsaturated C_{20-22}	0·7	0·6	1·1	0·6	0·6	0·7
	(ii) Fat ewes fasted					
Days fasted:	0	100	209	0	100	209
Live weight (lb.):	148	113	72	148	113	72
Lauric	0·1	0·1	—	0·7	0·6	0·3
Myristic	1·7	3·0	2·8	1·9	2·2	3·7
Palmitic	26·8	23·6	23·0	33·9	30·5	24·3
Stearic	30·1	31·7	37·8	15·3	20·1	24·6
Tetradecenoic	0·2	0·2	0·2	0·3	0·3	0·3
Hexadecenoic	0·9	1·3	1·0	0·9	1·2	0·7
Oleic	34·8	35·4	32·1	41·2	41·4	44·1
Octadecadienoic	4·3	3·9	2·2	4·9	2·8	1·5
Unsaturated C_{20-22}	1·1	0·8	0·9	0·9	0·9	0·5

(f) Loin fats (adipose and muscle tissues) of New Zealand sheep[74b]

	SHEEP I		SHEEP II	
	ADIPOSE	MUSCLE	ADIPOSE	MUSCLE
Myristic	2·9	1·4	2·9	0·6
Palmitic	21·8	24·3	22·5	26·1
Stearic	26·5	21·6	22·6	19·1
Arachidic	0·4	0·3	1·6	0·8
Tetradecenoic	0·3	0·2	0·4	Trace
Hexadecenoic	3·2	0·6	3·8	0·8
Unsaturated C_{18}	43·7 (− 2·2H)	48·4 (− 2·4H)	45·4 (− 2·4H)	49·3 (− 2·3H)
,, C_{20}	1·2 (− 6H)	3·2 (− 6H)	0·8 (− 6H)	3·3 (H)
[Total trans-unsaturated acids:	15·6	10·7	15·5	11·1]

(g) (i) New Zealand, Indian, and Somali Sheep Fats

	NEW ZEALAND[74a]		INDIAN (BANGALORE)[75a] PASTURE-FED	SOMALI[31a] (IN CAPTIVITY) GREENSTUFF DIET EXTERNAL TISSUE
	DEPOT	MUSCULAR		
Lauric	1·3	0·2	—	—
Myristic	3·5	4·1	2·9	2·2
Palmitic	25·0	24·6	27·8	23·0
Stearic	22·2	15·4	27·7	14·9
Arachidic	0·7	0·7	1·5	—
Tetradecenoic	0·5	0·5	0·4	0·3
Hexadecenoic	1·7	2·6	2·7	2·5
Oleic	42·0	45·1	33·0	55·7
Octadecadienoic	2·2	5·0	3·4	0·8
Unsaturated C_{20-22}	0·9	1·8	0·6	0·6

(ii) Somali Sheep Depot Fats (by gas-liquid chromatography)[75b]

	PERI-NEPHRIC	PERI-CARDIAL	BACK	NECK	TAIL	ABDOMINAL WALL
Myristic	2·3	2·2	2·3	2·4	3·0	2·4
Palmitic	23·8	23·3	22·5	25·2	24·0	22·1
Stearic	38·5	34·8	20·2	17·3	14·5	13·8
Hexadecenoic	0·6	0·8	1·1	1·4	1·5	1·3
Oleic	19·1	24·1	34·8	34·7	31·1	35·7
Oleic isomers	5·9	5·5	5·5	5·6	6·0	5·3
Linoleic	2·9	2·9	2·8	3·2	3·5	3·3

(Minor amounts of odd-numbered acids also observed: $n\text{-}C_{15}$ 1·1–3·4, $n\text{-}C_{17}$ 1·6–3·0, iso-C_{17} 1·1–3·2 per cent.)

The demarcation line between *trace* and *minor* component acids is not very clear in some instances, but for the most part the three categories are well differentiated.

(*a*) *Major component acids of ruminant depot fats.* Three fatty acids – palmitic, oleic and stearic – account for nearly 90 per cent. or more of the total acids in ruminant depot fats, as will be readily observed from Tables 35 and 36. These may be considered individually.

Palmitic acid. – Banks and Hilditch[67] first drew attention to the approximately constant proportions of palmitic acid – in the neighbourhood of 30 per cent. (mol.)* of the total fatty acids: consequently the rest of the fats is made up almost entirely of C_{18} acids, and the difference between a more

* In these depot fats the molar percentages of palmitic acid are 1·5–1·8 units per cent: higher than the weight percentages as given in Tables 35 and 36.

saturated and a less saturated tallow is due essentially to varying proportions in the stearic and oleic acid contents, the combined amounts of these
also being approximately constant. Hilditch and Longenecker,[68] who made
analyses in which minor components such as hexadecenoic acid were taken
into account, observed the same constancy and, on recalculating the earlier
figures to allow for hexadecenoic acid, found that the degree of constancy was
more exact than had at first appeared. They concluded that "the constancy of
the C_{18} acids at about 60–65 per cent. (mol.) of the total fatty acids of tallow
is even more marked than was at first thought, any increase in stearic acid
being closely balanced by diminution of oleic acid. At the same time, and largely
independently of the amount of unsaturated acids present, the palmitic acid
content of nearly all tallows which have been analysed lies within the relatively
constant limits of 30 ($\pm$ 3) per cent. (mol.)."

The characteristic content may vary somewhat according to the animal
species. Thus the value of 30 ($\pm$ 3) per cent. (mol.) which is normally observed
in ox depot fats appears to be slightly higher than that noted in sheep depot
fats ($28 \cdot 5 \pm 4$ per cent. mol.).

In certain of the Indian ox depot fats which were exceptionally low in
oleic acid, the stearic acid content did not increase beyond about 28 per
cent. (mol.) of the total fatty acids, and in these instances the extra saturated
acid over and above this proportion was palmitic; the content of palmitic
acid in such cases therefore exceeded considerably the normal figure of 30
per cent. (mol.), reaching in one example as much as 43 per cent. (mol.).
Such ox depot fats appear, however, to be exceptional in this respect, their
low degree of unsaturation being possibly dependent primarily on the tropical
conditions in which the animals in question were reared.

Stearic acid. – This is somewhat variable in both ox and sheep depot fats.
In each group (as also in pig depot fats, pp. 117–119) the perinephric fats are
more saturated than the external tissue fats, thus containing more stearic and
less oleic glycerides than the latter. This variation is usually considered to be
associated with the local body temperature of the animal at the site of the fat
deposits (*cf.* pig fats, p. 118). However, there are indications of a limit (at about
30 per cent. (mol.) of the total acids) beyond which the content of stearic acid
in the component acids of a sheep or ox depot fat rarely rises. Whilst the
perinephric (suet) fats contain the lowest proportions of oleic acid (about
40 per cent. or less), the back fats may contain up to nearly 50 per cent. of this
acid with correspondingly reduced stearic acid; thus the stearic content of ox
and sheep perinephric fats is in the range 21–29 per cent. and that of corresponding external tissue fats 14–17 per cent. Ox breast (brisket) fats[64a, 70] may
contain much less stearic acid (5–6 per cent.), much more hexadecenoic acid
(12–17 per cent.) and somewhat increased oleic acid contents compared with
fats from the main depots.

Oleic acid. – This is usually the most abundant single acid in ox and sheep
depot fats. Its general occurrence therein will have been gathered from the
preceding paragraph, since broadly speaking there is a reciprocal connection
between the oleic and the stearic acid contents of these fats. This relationship

has an important bearing upon the mode of formation of the depot glycerides of ruminants (*cf.* below, p. 112), wherein increase in stearic and corresponding decrease in oleic acid is accompanied by the appearance of unusually large amounts of fully saturated glycerides (palmitostearins) in relation to the total proportion of the saturated acids present.

Some proportion of the monoethenoid C_{18} acids recorded as oleic in Tables 35 and 36 is now known to consist of geometrical or positional isomers of oleic acid (these are mentioned below with other minor component acids and also later (p. 113) in connection with the origin of the specific type of ruminant depot fat).

(*b*) *Minor component acids* include myristic, hexadecenoic, the isomers of oleic just mentioned, and isomeric forms of diethenoid C_{18} acids.

Myristic acid usually forms from about 2 to 4 per cent. of the total depot fatty acids in both oxen and sheep. It is the only " minor" saturated component acid (as defined on p. 105) but many other saturated acids are present in "trace" proportions; these are detailed later (p. 110).

Hexadecenoic acid is usually present to the extent of about 2–3 per cent. of ox depot fatty acids, and to a slightly lesser amount in sheep depot fats. Traces of di- and/or tri-ethenoid C_{16} acids have sometimes been observed by spectrophotometric studies to accompany the hexadecenoic acid.

Monoethenoid C_{18} acids (other than oleic). In the fats of ruminant animals the predominating acid – oleic, *cis*-octadec-9-enoic – is accompanied by small amounts of isomeric monoethenoid acids. The first of these to be noticed was "vaccenic acid", the name given by Bertram[80] to traces (0·1 to at most 1 per cent.) of an acid isolated from ox and sheep depot and milk fats, and stated by him to be *trans*-octadec-11-enoic acid. The latter acid was synthesized in 1948 by Strong *et al.*[81] who found that its infra-red spectrum was identical with that of a highly purified specimen of natural "vaccenic acid"; Benedict and Daubert,[82] however, showed that the X-ray diffraction spectra of elaidic (*trans*-octadec-9-enoic) acid and the synthetic *trans*-octadec-11-enoic acid were identical but differed from that of the natural "vaccenic acid". In 1951 Gupta *et al.*[83] put forward chemical evidence which showed that natural "vaccenic acid" from ox or sheep depot and milk fats was a mixture of at least two isomers of elaidic acid, namely, *trans*-octadec-10-enoic and *trans*-octadec-11-enoic acids.

Meanwhile, in 1944, Millican and J. B. Brown[84] had scrutinized the individuality of the monoethenoid C_{18} acid present in various natural fats, finding only oleic acid in a number of vegetable fats but evidence of some small amounts of other isomeric acids in the octadecenoic acids of various fats from oxen, pigs, and the human body. In 1952 Swern *et al.*[85a] studied the infra-red spectra of the octadecenoic acids in a number of ox body fats and found that greater amounts of *trans*-acids (including elaidic as well as "vaccenic") were present than had previously been recognised: they put the proportion of *trans*-acids at as high as 10–15 per cent. of the total monoethenoid acids. Later, Shorland *et al.*[85b] similarly examined the infra-red spectra of body fats of a number of non-ruminant, ruminant, and marsupial animals. They could not detect any *trans*-acids in rat, horse, rabbit, pheasant or opossum fats (non-ruminants) and only 0·9 per cent. in pig fat, whereas *trans*-acid contents from 4–11 per cent. of the total fatty acids were observed in the fats of ox, cow, deer, goat and sheep (ruminants), and 18–21 per cent. in those of wallaby and quokka (marsupials which possess a *quasi*-rumen-like digestive system[58d]). From this evidence, Shorland *et al.* concluded that the *trans*-acids arise mainly from the hydrogenation of dietary unsaturated acids by bacteria in the rumen of ruminants, or in the rumen-like stomach in marsupials; this aspect is further referred to below (p. 113) in a general discussion of the origin of the typical acids produced in ruminant depot fats.

Other workers[85c] have also stated that pig, horse and a number of vegetable fats contain no *trans*-acids, but small amounts of these are present in beef fats and butter.

Polyethenoid C_{18} acids. These are specifically characteristic minor components, forming about 4 per cent. of the acids in sheep depot fats, but only about 1–2 per cent. in ox depot fats. In view of the relative abundance of linoleic and linolenic acids in the fats of pasture grasses, the small amount of diene acids in the ruminant depot fats is very striking (especially when contrasted with the substantial proportions of linoleic and linolenic acids in fats of the horse (p. 102) and of some other herbivorous animals). Hilditch and Longenecker[68] showed in 1937 that the diethenoid C_{18} acids of ox depot fats contained but little ordinary linoleic acid, and that apparently geometrical and possibly structural isomerides of octadecadienoic acids were the chief constituents present. More recent spectrophotometric studies of these acids before and after isomerisation with alkali have indicated the presence of very small proportions of conjugated acids, the remainder possessing partly the "pentadiene" grouping $-CH:CH.CH_2.CH:CH-$ and partly other structures, with very possibly the presence of *trans*- as well as *cis*-groupings (*cf.*, again, the general discussion below, p. 113). Weenink[85d] found that, in lamb caul fat, about 1·2 per cent. of the total fatty acids were isomers of linoleic acid with double bonds separated by two or more methylene groups, these forming about two-thirds of the total octadecadienoic acids.

(*c*) *Trace component acids* (present to the extent of less than 0·5 per cent. of the total fatty acids) include a wide variety of normal even-numbered saturated, normal and branched-chain odd-numbered saturated, and some unsaturated fatty acids in both bovine (oxen) and ovine (sheep and goat) fats.

Normal even-numbered saturated acids. Traces of *n*-decanoic acid have been noted in ewe external tissue fats[76a] and of lauric acid in ox perinephric[68] and other bovine[71b] and sheep[74a] depot fats. Traces of *n*-arachidic acid have often been reported in similar fats.

Normal odd-numbered saturated acids. Traces of *n*-heptadecanoic acid (0·4 per cent.) in ox,[76b] sheep [76c] and musk-ox fats[76d] and of *n*-nonadecanoic acid in ox fats[76e] have been observed.

Branched-chain odd-numbered acids, of which traces have been observed in various ox and sheep fats, include (+)-12-methyltetradecanoic,[77a] 13-methyltetradecanoic,[77a] 14-methylpentadecanoic,[77b] (+)-14-methylhexadecanoic,[77b] 15-methylhexadecanoic[77c] and 16-methylhexadecanoic.[77d]

The (+)-14-methylhexadecanoic acid isolated from ox and sheep fat[77b] was shown by Hansen *et al.* to be identical with that found by Weitkamp[78] in wool grease; the authors estimated that it constituted not less than 0·2 per cent. of the total acids in the sheep external tissue fat, and incline to the view that it is present as glycerides. The identity of the acid with that in wool wax and in tubercle bacilli wax suggests, however, that the presence of traces of such acids in animal body fats may result from traces of animal waxes which find their way into the adipose tissues.

Unsaturated acids. Traces of heptadec-9-enoic acid have been noted in lamb caul fat[77e] and in the back fat of the musk ox (*Ovibus moschatus*)[76d].

Unsaturated acids containing 20 or 22 carbon atoms are also present in ruminant body fats in very small quantities, usually much less than 1 per cent. of the total fatty acids. The presence of polyethenoid C_{20} (arachidonic) acid was noted in ox body fats in 1934 by J. B. Brown and Sheldon.[86] Later, in the course of ester-fractionation analyses of ox and sheep depot fats, it has appeared probable that the unsaturated acids may well include mono- and polyethenoid members of both the C_{20} and C_{22} series, the C_{20} acids predominating.

A review of all the trace component acids observed to date in hydrogenated ox perinephric fat has been contributed by Shorland and his co-workers[77f]; it is stated that, in all, these acids may amount to 2 per cent. and perhaps more of the total acids in the depot fat.

Fat synthesised by sheep. In one series of experiments, the results of which are illustrated in Table 36 (*e*) (i), it is possible to distinguish the kind of endogenous fat produced by a sheep whose diet included no added fats, so that its depot fats must have been almost wholly produced by biosynthesis in the animal from carbohydrate or protein. The increases in each component acid in the perinephric and external tissue fats between the ewe killed at 22 days and that killed at 81 days were approximately as follows:

	PERINEPHRIC		EXTERNAL	
	Weight (g.)	Molar ratio	Weight (g.)	Molar ratio
Lauric	—	—	39	1·3
Myristic	40	2·7	128	3·7
Palmitic	465	28·1	1182	30·0
Stearic	482	26·3	559	12·8
Tetradecenoic	5	0·3	8	0·2
Hexadecenoic	16	1·0	22	0·6
Oleic	684	37·5	2132	49·2
Octadecadienoic	56	3·1	71	1·6
Unsaturated C_{20-22}	20	1·0	29	0·6

Of the three major component acids, the perinephric and external tissue fats respectively show relative increases of 1 mol. palmitic acid to 2·28 and 2·07 mols. of combined stearic and oleic acids, suggesting that palmitodi-C_{18}-glycerides are the main types of fat synthesised by the animal. The more elaborate study of fats from pigs raised on a low fat diet (Table 39 and p. 121) led to a similar result, and also permitted conclusions to be drawn as to which acyl radicals were synthesised by the animal and which were derived by direct assimilation.

The data given in Table 36 (e) (ii) for ewes during fasting suggest that little selective removal of fatty acids takes place during mobilisation of the depot fats, especially the perinephric fat. To a slight extent, however, palmitic glycerides seem to be a little more readily removed from the perinephric fat, and still more so in the case of the fat of the external tissues. It should be remembered that, since all these depot fats consist of mixed glycerides (mainly palmitodioleins and oleopalmitostearins), any tendency in favour of withdrawal of a particular fatty acid must be partly obscured by other acids present in the mixed glycerides being inevitably and concurrently involved.

The cause of the characteristic (high) stearic acid content and the presence of isomeric mono- and di-ethenoid C_{18} acids in the fats of ruminants. Many years ago, in the early stages of detailed study of the glyceride structure of natural fats, it was recognised that animal depot fats rich in stearic acid contained fully saturated glycerides in large quantities (up to 25 per cent. or more of the fats) whereas vegetable seed fats with comparable proportions of palmitic and stearic acid contained only negligible amounts of fully saturated glycerides. Banks and Hilditch[67] suggested in 1931 that this marked difference in the glyceride structure of the two classes of fats could be explained if, in the stearic-rich (ruminant) depot fats, preformed palmito-oleo glycerides were later partly converted in the animal into palmito-stearo-glycerides by a bio-hydrogenation process. Cumulative evidence since 1951 that bacteria or protozoa present in the rumen of the ruminant and quasi-ruminant groups of mammals do in fact hydrogenate linolenic and linoleic glycerides present in pasture-grasses has confirmed the conclusions based on the earlier studies of the final products (the depot fats), although so far it appears that the bio-hydrogenation process may be mainly concerned with fatty acids in the rumen, rather than with glycerides as such.

The first experiments in this field were due to Reiser[79a] who in 1951 observed that incubation of linseed oil with sheep rumen contents caused marked reduction in linolenic acid and increase in linoleic acid. In 1952 Reiser et al.[79b] showed that 5 per cent. of cottonseed oil in the diet of steers increased the amount of stearic acid and reduced that of oleic acid in their depot fats, whilst their more elaborate studies[79c] in 1956, when goats were fed on an alfalfa diet with added cottonseed or linseed oil, showed that linoleic and linolenic acids largely disappeared, being replaced by much saturated and some oleic acid:

	COTTON-SEED OIL	GOAT FATS		LINSEED OIL	GOAT FATS	
		RUMEN	BACK		RUMEN	BACK
Saturated acids	31·5	63·5	56·1	18·5	58·4	45·5
Oleic	29·4	29·0	36·3	15·5	33·5	48·5
Linoleic	35·0	6·5	7·1	14·6	3·2	4·7
Linolenic	4·1	1·2	0·6	51·5	4·9	1·2

Meanwhile Shorland et al.[79d] (1955) and Holmberg et al.[79e] (1956) reported that the linolenic acid of pasture grass or clover lipids was more effectively hydrogenated than the linoleic acid; the former workers also made the important observation that *trans*-forms of mono- and di-ethenoid C_{18} acids were produced (to the extent of about 9 per cent.) in the rumen fats. Later, Shorland et al.[79f] incubated individual acids – oleic, linoleic or linolenic – with sheep rumen contents and found the following component acids (per cent. wt.) to have been produced from the added acids:

ACID INCUBATED:	OLEIC	LINOLEIC	LINOLENIC
Acids			
Stearic	22·6	15·6	16·8
Monoene	59·0	44·7	72·2
Diene (non-conjugated)	0·6	18·9	Trace
,, (conjugated)	1·4	15·0	1·4
Triene (non-conjugated)	1·0	0·2	0·7
,, (conjugated)	0·8	0·3	Trace
Trans-acids (as elaidic)	17·2	47·9	67·3

Similar results on the incubation of linseed oil with sheep rumen contents were obtained by Garton et al.,[79g] while in 1959 Reiser et al.[79h] found that the depot fat of a steer reared on a *non-fatty* diet had in its acids palmitic 27·3, stearic 29·2, oleic 35·0, and diene C_{18} 0·5 per cent. The latter workers therefore concluded that dietary di- or tri-ene acids were not necessary in order to produce ruminant–stearic-rich fats, and considered various alternative possibilities, including possible hydrogenation of palmitodioleins. That ruminants produce endogenous (biosynthesised) stearic-rich fats on a non-fatty diet was already evident, of course, as shown by, e.g., the ewe depot fats examined by Hilditch and Pedelty[73] in 1941, Table 36 (e) (i); conceivably, the enzyme systems in the rumen which cause hydrogenation might also be present in the site or sites where lipids are synthesised from carbohydrate in the ruminant.

Tove and Mochrie [79i] (1963) showed that intravenous injection of a cotton-seed oil emulsion to cows caused marked increase in the linoleic content of the milk fat. Thus, whilst dietary unsaturated glycerides are hydrogenated by the rumen microflora before deposition, bypassing the rumen leads to deposition of unsaturated glycerides without hydrogenation.

The demonstration that, in ruminants, unsaturated lipids undergo an efficient process of biohydrogenation is of great interest. The products include not only stearic glycerides but also a mixture of *cis*- and *trans*-forms of mono-ene and di-ene C_{18} acids, and are thus exactly similar to those produced by the present-day technical catalytic hydrogenation of vegetable fatty oils. So that the latter, which only dates from early in the present century, is merely an imitation of the procedure employed by cattle, sheep and other ruminants for many thousands of years. Moreover, those who object to the use of modern margarines and cooking fats on the grounds that "unnatural" (*trans*-, etc.) fatty acids have been introduced in the course of hydrogenation must now logically object also to the "natural" beef and mutton suets and butter, in which the allegedly "unnatural" acids are now proved also to be present.

Bone and hoof fats of oxen, sheep, and pigs. The general results of detailed studies on ox, sheep, and pig bone fats by Holmberg[87a,b], other figures for ox bone marrow fat (Hilditch and Murti[71a]), Argentine cattle bone fats (Cattaneo et al.[89]) and neat's foot oil (Hilditch and Shrivastava[88a]), with less complete data for neat's foot oil (Eckart[88b]) and for bone fat from a reindeer (Schmidt-Nielsen[90]), are collected in Table 37.

TABLE 37. Component Acids (per cent. wt.) of Ox, Sheep and Pig Bone Fats, and of Cattle Hoof Fat

BONE FATS	SATURATED					UNSATURATED					
						MONOENE			DIENE	TRIENE	
	C_{12} or lower	C_{14}	C_{16}	C_{18}	C_{20}	C_{14}	C_{16}	Oleic	C_{18}	C_{18}	C_{20-22}
Ox, Yellow marrow[71a]	0·1	2·6	32·3	15·5	—	0·7	3·0	43·2	2·6	—	—
Cow, 8 years old, lactating:[87a]											
Radius and ulna:											
Yellow marrow	—	4·1	31·0	13·0	0·8	0·8	2·5	43·7	2·5	1·0	0·6
Gelatinous marrow	0·2	2·0	25·2	6·3	0·3	0·9	5·4	55·2	1·7	0·9	1·9
Porous bone	0·7	2·7	24·2	9·9	0·6	1·1	5·1	52·5	1·6	0·7	1·0
Metatarsus:											
Gelatinous marrow	0·9	1·8	18·0	2·9	0·2	2·0	7·2	61·4	3·2	0·8	1·6
Porous bone	2·5	1·0	17·8	3·1	—	1·3	9·4	58·7	2·7	1·1	2·4
Calf, milk-fed[87a]											
Gelatinous marrow	0·6	3·6	18·2	7·1	1·8	1·7	4·7	56·6	3·3	0·8	1·6
Porous bone	1·6	4·9	20·5	8·8	1·0	1·3	5·8	53·2	1·3	1·0	0·6
Sheep[87b]											
Lamb, 6 months old*	0·9	4·9	18·9	8·3	0·3	1·2	5·5	54·7	3·9	1·5	Trace
Pig[87b]											
Sow, 4 years old*	0·3	1·8	19·2	6·1	0·6	0·5	2·5	51·4	12·2	1·3	4·3
Reindeer[90]*	—	5	26·5	12·5	—	←———54———→			2	—	—
HOOF FATS (CATTLE)											
Neat's Foot Oil (Irish)[88a]	—	0·7	16·9	2·7	0·1	1·2	9·4	64·4	2·3	0·7	1·6
Neat's Foot Oil (German)[88b]	—	—	18	3	—	←———————79———————→					
ARGENTINE CATTLE[89]											
Knee bones	—	1·1	21·3	6·4	0·4	0·6	3·1	57·3	9·1	—	0·7
Shin bones	—	1·6	25·3	5·2	—	0·8	5·8	48·7	12·1	—	0·5
Hoof bones	—	1·4	19·0	3·8	0·2	1·0	5·8	60·5	7·6	—	0·7

* Fats from mixed bones of animal.

Ox bone fats. The *yellow marrow* fats of the English ox[71a] and the radius and ulna of the Swedish cow[87b] are identical in composition with a typical ox body (rump) fat of the less saturated type, but the *gelatinous* marrow and *porous bone* fats in Holmberg's studies of the radial and metatarsal bones of the cow show interesting differences. In these the proportion of palmitic and stearic acids diminishes, compensated by lesser increase in hexadecenoic acid and more pronounced increase in oleic acid: the myristic acid content is also lessened, but that of the other minor component acids is little altered. The combined amounts of acids of the C_{16} and the C_{18} series in this group of fats is as follows (per cent. mol.):

BONE FAT:	PALMITIC	HEXA-DECENOIC	TOTAL C_{16}	STEARIC	OLEIC	TOTAL C_{18}
Yellow marrow	32·7	2·6	35·3	12·4	41·8	54·2
Radial:						
Gelatinous marrow	26·8	5·7	32·5	6·1	53·4	59·5
Porous bone	25·6	5·4	31·0	9·5	50·4	59·9
Metatarsal:						
Gelatinous marrow	19·2	7·7	26·9	2·8	59·3	62·1
Porous bone	18·9	10·0	28·9	2·9	56·3	59·2

There is thus a gradual decrease in the total C_{16} acids paralleled by corresponding increase in the total C_{18} acids. It is apparent, however, that the greater part (apart from the yellow marrow fat) of the ox bone fats contains 18–25 per cent. (wt.) of palmitic and about 55–60 per cent. (wt.) of oleic acid, with about 3–8 per cent. of stearic and about 5–9 per cent. of hexadecenoic acid.

Bone fats of calf, sheep, reindeer, and pig. Exactly the same relationships hold in these fats as in the ox bone and hoof fats. The palmitic acid contents of the calf, sheep, and pig bone fats lie between 18 and 20 per cent. (wt.), with 6–9 per cent. of stearic acid. So far as can be judged from the partial analysis quoted[90] the reindeer bone fatty acids follow a somewhat similar course. The calf bone fat is also interesting in that its content of acids with less than 14 carbon atoms is no greater than in the other bone fats, although the animal was feeding on cow's milk.

The unsaturated acids of this group of bone fats (and those of the horse, Table 34) again show close similarity to those of the body fats of the species concerned. In the calf and sheep, the unsaturated acids are qualitatively and also quantitatively similar to those in ox or sheep depot fats, but in the pig bone fat[87b] (as in pig body fats) ordinary (seed-fat) linoleic acid was present in relatively large amount: similarly horse bone fats (Table 34) contain linoleic and linolenic acids in the same proportions as in the corresponding body fats.

As Holmberg[87] has pointed out, therefore, animal bone fats exhibit characteristic differences from the corresponding depot fats (notably in their contents of palmitic and stearic acids); but their unsaturated acids are clearly made up of the same mixture which is characteristic for the body fats of the same animal species.

Cattle hoof fats. The analysis of Irish neat's foot oil[88a] (which is supported as regards palmitic and stearic acid contents by the earlier partial analysis[88b] of a German oil) shows a mixture of fatty acids which very closely resembles that in the bone fats of the Swedish cow. It is important to note, accordingly, that oleic acid (although it forms 64 per cent. of the total acids) is by no means so preponderant a component of neat's foot oils as was formerly supposed, and that these oils probably contain very little, if any, triolein. They are made up largely of palmitodiolein (*ca.* 35 per cent.), hexadeceno-diolein (*ca.* 25 per cent.) and palmito-hexadeceno-oleins (*ca.* 10 per cent.), with lesser amounts of other mixed oleo-glycerides and possibly a little triolein (*cf.* Chapter VII, p. 505).

The component acids of the cattle hoof fat should be compared with those of horse hoof fat[61] (Table 34, p. 103). Both fats contain the same amounts of palmitic acid, but the horse hoof fat has less stearic and more hexadecenoic acid. In the unsaturated acids it is interesting to note that the composition follows that of the unsaturated acids in the body fats of the respective species: in the cattle oil the proportions of oleic and the minor unsaturated acids are practically the same as in the softer ox depot fats, but the unsaturated acids of the horse hoof oil include the same proportions of linoleic and linolenic acids as are observed in the body fats of the same animal (Table 33, p. 102).

Depot fats (lards) of pigs (fed on diets low in fat). The records for pig depot fats are at present more numerous than for any other of the land animals. As in the ox and sheep depot fats, many of the component acid analyses (Table 38, p. 117; values given to nearest unit per cent.) do not take account of all the minor components (notably hexadecenoic acid); these older data embrace the following groups of investigations:

(i) Hogs of varying age fed on rations low in fat (Ellis and Zeller[91a]).

(ii) Hogs fed on brewers' rice or on corn (Ellis and Isbell[91b]).

(iii) Outer back, inner back, and perinephric fats of young pigs (Bhattacharya and Hilditch[92a]).

(iv) Outer back, inner back, and perinephric fats of a sow (Banks and Hilditch[92b]).

(v) Back fats at varying depths from the skin of a sow (Dean and Hilditch[92c]).

Subsequently, a number of analyses of pig depot fatty acids have been made,[93a] employing an electrically heated and specially packed fractionating column in the distillations of the unsaturated esters; some of these results are quoted in Table 39. The depot fats in question were from pigs reared on diets* low in fat at the School of Agriculture, Cambridge; the animals were fed on a "high" or a "low" ration to a final live weight of 200 lb., and in certain

* DETAILS OF DIET:

From weaning to 16 weeks.—

High plane ration. One gallon separated milk per pig daily, with *ad lib.* meal mixture No. 1 (20 per cent. dried separated milk, 30 per cent. white fish meal, 30 per cent. middlings, 20 per cent. flaked meal).

Low plane ration. Half gallon separated milk per pig daily, with restricted ration of meal mixture No. 1.

From 16 weeks onwards.—

High plane ration. One gallon separated milk per pig daily, with *ad lib.* meal mixture No. 2 (30 per cent. white fish meal, 30 per cent. barley meal, 30 per cent. flaked meal, 10 per cent. middlings).

Low plane ration. Half gallon separated milk per pig daily, with restricted ration of meal mixture No. 2.

Fat content of meal mixtures:

CONSTITUENT	MEAL	FAT (Per Cent.)	IODINE VALUE OF FAT
Dried separated milk	No. 1	1·0	42·5
White fish meal	Nos. 1 and 2	1·6	169·5
Wheat middlings	Nos. 1 and 2	4·1	116·0
Flaked maize	Nos. 1 and 2	1·3	114·6
Barley meal	No. 2	3·1	117·2

cases the "high" ration was changed to "low", or *vice versa*, when the pigs were sixteen weeks old.

In considering the figures in Tables 38 and 39 the following points must be borne in mind:

(*a*) The data in Table 39 may be taken as the most comprehensive analyses available at present.

(*b*) The figures in Table 38, (iii), (iv), and (v) have been calculated, in the cases of the fractionally distilled "liquid" or mainly unsaturated esters, as though only unsaturated C_{18} esters and esters of palmitic and myristic acids were present, no allowance being made for hexadecenoic esters; consequently the apparent contents of myristic acid are higher than the true values by nearly 3 per cent., whilst the palmitic acid figures are probably about 1 per cent. below the true values. The data in Table 38, (i) and (ii) are derived from ester-fractionation of the *saturated* acids, whilst the unsaturated acids are derived merely from the iodine values of the "liquid" acids; hence the figures for myristic and palmitic acids will be slightly low (no allowance having been made for the small quantities of these acids passing into the "liquid" acids), and also the proportions of linoleic acid will actually be higher than recorded.

TABLE 38. *Component Acids (per cent. wt.) of Pig Depot Fats*
(low fat diets) (Older analyses)

	FAT IOD. VAL.	SATURATED			UNSATURATED		
		C_{14}	C_{16}	C_{18}	Oleic	"Linoleic"	C_{20-22}
(i) Hogs (composite body fats) of varying age:[91a]							
Age (Days)							
110	61·2	1	26	8	58	7	—
134	57·4	1	28	9	58	4	—
246	53·3	1	26	12	60	1	—
257	55·1	1	25	11	62	1	—
(ii) Hogs fed on:[91b]							
Brewers' rice, etc. (Back fat)	52·6	2	26	12	59	1	—
Corn, etc. (Meat fat)	58·8	1	25	13	54	7	—
(iii) * Young pigs:[92b]							
Back, outer layer	62·6	2	25	11	53	9	—
,, inner ,,	55·0	1	30	14	47	8	—
Perinephric	45·7	4	29	21	41	5	—
(iv) † Back and perinephric fats of a sow:[92b]							
Back, outer, shoulder end	76·9	4	19	6	54	15	2
,, ,, central portion	72·6	4	20	8	54	13	1
,, ,, tail end	72·0	4	22	7	50	15	2
,, inner, shoulder end	71·1	4	23	9	47	16	1
,, ,, central portion	64·6	4	26	11	44	14	1
,, ,, tail end	64·6	4	23	14	44	14	1
Perinephric	59·0	4	28	17	36	14	1
(v) ‡ Back fats (varying depths) of a sow:[92c]							
Back, outer, central, outer layer	70·4	3	24	10	46	15	2
,, ,, ,, inner ,,	67·4	3	23	13	43	16	2
,, inner, ,, outer ,,	62·9	3	25	14	43	14	1
,, ,, ,, middle ,,	63·0	3	25	15	41	15	1
,, ,, ,, inner ,,	62·8	3	25	14	43	14	1

* Diet estimated to contain 1·5 per cent. of fat and 12 per cent. of protein.
† Diet included a small proportion of fish-meal.
‡ Diet included no fish-meal.

When due allowance is made for the minor variations in the analytical procedures used in the analyses recorded in Tables 38 and 39, it is clear that, with pigs reared on diets relatively low in fat, the major component depot fatty acids are palmitic, stearic, and unsaturated C_{18} acids (in which oleic acid predominates). Out of every 100 mols. of fatty acids, approximately 30 (or slightly less) are those of palmitic acid (the molar percentage of palmitic acid in these fats is 1·5–1·8 units per cent. more than the weight percentage recorded in the tables). Similarly, the combined molar content of C_{18} acids is in nearly all cases between 65 and 70 per cent. of the total fatty acids. As in ox and sheep depot fats the proportions of stearic acid are variable. In fats from different depots of the same pig it is also evident that the combined percentages of stearic and oleic acids are approximately constant, i.e. increase in stearic acid is mainly at the expense of oleic acid, or *vice versa*. These relationships will receive further consideration in connection with the glyceride structure of depot fats (Chapter V, pp. 405–408).

Concurrently with the general approximations to constancy in palmitic and total C_{18} acid contents, it will be noticed that the most unsaturated fats usually also contain somewhat less palmitic acid than usual. This is especially noticeable in the outer layers of back fat at the extreme ends (especially the shoulder) of this layer of adipose tissue.

The outer layers of the back fat of pigs are somewhat more unsaturated in character (higher oleic acid content) than the inner layers, whilst the perinephric fat of the animal is still more saturated and contains the greatest content of stearic acid. Henriques and Hansen[94] concluded that the determining factor here was the temperature of the site of the fat deposits in the animal (e.g. back of pig: 1 cm. deep, 33·7°C.; 4 cm. deep, 39·0°C.; rectum, 39·9°C.), and obtained further support for this hypothesis by maintaining three pigs from the same litter at different temperatures – one at 30–35°, one at 0°, and one at 0° but covered with a sheepskin coat; the iodine values of the outermost layers of the back fats from these animals, after two months, were respectively 69·4, 72·3 and 67·0. The detailed analyses of Dean and Hilditch[92c] (Table 38, (v)) afford general confirmation of Henriques and Hansen's views, but show that the increase in softness (i.e. unsaturation) is confined to the outermost layer of the outer back fat. The inner part of the outer layer, and the inner back fat (i.e. the portion beneath the "streak") which forms the greater part of the whole of the back fat are almost homogenous in composition throughout. It is noticeable that, in many of the outer back fats which have been analysed, the stearic acid content is close to 12–13 per cent. (wt.); in the inner back fats this usually rises by about 4 units per cent.

The proportions of "linoleic" acid also merit attention. In the first place it may be pointed out that the octadecadienoic acids of pig depot fat usually yield, on treatment with bromine, fair amounts of the tetrabromostearic acid, m.p. 114°; whilst alkaline permanganate oxidation gives the two tetra-hydroxystearic acids, m.p. 157° and 173°, characteristic of the linoleic acid of seed fats (*cf.* Chapter IX, p. 627). In this respect the octadecadienoic acids of pig depot fat therefore differ appreciably from the depot and milk fats of

TABLE 39. Component Acids (per cent. wt.) of Pig Back Fats (low fat diets)[93a]

	(i) Sixteen weeks old		(ii) Reared to 200 lb. live weight				
Animals:							
Sex:	GILT	GILT	GILT	HOG	HOG	GILT	GILT
Back fat:	OUTER	OUTER	OUTER	OUTER	OUTER	OUTER	INNER
Ration to 16 weeks	"HIGH"	"LOW"	"LOW"	"LOW"	"HIGH"	"HIGH"	"HIGH"
Ration after 16 weeks	—	—	"LOW"	"HIGH"	"LOW"	"HIGH"	"HIGH"
Fat, iodine value:	57·2	58·3	65·5	55·9	58·8	60·0	54·3
Component acids:							
Myristic	1·0*	1·3	0·8*	1·1*	0·7	1·3	1·0
Palmitic	29·8	28·1	25·9	28·2	25·3	28·3	30·1
Stearic	12·7	11·8	12·2	13·5	13·1	11·9	16·2
Tetradecenoic	0·2	Trace	0·2	0·2	0·1	0·2	0·3
Hexadecenoic	3·5	4·8	2·0	2·4	2·0	2·7	2·7
Oleic	47·8	42·9	48·1	47·0	51·0	47·5	40·9
Octadecadienoic	3·1	8·2	7·8	5·2	5·3	6·0	7·1
Unsaturated C_{20-22}	1·9	2·9	3·0	2·4	2·5	2·1	1·7

* Traces of lower saturated acid (probably lauric) included in this figure.

A more recent detailed analysis by Dahl[93c] of fats from pigs fed on a "fattening" diet gave similar results:

	SATURATED				UNSATURATED					
Acids (per cent. wt.):	C_{14}	C_{16}	C_{18}	C_{20}	C_{14}	C_{16}	Oleic	C_{18} diene	C_{18} triene	C_{20}
Abdominal fat	2·1	27·8	18·2	—	0·4	3·1	40·5	6·9	0·4	0·6
Back fat	3·0	25·5	12·1	0·4	0·7	3·1	47·2	6·5	1·2	0·3

119

oxen. The amounts of "linoleic" acid recorded in different cases vary widely, from 1 per cent. (or probably somewhat more) in young hogs (Ellis *et al.*[91]) to 14–15 per cent. in the case of sows several years old.[92b,c] In the latter cases it is evident that the high linoleic acid is approximately constant as compared with the differing oleic and stearic acid contents of fats from different sites in the same animal.

Of the minor component acids, it may be pointed out that small traces of lauric and of tetradecenoic acid are probably usually present. Myristic acid only amounts to about 1 per cent. of the total acids, whilst hexadec-9-enoic acid appears to be fairly constant at about 2–3 per cent. (wt.).

Of highly unsaturated acids of the C_{20} and C_{22} series Brown and Deck,[95] depending on the yield of ether-insoluble polybromo-additive products from the total depot fatty acids of the pig, recorded only 0·4 per cent, but fractionation analyses reveal the presence of 1–3 per cent. How far this depends on, for example, the ingestion of fish meal fatty acids is uncertain; the origin of these highly unsaturated minor components of pig depot fat therefore awaits the results of further investigation. De la Mare and Shorland[96a] have offered evidence of the presence of monoethenoid and diethenoid C_{20} acids in pig depot fats and consider that these exceed in quantity the polyethenoid acids which give rise to polybromo-adducts insoluble in ether; these authors consider that unsaturated acids of the C_{22} series may not be present in pig fats.

The pigs, from which the fats mentioned in Table 39 were derived, were reared on known diets and a complete record of the total weights of fat in each animal was available. Consequently it was possible to prepare a balance sheet of the weight of each fatty acid ingested as fat by the experimental animals, and, within approximate limits, of the weight of each fatty acid deposited as fat in the animal when it had reached 200 lb. live weight. The results were uniform for each of the four animals in Table 39 (ii), and may be illustrated by that fed on the "Low-High" rations:

FATTY ACIDS	IN DIET (kg.)	DEPOSITED (kg.)	DIFFERENCE (kg.)
Saturated:			
Below C_{14}	0·11	Trace	− 0·11
Myristic	0·24	0·29	+ 0·05
Palmitic	1·28	8·27	+ 6·99
Stearic	0·25	3·99	+ 3·74
Unsaturated:			
C_{16} (and C_{14})	0·22	0·89	+ 0·67
Oleic	3·24	13·87	+ 10·63
Linoleic	3·30	1·48	− 1·82
C_{20-22}	0·87	0·74	− 0·13
	9·51	29·53	+ 20·02

The greater part of the palmitic, stearic, oleic, and hexa- (with tetra-) decenoic acids have clearly been produced by the animal from carbohydrate (or protein) food. The small amount of myristic acid is of the same order as that in the ingested fats, and the evidence as to its origin is thus inconclusive. Saturated acids of lower molecular weight than myristic acid are neither synthesised nor laid down from dietary fat by the pig. The quantity of linoleic acid in the pig body fats is less than half of that available in the food, suggesting that, like the rat, the pig is not able to synthesise linoleic acid. This is further supported by the fact that the octadecadienoic acid of pig fats, unlike those of ox or sheep depot fats, is to a large degree seed fat linoleic acid. The quantity of unsaturated C_{20-22} acids in the pig depots likewise falls short of that present in the diet (as fish-meal constituents); but the disparity is less pronounced than in the case of linoleic acid, and it is possible that some of these acids are synthesised by the animal, perhaps from linoleic acid (*cf.* Nunn and Smedley-MacLean[47]).

Of the three main fatty acid products of synthesis – palmitic, stearic, and oleic – the ratio of increase of palmitic to the two C_{18} acids, in the four outer back fats (Table 39 (ii)), was $1:1\cdot86$, $1:2\cdot06$, $1:2\cdot18$, and $1:2\cdot50$ (wt.). The mean ratio for the four animals was $1:2\cdot08$ (wt.) or $1:1\cdot89$ (mol.), i.e. close to that demanded by predominant synthesis of palmitodi-C_{18}-glycerides from carbohydrate in the animal (*cf.* sheep depot fats, p. 111).

Other pigs which had been reared to 200 lb. live weight on the controlled diet* were subsequently starved for different periods, during which they would, of course, be dependent to a large extent on their depot fat as source of energy. The alteration in the composition of their depot fats during inanition is shown by the data in Table 40 (Hilditch and Pedelty[93b]).

TABLE 40. *Component Acids (per cent. wt.) of Depot Fats of Pigs during Starvation*

FAT	DAYS FAST-ED	FAT IOD. VAL.	SATURATED				UNSATURATED				
			C_{12}	C_{14}	C_{16}	C_{18}	C_{14}	C_{16}	Oleic	"Lino-leic"	C_{20-22}
Perinephric	0	56·4	—	0·9	29·3	17·4	0·3	1·8	40·3	8·1	1·9
,,	51	56·6	0·1	0·8	31·3	17·6	0·1	1·0	38·8	8·3	2·0
,,	135	54·8	—	0·9	30·3	21·5	0·2	2·2	34·1	7·3	3·5
Inner back	0	58·9	0·1	0·8	27·5	15·1	0·2	1·7	44·2	7·3	3·1
,, ,,	51	59·9	—	0·6	29·4	15·0	0·2	2·4	40·0	9·6	2·8
,, ,,	135	54·7	0·1	0·9	30·7	18·8	0·2	1·7	37·2	7·1	3·3
Outer back	0	63·9	0·1	0·9	26·5	12·8	0·2	1·9	46·8	7·9	2·9
,, ,,	51	65·0	—	0·9	26·0	13·0	0·2	1·7	45·6	9·1	3·5
,, ,,	135	60·0	—	0·9	30·1	15·1	0·2	2·6	39·5	8·2	3·4

Apart from minor differences, there is no great evidence of selectivity in mobilisation of any one fatty acid component of depot fats during starvation of the pig. The most prominent subsidiary effects are preferential removal of oleic acid during the later stages of inanition, and definite reluctance in the earlier stages to mobilise those acids (linoleic and unsaturated C_{20-22} acids) which are derived from ingested dietary fats. These findings, however, differ from observations on sheep during inanition, where palmito-glycerides seemed to be mobilised slightly more readily than the rest (p. 112).

It seems well to emphasise that the problem of fat mobilisation cannot be satisfactorily discussed in terms of the fatty acids – the various mixed

* *Cf.* footnote, p. 116.

glycerides in which these occur clearly have a profound bearing on the process. Thus, the most abundant glycerides in pig depot fats are palmitodioleins and oleopalmitostearins. If oleic acid is selectively desired, it must be found in molecules of these types. Similarly, a minor component acid, such as linoleic or unsaturated C_{20-22} acids, will in general contribute only one group to a triglyceride molecule, the others being oleic, or oleic and palmitic. Hence a molecule of linoleodiolein, for example, might be attacked, as it were, for the sake of its oleic groups, although the linoleic group is somewhat less readily amenable to utilisation. The problem of fat mobilisation is, in fact, fundamentally one from which considerations of glyceride structure cannot be excluded.

Depot fats of pigs fed on diets which included various fats. The changes brought about in the reserve fats of animals as a result of the presence of specific fats in the diet have received special notice in the case of the pig, chiefly as the result of the studies of Ellis and his colleagues.

The figures (Table 38 (i)) given by Ellis and Zeller[91a] for the component acids present in the composite body fats of hogs of varying age and weight, fed on a diet low in fat, together with those of Ellis and Isbell[91b] (Table 38 (ii) and Table 41, below), serve as a basis of comparison with their further analyses of fats from pigs whose diet included various kinds of added fats. Ellis and Isbell[91b] studied the influence of ingested fats on the composition of the pig body fats in a somewhat drastic manner by feeding different animals from the same litter on (*a*) brewer's rice, tankage, and grass; (*b*) maize, skim milk, and grass; (*c*) soya beans alone; and (*d*) groundnuts alone. The balanced diets (*a*) and (*b*) contained not more than 5 per cent. of vegetable fat, whereas (*c*) and (*d*) must have contained from 20 to 40 per cent. of the vegetable fats specific to soya beans and groundnuts respectively. The fatty acids in the various body fats were found to be composed as shown in Table 41:

TABLE 41. *Component Acids (per cent. wt.) of Depot Fats
of Pigs fed on Soya Beans or Groundnuts*

| | | | COMPONENT FATTY ACIDS (Per cent.) | | | | | | |
| | FAT | | SATURATED | | | | UNSATURATED | | |
FEED	FROM	IOD. VAL.	C_{14}	C_{16}	C_{18}	C_{20}	Oleic	Lino-leic	Lino-lenic
(*a*) Brewers' rice, etc.	Back	52·6	2	26	12	—	59	1	—
(*b*) Corn, etc.	Meat	58·8	1	25	13	—	54	7	—
(*c*) Soya beans alone	Back	90·7	1	17	10	—	40	32	Trace
(*c*) ,,　,,　,,	Back	100·6	Trace	14	8	—	39	38	1
(*d*) Groundnuts alone	Meat	84·1	,,	16	7	Trace	57	20	—
(*d*) ,,　　,,	Meat	91·8	,,	10	5	,,	65	20	—

This remarkable series shows that, whilst a balanced diet containing not more than 5 per cent. of vegetable fat leads to body fats of exactly the same type as those given in Tables 38 and 39, a ration of vegetable seeds alone leads to the following effects: (*a*) considerable diminution in the proportion of palmitic acid and the complete breakdown of the normal, approximately constant amount of the C_{18} acids as a whole (*cf*. p. 118), (*b*) increase in the linoleic acid to proportions approaching those in the ingested vegetable fats, and (c) failure to produce stearic acid even to the normal proportion observed in pigs fed on an ordinary balanced diet. Moreover, acids (respectively linolenic and arachidic in soya bean and groundnut oils) present in the vegetable fats in minor amounts appeared in the animal body fats as a result of this intensive vegetable seed diet.

The precise concentration of added fat in the diet beyond which the normal composition of the body fat is definitely altered is indicated by a further series of experiments by Ellis, Rothwell and Pool,[98] in which pigs were fed on a basal diet containing less than 1 per cent. fat, supplemented by varying amounts of cottonseed oil, with the results shown in Table 42.

TABLE 42. *Composite Back Fats of Hogs Fed on Varying Rations of Cottonseed Oil*

FEED	FAT IOD. VAL.	COMPONENT FATTY ACIDS (Per cent. wt.)				
		MYRIS-TIC	PAL-MITIC	STEARIC	OLEIC	LIN-OLEIC
Basal diet alone	60·6	2	25	14	50	9
,, ,, +4 per cent. C.S.O.	60·5	1	25	21	40	13
,, ,, +8 per cent. C.S.O.	64·4	1	22	23	36	18
,, ,, +12 per cent. C.S.O.	77·4	1	14	26	32	27

At some point between 4 and 8 per cent. of added fat in the diet, the total C_{18} acid content ceases to be approximately constant and commences to rise considerably, while the proportion of palmitic acid, of course, falls correspondingly. This is an especially good illustration of the fact that excessive fat in the diet cannot be dealt with by an animal in the same way as the fat which it itself normally produces; the palmitic acid content of the body fat of the hogs fed on a diet containing 12 per cent. of cottonseed oil was less than that of the cottonseed oil itself (component acids of cottonseed oil: myristic 0·5, palmitic 22, stearic 2, oleic 30·5, linoleic 45 per cent.). It is also observable that, with increasing proportions of cottonseed oil in the diet, the stearic acid content of the body fats was likewise augmented; whereas, in the cases of the pigs fed on soya beans or groundnuts alone, the stearic acid in the body fat declined below the normal figure.

J. B. Brown[95] found that lard from pigs fed on a diet which included 14 per cent. of menhaden oil contained 2·7 per cent. of C_{20} and C_{22} acids, which were slightly less unsaturated than the corresponding acids of the menhaden oil; Brown and Deck[95] had previously pointed out that pig body fats normally contain very small amounts (up to 0·4 per cent.) of the acids in question.

An extreme case of absorption of dietary fat was noted by Garton et al.[99a] in a pig which had been fed from weaning on a diet of which half was crude whale oil: in the later stages of fattening it received 4 lb. of whale oil daily. Large proportions of practically unchanged whale oil glycerides were removable from the pig depot fats by crystallising them from acetone at $-40°$, and the fats appeared to consist substantially of from 40 to over 60 per cent. of whale oil glycerides with from about 35 to 60 per cent. of pig synthetic fat, i.e., pig body fat of the nature produced in animals on a low-fat diet (as in Table 39). The mean unsaturation of the polyethenoid acids in the portion of the pig fat soluble in acetone was practically the same as that in whale oil, and there was no indication of any acyl interchange having taken place between the whale oil glycerides and the fat synthesised from carbohydrate by the pig. Table 43A shows (*a*) the component acids of the outer and inner back fats and the perinephric fat of the animal, and (*b*) gives a comparison of the component acids in the acetone-insoluble and acetone-soluble parts of the perinephric fat with those of, respectively, a typical perinephric fat from an animal on a low-fat diet, and a typical Antarctic whale oil.

TABLE 43A. *Component Acids (per cent. wt.) of Body Fats of a Pig Fed on Whale Oil*

(a) Component acids of outer and inner back fats and perinephric fat

		OUTER BACK	INNER BACK	PERINEPHRIC
Myristic		3·5	1·6	3·3
Palmitic		19·5	22·7	24·2
Stearic		8·2	10·6	13·5
Unsaturated	C_{14}	0·9 ($-2\cdot0$H)	1·4 ($-2\cdot0$H)	1·0 ($-2\cdot0$H)
,,	C_{16}	9·7 ($-2\cdot1$H)	7·4 ($-2\cdot1$H)	6·2 ($-2\cdot1$H)
,,	C_{18}	46·7 ($-2\cdot4$H)	47·3 ($-2\cdot4$H)	42·8 ($-2\cdot5$H)
,,	C_{20}	9·2 ($-5\cdot1$H)	7·6 ($-6\cdot2$H)	7·0 ($-7\cdot2$H)
,,	C_{22}	2·3 ($-7\cdot9$H)	1·4 ($-8\cdot5$H)	2·0 ($-10\cdot3$H)

(b) Comparison of solvent-segregated pig fat with normal pig fat and whale oil

		PERINEPHRIC (NORMAL, LOW-FAT DIET)	ACETONE-SEGREGATED PERINEPHRIC		ANTARCTIC WHALE OIL
			INSOLUBLE	SOLUBLE	
Myristic		0·9	2·1	1·5	9·2
Palmitic		29·3	25·7	14·3	15·6
Stearic		17·4	16·5	1·4	2·5
Unsaturated	C_{14}	0·3 ($-2\cdot0$H)	0·3 ($-2\cdot0$H)	0·8 ($-2\cdot0$H)	2·5 ($-2\cdot0$H)
,,	C_{16}	1·8 ($-2\cdot0$H)	5·4 ($-2\cdot1$H)	11·1 ($-2\cdot1$H)	13·9 ($-2\cdot1$H)
,,	C_{18}	48·4 ($-2\cdot3$H)	43·5 ($-2\cdot3$H)	44·3 ($-2\cdot9$H)	37·2 ($-2\cdot4$H)
,,	C_{20}	}1·9 ($-5\cdot0$H){	6·5 ($-6\cdot4$H)	21·2 ($-6\cdot8$H)	12·0 ($-7\cdot1$H)
,,	C_{22}		—	5·4 ($-10\cdot3$H)	7·1 ($-9\cdot4$H)

The above study was extended by Garton and Duncan[99b] by feeding a pig with a diet which included a mixture of equal parts of lard and of cod liver oil; the proportion of added dietary fat was increased until finally it formed 50 per cent. of the feed. This experiment was designed to test whether, during absorption of ingested fat, the latter is, as formerly supposed, completely hydrolysed and re-synthesised into glycerides. If this takes place, the resulting fat deposited would consist of glycerides in which the lard fatty acids and fish oil fatty acids would be assembled in a new mixture of mixed glycerides, in most of which acyl groups originally present in either dietary fat would be present in new combinations of mixed triglycerides. Actually, the resulting inner back fat of the pig was as readily separable by acetone at $-40°$ C. as those of the pigs fed heavily on whale oil, and furnished 67·5 per cent. of acetone-insoluble glycerides (iodine value 60·3) and 32·5 per cent. of acetone-soluble glycerides (iodine value 126·5). As Table 43B shows, the component acids of these acetone-segregated portions of the inner back fat (like those from the corresponding whale oil feeding experiment) were respectively very similar to those of the lard (or of fat synthesised by the pig itself) and of the cod liver oil which had been given in the diet. This experiment strongly supports the hypothesis of Frazer (cf. Chapter VIII, p. 564) that particulate absorption of dietary glycerides takes place without their intermediate hydrolysis and re-synthesis.

TABLE 43B. *Component Acids (per cent. wt.) of Inner Back Fat of a Pig fed on Lard and Cod Liver Oil*

	INNER BACK FAT[93b] (LOW-FAT DIET)	LARD	HOG INNER BACK FAT ACETONE-SEGREGATED		COD LIVER OIL
			INSOLUBLE	SOLUBLE	
Myristic	0·9	0·5	0·5	0·4	1·1
Palmitic	27·5	27·1	32·2	14·9	13·8
Stearic	15·1	15·6	9·0	2·4	2·7
Arachidic	—	0·7	0·2	—	—
Unsaturated:					
C_{14}	0·2 (−2·0H)	0·4 (−2·0H)	0·5 (−2·0H)	1·3 (−2·0H)	0·4 (−2·0H)
C_{16}	1·7 (−2·0H)	2·8 (−2·1H)	4·0 (−2·3H)	17·9 (−2·4H)	8·0 (−2·3H)
C_{18}	51·5 (−2·3H)	51·9 (−2·3H)	48·4 (−2·4H)	43·9 (−3·0H)	27·3 (−3·3H)
C_{20}	3·1 (−5·0H)	1·0 (−2·3H)	5·2 (−4·0H)	14·7 (−6·3H)	29·4 (−6·3H)
C_{22}			—	4·5 (−10·3H)	17·3 (−7·9H)

The fats of these animals, and those of pigs fed by Ellis and Isbell[91b] on soya beans or on groundnuts, are the most striking examples yet obtained of the capacity of the pig to store fat present in its diet.

The effect of skim milk and buttermilk diets, supplemented in some cases with maize meal or copra, upon the component acids of pig back fats, and the relation between growth rate of the animals and the composition of their body fats, has been discussed at some length by Shorland and de la Mare.[96b] The composition of the fats was not of course altered so drastically as in some of the foregoing examples in which fats formed unusually large proportions of the feed. Linoleic acid was more readily assimilated and deposited by slow-growing, and lauric and myristic acids by fast-growing, pigs. These authors conclude, however, that the composition of the fat in different parts of animals in general is probably mainly determined by the depot and species, and is not readily altered by mild dietary changes.

Further references to the influence of the basal diet on the composition of pig body fats will be found in the studies of Dahl.[93d]

Component acids of a wild boar fat. The fat from the upper thigh of an Indian male wild boar (*Sus cristatus indicus*) was found by Pathak et al.[97] to contain myristic 1·6, palmitic 29·5, stearic 16·8, tetradecenoic 0·7, hexadecenoic 13·2, oleic 36·3 and octadecadienoic 1·9 (acids, per cent. wt.). This closely resembles a typical pig fat, except for a higher hexadecenoic acid content (at the expense of oleic acid); in this respect it is reminiscent of the fats of the sloth bear (p. 101) and the Indian panther (p. 127).

Influence of dietary fat on depot fat of other animals. As regards tallows, it is generally accepted that the higher melting point and more saturated nature of beef tallows from South America and Australia as compared with the softer North American tallows is to be connected with the diet; in the first-named areas the cattle are practically entirely grass-fed, while in North America the practice is to fatten them to a large extent on oil-cakes (cottonseed, maize, linseed) rich in unsaturated glycerides. On the other hand, Thomas, Culbertson and Beard[100] found that liberal allowances of whole soya beans, menhaden oil, corn oil, or coconut oil fed to steer calves for 260 days had no perceptible effect on the unsaturation of their body fats. It may therefore be that different species of animals differ in the extent to which they utilize ingested fats in their reserve fats. (That oxen may be exceptional in this respect is further suggested by the observation that linoleic, linolenic, or erucic glycerides, fed to cows in the forms of linseed oil or rape oil (*cf.* pp. 155, 156), do not pass to any marked extent into the milk fat glycerides.)

Similar experiments on dogs by Lebedev and by Munk were carried out many years ago. In one instance,[101a] two dogs were first starved and then fed, one on linseed oil and the other on mutton tallow; the reserve fat of the first did not solidify at 0°, whereas that of the second melted at about 50°. Similarly, a dog fed with rape oil laid down adipose tissue fat in which erucic acid was detected.[101b]

From the above it will be fairly clear that animals can, and indeed do normally, provide adequate supplies of reserve fats mainly by synthesis from carbohydrates or other components of their diet; but that, in addition, they can utilise for this purpose the fatty acids present in the form of vegetable fats in their food. In view of the specifically constant nature of the various reserve fats deposited by animals which have lived on a diet containing only relatively small proportions of fat, and of the manner in which the normal composition of their reserve fats is changed by ingestion of unusually large proportions of fat in the food, it seems reasonable to conclude that the most natural, and therefore probably the most healthy, condition is for animals to synthesize, rather than to assimilate directly, the greater part of their own reserve fats.

Depot Fats of the Carnivora and Omnivora

As mentioned earlier, data in this field are still very scanty. Amongst the few detailed analyses so far made are those of body fats of five feline species and of five from the Mustelidæ and two from the Primates. The component acids of these fats are shown in Table 44.

The *feline* fats possess component acids which have much in common with those of the (mainly synthesized) depot fats of the herbivorous ox or sheep (Table 36). This may well be because they are derived from "stearic-rich" fats present in the bodies of ruminants (ox, deer, goats, etc.) which provided the main food of the wild animals. (The very small proportions of saturated acids of lower molecular weight than myristic acid in the lion and cat fats may not be significant, since they may well have been derived at second-hand, so to speak, from the flesh of animals which had fed on coconut cake at the Colombo Zoo.) The Mexican *puma* (*F. concolor*) is carnivorous, but feeds chiefly on herbivorous mammals, especially young deer and sheep. Its fat and those of the wild *panther* and *tiger* are marked by higher proportions of hexadecenoic acid and somewhat lower palmitic acid contents than usual, and by appreciable proportions of (seed fat) linoleic acid.

126

TABLE 44. Component Acids (per cent. wt.) of Body Fats of some Carnivorous or Omnivorous Animals

FELIDÆ

Acid	LION[31a] (Panthera Leo) BODY	PANTHER[103b] (P. pardus fusca) BODY	PUMA (Felix concolor) BODY[102]	PUMA ABDOMINAL[104b]	TIGER (Felix tigris) BODY[103a]	TIGER GROIN[104b]	CAT (Felix catus) BODY[31a]
Myristic	4·9 (a)	2·3	1·3	4·1	1·0	3·0	3·6 (c)
Palmitic	28·9	20·1	22·4	24·2	22·4	26·8	29·2
Stearic	17·8	13·7	26·9	10·5	24·6	10·7	16·6
Arachidic	0·1	1·7	3·7	0·8	1·2	—	—
Tetradecenoic	0·6	1·8	—	0·9	0·6	0·6	1·2
Hexadecenoic	1·9	10·8	12·6	4·6	7·1	6·0 (b)	4·3
Oleic	40·3	39·2	26·2	39·5	39·0	38·1	40·8
Octadecadienoic	—	2·1	2·3	8·6	4·1	6·2	1·9
Octadecatrienoic	—	—	—	3·6	—	6·8	—
Unsaturated C$_{20-22}$	3·0	8·3	4·6	3·2	—	1·8	Trace

MUSTELIDÆ / PRIMATES

Acid	BADGER[104a] (Meles meles) BODY	MINK[103c] (Putorius vison) SUBCUTANEOUS	FERRET[103d] (Mustela furo) SUBCUTANEOUS*	STOAT[103d] (M. erminea) SUBCUTANEOUS*	WEASEL[103d] (M. nivalis) BODY*	BABOON[31a] (Papio hamadryes) ABDOMINAL	CHIMPANZEE[104b] (Simia setyrus) BODY
Myristic	5·7	4·8	1·6	1·6	0·9	3·2	2·4 (e)
Palmitic	21·2	12·2	21·4	25·9	19·0	18·9	29·8
Stearic	8·2	9·1	15·3	8·3	6·5	5·8	6·8 (f)
Tetradecenoic	1·1	—	—	—	—	0·8	0·8 (f)
Hexadecenoic	6·2	22·2	2·5	5·2	3·1	3·8	5·1 (b)
Oleic	30·9	37·1	52·4	46·7	58·0	53·8	44·5
Octadecadienoic	8·4	12·3	3·5	9·3	10·3	13·2	8·0
Octadecatetraenoic	3·9	2·3	1·3	0·5	0·4	—	—
Unsaturated C$_{20-22}$	14·6 (d)	—	0·6	0·5	1·3	0·5	1·7

(a) Also 1·4 per cent. of decanoic and 1·1 per cent. of lauric acids.
(b) Traces of di- and tri-ene C$_{16}$ acids.
(c) Also 2·4 per cent. of lauric acid.
(d) Mean unsaturation –5·1H.
(e) Also 0·4 per cent. of lauric acid.
(f) Also 0·2 per cent. of arachidic and 0·3 per cent. of dodecenoic acids.
* Analyses (per cent. mol. by gas–liquid chromatography) also include traces of odd-numbered and branch-chain acids.

The two fats (*badger* and *mink*) from the Mustelidæ family are interesting in their unusually low contents of palmitic acid and in their high contents of hexadecenoic and of di- and tri-ene C_{18} acids. The *mink* fat has over 20 per cent. of hexadecenoic acid, the highest proportion so far reported in a mammalian depot fat. In both *mink* and *badger* fats the polyene C_{18} acids consist largely of the ordinary (vegetable) forms of linoleic (or linolenic) acid. The most remarkable feature of the *badger* fat is the presence of 14–15 per cent. of unsaturated C_{20} acids with an average unsaturation of $-5H$; it is conceivable, though perhaps not very likely, that frogs (on which badgers sometimes feed) are the source of the unsaturated C_{16} and C_{20} acids in the fat. How far these various components may be specific to the Mustelidæ family (which also includes the polecat, pine marten, etc.) or how far they are due to assimilated dietary fats, can at present only be a matter for speculation.

Of the two members of the Primates, the *baboon* fat has a low content of palmitic and a high content of diene C_{18} acids (chiefly ordinary linoleic), but the *chimpanzee* fat has the "normal" animal depot fat content of 30 per cent. of palmitic acid and a somewhat high proportion of diene C_{18} acids (again mainly linoleic). Both fats have comparatively little stearic acid, and also show considerable similarity to human body fats (Table 45A, below). The differences between the two fats may well arise from different fats present in the diets given to the animals, which were in captivity, respectively, in zoological gardens in Ceylon and in Scotland.

Human depot fats. There was little information in regard to the component acids of depot fats of human beings until in 1943 Cramer and Brown[105a] recorded data, based on ester fractionation coupled with low-temperature crystallisation, for five body fats from middle-aged and elderly persons who had died from pathological conditions not likely to be of significance in the history of the depot fats. Later, Calandra and Cattaneo[105b] gave figures for a female human abdominal subcutaneous fat, and Holmberg and Sellman[105c] for perinephric fat from a female who had died from cancer. These data are collected in Table 45A.

In the body fats, the saturated acids are the usual mixture, with relatively low stearic acid (as in the apes); the palmitic acid content is a few per cent. lower than the 28–30 per cent. met with in many animal fats (a similarly

TABLE 45A. *Component Acids (per cent. wt.) of Human Body Fats*

	FEMALE[105a] 53 YRS.	MALE[105a] 74 YRS.	MALE[105a] 61 YRS.	FEMALE[105b]	FEMALE[105c] (CANCER)
Lauric	0·1	0·6	—	—	1·7*
Myristic	2·7	5·9	2·6	1·5	5·9
Palmitic	24·0	25·0	24·7	20·8	22·8
Stearic	8·4	5·8	7·7	2·2	5·5
Tetradecenoic	0·2	0·6	0·4	0·4	2·4
Hexadecenoic	5·0	6·7	7·3	3·2	6·5
Oleic	46·9	45·4	45·8	38·7	43·2
Octadecadienoic	10·2	8·2	10·0	24·8	4·0
Unsaturated C_{20-22}	2·5	1·8	1·5	8·3 (−3·OH)	5·4

* Also decanoic 0·8, arachidic 1·0, dodecenoic 0·3, and linolenic 0·5 per cent. (wt.).

somewhat reduced palmitic acid content appears to characterise human milk fat as compared with cow milk fat, *cf.* p. 163). In the unsaturated acids, oleic acid forms nearly half of the total fatty acids, and ordinary linoleic acid is present in abundance in the 8–11 per cent. of octadecadienoic acids. Isomeric forms of both octadecenoic and octadecadienoic acid were, however, shown also to be present in the human body fat. Hexadec-9-enoic acid occurs in somewhat more than the usual proportion for a land animal body fat. In the C_{20-22} unsaturated acids (also slightly above the normal proportion) arachidonic acid was present in some quantity.

Since about 1955 much discussion has centred around the disputed connection of lipid deposits in linings of the aorta or coronary arteries with the onset of coronary arterial disease. At about the same period the technique of gas–liquid chromatography (G.L.C., *cf.* Chapter XI, pp. 697) commenced to be used in the analysis of fatty acid mixtures; this great advance permits much more rapid evaluation of mixed fatty acids and, moreover, can be applied to milligram amounts of material instead of the 50–100 grams desirable for ester-fractionation studies. It has therefore been widely used in the examination of lipid deposits in arterial and other tissues (*cf.* p. 138) and has also been applied in a few instances to human body fats. The first results in this field were published in 1956 by James and Wheatley,[106a] but for the present purpose it may suffice to reproduce a few selected figures from a later paper by Kingsbury *et al.*[106b] The gas–liquid chromatography procedure reveals, when they are present, trace component acids which are not always detectable by ester-fractionation; these are grouped together at the foot of Table 45B, which summarises typical results for abdominal body fats from normal (healthy) and atheromatous human subjects.

TABLE 45B. *Component Acids (per cent. wt.) of Healthy and Atheromatous Human Abdominal Fats*[106b]

	NORMAL			ATHEROMATOUS		
Lauric	1·0	1·5	1·0	1·0	1·5	1·5
Myristic	4·5	5·0	4·0	6·0	6·5	4·0
Palmitic	25·5	25·5	21·0	24·5	25·0	24·0
Stearic	5·0	5·5	7·5	6·5	6·5	6·0
Arachidic (and C_{19})	2·5	0·5	1·0	1·0	2·5	1·5
Tetradecenoic	0·5	0·5	0·5	0·5	0·5	0·5
Hexadecenoic	8·0	6·0	5·5	6·5	6·0	6·5
Oleic	47·5	48·5	51·0	46·5	45·5	46·0
Octadecadi- and tri-enoic	3·0	4·5	6·0	3·0	3·0	5·0
Eicosadi-, tri-, tetra-enoic	Trace	—	—	—	Trace	1·5
Saturated odd-numbered acids (total):						
C_{15}, C_{17}	1·0	1·0	1·0	1·5	1·0	1·0
Saturated branch-chain acids (total):						
C_{15}, C_{16}, C_{17}, C_{18}, C_{19}, C_{20}	2·0	2·0	1·5	2·5	1·5	2·0

The data in Table 45B are broadly similar to the earlier figures in Table 45A. Such differences as there are lie in slightly higher myristic acid contents, and definitely lower polyene C_{18} acids; these may easily be due to different dietary conditions. No significant differences (other than a possible increase in the small amounts of triene acids present) were detected between the depot fat composition of normal and atheromatous subjects, whilst a separate group of analyses showed that there was very little difference in composition between fats taken from the abdomen, buttocks or perirenal sites of the same individual.

Kummerow *et al.* [106c] have reported that human adipose tissue fats contain from 2·4 to 12·2 per cent. of *trans*-forms of unsaturated (oleic) acid.

The similarity of human body fat to the depot fats of many other land animals, especially in its contents of oleic and of palmitic acid, appears to be established by the above analyses.

Human bone fats. Bernhard and Korrodi[107a] in 1947 determined the chief component acids in the marrow fat of human bones, and later (1954) more detailed figures were obtained by Holmberg[107b] for the fatty acids in femoral bones from two male and one female human subject. As with other animals (*cf.* pp. 103, 114), the human bone fats bear considerable resemblance to the depot fats, but in some instances differ in one detail or another from these. Bernhard and Korrodi[107a] state that the 70 per cent of unsaturated acids shown in their analysis consisted mainly of oleic acid, with only small amounts of more highly unsaturated acids (amongst which ordinary linoleic acid was identified). The component acid data are summarised in Table 45C.

TABLE 45C. *Component Acids (per cent. wt.) of Human Bone Fats*

	BONE MARROW[107a]	FEMORAL[107b]			
		MALE	MALE	FEMALE (a)	FEMALE (b)
Decanoic	—	0·4	—	2·2	0·5
Lauric	0·1	0·9	0·4	—	0·7
Myristic	1·8	5·3	3·8	4·8	7·8
Palmitic	22·4	26·2	16·0	20·2	19·9
Stearic	5·7	6·4	3·3	7·8	4·0
Arachidic	—	0·5	0·2	—	0·7
Dodecenoic	⎱	0·1	0·3	—	—
Tetradecenoic		0·8	2·2	1·1	1·0
Hexadecenoic		4·9	15·5	8·8	8·3
Oleic	70·0	43·0	52·7	49·1	41·5
Linoleic		5·2	1·0	4·5	3·5
Linolenic		0·6	1·6	0·7	0·4
Unsaturated C_{20-22}	⎰	5·7	3·2	1·0	11·8

(a) gelatinous marrow; *(b)* porous bone.

ANIMAL DEPOT FATS – SUMMARY

The characteristic composition of the fatty acids in the depot fats of different species of animal, and the usual range of variations in the component acids of depot fats of one and the same species of animal, have been dealt with at some length in the preceding pages. It seems desirable, in concluding this section, to focus attention on the varying types of depot fat which have been considered by a table which includes examples, from the most detailed analyses available, of all the classes which have come under review. Table 46 (p. 131) therefore includes a selection of the data referred to in the previous pages; obviously it cannot take account of all the variations encountered within a single species, although two more or less extreme cases are quoted for both

TABLE 46. *Typical Component Acids (per cent. wt.) of Depot Fats of Different Classes of Animal*

CLASS	ANIMAL	DEPOT FAT	IOD. VAL.	SATURATED			UNSATURATED			
				C_{14}	C_{16}	C_{18}	C_{16}	Oleic	C_{18} Diene	C_{20-22}
Amphibian	Frog[16a]	Body	120	4	11	3	15	52	↑	15
Reptile	Tortoise[16b]	,,	87	1	14	4	9	65	↑	7
,,	Lizard[16b]	,,	76	4	18	7	10	56	↑	5
,,	Python[22a]	Intestinal	73.0	3	20	11	4	47	11	4
Bird	Crocodile[22b]	Body	80.5	3	27	5	7	34	17	4
Bird	Domestic hen[28]	Abdominal	79.7	1	25	4	7	43	18	1
,,	Emu[31a]	Subcutaneous	65.8	1	18	10	2	62	5	1
Rodent	Rat[44]	Body	57.3	7	24	5	6	49	5	1
,,	,,[45]	,,	62.5	3	27	5	16	47	2	Trace
Herbivora	Rabbit[51]	Perinephric	72.3	6	31	5	6	30	16	1
,,	Horse[63]	Mesenteric	95.6	5	26	5	7	34	5*	2
,,	Pig[93a]	Back, outer	60.0	1	28	12	3	48	6	2
,,	,,[93a]	Back, inner	54.3	1	30	16	3	41	7	2
,,	Ox[68]	Perinephric	43.2	3	29	21	3	41	2	Trace
,,	Deer[58a]	Body	35.5	4	25	35	3	25	5	—
,,	Sheep[73]	Perinephric	43.4	3	25	28	1	37	5	1
,,	,,[73]	External	49.1	3	28	16	1	47	4	1
,,	Camel[58a]	Mesenteric	35.1	6	29	27	3	26	2	3
,,	Kangaroo[31a]	Body	50.1	5	26	14	3	46	3	3
,,	Hippopotamus[58b]	,,	46.2	2	27	22	2	39	4	1
,,	Giant Panda[31a]	Abdominal	64.8	5	26	7	4	45	12	—
,,	Elephant[59c]	Body	41.7	6	44	7	5	27	6	3
Omnivora	Ceylon (Sloth) Bear[31a]	,,	60.3	3	29	3	11	51	1	2
,,	Badger[104a]	Abdominal	91.6	6	21	8	6	31	8†	15
,,	Sacred Baboon[31a]	,,	77.0	3	19	6	4	54	13	1
,,	Human[105a]	Male, 74 years	67.4	6	25	6	7	45	8	2
,,	,,	Female, 53 years	68.9	3	24	8	5	47	10	3
Carnivora	Cat[31a]	Body	43.6	4	29	17	4	41	2	—
,,	Lion[31a]	,,	41.0	5	29	18	2	40	—	3
,,	Tiger[103a]	,,	49.2	1	22	25	7	39	4	—

* Also 16 per cent. linolenic acid.   † Also 4 per cent. linolenic acid.

131

sheep and pig depot fats. The object of Table 46 is to illustrate the variations in depot fatty acid compositions as between one class of animal and another, rather than to give a complete picture of the range of fatty acid compositions within the depot fats of any given species. Since possible species variations in the body fats are under consideration, the illustrations are confined to animals known to have received diets low in fat, or, at least, their natural food (in which fat forms as a rule but a small proportion, say up to 5 per cent., of the whole diet).

Empirical relations between the component acids of depot fats and their iodine values have been considered by Dahl[108a] and by Gunstone and Russell.[108b]

Dahl[108a] found good correlation between iodine values and contents of oleic and of saturated acids in the harder animal fats such as beef fat or lard, but less in the cases of softer animal fats. Gunstone and Russell[108b] reviewed the data for 39 animal fats of iodine value 31–96 and containing little or no unsaturated C_{20-22} acids. They found that animal fats in the iodine value range 30–60 differed somewhat from those of higher iodine value (60–90); these two groups correspond to the categories of stearic-rich and stearic-poor fats and, moreover, divide the depot fats of ruminants, quasi-ruminants and ruminant-feeding animals from all others. These authors were able to derive equations empirically for each of the two groups whereby, from the iodine value, the approximate proportions of total saturated, stearic, hexadecenoic, oleic and polyene C_{18} acids may be calculated (except for 5 fats which showed poor correlation). They confirm that most land animals seem to lay down depot fat consisting of about one-third C_{16} acids (mainly palmitic) and two-thirds C_{18} acids (which may be saturated, mono-ene, or polyene, the relative amounts of each being directly related to the iodine value). In a fat of iodine value 60 the C_{18}-acids are largely oleic, with smaller amounts of stearic and polyene C_{18} acids. In fats of lower iodine value some oleic groups are replaced by stearic acid. In fats of higher iodine value the stearic acid content is rarely above 6 per cent. (and often only 3–4 per cent.), and some oleic acid groups are replaced by polyene C_{18} acids (mainly diene, but in the more unsaturated fats triene C_{18} acids may appear in significant amounts).

These relationships, although largely empirical, are of considerable interest.

Component Acids of the Lipids (Glycerides and Phosphatides) of Animal Organs

A certain amount of detailed information has appeared with reference to the component acids present in the lipids of various animal organs, especially the liver. In contrast to adipose tissue fats, which consist almost wholly of glycerides, and in which phosphatides are only present, if at all, in minute traces, the lipids of animal organs include both glycerides and phosphatides in important proportions. Fortunately, in a number of analyses, the glycerides and phosphatides have been separated from each other as completely as possible by taking advantage of the sparing solubility of the latter in acetone, and separate studies have thus been carried out on the respective component acids of the glyceridic and phosphatidic fractions. It should be observed that, owing to the sparing solubility of mono-oleodisaturated glycerides in cold acetone, the separation of glycerides and phosphatides by this solvent is probably not quite complete; on the other hand, the amount of such glycerides present in liver lipids will be relatively small, and the error thereby introduced will correspondingly also be comparatively small.

LIVER LIPIDS

(a) Liver Glycerides

The "glyceride" fraction of liver lipids includes any free fatty acids present in the liver, and also any fatty acids present in combination with cholesterol. The amount of the latter is small (1–3 per cent. of the glyceride fraction), but the free fatty acids present are variable and range, in Hilditch and Shorland's observations,[110a] from about 10–50 per cent. of the glyceride fractions of the liver lipids.

The component acid data available are collected in Table 47.

TABLE 47. Component Acids (per cent. wt.) of Animal Liver Glycerides

CLASS	ANIMAL	SATURATED				UNSATURATED				
		C_{14}	C_{16}	C_{18}	C_{20}	C_{14}	C_{16}	C_{18}	C_{20}	C_{22}
Amphibian	Frog[16a]	19–23 per cent. (mainly palmitic)				—	61	16–20		
Reptile	Greek tortoise[16b]	1	11	4	—	—	15	66 (−2·1H)	3 (−4·5H)	
Herbivora	Pig[110a]	0·1	22·5	9·5	—	—	8·9	47·0 (−2·4H)	10·6 (−6·8H)	1·4 (−6·8H)
,,	Ox[109a]	—	25	20	—	—	9	37 (−2·6H)	8 (−5·0H to −7·5H)	1
,,	Ox[110a]	1·4	30·4	6·6	—	1·1	9·9	40·3 (−3·0H)	8·5 (−6·9H)	1·8 (−6·9H)
,,	Sheep[110a]	0·2	21·9	12·9	—	—	4·9	44·7 (−2·8H)	11·6 (−7·3H)	3·8 (−7·8H)
,,	Horse[110b]	1·7	25·2	5·3	—	1·6	8·3	52·8 (−4·5H)	3·4 (−6·2H)	1·7 (−6·0H)
,,	Elephant[59c]	—	26·7	14·9	6·1	—	6·6	25·9 (−2·8H)	←—19·8—→ (−5·5H)	

Comparison of Tables 47 (liver glycerides) and 46 (depot glycerides) reveals some interesting features. In the first place, the content of palmitic acid in both groups of glycerides is approximately the same in each animal species (except the elephant); in the liver glycerides, as in the depot fats, the palmitic acid content rises from a figure reminiscent of marine animal fats (in the amphibia and reptiles) until it approaches 25–30 per cent. (ox, horse, and elephant); the corresponding figure for sheep and pig liver glycerides seems to be slightly lower (22 per cent.). Apart from this, the liver glycerides only resemble the corresponding depot fats quantitatively in the content of unsaturated C_{18} acids (the mean unsaturation of which is, however, definitely higher than in the corresponding depot fat acids).

Qualitatively, the liver glycerides differ from those of the adipose tissues in the presence of much greater amounts of unsaturated C_{20} and C_{22} acids, and of hexadecenoic acid. In the liver glycerides of pigs, oxen, and sheep, hexadecenoic acid forms, as a rule, about 9 per cent. of the total acids, whilst unsaturated acids of the C_{20} and C_{22} series (with a mean unsaturation equivalent of between 3 and 4 double bonds in the molecule) normally account for 10 per cent. or somewhat more of the total fatty acids. Stearic acid, on the other hand, although somewhat variable in proportion, is often much reduced in amount as compared with the corresponding depot fats.

The diethenoid C_{18} acids present in the liver, as in the depot, glycerides appear to be isomeric forms of ordinary or seed fat linoleic acid, since they do not yield more than small proportions of the tetrabromo- or tetrahydroxy-stearic acids characteristic of the latter. Bruce and Shorland[110b] note, however, that the unsaturated C_{18} acids of horse liver glycerides (52·8 per cent. in all) include linolenic 25·2, linoleic 10·1, and oleic 17·5 per cent. (wt.), whereas in horse liver phosphatides (v. infra) linoleic acid forms 61 per cent. of the unsaturated C_{18} acids. Linolenic acid which forms about 17 per cent. of the component acids of the depot fats of pasture-fed horses, is thus still more prominent in horse liver glycerides, but is only a minor component of the liver phosphatides.

In the elephant liver glycerides,[59c] in contrast to the extremely high proportion (45 per cent.) of palmitic acid in the body fat, this acid only makes the usual contribution of about 27 per cent. to the total fatty acids, indicating perhaps that the elephant body fats are abnormally constituted. The contents of stearic and of unsaturated C_{20-22} acids in the elephant liver glycerides are, however, greater, and that of the unsaturated C_{18} acids less, than in the other liver glycerides in Table 47.

Judged by the average composition of their component acids, therefore, the liver glycerides of all the higher land animals so far studied exhibit fundamental differences from the corresponding glycerides in their reserve fats, but usually resemble the latter in their total contents of unsaturated C_{18} acids and, especially, in the proportions of palmitic acid present. One is tempted to go further, and to suggest that, in the land animal group, the component acids of the liver glycerides often bear considerable quantitative resemblance to each other, irrespective of the species; but with the restricted data available this conclusion must clearly be uncertain.

(b) Liver Phosphatides

In Table 48 will be found component fatty acid analyses of liver phosphatides corresponding with those for the liver glycerides recorded in Table 47.

Liver phosphatide component acids differ from those of the liver glycerides much more even than the latter do from those of the depot fats. Of the saturated acids, palmitic acid is definitely less prominent than in the other two classes of fats, and usually (but not always) forms less than 15 per cent. of the total acids; stearic acid, on the other hand, is present in much greater proportions than in the liver glycerides, and in several cases exceeds the amount customarily found in the corresponding depot fats. In the unsaturated acids, those of the C_{18} series are usually somewhat more unsaturated than in the liver glycerides (and include little, if any, ordinary or "seed fat" linoleic acid), but form a somewhat lower proportion of the total acids; whilst hexadecenoic acid is also lower than in the liver glycerides, generally amounting to about one-half to two-thirds of its percentage in the latter. Unsaturated C_{20} and C_{22} acids are present, however, in greater amounts than in the liver glycerides; in the pig, ox, and sheep phosphatides the combined proportions of this group are in the neighbourhood of 20 per cent. of the total fatty acids.

It is interesting to recall that, amongst fish fats, similar relationships have been noted between the phosphatides and glycerides present in the roe of the New Zealand ling and also in the liver of the groper (Chapter II, p. 60).

TABLE 48. *Component Acids (per cent. wt.) of Animal Liver Phosphatides*

CLASS	ANIMAL	SATURATED				UNSATURATED				
		C_{14}	C_{16}	C_{18}	C_{20}	C_{14}	C_{16}	C_{18}	C_{20}	C_{22}
Amphibian	Frog[16a]	25 per cent. (mainly palmitic)				—	42 per cent. (mainly C_{18})	←———33———→		
Reptile	Greek tortoise[16b]	—	15	10	—	—	10	48 (−2·8H)	←———17———→ (−6H)	
Herbivora	Pig[110a]	—	12·1	15·4	1·8	—	4·8	39·9 (−2·2H)	24·1 (−6·5H)	1·9 (−6·5H)
"	Ox[110c]	—	12	30	—	—	—	40 (−3·4H)	18 (−8·0H)	—
"	Ox[109a]	—	12·5	27	—	—	5	27 (−3·0H)	18 (−5·3 to −8·2H)	10·5
"	Ox[110a]	1·3	28·2	14·4	0·2	0·7	3·8	31·5 (−2·9H)	←———19·9*———→ (−7·5H)	
"	Sheep[110a]	—	12·6	21·8	0·8	—	8·9	27·8 (−3·1H)	23·6 (−6·9H)	4·5 (—10·5H)
"	Horse[110b]	—	10·8	20·7	4·6	—	2·0	50·6 (−3·4H)	10·4 (−5·7H)	0·9 (−5·7H)
"	Elephant[59c]	—	16·4	23·6	11·3	—	0·3	25·4 (−3·5H)	21·6 (−5·6H)	1·4 (−7·5H)

* Mainly C_{20}.

The general result is that the component acids of liver phosphatides show a greater resemblance to each other, irrespective of the animal species, than those of either of the other two groups. It is true, of course, that this resemblance is by no means complete, but, so far as can be judged, the extreme variations in any one group are much smaller than in the liver or depot glycerides.

Futter and Shorland[52b] found that the phospholipids in the liver, kidney, and other tissues of the wild rabbit had higher contents of stearic, arachidic, octadecadienoic and unsaturated C_{20-22} acids, and lower contents of palmitic, hexadecenoic and octadecatrienoic acids than the corresponding glycerides.

A partial analysis of rat liver glycerides and phosphatides, showing the relative unsaturation of the acids present, was given by Charlot-Haimovici[111a] as follows:

	Saturated	Monoene	Diene	Triene	Tetraene	Pentaene	Hexaene
Glycerides	45·5	40	11	—	3·5	—	—
Phosphatides	52	7	14	2	21	2·5	1·5

135

These figures, which further illustrate the points made above, were for rats on a diet containing 10 per cent. of lard; when cottonseed oil was substituted for lard, unsaturated (mainly diene) acids were increased in the liver glycerides, but there was little alteration in the phosphatides.

Klenk and Oette[109d] found that, on a fat-free diet, the polyene acids of rat liver phosphatides were mainly of the "oleic" or hexadec-9-enoic acid type (C_{20} -5,8,11-triene and C_{20} -4,7,10,13-tetraene); with linoleic acid in the diet, the phosphatide polyene acids were of the "linoleic" type (chiefly arachidonic, C_{20} -5,8,11,14-tetraene) and, with linolenic acid, C_{20} -5,8,11,14,17-penta-ene and C_{22} -4,7,10,13,16,19-hexaene. Much other work on the structure of the polyunsaturated acids of liver lipids from a variety of animals has appeared from Klenk's laboratory, some references to which will be found at the end of this chapter.[109e]

In recent years, also, the various classes of lipids in liver and other organs – glycerides, phosphatidyl-choline, -ethanolamine, -inositol, plasmalogens, free sterols and sterol esters, etc. – have been separated by the various modern techniques of column, thin-layer or paper chromatography and considerable advances in our knowledge of the different kinds of lipids, and their proportions, in animal organs are becoming available. It would, however, take us too far from our main preoccupation here (the composition of the fatty acids present) to permit of any detailed account of these important investigations. Reference may be made to some other sources which deal with this aspect.[111b]

The data in Tables 46, 47, and 48 illustrate the broad similarities in fatty acid composition which are seen in the respective groups of (a) depot fats, (b) liver glycerides, and (c) liver phosphatides of a fairly wide range of land animal species. In Table 49 the weight percentages (to nearest unit) of the chief component acids in the depot and liver lipids of each of six species are

TABLE 49. *Comparison of Depot and Liver Lipids in Different Animal Species*

ACID	Depot Glycerides	Liver Glycerides	Liver Phosphatides	Depot Glycerides	Liver Glycerides	Liver Phosphatides
		OX			SHEEP	
Palmitic	29	30	13	25	22	13
Stearic	21	7	27	28	13	22
Hexadecenoic	3	10	5	1	5	9
Unsaturated C_{18}	43	40	27	42	45	28
Unsaturated C_{20-22}	Trace	10	28	1	15	28
		HORSE			PIG	
Palmitic	26	25	11	30	23	12
Stearic	5	5	21	16	9	15
Hexadecenoic	7	8	2	3	9	5
Unsaturated C_{18}	55	53	51	48	47	40
Unsaturated C_{20-22}	2	5	11	2	12	26
		TORTOISE			ELEPHANT	
Palmitic	14	11	15	44	27	16
Stearic	4	4	10	7	15	24
Hexadecenoic	9	15	10	5	7	Trace
Unsaturated C_{18}	65	66	48	33	26	25
Unsaturated C_{20-22}	7	3	17	3	20	23

arranged so that the respective amounts of each acid in each lipid may be more readily compared.

The distribution of these main component acids in the three groups of animal lipids is therefore roughly indicated by the following tabular statement:

ACID	DEPOT GLYCERIDES	LIVER GLYCERIDES	LIVER PHOSPHATIDES
Palmitic	High	High	Lower
Stearic (variable)	High or low	Low	High
Hexadecenoic	Very low or low	Higher	Medium or low
Unsaturated C_{18}	High	High	Lower
Unsaturated C_{20-22}	Very low	Medium	High

The differences in the relative proportions of palmitic, stearic, hexadecenoic, unsaturated C_{18}, and unsaturated C_{20} and C_{22} acids in the three groups are highly significant, and may be commended to the consideration of those who appear at times, perhaps, too ready to assume that organ and depot fats must be, if not nearly related, at all events closely derivable from each other by actions involving, as a rule, merely addition or removal of hydrogen. They indicate conclusively that each acid must be considered, very largely, independently of the others in any explanation which may ultimately be offered of their location in the respective fats of the higher land animals.

LIPIDS OF OTHER ANIMAL ORGANS

The fats of few animal organs, other than the liver, have yet been investigated in detail, but figures for individual component acids are available in the case of the lipids of the heart-muscle and adrenals of the ox. Broadly speaking, these analyses suggest closer resemblance to those of the liver glycerides or phosphatides than to those of depot glycerides. Unsaturated C_{20} (and C_{22}) acids are prominent in each case, whilst the palmitic contents are lower than in the depot glycerides; hexadecenoic acid was probably not allowed for in most of these studies:

Component Fatty Acids (per cent. wt.) of the Lipids from various Ox Organs

LIPIDS OF		OBSERVERS	SATURATED				UNSATURATED			
			C_{14}	C_{16}	C_{18}	C_{20}	C_{16}	C_{18}	C_{20}	C_{22}
Heart-	Glycerides	Klenk and Ditt[109b]	—	22	20	—	12	45	—	—
muscle	Phosphatides	,, ,,	—	14	21	—	—	45	14	1
Adrenals	Phosphatides	Ault and Brown[112a]	1·2	23·8	11·1	2·0	—	40·2	22·2	—

Some later information on the lipids in (ox) heart,[112b] spleen[112c] and brain tissues[112d] has appeared from time to time. Earlier, Klenk and Bongard[109c] separated from the phosphatides of brain tissue tri- and tetra-ethenoid acids of the C_{20} series, and tri-, tetra-, penta- and hexa-ethenoid acids of the C_{22} series.

The kidney tissues of the cat were reported by Turner[112e] to contain lipid matter in which, in addition to the more usual fatty acids, saturated acids apparently of the C_{14} and C_{16} group, which are liquid at the ordinary temperature, are present. Fatty acids of this kind have not yet been noted in other animal organ lipids, although they occur in certain animal waxes, e.g. that of sheep's wool, and in some glandular secretions such as those of the ear.

BLOOD LIPIDS

Until a few years ago knowledge about the lipids and their fatty acids in blood was restricted to two studies of ox blood plasma. Chiefly because of the wide discussion in recent years of a possible connection between arterial heart disease and deposition of lipids in arterial tissues (atherosclerosis) a good deal of information is now available concerning the different classes of lipids, and their component fatty acids, present in the blood plasma and in the arterial tissues of both healthy and atheromatous human subjects. The latter studies would not have been possible but for the concurrent development (i) of processes (silicic acid column chromatography) for effective separation of very small quantities of lipids into their constituent classes (triglycerides, sterol esters, free sterols, phospholipids) and (ii) of semi-micro or micro-methods of analysis of component fatty acids (e.g., gas–liquid chromatography or reversed-phase partition chromatography).

Ox blood lipids. Following an ester-fractionation analysis of the acids in the total lipids of ox blood in 1936 by Parry and Smith,[113a] Kelsey and Longenecker[113b] made a more comprehensive survey in 1941 of the lipids in 41 litres of plasma from 90 litres of blood taken from 6 Holstein cows; these (109 gm.) were separated as far as the methods then available permitted into the various classes of lipids, in two of which the component acids were determined by ester-fractionation. In 1957 Garton and co-workers[113c] similarly resolved the lipids in the plasma (*ca.* 2·7 litres) of a lactating cow by column chromatography, and analysed the fatty acids from the glycerides and sterol esters (0·02 to 0·1 gm.) by reversed-phase partition chromatography. The preliminary separations (per cent. wt.) obtained in each of these studies were as follows:

	Kelsey and Longenecker[113b]	Garton and Duncan[113c]
Triglycerides	9·6	7·5
Sterol esters	54·1	79·8
Sterols (free)	11·9	6·4
Phospholipids	13·8	3·8
		(including some non-lipid)
Free fatty acids	10·6	Traces
Unidentified	—	2·5
		(probably includes some sterol-esters)

The results of the corresponding component acid analyses for triglycerides and sterol esters are shown in Table 50.

It is evident from Table 50 that the later methods available to Garton and Duncan provided much more effective segregation of the different lipid classes. As regards component acids, the triglyceride fraction of Garton shows great similarity to cow depot fat, although the oleic acid content is lower, and the stearic acid content higher, than is usual in the depot fats. In contrast, the sterol-ester fatty acids are characterised by their high contents of linoleic,

138

TABLE 50. *Component Acids (per cent. mol.) in Cow Blood Plasma Triglycerides and Sterol Esters*

	TRIGLYCERIDES		STEROL ESTERS	
	Kelsey and Longenecker[113b]	Lough and Garton[113c]	Kelsey and Longenecker[113b]	Lough and Garton[113c]
Saturated:				
Myristic	0·2	4·6	—	4·4
Palmitic	33·7	29·3	11·1	1·6
Stearic	22·2	30·6	3·3	2·1
Arachidic	0·5	—	0·3	0·8
Unsaturated:				
Tetradecenoic	—	1·8	—	—
Hexadecenoic	2·6	7·2	4·2	11·2
Oleic	21·3	21·5	7·9	6·1
Linoleic	18·4	1·5	61·7	35·8
Linolenic	—	—	9·2	32·0
C_{20} monoene	—	2·9	—	—
C_{20} tetraene	1·1	—	2·3	6·0

linolenic (and arachidonic) acids, the C_{18} polyene acids together forming nearly 70 per cent. of the total acids. In contrast to the octadecadienoic acid of depot fat, the linoleic and linolenic acids combined as sterol esters are the natural (or seed-fat) forms, and Lough and Garton[113c] suggest that perhaps dietary linoleic and linolenic acids which escape hydrogenation in the rumen may become preferentially esterified with cholesterol.

In 1962 Duncan and Garton[113d] studied similarly the blood lipids from four grass-fed maiden heifers, but used gas–liquid chromatography on the respective fatty acids *per se* and the hydrogenated fatty acids of each lipid group to analyse their component fatty acids. The proportions of the lipid groups in heifer plasma were triglycerides 4·8, sterol esters 57·1, free sterols 9·6, phospholipids 25·8, free fatty acids 2·4 and hydrocarbons 0·3 per cent. The figures for component acids are quoted in Table 50A.

TABLE 50A. *Component Acids (per cent. wt.) in Heifer Blood Lipids*

	Triglycerides	Sterol esters	Phospholipids	Free acids
Saturated:				
Myristic	1·1	0·7	Trace	1·8
Palmitic	24·0	5·5	16·2	18·5
Stearic	30·0	1·5	26·8	24·1
Arachidic	—	0·9	Trace	—
Unsaturated:				
Tetradecenoic	—	—	—	—
Hexadecenoic	4·8	2·8	1·1	3·9
Oleic	24·3	5·6	16·3	39·3
Linoleic	4·6	52·4	14·1	5·2
Linolenic	1·9	22·9	2·4	3·3
Unsaturated C_{20}	—	4·6	9·7	—
,, C_{22}–C_{24}	—	—	8·7	—
	(a)	(b)	(c)	(d)

(a) Also saturated C_{15} 1·8, C_{17} 6·8; C_{11} diene 0·7 per cent.
(b) Also saturated C_{15} 2·3, C_{17} 0·5; C_{16} diene 0·3 per cent.
(c) Also saturated C_{15} 0·3, C_{17} 4·4; C_{16} diene *trace* per cent.
(d) Also saturated C_{12} 0·6, C_{15} 1·0, C_{17} 2·0; C_{16} diene 0·3 per cent.

The results for the glycerides and sterol esters are broadly similar to those for the blood lipids of lactating cows (Table 50); the phospholipids display the relatively low palmitic, high stearic, and prominent unsaturated C_{20-22} acid contents which are characteristic of most animal phospholipids (*cf.* pp. 134–136).

Human blood lipids. The component fatty acids of different lipids present in the blood plasma of normal healthy subjects (and also those in the corresponding lipids from the walls of the aortas and coronary arteries of both healthy and atheromatous subjects) have of late years been reported by a number of workers. In most instances the lipid groups were resolved by column chromatography, while their component acids were determined by gas–liquid chromatography or, in other cases, by spectrophotometric analysis of the acids after isomerisation with alkali by standard procedures (*cf.* Chapter XI, p. 695). The latter method leads to a statement of the different types of unsaturated acids present rather than to the proportions of individual unsaturated or saturated acids. Reference will be made to some typical figures reported by Tuna *et al.*,[114a] Luddy, Riemenschneider *et al.*,[114b] Wright, Morton *et al.*,[114c] Dole, James *et al.*,[114d] and Böttcher *et al.*,[114e] but other workers (for instance, Lewis,[114f] Ahrens *et al.*,[114f] Schrode *et al.*[114f]) have also contributed to knowledge in these fields.

Plasma lipids of normal subjects. Typical data are reproduced in Table 50B, which shows the percentage (wt.) of component acids of certain of the lipid groups in human plasma. Luddy, Riemenschneider *et al.*[114b] record the following proportions of the various lipids in normal human plasma: glycerides 14·0, phospholipids 32·2, sterol esters 40·3, free sterols 8·3, free fatty acids 2·3, hydrocarbons 2·9 per cent.

TABLE 50B. *Component Acids (per cent. wt.) in Individual Lipid Groups in the Blood Plasma of Normal Subjects*

ACIDS	(i) TRIGLYCERIDES Riemenschneider et al.[114b]	(ii) PHOSPHOLIPIDS Riemenschneider et al.[114b]	Dole, James et al.[114d]
Saturated	37·4	37·7	45·9
Monoene	44·7	35·5	21·1
Diene	14·3	14·5	16·0
Triene	1·3	1·0	1·8
Tetraene	1·3	8·2	4·3
Pentaene	0·5	1·7	—
Hexaene	0·5	1·4	—

ACIDS	(iii) STEROL ESTERS Riemenschneider et al.[114b]	Wright, Morton et al.[114c]	Tuna et al.[114a]
Saturated	18·7	11·9	16·2
Monoene	23·5	32·7	28·6
Diene	47·5	43·8	41·1
Triene	0·7	4·0	0·7
Tetraene	8·0	6·1	6·2
Pentaene	0·9	0·8	0·7
Hexaene	0·7	0·7	1·2

Broadly speaking, the figures for any one group recorded by different workers are of the same character, but at the same time individual variations occur (e.g., the saturated and monoene acids in the two plasma phospholipid analyses). These subordinate differences are even more marked in some of the component acid data recorded for normal and atheromatous arterial tissue lipids in Tables 50C and 50D; these may reflect true differences in the lipids of different human subjects, but it is perhaps not unfair to remark that the analyses have been contributed by a number of investigators of widely differing experience in the alkali-isomerisation and other recently developed techniques of fatty acid analysis, so that in some instances the analytical error might be greater than in others. (In Tables 50B, C and D "saturated" acids consist mainly of palmitic acid with lesser amounts of stearic acid, while "monoene" acids are largely oleic with subordinate proportions of hexadecenoic acid.)

The human plasma *triglycerides* seem (as in the case of the cow) to be not very different in composition from human body fats (Table 45A, p. 128), while the *phospholipid* fatty acids, like those of animal livers (Table 48, p. 135), appear to be marked by a lower content of monoene (oleic) acid and the appearance of definite proportions of polyunsaturated (arachidonic) acid. The *sterol esters* are the most distinctive group, and have great similarity to those in ox blood (Tables 50 and 50A); saturated and monoethenoid (oleic) acids are relatively low, whilst diethenoid (linoleic) acid is the major component and may form nearly half of the total acids; definite amounts of polyethenoid (notably the tetraene arachidonic) acids are also present.

Lipids deposited in certain arteries of normal and atherosclerotic human subjects. We must now consider the figures which have been recorded for the various classes of lipids observed in the interior lining (*intima*) of arteries which are liable to become blocked (thrombosis) or ruptured (infarction) in arterial diseases. Data are available for the aorta, coronary arteries, and the arteries of the brain; typical results for human subjects free from arterial disease will first be presented.

Böttcher et al.[114e] observed the following proportions of lipids in normal arterial walls:

	Triglycerides	Phospho-lipids	Sterol Esters	Free Sterols	Free Fatty Acids
Aorta	15·0	58·0	8·8	10·1	8·0
Coronary arteries	49·7	28·4	8·8	6·1	6·7
Brain arteries (Circulus Willisii)	20·0	58·2	7·5	9·3	5·7

It will be noticed that the lipids in the normal coronary artery contain a very large proportion of glycerides and corresponding less phospholipids than the aorta or cerebral artery. Recorded values for the component acids in the triglyceride, phospholipid and sterol ester fractions of these lipids are illustrated in Table 50C.

TABLE 50C. *Component Acids (per cent. wt.) in Lipids of Normal Human Arteries* (Bottcher et al.[114e])

	(i) TRIGLYCERIDES			(ii) PHOSPHOLIPIDS			(iii) STEROL ESTERS		
	Aorta	Coronary Artery	Brain Artery	Aorta	Coronary Artery	Brain Artery	Aorta	Coronary Artery	Brain Artery
Saturated	43·8	34·2	48·3	57·3	48·5	56·3	27·1	33·1	34·4
Monoene	41·1	56·6	38·3	17·5	27·5	24·3	39·8	43·8	40·7
Diene	10·1	7·8	8·4	4·7	5·5	3·2	27·3	18·2	19·1
Tri, Tetraene	5·0	1·4	5·0	20·5	18·5	16·2	5·8	4·9	5·8

The figures in Table 50C suggest that the *glycerides* of the aorta and brain arterial tissues have much in common, standing apart from those in the coronary arteries; the glycerides in the latter contain much less saturated, and much more unsaturated (oleic) acid. The *phosphatides* in all three arteries are more similar to each other, although again there is somewhat less saturated, and somewhat more monoethenoid acids present in those of the coronaries; the phosphatides resemble each other (and also those of blood plasma and of the livers and other organs of animals) in having important contents of highly unsaturated acids. The *sterol esters* are, as in other instances (Tables 50, 50A, 50B), distinguished by their relatively high contents of diene (linoleic) and still more unsaturated acids.

Lipids of diseased (atheromatous or atherosclerotic) arteries. Data for these (more numerous than the preceding and also less accordant) must next be considered. Proportions of the various classes in these atheromatous tissues have been observed as follows:

	Triglycerides	Phospho-lipids	Sterol Esters	Free Sterols	Free Fatty Acids
Aorta[114b]	19·4	13·7	28·0	38·9	Trace
Aorta[114e]	9·7	38·0	33·8	19·3	1·0
Coronary arteries[114e]	26·6	32·1	24·6	11·9	4·9
Brain arteries[114e]	16·0	37·5	28·1	14·7	4·1

It will be seen that the respective figures of Riemenschneider *et al.*[114b] and Böttcher *et al.*[114e] for the aorta lipids differ widely, and clearly much more information is required before any real conclusions can be reached. All that can be said, when comparison is made with the lipids of healthy tissues (above, p. 140), is that there is marked increase in the proportions of sterol esters and free sterols, chiefly at the expense of phospholipids (aortas and brain arteries) or of glycerides (coronary arteries).

Some component acid analyses of glycerides, phospholipids and sterol esters from atherosclerotic arterial tissues are illustrated in Table 50D.

The results in Table 50D differ among themselves even more than those in Tables 50B and 50C, and it is impossible at the present stage to decide how far the differences are real and how far they may be influenced by errors in analysis. Some remarks of Wright, Pitt and Morton[114c] in their own contribution to these results are apposite: "Technical difficulties in this field are not negligible" . . . "the general picture is confused"; yet the "reports of component acids in atheroma differ beyond what could readily be attributed to technical shortcomings". It will be noticed that the results of any one group of workers usually show some degree of consistency between themselves, although not parallel with those of other groups.

The detached observer may conclude that the following statement covers all that can reasonably be deduced from the existing information. Between normal and diseased arterial tissues the lipid *triglycerides* show no great variation, the saturated acids being perhaps reduced and the linoleic acid and monoene acids somewhat increased in the atheromatous tissues. In the *phospholipids* the saturated acids also seem to be increased somewhat, chiefly at the expense of the

TABLE 50D. *Component Acids (per cent. wt.) in Lipids of Atheromatous Arterial Tissues*

(i) GLYCERIDES

ACIDS	Aorta		Coronary Artery	Brain Artery
	Riemenschneider et al.[114b]	Böttcher et al.[114e]	Böttcher et al.[114e]	Böttcher et al.[114e]
Saturated	22·2	35·0	34·0	35·5
Monoene (chiefly oleic)	67·4	45·6	50·8	43·5
Diene (chiefly linoleic)	7·0	11·7	10·1	11·2
Triene	0·5	1·1	0·5	1·2
Tetraene	2·3	3·4	1·7	3·6
Pentaene	0·6	}3·2	2·9	5·0
Hexaene	—			

(ii) PHOSPHOLIPIDS

ACIDS	Aorta		Coronary Artery	Brain Artery
	Riemenschneider et al.[114b]	Böttcher et al.[114e]	Böttcher et al.[114e]	Böttcher et al.[114e]
Saturated	32·2	61·6	58·0	62·2
Monoene (chiefly oleic)	55·7	16·6	23·5	22·5
Diene (chiefly linoleic)	7·2	4·7	4·4	4·4
Triene	2·3	1·8	1·4	0·8
Tetraene	2·6	8·4	6·6	4·4
Pentaene	—	}6·9	6·1	5·7
Hexaene	—			

(iii) STEROL ESTERS

ACIDS	Aorta				Coronary Artery	Brain Artery
	Tuna et al.[114a]	Riemenschneider et al.[114b]	Morton et al.[114c]	Böttcher et al.[114e]	Böttcher et al.[114e]	Böttcher et al.[114e]
Saturated	10·7	4·2	26·1	16·1	22·2	20·5
Monoene (chiefly oleic)	41·3	61·5	35·1	37·5	38·5	47·1
Diene (chiefly linoleic)	37·6	23·6	29·5	37·2	33·6	25·5
Triene	1·6	1·4	3·0	3·4	1·5	1·9
Tetraene	7·4	7·0	4·7	4·6	2·5	3·0
Pentaene	0·9	1·3	1·0	0·8	}1·7	2·0
Hexaene	1·0	1·0	0·5	0·4		

more highly unsaturated acids. The *sterol esters* show more consistent changes, and it is fairly clear that in atheroma their saturated acid contents are definitely reduced, with possible slight increases in monoene acids and very definite increases in diene acids (which have been proved to be mainly linoleic); the range of linoleic acid recorded in sterol esters from diseased tissues lies between 23·6 and 37·6 per cent. of the total fatty acids.

The increase in cholesterol (free or esterified) in atheromatous tissues, at the expense of phospholipids or glycerides in normal arterial tissue, is the most positive result of the above studies.

Component Acids of Animal Milk Fats

The component fatty acids of some milk fats, especially those of ruminant mammals, differ from those of either the depot or organ fats of the same animal by including, in addition to palmitic, stearic, oleic, and linoleic acids, definite but small proportions of butyric, caproic, caprylic, capric, and lauric acids, with a somewhat larger amount of myristic acid than is present in the depot fats. Naturally, most of the detailed component acid analyses of milk fats are those of cow milk fats, although a few data are available for the milk fats of other herbivora – buffalo, sheep, goat, camel, pig, horse.

Before discussing these figures it should be pointed out that the component acids of other mammalian milk fats undoubtedly show wide variations in their proportions of lower saturated acids. Probably the 4 per cent. (weight) of butyric acid in ruminant milk fatty acids approaches the maximum amount present in any milk fat. At the other end of the scale we have the milk fats of marine mammals such as the whale and seal, which have been shown to contain no acids of lower molecular weight than those present in whale depot or liver fats, and whose component acids are quantitatively closely similar to those of the depot fats (cf. Chapter II, pp. 66, 71).

Some indication on this point is to be gained by comparing the average Reichert-Meissl and Polenske values of the milk fats of different animals. The Reichert-Meissl values,* being measures of the water-soluble, steam-volatile fatty acids present in a fat, give comparative indications of the amounts of butyric and hexanoic (caproic) acids; the Polenske values, giving similar measures of the content of water-insoluble, steam-volatile fatty acids, afford similar comparative indications of the relative proportions of octanoic and decanoic (caprylic and capric) acids. Typical data for a number of milk fats are as follows:

MILK FAT	REICHERT-MEISSL VALUE	POLENSKE VALUE
Dog	1·6	
Pig	1·7	
Human	1·4–3·4	1·5–2·2
Mouse	2·9	
Cat	4·4	
Horse	7·0	6·1
Ass	13·1	
Rabbit	16·1	
Camel	16·4	1·6
Goat	20–29	3·2–9·8
Sheep	23–33	2·2–6·9
Buffalo	26–34	1·6–2·4
Cow	33–36	1·3–3·5

It is evident that the proportion, if any, of butyric or hexanoic acid in milk fats such as those of the dog, pig, or human being is very small, and that the presence of 3–4 per cent. of butyric acid is confined to a particular group of animals, of which the cow is the best known example.

Detailed analysis of milk fatty acids. These were among the first to be attempted by means of the ester-fractionation procedure but the earlier results obtained for milk fatty acids were divergent and far from accurate. Later, however, a

* From chromatographic analyses, Sengupta[115] states that the Reichert-Meissl fraction of a sample of butter fat contained about 65 per cent. butyric, 30 per cent. hexanoic and 5 per cent. octanoic acid; and the Polenske fraction less than 1 per cent. of butyric and hexanoic, 22 per cent. octanoic, and about 77 per cent. capric (and some higher) acids.

number of more definite results have been published, mainly for the component acids of cow milk fat, but also including those of some other herbivorous animals.

In addition to lower saturated acids, it has been established that minor proportions of Δ^9-monoethenoid acids containing 10, 12, 14, and 16 carbon atoms are also present in cow and other milk fats. The presence of a decenoic acid was first deduced in 1912 by Smedley,[116a] and confirmed in 1922 by Grün and Wirth,[116b] who isolated it and determined its structure. The presence of C_{12}, C_{14}, and C_{16} unsaturated acids was indicated in a later paper by Grün,[116c] whilst in 1933 Bosworth and Brown[117] presented further evidence for decenoic and tetradecenoic acids but were unable to detect C_{12} or C_{16} unsaturated acids. In 1936 Riemenschneider and Ellis[118] found C_{10}, C_{14}, and C_{16} mono-ethenoid acids in goat milk fat; in 1936–1937 Hilditch and Paul[119a] and Longenecker[119b] isolated C_{10}, C_{12}, C_{14}, and C_{16} mono-ethenoid acids from cow milk fat and showed that in each case they were Δ^9-unsaturated acids. The possible bearing of these observations on the mode of production of typical milk fat glycerides will receive consideration in later chapters (V, p. 414; VIII, p. 550).

In many of the detailed analyses (Tables 51A, 53(a), and 54A) the presence of these minor proportions of lower unsaturated acids was not taken into account, but in more recent publications (Tables 51B–D, 52–55) they have been included. It is desirable, therefore, to record the respective data in separate tables. It is furthermore desirable to put on record the data for milk fat component acids in the form both of weight and of molar percentages. The wide variation in molecular weight of the component acids causes the latter to be quite different in some respects from the former. Weight percentages alone, therefore, do not present even an approximately accurate picture of the proportionate number of molecules of each fatty acid present.

Component acids of cow milk fats from pasture or stall-fed animals. Analyses of the component acids of milk fats from a variety of stall and pasture-fed cows are illustrated in Tables 51A (minor unsaturated components not included), 51B, 51C and 51D (fully detailed analyses). Tables 51A, 51B cover cows at spring, summer, and autumn pastures, or during winter feeding in the stall, when the diet of the Berkshire cows[119–121, 124] consisted of hay with roots, kale, and small proportions of concentrates, whilst that of the Cheshire cows[122a] was entirely of ensiled green fodder mixed with hay. Table 51C gives some more recent figures (1956) by Garton and Duncan[128a] for milk fats from stall-fed cows on winter rations consisting of oat straw with (i) silage alone, (ii) some silage with turnips or swedes, or (iii) turnips and cabbages with no silage.

Whilst the analyses in Tables 51B, 51C, and 51D must be regarded as the most comprehensive and the most accurate in detail, those in Table 51A conform to the more detailed analyses in all respects, save that the oleic acid figures are probably 3–5 per cent. too high (since they include unsaturation represented in reality by the small amounts of C_{10}, C_{12}, C_{14} and C_{16} mono-ethenoid acids). The effect of this upon the figures for the saturated acids in

TABLE 51A. Component Acids of Cow Milk Fats (minor unsaturated components not included)

(i) Weight Percentages

ACID	NEW ZEALAND MARKET SAMPLES I[123]	II[123]	III[123]	SPRING PASTURE 1928[124]	AUTUMN FED 1928[124]	BERKSHIRE, ENGLAND EARLY SUMMER PASTURE FED 1929[124]	STALL FED WINTER 1932[120]	STALL AND PASTURE 1932[120]	SPRING PASTURE 1932[120]	STALL FED WINTER 1934[121]	STALL FED WINTER 1934[121]	INDIAN "GHEE" I[125]	II[125]
Butyric	3·1	3·4	3·2	3·5	3·1	3·3	3·9	3·3	3·1	4·4	4·4	3·3	2·6
n-Hexanoic	1·9	1·8	1·7	1·7	1·7	1·3	1·5	1·7	1·7	2·2	1·4	2·1	1·9
n-Octanoic	0·8	0·9	0·8	1·3	1·6	1·2	0·7	0·7	0·7	2·4	1·8	1·0	1·4
n-Decanoic	2·0	1·9	2·3	3·1	2·1	2·2	1·9	1·8	1·8	3·8	1·9	2·3	3·6
Lauric	3·9	3·1	4·3	4·1	3·4	4·0	3·7	2·3	3·2	4·4	3·1	3·7	5·7
Myristic	10·6	9·7	10·8	11·1	6·9	10·4	8·4	8·8	7·1	10·9	9·3	5·8	10·6
Palmitic	28·1	27·6	28·4	27·3	29·0	26·1	22·0	21·8	22·8	23·1	27·5	30·0	29·1
Stearic	8·5	12·2	9·4	11·5	7·6	6·5	15·0	12·7	12·5	12·6	12·2	11·2	6·7
as Arachidic	1·0	0·7	0·5	0·6	0·9	—	0·7	0·4	0·7	0·7	1·0	—	—
Oleic	36·4	34·3	33·2	31·3	40·1	40·9	38·5	40·7	41·3	28·9	33·1	35·5	34·0
as Octadecadienoic	3·7	4·4	5·4	4·5	3·6	4·1	3·7	5·8	5·1	5·6	3·1	5·1	4·4
as Unsaturated C_{20-22}	—	—	—	—	—	—	—	—	—	1·0	1·2	—	—

(ii) Molar Percentages

ACID	NEW ZEALAND MARKET SAMPLES I[123]	II[123]	III[123]	SPRING PASTURE 1928[124]	AUTUMN FED 1928[124]	BERKSHIRE, ENGLAND EARLY SUMMER PASTURE FED 1929[124]	STALL FED WINTER 1932[120]	STALL AND PASTURE 1932[120]	SPRING PASTURE 1932[120]	STALL FED WINTER 1934[121]	STALL FED WINTER 1934[121]	INDIAN "GHEE" I[125]	II[125]
Butyric	8·4	9·2	8·7	9·2	8·4	8·9	10·6	8·9	8·5	11·5	11·7	8·8	6·9
n-Hexanoic	3·9	3·7	3·4	3·4	3·5	2·7	3·2	3·5	3·5	4·3	2·8	4·2	4·0
n-Octanoic	1·3	1·4	1·4	2·2	2·7	2·0	1·2	1·2	1·2	3·7	2·9	1·6	2·2
n-Decanoic	2·8	2·7	3·1	4·2	2·9	3·0	2·6	2·6	2·6	5·0	2·6	3·2	4·9
Lauric	4·6	3·7	5·1	4·7	4·1	4·7	4·4	2·7	3·8	5·0	3·6	4·4	6·7
Myristic	11·0	10·2	11·2	11·5	7·2	10·9	8·8	9·4	7·5	10·8	9·5	6·1	10·9
Palmitic	26·2	25·7	26·3	25·0	27·1	24·3	20·5	20·6	21·6	20·5	25·2	27·9	26·8
Stearic	7·1	10·2	7·8	9·5	6·4	5·4	12·6	10·8	10·7	10·1	10·0	9·4	5·5
as Arachidic	0·8	0·5	0·6	0·5	0·7	—	0·5	0·3	0·6	0·5	0·8	—	—
Oleic	30·8	28·9	27·9	26·1	33·9	34·6	32·5	35·0	35·6	23·3	27·4	30·0	28·4
as Octadecadienoic	3·1	3·8	4·5	3·7	3·1	3·5	3·1	5·0	4·4	4·5	2·6	4·4	3·7
as Unsaturated C_{20-22}	—	—	—	—	—	—	—	—	—	0·8	0·9	—	—

Table 51A is small in any individual case, because the result of the inclusion of the various lower unsaturated acids with oleic acid is spread, as it were, over a number of the homologous saturated acids.

The data in Table 51C show that the stall-fed cows on a diet of silage and straw produced milk fat of the same composition as that from pasture-fed cattle, but that substitution of roots for silage led to milk fats richer in the lower saturated acids and hexadecenoic acids but with lower contents of stearic and oleic acids.

The figures for the mammary gland tissue fats (Table 51D) seem interesting in that the fat of the lactating gland contained about half as much of the lower saturated acids as a typical milk fat, with compensating increases in stearic acid and perhaps palmitic acid; while that from the non-lactating gland differed and was more akin to a bovine depot fat in the relative proportions of the major component acids (but palmitic acid was much higher, and oleic acid lower, than in the typical depot fat).

Taking the more prominent individual acids of milk fats (and basing

TABLE 51B. *Component Acids of Cow Milk Fats (minor unsaturated components included)*

ACIDS	COW (BERKSHIRE, ENGLAND) STALL-FED WINTER 1935[119a]	STALL-FED WINTER 1937[119b]	COW (CHESHIRE, ENGLAND) SILAGE-FED WINTER 1940–41[122a]	EARLY SUMMER 1941[122a]	LATE SUMMER 1941[122a]	COW (INDIA) STALL-FED 1946[126]	COW (U.S.A.) COLOS-TRUM FAT 1944[127b]
			(i) *Weight Percentages*				
Butyric	3·7	3·0	3·6	3·7	3·5	4·0	2·6
n-Hexanoic (caproic)	2·0	1·4	2·0	1·7	1·9	1·8	1·6
n-Octanoic (caprylic)	1·0	1·5	0·5	1·0	0·7	1·0	0·5
n-Decanoic (capric)	2·6	2·7	2·3	1·9	2·1	1·9	1·6
Lauric	1·7	3·7	2·5	2·8	1·9	2·2	3·2
Myristic	9·3	12·1	11·1	8·1	7·9	12·9	9·5
Palmitic	25·4	25·3	29·0	25·9	25·8	31·3	31·7
Stearic	10·7	9·2	9·2	11·2	12·7	8·3	11·8
as Arachidic	0·4	1·3	2·4	1·2	1·5	0·9	0·6
Dec-9-enoic	0·2	0·3	0·1	0·1	0·1	0·1	0·1
Dodec-9-enoic	—	0·4	0·1	0·2	0·2	0·3	0·2
Tetradec-9-enoic	1·2	1·6	0·9	0·6	0·6	1·2	0 7
Hexadec-9-enoic	5·0	4·0	4·6	3·4	2·4	1·6	2·7
Oleic	32·4	29·6	26·7	32·8	34·0	28·0	28·5
as Octadecadienoic	4·0	3·6	3·6	3·7	3·7	3·8	2·5*
as Unsaturated C$_{20-22}$	0·4	0·3	1·4	1·7	1·0	0·7	1 8
			(ii) *Molar Percentages*				
Butyric	9·8	8·1	9·5	9·9	9·5	10·6	7·2
n-Hexanoic	4·1	2·8	4·1	3·5	4·0	3·7	3·4
n-Octanoic	1·6	2·5	0·8	1·6	1·1	1·6	0·8
n-Decanoic	3·5	3·7	3·2	2·6	2·9	2·6	2·3
Lauric	2·0	4·4	2·9	3·4	2·3	2·6	3·9
Myristic	9·6	12·5	11·5	8·5	8·2	13·1	10·1
Palmitic	23·4	23·2	26·7	24·0	24·1	28·4	29·9
Stearic	8·9	7·6	7·6	9·4	10·7	6·8	10·0
as Arachidic	0·3	1·0	1·8	0·9	1·1	0·7	0·5
Dec-9-enoic	0·3	0·4	0·1	0·1	0·1	0·2	0·2
Dodec-9-enoic	—	0·5	0·1	0·2	0·2	0·3	0·2
Tetradec-9-enoic	1·3	1·7	0·9	0·6	0·7	1·2	0·7
Hexadec-9-enoic	4·6	3·7	4·3	3·2	2·3	1·5	2·5
Oleic	27·0	24·8	22·4	27·7	28·8	23·1	24·3
as Octadecadienoic	3·3	2·9	3·1	3·1	3·2	3·1	2·2*
as Unsaturated C$_{20\ 22}$	0·3	0·2	1·0	1·3	0·8	0·5	1·5

* Also octadecatrienoic acid 0·4 (wt.) or 0·3 (mol.).

TABLE 51C. *Component Acids of Milk fats (minor unsaturated components included) from Cows fed on Silage or Roots*[128a]

	(i) Weight Percentages				(ii) Molar Percentages			
DIET:	Silage	Silage + roots	Roots		Silage	Silage + roots	Roots	
ACIDS								
Butyric	2·8	3·0	4·1	3·8	7·7	8·0	10·8	9·9
n-Hexanoic	2·0	3·0	2·4	2·6	4·2	6·1	4·8	5·1
n-Octanoic	0·7	0·9	0·5	0·7	1·2	1·5	0·8	1·1
n-Decanoic	1·7	2·1	2·1	3·2	2·4	2·9	2·8	4·3
Lauric	2·2	2·5	3·3	2·6	2·7	2·9	3·8	3·0
Myristic	5·4	6·9	7·5	8·0	5·7	7·1	7·6	8·0
Palmitic	29·7	35·9	35·7	41·3	28·1	33·0	32·2	37·0
Stearic	10·5	7·9	6·7	6·1	9·0	6·5	5·4	4·9
Arachidic	1·9	1·6	1·4	1·6	1·5	1·2	1·0	1·2
Dec-9-enoic	0·1	0·2	0·2	0·2	0·1	0·3	0·3	0·3
Dodec-9-enoic	0·3	0·3	0·6	0·4	0·4	0·4	0·7	0·5
Tetradec-9-enoic	1·4	1·1	1·6	1·3	1·5	1·1	1·6	1·2
Hexadec-9-enoic	3·4	3·0	5·2	5·9	3·2	2·8	4·8	5·4
Oleic	33·4	27·1	25·6	19·6	28·7	22·6	21·0	16·0
Octadecadienoic	0·9	1·2	1·2	1·0	0·8	1·2	0·9	0·8
Octadecatrienoic	0·6	0·7	0·7	0·9	0·5	0·5	0·6	0·7
Unsaturated C_{20-22}	3·0	2·5	1·2	0·8	2·3	1·9	0·9	0·6

TABLE 51D. *Component Acids of Mammary-gland Fat of Lactating and Non-lactating Cows*[128b]

	(i) Weight Percentages		(ii) Molar Percentages	
ACIDS	Lactating	Non-lactating	Lactating	Non-lactating
Butyric	2·3	0·4	6·5	1·2
n-Hexanoic	0·9	0·1	2·0	0·2
n-Octanoic	0·5	0·2	0·8	0·4
n-Decanoic	0·6	0·3	0·9	0·4
Lauric	2·1	1·6	2·6	2·1
Myristic	4·4	4·1	4·8	4·7
Palmitic	32·0	40·7	31·1	41·3
Stearic	14·3	18·1	12·6	16·5
Dec-9-enoic	0·2	0·1	0·3	0·2
Dodec-9-enoic	0·4	0·4	0·5	0·5
Tetradec-9-enoic	0·4	1·1	0·5	1·3
Hexadec-9-enoic	6·3	9·3	6·2	9·5
Oleic	29·3	20·2	25·8	18·6
Octadecadienoic	3·6	3·4	3·2	3·1
Octadecatrienoic	0·8	Trace	0·7	Trace
Unsaturated C_{20-22}	1·9	—	1·5	—

comparisons on their molar proportions), it is seen that, as in the corresponding depot fats, *palmitic* and *oleic* are the chief component acids. The content of *palmitic acid* again has some approach towards constancy, but is somewhat lower than in the depot fats. The average figure is probably in the region of 24–26 per cent., rather than 30 per cent. Milk fats from individual cows examined over a range of some years by Dean and Hilditch[120] suggest that the proportion of palmitic acid in the milk fat declines with progressive age of the lactating animal.

The proportions of *oleic acid* are likewise lower in the milk fats than in the depot fats of cows, and show a similar behaviour in that, the amount of palmitic acid being roughly constant, there is a reciprocal relation between the proportion of oleic acid and that of the total saturated acids. These relations are not so well defined as in the depot fats, and this is natural since the composition of milk fat is more liable to variation in consequence of seasonal and other causes.

148

This is most marked, perhaps, in the sudden change which occurs when English cattle pass from winter stall feeding to graze on early spring or summer pasture. Some influence connected with the seasonal change causes an increase of a few per cent. in the oleic acid content and a slight diminution in that of butyric acid and stearic acid. The precise character of these seasonal changes in the milk fat of cows is not easy to establish, since other factors also come into play, e.g. slight variations in composition in the milk fats of different individuals, and of the same individual as the number of lactations increases. Exactly similar changes are to be found in the case of the milk fat from cows fed on silage (Table 51B[122a]). Here the winter daily diet of 21 lb. of hay and 50–60 lb. of silage would have been almost identical in its proportions of lipids, carbohydrates, and proteins with a diet of approximately 120 lb. of pasture grass daily; yet the same increase in oleic acid content was noticed when the cows went out to grass. The unsaturation of the 1941 summer milk fats (secreted by comparatively young animals) is somewhat lower than that of summer samples previously studied, but this accords with the experience of Dean and Hilditch[120] that the unsaturated components (especially oleic acid) gradually augment with increasing age of the cows. The cause of the fall in oleic acid content during winter is thus not necessarily the ingestion of different dietary constituents from those in the summer food, but may lie in some other seasonal change such as temperature or, perhaps, difference in freedom of movement and exercise.

Hansen and Shorland[129a] discussed in 1952 the seasonal variations in New Zealand butterfats, and gave detailed figures (Table 52) for six specimens taken at two-monthly intervals over a period of one year. The seasonal effect is different from that in Great Britain, the oleic acid content being lower in summer (November–January) than in the winter months (May–July) whilst the butyric acid is highest in winter and spring (July–September). These authors point out that in New Zealand cows are at pasture throughout the year, and that the amount of pasture feed is at a minimum in May and June, when the oleic acid content of the milk fat is highest. The "plane of nutrition" of New Zealand cows is thus lower in May and June than in the spring and summer months. In Great Britain, however, when the cows change over from stall to pasture feeding in spring they may suffer a decline in the plane of nutrition with consequent increase in the unsaturated acids of the milk fat. On this view the observed changes in the milk fats are to be associated not with the precise season, but with the relative nutritive values of the cow diets at different seasons of the year in either country. Hansen and Shorland also considered the possible influence of other factors, and pointed out that in New Zealand the available data appeared to support the view that with progressive stages of lactation there tends to be increased production of oleic acid in the milk fat and concurrent diminution in some of the saturated acids. Gerson, Shorland and Barnicoat[129d] observed similar seasonal variations in the composition of Antipodean ewe milk fats, and this aspect of alterations in cow milk fat composition has also been dealt with by several other workers.[130]

As in ruminant depot fats, so in their milk fats slight amounts of isomers

TABLE 52. *Changes in Composition of New Zealand Butterfats*
in the course of a year
(Molar Percentages)

	SAMPLE TAKEN					
ACID	September 1947	November 1947	January 1948	April 1948	May 1948	July 1948
Butyric	11·5	10·8	11·4	9·6	9·5	12·0
n-Hexanoic	4·5	4·7	4·3	3·9	3·5	3·7
n-Octanoic	1·5	1·9	1·4	1·2	1·2	0·9
n-Decanoic	3·5	4·4	3·6	3·0	2·8	2·7
Lauric	3·5	4·4	3·7	3·1	2·9	2·9
Myristic	9·6	11·5	10·6	10·4	9·7	8·4
Palmitic	21·6	22·9	23·1	22·0	22·7	23·6
Stearic	11·3	11·1	11·2	11·9	12·2	11·3
Arachidic	0·7	0·6	0·7	0·6	0·8	0·4
Dec-9-enoic	0·2	0·4	0·3	0·2	0·2	0·2
Dodec-9-enoic	0·2	0·3	0·3	0·3	0·2	0·2
Tetradec-9-enoic	0·8	1·0	1·0	1·2	1·1	0·9
Hexadec-9-enoic	1·8	1·7	1·7	2·0	2·0	2·4
Oleic and octadecadienoic	28·1	23·4	25·6	29·2	29·8	29·5
Unsaturated C_{20}	1·3	1·2	1·1	1·4	1·4	0·9

of oleic (*cis*-octadec-9-enoic) acid accompany the latter. These were first observed (in their *trans*-forms) as "vaccenic acid" by Bertram[80] and were studied later by other workers[82,83] who showed that more than one structural *trans*-isomer was usually present. In 1953 Patwardhan[131a] reported that positional as well as geometric isomers of oleic acid may appear in traces in cow and buffalo milk fats. In 1958 Backderf and Brown[131b] found that the following monoethenoid acids accompanied oleic acid in traces or very small amounts in cow milk fat: *trans*-hexadec-9-enoic (*ca.* 0·4 per cent.), *trans*-octadec-9-enoic, elaidic (traces), *trans*- (and some *cis*-) octadec-11-enoic, "vaccenic" (*ca.* 3 per cent.) and *trans*-octadec-16-enoic acid (*ca.* 1 per cent.) of the total fatty acids. In 1959, Scott *et al.*[131c] confirmed the presence of both *cis*- and *trans*-forms of hexa- and octa-decenoic acids, and subsequently Hansen *et al.*[131e] isolated the *trans*-octadec-16-enoic acid of Brown[131b] and traces of a *cis*-heptadec-9-enoic acid,[131d] the only odd-numbered monoene acid so far observed in cow milk fat. By infra-red spectra studies Kaufmann *et al.*[131f] observed in 1961 that cow summer milk fat contained in all 6–9 per cent. of *trans*-acids, in contrast to less than 2 per cent. in winter milk fat and 0–4 per cent. in human milk fat.

The *lower unsaturated acids* of cow milk fats have already been discussed (p. 145). It may be added that Scott *et al.*[131c] found that in the C_{12} and C_{14} monoenoic acids the *cis*-forms predominate, although (as mentioned above) both *cis*- and *trans*-isomers of the hexa- and octa-decenoic acids are present in cow milk fat.

The characteristic acids of ruminant milk fats, like those of corresponding depot fats, are doubtless determined by the special metabolism of the ruminant. For the depot fats this was discussed on a previous page (p. 112) whilst further consideration of the mechanism of production of ruminant milk glycerides will be deferred to Chapter V (pp. 410–415), since their characteristic glyceride constitution is also material to discussion of this problem.

The *diethenoid* C_{18} *acids of cow milk fat* have been the subject of much discussion. Hilditch and Miss Jones[123] mentioned in 1929 that the acids then recorded as linoleic failed to give the usual yields of the tetrahydroxy-stearic acids (m.p. 157° and 173°) characteristic of linoleic acid from vegetable sources. In 1933, Bosworth and Brown[117] could not detect any linoleic acid in butter fat, whilst Eckstein[133a] could only find minute amounts of linoleic and linolenic acids, when isolated in the form of their characteristic tetra- or hexa-bromo-additive products. Green and Hilditch[133b] showed that the polyethenoid unsaturation of the C_{18} acids was not due, beyond a very limited extent, to tetra- or even tri-ethenoid unsaturation, and also found that the products of disruptive oxidation were hexanoic and azelaic acids, thus indicating the presence of double bonds in the 9:10 and 12:13 positions of the octadecadienoic acid. Brown[134a] and Hilditch[134b] considered in 1937–38 that, apart from minute proportions of seed-fat (*cis-cis-*) linoleic acid, the diethenoid C_{18} acids of cow milk fat were mainly other geometrical (*cis-trans-*) isomers of octadeca-9:12-dienoic acid. Hilditch and Jasperson[122a] obtained evidence of traces of a triene C_{18} acid and, by spectroscopic examination, of a small proportion of conjugated diene acid, and later[122b] showed that alkali isomerisation at 180° of a concentrate of the polyethenoid C_{18} acids of butter fat caused the production of considerably more conjugated diene and slightly more conjugated triene acids, indicating that the milk fat acids contained the "pentadiene" grouping $-CH:CH.CH_2.CH:CH-$. Scott *et al.*[131c] stated in 1959 that the C_{18} diene acids of butter fat were a mixture of non-conjugated and conjugated forms, the former a mixture of *cis-cis-* and either *cis-trans-* or *trans-trans-*isomers and the latter a mixture of *cis-cis-* and *trans-trans-*isomers. K. Sambasivarao and J. B. Brown[131g] (1962) in a further intensive study of the C_{18} diene and triene acids of butter fat, estimated that of the non-conjugated octadecadienoic acids about two-thirds is linoleic acid and the remainder *cis-trans-*isomers (largely linoleic isomers with widely separated double bonds); the *trans-trans-*form did not seem to be present.

Shorland[135] found that in New Zealand butterfat there were small but about equal proportions of triene and diene C_{18} acids; the former was largely "seed-fat" linolenic acid, but the octadecadienoic acids were similar to those of English cow milk fats,[122, 133] i.e. a mixture of conjugated and non-conjugated acids in which "seed-fat" linoleic acid was not detectable. Mattsson[136] has reported the presence of 0·7–2 per cent. of ordinary linolenic acid in Swedish butterfats. Scott *et al*[131c] state that the tri-, tetra- and penta-ene acids of butter fat all possess *cis-*configurations. The nature of the C_{18} di- and tri-ene acids has also been discussed by Sambasivarao.[131g]

The traces of *highly unsaturated acids of the* C_{20-22} *series* (or "arachidonic" type) present in milk fats appear to be similar to those in the corresponding depot fats (*cf.* p. 111).

The complex nature of the cow milk fat polyethenoid C_{18} acids is thus similar to that of the corresponding acids of ox and sheep depot and liver glycerides, and liver phosphatides. In contrast human milk fat (Bosworth[137]), like human body fat (Cramer and Brown[105a]), includes ordinary or seed-fat linoleic acid amongst its diethenoid C_{18} acids.

The *lower saturated acids of milk fats*, although collectively not so prominent as either oleic or palmitic acid, are the constituents which qualitatively differentiate many milk fats from all other fats. In cow milk fat, the acids from butyric to lauric account for about 18 to 22 mols. per 100 mols. of the total component acids; of these butyric usually amounts to 8–11 mols. per cent., and hexanoic to 3–4 mols. per cent. Butyric acid is thus the most abundant of the lower saturated acids in cow milk fat, but this statement does not apply to the milk fats of some other ruminants. Lauric acid has been isolated in the pure state from butter fat by Hansen and Cooke.[129c]

Of *higher saturated acids*, cow milk fats contain very minor proportions of arachidic acid, whilst trace amounts of the following higher saturated acids have been observed (Shorland, Hansen *et al.*):

Normal even-numbered: behenic C_{22}, lignoceric C_{24}, hexacosanoic C_{26}[129g]
Normal odd-numbered: C_{11},[129f] C_{13},[129e] C_{15},[129b] C_{17},[129h] C_{19},[129g] C_{21},[129g] C_{23}[129g]
Branched-chain: (+)-10-methyl- and 11-methyl-dodecanoic,[129e] methyl-tridecanoic,[129b] 12- and 13-methyltetradecanoic,[129b] 14-methylpenta-decenoic,[129i] two methylhexadecanoic[129b] acids and a tri- or tetra-methyl-eicosanoic acid[129b] (also 3,7,11,15-tetramethylhexadecanoic, Sonneveld *et al.*[129k]).

Shorland and Hansen have given a complete review of these trace components.[129j]

Several investigators[132a] have recently (1956–61) analysed the component acids of cow milk fats by gas–liquid chromatography; this procedure has given figures for major component acids in line with the ranges shown by ester-fractionation, but in addition has indicated the approximate proportions of many of the trace acids to which reference has just been made. It may be illustrated by a comprehensive study of Herb, Magidman, Luddy and Riemenschneider,[132b] in which prior fractionation (F) of the total methyl esters into eleven fractions and a residue was found to be advantageous, each of the ester fractions being then submitted to gas–liquid chromatography (GLC) and also examined by ultra-violet spectrophotometry (S) after alkali isomerisation. The complex residual fraction from the ester-distillation was further separated by column chromatography on silicic acid into seven fractions, each of which was separately analysed (S and GLC). "In all, 64 different acids were accounted for, 27 of which were present in less than 0·1 per cent. concentration in the milk fat and would account for only 1 per cent. of the total fatty acids". The following acids were reported (per cent. wt.):

Saturated (*even number*). Butyric 2·8, *n*-hexanoic 2·3, *n*-octanoic 1·1, *n*-decanoic 3·0, lauric 2·9, myristic 8·9, palmitic 23·8, stearic 13·2, arachidic 0·3, behenic 0·1 per cent.

152

Saturated (*odd number*). n-C_{15} 0·8, n-C_{17} 0·7, n-C_{19} 0·3 per cent.

Saturated (*branched-chain*). C_{14} 0·1, C_{15} 0·6, C_{16} 0·2, C_{17} 0·6 per cent.

Monoene. C_{10} 0·3, C_{12} 0·1, C_{14} 0·8, C_{16} 1·8, C_{17} 0·3, C_{18} 29·6, C_{20} 0·2 per cent.

Diene. C_{18} (*cis-cis-*) 2·1, (*cis-trans-*) 0·6 per cent.

Triene. C_{18} (all *cis-*) 0·5, C_{20} 0·1 per cent.

Tetra-ene. C_{20} 0·1 per cent.

Trace acids:

  Saturated. n-C_5, n-C_7, n-C_9, n-C_{11}, n-C_{13}, n-C_{21}, n-C_{23}, n-C_{24}, n-C_{25}, n-C_{26}; branched-chain C_{13}, C_{18}, C_{20}.

  Unsaturated. Monoene C_{15}, C_{19}, C_{21}, C_{22}, C_{23}, C_{24}; *Diene* C_{18} (*trans-trans-*), C_{20}, C_{22}; *Triene* C_{18} (conj.), C_{22}; *Tetraene* C_{22}; *Pentaene* C_{20}, C_{22}.

Some further observations on the production of milk fat glycerides under specific conditions of diet, etc.

The component acids (quoted in Table 51B) of the *colostrum* fat from an individual cow examined by Baldwin and Longenecker[127b] fall closely within the range of those of milk fats from pasture-fed cows so far as the unsaturated acids, and also most of the saturated acids, are concerned. The palmitic acid content, however, is somewhat higher than the average for cow milk fats, whilst the butyric and hexanoic acid contents are slightly lower. Anantakrishnan *et al.*[138a] examined the colostrum and milk fats of a cow during the first fifteen days of lactation. The first day's colostrum fat was much richer in oleic acid and poorer in short-chain saturated acids than normal cow milk fat and resembled more closely human milk fat (p. 163) or a soft cow depot fat; as lactation proceeded the oleic content of the fat fell whilst the short chain saturated acids rose, until after several days the normal composition of cow milk fat was attained. These workers[138a] observed a similar sequence of changes in buffalo milk fat at the commencement of lactation.

Effect of fasting or of certain pathological conditions on the component acids of cow milk fats. The effects of fasting and of conditions such as ketosis, whilst not wholly interrupting the secretion of milk fat by the cow, cause the composition of the milk fat to be widely altered from normal: in particular, the proportions of butyric and the other lower saturated acids are much reduced, whilst the oleic acid content is correspondingly increased. In other words, the milk fat from a starving cow, or a cow suffering from severe ketosis, resembles the depot fats in its component acids, rather than a normal milk fat. It is not unreasonable to infer that a normal metabolic conversion of oleoglycerides into lower saturated "milk fat" glycerides has been disturbed by the abnormal condition of the cow.

The effect of fasting (inanition) on the component acids of cow milk fat was first observed by Smith and Dastur,[139] who recorded the striking figures given in Table 52A. In the case of Cow No. 1, the molar contents of the C_4–C_{14} acids fell during fasting by a total of 24·2 per cent., whilst those of the C_{18} acids (oleic, stearic, and octadecadienoic) increased by a total of 24·7 per cent.

TABLE 52A. *Component Acids of Cow Milk Fat produced during Fasting (Smith and Dastur[139])*
(minor unsaturated components included)

| | COW No. 1 | | COW No. 2 |
	BEFORE FASTING	DURING FASTING* *Molar Percentages*	DURING FASTING†
Butyric	9·7	3·5	7·9
n-Hexanoic	1·2	—	0·1
n-Octanoic	1·6	0·2	0·2
n-Decanoic	2·5	0·3	1·5
Lauric	3·0	0·2	0·7
Myristic	12·5	3·2	4·3
Palmitic	22·1	20·9	22·1
Stearic	9·8	13·5	8·9
Arachidic	0·8	0·8	0·8
Dec-9-enoic	0·3	—	0·2
Dodec-9-enoic	0·3	—	0·3
Tetradec-9-enoic	1·0	0·5	0·5
Hexadec-9-enoic	3·0	1·5	2·0
Oleic	30·5	50·1	46·9
Octadecadienoic	1·0	2·4	0·7
Unsaturated C_{20}	0·6	2·9	2·9

* Sample from mixed fat secreted on 11th and 12th days of inanition.
† Pooled sample from fat secreted on the last six days (7th–12th) of inanition.

TABLE 52B. *Component Acids (per cent. mol.) of Milk Fats from Cows Giving Milk of Varying Fat Content*
(Holmberg et al.[141])

	HERD I		HERD II	
Fat content of milk (per cent.):	1·1	2·0	2·7	5·2
Unsaponifiable matter in fat:	2·1	2·4	0·5	0·8
ACID				
Butyric	1·7	5·6	8·2	9·2
n-Hexanoic	3·3	5·5	5·6	6·4
n-Octanoic	—	2·8	1·9	2·3
n-Decanoic	2·5	4·4	4·6	6·0
Lauric	5·5	7·3	4·2	4·5
Myristic	12·1	14·4	11·4	14·2
Palmitic	27·9	25·9	23·9	31·8
Stearic	4·1	7·6	6·2	5·8
Arachidic	0·9	—	0·7	—
Dec-9-enoic	0·4	0·4	0·3	0·2
Dodec-9-enoic	0·8	0·7	0·3	0·2
Tetradec-9-enoic	5·1	1·9	1·1	1·2
Hexadec-9-enoic	4·1	2·2	2·4	1·6
Oleic	26·6	19·8	25·4	16·4
Octadecadienoic	3·8	1·0	2·2	0·2
Octadecatrienoic	1·2	0·5	1·2	—
Unsaturated C_{20}	—	—	0·4	—

Again, Shaw et al.,[140] have shown from general characteristics of saponification, Reichert-Meissl, Polenske, and iodine values that in severe ketosis the short chain fatty acids of cow milk fall considerably below normal, whilst the oleic acid content augments. On treatment by glucose therapy the cow recovers and concurrently the milk fat reverts to its normal composition. The lower saturated acids are not decreased as much by ketosis as by short periods of fasting: qualitatively, however, the alterations produced in cow milk fat both by lack of food and by ketosis are similar.

In this connection some data obtained by Holmberg et al.[141] (1954) indicate that the milk fat of cows giving milk of low fat content is also relatively deficient in the lower saturated acids, although the inverse relationship between the oleic acid content and that of the lower saturated acids is not so clear as in the inanition experiments of Smith and Dastur (Table 52A). The results of Holmberg et al. (shown in Table 52B) were for individual cows from two different herds.

Component acids of milk fats from cows receiving specific fatty oils in their diets. Hilditch, with Sleightholme[124] and Thompson,[121] studied fats from the milk of Berkshire cows which had been given a regular ration of one or other fatty oil for some time previous to the period at which the milk was taken. Hilditch and Jasperson[122c] examined the milk fats of Ayrshire heifers from a Cheshire farm in which a basal control diet was supplemented with 8 ounces daily of refined groundnut oil, groundnut oil hydrogenated to iodine values of 45 or 17, or refined palm kernel oil (iodine value 17). The results of all these studies are summarised in Table 53.

Comparison with cow milk fats of animals on normal stall or pasture diets (Tables 51A, 51B, 53–II) shows that certain significant, although comparatively slight, effects result from the ingestion of specific dietary fats.

Cows which received fats (*coconut* or *palm kernel oils*) rich in lauric and myristic acids (*cf.* Chapter IV, Table 69B, p. 341) yielded milk fats with

TABLE 53. *Component Acids of Cow Milk Fats (effect of added fats in diets)*

I. INGESTED FAT*	COCO-NUT OIL[124]	SOYA BEAN OIL[124]	LINSEED OIL[121]	RAPE OIL[121]	COD LIVER OIL[121]	
					I	II
	(a)	(a)	(a)	(b)	(a)	(b)
	(a) Minor unsaturated components not allowed for.					
	(b) Minor unsaturated components included.					
ACID	*Molar Percentages*					
Butyric	9·0	9·6	11·2	9·9	6·1	5·7
n-Hexanoic	3·9	3·0	4·1	3·4	2·0	1·2
n-Octanoic	1·7	2·8	2·1	1·6	0·8	1·0
n-Decanoic	4·3	5·1	3·1	2·2	1·8	1·9
Lauric	8·3	7·5	3·6	2·2	3·9	1·1
Myristic	17·2	10·7	8·6	8·6	7·1	9·3
Palmitic	24·1	23·7	20·0	19·1	22·4	25·1
Stearic	3·9	6·7	8·2	11·7	6·0	7·3
as Arachidic	—	0·9	0·4	0·4	0·5	0·5
Decenoic	—	—	—	0·2	—	0·8
Tetradecenoic	—	—	—	1·4	—	1·5
Hexadecenoic	—	—	—	2·3	—	3·3
Oleic	25·7	27·0	32·8	30·8	38·8	33·8
Octadecadienoic	1·9	3·0	5·0	2·9	4·4	3·5
as Unsaturated C_{20-22}	—	—	0·9	0·7	6·2	4·0
as Erucic	—	—	—	2·6	—	—

* Fat added to basal ration:

Coconut oil cake	7 lb. coconut cake daily for two weeks previously.
Soya bean cake	5·2 lb. soya bean cake daily for two weeks previously.
Linseed oil	4 ounces linseed oil daily for two weeks previously.
Rape oil	4 ounces rape oil daily for two weeks previously.
Cod liver oil	4 ounces cod liver oil daily for two weeks previously.

TABLE 53—continued.

	CONTROL (Hay, swedes, oats)	PALM KERNEL OIL (I.V.17)	GROUND-NUT OIL (I.V.88)	HYDROGENATED GROUNDNUT OIL	
II. INGESTED FAT[122c]:				(I.V.45)	(I.V.17)
ACID			Minor unsaturated components included.		
			Molar Percentages		
Butyric	10·5	8·6	8·2	7·6	9·8
n-Hexanoic	4·6	3·4	3·2	3·3	4·3
n-Octanoic	1·3	1·9	0·8	0·9	1·9
n-Decanoic	2·7	1·8	1·9	2·1	2·1
Lauric	2·6	7·1	2·1	2·4	2·3
Myristic	9·6	11·3	7·9	6·7	8·5
Palmitic	23·4	20·6	22·8	21·0	23·2
Stearic	9·7	10·0	10·9	14·4	11·6
as Arachidic	0·6	0·8	1·0	0·8	0·9
Decenoic	0·3	0·2	0·1	0·1	0·2
Dodecenoic	0·2	0·5	0·2	0·2	0·2
Tetradecenoic	1·0	1·1	0·8	0·6	0·8
Hexadecenoic	2·1	2·2	2·1	2·2	1·4
Oleic	28·6	28·1	35·2	34·4	30·0
Octadecadienoic	1·8	1·0	1·6	2·9	1·5
Unsaturated C_{20-22}	1·0	1·4	1·2	0·4	1·3

definitely increased contents of these two acids, and consequently somewhat lowered oleic and palmitic acid: some of the dilauromyristins of the nut fats had apparently passed into the milk fats.

In spite of the high linoleic acid contents of *groundnut, rape, soya bean,* and *linseed oils,* and of the linolenic glycerides also present in the three latter oils, the amount of polyethenoid C_{18} acids in the milk fats of cows which had received any of these oils showed little significant increase, nor were ordinary linoleic or linolenic acids detectable as insoluble bromo-adducts. At the same time, the oleic acid contents of all these milk fats were normal or somewhat greater than normal, and (except for some reduction in the groundnut-oil-fed cows) the lower saturated acids were maintained at the usual level.

In contrast to the absence of linoleic or linolenic acid in the milk fats just discussed, small quantities of erucic glycerides appeared in the milk fats of cows fed on *rape oil,* and much larger proportions than usual (4–6 per cent. mol.) of highly-unsaturated C_{20} and C_{22} acids when the diet of the cow included *cod liver oil.* Concurrently with the appearance of these highly-unsaturated acids in the latter milk fats there was a marked departure from normal in their composition: the amount of butyric and other lower saturated acids was approximately halved, and a proportionately similar increase took place in the oleic acid contents. These results are still more striking when given in terms of the amount of each fatty acid produced daily by the lactating cow (see table opposite).

Golding[142] has shown that the component of cod liver oil responsible for the specific effects of lowered milk yield (and alteration in milk fat composition) is in the glyceride fractions, and not the unsaponifiable constituents. The effect on the cow milk fats is analogous to that of fasting or ketosis.

The effects of feeding *hydrogenated groundnut oil* were little different from ingestion of groundnut oil itself, except for slight increases in stearic acid

Approximate weight production of milk fatty acids in a cow receiving 4 oz. daily of cod liver oil in food

(Combined milk from 2 cows collected over 4-day periods in each case)

	BEFORE C.L.O. DIET LB.	DURING C.L.O. DIET LB.	AFTER C.L.O. DIET	
			IMMEDI-ATELY LB.	2 WEEKS LATER LB.
Milk fat production (2 cows) over 4 day period	7·91	5·60	5·33	7·76
Corresponding butter fatty acids	7·51	5·33	5·07	7·37
Butyric acid	0·33	0·11	0·11	0·33
Caproic acid	0·13	0·05	0·05	0·13
Caprylic acid	0·16	0·03	0·03	0·16
Capric acid	0·22	0·06	0·06	0·22
Lauric acid	0·28	0·16	0·16	0·27
Myristic acid	0·76	0·34	0·32	0·75
Palmitic acid	1·90	1·21	1·15	1·86
Stearic acid	0·93	0·36	0·34	0·91
Arachidic acid	0·06	0·03	0·03	0·06
Oleic acid	2·33	2·31	2·19	2·28
Octadecadienoic acid	0·33	0·26	0·24	0·32
Unsaturated C_{20-22} acids	0·08	0·41	0·39	0·08

content. The observed results are consonant with non-assimilation of high-melting fully saturated glycerides, and the absorption of a certain proportion of oleodistearin into the milk fat. There is no evidence that, as supposed by W. C. Brown *et al.*,[143] ingestion of highly hydrogenated fats leads to de-saturation of stearo-glycerides in the animal fats.

Component acids of cow milk phosphatides. Until it was demonstrated in 1936[144a] and confirmed later[144b,144c] that blood phosphatides are unaltered during passage of blood through the mammary gland of the cow, but that blood glycerides disappear as milk fat is produced, it was widely supposed that phosphatides played an important part in the production of the characteristic glycerides of cow milk. It is thus somewhat curious that the component acids of cow milk phosphatides were not studied in any detail until 1934. In that year Kurtz, Jamieson and Holm[145] examined the phosphatides from buttermilk powder and found that part was insoluble in ether at 0°: this fraction contained about 80 per cent. of lignoceric acid, probably emanating from a mixture of sphingomyelin and cerebrosides, but the acids of the ether-soluble portion were more akin to the usual fatty acids.

In 1941 Hilditch and Maddison[146] examined two specimens of crude phosphatides separated respectively from Swiss butter fat and from English butter fat clarification residues. It will be noticed that they contained a certain amount of higher saturated acids (calculated arbitrarily as $C_{26}H_{52}O_2$) from wax or cerebroside compounds admixed with the crude phosphatides. In 1959 Kaufmann and Mohr[147a] used a paper-chromatographic method to determine the acids of cow milk phosphatides, with results showing an ex-tremely small proportion of oleic acid and very high palmitic, stearic and behenic contents. The results of the three groups of workers are as follows in the table on page 158.

Component acids (per cent. wt.) of cow milk phosphatides

ACID	Kurtz et al.[145]	Hilditch and Maddison[146]		Kaufmann and Mohr[147a]
		SWISS	ENGLISH	
Myristic	5·2	3·2	5·5	6
Palmitic	—	21·0	13·4	43
Stearic	16·1	7·3	9·0	23
as Arachidic	1·8	12·3	20·9	1 (a)
as $C_{26}H_{52}O_2$	—	5·2	10·0	—
Hexadecenoic	—	4·3	4 9	—
Oleic	70·6	32·5	23·5	3
Octadecadienoic	—	6·4	—	—
Unsaturated C_{20-22}	6·3	7·8	12·8	18 (b)

(a) Also 8 per cent. behenic acid; *(b)* C_{22} diene 4, C_{24} triene 14 per cent.

Using spectrophotometric analysis, Smith and Jack[147b] (1959) observed the following proportions of different classes of acids in cow milk phosphatides and glycerides (the latter given in brackets): saturated 41·3 (63·5 including C_4-C_{12}), monoethenoid 39·8 (32·1), diene 11·1 (3·0), triene 3·6 (1·9), tetraene 2·0 (0·3) and pentaene 2·2 (0·2) per cent. Mattsson *et al.*[147c] isolated 1·7–2·5 gm. of phospholipids per kilo of butter and noted they contained much more, and much more highly, unsaturated acids than the butter glycerides.

Clearly, the phosphatide component acids differ entirely from those of cow milk glycerides. Acids of lower molecular weight than myristic are completely absent, so that the lower saturated acids – the most characteristic of the cow milk fat acids – have no counterpart in the cow milk phosphatide acids. These, however, resemble those of cow liver and other animal liver phosphatides (*cf.* Table 48, p. 135) in their general composition, and especially in the presence, entirely characteristic for phosphatides, of notable proportions of highly unsaturated acids of the C_{20} and C_{22} series. In detail the data are not accordant; but, nevertheless, the general resemblance to other animal phosphatides is as marked as is their essential difference in fatty acid composition from the cow milk glycerides.

By chromatographic separation Rhodes and Lea[148] estimate that cow milk phospholipids include phosphatidyl-choline 33, -ethanolamine 29, -serine 10 and sphingomyelin 19 per cent. (mol.). No lysophosphatides were detected; unsaturated acids were present in the 3(α')-and the 2(β)-glycerol positions (in contrast to other animal phosphatides in which unsaturated groups are mainly attached to the 3-, and saturated groups to the 2-positions).

Component acids of milk fats of other herbivorous mammals. The milk fats of a moderate number of species of animals, other than the cow, have been examined in detail. Table 54A gives data for goat, sheep, camel, and buffalo milk fatty acids (calculated without allowance for minor unsaturated acids), Table 54B similar data (including minor unsaturated components) for buffalo milk fatty acids, and Table 54C similar data (including minor unsaturated components) for other goat and sheep milk fats, and for those of the sow and mare.

Comparing the molar percentages of the acids in Tables 54A, 54B, and 54C, it is clear that (with the exception of mare milk fat) the proportion of palmitic acid does not vary greatly in the milk fats of any of the species listed. The buffalo, sow, and camel approach the value of 30 per cent. (mol.) which is characteristic for the depot fats of oxen, pigs, and many other animals.

This figure is appreciably lower in sheep and goat milk fats (20–26 per cent. mol.), and it may be recalled that the palmitic acid content of sheep depot fats (Tables 35, 36) is usually about 4 or 5 per cent. lower than that of ox depot fats.

TABLE 54A. *Component Acids of Goat, Sheep, Camel and Buffalo Milk Fats*
(minor unsaturated components not included)

ACID	GOAT[149a] INDIAN	SHEEP[149b] INDIAN	CAMEL[149b] INDIAN	BUFFALO[125] INDIAN	BUFFALO[150] TURKISH
		(i) *Weight percentages*			
Butyric	3·0	3·3	2·1	4·1	4·3
n-Hexanoic (caproic)	2·3	2·8	0·9	1·4	1·3
n-Octanoic (caprylic)	3·9	3·8	0·6	0·9	0·4
n-Decanoic (capric)	8·6	7·8	1·4	1·7	Trace
Lauric	4·6	5·4	4·6	2·8	3·0
Myristic	11·5	12·2	7·3	10·1	7·3
Palmitic	24·7	23·5	29·3	31·1	26·1
Stearic	9·3	6·9	11·1	11·2	16·5
as Arachidic	0·1	1·9	—	0·9	3·3
Oleic	30·5	28·3	38·8	33·2	35·8
as Octadecadienoic	1·5	4·1	3·8	2·6	2·0
		(ii) *Molar Percentages*			
Butyric	7·6	8·4	5·9	10·9	11·8
n-Hexanoic	4·5	5·4	1·9	2·8	2·7
n-Octanoic	6·2	5·8	1·1	1·5	0·7
n-Decanoic	11·1	10·1	2·1	2·4	Trace
Lauric	5·1	6·0	5·7	3·3	3·7
Myristic	11·2	11·8	7·9	10·5	7·8
Palmitic	21·5	20·4	28·3	28·7	24·5
Stearic	7·3	5·4	9·7	9·3	14·0
as Arachidic	0·1	1·3	—	0·7	2·5
Oleic	24·2	22·2	34·1	27·7	30·6
as Octadecadienoic	1·2	3·2	3·3	2·2	1·7

TABLE 54B. *Component Acids of Indian Buffalo Milk Fats*
(minor unsaturated components included)

Reichert-Meissl value of fat	37·4[72a]	30·8[72a]	22·7[72a]	20·7[72a]	28·8[126]
Iodine value of fat	27·4	28·9	34·9	37·0	30·2
ACID		(i) *Weight Percentages*			
Butyric	5·8	5·0	3·7	4·1	4·8
n-Hexanoic	0·6	0·2	0·3	—	1·7
n-Octanoic	0·9	0·3	1·3	0·1	0·5
n-Decanoic	1·0	0·6	1·3	0·3	1·3
Lauric	1·6	2·0	2·1	0·6	2·8
Myristic	9·0	11·9	6·7	4·4	11·5
Palmitic	35·2	34·2	23·7	25·8	29·0
Stearic	15·3	12·2	19·7	21·7	14·0
as Arachidic	0·1	—	1·3	1·4	1·4
Decenoic	0·1	0·1	0·2	Trace	Trace
Dodecenoic	0·1	0·1	0·2	0·1	0·1
Tetradecenoic	0·6	1·0	0·8	0·5	0·8
Hexadecenoic	3·3	3·2	5·3	3·0	3·8
Oleic	20·5	27·6	33·2	36·2	25·5
Octadecadienoic	1·5	0·5	0·2	1·1	1·6
Unsaturated C_{20-22}	4·4	1·1	—	0·7	1·2

159

TABLE 54B—*continued.*

	GOAT[149a] INDIAN	SHEEP[149b] INDIAN	CAMEL[149b] INDIAN	BUFFALO[125] INDIAN	BUFFALO[150] TURKISH
			(ii) *Molar Percentages*		
Butyric	15·4	13·5	10·1	11·5	12·6
n-Hexanoic	1·1	0·4	0·7	—	3·3
n-Octanoic	1·4	0·5	2·2	0·1	0·8
n-Decanoic	1·4	0·9	1·8	0·5	1·7
Lauric	1·9	2·4	2·6	0·8	3·3
Myristic	9·2	12·3	7·1	4·8	11·7
Palmitic	31·9	31·5	22·5	25·1	26·3
Stearic	12·5	10·1	16·8	19·0	11·5
as Arachidic	0·1	—	1·0	1·1	1·1
Decenoic	0·1	0·1	0·3	Trace	Trace
Dodecenoic	0·1	0·1	0·2	0·1	0·2
Tetradecenoic	0·6	1·0	0·8	0·5	0·8
Hexadecenoic	3·0	3·0	5·1	2·9	3·5
Oleic	16·8	23·0	28·6	32·0	21·0
Octadecadienoic	1·2	0·4	0·2	1·0	1·3
Unsaturated C_{20-22}	3·3	0·8	—	0·6	0·9

TABLE 54C. *Component Acids of Goat, Sheep, Sow, Mare and Eland Milk Fats*

ACID	GOAT[118] U.S.A.	GOAT[151a] ENGLISH	SHEEP[151a] ENGLISH	SOW[152] NEW ZEALAND	MARE[151a] ENGLISH	ELAND[151b] RHODESIA
			(i) *Weight Percentages*			
Butyric	2·1	3·0	2·8	⎫	0·4	0·9
n-Hexanoic	1·9	2·5	2·6	⎪	0·9	0·5
n-Octanoic	2·7	2·8	2·2	⎬ 1·3 ⎨	2·6	0·4
n-Decanoic	7·9	10·0	4·8	⎪	5·5	1·2
Lauric	3·5	6·0	3·9	⎭	5·6	—
Myristic	10·2	12·3	9·7	1·5	7·0	12·4
Palmitic	28·7	27·9	23·9	26·9	16·1	35·2
Stearic	8·1	6·0	12·6	6·5	2·9	15·2
as Arachidic	0·4	0·6	1·1	—	0·3	Trace
Decenoic	0·2	0·3	0·1	—	0·9	—
Dodecenoic	—	0·3	0·1	—	1·0	0·7
Tetradecenoic	0·4	0·8	0·6	—	1·8	1·2
Hexadecenoic	2·1	2·6	2·2	8·3	7·5	6·2
Oleic	31·1	21·1	26·3	36·7	⎱42·4(−3·7H)⎰	17·9
Octadecadienoic	—	3·6	5·2	14·6		2·0
Unsaturated C_{20-22}	0·7	0·2	1·9	4·2	5·1	1·6
			(ii) *Molar Percentages*			
Butyric	5·6	7·5	7·5	⎫	1·1	2·7
n-Hexanoic	3·8	4·7	5·3	⎪	1·9	1·1
n-Octanoic	4·3	4·3	3·5	⎬ 2·4 ⎨	4·4	0·7
n-Decanoic	10·6	12·8	6·4	⎪	7·9	1·8
Lauric	4·0	6·6	4·5	⎭	6·8	—
Myristic	10·3	11·8	9·9	1·8	7·4	14·4
Palmitic	25·9	24·1	21·6	28·3	15·4	36·3
Stearic	6·6	4·7	10·3	6·1	2·4	14·1
as Arachidic	0·3	0·4	0·8	—	0·2	—
Decenoic	0·3	0·3	0·2	—	1·3	—
Dodecenoic	—	0·3	0·2	—	1·2	0·9
Tetradecenoic	0·4	0·8	0·6	—	1·9	1·4
Hexadecenoic	1·9	2·2	2·0	8·8	7·2	6·5
Oleic	25·5	16·5	21·6	35·0	⎱36·9⎰	16·8
Octadecadienoic	—	2·8	4·3	14·0		1·2
Unsaturated C_{20-22}	0·5	0·2	1·3	3·6	4·0	1·3

The oleic acid content, as usual, varies somewhat widely, even in the case of milk fats of the same species of animal: thus in the three goat milk fats the range of oleic acid content is 16·5–25·5 per cent. (mol.).

The most striking differences, however, are manifested in the contents and kinds of the lower saturated acids present. In buffalo milk the proportions of butyric and of the other lower acids up to lauric are indistinguishable from those of cow milk fats, but in no other species do the proportions of butyric acid in the milk fats reach those of the bovine group. The detailed component acid analyses of four *buffalo milk fats* (*ghee*) of differing Reichert-Meissl and iodine values, given by Achaya and Banerjee[72a] (Table 54B), again reveal some approach to constancy in palmitic acid content. The milk fats with lowest palmitic and very high (17 and 19 per cent. mol.) stearic acid resulted after intensive feeding of the buffalo cows with cotton-seed. Anantakrishnan *et al.*[138b] have recorded similar effects on the milk fats of buffaloes in which a basal ration was supplemented by cottonseed oil, hydrogenated groundnut oil, or coconut oil. Dhingra and Chandra[153] observed that buffalo milk fat at early stages of lactation contained more butyric and lower saturated acids, and less oleic acid, than at the later stages; this accords with the observations of Shorland[129a] and others[120] on cow milk fats (*cf.* pp. 149, 150).

In the *milk fats of sheep and goats* the butyric acid content is already reduced by about one quarter compared with bovine milk fats, although the total content of butyric-decanoic acids amounts to 25–30 per cent. (mol.) of the total fatty acids, in consequence of specifically high proportions of decanoic (capric) and, to a less degree, octanoic (caprylic) acids in goat and sheep milk fats; the molar percentage of decanoic acid frequently reaches 10 or even somewhat higher in goat milk fats.

Camel milk fat appears to contain only about half the proportion of butyric acid present in bovine milk fats, the amount of oleic acid being correspondingly increased; whilst in *sow* and *mare milk fats* it would appear that the lower saturated acids occur only in very minor quantities, or even traces, so that to a large extent these milk fats closely resemble the corresponding depot fats.

The figures given by de la Mare and Shorland[152] for *sow milk fat* include a high content (14·6 per cent. wt.) of octadecadienoic acid, which failed to give more than traces of petrol-insoluble tetrabromo-adducts. The absence of ordinary or seed fat linoleic acid from the diethenoid C_{18} acids in the milk fats of the cow, ewe, goat, and sow, and in the depot fats of oxen and sheep, is one of the most characteristic features of all these fats; on the other hand the octadecadienoic acids of pig depot fats (usually present to the extent of only 5–7 per cent.) contain a fair proportion of ordinary linoleic acid (*cf.* p. 118).

The milk fat of the *mare*[151a] has several points of difference: its content of butyric acid, whilst definite, is only about one-tenth of that in cow milk fats; decanoic, lauric, and myristic acids each contribute about 7 per cent. (mol.). The palmitic acid content (15·4 per cent.) appears unusually low for a milk fat, but hexadecenoic acid (7·2 per cent.) is higher than usual, so that the total C_{16} acid content approaches 23 per cent. (mol.) of the total fatty acids. The unsaturated C_{20} and C_{22} acids are somewhat more prominent than in most milk fats, but the outstanding feature is the constitution of the unsaturated C_{18} acids. Here linolenic acid (the "seed-fat" form which gives a hexabromostearic acid, m.p. 181°) forms about 14 per cent. (mol). of the total fatty acids, the rest of the unsaturated C_{18} acids being oleic (16 per cent.) and octadecadienoic (7 per cent.), the latter being probably the "seed-fat" or linoleic form. The low proportion of oleic acid and the presence (as in horse depot fat, *cf.* p. 102) of substantial amounts of "seed-fat" linolenic acid combine to place the mare milk fat apart from any other milk fat yet examined.

The milk of the South Rhodesian eland antelope (*Taurotragus oryx*) contains about 11 per cent. of fat, the component acids of which were determined by reversed phase paper chromatography by Cmelik[151b]. They resemble those of horse milk fat in comparatively low contents of butyric-decanoic acids, whilst the relatively high proportions of palmitic, myristic and stearic acids resemble those in buffalo fats.

Component acids of human milk fat. It has long been known that human milk fat has marked differences in analytical characteristics from cow milk fat. In 1928 Elsdon[154] recorded Reichert-Meissl 3·4, Polenske 1·9, Kirschner 2·0, iodine value 35·9, for a mixed sample of human milk fat at an early stage of lactation. In 1934 Bosworth[137] separated the acids from about 3 lb. of human milk fat (saponification equivalent 273·4, iodine value 56·2, Reichert-Meissl value 2·5, Polenske value 0·1) into thirty fractions by distillation of the methyl esters. He found that the amount of butyric and hexanoic acids, if any, was extremely small, and that at least 0·02 per cent. of decenoic and 0·6 per cent. of tetradecenoic acids were present, and made the important observation that the octadecadienoic acids of human milk fat include considerable proportions of the ordinary or "seed fat" linoleic acid (*cis-cis*-octadeca-9,12-dienoic acid).

In 1944 Hilditch and Meara[155] determined the component acids of four human milk fats (from early, full, and late lactation periods) with the results given in Table 55A, and Baldwin and Longenecker[127a] determined those of human colostrum and milk fats (Table 55B). In 1946 J. B. Brown and Miss Orians[156] contributed a further detailed analysis of the component acids (Table 55B) of a mixed sample of human milk fat of iodine value 61·7.

The saturated acids of human milk fats in Tables 55A and 55B exhibit notable differences from those of cow (and other ruminant) milk fats. Although palmitic acid (the main saturated acid at about 22–24 per cent.), stearic, and myristic acids are present in proportions similar to those in which they occur in cow milk fats, the lower members of the series include only lauric and small proportions of decanoic acid. Careful examination of the steam-volatile acids from each specimen of milk fat studied by Hilditch and Meara[155] failed to reveal the presence of any butyric acid or of other acids of lower molecular weight than decanoic acid. Hence, whereas in cow milk fat, out of every 100 mols. of fatty acids, about 10 mols. consist of butyric acid, 4–5 mols. of hexanoic-octanoic acids, and 4–5 mols. of decanoic-lauric acids in human milk fat the three lower acids are not present and the combined amount of lauric and decanoic acids reaches 10–11 per cent. (mol.), with lauric acid predominating. Baldwin and Longenecker[127a] reported the presence of slightly more than 1 per cent. (mol.) of the three lower acids (chiefly butyric), but Brown and Orians[156] were unable to find more than traces of acids below C_{10}.

Subject to variation from one specimen to another in mean unsaturation (i.e. mainly in oleic acid content), it would appear that human milk fat component acids consist of saturated and unsaturated fatty acids in not far from equal proportions. In the unsaturated group oleic acid (the chief component acid of the whole fat) amounts to 30–40 per cent. (wt.), the minor components hexa- and tetra-decenoic acids occur in about the same proportions as in cow milk fat and in many animal body fats, but decenoic and dodecenoic acids are probably present in even lower proportions than in cow milk fat. The most arresting features of the unsaturated acids are the proportions of diethenoid C_{18} acids, unusually high for an animal fat and consisting, according to Bosworth,[137] Hilditch and Meara,[155] and Brown and Orians,[156] to a large extent of the linoleic acid characteristic of vegetable seed fats; and the amounts, also relatively high for a land animal fat, of unsaturated acids of the C_{20} and C_{22} series. At least 60 per cent. of the diethenoid C_{18} acids is the form of the linoleic (*cis-cis*-octadeca-9,12-dienoic) acid which is present in seed fats; so that human milk fat apparently differs both in the quantity and the nature of its octadecadienoic acids from the milk fats of the ruminants.

The general picture suggested by the data in Tables 55A and 55B is that, whatever the mechanism of formation of the lower fatty acids in milk fats, this process is carried on much more extensively, and to a lower range of acids, in the production of cow milk fat than in that of human milk fat. It may be said,

TABLE 55A. *Component Acids of Human Milk Fats*[155]

STAGE OF LACTATION:	COMPOSITE	EARLY	EARLY	FULL	LATE
Iodine value of fat	60·1	56·0	52·1	54·7	48·2

ACID	(i) *Weight Percentages*				
Decanoic	1·4	2·7	0·8	1·7	0·5
Lauric	5·9	5·1	6·1	6·4	7·0
Myristic	7·9	8·1	10·8	7·6	13·9
Palmitic	23·0	22·5	24·6	22·4	24·1
Stearic	7·0	8·3	7·3	9·0	9·6
as Arachidic	1·1	1·0	1·8	0·9	—
Decenoic	Trace	Trace	Trace	Trace	Trace
Dodecenoic	0·2	0·1	0·1	0·1	0·1
Tetradecenoic	0·7	1·3	0·4	0·5	0·9
Hexadecenoic	5·3	3·1	3·3	3·7	2·8
Oleic	35·6	36·4	32·8	36·6	30·2
Octadecadienoic	7·8	7·9	6·3	8·2	5·5
Unsaturated C_{20-22}	4·1	3·5	5·7	2·9	5·4

	(ii) *Molar Percentages*				
Decanoic	2·1	4·2	1·2	2·5	0·8
Lauric	7·7	6·7	8·0	8·3	9·0
Myristic	9·0	9·2	12·4	8·7	15·8
Palmitic	23·6	22·9	25·2	22·8	24·4
Stearic	6·5	7·7	6·7	8·3	8·8
as Arachidic	0·9	0·8	1·5	0·8	—
Decenoic	Trace	Trace	Trace	Trace	Trace
Dodecenoic	0·3	0·1	0·1	0·2	0·1
Tetradecenoic	0·8	1·5	0·5	0·6	1·1
Hexadecenoic	5·4	3·1	3·4	3·8	2·9
Oleic	33·2	33·6	30·4	33·9	27·6
Octadecadienoic	7·1	7·3	5·9	7·7	5·1
Unsaturated C_{20-22}	3·4	2·9	4·7	2·4	4·4

TABLE 55B. *Component Acids of Human Milk Fats*

ACID	COLOSTRUM[127a] 1st–2nd day	COLOSTRUM[127a] 3rd day	MILK (MATURE)[127a] 22nd–43rd day	MILK[156]
		(i) *Weight Percentages*		
Butyric	0·2	0·3	0·4	Trace(?)
Hexanoic	0·1	0·1	0·1	—
Octanoic	0·8	0·1	0·3	0·1
Decanoic	3·5	0·9	2·2	2·1
Lauric	0·9	2·6	5·5	4·8
Myristic	2·8	4·9	8·5	6·6
Palmitic	24·6	27·8	23·2	21·6
Stearic	9·9	7·7	6·9	6·8
as Arachidic	4·9	2·7	1·1	*
Decenoic	0·2	0·1	0·1	Trace
Dodecenoic	0·1	0·1	0·1	Trace
Tetradecenoic	0·1	0·2	0·6	0·4
Hexadecenoic	1·8	2·9	3·0	2·6
Oleic	36·0	37·1	36·5	39·5
Octadecadienoic	7·5	6·2	7·8	10·4
Octadecatrienoic	0·3	0·3	0·4	0·5
Eicosadienoic	4·6	4·7	2·4	*
Eicosatetraenoic	1·8	1·6	0·9	0·8
		(ii) *Molar Percentages*		
Butyric	0·7	0·8	1·1	Trace (?)
Hexanoic	0·3	0·2	0·1	—
Octanoic	1·5	0·1	0·6	0·1
Decanoic	5·3	1·4	3·3	3·2
Lauric	1·2	3·4	7·1	6·3
Myristic	3·3	5·7	9·6	7·6
Palmitic	25·4	28·9	23·4	22·2
Stearic	9·2	7·2	6·3	6·3
as Arachidic	4·1	2·3	0·9	*
Decenoic	0·3	0·1	0·1	Trace
Dodecenoic	0·1	0·1	0·1	Trace
Tetradecenoic	0·1	0·2	0·7	0·5
Hexadecenoic	1·9	3·0	3·0	2·7
Oleic	33·8	35·1	33·3	36·9
Octadecadienoic	7·1	5·9	7·2	9·8
Octadecatrienoic	0·3	0·2	0·4	0·5
Eicosadienoic	3·9	4·0	2·0	*
Eicosatetraenoic	1·5	1·4	0·8	0·7

* Also 0·2 per cent. (wt.) octadecatetraenoic and 3·6 per cent. (wt.) of other saturated and unsaturated C_{20} acids.

in consequence, that human milk fat has more resemblance to many types of soft margarine fats than to the butter fat from cow's milk.

In 1959 Insull and Ahrens[157a] analysed the acids in human milk fat (from 11 mothers on unrestricted diets) by means of gas–liquid chromatography assisted by spectrophotometric analysis. The major component acids included lauric 7, myristic 9, palmitic 21, stearic 7, hexadecenoic 2, oleic 29, isomeric forms of oleic 7 and linoleic 7 per cent. (wt.); the remaining 11 per cent. was made up of 30 minor or trace component acids, the latter including odd-numbered and branch-chain acids and a variety of unsaturated C_{19} and C_{20} acids. The percentage of fat in the milk varied considerably at different periods of lactation, but the composition of the milk fat (as in Tables 55A and 55B) was substantially the same throughout. These authors[157b] also studied the influence of diet on human milk fat composition. With diets deficient in calories, the milk fat approached the composition of human depot fat, and when the calorie balance was made normal or excessive by ingestion of dietary fats the milk fats commenced to show similarities to the latter in some respects. On the other hand when excess calories were supplied by a non-fatty diet there was a striking increase in the lauric and myristic contents of the milk fat (although the blood glycerides remained unaltered). The authors deduce that fat-synthesis in the breast is promoted by excess dietary calories, and that the specific proportions of lauric and myristic acids in human milk fat suggest that this synthesis operates differently from that in sites other than the mammary system.

References to Chapter III

1. (a) J. A. Lovern, *Biochem. J.*, 1940, **34**, 709; (b) S. Cmelik and Z. Bartl, *Z. Physiol. Chem.*, 1956, **305**, 170.
2. W. Kimura, *Chem. Umschau*, 1929, **36**, 185.
3. W. Bergmann, *J. Biol. Chem.*, 1936, **114**, 27.
4. M. Bachstez and A. Aragon, *J. Amer. Pharm. Assoc.*, 1942, **31**, 145.
5. E. Hastings and J. H. Pepper, *Arch. Biochem.*, 1944, **4**, 89.
6. H. Thoms, *Arb. Pharm. Inst. Univ. Berlin*, 1913, **10**, 180; *Chem. Zentr.*, 1913, II, 2052.
7. M. Tsujimoto, *J. Soc. Chem. Ind. Japan*, 1929, **32**, 52B.
8. (Miss) A. P. Dale and M. L. Meara, privately communicated.
9. (a) J., F., and M. L. Giral, *J. Biol. Chem.*, 1946, **162**, 55; (b) F. Giral, *ibid.*, 1946, **162**, 61.
10. A. P. Oliver, *Trans. Roy. Soc. New Zealand*, 1949, **77**, 321.
11. B. H. Iyer and P. R. Ayyar, *J. Indian Inst. Sci.*, 1931, **14**, A, 40.
12. M. M. Janot and P. Faudemay, *Bull. Soc. chim.*, 1937, (v), **4**, 1149.
13. N. Schultz, *Biochem. Z.*, 1922, **127**, 122.
14. (a) G. Collin, *Biochem. J.*, 1933, **27**, 1373; (b) D. N. Grindley, *J. Exptl. Biol.*, 1952, **29**, 440.
15. (a) M. Tsujimoto, *J. Soc. Chem. Ind. Japan*, 1920, **23**, 41, 1099; (b) P. Cattaneo and G. K. de Sutton, *Rev. Brasil Quim.*, 1951, **32**, 388.
16. (a) E. Klenk, *Z. Physiol. Chem.*, 1933, **221**, 67, 259, 264; (b) E. Klenk, F. Ditt and W. Diebold, *ibid.*, 1935, **232**, 54.
17. T. P. Hilditch and H. Paul, *Biochem. J.*, 1937, **31**, 227.
18. T. G. Green and T. P. Hilditch, *ibid.*, 1938, **32**, 681.
19. A. Ogata and A. Minato, *J. Pharm. Soc. Japan*, 1940, **60**, 76.
20. (a) J., F., and M. L. Giral, *Arch. Biochem.*, 1948, **16**, 181; (b) F. Giral and A. Marquez, *ibid.*, 1948, **16**, 187; (c) F. Giral, *ibid.*, 1948, **16**, 191; (d) S. P. Pathak and L. M. Dey, *Biochem. J.*, 1956, **62**, 448.
21. (a) C. B. Pollard and J. McLaughlin, Jr., *J. Amer. Oil Chem. Soc.*, 1952, **29**, 631; (b) Y. D. Karkhanis and N. G. Magar, *Biochem. J.*, 1955, **60**, 565.
22. (a) F. D. Gunstone and R. P. Paton, *Biochem. J.*, 1953, **54**, 621; (b) F. D. Gunstone and W. C. Russell, *ibid.*, 1954, **57**, 462.
23. S. P. Pathak and G. D. Pande, *J. Sci. Food Agric.*, 1955, **6**, 48.
24. M. Tsujimoto, *J. Soc. Chem. Ind. Japan*, 1937, **40**, 185B.
25. C. Hata, *J. Soc. Chem. Ind. Japan*, 1939, **42**, 88B; C. Hata and M. Fujikama, *ibid.*, 329B.
26. A. Bömer and H. Merten, *Z. Unters. Nahr. Genussm.*, 1922, **43**, 101.
27. J. Grossfeld, *Z. Unters. Lebensm.*, 1930, **60**, 64; 1931, **62**, 553.
28. T. P. Hilditch, E. C. Jones and A. J. Rhead, *Biochem. J.*, 1934, **28**, 786.
29. (Miss) E. M. Cruickshank, *Biochem. J.*, 1934, **28**, 965.
30. M. K. Nutter, E. E. Lockhart and R. S. Harris, *Oil and Soap*, 1943, **20**, 231.
31. (a) T. P. Hilditch, I. C. Sime and L. Maddison, *Biochem. J.*, 1942, **36**, 98; (b) F. D. Gunstone and W. C. Russell, *ibid.*, 1954, **57**, 459; *J. Sci. Food Agric.*, 1957, **8**, 287.

32. F. B. Shorland and Joan P. Gass, *J. Sci. Food Agric.*, 1961, **12**, 174.
33. (*a*) R. Koyama, *J. Soc. Chem. Ind. Japan*, 1928, **31**, 298B; (*b*) J. A. Lovern, *Biochem. J.*, 1938, **32**, 2142.
34. S. Ueno and T. Aoki, *J. Soc. Chem. Ind. Japan*, 1938, **41**, 362B.
35. (*a*) F. J. McClure and R. H. Carr, *Amer. J. Physiol.*, 1925, **74**, 70; (*b*) J. S. Hepburn and A. B. Katz, *J. Franklin Inst.*, 1927, **203**, 835.
36. (*a*) R. W. Riemenschneider, N. R. Ellis and H. W. Titus, *J. Biol. Chem.*, 1938, **126**, 255; (*b*) F. B. Shorland, *J. New Zealand Sci. Tech.*, 1951, **33**, 224; (*c*) D. N. Rhodes and C. H. Lea, *Biochem. J.*, 1957, **65**, 526; (*d*) J. C. Hawke, *Chem. and Ind.*, 1962, 1761; (*e*) J. W. Airan and D. G. Kalyankar, *J. Indian Chem. Soc., Ind. News Ed.*, 1952, **15**, 175.
37. H. and I. S. MacLean, "Lecithin and Allied Substances" (1927), Longmans, Green & Co., London.
38. V. Henriques and C. Hansen, *Skand. Arch. Physiol.*, 1903, **14**, 390.
39. L. Horlick and J. B. O'Neil, *Lancet*, 1958, **ii**, 243; 1960, **i**, 438; J. H. Skellon and D. A. Windsor, *J. Sci. Food Agric.*, 1962, **13**, 300.
40. (*a*) D. N. Rhodes, *Biochem. J.*, 1958, **68**, 380 (*see also* D. N. Rhodes and C. H. Lea, *Nature*, 1956, **177**, 1129; P. Wheeler *et al.*, *J. Nutrition*, 1959, **69**, 253); (*b*) N. L. Murty and R. Reiser, *J. Nutrition*, 1961, **75**, 287; (*c*) J. B. M. Coppock, *Chem. and Ind..*, 1962, 886.
41. C. H. Lea and J. C. Hawke, *Biochem. J.*, 1951, **50**, 67; 1952, **52**, 105; 1953, **54**, 475, 479; *see also* F. J. Joubert and W. H. Cook, *Canad. J. Biochem. Physiol.*, 1958, **36**, 389, 399.
42. A. Banks, T. P. Hilditch and E. C. Jones, *Biochem. J.*, 1933, **27**, 1375.
43. J. M. Spadola and N. R. Ellis, *J. Biol. Chem.*, 1936, **113**, 205.
44. H. E. Longenecker and T. P. Hilditch, *Biochem. J.*, 1938, **32**, 784.
45. H. E. Longenecker, *J. Biol. Chem.*, 1939, **128**, 645; 1939, **129**, 13; **130**, 167.
46. G. O. Burr and M. M. Burr, *J. Biol. Chem.*, 1930, **86**, 587.
47. L. C. A. Nunn and I. Smedley-MacLean, *Biochem. J.*, 1938, **32**, 2178; E. M. Hume, L. C. A. Nunn, I. Smedley-MacLean and H. H. Smith, *ibid.*, 1940, **34**, 879, 884; I. Smedley-MacLean and E. M. Hume, *ibid.*, 1941, **35**, 990.
48. (*a*) R. Reiser and co-workers, *J. Nutrition*, 1950, **40**, 429; 1950, **42**, 325; 1951, **44**, 159; *Arch. Biochem. Biophys.*, 1951, **32**, 113; (*b*) J. F. Mead and co-workers, *J. Nutrition*, 1951, **44**, 507; *J. Biol. Chem.*, 1953, **205**, 683; 1956, **219**, 705; **218**, 401; **220**, 257; 1957, **224**, 841; **227**, 1025; 1958, **229**, 575; 1959, **234**, 1411; 1960, **235**, 3385.
49. H. J. Thomasson, *Int. Z. Vitaminf.*, 1953, **25**, 62; *Nature*, 1954, **173**, 452.
50. (*a*) H. Wagner, *Internat. Z. Vitaminforsch.*, 1957, **28**, 192; H. Wagner, E. Seelig and K. Bernhard, *Schweiz. Med. Wochenschr.*, 1957, **87**, 1423; (*b*) C. Y. Hopkins, M. J. Chisholm, T. K. Murray and J. A. Campbell, *J. Amer. Oil Chem. Soc.*, 1957, **34**, 505.
51. (*a*) A. R. Baldwin and H. E. Longenecker, *Arch. Biochem.*, 1944, **5**, 147; (*b*) G. Clément and M. L. Meara, *Biochem. J.*, 1951, **49**, 561; (*c*) F. D. Gunstone and W. C. Russell, *J. Sci. Food Agric.*, 1957, **8**, 283; (*d*) G. Rankov and A. Popov, *Compt. Rend. Acad. Bulga. Sci.*, 1954, **7**, (1), 9.
52. (*a*) J. R. Vickery, privately communicated; (*b*) J. H. Futter and F. B. Shorland, *Biochem. J.*, 1957, **65**, 689.
53. (*a*) C. Amthor and J. Zink, *Z. Anal. Chem.*, 1897, **36**, 8; I. Klimont, *Monatsh.*, 1912, **33**, 441; (*b*) M. Grübler, *Z. österr Apoth-Vereins.*, 1907, **45**, 745; J. Pritzker and R. Jungkunz, *Pharm. Acta. Helv.*, 1927, **2**, 5.
54. V. R. Wheatley and A. T. James, *Biochem. J.*, 1957, **65**, 36.
55. J. L. E. Erickson and H. B. Hix, *J. Amer. Oil Chem. Soc.*, 1948, **25**, 447.
56. D. R. Dhingra and D. N. Sharma, *J. Soc. Chem. Ind.*, 1938, **57**, 369.
57. W. F. Baughman, G. S. Jamieson and R. S. McKinney, *Oil and Fat Ind.*, 1929, **6**, (8), 11.

58. (a) F. D. Gunstone and R. P. Paton, *Biochem. J.*, 1953, **54**, 617; (b) S. P. Pathak and B. N. Trivedi, *J. Sci. Food Agric.*, 1958, **9**, 533; (c) C. Barker and T. P. Hilditch, *J. Chem. Soc.*, 1950, 3141; (d) R. J. Moir, M. Somers, G. Sharman and H. Waring, *Nature*, 1954, **173**, 269.

59. (a) S. P. Pathak, B. N. Trivedi and S. K. Roy, *J. Chem. Soc.*, 1959, 1645; (b) H. Steger and F. Püschel, *Pharmazie*, 1957, **12**, 821; (c) J. S. Cama and M. L. Meara, privately communicated.

60. C. R. Treadwell and H. C. Eckstein, *J. Biol. Chem.*, 1939, **128**, 373.

61. E. G. Brooker and F. B. Shorland, *Biochem. J.*, 1950, **46**, 80.

62. (a) J. Holmberg and (Miss) U. Rosenqvist, *Svensk. Kem. Tidskr.*, 1949, **61**, 89; (b) (Miss) U. Bergqvist and J. Holmberg, *ibid.*, 1953, **65**, 139.

63. S. S. Gupta and T. P. Hilditch, *Biochem. J.*, 1951, **48**, 137.

64. O. Dahl, (a) *Z. Lebensm-Untersuch.*, 1957, **106**, 81; *Acta. Chem. Scand.*, 1957, **11**, 1073; (b) *J. Sci. Food Agric.*, 1962, **13**, 520.

65. E. F. Armstrong and J. Allan, *J. Soc. Chem. Ind.*, 1924, **43**, 216т.

66. G. Collin, T. P. Hilditch and C. H. Lea, *J. Soc. Chem. Ind.*, 1929, **48**, 46т.

67. A. Banks and T. P. Hilditch, *Biochem. J.*, 1931, **25**, 1168.

68. T. P. Hilditch and H. E. Longenecker, *Biochem. J.*, 1937, **31**, 1805.

69. T. P. Hilditch and S. Paul, *Biochem. J.*, 1938, **32**, 1775.

70. L. R. Dugan, J. E. Maroney and (Miss) M. Petheram, *J. Amer. Oil Chem. Soc.*, 1952, **29**, 298.

71. T. P. Hilditch and K. S. Murti, (a) *Biochem. J.*, 1940, **34**, 1299; (b) *ibid.*, 1301.

72. (a) K. T. Achaya and B. N. Banerjee, *Biochem. J.*, 1946, **40**, 664; *cf.* also V. V. R. Subramanian and K. T. Achaya, *J. Amer. Oil Chem. Soc.*, 1958, **35**, 467; (b) D. R. Dhingra, S. N. Kapoor, G. Chandra and R. C. Sharma, *J. Indian Chem. Soc.*, *Ind. News. Ed.*, 1953, **16**, 172.

73. T. P. Hilditch and W. H. Pedelty, *Biochem. J.*, 1941, **35**, 932.

74. (a) F. B. Shorland, *J. New Zealand Inst. Chem.*, 1948–1949; (b) L. Hartman and F. B. Shorland, *J. Sci. Food Agric.*, 1957, **8**, 428.

75. (a) T. P. Hilditch and R. K. Shrivastava, *J. Amer. Oil Chem. Soc.*, 1949, **26**, 1; (b) W. W. C. Read and Z. Awdeh, *J. Sci. Food Agric.*, 1963, **14**, 770.

76. (a) R. P. Hansen and N. J. Cooke, *Biochem. J.*, 1953, **54**, 14; (b) R. P. Hansen, F. B. Shorland and N. J. Cooke, *J. Sci. Food Agric.*, 1957, **8**, 331; (c) *Biochem. J.*, 1957, **65**, 18; (d) M. J. Chisholm and C. Y. Hopkins, *Canad. J. Chem.*, 1957, **35**, 1434; (e) R. P. Hansen, F. B. Shorland and N. J. Cooke, *Nature*, 1955, **176**, 882.

77. (a) R. P. Hansen, F. B. Shorland and N. J. Cooke, *Biochem. J.*, 1951, **50**, 581; 1952, **52**, 203; 1953, **53**, 374; 1954, **58**, 513, 516; *Chem. and Ind.*, 1954, 1229; *Nature*, 1954, **174**, 39 (*see also* F. B. Shorland, *ibid.*, 1954, **174**, 603); (b) *idem.*, *Biochem. J.*, 1955, **61**, 547; *Chem. and Ind.*, 1956, 1149; (c) *Biochem. J.*, 1955, **61**, 141; (d) *ibid.*, 1956, **64**, 214; (e) F. B. Shorland and A. S. Jessup, *Nature*, 1955, **176**, 737; (f) *J. Sci. Food Agric.*, 1958, **9**, 391.

78. A. W. Weitkamp, *J. Amer. Chem. Soc.*, 1945, **67**, 447.

79. (a) R. Reiser, *Fed. Proc.*, 1951, **10**, 236; (b) N. B. Willey, J. K. Riggs, R. N. Colby, O. D. Butler and R. Reiser, *J. Anim. Sci.*, 1952, **11**, 705; (c) R. Reiser and H. G. R. Reddy, *J. Amer. Oil Chem. Soc.*, 1956, **33**, 155; (d) F. B. Shorland, R. O. Weenink and A. T. Johns, *Nature*, 1955, **175**, 1129; (e) S. Hofland, J. Holmberg and G. Sellmann, *Cornell Vet.*, 1956, **46**, 53; (f) F. B. Shorland, R. O. Weenink, A. T. Johns and I. R. C. McDonald, *Biochem. J.*, 1957, **67**, 328; (g) G. A. Garton, P. N. Hobson and A. K. Lough, *Nature*, 1958, **182**, 1511; G. A. Garton, A. K. Lough and E. Vioque, *J. Gen. Microbiol.*, 1961, **25**, 215; (h) R. Reiser, R. B. R. Choudhury and R. E. Leighton, *J. Amer. Oil Chem. Soc.*, 1959, **36**, 129; (i) S. B. Tove and R. D. Mochrie, *J. Dairy Sci.*, 1963, **46**, 686.

80. S. H. Bertram, *Biochem. Z.*, 1928, **197**, 433.

81. K. Ahmad, F. M. Bumpus and F. M. Strong, *J. Amer. Chem. Soc.*, 1948, **70**, 3391.

82. J. H. Benedict and B. F. Daubert, *J. Amer. Chem. Soc.*, 1949, **71**, 4113.

83. S. S. Gupta, T. P. Hilditch, S. Paul and R. K. Shrivastava, *J. Chem. Soc.*, 1950, 3484; *cf. also*, D. G. Bounds, R. P. Linstead and B. C. L. Weedon, *J. Chem. Soc.*, 1954, 4219.

84. R. C. Millican and J. B. Brown, *J. Biol. Chem.*, 1944, **154**, 437.

85. (a) D. Swern, H. B. Knight and C. R. Eddy, *J. Amer. Oil Chem. Soc.*, 1952, **29**, 44; (b) L. Hartman, I. R. C. McDonald and F. B. Shorland, *Nature*, 1954, **174**, 185; *Biochem. J.*, 1955, **61**, 603; (c) D. Firestone and M. De la Luz Villadelmar, *J. Assoc. Offic. Agric. Chemists*, 1961, **44**, 459; (d) R. O. Weenink, *Nature*, 1956, **178**, 646.

86. J. B. Brown and C. C. Sheldon, *J. Amer. Chem. Soc.*, 1934, **56**, 2149.

87. J. Holmberg and (Miss) U. Rosenqvist, (a) *Svensk Kem. Tidskr.*, 1951, **63**, 12; (b) *ibid.*, 1951, **63**, 272.

88. (a) T. P. Hilditch and R. K. Shrivastava, *J. Soc. Chem. Ind.*, 1948, **67**, 139; (b) H. Eckart, *Z. Unters. Nahr. Genussm.*, 1922, **44**, 1.

89. P. Cattaneo, G. K. de Sutton and M. J. Hazan, *Anales Asoc. Quim. Argentina*, 1959, **47**, 255.

90. S. Schmidt-Nielsen and A. Espeli, *Kong. Norske Vidensk. Selsk. Forhandl.*, 1941, **14**, 13, 17.

91. (a) N. R. Ellis and J. H. Zeller, *J. Biol. Chem.*, 1930, **89**, 185; (b) N. R. Ellis and H. S. Isbell, *ibid.*, 1926, **69**, 239.

92. (a) R. Bhattacharya and T. P. Hilditch, *Biochem. J.*, 1931, **25**, 1954; (b) A. Banks and T. P. Hilditch, *ibid.*, 1932, **26**, 298; (c) H. K. Dean and T. P. Hilditch, *ibid.*, 1933, **27**, 1950.

93. (a) T. P. Hilditch, C. H. Lea and W. H. Pedelty, *Biochem. J.*, 1939, **33**, 493; (b) T. P. Hilditch and W. H. Pedelty, *ibid.*, 1940, **34**, 40; (c) O. Dahl, *Z. Lebensm. Untersuch.*, 1957, **106**, 81; (d) *idem*, *Acta. Agric. Scand.*, 1958, **8**, 106.

94. V. Henriques and C. Hansen, *Skand. Arch. Physiol.*, 1901, **11**, 151.

95. J. B. Brown and E. M. Deck, *J. Amer. Chem. Soc.*, 1930, **52**, 1135; J. B. Brown, *J. Biol. Chem.*, 1931, **90**, 133.

96. F. B. Shorland and P. B. D. de la Mare, (a) *Analyst*, 1944, **69**, 337; *Biochem. J.*, 1945, **39**, 246; *New Zealand J. Sci. Technol.*, 1946, **27**, B, 465; (b) *J. Agric. Sci.*, 1945, **35**, 33, 39.

97. S. P. Pathak, S. K. Roy and B. N. Trivedi, *Biochem. J.*, 1959, **71**, 593.

98. N. R. Ellis, C. S. Rothwell and W. O. Pool, *J. Biol. Chem.*, 1931, **92**, 385.

99. (a) G. A. Garton, T. P. Hilditch and M. L. Meara, *Biochem. J.*, 1952, **50**, 517; (b) G. A. Garton and W. R. H. Duncan, *ibid.*, 1954, **57**, 120.

100. B. H. Thomas, C. C. Culbertson and F. Beard, *Amer. Soc. Animal Production Rec. Proc.*, 27th Annual Meeting, 1934, 193.

101. (a) Lebedev, *Pfluger's Archiv.*, 1883, **31**, 11; (b) I. Munk, *Arch. Path. Anat. Physiol.*, 1884, **95**, 407.

102. F. Giral, *J. Chem. Soc.*, 1945, 112.

103. (a) S. P. Pathak and C. V. Agarwal, *J. Sci. Food Agric.*, 1952, **3**, 136; (b) S. P. Pathak and B. N. Trivedi, *Biochem. J.*, 1958, **70**, 103; (c) J. M. Cross and J. Ehrlich, *Drug and Allied Indust.*, 1957, **43**, (7), 10; (d) L. Hartman and A. R. Johnson, *J. Sci. Food Agric.*, 1964, **15**, 127.

104. (a) S. S. Gupta, T. P. Hilditch and M. L. Meara, *J. Chem. Soc.*, 1950, 3145; (b) F. D. Gunstone, *Biochem. J.*, 1955, **59**, 454, 455.

105. (a) D. L. Cramer and J. B. Brown, *J. Biol. Chem.*, 1943, **151**, 427; (b) (Miss) E. Calandra and P. Cattaneo, *Rev. Soc. Arg. Biol.*, 1948, **24**, 275; (c) J. Holmberg and G. Sellmann, privately communicated.

106. (a) A. T. James and V. R. Wheatley, *Biochem. J.*, 1956, **63**, 269; (b) K. J. Kingsbury, S. Paul, A. Crossley and D. M. Morgan, *ibid.*, 1961, **78**, 54; (c) P. V. and O. C. Johnson and F. A. Kummerow, *Science*, 1957, **126**, 698.

107. (a) K. Bernhard and H. Korrodi, *Helv. Chim. Acta*, 1947, **30**, 1786; (b) J. Holmberg, privately communicated.

108. (a) O. Dahl, *Z. Lebensm.-Untersuch.*, 1957, **106**, 349; (b) F. D. Gunstone and W. C. Russell, *J. Sci. Food Agric.*, 1957, **8**, 290.

109. (a) E. Klenk and O. V. Schoenebeck, *Z. physiol. Chem.*, 1932, **209**, 112; (b) E. Klenk and F. Ditt, *ibid.*, 1934, **226**, 213; (c) E. Klenk and W. Bongard, *ibid.*, 1952, **291**, 104; (d) E. Klenk and K. Oette, *ibid.*, 1960, **318**, 86; (e) E. Klenk and A. Dreike, *ibid.*, 1955, **300**, 113; E. Klenk and F. Lindlar, *ibid.*, 1955, **301**, 156; E. Klenk and G. Krickau, *ibid.*, 1957, **308**, 98; E. Klenk and H. J. Tomuschat, *ibid.*, 1957, **308**, 165; E. Klenk and D. Eberhagen, *ibid.*, 1960, **322**, 258; E. Klenk and W. Montag, *Annalen*, 1957, **604**, 4; *J. Neurochem.*, 1957, **2**, 226, 233; W. Montag, E. Klenk, H. Hayes and R. T. Holman, *J. Biol. Chem.*, 1957, **227**, 53.

110. (a) T. P. Hilditch and F. B. Shorland, *Biochem. J.*, 1937, **31**, 1499; (b) L. W. Bruce and F. B. Shorland, *Nature*, 1951, **167**, 236; L. W. Bruce, F. B. Shorland and A. S. Jessop, *Biochem. J.*, 1952, **52**, 400; (c) R. H. Snider and W. R. Bloor, *J. Biol. Chem.*, 1933, **99**, 555.

111. (a) D. Charlot-Haimovici, *Arch. Sci. Physiol.*, 1957, **11**, 169, 185; (b) *E.g.*, D. N. Rhodes, *Chem. and Ind.*, 1956, 1010; J. Olley, *ibid.*, 1956, 1120; G. M. Gray, *Biochem. J.*, 1960, **77**, 82; T. Malkin, *Chem. and Ind.*, 1961, 605; B. G. Creech, *J. Amer. Oil Chem. Soc.*, 1961, **38**, 538; G. Rouser *et al.*, *ibid.*, 544, 565; J. G. Hamilton and J. E. Muldrey, *ibid.*, 582; H. K. Mangold, *ibid.*, 708, etc.

112. (a) W. C. Ault and J. B. Brown, *J. Biol. Chem.*, 1934, **107**, 607; (b) G. M. Gray, *Biochem. J.*, 1958, **70**, 409, 425; (c) G. V. Marinetti and E. Stotz, *J. Amer. Chem. Soc.*, 1957, **79**, 145; G. M. Gray, *Biochem. J.*, 1960, **77**, 82; (d) E. Klenk and F. Lindlar, *Z. Physiol. Chem.*, 1955, **299**, 74; A. Rosenberg and E. Chargoff, *Biochim. Biophys. Acta.*, 1956, **21**, 588; H. P. Kaufmann and H. Kirschnek, *Fette u. Seifen*, 1959, **61**, 1119; J. C. Dittmer and R. M. C. Dawson, *Biochim. Biophys. Acta*, 1960, **40**, 379; (e) K. T. Turner, *Biochem J.*, 1931, **25**, 49.

113. (a) T. W. Parry and J. A. B. Smith, *Biochem. J.*, 1936, **30**, 592; (b) F. E. Kelsey and H. E. Longenecker, *J. Biol. Chem.*, 1941, **139**, 727; (c) G. A. Garton and W. R. H. Duncan, *Biochem. J.*, 1957, **67**, 340; A. K. Lough and G. A. Garton, *ibid.*, 345; (d) W. R. H. Duncan and G. A. Garton, *J. Lipid Res.*, 1962, **3**, 53.

114. (a) N. Tuna, L. Reckers and I. D. Frantz, *J. Clin. Invest.*, 1957, **36**, 932; 1938, **37**, 1153; (b) F. E. Luddy, R. W. Riemenschneider, R. A. Barford and J. D. Evans, *J. Biol. Chem.*, 1958, **232**, 843; (c) A. S. Wright, G. A. J. Pitt and R. A. Morton, *Lancet*, 1959, ii, 594; (d) V. P. Dole, A. T. James, J. P. W. Webb, M. A. Rizack and M. F. Sturman, *J. Clin. Invest.*, 1959, **38**, 1544; (e) C. J. F. Böttcher, F. P. Woodford, C. Ch. Ter Haar Romeny Wachter, E. Boelsma-van Houte and C. M. van Gent, *Lancet*, 1960, i, 1378; 1960, ii, 1162; (f) B. Lewis, *Lancet*, 1958, ii, 71; E. H. Ahrens, Jr., H. J. Thomasson *et al.*, *Lancet*, 1959, i, 115, 315; W. Schrode, E. Böhle and R. Biegler, *Klin. Woch.*, 1959, **37**, 1101. *See also* K. J. Kingsbury, D. M. Morgan *et al.*, *Clin. Sci.*, 1962, **22**, 161.

115. A. Sengupta, *Dissert. Abstr.*, 1959, **19**, 2204.

116. (a) I. Smedley, *Biochem. J.*, 1912, **6**, 451; (b) A. Grün and T. Wirth, *Ber.*, 1922, **55**, 2197; (c) A. Grün, *Z. angew. Chem.*, 1924, **37**, 228.

117. A. W. Bosworth and J. B. Brown, *J. Biol. Chem.*, 1933, **103**, 115; A. W. Bosworth and E. W. Sisson, *ibid.*, 1934, **107**, 489.

118. R. W. Riemenschneider and N. R. Ellis, *J. Biol. Chem.*, 1936, **113**, 219.

119. (a) T. P. Hilditch and H. Paul, *Biochem. J.*, 1936, **30**, 1905; (b) H. E. Longenecker, *J. Soc. Chem. Ind.*, 1937, **56**, 199T; T. P. Hilditch and H. E. Longenecker, *J. Biol. Chem.*, 1938, **122**, 497.

120. H. K. Dean and T. P. Hilditch, *Biochem. J.*, 1933, **27**, 889.

121. T. P. Hilditch and H. M. Thompson, *Biochem. J.*, 1936, **30**, 677.

122. (a) T. P. Hilditch and H. Jasperson, *J. Soc. Chem. Ind.*, 1941, **60**, 305; (b) *ibid.*, 1945, **64**, 109; (c) *Biochem. J.*, 1943, **37**, 238.

123. T. P. Hilditch and (Miss) E. E. Jones, *Analyst*, 1929, **54**, 75.

124. T. P. Hilditch and J. J. Sleightholme, *Biochem. J.*, 1930, **24**, 1098.

125. R. Bhattacharya and T. P. Hilditch, *Analyst*, 1931, **56**, 161.
126. K. T. Achaya and T. P. Hilditch, *Proc. Roy. Soc.*, 1950, **B**, 137, 187.
127. (*a*) A. R. Baldwin and H. E. Longenecker, *J. Biol. Chem.*, 1944, **154**, 255; (*b*) *ibid.*, 1944, **155**, 507.
128. (*a*) G. A. Garton and W. R. H. Duncan, *J. Sci. Food Agric.*, 1956, **7**, 734; (*b*) G. A. Garton, *ibid.*, 1954, **5**, 247.
129. R. P. Hansen and F. B. Shorland, (*a*) *Biochem. J.*, 1952, **52**, 207 (*see also* A. K. R. McDowell, *J. Dairy Research*, 1953, **20**, 101); (*b*) *Biochem. J.*, 1951, **50**, 207, 358; 1953, **55**, 662; 1954, **57**, 297; 1954, **58**, 358; 1955, **59**, 350; (*c*) R. P. Hansen and N. J. Cooke, *J. Sci. Food Agric.*, 1953, **4**, 351; (*d*) T. Gerson, F. B. Shorland and C. R. Barnicoat, *Biochem. J.*, 1958, **68**, 644; (*e*) F. B. Shorland, T. Gerson and R. P. Hansen, *Biochem. J.*, 1955, **61**, 702; (*f*) R. P. Hansen, F. B. Shorland and N. J. Cooke, *Chem. and Ind.*, 1955, 92; *New Zealand J. Sci.*, 1963, **6**, 101; (*g*) *idem*, *J. Dairy Res.*, 1959, **26**, 190; (*h*) *idem*, *Nature*, 1957, **179**, 98; (*i*) *Chem. and Ind.*, 1959, 124; (*j*) F. B. Shorland and R. P. Hansen, *Dairy Sci. Absts.*, 1957, **19**, 168; (*k*) W. Sonneveld, P. H. Begemann *et al.*, *J. Lipid Research*, 1962, **3**, 351.
130. J. W. Mayhead and C. R. Barnicoat, *J. Dairy Res.*, 1956, **23**, 238; J. Stadthouders and H. Mulder, *Neth. Milk Dairy J.*, 1956, **10**, 53; F. W. Wood and W. Haab, *Canad. J. Anim. Sci.*, 1957, **37**, 1.
131. (*a*) S. S. Phatak and V. N. Patwardhan, *Nature*, 1953, **172**, 456; (*b*) R. H. Backderf and J. B. Brown, *Arch. Biochem. Biophys.*, 1958, **76**, 15; (*c*) W. E. Scott, S. F. Herb, P. Magidman and R. W. Riemenschneider, *J. Agric. Food Chem.*, 1959, **7**, 125; (*d*) R. P. Hansen, F. B. Shorland and N. J. Cooke, *Biochem. J.*, 1960, **77**, 64; (*e*) R. P. Hansen and N. J. Cooke, *ibid.*, 1961, **81**, 233; (*f*) H. P. Kaufmann, F. Volbert and G. Mankel, *Fette, Seifen, Anstrichm.*, 1961, **63**, 261; (*g*) K. Sambasivarao and J. B. Brown, *J. Amer. Oil Chem. Soc.*, 1962, **39**, 340.
132. (*a*) A. T. James, G. Peeters and M. Lauryssens, *Biochem. J.*, 1956, **64**, 726; J. C. Hawke, *J. Dairy Res.*, 1957, **24**, 366; M. P. Thompson, J. R. Brunner and C. M. Stine, *J. Dairy Sci.*, 1959, **42**, 1651; T. Gerson, T. C. Hawke, F. B. Shorland and W. H. Melhuish, *Biochem. J.*, 1960, **74**, 366; E. R. Samuels, A. Coffin, J. P. Julien and B. E. Baker, *J. Dairy Sci.*, 1960, **43**, 624; S. R. Patton, R. D. McCarthy, L. Evans and T. R. Lynn, *ibid.*, 1960, **43**, 1187, 1196; L. M. Smith, *ibid.*, 1961, **44**, 607; (*b*) S. F. Herb, P. Magidman, F. E. Luddy and R. W. Riemenschneider, *J. Amer. Oil Chem. Soc.*, 1962, **39**, 137, 142.
133. (*a*) H. C. Eckstein, *J. Biol. Chem.*, 1933, **103**, 135; (*b*) T. G. Green and T. P. Hilditch, *Biochem. J.*, 1935, **29**, 1564.
134. (*a*) J. B. Brown, *Oil and Soap*, 1938, **15**, 102; (*b*) T. P. Hilditch, *Analyst*, 1937, **62**, 252.
135. F. B. Shorland, *Nature*, 1950, **166**, 745.
136. S. Mattsson, *XIIth Int. Dairy Congress, Stockholm*, 1949, **2**, Sect. 11, 308.
137. A. W. Bosworth, *J. Biol. Chem.*, 1934, **106**, 235.
138. C. P. Anantakrishnan, V. R. B. Rao and T. M. Paul, (*a*) *Biochem. J.*, 1946, **49**, 292; (with M. C. Rangaswamy) *J. Biol. Chem.*, 1947, **166**, 31; (*b*) *Arch. Biochem.*, 1947, **13**, 389.
139. J. A. B. Smith and N. N. Dastur, *Biochem. J.*, 1938, **32**, 1868.
140. J. C. Shaw, R. C. Powell and C. B. Knodt, *J. Dairy Sci.*, 1942, **25**, 909; J. C. Shaw, *ibid.*, 1941, **24**, 502; 1941, **A**, 3, 145.
141. S. Hoflund, J. Holmberg and G. Sellman, privately communicated.
142. J. Golding, *Proc. 8th World's Dairy Congress*, 1928, 44.
143. W. C. Brown, R. B. Dustman and C. E. Weakley, *J. Dairy Sci.*, 1941, **24**, 265.
144. (*a*) W. R. Graham, T. S. G. Jones and H. D. Kay, *Proc. Roy. Soc.*, 1936, **B**, 120, 330; (*b*) L. A. Maynard, C. M. McCay, G. H. Ellis, A. Z. Hodson and G. K. Davis, *Cornell University Agric. Expt. Station*, 1938, Memoir 211; (*c*) J. C. Shaw and W. E. Petersen, *J. Dairy Sci.*, 1938, **21**, 122; 1940, **23**, 1045.
145. F. E. Kurtz, G. S. Jamieson and G. E. Holm, *J. Biol. Chem.*, 1934, **106**, 717; F. E. Kurtz and G. E. Holm, *J. Dairy Sci.*, 1939, **22**, 1011.

146. T. P. Hilditch and L. Maddison, *Biochem. J.*, 1941, **35**, 24.
147. (*a*) H. P. Kaufmann and E. Mohr, *Fette, Seifen, Anstrichm.*, 1959, **61**, 285; (*b*) L. M. Smith and E. L. Jack, *J. Dairy Sci.*, 1959, **42**, 767; (*c*) A. Deutsch, S. Mattsson and P. Swartling, *Milk Dairy Research (Swedish) Rept.*, 1958, **No. 54**, 9; *cf.* S. Mattsson, *Svensk. Kem. Tidskr.*, 1961, **73**, 102.
148. D. N. Rhodes and C. H. Lea, *J. Dairy Research*, 1958, **25**, 60.
149. D. R. Dhingra, (*a*) *Biochem. J.*, 1933, **27**, 851; (*b*) *ibid.*, 1934, **28**, 73.
150. A. Heiduschka and F. Cicekdagi, *Z. Unters. Lebensm.*, 1940, **79**, 150.
151. (*a*) T. P. Hilditch and H. Jasperson, *Biochem. J.*, 1944, **38**, 443; (*b*) S. H. W. Cmelik, *J. Sci. Food Agric.*, 1962, **13**, 662.
152. P. B. D. de la Mare and F. B. Shorland, *Nature*, 1944, **153**, 380.
153. D. R. Dhingra and G. Chandra, *J. Proc. Inst. Chem. (India)*, 1949, **21**, 5.
154. G. D. Elsdon, *Analyst*, 1928, **53**, 78.
155. T. P. Hilditch and M. L. Meara, *Biochem. J.*, 1944, **38**, 29, 437.
156. J. B. Brown and (Miss) B. M. Orians, *Arch. Biochem.*, 1946, **9**, 201.
157. (*a*) W. Insull, Jr., and E. H. Ahrens, Jr., *Biochem. J.*, 1959, **72**, 27; (*b*) W. Insull, Jr., J. Hirsch, A. T. Jones and E. H. Ahrens, Jr., *J. Clin. Investn.*, 1959, **38**, 443.

CHAPTER IV

The Component Acids of Vegetable Fats

I N this chapter we shall be occupied for the most part with a very large number of fats from the seeds or fruit-coats of the higher land flora. Before proceeding to deal with these it is logical to consider the comparatively few accounts to hand of the fatty acid components of fats present in the simpler plants, such as moulds, fungi, mosses, and other cryptogams. An interesting part of the plant kingdom – the aquatic flora – has already received attention, of course, in Chapter II (pp. 27–31), wherein the fats present in phytoplankton, algæ, and other aquatic vegetation were discussed.

Cryptogam Fats

The component acids of glycerides from several species of these simpler forms of vegetable life have been reported from time to time. Until recent years, they were usually given as a mixture of palmitic, stearic, oleic, and linoleic acids, but it has lately been shown that hexadecenoic acid is usually also fairly prominent. **Bacteria.** The lipid matter of bacteria has received attention, especially in the cases of tubercle bacilli and diphtheria bacteria. Those of tubercle and leprosy bacilli are mainly composed of waxes, and the extensive studies of Anderson[1a] et al. have shown that the acidic components do not belong solely to the same series as the fatty acids of glycerides, but are to a considerable extent saturated acids possessing branched carbon chains (cf. Chap. IX, p. 586). Their melting points are much lower than those of the corresponding normal saturated aliphatic acids. Chargaff and Levine[2a] reported that the acetone soluble lipids of *Phytomonas tumefaciens* contain palmitic, stearic, oleic, and 13 per cent. of a liquid saturated acid $C_{21}H_{42}O_2$, whilst Geiger and Anderson[1b] found that the phosphatides of this bacterium also contained a saturated acid liquid at ordinary temperatures. Anderson *et al.*[1c] were the first to report the presence, in *Mycobacterium tuberculosis* from human, bovine, and avian strains, of acids of very large molecular weight which formed about 8 per cent. of the weight of the dried bacilli. Anderson and co-workers[1d] gave the formula of these acids, termed *mycolic* acids, as $C_{88}H_{176}O_4$ in 1938. Some ten years later, Lederer with Asselineau[3a] and others[3b] were able to show that the mycolic acids (of which three had been isolated) were a hitherto unknown type of natural fatty acids, consisting of hydroxy-acids derived from *n*-hexacosanoic acid by substitution of a complex aliphatic side-chain at the carbon atom adjacent to the carboxylic group:

$$CH_3.[CH_2]_{23}.\underset{\underset{\displaystyle CH(OH).R}{|}}{CH}.COOH$$

The alkyl group R is represented in one acid as about $C_{60}H_{121}$, whilst in the others R is either *ca.* $C_{60}H_{120}(OCH_3)$ or *ca.* $C_{60}H_{120}(OH)$, (with a possible uncertainty of about ± 5 carbon atoms in each group).

Cason[4a] (1953) gave the approximate composition of tubercle bacilli fatty acids as palmitic 28–34, C_{18} and C_{19} acids 32–39, and acids of higher molecular weight (about one-third of which were 2-methyl-2-enoic acids) 16–21 per cent. (wt.). Later (1956) he stated that they were a much more complex mixture, and in 1959 gave their approximate composition as palmitic 33 per cent., C_{18} and C_{19}, 33 per cent., *iso*-C_{19} (10-methylstearic) about 10 per cent., and other acids (all *n*-acids from C_{14} to C_{19}, *iso*-acids from C_{14} to C_{19}) less than 1 per cent. Polgar[4b] (1954) identified *d*-2,4,6-trimethyltetracos-2-enoic (mycolipenic) acid and mycoceranic acid (a mixture of 2,4,6-trimethyl saturated C_{25}, C_{26}, C_{27} and C_{29} acids and 2,4,6,8-tetramethyl saturated C_{30}, C_{31} and C_{32} acids)[4c] amongst the high molecular weight acids in tubercle bacilli lipids.

Chargaff[2b] found in 1933 that diphtheria bacteria (*Corynebacterium diphtheriæ*) contain glyceridic fat, the component acids of which, in addition to about 30 per cent. of palmitic acid, consist mainly of hexadec-9-enoic acid. Lederer and Pudles[3c] in 1951 isolated from diphtheria bacilli lipids about 6 per cent. of a high molecular weight acid, $C_{32}H_{64}O_3$, somewhat analogous to the mycolic acids of tubercle bacilli. This, which they termed *corynomycolic* acid, was shown to have the structure

$$CH_3.[CH_2]_{13}.\underset{\underset{CH(OH).[CH_2]_{14}.CH_3}{|}}{CH}.COOH$$

The natural acid is dextrorotatory, and its racemic form has been synthesised.[3d]

Amongst the fatty acids in the lipids of *Lactobacillus arabinosus* Hofmann and Lucas[5a] (1950) isolated a very unusual saturated acid $C_{19}H_{36}O_2$, which contains a cyclopropane ring, shown later to be in the 11:12 position (I):[5c]

$$CH_3.[CH_2]_5.\underset{\underset{CH_2}{\diagdown\diagup}}{CH\!-\!CH}.[CH_2]_9.COOH \qquad CH_3.[CH_2]_7.\underset{\underset{CH_2}{\diagdown\diagup}}{C\!=\!C}.[CH_2]_7.COOH$$

$$\text{I} \qquad\qquad\qquad\qquad\qquad\qquad \text{II}$$

A similar unsaturated acid (II) occurs in the seed fat of *Sterculia fœtida* (see p. 323).

Hofmann *et al.* have given the following figures for the fatty acids present in two species of *Lactobacillus* and in *Phytomonas tumifaciens*:

	L. arabinosus[5b]	L. casei[5b]		P. tumifaciens[5d]
Palmitic	37	28	23	10
Stearic	2	5	4	—
cis-Octadec-11-enoic	20	45	38	68
Lactobacillic	31	19	16	13
(Unaccounted for	10	3	19	9)

cis-Octadec-11-enoic acid (the *trans*-form of which, " vaccenic acid," occurs in small amounts in some animal fats) has hitherto only been found in certain

173

lipids of the horse (*cf.* Chapter IX, p. 624). Hofmann[5e] suggests that the cyclopropane lactobacillic acid may arise from the addition of a —CH_2— unit to the double bond of the *cis*-octadec-11-enoic acid.

Yeasts. Yeast lipids have been studied by several workers, whose results include some earlier analyses in which ester-fractionation was not available. Newman and Anderson,[7] for instance, showed that, whilst the saturated acids of baker's yeast were made up of 75 per cent. palmitic and 25 per cent. stearic acids, the unsaturated acids yielded on hydrogenation a mixture of 25 per cent. palmitic and 75 per cent. stearic acids. In other words, a quarter of the unsaturated acids, according to Newman and Anderson's data, must consist of hexadecenoic acid.

More detailed analyses, using the ester-fractionation technique, have been made of the fatty acids in the total lipids of the following yeasts: *Torulopsis utilis* (Reichert[8]), and fat-rich yeasts of an unknown strain (probably *Rhodotorula*, Hilditch and Shrivastava[9]), of *R. gracilis* (Holmberg[10a]) and of *R. graminis* (Hartman et al.[10b]) with results shown in Table 56A.

TABLE 56A. *Component Acids (per cent. wt.) of Yeast Fats*

	T. utilis[8]	Strain No. 12[9]	*R. gracilis*[10a]	*R. graminis*[10b]
Steam-volatile acids	4·6	—	—	—(a)
Myristic	0·3	0·1	1·1	3·9
Palmitic	7·9	25·6	29·8	31·9
Stearic	3·8	5·9	8·8	3·2
Saturated C_{20}, C_{22}, C_{24}	0·2	5·1	1·4	—
Hexadecenoic	7·6	1·3	1·8	0·3
Oleic	21·5	54·5	40·1	37·2
Linoleic	49·7	5·7	11·2	10·2
Linolenic	4·4	0·7	4·8	4·6
Unsaturated C_{20}	—	1·1	1·0	2·5

(a) Also decanoic 0·3, lauric 0·4, decenoic 0·1, tetradecenoic 1·1, and unidentified 4·3 per cent.

These figures may suggest that ordinary yeasts with lipid contents not exceeding 7 or 8 per cent. may contain fatty acids low in palmitic and oleic and relatively high in hexadecenoic and polyethenoid C_{18} acids, whilst intensively grown yeasts of high (*ca.* 50 per cent.) lipid content produce a fatty acid mixture with large proportions of palmitic and oleic acids, very small amounts of hexadecenoic and much smaller linoleic acid contents. The latter fats in both instances are rather similar in composition to those of some seed fats and some animal depot fats. Bass and Hospodka[11] stated that *Rhodotorula* produces a more saturated fat when grown at higher than at lower temperatures, and that different proportions of palmitic, oleic, linoleic, and linolenic acids result from growth at different temperatures.

Rewald[12] found that brewer's yeast phosphatides contain about 65–69 per cent. of lecithin and 35 per cent. of kephalin; Newman and Anderson[7] observed about 80 per cent. of lecithin with 20 per cent. of kephalin in the phosphatides of baker's yeast.

Moulds and fungi. The plasmodia of *Lycogala epidendrum* and of *Reticularia lycoperdon* contain respectively 37 per cent. and 23 per cent. of fatty matter;

according to Kiesel,[13] the fatty acids present included 8–16 per cent. of palmitic, 70–77 per cent. of oleic, and 13–15 per cent. of linoleic acid.

The component acids of the lipids in a number of species of *Penicillium* moulds have been recorded, including those of *P. javanicum* (1934[14a]), an unknown species (1944[14b]), *P. chrysogenum* (1949[14c]), *P. flavo-cinereum* (1956[16a]), *P. lilacinum* (1956[16b]), *P. soppii* (1957[16c]) and *P. spinulosum* (1959[16d]), with the results shown in Table 56B.

TABLE 56B. *Component Acids (per cent. wt.) of* Penicillium *Lipids*

ACIDS	P. javani-cum[14a]	Unknown sp.[14b]	P. chryso-genum[14c]	P. flavo-cinereum[16a]	P. lila-cinum[16b]	P. soppii[16c]	P. spinul-osum[16d]
Myristic	—	3·5	3·7	0·3	0·1	0·3	—
Palmitic	23·4	40·5	12·0	19·4	32·3	22·0	18·0
Stearic	9·4	8	5·7	9·9	9·4	7·6	11·9
Satd. C$_{20}$ and above	0·8	1	0·7	0·7	1·4	0·9	1·4
Hexadecenoic	—	8	—	1·5	3·4	3·3	3·8
Oleic	34·6	19	53·6	39·4	38·6	45·2	43·4
Linoleic	31·8	20	20·3	27·1	13·4	20·0	21·1
Linolenic	—	—	} 4 {	0·8	—	0·3	0·3
Unsatd. C$_{20}$	—	—		0·9	1·4	0·4	0·2

Table 56C gives similar results for the lipids in some other moulds and fungi (*Citromyces* sp., 1937[6]; *Oidium lactis*, 1938[15]; *Aspergillus nidulans*, 1955[16e]; *A. flavus*, 1957[16f]; *Phycomyces blakesleeanus*, 1948[17a]; *Neurospora crassa*, 1957[17b]; *Pithomyces chartarum*, syn. *Sporidesmium bakeri*, 1960[17c]).

TABLE 56C. *Component Acids (per cent. wt.) of Lipids in Moulds and Fungi*

ACIDS	Citro-myces sp.[6]	Oidium lactis[15]	Aspergillus nidu-lans[16e]	Aspergillus flavus[16f]	Phyco-myces blakes-leeanus[17a]	Neuro-spora crassa[17b]	Pithomyces chartarum[17c] (i)	Pithomyces chartarum[17c] (ii)
Myristic	—	—	0·7	0·5	—	—	0·2*	0·6*
Palmitic	6·8	} 42·8 {	20·9	24·0	24	10–12	29·5	18·3
Stearic	11·8		15·9	21·5	5	2·2–2·6	8·1	5·9
Satd. C$_{20}$ and above	—	—	1·4	0·7	5	—	—	—
Hexadecenoic	—	—	1·2	2·4	—	2·0–2·5	0·7	1·3
Oleic	40·7	41·2	40·3	25·3	29	4–5	15·0	8·2
Linoleic	40·7	11·8	17·0	23·7	26 (b)	40–42	41·3	59·0
Linolenic	—	Trace	0·2	—	—	32–34	1·1	2·8
Unsatd. C$_{20}$ or above	—	— (a)	2·4	1·9	—	1·4–2·0	—	—

(a) Also ca. 4 per cent. hydroxy-acids.
(b) Also octadeca-6,9,12-trienoic 3, tetracos-17-enoic 3, and a hexacosenoic acid 1 per cent.
* Analyses by gas–liquid chromatography. Traces of *n*-C$_8$ to *n*-C$_{15}$ and *n*-C$_{17}$ saturated acids, and of branched-chain C$_{11}$ to C$_{17}$ saturated acids, also detected (amounting in all to about 4 per cent. of the total acids).

Hartman *et al.*[17d] have given more detailed figures, determined by gas–liquid chromatography, for the component acids of the glycerides and phospholipids in the lipids of *P. chartarum* and of two other linoleic-rich fungi (Table 56D).

The lipid fatty acids in *Choanephora cucurbitarium* were examined (1962[17e]) at different stages of growth of the fungus, with results (Table 56E) which are informative since they seem to throw light on the somewhat different figures for yeasts and moulds which have been given by various workers. The data in Table 56E indicate that, as growth progresses, the palmitic acid content rises from a comparatively low figure to about 30 per cent., the hexadecenoic and

TABLE 56D. *Chief Component Acids (per cent. mol.)* of Lipids in Three Fungi*

ACIDS	Pithomyces chartarum		Stemphylium dendriticum		Cylindrocarpon radicicola	
	Glycerides	Phospho-lipids	Glycerides	Phospho-lipids	Glycerides	Phospho-lipids
Myristic	2·6	0·4	0·7	0·9	0·3	0·4
Palmitic	33·9	15·4	21·9	12·1	23·5	16·8
Stearic	8·6	5·4	2·9	2·6	8·2	3·1
Hexadecenoic	0·4	2·3	2·0	1·1	0·6	0·7
Oleic	17·6	6·9	21·7	7·6	28·6	11·3
Linoleic	35·6	56·2	47·7	69·3	27·9	49·3
Linolenic	0·9	6·1	2·7	2·0	10·9	13·3
Eicosenoic	—	4·9	—	1·5	—	0·4

* Traces (up to 1 per cent.) of C_{11}, C_{12}, C_{13}, C_{15}, and C_{17} saturated acids were also observed in some cases (especially in the phospholipids).

TABLE 56E. *Alterations in Component Acids (per cent. wt.) during Growth of* Choanephora Cucurbitarium *Fungus*[17e]

Incubation time (hours):	20	28	44	56	80
Per cent. lipids (dry wt.):	18	16	23	22	22
ACIDS					
Lauric	0·2	0·1	0·1	0·1	0·1
Myristic	2·6	1·8	1·7	2·0	2·0
Palmitic	11·0	13·1	33·9	34·4	32·2
Stearic	2·5	2·6	7·1	5·9	4·6
Hexadecenoic	17·2	10·2	3·4	3·7	4·7
Oleic	42·0	49·8	35·4	28·4	22·8
Linoleic	9·3	8·7	11·3	14·8	19·7
Unsatd. C_{14}–C_{18} unidentified	4·1	2·1	0·4	0·5	0·7
Unsatd. above C_{18} unidentified	11·1	11·6	6·7	10·0	13·5

oleic acid proportions fall considerably, and the content of linoleic acid is approximately doubled. These analyses were carried out by means of gas–liquid chromatography.

Factors governing the development of lipids and alteration in their component acids during the growth of *Aspergillus nidulans* and of species of *Penicillium* have been considered in a number of communications by Walker and Singh.[16g]

The fatty acids present in the fats of ergot (of rye) and maize blight have also received some notice. Ergot (*Secale cornutum*) contains from 15 to 30 per cent. of lipids, the acids of which are unusual since they include 35–40 per cent. of ricinoleic (12-hydroxy-oleic) acid. Figures for the component acids of ergot lipids have been recorded as follows by Fiero,[18] Van der Meulen,[19] and Bharucha and Gunstone[20]:

Acids (per cent. wt.)	Fiero[18]	Van der Meulen[19]	Bharucha and Gunstone[20]
Myristic	3·0	—	0·9
Palmitic	25·0	30·3	23·9
Stearic	2·1	12·1	3·2
Arachidic	—	—	0·9
Hexadecenoic	—	—	3·8
Oleic	20·9	23·2	20·9
Linoleic	13·2	Trace	12·3
Ricinoleic	35·8	34·4	34·1

The fat (6 per cent. of the air-dried fungus) in maize blight (*Ustilago Zeæ*) was examined by the older methods in 1910 by Zellner,[21] who reported the usual 10–15 per cent. of saturated acids and 85–90 per cent. of oleic acid as the component acids.

The spores of a toadstool, *Amanita muscaria*, contain 1·4 per cent. of fat, the acids of which were stated by Heinisch and Zellner[22] to consist of about 10 per cent. of saturated (palmitic) and 90 per cent. of unsaturated (oleic) acids.

The pathogenic fungus *Monilia albicans* was observed by Peck and Hauser[23] to contain 5·3 per cent. of lipids (3 per cent. phosphatides, 97 per cent. acetone-soluble); the acetone-soluble portion contained 13·6 per cent. of sterols, whilst its fatty acids included palmitic 19·5, stearic 6·5, oleic 61, and linoleic 13 per cent. (wt.).

Clubmoss. The spores of *Lycopodium clavatum* contain about 50 per cent. of fat, the acids of which (apart from about 4 per cent. of myristic, palmitic, and stearic acids) were stated by Rathje[24] to consist, to the extent of over 90 per cent., of "lycopodic" acid, said to be an isomeric form of hexadecenoic acid. Riebsomer and Johnson[25] showed in 1933 that the *Lycopodium* spore-fat acids were made up of 55–60 per cent. of ordinary oleic acid with 30–35 per cent. of hexadec-9-enoic acid, accompanied by palmitic and linoleic acids.

Ferns. The fats in the spores of the larger ferns have not yet received much notice. The spores of the crested fern (*Aspidium dilatatum*, Polypodiaceæ), however, are stated by Maizite[26] to contain 35–40 per cent. of fat, with 14–21 per cent. of unsaponifiable matter (chiefly higher fatty alcohols), and fatty acids made up approximately of saturated 6, oleic 76, and linoleic 18 per cent. (wt.).

It is fairly evident that saturated acids may form from about 10 to 30 per cent. of the mixed acids of the fats of moulds, of fungi, and of the spores of mosses or ferns, and that palmitic acid is, as usual, the most abundant saturated acid, although stearic acid is sometimes present in fair quantity. The nature of the unsaturated acids is more variable. Oleic acid is usually the major component, while linoleic acid sometimes but not always approaches it in quantity. Hexadecenoic acid is often present in small amounts, but in some instances forms 10 per cent. or more of the total acids; this acid and a few others were not able to be recorded in most of the earlier (pre-1930) studies, and re-investigation of the latter and of other fungoid lipids by the modern methods is necessary before reaching any general conclusions as to the characteristic composition of these fats.

Phanerogam Fats

Fats occur in most parts of phanerogams – plants whose mode of reproduction is by seeds. During the period of growth they are present in the physiologically active cells of the leaf and stem systems, but, as a rule, form only a small proportion of the whole of the components. Moreover, they are accompanied by phosphatides (perhaps phosphatidic salts,[27a] $C_3H_5(OR)_2.O.PO_3M$,* rather than actual phosphatides, $C_3H_5(OR)_2.O.PO(OH).O.[CH_2]_2.N(CH_3)_3OH$, the

* R = fatty acyl radical; M = metallic component (calcium, or, sometimes, magnesium).

amount being apparently of about the same order as that of the glycerides themselves.[27c] In contrast to the glycerides associated with the growing plant, fats are also accumulated as reserve material in the maturing fruit and, in a few cases, in rhizomes or tubers. When they are deposited in this manner, they subsequently serve as a source of nutrition for the germinating seed (or, in the case of rhizome fats, during the commencing stages of growth in the following season). Very frequently fatty material forms a large part (25–50 per cent., or more) of the reserve material in the seed itself and, most often, reserve fat is practically wholly glyceride and is not accompanied by any appreciable proportion of phosphatidic compounds.

It is a natural consequence of the relative abundance of glycerides in fruit, and especially in seed, fats that our knowledge of their components is at present much more complete than in the case of leaf and similar fats. Seed fats can often be isolated in a pure condition, accompanied by only a few per cent. at most of non-glyceridic compounds; but in the leaf, for example, the glycerides may amount to little more than 1 per cent. or so of the dry weight, and their isolation and separation from ether-soluble plant pigments, as well as from the phosphatides which are also present, has been a matter of great difficulty, especially if a sufficient amount of the glycerides for a complete examination is to be accumulated. This drawback is now largely removed, however, since modern chromatographic methods of separation of lipids from other material, and of different groups of lipids from each other, together with the use of gas–liquid chromatography (instead of ester-fractionation) for analysis of fatty acids or their methyl esters, permits very small quantities of lipid material to be accurately studied. To the plant physiologist and others interested in the chemical changes connected with the living plant cell the scarcity of data with reference to leaf and similar fats is unfortunate. On the other hand, the more extensive figures available for many fruit fats are of use not only to the biochemist but also to the technologist, since many seed fats are, of course, employed in the edible fat, soap, paint, and other industries.

Although, owing to the circumstances described in the preceding paragraph, it is not possible to present a properly balanced and comprehensive account of the component fatty acids of glycerides from all parts of plants, an attempt will be made to indicate the available data for each class (leaf, stem, root, fruit-coat, seed). The seed fats, in particular, will be discussed in groups, the classification depending upon the acids which are most prominent in each fat – the *major component acids* (*cf.* Chapter I, p. 7). Each group will therefore be prefaced by a sub-heading which indicates clearly both the chief major and minor component acids characteristic of the fats under consideration.

Since the first edition of this book appeared (1940), the fatty acid compositions of very many specimens of the more widely used vegetable fats (palm, olive, linseed, sunflower seed, tobacco seed, and other oils) have been recorded. To incorporate all these into their appropriate places in the general Tables in this chapter would have been, if not impracticable, unduly cumbersome. In such cases, therefore, an indication merely of the range of the observed fatty acid proportions is given in the general Tables, leaving the individual records to be more fully dealt with separately in the course of general discussion of the fruit-coat fats and of each group of seed fats.

For uniformity and ease of comparison, the data quoted in this chapter from the literature have for the most part been transformed into *percentages of the total fatty acids*, in cases in which they were not originally published in this form (*cf.* Preface, p. vi and Chapter I, p. 4, footnote). Data involving the computation of linolenic, linoleic, and oleic acids together, and also all data in which ester-fractionation, reversed-phase partition chromatography, or gas–liquid chromatographic analysis was not employed, are in general given only to the nearest unit or half-unit per cent.

A word may be added here with reference to the utilisation of some of the older published data on the quantitative composition of mixed fatty acids from vegetable fats. Wherever possible, preference is given, in the succeeding tables, to analyses made, wholly or in part, by the more modern procedures (ester-fractionation, denoted in the Tables in column "Method" by "F", reversed-phase partition chromatography, "RPC", or gas–liquid chromatography, "GLC"). Many of the earlier data, especially when a fat contains only palmitic, stearic, oleic, and linoleic acids, are probably well-founded (although some, unfortunately, are not so). The original literature has therefore been consulted whenever possible; when the methods employed by the investigators have appeared trustworthy and the whole determination has been made on a quantitative basis the results have frequently been utilised in the tables which follow. Whilst care has been taken as far as possible to avoid inclusion of uncertain figures, it should be remembered that, in general, results obtained by methods not including separation by fractional distillation or chromatography should be regarded as less certain than those in which one of the latter has been employed.

The procedures (other than ester-fractionation "F", reversed-phase partition chromatography "RPC", or gas–liquid chromatography "GLC") used in individual cases are indicated as follows in the tables:

L. Separation of saturated acids by the lead salt–ether (Gusserow-Varrentrapp) or the lead salt–alcohol (Twitchell) processes or variants thereof; or, in a few cases, by other metallic salts.

C. Preliminary resolution of mixed acids by crystallisation at low temperatures from acetone, ether, etc. (*cf.* Chapter XI, p. 680).

B. Estimation of saturated acids by the Bertram oxidation method.

H. Estimation of linolenic and linoleic acids by isolation and analysis of bromo-addition products ("hexabromides" in the case of linolenic acid).

K. Estimation of linolenic, linoleic, and oleic acids by the Kaufmann thiocyanogen method, employing Kaufmann's assumed values for linoleic and linolenic acids.

T. Estimation of linolenic, linoleic, and oleic acids from thiocyanogen values, employing the correct and empirically determined values for linoleic and linolenic acids.[28] Wherever possible the compositions of fatty acids, in the determination of which thiocyanogen values have been employed, have now been recalculated in terms of the more correct thiocyanogen values for linoleic and linolenic acids, and distinguished by the letter T in place of K in this chapter (including Tables 57 to 69).

S. Estimation of linolenic and linoleic acids spectrophotometrically after alkali-isomerisation to conjugated acids.[29] The spectrophotometric method S for determination of linoleic and linolenic acids (and also elaeostearic and other natural conjugated acids) is now recognised as much the best means for the analysis of fatty acid mixtures in which these natural diene and triene C_{18} acids are present, and in most of the recent investigations of component fatty acids of natural fats this procedure has been followed. If slight autoxidation has taken place, the initial products (hydroperoxides) are already thereby conjugated, and spectrophotometric examination of them prior to alkali-isomerisation may indicate traces of conjugated acids. It is essential to take every precaution against accidental exposure of unsaturated acids or esters prior to determining linoleic or other acids by this means. It is probable that some at least of the traces of conjugated acids reported as present in some natural fatty oils are in fact artefacts produced in the course of incipient autoxidation.

Leaf Fats

Major component acids: LINOLEIC, LINOLENIC (OLEIC, PALMITIC).
Minor component acids: Stearic, cerotic.

The composition of leaf lipids has special interest in the case of pasture grasses, but the complexity of these products has so far prevented any very detailed account of their components. In general, the dry matter in pasture grasses contains 4–6 per cent. of total lipids, made up of glycerides 1·5–4, waxes (chiefly *n*-hexacosanol) 0·5–1, other unsaponifiable matter (sitosterols) 0·5–1, phosphatides and phosphatidic acid salts (*cf.* p. 177) 0·2–0·3 per cent. (of total dry weight).

The first attempt to obtain quantitative information of the fatty acids of leaf glycerides was made by Smith and Chibnall[30](1932) on two grasses, cocksfoot (*Dactylis glomerata*) and perennial ryegrass (*Lolium perenne*); glycerides were present in these to the respective extents of 2·2 per cent. and 1·7 per cent. of the dry weights. Smith and Chibnall's figures suggest that palmitic acid forms about 10 per cent. of the mixed fatty acids in these two grass fats, and that, calculated from the iodine and thiocyanogen (K) values, the component acids of the leaf glycerides in both cocksfoot and perennial ryegrass are made up somewhat as follows: saturated 10–17, oleic 16–23, linoleic 30–21, and linolenic 44–39 per cent. (wt.).

Shorland made similar general observations on the lipids present in New Zealand pasture grasses[31a] (chiefly ryegrass 55, Yorkshire fog 12, white clover 11, sweet vernal 10, and cocksfoot 5 per cent.), finding the average percentages (on the dry weight) of the lipid constituents of cocksfoot[31b] (*Dactylis glomerata*) to be glycerides 3·2, waxes 0·9, other unsaponifiable matter 1·0, phosphatides and phosphatidic acids 0·2 per cent. By ester-fractionation the component acids of the glyceride fraction were found to be myristic 1·4, palmitic 11·2, stearic 2·6, as arachidic 1·5, tetradecenoic 0·4, hexadecenoic 6·4, and unsaturated C_{18} 76·5 ($-5·1$H) per cent. (wt.). These figures again suggest that octadecadienoic and octadecatrienoic acids are the major component acids of grass glyceride fats.

A subsequent ester-fractionation study by Jasperson and Burke[32a] gave the component acids from a sample of mixed pasture grasses as: saturated, C_{12} 2·9, C_{14} 3·3, C_{16} 9·4, C_{18} 1·5, C_{20} 0·7; unsaturated, C_{12} 0·3 (-2H), C_{14} 0·4 (-2H), C_{16} 3·0 (-2H), C_{18} 78·5 ($-4·6$H) per cent. (wt.). The unsaturated C_{18} acids appeared to include about 50 per cent. of linolenic with perhaps 15–25 per cent. of linoleic, the rest being oleic (Hilditch and Jasperson[32b]).

In 1959 Weenink[31f] made the important observation that much of the lipid in pasture grasses and clover leaves consists not of simple triglycerides as previously supposed, but as unsaturated (largely linolenic) esters of galactosyl-1-glycerol and digalactosyl-1-glycerol; in the leaf of red clover (*Trifolium pratense*) galactoso-lipids form about 60 per cent. of the total neutral lipids. Garton[33] (1960) confirmed the presence of galactosyl-glyceryl esters in the lipids of a mixture of pasture grasses (rye 50, cocksfoot 25, timothy 15 and Italian rye 10 per cent.) to the extent of over 50 per cent. of the total lipids, in which free fatty acids (*ca.* 12 per cent.) and neutral fat (triglycerides, *ca.* 2 per cent.) were also present in much smaller amounts. Garton determined the component acids by gas–liquid chromatography in each of the three groups:

	Free Acids	Triglycerides	Galactosyl-glyceride esters
Myristic	2	3	Trace
Palmitic	13	15	7
Stearic	2	3	2
Hexadecenoic	2	2	1
Oleic	4	8	2
Linoleic	17	23	6
Linolenic	60	46	82

Shorland[31e] showed that the lipids in the leaves of rye grass, cocksfoot, white clover (*T. repens*) and rape (*Brassica napus*) all contained large proportions of galactoso-lipids. In the case of rye grass these were separated by dialysis from triglycerides and free fatty acids, which passed through the semi-permeable (rubber) membrane. The proportions of each group, and their main component fatty acids (by GLC), were found to be:

	Dialysable		Non-dialysable Galactosyl-glyceride esters
	Free Acids	Triglycerides	
Proportion (per cent.)	3·4	25·3	71·3
ACIDS			
Myristic	1·3	5·2	0·3
Palmitic	21·3	24·6	5·8
Stearic	7·5	7·4	—
Saturated C_{20} and above	16·7	—	—
Hexadecenoic	0·8	1·5	—
Oleic	7·8	7·4	—
Linoleic	4·9	14·2	5·8
Linolenic	36·7	32·1	88·1
(Trace saturated acids, total:	3·0	7·6	—)

In red clover leaves, similarly, Weenink[31g] found that the galactoso-lipid fatty acids consisted of palmitic 2·3, linoleic 1·9 and linolenic 95·8 per cent. All three studies thus suggest that linolenic acid constituted by far the greater part of the ester groups in these galactoso-glyceryl lipids.

Shorland *et al.* [31h] have also examined the lipids in the seeds as well as the leaves of the common pea (*Pisum sativum*, Leguminosæ); here also the leaf lipids are largely galactoso-lipids with not more than minor amounts of triglycerides, whilst in the seeds traces at least of galactoso-lipids may accompany the overwhelmingly predominating triglycerides.

181

Other leaf fat analyses available are for single species from each of the families Cruciferæ, Labiatæ, Chenopodiaceæ, and Leguminosæ.

In the course of a study of cabbage (*Brassica oleracea*) leaf cytoplasm, Chibnall and Channon[27b] found that about 1·7 per cent. of the leaf solids consisted of ether-soluble material, and showed that the glycerides present contained about 10 per cent. of saturated acids (about 70 per cent. of which was palmitic acid). The unsaturated acids contained much linoleic and a fair amount of linolenic acid; oleic acid was not identified and, if present, was evidently a minor component.

The dried leaves of peppermint (*Mentha aquatica*, Labiatæ) were found by Gordon[34] to contain nearly 5 per cent. of their weight of fatty components (as acids). The chief members present were palmitic, oleic, linoleic, and linolenic acids; and the proportion of saturated to unsaturated acids was apparently much greater than in the other leaf fats now under discussion.

Spinach leaves (from *Spinacea oleracea*, Chenopodiaceæ) have been similarly studied by Speer, Wise, Hart and Heyl,[35] who isolated 0·4 per cent. of neutral fat from the dried leaves. The unsaturated acids were made up of about 30 per cent. oleic, 50 per cent. linoleic, and 20 per cent. linolenic acids, and there was a small amount of saturated acids (palmitic and stearic, with small amounts of cerotic). According to Menke and Jacob,[36] about half of the lipids of spinach leaves consist of glycerides, the rest including 15–17 per cent. of wax alcohols, 2–7 per cent. of phosphatides, and 2–2·5 per cent. of sterols.

The fat of nettle (*Urtica dioica*) leaves contains very little (nil–5 per cent.) saturated acid, with 82–86 per cent. oleic acid as main component; the remaining 13–14 per cent. is linoleic, with perhaps some linolenic, acid (Hilditch and Meara[14b]).

Tsujimoto[37] identified linolenic acid in the leaf fats of clover, ginger, and three other plants, but did not detect it in the leaves of the black pine (*Pinus thunbergii*); Tang and Hsu[38] found lauric, oleic, linoleic, and linolenic acids in the leaves of *Leonorus sibiricus*.

Shorland[31c] found the component acids of rape (*Brassica napus*) leaves to be: saturated (chiefly palmitic) 15–16, tetradecenoic 0·5–0·7, hexadeca-7,10,13-trienoic[31d] 17–11, and unsaturated C_{18} acids (of mean unsaturation over − 5H) 67–72 per cent. (wt.). The presence of so much triethenoid C_{16} acid, and also the absence of erucic acid (the monoethenoid C_{22} acid which forms over 40 per cent. of rape seed fatty acids), is noteworthy.

The lipids of dehydrated alfalfa (lucerne, *Medicago sativa*) leaf were examined by Jackson and Kummerow,[39a] who found that the 6·6 per cent. of extracted material contained 33 per cent. of glycerides and 3·7 per cent. of phosphatides. The component acids (by method S, p. 179) of the glyceride and phosphatide fractions were respectively: saturated 19·9, 13·3; oleic 31·0, 36·8; linoleic 16·9, 14·7; and linolenic 32·2, 35·2 per cent. (wt.). Krewson[39b] records the acids in buckwheat (*Polygonum fagopyrum*) leaf fat as palmitic 16, oleic 26, linoleic 17, and linolenic 30 per cent. (wt.), with about 1 per cent. each of stearic and of saturated C_{20}, C_{26}, and C_{28} acids.

The scanty evidence thus available may be summed up in the statement that

182

the leaf fats (from several very diverse families) so far examined show considerable similarity in their component acids. The latter consist mainly of the C_{18} unsaturated group, in which linoleic and linolenic acids frequently predominate; oleic acid is reported definitely in peppermint and spinach leaf fats, and as the chief component of nettle leaf fat, but is present only in minor amounts in other cases. The saturated members, which appear usually to form only about 10 per cent. of the whole, consist mainly of palmitic acid, with smaller amounts of stearic and (sometimes) cerotic acid, the latter probably emanating from small proportions of leaf waxes.

Bark and Stem Fats

Major component acids: OLEIC, LINOLEIC (PALMITIC).
Minor component acids: Linolenic, stearic.

The component fatty acids of fat from the bark of trees or shrubs have been investigated in some detail in a few instances; in most the main component appears to be oleic acid, but in one or two cases, saturated (palmitic and stearic) acids form over one-third of the whole, whilst in others they are almost negligible.

The bark of *Tilia cordata* (basswood, winter lime, Tiliaceæ) was found by Pieraerts[40] to contain 2·3 per cent. of fat. The component acids of the latter were mainly oleic (94 per cent.), with a little linoleic (4 per cent.) and palmitic or stearic (2 per cent.) acids.

Ruchkin[41] examined fat from the bark of the sea buckthorn (*Hippophaë rhamnoides*, Elæagnaceæ), in which it was present to the extent of 3 per cent., and reported that it contained 37·4 per cent. of saturated (palmitic and stearic) acids and 62·6 per cent. of unsaturated (oleic) acid.

Dieterle and Dorner[42] reported that the bark fat of the hawthorn (*Cratægus oxyacantha*, Rosaceæ) also contains oleic, palmitic, stearic, and myristic amongst the higher fatty acids.

The small amount of fat in the wood of the rosewood tree (*Dalbergia sissoo*, Papilionatæ) is comparatively saturated (iodine value 31) and its component acids, determined by Kathpalia and Dutt[43a] are myristic 6, palmitic 24, stearic 27, arachidic 21, oleic 10, and linoleic 12 per cent. (wt.). The 0·5 per cent. of fat in the wood of another Papilionate tree, *Pterocarpus marsupium*, is much more unsaturated and, according to Bhargava,[43b] contains palmitic and stearic 7, oleic 48, linoleic 41, and linolenic 4 per cent. (wt.) as its component acids.

The small amounts of fat in the wood and the bark of the winter lime (*Tilia cordata*, Tiliaceæ) consist of about 14 per cent. saturated, 26 per cent. oleic, 58 per cent. linoleic and 2 per cent. linolenic acids.[43c]

The small amounts of lipids in the bark, wood and stems of some members of the families Santalaceæ and Olacaceæ (including *Leptomeria aphylla*, *Santalum acuminatum*, *Ximenia americana*) have been observed by Hatt *et al.*[44a] to contain small proportions (but in isolated instances major amounts) of some or all of the following acetylenic acids:

Octadeca-*trans*-13-en-9,11-diynoic,
Octadeca-*trans*-11-*trans*-13-dien-9-ynoic,

Octadeca-*trans*-11-en-9-ynoic (ximenynic),

Octadeca-*trans-trans*-diendiynoic (probably a conjugated *trans-trans*-diene) of uncertain structure.

The lipids of the sugar cane ("sugar cane wax") have been studied by a number of workers who have reached very different conclusions. The earliest report by Vidyarthi and Narasingaro[45a] in 1939 quoted a content of about 44 per cent. of "unsaponifiable matter" consisting of *ca.* 80 per cent. of melissyl alcohol, 10 per cent. sterols and 5 per cent. of n-$C_{35}H_{72}$; the acids (present as wax esters) included palmitic 29, stearic 23, arachidic 4, and oleic 44 per cent. A more recent reference to sugar cane wax from Indian sources[45b] quotes 60 per cent. "unsaponifiable" (made up of n-fatty alcohols 32, sterols 17, and hydrocarbons 3 per cent.) with 36 per cent. fatty acids, of which 20 per cent. were hydroxylated and 55 per cent. normal fatty acids, 68 per cent. of which were of the saturated C_{30} to C_{36} series. On the other hand Whyte and Hengeveld (1950)[45c] found that Cuban sugar cane contained a solid wax and a dark green oil; the latter contained about 7 per cent. of sterols and 16 per cent. of alcohols and hydrocarbons, with combined fatty acids n-C_8 to n-C_{14} 10, n-C_{16} 25, n-C_{18} 5, n-C_{20} 7, oleic 10, linoleic 36 and linolenic 7 per cent. Again, Horn and Matic (1957)[45d] reported only 16 per cent. of acids in combination in sugar cane wax with 84 per cent. of "unsaponifiable", 60 per cent. of which was "high-boiling alcohols" of molecular weight 800–1200, with 20 per cent. of the n-C_{28} and higher n-alcohols, and small amounts of hydrocarbons and of $\alpha\beta$-unsaturated ketones.

The most recent (1959–1960) work of Lamberton and Redcliffe[46] on Queensland sugar cane wax however suggests a quite different composition. About half of the wax, after distillation in a high vacuum, consisted of aldehydes of high molecular weight, probably produced by thermal depolymerisation of their polymeric (trioxane) forms which were present in the original wax. The rest of the wax included alcohols (chiefly n-C_{28}) 25–27, acids (from esters in the original wax) chiefly C_{28} (but with minor amounts of all odd and even acids from C_{16} to C_{34}) 7–8, and hydrocarbons (chiefly C_{27} and C_{29}) 8–9 per cent.

Reference is also due, whilst discussing bark and stem fats, to the industrial product known as "talloel", a dark-coloured liquid resinous product obtained to some extent as a by-product in the manufacture of rosin, but mainly from the "black liquor" produced as a residue in the manufacture of paper from wood pulp. This material, representing some of the fats present in the spruce or other coniferous wood employed in the paper industry, is said to have a possible annual production in the United States of 150,000–200,000 tons.[47] Somewhat variant statements as to the acidic components of talloel have been given by Becher,[48] Niesen,[49] Anderson and Wheeler,[50] Jennings,[51a] and Burch *et al.*[51b] as follows (Table, p. 185).

New Zealand tall oil (from *Pinus radiata*) also contains rosin acids *ca.* 50, fatty acids *ca.* 43, and "unsaponifiable" matter *ca.* 7 per cent.[52a] In the fatty acids oleic and linoleic largely predominated (together *ca.* 93 per cent.), with palmitic *ca.* 6 and stearic less than 1 per cent. Very small traces of 14-methylhexadecanoic, n-C_{17}, n-C_{20}, n-C_{22} and n-C_{24} acids have also been noted by Hansen and Cooke[52b] in New Zealand tall oil.

| TALLOEL | ACID CONTENT | | COMPONENT FATTY ACIDS (PER CENT. WT.) | | | |
	ROSIN	FATTY	SATURATED	OLEIC	LINOLEIC	LINOLENIC
Crude[48]	ca. 30	ca. 60				
Distilled[48]	ca. 12	ca. 85				
Distilled[49]	33	67	—	15	79	6
Crude[50]	46–38	26–45 ⎫	7	45	48	—*
Refined[50]	32	61 ⎭				
Refined[51a]	—	—	?	17–45	50–80	5–15
Crude[51b]	28	46	50	2	47	1

* The saturated acids were chiefly palmitic acid, and about 11 per cent. of conjugated octadecadienoic acid (probably formed from linoleic acid during processing of the wood pulp) was present.

Root Fats

Major component acids: OLEIC, PALMITIC, (LINOLEIC).
Minor component acids: Stearic, arachidic, etc.

The most conspicuous example of a fatty oil derived from the roots of a plant is probably sedge (or chufa) oil, which forms 20–30 per cent. of the substance of the small tubers of the tropical sedge (*Cyperus esculentus*, Cyperaceæ). This oil was examined by the modern methods by Baughman and Jamieson,[53] who found that the component fatty acids were myristic (traces), palmitic (12·2), stearic (5·4), arachidic (0·5), lignoceric (0·3), oleic (75·5), and linoleic (6·1 per cent.); Josephs[54a] found 14·4 per cent. of oil in chufa tubers, the component acids being saturated (15), oleic (68), and linoleic (17 per cent.), whilst in 1959 by spectrophotometry after alkali-isomerisation, Earle *et al.*[54b] reported saturated 20, oleic 64 and linoleic 11 per cent. in the fat which formed 27 per cent. of the roots.

The component acids of poke root oil, from *Phytolacca americana* (Phytolaccaceæ) are, according to Goldstein and Jenkins,[55] somewhat similar: palmitic 11, stearic 2, arachidic 6, and oleic about 80 per cent.

Mangel roots (*Beta rapa vulgaris*, Chenopodiaceæ), according to Neville,[56] contain about 7 per cent. of fatty oil, the component acids of which consist of palmitic 14, oleic 57, and erucic 29 per cent.; whilst senega root (*Polygala senega*, Polygalaceæ) was observed by Schröder[57] to contain 5–9 per cent. of oil, the acids of which were oleic (ca. 90 per cent.) and palmitic (ca. 10 per cent.). The component acids of oil from the roots of *Courbonia virgata* (Capparidaceæ) were found by Henry and Grindley[58] to be saturated 1·7, oleic 37·7, linoleic 57·1, and linolenic 3·5 per cent. (wt.). The component acids of oils from roots of some other plants are given as follows:

	Saturated	Oleic	Linoleic	Linolenic
Burdock *(Arctium lappa,* Compositæ)[43c]	21	31	47	2
Pæony *(Pæonia officinalis,* Ranunculaceæ)[43c]	18	34	46	3
Pachypleurum alpinum[59]	1	20	64	14

As in the corresponding bark and stem fats, some or all of the four polyunsaturated acetylenic acids found by Hatt *et al.* in certain members of Santalaceæ and Olacaceæ have also been observed[44a,b] in the roots of *Exocarpus*

185

cupressiformis, E. strictus, Leptomeria aphylla, Santalum acuminatum, and *Ximenia americana.*

It should be noted that, up to the present (with the exception of these latter acids and of 30 per cent. of erucic acid in mangel root oil), the only major components of fatty oils from leaves, stems, and roots of plants, or from fungi, have been found to be oleic and palmitic acids, with linoleic (and linolenic) acids in addition to, or perhaps (in leaf fats) even replacing, oleic acid.

Lipids of Petals and Stamens

Little has yet been reported on the lipids of flowers, but Rewald[60] observed the following percentages of glycerides and phosphatides in dry petals and stamens of different species:

	GLYCERIDES (Per cent.)	PHOSPHATIDES (Per cent.)
Daffodil petals	5·8	1·4
Dandelion petals	*ca.* 6	3·0
,, stamens	9·1	2·9
Poppy petals	3·4	0·7
,, stamens	6·3	1·4
,, seeds (green, young)	6·7	2·8
Rose petals	2·9	3·5
Tulip petals	3·2	1·8
,, stamens	1·8	2·2

The phosphatides thus nearly always formed over 20 per cent., and sometimes as much as 45–50 per cent., of the total lipids. The iodine values of the glycerides in the petals, stamens, and undeveloped seeds of the poppy were respectively 88, 97, and 95, compared with about 140 for those in the ripened seeds.

The fats in the flower petals of poppies (*Papaver Rheas*) and of *Arnica montana* have been stated to contain mainly oleic acid, together with some palmitic and minor amounts of stearic and lower saturated acids.[61] *Artemisia scoparia* flowerheads contain 4·5 per cent. of fatty oil, the approximate fatty acid composition of which (Panihar and Dutt[62]) is myristic 5, palmitic 26, stearic 26, arachidic 20, oleic 11, and linoleic 12 per cent. (wt.). Neem (*Azadirachta indica*) flowers, according to Mitra *et al.*[63], contain a similar amount of fat, with palmitic 14, stearic 9, arachidic and behenic 2, oleic 69, and linoleic 6 per cent. (wt.) as component acids.

Shorter Chain Unsaturated Acids in Flowers and Leaves

Some interesting unsaturated acids of the normal C_{10} series have been observed in flowerheads of various species in the family Compositæ, and unsaturated alcohols of the normal C_6 and C_9 series in the leaves of many plants. These are of course not directly connected with fats, but the possibility (perhaps remote) that they may be found to have some kind of connection with stages of biosynthesis of unsaturated fatty acids in plants makes a brief reference to them desirable.

The occurrence of methyl esters of a group of unsaturated acids derived from *n*-decanoic acid and containing both ethylenic and acetylenic groups has been observed in the flowers of several Compositæ species by N. A. Sörensen and his colleagues.[64] The first to be isolated [64a] was "matricaria ester", the methyl ester of *n*-deca-2,8-dien-4,6-diynoic acid (I) from *Matricaria inodora*, in the flowers of which the methyl ester of *n*-deca-2,3,4-trienoic acid (II) was later also found[64b]; subsequently methyl esters of the following acids were also recorded: a *n*-dec-en-triyn-oic acid (III) from *Artemisia vulgaris*[64c] and *n*-dec-2-en-4,6-diynoic acid (IV) (with the three preceding methyl esters) from several species of *Erigeron*.[64d] This last occurs as the *cis*-ene form, and the related *trans*-isomeride has been synthesised.[64e]

I "Matricaria ester"
$C_{11}H_{10}O_2$
$CH_3.CH:CH.C:C.C:C.CH:CH.COOCH_3$

II "Hexahydromatricaria ester"
$C_{11}H_{16}O_2$
$CH_3.[CH_2]_4.CH:C:C:CH.COOCH_3$

III "Dehydromatricaria ester"
$C_{11}H_8O_2$
$(?)CH_3.C:C.C:C.C:C.CH:CH.COOCH_3$

IV "Lachnophyllum ester"
$C_{11}H_{12}O_2$
$CH_3.[CH_2]_2.C:C.C:C.CH:CH.COOCH_3$

The unsaturated aliphatic alcohols containing six and nine carbon atoms which have been identified in the leaves of various plants include *cis-n*-hex-3-enol, $CH_3.CH_2.CH:CH.CH_2.CH_2.OH$ in the growing leaves of tea, ivy, clover, oak, wheat, and other plants (often accompanied by *n*-hex-2-enal, $CH_3.[CH_2]_2.CH:CH.CHO$), whilst *n*-nonadienols and *n*-nonadienals have been found in the leaves of the cypress and the violet, and in cucumbers.[65] The leaf hexenol was originally given as *trans-n*-hex-4-enol, but syntheses[66] of *trans*- and *cis*-hex-3-enol have proved that the "leaf alcohol" of peppermint has the latter constitution.

Fruit Fats

It has already been said that far more information is available with reference to the component acids of fruit fats than is the case in those of fats from the rest of the organs of plants. In classifying this mass of data it will be useful to consider first the many cases in which the major components are practically confined (as in leaf, stem, and root fats) to oleic, linoleic, and palmitic acids. This will lead us, in the first place, to the category of fruitcoat fats, which appear to be made up almost exclusively of these acids, although in quite a number of cases the proportion of linoleic acid is not great, and in some cases subordinate amounts of stearic acid are found. Then, in the seed fats, it will be convenient first to deal with the numerous and important groups in which, again, only these acids occur as major components.

It may not be out of place here to describe very briefly the various formations which are met with in different fruits. In the flower the ovary is attached to the extremity of the stalk (peduncle) bearing the flower. This apex, termed the *receptacle*, may be extremely small, but is often more or less elongated, thickened, or otherwise enlarged; it may be connected with the ovary as indicated in Fig. 1 (*a*), when the ovary is said to be *superior* or *free*, or it may partially surround the ovary in such a way that it adheres to it above the level of the insertion of the lowest ovule, in which case the ovary is described as *inferior* or *adherent* (Fig. 1 (*b*)). Figs. 1 (*a*) and 1 (*b*) actually refer to the development of the fruit after fertilisation has taken place. In flowers with a superior ovary the fruit itself is seen distinct from the receptacle and consists essentially of a *fruit-wall* or *pericarp* enclosing the seed.

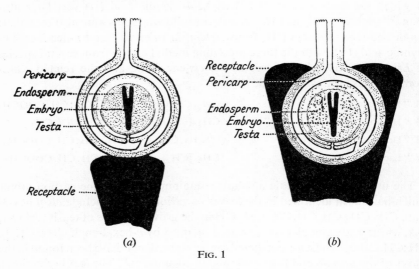

(*a*) (*b*)

FIG. 1

The seed consists of the *embryo* or *germ* which may either fill or almost fill the seed cavity or be set in a mass of reserve food tissue termed the *endosperm* or "*albumen*"; the food reserves in the endosperm include carbohydrate, proteins, and fats in varying proportions. If, during development of the seed, the embryo grows so as to absorb all the endosperm (the mature seed then being termed non-endospermic or exalbuminous), the food reserves are then in the embryo which in this case makes close contact with the *testa* or seed coat. The *testa* or outer covering of the seed may be a thin skin or it may be hard and woody.

Seed fats, as discussed in this book, are fats present in the endosperm or embryo of the seed. In a few cases reference will also be made to fats present in the seed covering and these will be termed *testa fats*.

The seed is connected to the inner side of the pericarp (originally the placenta of the ovary) by a short stalk or *funicle*, which sometimes (e.g. in the mace of *Myristica* species) carries a fleshy appendage termed an *arillus*, which may contain fat.

Returning now to the *fruit-wall* or *pericarp*, we find in the first place that this, the developed ovary enclosing the ripened seed, may also often be divided into three zones: (i) an exterior, relatively hard, skin or rind (*epicarp*) enclosing (ii) a more or less fleshy or pulpy substance (*mesocarp*) whilst in some cases there is, between the latter and the seed or seeds, (iii) a thin inner skin known as the *endocarp*.

Except in the class of *Gymnosperms* (e.g. the Coniferæ), in which the seeds are naked and without any real pericarp, this fruit-wall system is present whether

188

the ovary is superior or inferior; but in the latter case (Fig. 1 (*b*)) the *receptacle* frequently, in the mature fruit, acquires some or most of the characteristics of the pericarp. The outer limits of the pericarp and the inner zones of the receptacle may lose their identity or become fused to a large degree; or the ripened receptacle may become fleshy whilst the pericarp, or the inner part thereof, becomes hard and woody.

Fats are found indifferently in either type of *Angiosperm* fruit, that is, in true pericarp, receptacle, or in pericarp and receptacle. Often these have been indiscriminately termed "pericarp fats" but, for purposes of convenience in these pages, the term "*fruit-coat fat*" will be employed to denote *fats from parts of a fruit other than the seed* (embryo, endosperm, or testa). Fruit-coat fats, thus defined, may be found, in different instances, either exclusively in the pericarp or in the receptacle, or in both of these, or occasionally, in arils attached to the funicle.

Fruit-coat Fats

Major component acids: PALMITIC, OLEIC, LINOLEIC.
Minor component acids: Myristic, stearic (linolenic).

The fleshy or succulent part of many fruits contains more or less fatty oil. In some cases the proportion of fat is considerable and the fruits have become, in consequence, sources of edible oils or of raw material for the fat industries; the most familiar examples are olive oil and the red palm oil of *Elæis guineensis*.

Quite a number of determinations of the component acids of fruit-coat fats have been made from about 1930 onwards, mostly by the ester-fractionation method. These are collected in Table 57, in approximately descending order of palmitic acid contents: but figures for the many different varieties of palm oils and olive oils which have been examined are detailed separately in Tables 57A and 57B respectively.

The material in Tables 57, 57A, and 57B invites comment from several aspects. In the first place, the general characteristics of all the fruit-coat fats are the same: the main components are palmitic and oleic acids, the former reaching 70 per cent. or more of the whole in *Rhus* and *Stillingia* fruit-coat fats, about 40 per cent. in palm oil, and falling to somewhat less than 10 per cent in other cases, whilst oleic acid varies from negligible proportions in the myrtle and Rhus "tallows" to 40–50 per cent. in palm oils and 75–80 per cent. in the more liquid oils such as olive or elderberry. With the exception of linoleic acid, other component acids rarely form more than 2–5 per cent. of the mixed acids.

The only exceptions to the last statement are the fruit-coat fats of *Myrica* species and of some Lauraceæ fruits. In the *Myrica* fruit-coat fats myristic shares with palmitic acid the place of a major component: these are indeed the only acids present in major amounts and, in the three species whose fruit-coat fats have been studied, together make up nearly the whole of the fatty acids present. Myristic acid, in these three fats, forms from 35 to 61 per cent. of the total acids.

The seed fats of some members of the Lauraceæ contain exceedingly high

189

TABLE 57. *Component Acids of Fruit-coat Fats*

Major component acids: PALMITIC, OLEIC, LINOLEIC.
Minor component acids: Myristic, stearic (linolenic).

COMPONENT FATTY ACIDS PER CENT. (WT.)

	HABITAT	SATURATED			UNSATURATED		METHOD	OBSERVERS
		C_{14}	PALMITIC	C_{18}	OLEIC	LINOLEIC		
ANACARDIACEÆ								
Rhus succedanea Sumach	Japan, etc.	—	77	5	12	Trace (a)	F	Tsujimoto[1]
	"	1·9	67·5	11·6	13·6	— (a')	F	Schuette and Christenson[2]
EUPHORBIACEÆ								
Sapium sebiferum Stillingia or syn. *Stillingia sebifera* Chinese vegetable tallow.	China	5·8	69·6	3·1	20·7	— (b)	F	Hilditch and Priestman[3]
" " "	Hong Kong	3·6	57·6	1·8	34·5	— (b)	F	Hilditch and Priestman[3]
" " "	Florida	0·5	63·2	7·6	27·1	1·6	F	Gupta and Meara[4]
" " "	South Texas	3·7	66·3	1·2	26·9	— (b)	F	Hilditch and Priestman[3]
" " "	India	3·4	72·1	1·6	20·4	1·0 (c)	F	Gupta and Meara[4]
S. discolor "	India	4·2	62·3	5·9	27·4	— (m)	F	Narang and Sadgopal[45]
" " "	Hong Kong	1·7	46·8	2·0	46·4	3·1	F	Gupta and Meara[4]
CUCURBITACEÆ								
Tricosanthes cucumeroides Snake gourd	Japan	← 32 →			30·8	23·4 (n)	F,S	Kato[46]
PALMÆ								
Elæis guineensis Oil palm	Tropics	1·6	32–47	1–6	40–52	5–11	F	See *Table* 57A, p. 194
Elæis melanococca " "	Belgian Congo	1·0	32·6	4·7	47·5	12·0 (d)	C,F,S	Roels and Thuriaux[5]
Jessenia batava	Brazil	—	7·6	9·4	77·5	5·5	F	Pinto[47]
Œnocarpus batava Patua palm	Brazil	—	9·3	5·9	81·1	3·6	F	Jamieson and McKinney[6]
" *bucaba* " "		—	6·0	6·0	79·2	8·8	F	Chaves and Pechnik[7]
" " "		—	11·8	9·6	64·8	13·8	F	Pinto[47]
CARYOCARACEÆ								
Caryocar villosum Piqui-a oil	Malaya	1·5	41·2	0·8	53·9	2·6	F	Hilditch and Rigg[8]

Species	Common name	Source						Method	Reference
MELIACEÆ									
Trichilia emetica		Sudan		←—— 44 ——→	18·2	29	27	B,T	Henry and Grindley[9a]
CAPPARIDACEÆ									
Courbonia virgata		Sudan	—	13·2	18·2	57·9	10·7	F,T	Grindley[9b]
STERCULIACEÆ									
Sterculia fœtida	"Java olive"	Java	2·3	←— ca.40 —→	9·0	37·6	←— ca.60 —→ 22·2(e)	B	Steger and van Loon[10]
" *parviflora*		Malaya		27·6		63	5	F	Hilditch and Meara[11]
" *tomentosa*		Sudan		←— 32 —→			16-9	B,T	Henry and Grindley[9a]
Theobroma cacao	Cacao bean shell	Tropics		←— 51–56 —→		33–35		B,T	Bauer and Seber[12]
BURSERACEÆ									
*Dacryodes rostrata**	"Java almond"	Malaya		33·9	2·7	59·3	4·1	F	Hilditch and Stainsby[13]
MYRICACEÆ									
Myrica cerifera	Bayberry, myrtle	U.S.A.	ca.33	ca.45	ca.20	?	—	?	McKay[14]
" *cordifolia*		S. Africa	49·9	49·0	0·2	0·5	—	F	Schoeman and Hawke[15]
" *mexicana*		Central America	61·1	37·5	—	1·4	(f)	F	Jamieson et al.[16]
LAURACEÆ		LAURIC							
Laurus nobilis	Laurel, bay	Mediterranean coasts	—	24	—	57	19	?	Wallrabe[17]
" "	"	Adriatic	2·7	20·3	—	63·0	14·0	F	Collin[18a]
" "	"	Ceylon	1·0	19·0	—	56·5	21·0(c)	?	Krajčinović[18b]
Neolitsea involucrata	Wild cinnamon		10·2	28·2	3·1	48·2	10·3	F	Gunde and Hilditch[19]
Actinodaphne hookeri		India	33	—	—	56	—(g)	?	Puntambekar and Krishna[20]
Persea gratissima	Avocado pear	Sub-tropics	—	7·2	0·6	80·9	11·3	F	Jamieson, Baughman and Hann[21]
"	"	Puerto Rico	2·2	26·1	0·6	64·8	6·3	F	Asenjo and Goyco[22a]
"	"	Argentine	0·3	17·5	0·4	55·3	16·5(h)	F	Cattaneo et al.[23a]
"	"	"	0·3	24·7	1·3	46·9	15·7(i)	F	Cattaneo et al.[23a]
"	"	Florida	0·2	19·1	0·4	55·8	17·0(p)	GLC	French[22b]
"	"	"	—	22·5	0·8	46·6	17·5(q)	GLC	French[22b]

191

TABLE 57. Component Acids of Fruit-coat Fats—continued.

	HABITAT	COMPONENT FATTY ACIDS (PER CENT. WT.)					METHOD	OBSERVERS
		SATURATED			UNSATURATED			
		C_{14}	PALMITIC	C_{18}	OLEIC	LINOLEIC		
CELASTRACEÆ								
Celastrus paniculatus	India	3·0	26·2	4·0	36	8 (j)	F, T	Gunde and Hilditch[24]
Maytenus disticha	Patagonia	1	27·5	1	35	28 (k)	F	Cattaneo et al.[23b]
VALERIANACEÆ								
Valerianella olitoria Corn salad	Europe	←————20·5————→			5·5	74 (l)	L, T	Steger and van Loon[25]
CAPRIFOLIACEÆ								
Sambucus racemosa Elderberry	General	—	23	—	71	6	L	Byers and Hopkins[26]
OLEACEÆ								
Olea europæa sativa Olive Oil	Various	0-1	7-20	0-3	65-86	5-15	—	See Table 57B, p. 196
ELÆAGNACEÆ								
Hippophaë Sea Buckthorn rhamnoides	Siberia	←————12·3————→			75·2	12·5	?	Ruchkin[27]

* This was published as the fruit-coat fat of Sterculia foetida, but the fruits have subsequently been found to be not of this plant, but of Dacryodes rostrata, a plant known (with related Canarium sp.) as "Java almond".

Rhus species (a), (a') also contained 5–6 per cent. of saturated dibasic acids of C_{23} and C_{22} series.

Minor and other component acids recorded as follows (per cent. wt.):

	LAURIC	ARACH-IDIC	HEXA-DECENOIC	LINO-LENIC
(b) Sapium sebiferum	1-2·5	—	—	—
(c) "	1·5	—	—	—
(d) Elæis melanococca	—	0·5	0·9	0·8
(e) Sterculia parviflora	—	1·3	—	—
(f) Myrica cordifolia	0·4	—	—	—
(g) Actinodaphne hookeri	(Also 11 per cent. resin acids)			
(o) Laurus nobilis	—	—	—	2·5
(p) Persea gratissima	—	—	7·0	0·8
(q) "	—	0·3	11·0	1·3

	LAURIC	ARACH-IDIC	HEXA-DECENOIC	LINO-LENIC	UNSATD C_{20}
(h) Persea gratissima	—	0·4	6·4	—	3·2
(i) "	—	—	8·3	—	2·6
(j) Celastrus paniculatus	—	—	—	23	5·5
(k) Maytenus disticha	1·0	1·0	—	5	—
(l) Valerianella olitoria	—	—	—	9·3	—
(m) Sapium sebiferum	0·3	—	—	—	0·3
(n) Tricosanthes cucumeroides	(Also conjugated-diene 4·0, -triene 0·2)				

192

References to Tables 57, 57A, *and* 57B

1. M. Tsujimoto, *Bull. Chem. Soc. Japan*, 1931, **6**, 325, 337; 1935, **10**, 212.
2. H. A. Schuette and R. M. Christenson, *Oil and Soap*, 1942, **19**, 209.
3. T. P. Hilditch and J. Priestman, *J. Soc. Chem. Ind.*, 1930, **49**, 397T.
4. S. S. Gupta and M. L. Meara, *J. Chem. Soc.*, 1950, 1337.
5. O. A. Roels and L. Thuriaux, *Bull. Inst. Roy. Col. Belge*, 1950, **21**, 730.
6. G. S. Jamieson and R. S. McKinney, *Oil and Soap*, 1934, **11**, 207, 217.
7. J. M. Chaves and E. Pechnik, *Quim. e Ind. (S. Paulo)* 1946, **14**, 2.
8. T. P. Hilditch and J. G. Rigg, *J. Soc. Chem. Ind.*, 1935, **54**, 109T.
9. (*a*) A. J. Henry and D. N. Grindley, *J. Soc. Chem. Ind.*, 1944, **63**, 188; (*b*) D. N. Grindley, *J. Sci. Food Agric.*, 1950, **1**, 153.
10. A. Steger and J. van Loon, *Rec. trav. chim.*, 1941, **60**, 87.
11. T. P. Hilditch and M. L. Meara, *J. Soc. Chem. Ind.*, 1944, **63**, 112.
12. K. H. Bauer and L. Seber, *Fette u. Seifen*, 1938, **45**, 293.
13. T. P. Hilditch and W. J. Stainsby, *J. Soc. Chem. Ind.*, 1934, **53**, 197T.
14. A. F. McKay, *J. Org. Chem.*, 1948, **13**, 86.
15. D. J. Schoeman and F. Hawke, *J. S. African Chem. Inst.*, 1948, **1**, 5.
16. G. S. Jamieson, R. S. McKinney and S. I. Gertler, *cf.* Jamieson, " Vegetable Fats and Oils", New York, 1932, p. 37.
17. G. Wallrabe, *Chem. Umschau*, 1929, **36**, 293.
18. (*a*) G. Collin, *Biochem. J.*, 1931, **25**, 95; (*b*) M. Krajčinović and M. Filajdić, *Kem. i. Ind. (Zagreb)*, 1957, **6**, 141.
19. B. G. Gunde and T. P. Hilditch, *J. Chem. Soc.*, 1938, 1610.
20. S. V. Puntambekar and S. Krishna, *J. Indian Chem. Soc.*, 1933, **10**, 395.
21. G. S. Jamieson, W. F. Baughman and R. M. Hann, *Oil and Fat Ind.*, 1928, **5**, 202.
22. (*a*) C. F. Asenjo and J. A. Goyco, *Oil and Soap*, 1942, **19**, 129; (*b*) R. B. French, *J. Amer. Oil Chem. Soc.*, 1962, **39**, 176.
23. (*a*) J. Alvarez, P. Cattaneo *et al.*, *Anales Asocn. Quim. Argentina*, 1949, **37**, 34; (*b*) P. Cattaneo, L. M. Darnet *et al.*, *ibid.*, 1947, **35**, 164.
24. B. G. Gunde and T. P. Hilditch, *J. Chem. Soc.*, 1938, 1980.
25. A. Steger and J. van Loon, *J. Soc. Chem. Ind.*, 1937, **56**, 298T.
26. H. G. Byers and P. Hopkins, *J. Amer. Chem. Soc.*, 1902, **24**, 771.
27. V. Ruchkin, *Maslob. Shir. Delo*, 1929, No. 2, 47.
28. G. S. Jamieson and R. S. McKinney, *Oil and Fat Ind.*, 1929, **6**, (6), 15.
29. T. P. Hilditch and (Miss) E. E. Jones, *J. Soc. Chem. Ind.*, 1930, **49**, 363T.
30. G. S. Jamieson and S. I. Gertler, *cf.* Jamieson, " Vegetable Fats and Oils", New York, 1932, p. 109.
31. H. K. Dean and T. P. Hilditch, *J. Soc. Chem. Ind.*, 1933, **52**, 165T.
32. A. Steger and J. van Loon, *Rec. trav. chim.*, 1935, **54**, 284.
33. T. P. Hilditch, M. L. Meara and O. A. Roels, *J. Soc. Chem. Ind.*, 1947, **66**, 284.
34. T. P. Hilditch and (Miss) E. E. Jones, *J. Soc. Chem. Ind.*, 1931, **50**, 171T.
35. A. Heiduschka and A. Endler, *Pharm. Zentr.*, 1932, **73**, 481.
36. L. Kehren, *An. fac. farm. Bahia*, 1952, **10**, 101.
37. (*a*) G. S. Jamieson and W. F. Baughman, *Oil and Fat Ind.*, 1925, **2**, 40; (*b*) *ibid.*, 1925, **2**, 110.
38. G. S. Jamieson, R. M. Hann and W. F. Baughman, *Oil and Fat Ind.*, 1927, **4**, 63.
39. G. S. Jamieson, *Oil and Fat Ind.*, 1927, **4**, 426.
40. T. P. Hilditch and E. C. Jones, *J. Chem. Soc.*, 1932, 805.
41. B. G. Gunde and T. P. Hilditch, *J. Soc. Chem. Ind.*, 1940, **59**, 47.
42. T. P. Hilditch and H. M. Thompson, *J. Soc. Chem. Ind.*, 1937, **56**, 434T.
43. V. Brandonisio, *Chim. e. Ind.*, 1936, **18**, 14.
44. (*a*) P. Cattaneo, *Anales Asocn. Quim. Argentina*, 1950, **38**, 83; (*b*) P. Cattaneo, G. K. de Sutton and J. Schmidt, *ibid.*, 1950, **38**, 268.
45. S. A. Narang and Sadgopal, *J. Amer. Oil Chem. Soc.*, 1958, **35**, 68.
46. A. Kato, *Yukagaku*, 1961, **10**, 174.
47. G. P. Pinto, *Rev. Quim. Ind., Rio de Janeiro*, 1955, **24**, 72.
48. M. R. Fuhrmann, *Rev. Francaise des Corps Gras*, 1955, **2**, 237.
49. B. M. Craig and N. L. Murti, *J. Amer. Oil Chem. Soc.*, 1959, **36**, 549.
50. W. Mary L. Crombie and S. G. Boatman, *J. W. Afr. Inst. Oil Palm Res.*, 1955, **1**, 64.

TABLE 57A. *Component Acids of Palmæ Fruit-coat Fats*
(*For references, see p. 193*)

Major component acids: PALMITIC, OLEIC, LINOLEIC
Minor component acids: Myristic, stearic.

		COMPONENT FATTY ACIDS PER CENT. (WT.)						
		SATURATED			UNSATURATED			
		C_{14}	PALMITIC	C_{18}	OLEIC	LINOLEIC	METHOD	OBSERVERS
Elæis guineensis	Oil palm							
	Plantation Oils							
	Congo	0·5	41·0	5·2	47·6	5·6(a)	F	Jamieson and McKinney[28]
	"	1·2	43·0	4·4	40·2	11·2	F	Hilditch and (Miss) Jones[29]
	Malaya	2·5	40·8	3·6	45·2	7·9	F	Hilditch and (Miss) Jones[2]
	Sumatra	0·6	43·8	2·9	43·1	9·5	F	Jamieson and Gertler[30]
	"	2·5	41·8	4·2	42·1	9·4	F	Dean and Hilditch[31]
	"	1·5	42·9	4·7	39·8	11·3	F	Steger and van Loon[32]
	N'Dian	3·1	42·4	3·6	39·5	10·0(b)	C,F,S	Hilditch, Meara and Roels[33]
	Native Oils							
	Sierra Leone	2·0	35·9	6·1	48·0	8·0	F	Dean and Hilditch[31]
	Liberia, Sherbro	1·6	35·0	5·3	50·1	8·0	F	Dean and Hilditch[31]
	" Grand Bassa	2·0	33·5	6·4	50·5	7·6	F	Dean and Hilditch[31]
	" Cape Palmas	1·6	32·3	5·5	52·4	8·2	F	Dean and Hilditch[31]
	Ivory Coast, Drewin	2·3	34·3	5·6	49·5	8·3	F	Hilditch and (Miss) Jones[29]
	" " "	2·2	35·3	5·2	52·3	5·0	F	Hilditch and (Miss) Jones[34]

Source						Method	Reference
Ghana, Takoradi	1·9	40·8	4·9	43·3	9·1	F	Dean and Hilditch[31]
Nigeria, Lagos	—	47·0	1·0	50·0	2·0	F	Heiduschka and Endler[35]
,, ,,	1·2	39·6	5·8	42·4	11·0	F	Dean and Hilditch[31]
,, ,, Benin	2·7	42·5	3·4	40·9	10·5	F	Dean and Hilditch[31]
,, ,, Benin	4·5	37·5	4·2	47·3	6·5	F	Hilditch and (Miss) Jones[34]
,, ,, ,,	0·8	42·4	7·5	40·9	6·2 (d)	RPC	Crombie and Boatman[50]
,, ,, Bonny Old Calabar	4·1	40·1	4·4	41·5	9·9	F	Hilditch and (Miss) Jones[34]
Niger	5·9	39·3	2·2	42·7	9·9	F	Hilditch and (Miss) Jones[34]
Cameroons	1·0	38·9	5·9	43·9	10·3	F	Hilditch and (Miss) Jones[34]
Bahia (Brazil)	1·6	33·0	4·5	52·5	8·4	F	Hilditch and (Miss) Jones[29]
Elæis melanocca ,, Noli palm, Congo (S. American)	1·0	32·6	4·7	47·5	12·0 (c)	C,F,S	Kehren[36] Roels and Thuriaux[5]
Œnocarpus batava Patua palm, Brazil	—	9·3	5·9	81·1	3·6	F	Jamieson and McKinney[6]
,, ,, ,,	—	6·0	6·0	79·2	8·8	F	Chaves and Pechnik[7]
,, *bacaba* Bacaba oil, Brazil	—	11·8	9·6	64·8	13·8	F	Pinto[47]
Jessenia batava Brazil	—	7·6	9·4	77·5	5·5	F	Pinto[47]

195

Minor component acids also recorded as follows (per cent. wt.):

	ARACHIDIC	LIGNOCERIC	HEXADECENOIC	LINOLENIC
(a) *Elæis guineensis* (Congo)	—	0·1	—	—
(b) ,, ,, (N'Dian)	0·2	—	0·9	0·3
(c) *Elæis melanocca*	0·5	—	0·9	0·8
(d) ,, *guineensis* (Nigeria, Benin)	1·1	—	—	—

TABLE 57B. *Component Acids of Olive Fruit-coat Fats*
(For references, see p. 193)

Major component acids: PALMITIC, OLEIC, LINOLEIC
Minor component acids: Myristic, stearic.

Olea europaea, sativa

| | COMPONENT FATTY ACIDS PER CENT. (WT.) | | | | | | |
| | SATURATED | | | UNSATURATED | | | |
	C_{14}	PALMITIC	C_{18}	OLEIC	LINOLEIC	METHOD	OBSERVERS
Olive oils from:							
California	—	7·0	2·3	85·8	4·7 (a)	F	Jamieson and Baughman[37a]
Corsica	—	9·4	2·0	84·5	4·0 (a)	F	Jamieson and Baughman[37b]
Tunisia	0·1	14·7	2·4	70·3	12·2 (a)	F	Jamieson, Hann and Baughman[38]
"	0·7	13·9	1·9	64·0	15·1 (a')	C,F	Fuhrmann[48]
Canada	—	13·6	3·2	74·0	7·0 (m)	GLC	Craig and Murti[49]
Spain	0·2	9·5	1·4	81·6	7·0 (a)	F	Jamieson[39]
Italy (Tuscany)	1·1	9·7	1·0	79·8	7·5	F	Hilditch and Jones[40]
" "	1·2	15·6	2·0	64·6	15·0 (b)	F	Gunde and Hilditch[41]
Palestine	0·5	10·0	3·3	77·5	8·6 (a)	F	Hilditch and Thompson[42]
Mediterranean Islands—							
Arcangelo	0·9	19·7	—	68·7	10·7	?	Brandonisio[43]
Afando	0·4	18·7	—	67·6	13·3	?	Brandonisio[43]
Alaerma	0·6	18·4	—	68·5	12·5	?	Brandonisio[43]
Cos	0·4	17·1	—	68·8	13·7	?	Brandonisio[43]

Peveragno	0·8	19·1	—	69·5	10·6	?	Brandonisio[43]
Rhodes	—	19·7	0·3	69·6	10·4	?	Brandonisio[43]
Argentina—							
Patagonia	0·5	9·8	2·0	76·3	7·0 (c)	F	Cattaneo[44a]
Bahia Blanca	0·8	12·3	0·6	73·6	6·4 (d)	F	Cattaneo[44a]
Mendoza	0·7	12·2	2·7	67·6	14·8 (e)	F	Cattaneo[44a]
Cordoba	0·8	16·3	0·7	61·5	15·9 (f)	F	Cattaneo[44a]
La Rioja	0·7	20·0	1·5	56·6	18·1 (g)	F	Cattaneo[44a]
Mendoza	1·7	18·8	0·8	53·1	19·6 (h)	F	Cattaneo[44a]
Cuyo (var. *arbequina* at different stages of maturity):							
Collected January 28th	—	13·8	0·8	74·5	6·6 (i)	F	Cattaneo et al.[44b]
,, March 23rd	—	16·3	1·2	64·5	15·2 (j)	F	Cattaneo et al.[44b]
,, April 19th	—	14·5	0·9	62·6	18·7 (k)	F	Cattaneo et al.[44b]
,, June 6th	0·2	13·9	0·9	59·5	22·5 (l)	F	Cattaneo et al.[44b]

Minor component acids also recorded as follows (per cent. wt.):

	LAURIC	ARACHIDIC	HEXADECENOIC	as EICOSENOIC
(a)	—	Traces	—	—
(a')	—	0·7	1·6	2·1
(b)	—	—	1·6	—
(c)	0·2	0·5	1·8	1·9
(d)	0·2	1·0	2·0	3·1
(e)	—	0·2	1·6	0·2
(f)	—	1·3	2·5	1·0

	LAURIC	ARACHIDIC	HEXADECENOIC	as EICOSENOIC
(g)	—	0·9	2·2	1·8
(h)	0·7	1·2	2·3	2·5
(i)	—	1·4	0·4	0·8
(j)	—	1·1	0·9	0·9
(k)	—	0·8	1·6	0·8
(l)	—	1·0	1·2	0·8
(m)	Also hexadecenoic 1·3, linolenic 0·9 per cent.			

197

proportions of lauric acid (80 per cent. or more, *cf.* pp. 333, 335, 336), and, from the few analyses available it seems that in these plants the fruit-coat fats also contain a certain amount of combined lauric acid. The amounts are, however, small in comparison with those in the corresponding seed fats, and, moreover, palmitic acid is usually present in considerably larger quantities than lauric acid in these fruit-coat fats, whilst oleic acid (a very minor component of the seed fats) forms 50 per cent. or more of the Lauraceæ fruit-coat fatty acids.

A point of interest about avocado (*Persea*) fruit coat fats is their content of about 10 per cent. of hexadecenoic acid which, except for seed fats belonging to the family Proteaceæ (pp. 219, 237, 239), has only been reported in very minor quantities in the higher flora, although it is widely distributed in fats of terrestial and (especially) marine fauna.

The fruit-coat fat of sumach (*Rhus* sp.) berries, commonly known as "Japan wax", is unusual not only in its extremely high content of palmitic glycerides but also because it contains up to 6 per cent. of saturated dibasic acids, first reported by Eberhardt[67] as $C_{18}H_{36}(CO_2H)_2$ and later by Geitel and van der Want[68] as "Japanic acid", $C_{20}H_{40}(CO_2H)_2$. In 1931 Tsujimoto[69a] showed that the dibasic acids were a mixture of at least two homologues, $C_{21}H_{42}(CO_2H)_2$, m.p. 123·5°, and $C_{20}H_{40}(CO_2H)_2$. The presence of these acids (which, incidentally, belong to the normal series $COOH.[CH_2]_n.COOH$) is held to confer on "Japan wax" its characteristic properties of toughness and ability to be kneaded without crumbling. In 1954 Toyama and Hinai[69b] separated by chromatographic adsorption concentrates of glycerides of the dibasic acids of high molecular weight, and found that two glyceryl residues were linked by dibasic acids, the remaining hydroxyl groups of the glycerol molecules being either free or united with palmitic acid.

In the next place, although the data cover members of only sixteen botanical families, the seed fats of the latter are so diverse in composition that we are presented with a very striking series of fruit-coat fats qualitatively similar in component acids, coupled with corresponding seed fats ranging from almost saturated to extremely unsaturated, and containing a wide variety of saturated fatty acids. This is clearly illustrated by the summary in Table 58.

We shall find, when discussing the component acids of seed fats, that a wide variety of fatty acids enters into their composition, but that the mixture found within the limits of any given botanical family is nearly always qualitatively, and to some extent quantitatively, the same. Thus the proportions and kinds of fatty acids present in palm kernel oil are closely simulated in the other Palmæ seed fats (*Areca catechu*, *Astrocaryum* species, *Attalea* species, *Cocos nucifera*, etc.) which have been submitted to detailed analysis, whilst still other Palmæ seed fats have saponification values (240–250) and iodine values (7–30) which suffice to indicate that their component acids are closely similar to those which have been studied in detail. The saponification values (190–200) and iodine values (50–80) of the fruit-coat fats corresponding with these latter seed fats are, in contrast, similar to those of palm oils and other fruit-coat fats. Thus, whilst seed fats of the Palmæ, Myristicaceæ, and Lauraceæ contain very large

TABLE 58. Contrasts in Composition of Fruit-coat and Seed Fats from the Same Fruit

Family	Species	FRUIT-COAT FAT COMPONENT ACIDS				SEED FAT COMPONENT ACIDS				
		LAURIC	PALMITIC	OLEIC	LINOLEIC	LAURIC	PALMITIC	OLEIC	LINOLEIC	OTHERS
ANACARDIACEÆ	Rhus sp.	—	77	12	Trace	—	Small	Much	Much	—
EUPHORBIACEÆ	Sapium sebiferum†	—	60–70	20–35		—	6	16	46	29 per cent. linolenic
CUCURBITACEÆ	Trichosanthes cucumeroides	—	32‡	31	23*	—	9‡	20	42	29 per cent. trichosanic
PALMÆ	Elæis guineensis	—	35–40	40–50	5–11	47	9	18	1	14 per cent. myristic, etc.
CARYOCARACEÆ	Caryocar villosum	—	41	54	3	—	48	46	3	—
STERCULIACEÆ	Theobroma cacao	—	ca. 50‡	ca. 35	ca. 10	—	ca. 60‡	ca. 37	ca. 2	—
BURSERACEÆ	Dacryodes rostrata	—	34	59	4	—	11	44	3	40 per cent. stearic.
LAURACEÆ	Laurus nobilis	3	20	63	14	43	6	32	18	—
	Neolitsea involucrata	10	28	48	10	86	—	4	3	—
CELASTRACEÆ	Celastrus paniculatus	—	26	36	8§	—	22	22	35	16 per cent. linolenic.
CAPRIFOLIACEÆ	Sambucus racemosa	—	23	71	6	—	23	45	24	8 per cent. linolenic.
OLEACEÆ	Olea europœa	—	7–15	70–85	4–12	—	6	83	7	4 per cent. stearic.
ELÆAGNACEÆ	Hippophæ rhamnoides	—	12	75	12	—	11	41	33	15 per cent. linolenic.
MYRISTICACEÆ	Myristica officinalis	—	?	ca. 80	?	—	10	10	—	77 per cent. myristic.

* Also 9 per cent. linolenic acid.   † Syn. Stillingia sebifera.   ‡ Total saturated acids (palmitic and stearic).   § Also 23 per cent. linolenic acid.

199

amounts of lauric and/or myristic acids, their fruit-coat fats are mainly made up of palmitic, oleic, and linoleic acids in varying proportions.

There is, then, no apparent connection between the general nature of the component acids of fruit-coat and seed fats. Sometimes, as in the fruits of the olive, piquia, or cacao plants, the seed fat is closely similar to the fruit-coat fat, but this seems to be exceptional rather than otherwise (in six or seven of the plant species illustrated in Table 58, however, it may be noticed that the fruit-coat and seed fats contain about the same proportion of palmitic acid). A fruit-coat fat of comparatively high melting point (i.e. relatively rich in combined palmitic acid) may be associated with a highly unsaturated liquid seed fat (*Stillingia*) or an almost saturated solid fat (Palmæ); liquid ("non-drying" oil) fruit-coat fats, equally, are found in instances where the seed fats are soft solids and their component acids mainly saturated (Lauraceæ, Myristicaceæ), or where the seed fats are "drying" oils (elderberry, buckthorn); and so on. It is clear that, whereas seed fats contain a wide range of specific component acids, according to their botanical origin, fruit-coat fats almost invariably include only palmitic and oleic, with occasionally linoleic, amongst their major component acids.

It will be observed that, in spite of the general constancy in the qualitative nature of their components, fruit-coat fats vary almost as widely as seed fats in their physical properties. Whereas, however, relatively high melting point in a seed fat is almost always due to the presence in quantity of saturated acids other than palmitic acid, the consistencies of different fruit-coat fats at the ordinary temperature are controlled in all the foregoing instances by variation in the respective proportions of palmitic and oleic (with linoleic) acids. The physical properties of either fruit-coat or seed fats are, of course, in a sense accidental, in that they are determined by the component fatty acids and glyceride structure; the causes which in turn determine the kind and amount of the various acids and their combination into natural glycerides of specific structure remain unknown.

Sufficient stillingia tallows, palm, and olive oils have been examined to permit in each of these fats some consideration of the extent to which the fatty acid compositions may vary. In stillingia fruit-coat fats (the name "*Stillingia*" came into use for the fats before botanists finally made up their minds to call the genus "*Sapium*") there is evidence of a species distinction: that of *S. discolor* contains about equal amounts (46–47 per cent.) of palmitic and oleic acids, whereas in the more unusual *S. sebiferum* the fruit-coat fat is much richer in palmitic acid. Within this species, however, ranges from 58 to 72 per cent. in palmitic acid, and from 35 to 20 per cent. in oleic acid, have been observed.

Palm oils. A much greater number of specimens is available for scrutiny in palm oils. Here, as in stillingia tallows, the two major component acids, palmitic and oleic, together form an approximately constant proportion (about 80 per cent.) of the total fatty acids. Nevertheless in different palm oils there is a subordinate but quite definite variation in the respective proportions of palmitic and oleic acids; this seems to be connected with the locality in which the oil palm is grown. Roughly speaking, the oils from palms grown east of about longitude

4–6° W. (i.e. from the Ivory Coast and Ghana eastwards) all contain about 40 per cent. of palmitic, about 43–44 per cent. of oleic, and about 9–10 per cent. of linoleic acid; but in the oils derived from more westerly parts of the coast (Liberia and Sierra Leone) another type is met with, characterised by a lower content of palmitic acid (about 35 per cent.) and correspondingly higher oleic acid (about 50 per cent.). The cause of this variation is unknown; it was first noticed in 1928 by Dyke,[70] who pointed out that the setting point of the mixed fatty acids of the oils from the more westerly regions was slightly lower (*ca.* 41° C.) than that (*ca.* 44° C.) of Ghana or Nigerian oils. The geographical difference is one of longitude, not latitude, and it seems unlikely that climatic variations will come into consideration; there may be differences in the soil or, perhaps, the oil palm in the western districts may be a different variety from that indigenous to Ghana and Nigeria.

The plantation oils from the Congo, Malaya, and Sumatra all show close similarity between themselves and also to the native oils of the Ghana and Niger regions; this is probably in consequence of seed having been originally drawn from the variety indigenous to one or other of these districts.

The Noli palm is a species of *Elæis* (*E. melanococca*) indigenous to South America: the fruit-coat fat from a specimen grown at Yangambi (Congo) was found by Roels and Thuriaux[71] to be similar to those of *E. guineensis* palm oils with the lower palmitic and higher oleic acid contents. The fruit-coat fats of the Brazilian genera *Œnocarpus* and *Jessenia* (patua palms) differ from those of *Elæis* species in that they contain up to 80 per cent. of oleic acid and only 10 per cent. (or less) of palmitic acid.

Olive oils. Olive fruit-coat fats seem to vary rather widely in their contents of oleic, palmitic, and also linoleic, acids. Many olive oils from Italy, Spain, Asia Minor, or California agree closely in containing about 9–10 per cent. palmitic acid, about 2 per cent. of stearic acid, and not more than about 7 per cent. of linoleic acid; these oils are so similar in composition that, for the acids mentioned, the variations are not far outside the limits of experimental error of the ester-fractionation method. The oleic acid content lies between the extremes of 77 and 86 per cent. (in all but two of the analyses between 77·5 and 81·6 per cent.). On the other hand, the Mediterranean (Dodecanese) Island oils examined by Brandonisio,[72] the Tunisian oils analysed by Jamieson and Baughman[73a] and by Fuhrmann[73b] and an oil reputedly of Italian (Tuscany) origin studied by Gunde and Hilditch[73c] show oleic acid contents of 70–65 per cent., with 10–15 per cent. of linoleic acid and 15 per cent. or more of palmitic acid, whilst the Argentine olive oils investigated by Cattaneo et al.[75] include palmitic acid contents between 10 and 20 per cent., linoleic acid contents between 6 and 22 per cent., and oleic acid between 54 and 79 per cent. In one instance specimens of olive fruits were collected at four different stages of maturity (between January and June, 1949, *cf.* Table 57B, p. 197): Cattaneo et al[75b] observed that whilst the palmitic acid in the four oils remained fairly constant at 14–16 per cent. of the total acids, oleic acid progressively decreased during ripening from 75 to 60 per cent., linoleic acid increasing from 7 to 23 per cent. The oils with highest linoleic contents occurred in the Argentine winter season, so that this series may appear to be similar to certain seed fats (linseed, sunflower) in which growth in cooler conditions seems to result in higher linoleic and lower oleic acid with but little change in the proportion of saturated acids (*cf.* Chapter IV, pp. 210, 227, Chapter VIII, p. 538). Brandonisio[72] suggests, on the contrary, that olive oils contain more linoleic acid when the trees are grown in warmer climates. Moreover, in the European oils in Table 57B it is noticeable that increased linoleic acid is accompanied by very similar increases in palmitic acid as well as reduction in oleic acid percentages.

It is therefore difficult, with the information at present available, to assess, in the case of olive oils, whether these subordinate differences in quantitative composition are to be correlated with growth conditions, climate, or varietal differences in the parent trees.

Seed Fats

What does a sample of a seed fat represent? This is a convenient place to consider how far a specimen of fat extracted from a seed represents the composition of the fat in, for instance, individual cells of the endosperm. In most cases the specimen is extracted from a large number (often many thousands) of individual seeds, so that the fatty acid composition determined is the *average* for the fat from a great number of seeds; fat from different seeds may vary to some extent in fatty acid composition although probably not to any marked degree (*cf.* candlenut oil, p. 246).

Recently (1963) Kartha[225] observed variations in the content of oil and in its iodine value at different sites, either vertically from top to bottom, or laterally from side to side, in a number of fairly large seeds. The oil content decreases, while its iodine value increases, from the centre to the periphery, in groundnuts, pistachio, almond and apricot seeds; in coconuts, areca and hazel nuts, in contrast, both oil content and iodine value increase from the centre outwards. Whilst the observed differences are not very large, and also not always in the same direction, it is nevertheless clear that the composition of a seed fat is by no means the same in different sectors of the seed.

It is in any case essential to ensure that the botanical origin of the seed studied is fully authenticated and, again, that the seed fat is extracted from mature, dry seed in the laboratory in which the component fatty acid analysis is to be performed.

In this connection a word of caution may be added in regard to the employment of fats or fatty oils drawn from storage in an oil mill. In spite of every effort to supply the investigator with a true sample there are two factors which must be guarded against carefully:

(i) Inadvertent contamination (from pipe lines, etc.) with small proportions of another oil;

(ii) Withdrawal of a sample from a tank which has stood for a long time, in which case settling and deposition of solid glycerides may have proceeded, with the result that the sample obtained is not a true average of the total seed or other fat to be supplied.

Classification of seed fats based upon their major component acids. A very large number of seed fats contain, as major component acids, only those – palmitic, oleic, linoleic, and sometimes linolenic – which have been found to characterise fats from parts of plants other than the seed. Many others, again, in addition to one or more of the acids mentioned, have as major components one or more distinctive acids, either saturated or unsaturated. It is therefore possible to group most seed fats according to their predominating component acids, although in a minority of instances this method of grouping is somewhat ill-defined: for example, in consequence of more than one of the more usual mixtures of major components occurring in the seed fats of a single family (e.g., in the Leguminosæ, Rosaceæ, Euphorbiaceæ, Olacaceæ, or Simarubaceæ families). As already mentioned in Chapter I (p. 10) grouping of seed fats according to their chief component acids leads at once to the circumstance that seed fats of plants in the same botanical family usually fall in the same group, and often show great similarity in their composition. The grouping of seed fats adopted in this book is therefore *primarily* based upon *similarities in their major component acids.*

The seed fats in which only palmitic, oleic, linoleic, and/or linolenic acids are major components will be discussed first of all. These may be subdivided into the following groups:

I. Those in which linoleic and linolenic acids predominate.
II.   „   „   „   oleic and linoleic   „   „
III.   „   „   „   oleic and palmitic   „   „

Groups I, II, and III, of course, correspond approximately with the empirical divisions of "drying", "semi-drying", and "non-drying" oils and, indeed, many of the more familiar of these oils will be found in these three groups.

There are a number of fats, however, in which linoleic acid is prominent, which also contain specific saturated acids, and there are others in which linoleic acid or linolenic acid is abundant in the seed fat of one species, whilst in another related species a quite different unsaturated acid replaces these almost entirely. The most familiar examples of the latter are: (i) the prominence of elæostearic glycerides in the seeds of *Aleurites fordii* and *montana*, whilst in other species of *Aleurites* polyethenoid unsaturation is confined to linoleic and linolenic glycerides; and (ii) the abundance of ricinoleic glycerides in the seeds of *Ricinus* species. Such cases are therefore classified separately, as a sub-group to I and II (above), according to the plant families concerned (Euphorbiaceæ, Rosaceæ, Cucurbitaceæ).

The other type, in which specific saturated acids (other than palmitic) are a feature of the seed fats, are grouped primarily with reference to their specific saturated acids, irrespective of whether linoleic acid is also a major component. Similarly, the occurrence of specific unsaturated acids, such as erucic, petroselinic, chaulmoogric, and hydnocarpic, has been dealt with by separating into corresponding groups the seed fats in which they occur as major components of the mixed glycerides.

203

General classification of seed fats according to their major component acids

Table	Major component acids	Botanical families represented
59	Linolenic, linoleic (oleic)	Coniferæ; Moraceæ, Celastraceæ, Aquifoliaceæ, Labiatæ, Valerianaceæ, Onagraceæ, Linaceæ, Elæagnaceæ, Rhamnaceæ, Boraginaceæ, Ericaceæ, Nyctaginaceæ, Dilleniaceæ.
60	Linoleic, oleic	Betulaceæ, Fagaceæ, Juglandaceæ, Hippocastanaceæ, Ulmaceæ, Olacaceæ, Vitaceæ, Papaveraceæ, Passifloraceæ, Typhaceæ, Compositæ, Solanaceæ, Pedaliaceæ, Scrophulariaceæ, Plantaginaceæ, Dipsaceæ, Asclepiadaceæ, Staphyleaceæ, Myrtaceæ, Urticaceæ, Theaceæ, Oleaceæ, Ranunculaceæ, Calycanthaceæ, Campanulaceæ, Symplocaceæ, Polemoniaceæ, Chenopodiaceæ, Hamamelidaceæ, Loasaceæ, Portulacaceæ, Agavaceæ, Liliaceæ, Proteaceæ.
61	Linoleic, oleic, or linolenic; or elæostearic, licanic; or ricinoleic	Rosaceæ, Euphorbiaceæ, Cucurbitaceæ.
62	Palmitic, oleic, linoleic	Berberidaceæ, Magnoliaceæ, Anonaceæ, Rutaceæ, Zygophyllaceæ, Anacardiaceæ, Capparidaceæ, Hernandiaceæ, Tiliaceæ, Malvaceæ, Bombacaceæ, Caryocaraceæ, Caricaceæ, Lecythidaceæ, Combretaceæ, Apocynaceæ, Amarantaceæ, Martyniaceæ, Acanthaceæ, Bignoniaceæ, Rubiaceæ, Caprifoliaceæ, Loganiaceæ.
63	Palmitic, oleic, linoleic	Gramineæ.
64	Petroselinic, oleic, linoleic Acetylenic acids: Tariric Octadecen-ynoic	Umbelliferæ, Araliaceæ, (Simarubaceæ). Simarubaceæ *(Picramnia* sp.). Olacaceæ *(Onguekoa* sp., *Ximenia* sp.), Santalaceæ.
65	Cyclic unsaturated acids (chaulmoogric, hydnocarpic, gorlic). Eicosenoic, (oleic, linoleic)	Flacourtiaceæ. Olacaceæ (*Ximenia* sp.); Sapindaceæ; Buxaceæ (*Simmondsia* sp.).
66	Erucic, oleic, linoleic (linolenic, eicosenoic)	Cruciferæ, Tropæolaceæ.
67	Oleic, linoleic, arachidic, behenic, lignoceric	Leguminosæ, Moringaceæ, Ochnaceæ, Sapindaceæ.
68	Stearic, palmitic, oleic	Gnetaceæ; Meliaceæ, Menispermaceæ, Sterculiaceæ, Guttiferæ, Dipterocarpaceæ, Burseraceæ, Sapotaceæ, Convolvulaceæ, Verbenaceæ, Zingiberaceæ.
69A	Capric, lauric.	Ulmaceæ, Lythrarieæ.
69A	Lauric, myristic (palmitic)	Lauraceæ, Myristicaceæ, Simarubaceæ, Vochysiaceæ, Salvadoraceæ.
69B	Lauric, myristic (palmitic)	Palmæ.

The above classification of seed fats shows at a glance the very marked degree of alignment of typical seed fatty acid mixtures with their botanical sources, not only when the acids concerned are those most common (palmitic, oleic, linoleic, linolenic) but also when another specific fatty acid is prominent (e.g., petroselenic, erucic, stearic, lauric in different families). These regularities obtain in what must be many thousands – probably the great majority – of plant species; yet (as usually happens in natural organisms and their products) quite a number of unusual fatty acids crop up here and there to provide exceptions to what seems to be the more general practice. To the investigator the abnormal and unexpected has more excitement and interest than the rather prosaic evaluation of seed fats whose major components are confined to the usual quartet (albeit in varying proportions of the latter); and in the literature more emphasis on the rarities is often evident than on the far larger number of seed fats which ring the changes on oleic, linoleic, linolenic and palmitic acid. Both aspects are equally interesting and equally important, but it is necessary to endeavour to maintain a correct sense of perspective and to remember that the wide distribution and quantities of the "common" fatty acids in seed fats is just as worthy of consideration as the more exciting discovery of quite unusual forms.

Some of the rather curious rarities are mentioned in the foregoing general classification and reference may be made to a few others of the more exceptional types. Hexadec-9-enoic acid, more familiar in animal fats and in the lower forms of vegetation, has so far only been noted as a major component (10–20 per cent.) of the acids in the seed fats of Proteaceæ (p. 219) and the fruit-coat fat of *Persea gratissima* (Lauraceæ). Epoxy-oleic (vernolic) acid is the major component in *Vernonia anthelmintica* (Compositæ), and the cyclopropene sterculic and malvalic acids occur in *Sterculia fœtida* (Sterculiaceæ) and some Malvaceæ species. Deca-2,4-dienoic acid is an unusual natural fatty acid present in stillingia oil (Euphorbiaceæ) and dec-4-enoic, dodec-4-enoic and tetradec-4-enoic acids have been found in seed fats of *Lindera* and *Litsea* species (Lauraceæ).

More specific reference may also be made here – since they do not fit in to any of the general tables which follow – to two quite exceptional seed fatty acids which have recently (1960) been reported. The seed oil of *Limnanthes douglassii* (Limnanthaceæ) contains a mixture, at present unique, of fatty acids[74a]: eicos-*cis*-5-enoic *ca.* 65, docos-*cis*-5-enoic *ca.* 7, docos-*cis*-13-enoic (erucic) *ca.* 13, and docos-*cis*-5-*cis*-13-dienoic *ca.* 10 per cent. (with 2 per cent. each of oleic and arachidic acids, and traces of myristic, palmitic, stearic and linoleic acids). The seed fat of ratsbane, *Dichapetalum toxicarium* (Dichapetalaceæ Engler, Chailletaceæ Bentham and Hooker), is even more unusual in that it contains fluoro-fatty acids, including *ca.* 20 per cent. of ω-fluoro-octadec-*cis*--9-enoic acid, $CH_2F.[CH_2]_7.CH:CH.[CH_2]_7.COOH$, and traces of a C_{17} saturated fluoro-fatty acid.[74b] The identity of the ω-fluoro-oleic acid has been confirmed[74c] by its synthesis from 8-fluoro-octyl bromide, which with sodium acetylide yielded 10-fluoro-1-decyne; this was condensed with 7-iodo-heptyl chloride by metallic lithium in liquid ammonia to give 1-chloro-17-fluoro-heptadec-8-yne, leading to 18-fluoro-octadec-*cis*-9-enoic acid by the conventional routes (*cf.* Chapter IX, p. 606).

Seed Fats with Palmitic, Oleic, Linoleic, and/or Linolenic Acids as Major Components

I AND II. SEED FATS IN WHICH LINOLEIC AND/OR LINOLENIC ACID PREDOMINATES

("LINOLENIC-RICH" AND "LINOLEIC-RICH" SEED FATS)

Major component acids: LINOLEIC, LINOLENIC, OLEIC.
Minor component acids: Palmitic (stearic).

Tables 59 (p. 213) and 60 (p. 229) give practically all the detailed figures which have been published for seed fats in which *linoleic, linolenic,* and *oleic* acids are the most important constituents. These groups, in spite of the small number of fatty acids concerned, were not easy to investigate until methods of analysis had been devised for the determination of oleic, linoleic, and linolenic acids in presence of each other. The ester-fractionation method does not help, of course, in this respect. Some earlier figures quoted are based either upon analyses of the unsaturated acid fraction (obtained by a lead salt separation ("L"), by means of the bromo-addition products (hexa-bromo- and tetrabromo-stearic acids) ("H"), or upon a combination of the Bertram oxidation process ("B") (for the total saturated acids) with the thiocyanogen method for estimating the three unsaturated acids ("T" or "K"). The most reliable figures, however, are those in which the most modern procedures have been employed, namely, preliminary resolution of the mixed fatty acids by low-temperature crystallisation from solvents ("C"), followed by ester-fractionation ("F"), reversed-phase partition chromatography ("RPC"), or gas–liquid chromatography ("GLC") of each group of acids obtained, and with determinations of linoleic and linolenic acids by spectrophotometric analysis after alkali-isomerisation ("S", p. 179); when possible, component fatty acid figures obtained by these procedures have been given, sometimes in preference to those obtained by earlier methods.

It should be appreciated that for linoleic and linolenic acids data obtained by the spectrographic method ("S") or with the aid of thiocyanogen values based on the empirically determined values ("T") are the more reliable. Those derived from the older form of calculation ("K") from thiocyanogen values give considerably less accurate figures for the proportions of the three unsaturated acids, whilst those based upon determinations of insoluble forms of tetra- or hexa-bromostearic acids ("H") are liable to record considerably less than the amount of linoleic or linolenic acid actually present.

There is, perhaps, no very sharp line to be drawn, as regards component fatty acids, between the seed fats in Table 59 and those in Table 60, but it is convenient to subdivide them roughly into those in which linolenic acid is prominent and those in which it is not. It will be noticed that in both groups the fats are derived from the seeds of (i) large trees (conifers, beech, walnut, etc.), (ii) shrubs, and (iii) herbs of various families (e.g. Labiatæ, Compositæ, etc.).

"Drying", "semi-drying" and "non-drying" oils. Of the more common oils mentioned in Tables 59 and 60, those of perilla, chia, linseed, argemone, poppy, walnut, and hemp are usually termed "drying" oils, as also are soya bean, safflower, and sunflower seed oils, although these are sometimes classed with the "semi-drying" type. This is because the latter oils may differ in their relative proportions of oleic and linoleic acids when grown in different circumstances. Other oils, such as sesame and grape seed oils in the groups under consideration, and others such as cottonseed oil, maize oil, and many more which fall to be considered later (under other major component acid groups) and which contain perhaps 40–60 per cent of linoleic acid, are definitely "semi-drying" oils, whilst groundnut, olive, almond, and other oils which contain about 20 per cent. or less of linoleic acid belong to the group of "non-drying" oils.

Rather more specific criteria[76] can now be offered for different kinds of "drying" oils than was formerly possible. These fall into three groups: (*a*) oils very rich in linolenic acid, (*b*) oils very rich in linoleic acid, and (*c*) oils containing somewhat less linoleic acid than group (*b*) but with some relatively small proportions of linolenic acid as well. A good "linolenic-rich drying oil" (*a*) must contain[76b] not less than about 70 per cent. of total polyethenoid (linolenic + linoleic) acids, and linolenic should form at least 50 per cent. of the total fatty acids (linseed oil type). On the other hand linolenic acid is not an essential ingredient of a "drying" oil so long as sufficient linoleic acid is present: the criterion[76a] for a good "linoleic-rich drying oil" (*b*) is that linoleic acid must form 66 per cent. or more of the total fatty acids. Finally, oils (*c*), such as those of hemp seed or of the soya bean, which contain not less than 50 per cent. of linoleic acid accompanied by 10 per cent. or more of linolenic acid, or some others such as candlenut or rubberseed oils which have about 40 per cent. of linoleic acid with 25–30 per cent. of linolenic acid, also possess useful "drying" properties.

Influence of environment on unsaturation of seed fats. Some of the figures for seed fats in Tables 59A (linseed) and 60A, B (sunflower, safflower, and other seeds), and also in some later tables (e.g., 61 almond, 61A candlenut; 67B soya bean, 67A groundnut) form suitable material for considering the connection between temperature of habitat and relative unsaturation of the seed oils. The detailed data given later (pp. 211, 221–228, 306, 309) for the oils referred to amply confirm earlier evidence of Ivanov[77] and others that a given plant species, capable of existence in different climates, produces when grown in a cold climate more unsaturated (linoleic and linolenic) acids in its seed fat than when it is grown in a warmer climate. To argue in addition, as has been attempted, that tropical plants tend to produce more saturated kinds of seed fats than those of cooler habitat appears to be far too sweeping and, moreover, is not by any means substantiated by the facts. It is, of course, obvious that seeds in whose fats the higher saturated acids predominate will be those of tropical or subtropical growth, since the seed fats must be fluid at the temperature of the living plant. Let us, however, consider the case of species with varying proportions of the different unsaturated acids, the mixed glycerides of which are liquid at the ordinary temperature of the temperate or even sub-arctic regions.

Cases for relation between temperature of growth and component unsaturated acids in the seed fats could be made out for members of the Coniferæ,

Moraceæ, and Celastraceæ listed in Table 59. In the Moraceæ, the West African *Treculia africana* seed fat is much less unsaturated in composition than those of hempseed or mulberry, which grow in temperate climates; again, the seed fat of the North American *Celastrus scandens* obviously contains much more linoleic and linolenic acids, and less oleic and saturated acids, than the sister species, *C. paniculatus*, from India. Similarly, in the data (Table 60) for species of oak (Fagaceæ), of the Papaveraceæ, of sesame (Pedaliaceæ), of sunflower and safflower (Compositæ), and again in Argentine as contrasted with West African groundnut oil (Leguminosæ, Table 67A), there is evidence for greater proportions of the more unsaturated acids in the respective plants which inhabit cooler, as compared with those from warmer, regions.

On the contrary, however, seed fats of numerous tropical or sub-tropical plants (e.g., those of sweet basil, perilla, or chia seeds), are as highly unsaturated as any of temperate climatic origin. Among the Rosaceæ and Euphorbiaceæ species (Table 61, pp. 253–263) the absence of any general correlation between degree of general unsaturation and climatic temperature becomes absolutely clear. In the rose family, the species common to temperate regions – *Prunus* species, hawthorn, blackberry – usually contain much oleic and linoleic acids in their seed fats, with occasionally some linolenic acid in addition; but certain tropical species, namely, *Licania rigida* and *Parinarium* species, are characterised by the presence in their seed fats of large amounts of conjugated triethenoid and, in one instance, *tetraethenoid* acids of the C_{18} series. Similarly, in the Euphorbiaceæ, whilst the caper spurge appears to contain over 90 per cent. of oleic acid in its seed fat, tropical species such as those of *Hevea* and *Aleurites* are uniformly characterised by high proportions of highly unsaturated acids, notably in the case of the conjugated triethenoid elæostearic acid.

It has seemed convenient to mention the above features (which refer to seed fats to be discussed later as well as to those in Tables 59 and 60) in one place before proceeding to discuss those seed fats whose characteristic major component acids are linoleic and/or linolenic.

Mainly Linolenic-rich Seed Fats (Table 59, p. 213). The linolenic acid content of oils in this Table attains to over 60 per cent. of the total acids in some instances, but is much less in others, and even absent in a few cases: when linolenic acid is present in smaller proportions, however, the linoleic acid content is usually of the order of 50 per cent. or so of the total fatty acids. In all these fats saturated acids form only about 10 per cent. or less of the whole, and palmitic acid generally forms about 70 per cent. of the saturated acids; small proportions (1–3 per cent.) of stearic acid are usually also present.

The seed fats of Conifers sometimes contain fairly large proportions of linolenic acid but in other instances this acid is only present in small quantity or absent. It is unfortunate that all but one of these oils listed in Table 59 were studied by the more archaic methods of component acid determination. It is however interesting to observe that, in contrast to coniferous gymnosperms, the only seed fat yet examined from the relatively few tropical gymnosperms (*Gnetum scandens*, Table 68, p. 324) contains a quite different mixture of acids (palmitic 14, stearic 56, oleic 27, linoleic 3 per cent.) thus closely resembling certain families (Sapotaceæ, Guttiferæ) of tropical angiosperms in the general composition of its seed fatty acids (especially the high stearic acid content).

Whilst linolenic acid frequently forms from about 15 to 30 per cent. of seed fats of species of the families Moraceæ, Celastraceæ, Rhamnaceæ, Eleagnaceæ, it is generally much more abundant in Linaceæ and Labiatæ seed fats. In some species of the latter family (*Hyptis, Ocimum, Thymus, etc.*) it exceeds 60 per cent. of the total acids of the seed fats and in these cases the linoleic acid content is usually below 20 per cent. Other seed fats characterised by similar very high contents of linolenic acid are met with in certain species of Euphorbiaceæ (Table 61), and the characteristic compositions of this group of fats, extremely rich in linolenic acid, will receive further mention when the latter are considered (p. 245).

In contrast to the general predominance of linolenic and linoleic acid in the seed fats enumerated in Table 59, there are a very few instances in which oleic is the chief fatty acid present. Thus, in the Labiatae (so often characterised by seed fats very rich in linolenic acid) oleic acid forms over 60 per cent. of the seed fat acids in *Lallemantia royleana* and *Leonatis nepetæfolia*, and 40 per cent., or more, in the seed fats of a few other species (e.g., *Treculia africana*, Moraceæ; *Mirabilis jalapa*, Nyctaginaceæ; *Lycopus asper*, Labiatæ; *Rhamnus purshiana*, Rhamnaceæ; and in a few *Pinus* seed fats). Such seed fats are however only a small proportion of those quoted in Table 59.

It is important to note that the 10 per cent. of triene C_{18} acid in the seed oils of *Œnothera* species (Evening Primrose) is octadeca-6,9,12-trienoic acid (isomeric with linolenic (-9,12,15-) acid), although its main component acid (linoleic, 60–70 per cent.) is the usual octadeca-9,12-dienoic acid. The only other seed fat of this family (Onagraceæ) yet examined, that of *Clarkia elegans*, is reported[78a] to contain about 10 per cent. of 12,13-epoxy-octadec-9-enoic (vernolic) acid (*cf.* p. 219).

Of the two seed fats of the valerian family whose composition has been reported, one (corn salad, *Valerianella olitaria*) is similar to many other fats in Tables 59 and 60, but the other (common valerian, *Valeriana officinalis*) was found by Earle *et al.*[78b] to contain 42 per cent. of the conjugated triene elæostearic acid.

Another unusual feature in the seed fats in Table 59 is the presence in those of *Celastrus* species of appreciable proportions of formic, acetic and benzoic acids in addition to the usual higher fatty acids: it is, however, probable that the acids in question are not present as glycerides, but are in combination with a water-soluble polyhydric, and probably cyclic, alcohol whose constitution is not yet known.[78c] The naturally occurring lower acyl esters of this substance are evidently soluble in the seed glycerides, and are removed to some extent during extraction of the latter from the seed by solvents.

Linseed oil. The technical importance of linseed oil has resulted in many more figures being available for its component acids than in the case of any other seed fat in Table 59. An account of these is therefore given separately from the main Table at this point. Owing to the inadequacy, until comparatively recent years, of accurate methods for determining linolenic and linoleic acids many of the earlier figures are uncertain; in Table 59A (in which the component acids of linseed oils from many regions are recorded) the analyses quoted have been confined to those of comparatively recent date in which reasonably trustworthy methods have been used.

The data in Table 59A indicate that linseed oils from different parts of the world differ somewhat in composition. Argentine linseed oils are low in linolenic acid (45–53 per cent.) whilst those from India, Canada, New Zealand, or from linseed grown in England, have linolenic acid contents which approach (and in some cases exceed) 60 per cent. These differences are in part due,

TABLE 59A. *Component Fatty Acids (per cent. wt.) of Linseed Oils*

SOURCE	SATURATED			UNSATURATED			METHOD	OBSERVERS
	C_{16}	C_{18}	C_{20}	OL.	LIN.	LEN.*		
Argentine	←	11	→	14	29	45	L,T	Kaufmann and Keller[79]
,,	←	11	→	21	15	53	B,T	Gay[80]
,,	5·4	3·5	0·6	19	24	47	F,T	Griffiths et al.[81a,b]
,,	←	6	→	29	18	47	S	Mitchell et al.[29]
Canada								
(Saskatchewan)								
var. Redwing	←	6·6	→	22·5	12·1	58·7	L,T	Sallans and Sinclair[82]
,, Bison	←	7·0	→	27·0	11·7	54·3	L,T	Sallans and Sinclair[82]
,, Royal	←	7·6	→	26·9	11·0	54·5	L,T	Sallans and Sinclair[82]
India	9·3	4·7	1·1	13·1	17·1	54·7	C,F,S	Gunstone and Hilditch[81c]
,,	8·2	6·8	0·5	13·9	14·4	56·2	C,F,S	Hilditch and Seavell[76b]
Argentine	8·2	7·3	0·5	15·7	15·3	53·0	C,F,S	Hilditch and Seavell[76b]
India	←	16·9	→	13·6	8·3	61·2	S	Edwards and Robb[84]
New Zealand								
var. Bison	←	8·6	→	15·6	15·5	60·3	S	Edwards and Robb[84]
,, Walsh	←	9·3	→	16·3	13·5	60·9	S	Edwards and Robb[84]
,, Golden								
Viking	←	13·4	→	9·0	10·6	67·0	S	Edwards and Robb[84]
India	9·4	7·2	1·0	18·9	13·2	50·3	C,F,S	Hilditch et al.[85a]
South Africa	←	11·8	→	17·1	13·8	57·3	S	Hilditch et al.[85b]
England (1947)	8·5	3·9	0·4	14·9	16·8	55·5	C,F,S	Hilditch et al.[85c]
,, (1948)	6·9	6·4	—	14·6	15·5	56·6	C,F,S	Hilditch et al.[85d]
,, (1955)	4·5	4·3	0·6	15·1	15·3	54·1†	RPC	Crombie et al.[83a]
Canada (1959)	6·9	3·6	—	16·0	15·0	58·5	GLC	Craig and Murti[83b]
U.S.A. (1960)	←	11	→	22	14	49	S	Earle et al.[83c]

* "Ol."=Oleic; "Lin."=Linoleic; "Len."=Linolenic.

† Also 6 per cent. saturated acids C_{14}–C_8, part of which believed to be products of autoxidation of the oil.

(*Literature references 29, 79–85 are in the general bibliography to Chapter IV, p. 352.*)

obviously, to climatic or other environmental causes ,but there is some indication in the Canadian and New Zealand oils that the oil composition is somewhat different in different varieties of seed. The relative influences of variety of seed and environment have been further clarified by several investigators whose results will now be considered in some detail.

In 1939 Woodward[86] published data (based on lead salt separations, Bertram oxidations, and thiocyanometric (T) analyses) for specimens of four main types of linseed oil, as follows:

VARIETY	SATD.	OL.	LIN.	LEN.
Indigene	11	13	15	61
Baltic	7	20	16	57
Calcutta	9	24	14	53
La Plata	10	26	12	52

In 1939, also, Rose and Jamieson[87] gave data for three varieties of linseed grown in different parts of the United States, based on analyses by the esterfractionation and thiocyanogen (T) methods. Their results were as follows (including the individual proportions of palmitic (P) and stearic (S) acids):

VARIETY	GROWN IN	OIL I.V.	P	S	OL.	LIN.	LEN.
Bison	N. Dakota (south)	144·1	6·7	4·7	36	21	30
,,	,, (north)	160·7	6·3	4·2	29	22	38
,,	,, ,,	179·8	6·3	2·5	19	24	47
,,	Texas	174·0	4·6	3·5	25	24	42
Punjab	,,	168·1	4·1	5·0	28	20	43
,,	California	184·9	5·2	5·1	22	10	58
Abyssinian	,,	197·3	7·2	2·3	16	10	64

In 1943 Painter and Nesbitt,[88] by means of the Bertram oxidation (B) and thiocyanogen (T) procedures, made analyses of a very large number of linseed oils from flax seed grown in various parts throughout the United States and Canada. Samples with a range in iodine values of from 128 to 203 were collected. The authors say "Adverse climatic conditions, high temperature, and insufficient moisture while the seed ripens sometimes produce linseed oils with low iodine values." These workers concluded from their results that each variety has its own characteristics as regards the composition of the oils produced in the seeds, but that the composition is always affected by the location and conditions of growth. Oils from each variety produced in Nebraska had most oleic and least linolenic acid, whilst those from seed grown in Nova Scotia had most linolenic and least oleic acid. A selection from the data of Painter and Nesbitt is appended:

VARIETY	GROWN IN	OIL I.V.	COMPONENT FATTY ACIDS[88]			
			SATD.	OL.	LIN.	LEN.
Bison	Nebraska	155·4	12	32	21	35
,,	Minnesota	162·8	11	30	18	40
,,	N. Dakota	164·7	10	34	12	44
,,	S. Dakota	171·5	10	27	19	44
,,	Montana	177·0	10	25	18	47
,,	Oregon	182·4	9	22	20	49
,,	Saskatchewan	187·0	9	22	15	54
,,	Nova Scotia	196·0	9	16	16	59
Redwing	Nebraska	171·6	10	25	22	43
,,	Minnesota	181·8	10	23	15	52
,,	N. Dakota	178·2	9	25	17	49
,,	S. Dakota	180·5	10	23	17	50
,,	Montana	187·6	9	19	20	52
,,	Oregon	196·5	9	17	14	60
,,	Saskatchewan	195·1	8	16	18	57
,,	Nova Scotia	201·7	9	12	18	61
Linota	Nebraska	170·6	9	26	25	40
,,	Minnesota	179·0	9	25	18	48
,,	N. Dakota	176·9	9	26	18	47
,,	S. Dakota	181·6	9	19	27	45
,,	Montana	188·2	8	21	18	53
,,	Oregon	190·4	8	21	16	55
,,	Saskatchewan	196·6	7	18	16	59
,,	Nova Scotia	202·8	7	14	17	62
Rio	Nebraska	155·8	14	31	15	40
,,	Minnesota	161·6	14	29	13	44
,,	N. Dakota	162·9	14	28	14	44
,,	S. Dakota	172·4	13	21	21	45
,,	Montana	177·8	12	25	10	53
,,	Oregon	186·8	9	19	20	52
,,	Saskatchewan	189·4	10	16	20	54
,,	Nova Scotia	194·7	10	14	17	59

It is to be concluded that, frequently, different varieties of seed grown in the same area may produce linseed oils of very similar composition; but, as pointed out by Dillman,[89] Sallans and Sinclair,[82] and Edwards and Robb,[84] varietal differences may be distinguished in some instances, notably that of the "Golden Viking" variety grown by the last-mentioned authors in New Zealand. Such varietal differences are nevertheless much smaller than those observed (e.g. by Painter and Nesbitt[88]) in oils from seeds of the same variety grown in widely different climatic conditions. Whilst the environmental causes which lead to different degrees of unsaturation in linseed oils from a given variety of seed may include differences in soil, moisture, etc., it is clear that the main factor concerned is the atmospheric temperature in which the seed is developed. In the light of experience with other seeds (e.g. sunflower, *cf.* p. 226) it may well be that the rate of production of the seed-endosperm and its contents (which of course will depend largely on the climatic temperature) is an essential factor. The most unsaturated linseed oils are produced in the coolest regions, and conversely. The difference in component fatty acids is greatest in linolenic acid, mainly at the expense of oleic acid: the linoleic acid contents do not vary so greatly with the temperature conditions of growth, nor do the saturated acids (which indeed remain almost constant).

The relation between environment during growth and the composition of seed oils will receive further attention in later pages (this Chapter, pp. 226, 308, 310; Chapter VIII, pp. 537–539).

TABLE 59. *Component Acids of Seed Fats (mainly "Linolenic-rich")*

Major component acids: All unsaturated C_{18} acids: LINOLEIC, LINOLENIC (OLEIC).
Minor component acids: Palmitic, stearic, and occasionally traces of arachidic.

			COMPONENT FATTY ACIDS PER CENT. (WT.)						
Species		HABITAT	PALMITIC	STEARIC	OLEIC	LINOLEIC	LINOLENIC	METHOD	OBSERVERS
GYMNOSPERMS									
CONIFERÆ (PINACEÆ)									
Pinus cembra	Cedar nut oil	W. Siberia	—	← 8·2 →	33–36	31–34	17–28	K	Ivanov and Resnikova [1]
" *excelsa*	Red pine seed	Europe, N. America	7·7	6·5	12	57	22	L, H	Eibner and Reitter [2]
" *griffithii*		Himalaya	2·9	0·4	13·3	52·2	20·3	F	Prakash et al. [3]
" *monophylla*	Pine nut	Southern U.S.A.	—	—	61·7	29·6	— (a)	F	Gill [4]
" *pumila*		Russia	← 5 →		12	76	7	B, T	Pigulevski and Ivanova [5]
" *sabiniana*	Digger pine	U.S.A.	← 7 →		48	45	—	T	Semb [6]
" *sylvestris*	Pine seed	Europe, Asia, N. America	4·1	3·1	9·5	58	25	L, H	Eibner and Reitter [2]
Abies balsamea		U.S.A.	← 2 →		35	61	2	B, T	Benson and Calderwood [7]
ANGIOSPERMS									
MORACEÆ									
Broussonetia papyrifera	Mulberry	Japan	← 9 →		15·0	76·0	—	T	Koyama and Toyama [8]
	"	U.S.A.	← 10 →		14	71	1	S	Earle et al. [9a]
Cannabis sativa	Hemp seed	Temperate zones	← 10·1 →		16	46	28	B, T	Kaufmann and Juschke-witsch [10]
" "	"	Cyprus	5·8	1·7	6	70	15 (b)	F, T	Griffiths and Hilditch [11a]
" "	"	Bedford	9·9	5·6	11	54	19 (c)	C, F, S	Hilditch and Seavell [11b]
" "	"	Essex	9·5	2·5	7	55	23 (d)	C, F, S	Bridge and Hilditch [11c]
" "	"	England	9·5	2·0	8	56	22 (e)	C, F, S	Bridge and Hilditch [11c]
" "	"	England	7	3	17	59	14	GLC	Roberts and Stevens [11e]
Ficus carica	Fig	U.S.A.	5·5	2·3	19·8	35·1	34·2 (e')	F	Jamieson and McKinney [11d]
Humulus lupulus	Hop	England	7	3	10	60	15†	GLC	Roberts and Stevens [11e]
" *scandens*		U.S.A.	← 14 →		15	54	—	S	Earle et al. [11f]
Maclura pomifera		U.S.A.	← 9 →		14	72	—	S	Earle et al. [12a]
Treculia africana	Bread fruit	Sierra Leone	24·1	11·7	46	18	—	F	Ichaporia [12b]

TABLE 59. *Component Acids of Seed Fats—continued.*

		Habitat	Component fatty acids per cent. (wt.)					Method	Observers
			Palmitic	Stearic	Oleic	Linoleic	Linolenic		
CELASTRACEÆ									
Celastrus orbiculata	Bittersweet	U.S.A.	← 36 →		16	20	21	S	Earle *et al.*[12a]
,, *paniculatus*	,,	India	22·3	4·3	22	35	16 (*f*)	F, T	Gunde and Hilditch[14]
,, *scandens*	,,	U.S.A.	12·1	2·7	1	45	39	L, T	Barkenbus and Krewson[13]
Euonymus alatus		U.S.A.	← 32 →		25	34	3	S	Earle *et al.*[9a]
,, *verrucosa*		Caucasus	← 19·3 →		55·8	19·3	5·6	S	Simonova[12c]
Maytenus disticha		Patagonia	12·8	0·3	36	46	— (*g*)	F	Cattaneo *et al.*[15a]
AQUIFOLIACEÆ									
Ilex paraguariensis	Yerba maté	Argentina	10·0	3·8	34·4	49·1	— (*g′*)	F	Cattaneo *et al.*[15b]
LABIATÆ									
Hyptis spicigera	Black sesame	Tropical Africa and America	8·7	—	4·8	16·7	65·9 (*h*)	C,F,S	Barker *et al.*[16]
,, ,,			4·4	3·2	9·2	23·3	59·9	F, T	Grindley[17a]
,, *suaveolens*	Bushmint	U.S.A.	← 12 →		6	77	Trace	S	Earle *et al.*[12a]
Lallemantia iberica	Lallemantia	Russia	← 9 →		1	36	53	B, K	Steger and van Loon[19a]
,, *royleana*	,,	India	10·2	3·3	60·1	26·4	—	L	Malavya and Dutt[20]
Leonatis nepetœfolia	Molinillo	Puerto Rico	12·2	8·5	65·8	12·1	— (*i*)	F	Asenjo *et al.*[18]
Leonurus cardiaca	Motherwort	U.S.A.	← 6 →		35	53	2	S	Earle *et al.*[12a]
Lycopus asper	Bugleweed	U.S.A.	← 0 →		49	16	30	S	Earle *et al.*[12a]
Majorana hortensis	Sweet marjoram	U.S.A.	← 5 →		16	20	55	S	Earle *et al.*[9b]
Mentha arvensis	Field mint	U.S.A.	← 9 →		13	16	58	S	Earle *et al.*[12a]
Monarda fistulosa	Wild bergamot	U.S.A.	← 0 →		19	18	58	S	Earle *et al.*[9b]
Nepeta cataria	Catnip	U.S.A.	← 8 →		12	18	57	S	Earle *et al.*[12a]
,, *mussinii*	Catmint	U.S.A.	← 6 →		17	18	55	S	Earle *et al.*[9b]
Ocimum basilicum	Sweet basil	U.S.A.	← 8 →		15	22	50	S	Earle *et al.*[9b]
,, *kilimand-scharicum*		Sudan	← 8 →		17	14	61	L, T	Henry and Grindley[22]
		Sudan	8·2	—	5·3	16·2	65·0 (*j*)	C,F,S	Barker *et al.*[16]
,, *sanctum*		India	7	2	9	66	16	F	Patwardhan *et al.*[21]
,, *viride*		Nigeria	8·7	2·7	14·3	32·5	39·2 (*k*)	C,F,S	Barker *et al.*[16]

TABLE 59. *Component Acids of Seed Fats (mainly "Linolenic-rich")*

Major component acids: All unsaturated C_{18} acids: LINOLEIC, LINOLENIC (OLEIC).
Minor component acids: Palmitic, stearic, and occasionally traces of arachidic.

COMPONENT FATTY ACIDS PER CENT. (WT.)

Species	Common name	HABITAT	PALMITIC	STEARIC	OLEIC	LINOLEIC	LINOLENIC	METHOD	OBSERVERS
GYMNOSPERMS									
CONIFERÆ (PINACEÆ)									
Pinus cembra	Cedar nut oil	W. Siberia	← 8·2 →	—	33–36	31–34	17–28	K	Ivanov and Resnikova[1]
" *excelsa*	Red pine seed	Europe, N. America			12	57	22	L,H	Eibner and Reitter[2]
" *griffithii*	Pine nut	Himalaya	7·7	6·5	13·3	52·2	20·3	F	Prakash et al.[3]
" *monophylla*	Pine nut	Southern U.S.A.	2·9	0·4	61·7	29·6	—(a)	F	Gill[4]
" *pumila*	Digger pine	Russia	5		12	76	7	B,T	Pigulevski and Ivanova[5]
" *sabiniana*	Pine seed	U.S.A.	7		48	45		T	Semb[6]
" *sylvestris*		Europe, Asia, N. America	4·1	3·1	9·5	58	25	L,H	Eibner and Reitter[2]
Abies balsamea		U.S.A.	← 2 →		35	61	2	B,T	Benson and Calderwood[7]
ANGIOSPERMS									
MORACEÆ									
Broussonetia	Mulberry	Japan	9		15·0	76·0	—	T	Koyama and Toyama[8]
papyrifera		U.S.A.	10		14	71	1	S	Earle et al.[9a]
Cannabis sativa	Hemp seed	Temperate zones	10·1		16	46	28	B,T	Kaufmann and Juschke-witsch[10]
" "	"	Cyprus	5·8	1·7	6	70	15 (b)	F,T	Griffiths and Hilditch[11a]
" "	"	Bedford	9·5	5·6	11	54	19 (c)	C,F,S	Hilditch and Seavell[11b]
" "	"	Essex	9·9	2·5	7	55	23 (d)	C,F,S	Bridge and Hilditch[11c]
" "	"	England	9·5	2·0	8	56	22 (e)	C,F,S	Bridge and Hilditch[11c]
Ficus carica	Fig	England	7	3	17	59	14	GLC	Roberts and Stevens[11e]
Humulus lupulus	Hop	U.S.A.	5·5	2·3	19·8	35·1	34·2 (e')	F	Jamieson and McKinney[11d]
" *scandens*	"	England	7	3	10	60	15†	GLC	Roberts and Stevens[11e]
Maclura pomifera		U.S.A.	14		15	54	—	S	Earle et al.[11f]
"		U.S.A.	9		14	72	—	S	Earle et al.[12a]
Treculia africana	Bread fruit	Sierra Leone	24·1	11·7	46	18	—	F	Ichaporia[12b]

213

TABLE 59. Component Acids of Seed Fats—continued.

Species	Common name	Habitat	Palmitic	Stearic	Oleic	Linoleic	Linolenic	Method	Observers
CELASTRACEÆ									
Celastrus orbiculata	Bittersweet	U.S.A.	36 →		16	20	21	S	Earle et al.[12a]
" *paniculatus*	"	India	22·3	4·3	22	35	16 (f)	F, T	Gunde and Hilditch[14]
" *scandens*	"	U.S.A.	12·1	2·7	1	45	39	L, T	Barkenbus and Krewson[13]
Euonymus alatus		U.S.A.	32 →		25	34	3	S	Earle et al.[9a]
" *verrucosa*		Caucasus	19·3 →		55·8	19·3	5·6	S	Simonova[12c]
Maytenus disticha		Patagonia	12·8	0·3	36	46	— (g)	F	Cattaneo et al.[15a]
AQUIFOLIACEÆ									
Ilex paraguariensis	Yerba maté	Argentina	10·0	3·8	34·4	49·1	— (g')	F	Cattaneo et al.[15b]
LABIATÆ									
Hyptis spicigera	Black sesame	Tropical Africa and America	8·7	—	4·8	16·7	65·9 (h)	C, F, S	Barker et al.[16]
" *suaveolens*	Bushmint	U.S.A.	4·4	3·2	9·2	23·3	59·9	F, T	Grindley[17a]
Lallemantia iberica	Lallemantia	Russia	12 →		6	77	Trace	B, K	Steger and van Loon[19a]
" *royleana*	Molinillo	India	9 →		1	36	53	L	Malavya and Dutt[20]
Leonotis nepetæfolia	Motherwort	Puerto Rico	10·2	3·3	60·1	26·4	—	F	Asenjo et al.[18]
Leonurus cardiaca	Bugleweed	U.S.A.	12·2	8·5	65·8	12·1	— (i)	S	Earle et al.[12a]
Lycopus asper	Sweet marjoram	U.S.A.	6 ↑		35	53	2	S	Earle et al.[12a]
Majorana hortensis	Field mint	U.S.A.	0 ↑		49	16	30	S	Earle et al.[12a]
Mentha arvensis	Wild bergamot	U.S.A.	5 ↑		16	20	55	S	Earle et al.[9b]
Monarda fistulosa	Catnip	U.S.A.	9 ↑		13	16	58	S	Earle et al.[12a]
Nepeta cataria	Catmint	U.S.A.	0 ↑		19	18	58	S	Earle et al.[9b]
" *mussinii*	Sweet basil	U.S.A.	8 ↑		12	18	57	S	Earle et al.[12a]
Ocimum basilicum		U.S.A.	6 ↑		17	22	55	S	Earle et al.[9b]
Ocimum basilicum		U.S.A.	8 ↑		15	14	50	S	Earle et al.[9b]
" *kilimandscharicum*		Sudan	8 ↑		17	16·2	61	L, T	Henry and Grindley[22]
" *sanctum*		Sudan	8·2	—	5·3	16·2	65·0 (j)	C, F, S	Barker et al.[16]
" *sanctum*		India	7	2	9	66	16	F	Patwardhan et al.[21]
" *viride*		Nigeria	8·7	2·7	14·3	32·5	39·2 (k)	C, F, S	Barker et al.[16]

COMPONENT FATTY ACIDS PER CENT. (WT.)

Species	Common name	Source						Method	Reference
Perilla frutescens		U.S.A.	←——9——→		21	11	55	S	Earle et al.,[9b]
" *ocimoides*	Perilla seed	Japan, East Indies	←—6·7—→		23	—	70	B,T	Kaufmann[23]
Pycnanthemum muticum	"	U.S.A.	←—7·6—→		14	16	63	B,T	Kaufmann[23]
	" Mountain mint	"	←——0——→		19	14	62	S	Earle et al.,[12a]
Salvia columbariae	California chia	U.S.A.	5·3——5	2·9	18	15	56	S	Earle et al.,[9b]
" *hispanica*	Chia seed	Mexico		2·9	12	32·5	47	F,H	Baughman and Jamieson[24]
" "	"	Holland	←—10·5—→		10·5	10	69	B,T	Steger and van Loon[19b]
" "	"	Mexico	←——9——→		4	28	59	L,T	Palma et al.,[25]
Satureja hortensis	Summer savory	U.S.A.	←——4——→		12	18	62	S	Earle et al.,[9b]
Stachys lanata	Woolly betony	U.S.A.	←——5——→		24	65	0·6	S	Earle et al.,[9a]
Thymus vulgaris	Thyme	U.S.A.	←——3——→		18	13	62	S	Earle et al.,[9b]

VALERIANACEÆ

Species	Common name	Source						Method	Reference
Valerianella olitoria	Corn salad	Europe	←—12·4—→		18	61	9	B,T	Steger and van Loon[26]

ONAGRACEÆ

Species	Common name	Source						Method	Reference
Clarkia elegans	—	U.S.A.	←——14——→		20	57	1·3	S	Earle et al.,[9a]
Godetia amoena	—	U.S.A.	5·7——21		2	71	0·7	S	Earle et al.,[11f]
Œnothera biennis	Evening prim-rose seed	Temperate zones	8·8———	— 1·3	26	58	10*	L,H	Eibner and Schild[27]
				1·3	7·0	71·7	10·2*(*l*)	C,F,S	Riley[28a]
" *lamarckiana*	"	U.S.A.	←——3——→		24	61	8*	S	Earle et al.,[12a]
"	"	Bulgaria	←—6·5—→		10·6	73·8	2·6*	S	Popov[28b]
" *rhombipetala*	"	U.S.A.	←—6·2—→		18	62	8·3*	S	Earle et al.,[9a]
"	"	U.S.A.	←——8——→		13	69	5*	S	Earle et al.,[12a]

LINACEÆ

Species	Common name	Source						Method	Reference
Linum usitatissimum	Linseed	Widely distributed	←—6–16—→		13–36	10–25	60–30	—	See Text p. 210 (Table 59A).

RHAMNACEÆ

Species	Common name	Source						Method	Reference
Frangula crenata	Buckthorn	Japan	←—15·6—→		37·6	42·9	3·9	T	Koyama and Toyama[8]
Rhamnus cathartica	"	U.S.A.	←——10——→		19	36	31	S	Earle et al.,[12a]
" *davurica*	"	U.S.A.	←——11——→		18	42	24	S	Earle et al.,[12a]
" *purshiana*	Cascara sagrada	U.S.A.	←——10——→		55	28	3	S	Earle et al.,[12a]
Zizyphus jujuba		India	13·0———	— 22·6	71·7	15·3	—	S	Mehta et al.,[29a]
" *spinachristi*		Sudan	2·3	22·6	51·1	24·0	—	L,T	Grindley[17b]

215

TABLE 59. *Component Acids of Seed Fats—continued.*

| | HABITAT | COMPONENT FATTY ACIDS PER CENT. (WT.) | | | | | METHOD | OBSERVERS | SATURATED | | |
		PALMITIC / STEARIC	OLEIC	LINOLEIC	LINOLENIC				C14	C20	C22 and C24
ELÆAGNACEÆ											
Elæagnus angustifolia Russian olive	U.S.A.	←— 1 —→	32	48	14	S	Earle et al.,[12a]		3·1	0·3	⎱ 1·2
Hippophæ rhamnoides Sea buckthorn	Europe	←— 11·6 —→	23·1	36·0	27·6	S	Kaufmann[29b]		—	0·5	⎪
BORAGINACEÆ											
Anchusa capensis Cape bugloss	U.S.A.	←— 11 —→	28	28	24	S	Earle et al.[9a]		—	3·9	⎪
„ italica Italian bugloss	U.S.A.	←— 12 —→	32	40	12	S	Earle et al.[9a]		1·4	—	⎪
Borago officinalis Borage	U.S.A.	←— 16 —→	26	35	19	S	Earle et al.[9a]		—	5·3	⎪
Cynoglossum amabile Hounds-tongue	U.S.A.	←— 14 —→	42	24	13	S	Earle et al.[9a]		—	2·6	⎪
ERICACEÆ											
Arctostaphylos glauca	U.S.A.	←— 6 —→	32	33	25	S	Earle et al.[12a]		—	1·3	⎰ 1·0
NYCTAGINACEÆ											
Mirabilis jalapa Marvel of Peru	Japan	←— 24·4 —→	46·9	13·6	15·1	T	Koyama and Toyama[8]				
DILLENIACEÆ											
Actinidia arguta Tara Vine	U.S.A.	←— 3 —→	35	7	44	S	Earle et al.[12a]				

* "Linolenic" acid of Œnothera oil is octadeca-6,9,12-trienoic acid. † Also 5 per cent. octadeca-6,9,12-trienoic acid.

Minor component acids also recorded as follows (per cent. wt.):

| | | SATURATED | |
		C14	C20
(a)	Pine nut	5·4	—
(b)	Hemp seed	—	1·1
(c)	„ „	—	1·0
(d)	„ „	0·6	1·7
(e)	„ „	0·2	1·9
(e')	Fig	—	1·1
(f)	Celastrus paniculatus	0·1	0·3

(g)	Maytenus disticha
(g')	Ilex: (Lauric 0·8, hexadecenoic 1·4)
(h)	Hyptis spicigera
(i)	Molinillo
(j)	Ocimum kilimandscharicum
(k)	Ocimum viride
(l)	Œnothera biennis

References to Table 59

1. S. L. Ivanov and S. B. Resnikova, *Schr. zentr. biochem. Forsch. Nahr. Genussm.*, *Russia*, 1933, **3**, 239.
2. A. Eibner and F. Reitter, *Chem. Umschau*, 1926, **33**, 114, 125.
3. O. Prakash, T. R. Sharma and A. Satta, *J. Proc. Oil Techn. Assocn.*, *India*, 1957, **13**, 47.
4. A. H. Gill, *Oil and Soap*, 1933, **10**, 7.
5. G. V. Pigulevski and M. A. Ivanova, *J. Appl. Chem. Russia*, 1934, **7**, 569.
6. J. Semb, *J. Amer. Pharm. Assoc.*, 1935, **24**, 609.
7. S. R. Benson and H. N. Calderwood, *J. Amer. Chem. Soc.*, 1936, **58**, 523.
8. Y. Koyama and T. Toyama, *J. Japan Oil Chem. Soc.*, 1956, **5**, 359.
9. (a) F. R. Earle, I. A. Wolff et al., *J. Amer. Oil Chem. Soc.*, 1959, **36**, 304; (b) ibid., 1960, **37**, 48.
10. H. P. Kaufmann and S. Juschkewitsch, *Z. angew. Chem.*, 1930, **43**, 90.
11. (a) H. N. Griffiths and T. P. Hilditch, *J. Soc. Chem. Ind.*, 1934, **53**, 75T; (b) T. P. Hilditch and A. J. Seavell, *J. Oil Col. Chem. Assocn.*, 1950, **33**, 24; (c) R. E. Bridge and T. P. Hilditch, *J. Sci. Food Agric.*, 1951, **2**, 547; (d) G. S. Jamieson and R. S. McKinney, *Oil and Soap*, 1935, **12**, 88; (e) J. B. Roberts and R. Stevens, *Chem. and Ind.*, 1963, 608; (f) F. R. Earle et al., *J. Amer. Oil Chem. Soc.*, 1962, **39**, 381.
12. (a) F. R. Earle, I. A. Wolff et al., *J. Amer. Oil Chem. Soc.*, 1960, **37**, 440; (b) M. B. Ichaporia, *Dissertation*, Liverpool, 1937; (c) N. I. Simonova, *Zhur. Priklad. Khim.*, 1959, **32**, 1637.
13. C. Barkenbus and C. F. Krewson, *J. Amer. Chem. Soc.*, 1932, **54**, 3993.
14. B. G. Gunde and T. P. Hilditch, *J. Chem. Soc.*, 1938, 1980.
15. (a) P. Cattaneo, L. M. Darnet, J. B. Etchigoin, G. Karman and F. O. Peruzzotti, *Anales Asocn. Quim. Argentina*, 1947, **35**, 164; (b) P. Cattaneo, G. K. de Sutton, and M. L. Rodriguez, *Anales Direc. Nacl. Quim.*, 1952, **5**, No. 9, 9.
16. C. Barker, H. C. Dunn, and T. P. Hilditch, *J. Soc. Chem. Ind.*, 1950, **69**, 71.
17. D. N. Grindley, (a) *J. Sci. Food Agric.*, 1950, **1**, 152; (b) *J. Soc. Chem. Ind.*, 1948, **67**, 230.
18. C. F. Asenjo, J. A. Goyco, and Z. Martinez-Pico, *J. Amer. Chem. Soc.*, 1945, **67**, 1936.
19. A. Steger and J. van Loon, (a) *Fette u. Seifen*, 1944, **51**, 1; (b) ibid., 1942, **49**, 241.
20. B. K. Malavya and S. Dutt, *Proc. Indian Acad. Sci.*, 1941, **14**, A, 80.
21. G. B. Nadkarri and V. A. Patwardhan, *Current Sci.* (*India*), 1952, **21**, 68.
22. A. J. Henry and D. N. Grindley, *J. Soc. Chem. Ind.*, 1944, **63**, 188.
23. H. P. Kaufmann, *Allgem. Oel-Fett-Ztg.*, 1930, **27**, 39.
24. W. F. Baughman and G. S. Jamieson, *Oil and Fat Ind.*, 1929, **6**, (9), 15.
25. F. Palma, M. Donde and W. R. Lloyd, *J. Amer. Oil Chem. Soc.*, 1947, **24**, 27.
26. A. Steger and J. van Loon, *J. Soc. Chem. Ind.*, 1937, **56**, 298T.
27. A. Eibner and E. Schild, *Chem. Umschau*, 1927, **34**, 312, 339.
28. (a) J. P. Riley, *J. Chem. Soc.*, 1949, 2728; (b) P. Mazhdrakov and A. Popov, *Bulgar. Akad. Nauk. Invest. Khim. Inst.*, 1957, **5**, 209.
29. (a) T. N. Mehta, C. V. N. Rao and V. Laxnikantam, *Indian Soap J.*, 1953, **19**, 94; (b) H. P. Kaufmann and A. V. Roncero, *Grasas y Aceites*, 1955, **6**, 81.

Mainly Linoleic-rich Seed Fats. (Table 60, p. 229). We next pass on to numerous seed fats in which saturated acids (including palmitic acid) are still very minor components but in which the unsaturated major component acids are mainly confined to linoleic and oleic, the former largely predominating in many cases. It will be noticed, perhaps, that no plant family falling in either Table 59 or Table 60 appears again in any of the subsequent tables,* so that a specific relationship between seed fat component acids and botanical grouping commences to appear even in the relatively simple mixtures of the more common natural vegetable fatty acids which form the bulk of the linolenic-rich and linoleic-rich oils enumerated in Tables 59 and 60. This relationship becomes more marked as seed fats are subsequently considered in which other acids appear as major components in addition to, or in substitution for, linoleic and oleic acids.

At the same time, since linoleic (with oleic) acid is a constituent in greater or less degree of practically all seed fats, many of the fats considered in subsequent groups also contain linoleic acid as a major component. Two categories of plant families and their seed fats are to be distinguished here:

(*a*) In certain families (Rosaceæ, Euphorbiaceæ, Cucurbitaceæ, Table 61) many species produce seed fats of the same type as those in Table 60 (or, occasionally, Table 59); but other genera in these families elaborate unusual unsaturated acids (elæostearic, ricinoleic, licanic, etc.) which cause their seed fats to be quite different in character from the simple linoleic- (or linolenic-) rich oils.

(*b*) In many other families linoleic acid is quite often a major component of the seed fats but is accompanied by some other acid or acids in major proportions. Such major component acids may be palmitic (Tables 62 and 63) or other saturated acids (Tables 67, 68, 69A), or may be specific unsaturated acids (Tables 64 (petroselinic), 65 (chaulmoogric and hydnocarpic), 66 (erucic, etc.), or acetylenic acids in rare cases as in some Simarubaceæ and Olacaceæ species).

The seed fats in Table 60, therefore, include most of those in which linoleic is, apart from oleic acid, the only major component acid.

The general features of the seed fats listed in Table 60 may be distinguished more or less by the following statement. Very many of them are characterised by remarkably high proportions of linoleic acid (exceeding 60 per cent. and even 70 per cent. or more of the total acids). Thus seed fats of walnut, hackberry, poppy and passion fruit usually have linoleic acid contents approaching or somewhat exceeding 70 per cent., as do those of many species in the Compositæ and Solanaceæ families. Other species, notably henbane and safflower, produce seed fats with from 75 to 80 per cent. of linoleic acid in the total fatty acids, whilst seed fats of species from the Agave family so far examined have been found to contain up to 88 per cent. of linoleic acid, the highest proportions yet reported in linoleic-rich seed fats.

In other cases in this group of fats the linoleic acid is only of the order of about 40 ± 10 per cent., for instance, in some beech nuts, hickory, sesame, some Solanaceæ and Compositæ species, milkweed, and seed fats of *Plantago*

* Except Ulmaceæ (*cf.* p. 219, and Table 69A, p. 335).

and teazle. In a minority of instances linoleic acid falls to about 20 per cent. or still less of the total fatty acids and oleic takes its place as the predominating component (e.g. seed fats of the tea plant, olive, some beech nuts, some Myrtaceæ species and horse chestnuts).

Exceptional acids present in certain seed fats listed in Table 60. The general monotony of this group of seed fats (in which the only change as a rule is the varying proportions of linoleic and oleic acids which make up 80–90 per cent. of the total fatty acids) is broken in a few instances by the intrusion of one or other quite abnormal acid.

Perhaps the most extraordinary of these exceptional cases are seed fats of species in the family Proteaceæ, which is thought to be a survival of primitive flora. The first instance studied[90a] (1950) was the Australian *Macadamia ternifolia* seed fat, the acids of which include oleic 60, saturated 11, and linoleic 2 per cent., accompanied by 20 per cent. of hexadec-9-enoic (palmitoleic) acid. More recently (1962) the seed fats of three Argentinian species of this family were examined,[90b] and in each case their component acids included over 20 per cent. of a hexadecenoic acid; in the seed fats of *Embothrium* and *Lomatia*, as in that of *Macadamia*, this was hexadec-9-enoic acid, but in that of *Geruina* (which also contained 11 per cent. of eicos-11-enoic and 9 per cent. of erucic acid) it was entirely hexadec-11-enoic acid. At present hexadec-9-enoic acid has only been reported as a major component in one other seed fat, that of *Anogeissus*[90c] (*cf.* Table 62, pp. 272, 276).

Another peculiarity in this group lies in seed fats of the elm and of some other species of the Ulmaceæ. Those of other species of this family which have been examined conform to the general features of the rest in Table 60 (except that saturated acids, in which stearic acid seems to be prominent, are higher than usual). Schuette *et al.*[91a] observed in 1936 that elm seed fat (*Ulmus americanus*) contained over 60 per cent. of *n*-decanoic (capric) acid, and this was also observed in the seed fat of the European elm (*U. campestris*)[91b,c,d] whilst that of *Zelkova serrata* of the same family contains over 70 per cent. of *n*-decanoic acid.[91e] The component acids of these fats are therefore included in Table 69A (p. 335) with other seed fats which are rich in decanoic, lauric or myristic acids.

With but very few exceptions, the many Compositæ seed fats which have been studied contain the conventional mixture of much linoleic, less oleic, and minor proportions of saturated acids; but in the seed fat of *Vernonia anthelmintica* all these are present only in small proportions (linoleic forming only 10–15 per cent. of the total acids), and the chief acid present is "vernolic" acid, $C_{18}H_{32}O_3$ (64^{92}–72^{93a} per cent.), which is 12,13-epoxy-octadec-9-enoic acid.[93a] So far this and *Cephalocroton cordofanus* (Euphorbiaceæ) are the only known seed fats with so high a proportion of a higher fatty acid containing an epoxy group, but several instances have now been recorded of the presence of minor proportions (and in a few cases as much as 10–20 per cent.) of epoxy-monoethenoid acids in seed fats. In the Compositæ family, Smith, Wolff *et al.*[93b] have recorded the following percentages: *Artemisia absinthium* 23, *Chrysanthemum coronarium* 15, *Cynara cardunculus* 12, *Heliopsis pitcheriana* 13, *Arctotis grandis* 7. The epoxy-acid in *Chrysanthemum coronarium* seed fat is an isomeric form of vernolic acid, namely, cis-9,10-epoxy-cis-octadec-12-enoic acid,[93c] but the structure of epoxy-acids in the other instances has not yet been given.

Small proportions of epoxy-oleic acids have also been reported in a few seed fats of the families Onagraceæ, Leguminosæ and Umbelliferæ.

Further analyses (additional to those given in Table 60) for the component acids of seed fats of seven species of *Vernonia* were subsequently made by Badami and Gunstone[93j] by means of reversed phase chromatography coupled with direct determinations of epoxy-acids (the values for "oxygenated acids" recorded by RPC. exceeded those indicated by "epoxide values"):

ACID	V. anthel-mintica	V. amyg-dalina	V. colorata	V. cinerea	V. biafrae	V. nigritana	V. camp-orum
Myristic	1	1	9	8	6	2	—
Palmitic	5	8	11	23	21	18	14
Stearic	2	5	6	8	8	8	9
Arachidic	1	1	2	3	2	1	—
Behenic	1	1	2	4	4	1	—
Hexadecenoic	—	—	5	—	10	—	—
Oleic	1	6	12	4	15	19	22
Linoleic	9	20	15	22	21	43	55
"Oxygenated" (RPC)	80	58	38	28	13	8	—
(Epoxy-acids (direct)	68	50	19	14	5	—	—)

Analyses (GLC.) by Miwa et al.[93k] of the fatty acids in developing seeds of *V. anthelmintica* showed that oleic and linoleic acids were major components in the earliest stages, the latter remaining fairly constant throughout maturity. Oleic acid, however, fell to about half its earlier proportion whilst, concurrently, (+)-*threo*-12,13-dihydroxyoctadec-cis-9-enoic acid was produced and increased until the final stages, when it declined markedly and epoxy-oleic acid appeared in quantity. This may suggest that the 12,13-dihydroxy-oleic may be the precursor of epoxy-oleic acid.

The seed fat of *Artemisia absinthium* has also been found[93b,d] to contain 7–9 per cent. of one or more hydroxy-conjugated C_{18} dienoic acids, a very unusual type which, however, forms 55–58 per cent. of the seed fat acids of *Dimorphotheca aurantiaca*.[93b,d,e] In this species the acid ("dimorphecolic") is 9-hydroxy-octadeca-trans-10-trans-12-dienoic,[93d] but that present in *Artemisia* seed fat,[93d] in very small proportions in two other Compositæ seed fats,[93d] and to the extent of about 4 per cent. in the seed fatty acids of *Tragopogon porrifolius*[93f] (Compositæ) is a mixture of 9-hydroxy-octadeca-10,12-dienoic and 13-hydroxy-octadeca-9,11-dienoic acids.

Chisholm and Hopkins[93f] have also observed that the seed fatty acids of *Calendula officinalis* (Compositæ) include about 47 per cent. of an usual conjugated triene, octadeca-trans-8-trans-10-cis-12-trienoic acid.

It is gradually becoming clear that, in the Compositæ, curious and unusual fatty acids appear in very selective fashion in a few specific instances. Although it is only here and there that a particular species elaborates major proportions of such acids, it seems quite possible that, with further improvements in experimental techniques, it may be found that minor amounts of them occur in some other species. Inspection of Table 60 will nevertheless reveal that the outstanding characteristic of Compositæ seed fats is the presence of major proportions (usually 50–70 per cent.) of linoleic acid.

Similar general proportions of linoleic acid are evident in Table 60 in, for example, seed fats in the families Papaveraceæ, Solanaceæ, Scrophulariaceæ, Ranunculaceæ and Liliaceæ.

Sporadic appearances of unusual acids in the last two families include eicos-11-enoic in *Delphinium*[93g] (18 per cent.) and *Asparagus* (1·5 per cent.)[93h] whilst *Asclepias syriaca* seed fat has 15 per cent. of octadec-11-enoic in its component acids.[93i]

The few seed fats of the Olacaceæ which have been studied have been included for the present in Table 60, although this family (like Simarubaceæ, Table 69A, and to a less extent Rosaceæ and Euphorbiaceæ, Table 61) seems to be one of the few which specialise in seed fats of heterogeneous and unusual constitution. Of the five species studied, only the seed fats of *Coula edulis* and *Mappia fœtida* contain the usual unsaturated acids: even here, coula seed fat is marked by extremely high oleic acid content (95 per cent.), whilst that of *Mappia fœtida* is reported to contain 37 per cent. of linolenic and *no* linoleic acid (a feature which seems difficult to accept). Ivory wood seed fat contains, in addition to linoleic and oleic acids, nearly 50 per cent. of a hydroxy-oleic (ricinoleic) acid,[94] whilst *Ximenia* seed fat has as its main component ximenynic (octadec-11-en-9-ynoic) acid, accompanied by smaller amounts of hexaco-sanoic and hexacos-17-enoic acids.[95] The remaining seed fat, that of *Onguekoa Gore*, is still more peculiar since it consists largely of glycerides of a C_{18} acid containing one ethenoid and two ethynoid linkings together with a hydroxy-derivative of this acid.[96] Further references will be made later in this Chapter (pp. 289, 290) to the seed fats of *Ximenia* and of *Onguekoa*.

Niger seed, tobacco, safflower, and sunflower seed oils. Analyses of these oils are much more numerous than in most of the other seed fats dealt with in Table 60, and for this reason will now be given separately instead of in the main table. Figures for Niger seed, tobacco, and safflower oils from various localities will be found in Table 60A, and for sunflower seed oils (which have been recorded more fully than any) in Table 60B. It will be noticed that three of these oils come from the Compositæ family, whilst the tobacco plant belongs to the Solanaceæ.

All four fatty oils in Tables 60A and 60B contain only linoleic and oleic acids as major components; linoleic acid in many cases approaches or exceeds 70 per cent. of the total acids. Linoleic and oleic acids are usually in inverse proportions, the saturated acid contents being fairly constant in the oils of any one of the four species. Thus in *sunflower seed oil* saturated acids form 12–14 per cent. of the total acids; about half is palmitic acid, stearic acid usually forms 25–30 per cent. and the remaining acids consist of much smaller proportions of arachidic and behenic acids. The saturated acids of *safflower seed oil* amount to only about 5–10 per cent. of the total acids, and consist mainly of palmitic with a smaller proportion of stearic and very small amounts of arachidic acid. The saturated acids of *tobacco seed oils* are similar in nature but amount usually

TABLE 60A. *Component Acids (per cent. wt.) of Niger Seed, Tobacco Seed and Safflower Seed Oils*

ORIGIN	SATURATED				UNSATURATED			METHOD	OBSERVER
	C14	C16	C18	C20	OL.	LIN.	LEN.		
NIGER SEED (Guizotia abyssinica)									
India	3·3	8·2	4·8	0·5	30·3	52·9	—	F	Kale et al.[97]
India	1·7	5·0	2·3	—	39·4	51·6	—	F	Vidyarthi[98]
India	—	12·4	11·6	2·8	4·5	67·7	1·0	C, F, S	Chakrabarty[99a]
India	←— 10 —→				16	72	2	T	Pye[100]
West Africa	1·1	7·0	3·2	0·6	17·0	68·1	3·0	C, F, S	Hilditch et al.[101]
S. Rhodesia	—	7·9	10·6	1·0	7·0	72·6	0·9	C, F, S	Dunn and Hilditch[102]
TOBACCO SEED (Nicotiana tabacum)									
India	1·8	7·8	5·6	—	30·2	54·6	—	F	Venkatarao et al.[103]
India	←— 16·1 —→				28·1	55·8	—	?	Mahant and Pandit[104]
India	—	7·6	3·1	0·9	17·9	69·4	1·1	C, F, S	Crawford and Hilditch[105]
India	—	9·0	4·8	1·2	10·9	73·1	1·0	C, F, S	Chakrabarty[99a]
India, West Bengal	←— 15·3 —→				19·3	63·6	1·8	S	Chakrabarty[99b]
India, West Bengal	←— 15·8 —→				13·7	68·9	1·6	S	Chakrabarty[99b]
India, United Provinces	←— 17·3 —→				10·7	70·4	1·6	S	Chakrabarty[99b]
India, Andhra	←— 16·8 —→				10·1	71·7	1·4	S	Chakrabarty[99b]
Philippine Is.	0·1	7·2	3·1	0·4	27·2	62·0	—	F	Cruz and West[106]
Wisconsin, U.S.A.	—	3·3	5·1	—	17·1	74·5	—	F	Roberts and Schuette[107]
Connecticut, U.S.A.	—	9·8	5·9	—	28·0	56·3	—	F	Salisbury[108]
U.S.A.*	—	7	3	—	15	75	—	C, F, S	Riemenschneider et al.[109]
Turkey	—	8·3	4·1	0·4	12·0	74·6	0·6	C, F, S	Crawford and Hilditch[105]
Rhodesia (Turkish)	—	7·5	3·7	0·8	12·9	74·0	1·1	C, F, S	Crawford and Hilditch[105]
(Virginian)	—	7·8	2·8	0·8	12·9	74·0	1·7	C, F, S	Crawford and Hilditch[105]
England (Virginian) (1949)	←— 11·4 —→				8·0	79·1	1·5	C, F, S	Crawford and Hilditch[105]
(Virginian) (1950)	←— 10·7 —→				11·4	76·8	1·1	S	Bridge[110a]

						Method	Reference
India (range of acids in 15 specimens)	12·8-19·5	9·3-19·3	64·7-72·6	1·1-2·0		S	Chakrabarty[99c]

* Average of 12 tobacco seed oils from different varieties.

SAFFLOWER SEED (Carthamus tinctorius)

Source						Method	Reference
India	0·4	2·1	2·0	37·6	56·7	—	F	Lagawankar et al.[111a]
India	—	4·4	2·0	31·4	58·4	—	F	Mehta et al.[111b]
India	—	3·8	2·2	28·4	61·1	—	F	Mehta et al.[111b]
India	1·5	3	1	33	61	—	F	Vidyarthi[112]
India	—	8·4	4·2	8·2	78·4	—	C,F,S	Chakrabarty[99a]
U.S.A.	—	4·2	1·6	26·3	67·4	0·1	F,H	Jamieson and Gertler[113]
U.S.A.	9		13	78		—	B,T	van Loon[114]
Germany	8		13	78		1	B,T	Kaufmann and Fiedler[115]
New Mexico	7		19	71		3	B,T	Bickford et al.[116]
Montana, U.S.A.*	5-7		15-17	76-79		—	S	Milner et al.[117a]
S. Australia	7·6		15·5	76·9		—	S	Winter[118]
Kenya	—	6·4	3·1	13·4	76·9	—	C,F,S	Barker and Hilditch[119a]
N. Dakota, U.S.A.	—	5·1	6·5	7·5	78·5	—(a)	F,S	Craig[117b]
Saskatchewan, Canada	0·4	4·1	5·4	7·1	80·0	—(b)	F,S	Craig[117b]
Australia: Variety I.P. (most specimens)	6		15-22	79-72		—	S	Horowitz and Winter[125]
" " (2 individual plants)	4-8		74-79	11-19		—	S	(See text, p. 226)[125]

* Range of 8 varieties.

(a) Also 1·2 per cent. behenic and traces of hexadecenoic, linolenic, eicosenoic, and erucic acids.
(b) Also 0·5 per cent. behenic, 0·9 per cent. erucic, and traces of hexadecenoic, linolenic, and eicosenoic acids

(Literature references 97–125 are in the general bibliography to Chapter IV, p. 353.)

TABLE 60B. Component Acids (per cent. wt.) of Sunflower Seed Oils

ORIGIN	SEED	SATD.	OLEIC	LINOLEIC	METHOD	OBSERVER
India	Striped	8·4	38·2	53·4	C, F, S	Chakrabarty[99a]
North China	?	9·1	37·4	53·5	F	Ueno and Wan[120c]
Japan	?	9·8	33·7	56·5	F	Nobori[121]
Russia	?	10	33	57	B, K	Rankoff[122]
U.S.A.	?	7·4	34·1	58·5	F	Baughman and Jamieson[123a]
U.S.A. (range of 4 varieties grown in 7 locations)		9–12	21–40	51–68	S	Milner et al.[117a]
Argentina	?	12·0	22·8	65·2	B, K	Viollier and Iselin[123b]
Argentina	?	12·2	20·1	67·7	C, F, S	Barker and Hilditch[119b]
Africa:						
Congo	?	6·0	42·0	52·0	F	Pieraerts[124]
S. Rhodesia	Black	13·5	14·1	72·4	C, F, S	Barker and Hilditch[119b]
S. Rhodesia	Striped	13·9	14·3	71·8	C, F, S	Barker and Hilditch[119b]
Kenya	Cream	14·1	17·3	68·6	C, F, S	Barker and Hilditch[119b]
Kenya	Black	14·0	18·5	67·5	C, F, S	Barker and Hilditch[119b]
Tanganyika (Southern Highlands)	Cream	14·2	20·9	64·9	C, F, S	Barker and Hilditch[119b]
Nigeria (Zaria)	Striped	12·0	29·8	58·2	C, F, S	Barker and Hilditch[119b]
Tanganyika (Lake Province)	Black	11·0	30·8	58·2	C, F, S	Barker and Hilditch[119b]
Tanganyika (Kongwa)	Striped	12·1	31·1	56·8	C, F, S	Barker and Hilditch[119b]
East Africa	Cream	11·9	42·1	46·0	C, F, S	Barker and Hilditch[119b]
Tanganyika (Lake Province)	Cream	12·7	43·1	44·2	C, F, S	Barker and Hilditch[119b]
Zanzibar						
Kizimbani	Cream	8·2	58·2	33·6	C, F, S	Barker and Hilditch[119c]
Pemba	Cream	9·1	71·8	19·1	C, F, S	Barker and Hilditch[119c]
Nigeria						
Mokwa	Striped	13·5	22·5	64·0	S	Crawford[126]
E. of R. Niger	Striped	9·2	57·8	52·4	S	Crawford[126]
W. of R. Niger	Striped	9·7	52·4	37·9	S	Crawford[126]

Source	Variety				Method	Reference
Sudan Summer	Striped	10.4	56.3	33.3	B, T	Grindley[127]
Sudan Winter	Striped	10.9	34.5	54.6	B, T	Grindley[127]
Australia:						
N. Territory (Lat. 14½° S.)	"Mennonite"	13.4	52.4	34.2	C, F, S	Bridge and Crossley[119d]
N. Territory (Lat. 14½° S.)	"Sunrise"	13.5	50.8	35.7	C, F, S	Bridge and Crossley[119d]
Queensland (Lat. 27½° S.)	"Mennonite"	15.5	23.2	61.3	C, F, S	Bridge and Crossley[119d]
Queensland (Lat. 27½° S.)	"Sunrise"	14.7	29.7	55.6	C, F, S	Bridge and Crossley[119d]
N. S. Wales (Lat. 32° S.)	"Sunrise"	14.7	27.3	58.0	C, F, S	Bridge and Crossley[119d]
Victoria (Lat. 36° S.)	"Mennonite"	17.1	16.7	66.2	C, F, S	Bridge and Crossley[119d]
Victoria (Lat. 36° S.)	"Sunrise"	15.9	19.2	64.9	C, F, S	Bridge and Crossley[119d]
Victoria (Lat. 37½° S.)	"Mennonite"	15.2	17.8	67.0	C, F, S	Bridge and Crossley[119d]
New Zealand	"Jupiter"	13.3	9.9	76.8	S	Crawford[126]
New Zealand	"Large Grey"	14.4	12.5	73.1	S	Crawford[126]
England	Striped	11.1	24.4	64.5	S	Barker and Hilditch[119e]
England	Black	9.3	20.3	70.4	S	Barker and Hilditch[119e]
England	Cream	8.8	20.9	70.3	S	Barker and Hilditch[119e]
England	Striped	12.2	21.5	66.3	C, F, S	Bridge[110b]
Canada		10.6	15.5	73.9	GLC	Craig and Murti[120a]
United States of America:						
Helianthus annuus		14	11	68	S	Earle et al.[120b]
Helianthus annuus		15	11	68	S	Earle et al.[120b]
" maximilliani		9	13	73	S	Earle et al.[120b]
" petiolaris (Prairie sunflower)		5	26	65	S	Earle et al.[120b]
" rydbergi		6	28	62	S	Earle et al.[120b]
" scaberrimus		8	21	67	S	Earle et al.[120b]
" tuberosus (Jerusalem artichoke)		0	31	64	S	Earle et al.[120b]

(Literature references 99–127 are in the general bibliography to Chapter IV, p. 353.)

to 10–15 per cent. of the total acids; those of *Niger seed oil* are somewhat more abundant (12–20 per cent.) and contain a similar mixture of palmitic, stearic, and arachidic acids (1–2 per cent. of myristic acid has also been reported in some oils).

Small proportions (probably not much exceeding 1 per cent. of the total acids) of *linolenic acid* accompany linoleic and oleic acids in *Niger seed* and *tobacco seed oils*, but this acid is absent from *sunflower seed* and *safflower seed oils*; small amounts of it were recorded earlier in the last mentioned oil, but spectrophotometric analysis has shown that it is not in fact present.[118, 119a]

In *Niger seed, tobacco seed,* and *safflower seed oils* it will be seen that in most of the specimens recorded the linoleic acid contents are respectively 68–73, 73–79, and 76–79 per cent. of the total fatty acids. In a few instances (usually oils from seed grown in the tropics) linoleic acid contents of only 52–62 per cent. have been reported for oils of all three species. In view of the more abundant evidence available with regard to the influence of environment on the composition of sunflower seed oils (*v. infra*) it is almost certain that these differences in proportions of linoleic and oleic acids are the result of growth of the Niger seed, tobacco, or safflower plants in climates of different temperature and, possibly, other conditions.

An exceptional instance of a safflower seed oil observed by Horowitz and Winter[125] is however worthy of mention. Trials of safflower seed cultivation were made at the Waite Agricultural Research Institute in Australia with a single variety of seed. Most of the seed oils were of the usual type with iodine values 145–148, linoleic acid 79–72 and oleic acid 15–22 per cent., but the oils from two individual plants had iodine values of only 91–101, with linoleic 11–19, and oleic acid 74–79 per cent. The progeny of one of these plants (up to the fourth generation) continued to give seed oils with low iodine values (88–97).

Influence of environment on the unsaturated acid composition of sunflower seed oils. There is now a considerable body of evidence of the growth factors which may lead to wide differences in the linoleic and oleic acid contents of *sunflower seed* oils.

In 1947 Singh and Kumar[128a] recorded the case of an originally Russian strain of sunflower seed which had been grown for four generations in the United States, where the seeds yielded oil of the high linoleic acid content of typical American oils (60–68 per cent., *cf.* Table 60B); when grown in India, the component acids of the resulting seed oil were linoleic 40, oleic 49, and saturated 11 per cent. (wt.).

The African sunflower seed oils investigated by Barker and Hilditch[119b,c] (Table 60B) afforded further general evidence that the high linoleic oils result from plants grown in cooler regions, and *vice versa*. That the observed differences were almost wholly caused by different temperatures of growth and consequent varying rates of development of the seed endosperm, rather than by varietal differences in the plants grown, was strikingly confirmed when African-grown seeds with oils of differing composition were grown side by side in English gardens. The average composition of the seed oils resulting from growth in England (b), compared with those of the seed oils grown in Africa (a) were found by Barker and Hilditch[119e] to be as follows:

Component Fatty Acids (per cent. wt.)

SOURCE	SEED	(a) *Grown in Africa*			(b) *Grown in England*		
		SATD.	OL.	LIN.	SATD.	OL.	LIN.
Southern Rhodesia	Black	14	14	72	9	20	71
Tanganyika (Southern Highlands)	Cream	14	21	65	9	22	69
Nigeria (Zaria)	Striped	12	30	58	11	15	74
Tanganyika (Kongwa)	Striped	12	31	57	11	24	65
„ (Lake Province)	Cream	13	43	44	9	21	70

Clearer evidence of the relatively small and indefinite influence of the particular variety of seed grown as compared with the temperature of growth (and very possibly the intensity of light or variable amount of ultra-violet rays during growth[119e]), resulting in different rates of development of the endosperm, is available in some cases in which the same variety of seed was grown in different regions. This is well illustrated by the varieties "Mennonite" and "Sunrise" which were grown in different parts of Australia under the auspices of the Division of Plant Industry of the Commonwealth Scientific and Industrial Research Organisation, the seed oils of which (Bridge and Crossley[119d]) are quoted in Table 60B. The data quoted are only a few of those given in the original paper, which includes oils of several other varieties. All the other results were extremely alike: oils from the hot region of Katherine (Northern Territory, Lat. $14\frac{1}{2}°$ S.) had only 31–36 per cent., those from Queensland (Lat. $26\frac{1}{2}$–$27\frac{1}{2}°$S.), 50–61 per cent., and those from Victoria (Lat. 36–$37\frac{1}{2}°$ S.), 63–68 per cent. of linoleic acid in their total acids.

Similar phenomena are seen in the following oils from different varieties of seed grown in different parts of Africa (Barker and Hilditch[119c]):

Component Fatty Acids (per cent. wt.)

	"Mars"			"Jupiter"			"Giant Black"		
	SATD.	OL.	LIN.	SATD.	OL.	LIN.	SATD.	OL.	LIN.
S. Rhodesia	13	22	65	13	22	65	13	16	71
Kenya	14	14	72	13	15	72	14	13	73
Tanganyika (Kongwa)	11	28	61						

	Period of growth (sowing to harvest)	Black-seeded			Cream-seeded		
		SATD.	OL.	LIN.	SATD.	OL.	LIN.
Zanzibar:							
Hanyegwa Mchana	5 months	12	24	64	11	37	52
Kizimbani	3·3 „	11	44	45	8	58	34
Ole, Pemba	2·2 „	8	65	27	9	72	19

In the Zanzibar trials, the black-seeded varieties consistently produced somewhat more unsaturated oils than the cream-seeded when grown in the same location, but these differences were far smaller than those between oils of the same variety grown in different areas. On the other hand no significant differences appeared between oils from the varieties "Mars", "Jupiter" and

227

"Giant Black" when grown respectively in Southern Rhodesia or Kenya. From the consensus of all their data Barker and Hilditch concluded that environment is the main cause of difference in the seed oil composition, and that the predominant factor is apparently the rate of development or ripening of the newly-formed seed in the flower heads. Quick ripening tends to give sunflower seed oils of medium or low linoleic and higher oleic content, and slower ripening gives oils of high linoleic and low oleic content.

Grindley,[127] from his experiments at Khartoum (recorded in Table 60B), is of the opinion that difference in temperature alone, rather than varying amount of sunlight or rate of development of fatty oil in the seed, is the operative factor which determines the degree of unsaturation in the seed oils.

It has been pointed out already that there is little alteration in the amount of saturated acids, however different are the proportions of linoleic and oleic acids in sunflower seed oils. In fact, as will be seen from the analyses recorded above, there is a consistent tendency for the oils richest in linoleic acid to contain slightly greater proportions of saturated acids than those of lower linoleic acid content. This feature, paradoxical at first sight, appears to have some bearing upon the respective modes of biosynthesis of the saturated acids and of the unsaturated (oleic, linoleic, and linolenic) acids of seed fats, a matter which will be further considered in Chapter VIII (pp. 557–560).

In conclusion, it should be pointed out that the somewhat large number of seed oils (those of sunflower, safflower, Niger seed, tobacco, poppy, passion fruit, grapes, and others), all of which contain about 70 per cent of linoleic acid with about 25–20 per cent. of oleic acid and about 10 per cent. of saturated acids, approximate to much the same mixture of mixed glycerides irrespective of their botanical origin. This circumstance has important implications in regard to the interavailability of such seed oils for a number of technical uses.

The component acids of pecan (hickory, *Hickoria pecan*) nuts from 12 varieties grown in north-central Florida have been determined by French.[128b] The results for five of these are given for illustration below:

Variety	Palmitic	Stearic	Arachidic	Oleic	Linoleic	Linolenic
Moneymaker	6·3	2·6	0·4	51·0	37·8	1·7
Big Z	5·9	2·9	0·4	59·7	30·3	1·6
Frotscher	6·5	2·5	0·2	63·9	25·5	1·1
Seedling 1	6·3	3·2	0·1	71·0	18·5	0·9
Success	5·4	2·9	0·4	76·5	13·5	1·3

The wide range of percentages of the unsaturated acids (oleic from 51 to 76·5, linoleic from 38 to 13·5) suggests that, as in groundnut oils (p. 308), genetic factors play an important role in the composition of pecan oils, since all these varieties were grown in similar environments. The contents of saturated acids showed little difference in all the varieties.

TABLE 60. Component Acids of Seed Fats (mainly "Linoleic-rich")

Major component acids: All unsaturated C_{18} acids—LINOLEIC and/or OLEIC.
Minor component acids: Small amounts of palmitic and less stearic (linolenic, myristic, arachidic).

COMPONENT FATTY ACIDS PER CENT. (WT.)

Species	Common name	HABITAT	PAL-MITIC	STEARIC	OLEIC	LINO-LEIC	LINO-LENIC	METHOD	OBSERVERS
BETULACEÆ									
Corylus avellana	Hazelnut, filbert	Italy	3·2	1·7	91	4	—(a)	F, T	Schuette and Chang[1a]
"	" "	France	8·4 →		82	10	—	B, H	Bertram[1b]
"	" " var. Barcelona	Canada	3	4	82	11	—	F	Hopkins and Chisholm[2a]
"	" " var.	Oregon, U.S.A.	2·3	1·6	56	17	—(b)	F, T	Fang and Bullis[3]
"	" " var. Du Chilly	" "	0·5	0·8	65	15	—(c)	F, T	Fang and Bullis[3]
FAGACEÆ									
Fagus sylvatica	Beech nut	Temperate zones	12·0 →		48	38	2	B, T	Delvaux[4]
" "	" "	" "	10 →		57	33	—	B, T	Pritzker and Jungkunz[5]
Quercus alba	Oak	Canada	10	2	48	40	—	F	Hopkins and Chisholm[2b]
" *incana*	Indian Oak	India	17·1	—	82·0	—	—	F	Puntambekar and Krishna[6]
" *palustris*	Pin, swamp oak	U.S.A.	16 →		55	29	—(d)	B, T	Hutchins and Simpson[7]
JUGLANDACEÆ									
Carya cordiformis syn. *Hicoria pecan*	Hickory, pecan nut	U.S.A.	3·3	1·9	78·7	16·1	—	F	Jamieson and Gertler[8]
"	"	U.S.A.	6·5	5·5	88	—	—	L, H	Riebsomer *et al.*[9]
"	"	Canada	4 →		71	25	—	B, T	Bickford *et al.*[10]
"	"	U.S.A.	6	1	72	19	—(da)	F	Hopkins and Chisholm[2b]
									(See text, p. 228)
Juglans regia	Walnut	Europe, Asia, N. America	4·7	2·3	51–77	38–14	1–2(l')	GLC	(See text, p. 228)
"	"	"	4·6	0·9	18	73	3	F, H	Jamieson and McKinney[11a]
"	"	" "	3·5	1·9	35	57	3(e)	F, T	Jamieson and McKinney[11b]
"	"	" "	7·0	1·1	16	72	4	F, T	Griffiths and Hilditch[12a]
"	"	Moldavia	8·5 →		28	55	8·5	S	Aizenberg[12b]
"	"	Japan	10·8 →		9	76	4	L, T	Ueno and Nishikawa[13]
" *manchurica*	"	Manchuria	2·9	0·6	19	76	2	L, H	Branke and Komissartschuk[14]
" *sieboldiana*	"	Japan	6·6 →		20	67	6	B, T	Ueno and Nishikawa[13]

229

TABLE 60. Component Acids of Seed Fats—continued

	HABITAT	COMPONENT FATTY ACIDS PER CENT. (WT.)					METHOD	OBSERVERS
		PAL-MITIC	STEARIC	OLEIC	LINO-LEIC	LINO-LENIC		
HIPPOCASTANACEÆ								
Æsculus hippocastanum Horse chestnut	Temperate zones	4·4	3·6	66	25	1	F, T	Kaufmann and Baltes[15]
" "	New England, U.S.A.	2·3	5·2	70	22	Trace	F	Ehlers and Hill[16]
ULMACEÆ (See also Text, pp. 219, 335)								
Celtis integrifolia	Sudan	—	13·6	12·7	73·7	—	B, T	Grindley[17a]
" *occidentalis* Hackberry	U.S.A.	—	5·3	16	78	—	L	Schuette and Zehnpfennig[18]
Chætacme microcarpa	Sudan	—	12·4	5·6	82·0	—	B, T	Grindley[17a]
Holoptelea integrifolia	India	37·6	10·0	46·7	3·6	(m')	F	Farooq and Siddiqui[17b]
"	India	35·1	4·5	53·3	—		RPC	Badami[17c]
Trema guineensis	Sudan	17·1	6·2	23·7	53·0	(n')	B, T	Grindley[17a]
OLACACEÆ								
Agonandra brasiliensis Ivory wood seed	Argentine	1·4	← 1·7 →	12	37	(f)	F	Gurgel and de Amorim[19]
Coula edulis Coula seed	Tropical Africa			95	3	—	B, K	Steger and van Loon[20]
Mappia fœtida	India	7·1	17·7	38·4	(l)	36·8	L, F	Nadkarni et al.[21]
Ximenia americana	India	—	1·2	60·8	6·7	(g)	F	Puntambekar and Krishna[22]
"	W. Africa	—	4	54	10	(h)	F	Boekenoogen[23]
Onguekoa Gore Engler Isano nut syn. *Ongokea Klaineana* Pierre	Congo	(Later work shows large proportions of C_{18}-11-en-9-ynoic acid)						(See text, p. 221, 290) (See text, p. 221, 289)
VITACEÆ								
Vitis riparia Wild grape seed	Temperate zones	3·4	1·9	44	50	—	L, H	Beal and Beebe[24]
" *rotundifolia* Muscadine grape seed	Southern U.S.A.	← 15 →		20	65	—	T	Pickett[25]
" *vinifera* Grape seed	Sub-tropics	5·5	2·4	37	55	(i)	L	Rabak[26]
" "	Sub-tropics	5	10	20	50	—		Carriére and Brunet[27]
" "	Bessarabia	6·5	2·3	33	46	Trace (j)	L, H	Otin and Dima[28]
" "	California	6·5	2·9	31	60		F, T	Jamieson and McKinney[29]
" "	S. Germany	← 12 →		17	71	(k)	B, K	Kaufmann and Fiedler[30a]

Family / Species	Common name	Source	Sat. acids (12–16 / 16·5)	Oleic (23–15 / 14·5)	Linoleic (65–69 / 69)	—		Reference
" " "		Pfalz, Germany	15	23–15	65–69	—	B, K	Kaufmann and Sprick[30b]
" " "		Swiss	12	14·5	69	—	T	Viollier and Iselin[31]
PAPAVERACEÆ								
Argemone hispida	Prickly poppy	U.S.A.		24	57	—	S	Earle *et al.*[91a]
" " *intermedia*		U.S.A.		18	65	—	S	Earle *et al.*[91a]
" " *mexicana*	Argemone seed	Tropics	8·0 → 6·0	21·8	48·0	0·6 (l)	F, H	Iyer, Sudborough and Ayyar[32]
"		Mexico	11·8 → 1·9	22·7	62·3	— (m)	F	Jamieson and Rose[33]
"		Argentine	6·6 → 3·8	30·5	55·9	— (o')	F	Cattaneo *et al.*[91b]
"		India	14·5 → 3·8	18·5	61·4	— (p')	F	Chakrabarty[91c]
"		Jamaica	9 → 5	33	53		F	Badami and Gunstone[91d]
"		India	12 → 5	23	58		F	Badami and Gunstone[91d]
"		U.S.A.	15	25	55	— (q')	S	Earle *et al.*[91e]
"		U.S.A.	9	16	70	0·3	S	Earle *et al.*[91e]
"		U.S.A.	10	16	67	0·5	S	Earle *et al.*[91e]
Dicentra ochraleaca		Temperate and sub-tropics	4·8 → 2·9	30·1	62·2	2·5	L, H	Eibner and Wibelitz[34]
Macleaya cordata		Russia	10	25	65	—	B, K	Juchnovski[35]
Papaver rhoeas	Corn poppy	Europe	10	25	65	—	B, K	Iselin[36]
Papaver somniferum	Poppy seed	England (1947)	9·5 → 1·4	16·5	71·6	— (n)	C, F, S	Bridge *et al.*[37]
"	(1948)	England	8·3 → 2·7	16·4	72·6		C, F, S	Bridge *et al.*[37]
"	(1949)	India	11·0 → 4·2	11·4	73·0	— (o)	C, F, S	Bridge *et al.*[37]
"		Argentina	7·4 → 1·2	20·5	69·7	— (oa)	L, F	Cattaneo *et al.*[91g]
"		"	10·6 → 1·3	16·0	70·3	— (ob)	L, F	Cattaneo *et al.*[91g]
PASSIFLORACEÆ								
Passiflora edulis	Passion fruit	U.S.A.	7·3 → 1·9	17	73	— (p)	F, T	Jamieson and McKinney[38]
" "	Granadilla	S. Africa	8·8 → 3·3	13·8	73·7	0·4	C, F, S	Seavell[39]
TYPHACEÆ								
Typha latifolia	Reed-mace, Cat-tail	U.S.A.	23	17	60	—	L	Schuette and Gagneron[40]
" "		U.S.A.	12·5	15	72·5	—	T	Clopton and von Korff[41]
COMPOSITÆ								
Ambrosia elator	Ragweed	U.S.A.	5·5 → 4·8	19·9	69·8	—	T	Roedel and Thornton[42]
" *trifida*		U.S.A.	10	18	67	Trace	S	Earle *et al.*[91a]
Ageratum houstonianum		U.S.A.	13	19	53	10	S	Earle *et al.*[91f]
Anthemis sancti-johannis	Camomile	U.S.A.	12	10	72	Trace	S	Earle *et al.*[91a]

231

TABLE 60. *Component Acids of Seed Fats—continued*

COMPONENT FATTY ACIDS PER CENT. (WT.)

COMPOSITÆ, continued		HABITAT	PALMITIC	STEARIC	OLEIC	LINOLEIC	LINOLENIC	METHOD	OBSERVERS
Anthemis tinctoria	Camomile	U.S.A.	2 →	→	18	73	0·4	S	Earle et al.[92d]
Arctium lappa	Burdock	Europe	7	—	20	69	4	K	Gerloff[97]
Arctotis grandis	African daisy	U.S.A.	13 →	→	27	53	Trace (t')	S	Earle et al.[91a]
Artemisia absinthium	Wormwood	U.S.A.	18 →	→	?	45	—(u')	S	Earle et al.[91f]
Aster ericoides	Michaelmas daisy	U.S.A.	3 →	→	26	66	Trace	S	Earle et al.[91a]
Bidens frondosa		U.S.A.	16 →	→	17	62	0·3	S	Earle et al.[92d]
Boltonia asteroides		U.S.A.	2 →	→	39	54	1	S	Earle et al.[91a]
Brachycome iberidifolia	Swan River daisy	U.S.A.	14 →	→	25	51	—(v')	S	Earle et al.[91a]
Carthamus lanatus	Saffron thistle	Australia	7·7	6·8	12·8	72·7		F,T	Hatt and Troyhan[43]
" *oxyacantha*		India	3·1	3·6	55·8	36·8	—(q)	F,T	Singh and Kumar[44]
" *tinctorius*	Safflower	Various	5-10 →	→	37–13	57–59	Trace	—	(See text, p.223)
Centaurea cyanus	Cornflower	U.S.A.	6 →	→	22	67	1	S	Earle et al.[91f]
Chrysanthemum coronarium	Chrysanthemum	U.S.A.	11 →	→	24	59	8	S	Earle et al.[91f]
Cichorium intybus	Chicory seed	India	22 →	→	33	45	—	L	Misra and Dutt[45]
Cirsium altissimum	Plumed thistle	U.S.A.	10 →	→	23	55		S	Earle et al.[91a]
Cnicus benedictus	Thistle	U.S.A.	12 →	→	22	62		S	Earle et al.[91a]
Coreopsis lanceolata		U.S.A.	14 →	→	22	56	Trace	S	Earle et al.[92d]
Cosmos bipinnatus		U.S.A.	30 →	→	14	49	2	S	Earle et al.[91f]
Cynara cardunculus	Cardoon	S. America	12 →	→	22	64	2	?	Eckstein[47]
"		Spain	10·0	1·7	21·5	62·1	—(r)	F	Cattaneo et al.[48]
"		U.S.A.	8·7	1·8	27·2	53·6	—(s)	F	Cattaneo et al.[48]
Dimorphotheca aurantiaca	Cape marigold	U.S.A.	18 →	?	4	10	—(w')	S	Earle et al.[91a] Chisholm and Hopkins,[92b] Smith, Wolff et al.[92c]
Doronicum caucasicum	Coneflower	U.S.A.	9 →	→	26	60	1	S	Earle et al.[92d]
Echinacea angustifolia	Globe thistle	U.S.A.	8 →	→	22	64	1	S	Earle et al.[91a]
Echinops exaltatus	Brittlebush	U.S.A.	12 →	→	14	66	1 (x')	S	Earle et al.[91a]
Encelea farinosa		U.S.A.	18 →	→	23	55	—	S	Earle et al.[91a]
Eupatorium rugosum	Eupatory	U.S.A.	8 →	→	18	70	Trace	S	Earle et al.[91a]
Gaillardia aristata	Gaillardia	U.S.A.	10 →	→	16	65	1	S	Earle et al.[91a]
" *pulchella*	"	U.S.A.	16 →	→	17	60	Trace	S	Earle et al.[91a]

Species	Common name	Country	Sat.		Oleic	Linoleic	Minor	Type	Reference
Grindelia squarrosa	Gumweed	U.S.A.	← 6 →		28	61	1	S	Earle et al.[91a]
Guizotia abyssinica	Niger seed	Africa, India	5–12		40–45	52–72	2·0	—	(See text, p. 222)
Helianthus annuus	Sunflower	Various	9–16	2–11	14–70	20–72	Trace (y')	—	(See text, p. 224)
Heliopsis helianthoides		U.S.A.	13	→	22	56	Trace	S	Earle et al.[91f]
Hulsea heterochrome		U.S.A.	13	→	28	55	1	S	Earle et al.[91a]
Iva xanthifolia		U.S.A.	8	→	14	73		S	Earle et al.[91a]
Kuhnia glutinosa		U.S.A.	8	→	27	60	1	F	Earle et al.[91a]
Lactuca scariola	Indian lettuce	India	1·9	1·3	39	58	—(t)	F	Dhingra and Pershad[49]
" "	" "	India	4·3	4·0	40·2	51·1	—(u)	S	Gambhir and Dutt[50]
" "	Bitter lettuce	U.S.A.	9	→	22	63	2	S	Earle et al.[91a]
Liatris punctata	Blazing star	U.S.A.	12	→	28	54	1	S	Earle et al.[91a]
Listris pycnostachya		U.S.A.	7	→	30	58	1	S	Earle et al.[91a]
Matricaria capensis		U.S.A.	22	→	11	45	11	S	Earle et al.[92d]
Onopordon acanthium	Cotton thistle	Holland	7	→	25	64	4	B, K	Steger and van Loon[51]
Ratibida columnaris		U.S.A.	2	→	26	66	Trace	S	Earle et al.[91a]
Rudbeckia bicolor	Coneflower	U.S.A.	10	→	59	27		S	Earle et al.[91f]
" *laciniata*		U.S.A.	4	→	26	60	6	S	Earle et al.[91a]
Solidago canadensis	Golden Rod	U.S.A.	2	→	32	62	1	S	Earle et al.[91a]
Tithonia speciosa		U.S.A.	28	→	8	58		S	Earle et al.[91a]
**Vernonia anthelmintica*	Purple fleabane	India	7	6	6	10	—(v)	F	Vidyarthi[52]
" "		India	3·5	1·5	6·0	16·5	—(w)	F	Gunstone[53]
" *baldwini*		U.S.A.	10	→		17	—(z)	S	Earle et al.[91f]
" "		U.S.A.	7	→	25	63	1 (a″)	S	Earle et al.[91f]
" *camporum*		U.S.A.	2	→	33	60	1 (r')	S	Earle et al.[91f]
" *fasciculata*		Sierra Leone	13·6	8·5	22·1	55·2	1	RPC	Gunstone and Sykes[46]
" *missurica*		U.S.A.	9	→	29	56	1	S	Earle et al.[91a]
Viquiera laciniata		U.S.A.	8	→	30	57		S	Earle et al.[91f]
Wyethia helenioides		U.S.A.	17	→	9	69		S	Earle et al.[91a]
Xanthium italicum	Cockle burr	U.S.A.	9	→	34	50	Trace	S	Earle et al.[91a]
" *spinosum*		Bulgaria	4·6	→	24·5	65·5		T	Popov and Ivanov[54a]
" *strumarium*		Bulgaria	3·5	→	26·5	64·6		T	Popov and Ivanov[54a]
" "		Bulgaria	3·8	→	28·0	63·3		T	Popov and Ivanov[54a]
" "		Russia	1	7	27	65		L, H	Branke and Gutt[54b]
" "		Russia	8·3	→	27·5	64·2		L	Maximov[55a]
" "		India	11·1	→	36·7	52·2		T	Rao and Kebra[55b]
Ximenesia encelioides		U.S.A.	5	→	64	27	Trace	S	Earle et al.[91a]

* For further details of seed fatty acids of *Vernonia* species, see p. 220.

TABLE 60. *Component Acids of Seed Fats—continued*

COMPONENT FATTY ACIDS PER CENT. (WT.)

		HABITAT	PAL-MITIC	STEARIC	OLEIC	LINO-LEIC	LINO-LENIC	METHOD	OBSERVERS
SOLANACEÆ									
Atropa belladonna	Belladonna	Europe, etc.	5·9	1·8	25·5	66·8	—	F	Hilditch and Ichaporia[56]
Datura alba	Datura seed	E. Africa	7	—	65	28	—	L,H	Dieterle[57]
"	" "	Sudan	13·1	3·0	31·8	52·1	1	B,T	Grindley[58]
" *metel*	" "	India	16	⟶	39	40	1	S	Earle et al.[91a]
" *stramonium*	Thorn apple	Tropics	11·5	⟶	27·5	61	(x)	B,T	Lutenberg and Ivanov[59a]
" "	" "	Tropics	10·8	1·2	33·1	53·6	—	F	Hilditch and Ichaporia[56]
Hyoscyamus niger	Henbane seed	Sudan	11·4	4·4	23·4	60·8	—	B,T	Grindley[58]
" "	" "	Europe, etc.	6·5	0·4	16	74	(y)	F	Lutenberg and Ivanov[59b]
" "	" "	Europe, etc.	6·5	1·6	11·1	82·0	—	F	Hilditch and Ichaporia[56]
Nicotiana tabacum	Tobacco seed	India	—	—	35·2	56·4	—	F	Pathak et al.[60]
Physalis peruviana	Cape gooseberry	Sub-tropics	9–13	—	30–15	55–78	—	—	(*See text*, p. 000)
Solanum esculentum	Tomato seed	India	7·2	6·0	46·1	40·7	—	F	Gupta and Lal[61]
syn. *lycopersicum*	" "	Formosa	22	⟶	16	62	—	L	Hata[62]
"	" "	Australia	17·9	⟶	23·8	56·5	1·8	S	Winter and Nunn[63]
indicum	" "	India	7·2	6·6	35·5	49·5	(a')	F	Puntambekar and Krishna[64]
nigrum	" "	India	1·8	1·9	49·7	46·6	0·8	B,T	Singh and Kumar[65]
nudiflorum	" "	U.S.A.	10	⟶	20	65	—	S	Earle et al.[92d]
xanthocarpum	" "	India	5·7	10·3	45·4	38·2	(b')	F	Gupta and Dutt[66]
PEDALIACEÆ									
Sesamum indicum	Sesame seed	India	7·8	4·7	49·4	37·7	(c')	F,H	Jamieson and Baughman[67]
"	"	Siberia	16	⟶	37	47	—	B	Rudakov and Belopolski[68]
"	"	India	9·1	4·3	45·4	40·4	(d')	F	Hilditch, Ichaporia and Jasperson[69]
"	"	India	8·2	3·6	45·3	41·2	(e')	C,F,S	Hilditch and Riley[70]
"	"	India	9·4	5·7	35·0	48·4	(f')	C,F,S	Chakrabarty and Hilditch[71]
"	"	Nicaragua	14·3	⟶	41·7	44·0	—	T	Andraos et al.[72]
SCROPHULARIACEÆ									
Antirrhinum majus	Snapdragon	U.S.A.	9	⟶	17	69	—	S	Earle et al.[91a]
Chelone barbata		U.S.A.	11	⟶	32	51	1	S	Earle et al.[91e]
Digitalis purpurea	Foxglove	U.S.A.	7	⟶	23	58	7	S	Earle et al.[91e]
Linaria maroccana	Toadflax	U.S.A.	7	⟶	22	66	1	S	Earle et al.[91e]
Nemesia suttonii		U.S.A.	16	⟶	18	60	2	S	Earle et al.[91e]
Paulownia tomentosa		U.S.A.	9	⟶	19	66	—	S	Earle et al.[91a]

Species	Common name	Source	Sat.	Oleic	Linoleic	Linolenic, etc.		Reference
Pentstemon grandiflorus		U.S.A.	4	42	49	—	S	Earle et al.[91a]
" *murraya x grandiflorus*		U.S.A.	3	45	47	1	S	Earle et al.[91e]
Verbascum thapsus	Mullein seed	Bohemia	6	28	57	8	B, K	Votoček, Valentin and Buliř[73]
Veronica spicata	Spiked speedwell	U.S.A.	3	21	70	2	S	Earle et al.[91a]
PLANTAGINACEÆ								
Plantago ovata	Isabghol	India	4·2 → 7·7	38·0	49·2	Trace (g')	L, F	Pendse and Dutt[74]
DIPSACACEÆ								
Dipsacus fullamum	Teazlewort	Russia	4	53	43	—	B	Ivanov[75]
Scabiosa atropurpurea	Scabious	U.S.A.	22	35	34	Trace	S	Earle et al.[91e]
ASCLEPIADACEÆ								
Asclepias cornuti	Milkweed	Russia	5·1 → 11	35	54	— (h')	B	Matzurevitsch[76]
"		E. Europe	2·7	83·6	7·8		?	Juillet and Delga[77]
"		U.S.A.	6	53	34	2	S	Earle et al.[91a]
" *engelmanniana*		U.S.A.	6	48	39	2	S	Earle et al.[91a]
" *incarnata*		U.S.A.	3	50	47	—	B, T	Lanson et al.[78]
" *syriaca*		Canada	4·4	51·8	43·8		T	Watson and Levetin[79]
" *syriaca*		Canada	4 → 20	15	53	<1 (b'')	GLC	Chisholm and Hopkins[80]
Marsdenia edulis		U.S.A.	<1	58	18	—	S	Earle et al.[91a]
STAPHYLEACEÆ								
Staphylea pinnata		Mid-Europe	4	56	40	—	B	Pavlov[81]
MYRTACEÆ								
Meratia praecox	Japanese allspice	Japan	8·9 → 22	46	25	7	T	Kusurose[93a]
Psidium guaiva	Guava	India	4·8	53·9	29·2	1·1 (e'')	F	Achaya et al.[93b]
" *guyova*	Guyova seed	India	16	56	28	—	B, T	Varma et al.[82]
URTICACEÆ								
Urtica dioica	Stinging nettle	Europe	7	12	79	2	B, K	Prögler[83]
THEACEÆ								
Camellia japonica	Japanese tea seed	Japan	11	87	2	—	B, K	Kaufmann and Baltes[87]
" *sasanqua*	Ceylon "	Ceylon	13	72	15	—	T	Child[88]
Thea sinensis	Tea seed	China, India, etc.	7·6 → 6	83·3	7·4	(i')	F	Griffiths and Hilditch[84]
" "	Chinese tea seed	China		84	10	0·8	L	Ueno and Ueda[85]
" "		China	8·9	79·2	8·2	3·7	C, F, S	Weerakoon[86a]
" *sasanqua*	Indian "	Assam	15·0	58·4	24·3	0·3 (i')	F, S	Chakrabarty[86b]
" "	sasanqua "	Darjeeling	16·1	59·0	22·3	0·4 (s')	F, S	Chakrabarty[86b]

TABLE 60. Component Acids of Seed Fats—continued

	HABITAT	COMPONENT FATTY ACIDS PER CENT. (WT.)					METHOD	OBSERVERS
		PAL-MITIC	STEARIC	OLEIC	LINO-LEIC	LINO-LENIC		
OLEACEÆ								
Olea europæa	Olive kernel	6	4	83	7	—	L	Klein[89]
RANUNCULACEÆ								
Anemone coronaria	Anemone	13 ⟶		17	62	1	S	Earle et al,[91e]
Delphinium hybridum	Larkspur	4	1	53	16	3 (d″)	F	Chisholm and Hopkins[92a]
Nigella hispanica	Love-in-a-mist	4 ⟶		48	44	—	S	Earle et al,[91e]
Pæonia brownii	Pæony	11 ⟶		27	56	2	S	Earle et al,[91e]
" *officinalis*	"	12 ⟶		31	19	34	S	Earle et al,[91a]
"		2·5 ⟶		23·3	35·0	39·2	K	Gerloff[97]
CALYCANTHACEÆ								
Calycanthus floridus	Californian allspice	10 ⟶		24	62	—	S	Earle et al,[91a]
Chimonanthus præcox	Wintersweet	20 ⟶		23	52	1	S	Earle et al,[91a]
CAMPANULACEÆ								
Lobelia erinus	Lobelia	9 ⟶		17	69	1	S	Earle et al,[91e]
SYMPLOCACEÆ								
Styrax americana		16 ⟶		39	28	9	S	Earle et al,[91a]
Symplocos paniculata		6 ⟶		53	36	—	S	Earle et al,[91a]
POLEMONIACEÆ								
Cobæa scandens		22 ⟶		51	23	Trace	S	Earle et al,[91e]
CHENOPODIACEÆ								
Kochia scoparia		5 ⟶		38	48	5	S	Earle et al,[91a]
Salsola pestifer		10 ⟶		30	50	5	S	Earle et al,[91a]
HAMAMELIDACEÆ								
Liquidambar styraciflua	Sweet gum	8 ⟶		20	67	1	S	Earle et al,[91a]

236

Species	Common/Variety	Source						Method	Reference
LOASACEÆ									
Mentzelia decapetala		U.S.A.	⟵ 8 ⟶		26	58	4	S	Earle et al.[91a]
PORTULACACEÆ									
Portulaca oleracea		India	10·9	3·7	28·7	38·9	9·9	F	Choudhuri et al.[94]
LILIACEÆ									
Allium porrum	Leek	U.S.A.	9		24	61	—	S	Earle et al.[91a]
Asparagus officinalis	Asparagus	Canada	3	2	27	57	—(c'')	F	Hopkins and Chisholm[95a]
"	"	U.S.A.	3		40	52	—	S	Earle et al.[91a]
Asphodelus fistulosus		Lahore	5·7	3·6	33·1	54·9	—(f'')	L, H, F	Khan et al.[95b]
Dasylirion wheeleri		U.S.A.	8		14	73	1	S	Earle et al.[91a]
Hemerocallis sp.	Day lily	U.S.A.	9		26	59	—	S	Earle et al.[91a]
Yucca constricta		U.S.A.	8		24	63	—	S	Earle et al.[91a]
" *elata*		U.S.A.	9		32	55	—	S	Earle et al.[91e]
" *glauca*		U.S.A.	8		19	69	—	S	Earle et al.[91a]
" *peninsularis*		U.S.A.	8		29	56	—	S	Earle et al.[92d]
AGAVACEÆ									
Agave Schottii	Agave	U.S.A.	⟵ 13 ⟶		12	75	Trace	S	Earle et al.[91a]
"	"	U.S.A.	5		24	70	—	S	Earle et al.[91e]
Cordyline australis		New Zealand	8·1	0·8	7·3	83·8	—	GLC	Morice[96]
"		(from New Plymouth)	3·5	1·0	6·9	88·6	—	GLC	Morice[96]
"		(from Auckland)	3·1	0·7	7·1	89·1	—	GLC	Morice[96]
"		(from Wellington)	6·1	1·1	12·2	80·6	—	GLC	Morice[96]
" *banksii*		"	6·0	0·7	5·3	88·0	—	GLC	Morice[96]
" *indivisa*		"	4·5	1·4	14·6	79·5	—	GLC	Morice[96]
" *kaspar*		"	5·5	1·5	6·9	86·1	—	GLC	Morice[96]
" *pumilio*		"	6·0	2·5	15·5	76·0	—	GLC	Morice[96]
Phormium colensoi		(from Wellington)	6·9	1·3	10·5	81·3	—	GLC	Morice[96]
" *tenax*		(from Moutoa)	10·3	1·8	12·9	75·0	—	GLC	Morice[96]
PROTEACEÆ									
Macadamia ternifolia		Queensland	8·0	3·3	59·3	2·2	—(k')	C, F, S	Bridge and Hilditch[90a]
Embothrium coccineum		Argentina	7·9	0·9	45·7	11·8	—(g'')	F	Cattaneo et al.[90b]
Geruina avellana		"	3·7	0·8	37·0	11·2	—(h'')	F	Cattaneo et al.[90b]
Lomatia hirsuta		"	11·6	1·6	50·4	11·5	—(i'')	F	Cattaneo et al.[90b]

TABLE 60. Component Acids of Seed Fats—continued

Minor and other component acids recorded as follows (per cent. wt.):

		SATURATED				UNSATURATED			
		C_{14}	C_{20}	C_{24}	C_{26}	C_{16}	C_{20}	C_{22}	
(a)	Filbert	0·2	—	—	—	—	—	—	
(b)	"	—	1·4	—	—	—	21	0·4	
(c)	"	—	3·1	—	—	—	15	—	
(d)	Indian oak	—	—	0·9	—	—	—	—	
(da)	Hickory	0·5	0·5	—	—	—	—	—	
(e)	Walnut	2·3	—	—	—	—	—	—	
(f)	Ivory wood seed	—	—	—	15	—	—	—	(Ricinoleic 47)
(g)	Ximenia americana	—	—	—	2	—	—	—	($C_{26}H_{50}O_2$, 15; $C_{30}H_{58}O_2$, 5)
(h)	Lumeque seed	—	—	—	—	—	—	—	($C_{26}H_{50}O_2$, 25; $C_{30}H_{58}O_2$, 5)
(i)	Grape seed	—	—	—	—	—	—	5	(Ricinoleic 10)
(j)	"	—	—	—	—	—	—	—	(Hydroxy acids 12·5)
(k)	"	—	0·1	—	—	5·8	—	—	
(l)	Argemone seed	—	—	0·1	—	0·9	—	—	(Ricinoleic 9·8)
(m)	" "	0·3	0·3	—	—	—	—	—	
(n)	Poppy seed "	0·7	0·4	—	—	—	—	—	
(o)	" "	0·3	0·1	—	—	0·8	—	—	
(oa)	" "	0·1	0·1	—	—	1·6	—	—	
(ob)	" "	—	0·3	—	—	—	—	—	
(p)	Passion fruit	0·7	0·9	—	—	—	—	—	
(q)	Carthamus oxyacantha	0·7	0·9	—	—	0·8	2·3	—	
(r)	Cardoon	1·2	0·9	—	—	3·7	2·9	—	
(s)	"	—	0·1	—	—	—	—	—	
(t)	Indian lettuce	—	0·4	—	—	—	—	—	
(u)	"	7	—	—	—	—	—	—	
(v)	Vernonia	0·5	—	—	—	—	—	—	
(w)	"	1·3	—	—	—	—	—	—	
(x)	Datura stramonium	0·3	—	—	—	—	—	—	
(y)	Hyoscyamus niger	—	—	—	—	—	—	—	("Vernolic", 64*)
(a')	Solanum indicum	—	1·2	—	—	—	—	—	("Vernolic", 72*)
(b')	Solanum xanthocarpum	—	0·4	—	—	—	—	—	

238

(c')	Sesamum indicum	—	0.4	—	—	—	—
(d')	" "	—	0.8	—	—	—	—
(e')	" "	Trace	—	—	—	—	—
(f')	" "	0.3	1.1	—	—	0.5	—
(g')	Plantago ovata	1.2	—	0.9	—	—	—
(h')	Asclepias cornuti	—	—	—	—	—	—
(i')	Thea sinensis	0.3	0.6	0.8	—	—	—
(j')	" sasanqua	2.0	—	—	—	—	—
(k')	Macadamia ternifolia	1.6	2.2	0.8	—	20.4	2.2
(l')	Hicoria pecan	—	0.5	—	—	0.2	—
(m')	Holoptelia integrifolia	3.5	2.0	—	—	—	—
(n')	" "	0.8	1.1	0.4	—	1.9	—
(o')	Argemone mexicana	0.8	0.5	—	—	1.9	—
(p')	" "	1	1.0	—	—	—	—
(q')	" "	—	—	—	—	—	—
(r')	Vernonia camporum	2.6	0.6	—	—	—	—
(s')	Thea sasanqua						
(t')	Arctotis grandis	Also 3 per cent. conjugated dienoic acid.					
(u')	Artemisia absinthium	Also 23 per cent. epoxy-oleic acid.					
(v')	Brachycome iberidifolia	Also 6 per cent. conjugated dienoic acid.					
(w')	Dimorphotheca aurantiaca	Also 48 per cent. dimorphecolic, (+)-9-hydroxy-octadeca-*trans*-10-*trans*-12-dienoic acid.					
(x')	Echinops exaltatus	Also 3 per cent. conjugated dienoic acid.					
(y')	Heliopsis helianthoides	Also 5 per cent. conjugated dienoic acid.					
(z')	Vernonia anthelmintica	Also 68 per cent. epoxy-oleic acid.*					
(a")	" baldwini	Also 2 per cent. epoxy-oleic acid.					
(b")	Asclepias syriaca	Also hexadec-*cis*-9-enoic 10, hexadeca-*cis*-9-*cis*-12-dienoic 2, octadec-*cis*-11-enoic acid 15 per cent.					
(c")	Asparagus officinalis	Also arachidic 0.6, eicos-11-enoic 1.5 per cent.					
(d")	Delphinium hybridum	Also hexadec-9-enoic less than 1, eicos-11-enoic 18, eicosadienoic 1 per cent.					
(e")	Psidium guaiava	Also myristic 1.2 per cent.					
(f")	Asphodelus fistulosus	Also myristic 0.5 per cent.					
(g")	Embothrium coccineum	2.2	0.1	—	23.1	2.5	—
(h")	Geruina avellana	0.4	1.6	2.1	22.0	11.5	9.3
(i")	Lomatia hirsuta	0.4	0.7	—	22.8	1.0	—

* "Vernolic" acid (12,13-epoxy-octadec-9-enoic acid[53]) is the main component of *Vernonia anthelmintica* seed fat.

239

References to Table 60

1. (*a*) H. A. Schuette and C. Y. Chang, *J. Amer. Chem. Soc.*, 1933, **55**, 3333; (*b*) S. H. Bertram, *Ole, Fette, Wachse, Seife, Kosmetik*, 1936, **14**, 2.
2. C. Y. Hopkins and M. J. Chisholm, (*a*) *Canad. J. Chem.*, 1953, **31**, 1131; (*b*) *ibid.*, 1953, **31**, 1173.
3. S. C. Fang and D. E. Bullis, *J. Amer. Oil Chem. Soc.*, 1949, **26**, 512.
4. E. Delvaux, *Fette u. Seifen*, 1936, **43**, 183.
5. J. Pritzker and R. Jungkunz, *Mitt. Lebensm. Hyg.*, 1943, **34**, 107.
6. S. V. Puntambekar and S. Krishna, *J. Indian Chem. Soc.*, 1934, **11**, 721.
7. W. D. Hutchins and R. M. Simpson, *Oil and Soap*, 1937, **14**, 148.
8. G. S. Jamieson and S. I. Gertler, *Oil and Fat Ind.*, 1929, **6**, (10), 23.
9. J. L. Riebsomer, R. Larson and L. Bishman, *J. Amer. Chem. Soc.*, 1940, **62**, 3065.
10. W. G. Bickford, G. E. Mann and K. S. Markley, *Oil and Soap*, 1943, **20**, 85.
11. G. S. Jamieson and R. S. McKinney, (*a*) *Oil and Fat Ind.*, 1929, **6**, (2), 21; (*b*) *Oil and Soap*, 1936, **13**, 202.
12. (*a*) H. N. Griffiths and T. P. Hilditch, *J. Soc. Chem. Ind.*, 1934, **53**, 75т; (*b*) R. S. Aizenberg, *Trudy Kishinev Inst.*, 1956, **11**, 63.
13. S. Ueno and Y. Nishikawa, *J. Soc. Chem. Ind. Japan*, 1937, **40**, 313в.
14. J. V. Branke and A. A. Komissartschuk, *Bull. Far East Branch Acad. Sci. U.S.S.R.*, 1935, No. 14, 85.
15. H. P. Kaufmann and J. Baltes, *Fette u. Seifen*, 1938, **45**, 175.
16. V. B. Ehlers and G. A. Hill, *J. Amer. Oil Chem. Soc.*, 1951, **28**, 45.
17. (*a*) D. N. Grindley, *J. Soc. Chem. Ind.*, 1948, **67**, 230; (*b*) M. O. Farooq and M. S. Siddiqui, *Fette, Seifen, Anstrichm.*, 1955, **57**, 389; (*c*) R. C. Badami, *J. Sci. Food Agric.*, 1962, **13**, 297.
18. H. A. Schuette and R. G. Zehnpfennig, *Oil and Soap*, 1937, **14**, 269.
19. L. Gurgel and T. F. de Amorim, *Mem. Inst. Chim. Rio de Janeiro*, 1929, No. 2, 31.
20. A. Steger and J. van Loon, *Rec. trav. chim.*, 1935, **54**, 502.
21. M. D. Nadkarni, J. W. Airan and S. V. Shah, *J. Univ. Bombay*, 1946, **A, 14**, 26.
22. S. V. Puntambekar and S. Krishna, *J. Indian Chem. Soc.*, 1937, **14**, 268.
23. H. A. Boekenoogen, *Fette u. Seifen*, 1939, **46**, 717.
24. G. D. Beal and G. K. Beebe, *Ind. Eng. Chem.*, 1915, **7**, 1054.
25. T. A. Pickett, *Oil and Soap*, 1940, **17**, 246.
26. F. Rabak, *Ind. Eng. Chem.*, 1921, **13**, 919.
27. E. Carrière and Brunet, *C. R. Acad. Sci., Paris*, 1927, **185**, 1516.
28. C. Otin and M. Dima, *Allgem. Oel-Fett-Ztg.*, 1934, **31**, 107.
29. G. S. Jamieson and R. S. McKinney, *Oil and Soap*, 1935, **12**, 241.
30. (*a*) H. P. Kaufmann and H. Fiedler, *Fette u. Seifen*, 1937, **44**, 286; (*b*) H. P. Kaufmann and M. Sprick, *Fette u. Seifen*, 1938, **45**, 288.
31. R. Viollier and E. Iselin, *Mitt. Lebensm. Hyg.*, 1942, **33**, 295.
32. S. N. Iyer, J. J. Sudborough and P. R. Ayyar, *J. Indian Inst. Sci.*, 1925, **8, A**, 29.
33. G. S. Jamieson and W. G. Rose, *Oil and Soap*, 1943, **20**, 33.
34. A. Eibner and B. Wibelitz, *Chem. Umschau*, 1924, **31**, 109, 121.
35. G. Juchnovski, *Maslob. Shir. Delo*, 1931, No. **6-7**, 36.
36. E. Iselin, *Mitt. Lebensmitt. Hyg.*, 1945, **36**, 377.
37. R. E. Bridge, M. M. Chakrabarty and T. P. Hilditch, *J. Oil Col. Chem. Assocn.*, 1951, **34**, 354.
38. G. S. Jamieson and R. S. McKinney, *Oil and Soap*, 1934, **11**, 193.
39. A. J. Seavell (1950, privately communicated).
40. H. A. Schuette and L. Gagneron, *Amer. Oil Chem. Soc.*, 1945, 19th Autumn Meeting (Chicago).
41. J. R. Clopton and R. W. von Korff, *Oil and Soap*, 1945, **22**, 330.
42. G. F. Roedel and M. H. Thornton, *Oil and Soap*, 1942, **19**, 153.
43. H. H. Hatt and W. J. Troyhan, *J. Counc. Sci. Ind. Res., Australia*, 1946, **19**, 86.

44. B. K. Singh and A. Kumar, *Proc. Indian Acad. Sci.*, 1948, **27, B,** 147.
45. R. N. Misra and S. Dutt, *J. Indian Chem. Soc.*, 1937, **14**, 141.
46. F. D. Gunstone and P. J. Sykes, *J. Sci. Food Agric.*, 1961, **12**, 115.
47. G. Eckstein, *Ind. y. Quim.*, 1941, **3**, 81.
48. J. C. Fernandez, P. Cattaneo, G. Karman and I. J. Rodrigo, *Anales. Asoc. Quim. Argentina*, 1949, **37**, 139.
49. D. R. Dhingra and K. Pershad, *J. Indian Chem. Soc.*, 1945, **22**, 127.
50. I. R. Gambhir and S. Dutt, *Indian Soap Journal*, 1946, **12**, 49.
51. A. Steger and J. van Loon, *Rec. trav. chim.*, 1942, **61**, 120.
52. N. L. Vidyarthi, *Patna Univ. J.*, 1945, **1**, 51.
53. F. D. Gunstone, *J. Chem. Soc.*, 1954, 1611.
54. (*a*) A. Popov and S. Ivanov, *C. R. Bulgare Sci.*, 1957, **10**, 229; (*b*) Y. V. Branke and E. F. Gutt, *Bull. Far East Branch Acad. Sci. U.S.S.R.*, 1935, **13**, 17.
55. (*a*) N. M. Maximov, *Compt. rend. Acad. Sci. U.S.S.R.*, 1940, **26**, 393; (*b*) C. V. N. Rao and P. D. Kebra, *Indian Soap J.*, 1954, **20**, 103.
56. T. P. Hilditch and M. B. Ichaporia, *J. Soc. Chem. Ind.*, 1936, **55**, 189т.
57. H. Dieterle, *Arch. Pharm.*, 1926, **264**, 140.
58. D. N. Grindley, *J. Sci. Food Agric.*, 1954, **5**, 92.
59. C. Lutenberg and S. Ivanov, (*a*) *Allgem. Oel-Fett-Ztg.*, 1935, **32**, 141; (*b*) *ibid.*, 1935, **32**, 189.
60. S. P. Pathak, B. G. Gunde and N. N. Godbole, *Indian Soap J.*, 1944, **9**, 5.
61. M. P. Gupta and J. B. Lal, *Proc. Nat. Acad. Sci. India*, 1938, **7**, 131.
62. T. Hata, *J. Chem. Soc. Japan*, 1938, **59**, 1099.
63. G. Winter and W. Nunn, *Paint Notes, Australia*, 1948, **3**, 43.
64. S. V. Puntambekar and S. Krishna, *J. Indian Chem. Soc.*, 1941, **18**, 329.
65. B. K. Singh and K. Kumar, *Proc. Indian Acad. Sci.*, 1945, **22, A,** 310.
66. M. P. Gupta and S. Dutt, *J. Indian Chem. Soc.*, 1936, **13**, 613.
67. G. S. Jamieson and W. F. Baughman, *J. Amer. Chem. Soc.*, 1924, **46**, 775.
68. Rudakov and M. A. Belopolski, *Maslob. Shir. Delo*, 1931, No. 2–3, 60.
69. T. P. Hilditch, M. B. Ichaporia and H. Jasperson, *J. Soc. Chem. Ind.*, 1938, **57**, 363.
70. T. P. Hilditch and J. P. Riley, *J. Soc. Chem. Ind.*, 1945, **64**, 204.
71. M. M. Chakrabarty and T. P. Hilditch, *J. Sci. Food Agric.*, 1951, **2**, 255.
72. V. Andraos, C. E. Swift and F. G. Dollear, *J. Amer. Oil Chem. Soc.*, 1950, **27**, 31.
73. E. Votoček, F. Valentin and J. Buliř, *Coll. Czech. Chem. Comm.*, 1936, **8**, 455.
74. G. P. Pendse and S. Dutt, *Proc. Acad. Sci. Agra and Oudh*, 1934–1935, **4**, 133; G. P. Pendse, *Proc. Nat. Acad. Sci, India*, 1938, **7**, 137.
75. S. Ivanov, *Chem. Umschau*, 1932, **39**, 173.
76. I. Matzurevitsch, *J. Appl. Chem. Russia*, 1936, **9**, 509.
77. A. Juillet and J. Delga, *Mem. Serv. Chim. Etat*, 1945, **32**, 378.
78. H. J. Lanson, D. Habib and P. E. Spoerri, *Ind. Eng. Chem.*, 1945, **37**, 179.
79. R. W. Watson and N. Levitin, *Canad. J. Res.*, 1946, **24, F,** 95.
80. M. J. Chisholm and C. Y. Hopkins, *Canad. J. Chem.*, 1960, **38**, 805; *Canad. J. Biochem. Physiol.*, 1961, **39**, 829.
81. G. Pavlov, *Maslob. Shir. Delo*, 1932, No. 4–5, 93.
82. P. S. Varma, N. N. Godbole and P. D. Srivastava, *Fettchem. Umschau*, 1936, **43**, 8.
83. R. Prögler, *Fette u. Seifen*, 1941, **48**, 540.
84. H. N. Griffiths, T. P. Hilditch and E. C. Jones, *J. Soc. Chem. Ind.*, 1934, **53**, 13т, 75т.
85. S. Ueno and S. Ueda, *J. Soc. Chem. Ind. Japan*, 1938, **41**, 326в.
86. (*a*) A. H. Weerakoon, Thesis, University of Liverpool, 1952; (*b*) S. R. and M. M. Chakrabarty, *Indian Soap J.*, 1954, **20**, 16; *Science and Culture* (*India*), 1954, **20**, 186.
87. H. P. Kaufmann and J. Baltes, *Fette u. Seifen*, 1938, **45**, 152.
88. R. Child, *Trop. Agric.*, 1935, **84**, No. 2, 1.
89. O. Klein, *Z. angew. Chem.*, 1898, **12**, 847.
90. (*a*) R. E. Bridge and T. P. Hilditch, *J. Chem. Soc.*, 1950, 2396; (*b*) P. Cattaneo *et al.*, *Anales Asoc. Quim. Argentina*, 1962, **50**, 1.

91. (a) F. R. Earle, I. A. Wolff, *et al.*, *J. Amer. Oil Chem. Soc.*, 1960, **37**, 440; (b) M. L. Aceiro, M. H. Bertoni and P. Cattaneo, *Anales Asoc. Quim. Argentina*, 1957, **45**, 59; (c) S. R. and M. M. Chakrabarty, *J. Indian Chem. Soc.*, (*Ind. News. Edn.*), 1957, **20**, 33; (d) R. C. Badami and F. D. Gunstone, *J. Sci. Food Agric.*, 1962, **13**, 255; (e) F. R. Earle, I. A. Wolff, *et al.*, *J. Amer. Oil Chem. Soc.*, 1959, **36**, 304; (f) *idem*, *ibid.*, 1960, **37**, 254; (g) P. Cattaneo, G. K. de Sutton and J. C. Pantolini, *Anales Div. Nac. Quim.*, 1953, **6**, No. 2.

92. M. J. Chisholm and C. Y. Hopkins, (a) *Canad. J. Chem.*, 1956, **34**, 459; (b) 1957, **35**, 358; (c) C. R. Smith, Jr., I. A. Wolff *et al.*, *J. Amer. Chem. Soc.*, 1960, **82**, 1417; (d) F. R. Earle *et al.*, *J. Amer. Oil Chem. Soc.*, 1962, **39**, 381.

93. (a) K. Kusurose and A. Adachi, *J. Japan Oil Chem. Soc.*, 1959, **8**, 76; (b) V. V. R. Subramanian and K. T. Achaya, *J. Sci. Food Agric.*, 1957, **8**, 657.

94. K. L. Handa, R. Vasuder, V. Paul and S. S. Choudhuri, *J. Sci. Indust. Res.* (*India*), 1957, **15**, **B**, 726.

95. (a) C. Y. Hopkins and M. J. Chisholm, *J. Amer. Oil Chem. Soc.*, 1957, **34**, 477; (b) S. A. Khan, M. I. Qureshi, M. K. Bhatty and Karimullah, *ibid.*, 1961, **38**, 452.

96. I. M. Morice, *J. Sci. Food Agric.*, 1962, **13**, 666.

97. U. Gerloff, *Planta*, 1936, **25**, 667 (*Chem. Abst.*, 1937, **31**, 131).

I A. SEED FATS OF THE FAMILIES ROSACEÆ, EUPHORBIACEÆ, CUCURBITACEÆ

Major component acids: LINOLEIC, OLEIC, with LINOLENIC or a conjugated poly-ethenoid acid (ELÆOSTEARIC, LICANIC, etc.).
Minor component acids: Palmitic, (stearic), (oleic, linoleic).
(See Table 61, p. 253).

Until comparatively recently it seemed as though the Euphorbiaceæ family was somewhat exceptional in possessing a few species which elaborated unusual acids in the seed fats – on the one hand ricinoleic (hydroxy-oleic) acid in *Ricinus* species, and on the other hand α-elæostearic (octadeca-9,11,13-trienoic) acid in two species of *Aleurites*. Within the last few years this pecu-liarity has not only been emphasised by the discovery that other species of this family (*A. trisperma* and *Ricinodendron africanum*) also contain α-elæostearic glycerides in their seeds, but the occurrence of the latter acid in quantity in the seed fats of several tropical species of plants belonging to the rose and the cucumber families has been recorded, whilst in addition isomeric forms of elæostearic acid, 4-keto-α-elæostearic (licanic, couepic), and the conjugated tetraethenoid parinaric acid have also been observed in other seed fats of the two latter families. Therefore, since many other species in these three families confine polyethenoid unsaturation in their seed fats to the common forms of linoleic and linolenic glycerides, it is well to consider the three plant families together. The data available at present are given in Table 61 (p. 253).

Rosaceæ seed fats. For so large a botanical family, the data are, of course, relatively meagre. So far as they go (seed fats from species of only eleven different genera have been examined in any detail), they fall into two well-defined groups:

(*a*) Shrubs of temperate or sub-tropical habitat (*Prunus, Rubus, Cratægus, Cydonia, Geum, Sanguisorba*), the seed fatty acids of which are mainly linoleic and oleic, with occasionally linolenic, but usually with only about 5 per cent. of saturated acids (mainly palmitic).

The unsaturated acids in the seed oils of *Prunus* species, including almonds, apricots, cherries, plums, and laurels, are confined to linoleic and oleic, the latter often predominating, although linoleic acid forms from 20 to over 40 per cent. of the total acids. Seed oils of the quince, hawthorn, and blackberry are similar, but also contain small proportions (1–5 per cent.) of linolenic acid. Members of the genus *Rosa* and also meadowsweet, avens and burnet, how-ever, seem to produce more linolenic glycerides in their seed fats, from 14 to 47 per cent. of linolenic acid accompanying linoleic and oleic acids as the chief components in the species so far recorded.

(*b*) Seed fats of the tropical genera *Licania* and *Parinarium*, in which the proportion of saturated acids is somewhat higher (usually 10–11 per cent.), oleic and linoleic acids are often present in only about the same amounts as the saturated acids, and the predominant components are highly unsaturated, conjugated C_{18} acids.

Licania seed fats. In those of the four species which have been examined the

243

chief component acid is licanic or 4-keto-α-elæostearic acid, which usually forms about 60 per cent. or more of the total fatty acids. Until recently, methods for determining mixtures of licanic and elæostearic acids have not been very satisfactory, but a colorimetric method for determination of licanic acid by means of its 2,4-dinitrophenylhydrazone, together with spectrophotometric analysis of the total conjugated triene acids present (Mendelowitz and Riley[129a]), has shown that elæostearic (octadeca-9,11,13-trienoic) acid accompanies the ketonic acid in smaller proportions. Thus, in *Licania rigida* seed fat (oiticica oil), Mendelowitz[129b] found α-licanic 61, and α-elæostearic 17 per cent. of the total seed fatty acids.

Parinarium *seed fats*. Of the seven species of this genus, the seed fats of *P. campestre*, *P. curatellifolia*, and *P. macrophyllum* (neou seed) have been reported to contain only α-elæostearic acid as major component with lesser amounts of saturated, oleic, and linoleic acids.

Those of *P. corymbosum*, *P. glaberrimum*, and *P. sherbroense* (po-yoak oil) contain α-licanic acid as well as α-elæostearic acid; thus Mendelowitz[129b] records α-licanic 35, α-elæostearic acid 37 per cent. in the fatty acids of po-yoak oil.

The seed fat of *P. laurinum* (makita oil) is almost unique in that its chief fatty acid is the tetraene α-parinaric (octadeca-9,11,13,15-tetraenoic) acid, which is accompanied by fairly large amounts of the triene α-elæostearic acid. The seed fatty acids of makita oil may contain about 46–56 per cent. of the conjugated tetraene parinaric acid with about 30–35 per cent. of elæostearic acid, the remainder being made up of small amounts of palmitic, oleic, and linoleic acids.

Parinaric acid was also observed by Tutiya[130] to be a constituent of balsam seed fat from *Impatiens balsamina*, a member of the family Balsaminaceæ indigenous to India and Japan. Kaufmann and Keller[131a] found the following percentages of parinaric acid in the species of *Impatiens* mentioned: *I. fulva* 51, *I. Holstii* 13, *I. hortensis* 27, *I. noli-me-tangere* 32, *I. parviflora* 46, *I. Roylei* 40–50, and *I. sultanii* 27 per cent.; they also found acetic acid to be present in all these fats. Later, Sarkar and Chakrabarty[131c] gave the component acids of *I. balsamina* seed fat as palmitic 4·7, stearic 5·8, arachidic 2·8, oleic 18·3, linoleic 9·2, linolenic 30·1 and parinaric 29·1 per cent.; and Kaufmann and Such,[131d] by paper-chromatographic analysis, arrived at the following figures: saturated 5·7, oleic 16·1, linoleic 3·1, linolenic 32·6 and parinaric 42·5 per cent. Kaufmann[131b] has also reported the presence in seed fats of certain aquatic plants (*Iris* species and *Nymphæa alba*) of considerable amounts of conjugated di-, tri-, and/or tetra-ene acids. These observations are some of the few reports (*cf.* p. 252) of the occurrence of any of these conjugated polyethenoid acids in the seed fat of a plant belonging to a family other than Rosaceæ, Euphorbiaceæ, or Cucurbitaceæ.

Euphorbiaceæ seed fats. The position here is not so simple as in Rosaceæ. Only one seed fat from the many species inhabiting cool regions has so far been studied in detail – the caper spurge, *Euphorbia lathyris*, which contains a very simple mixture of seed fatty acids with over 90 per cent. of oleic acid. The tropical species include both the ordinary type of "drying oil" seed fats (similar to those in Tables 59 and 60) and seed fats in which elæostearic acid is prominent; in *Aleurites* the two types of seed fatty acids are found in different species of the same genus. Elæostearic acid also occurs in the seed fats of some species of *Garcia* and *Ricinodendron*, whilst *Ricinus* seed fats contain large proportions of 12-hydroxy-oleic (ricinoleic) acid, and a hydroxyelæostearic acid is the chief component of *Mallotus* seed fat. *Cephalocroton* seed fats exceptionally contain high proportions of epoxy-oleic (vernolic) acid, thus resembling that of *Vernonia anthelmintica* (Compositæ, *cf.* p. 219). The seed fats of some *Sapium* and *Sebastiana* species are unique in including glycerides of short-chain (C_{10} or C_{12}) conjugated dienoic acids in their seed fats (*v. infra*). Throughout the whole group, the proportions of saturated acids are low, usually 4–10 per cent., although in one or two instances they rise to 15–18 per cent. of the total fatty acids.

Euphorbiaceæ seed fats containing only linoleic (linolenic), oleic, and saturated acids. Simple mixtures of linoleic (30–60 per cent.) with oleic (60–30 per cent.) acid, accompanied by small proportions of palmitic and other saturated acids, are seen in the seed fats of *Chrozophora*, *Hura*, *Jatropha*, *Joannesia*, and *Putranjiva*; in several of these the amount of palmitic and/or stearic acid approaches or exceeds 20–25 per cent., so that these seed fats are more akin to those discussed in the next section (Table 62) than to those previously discussed (Table 60).

Rather more species of Euphorbiaceæ have so far been observed to produce "linolenic-rich" seed fats of the type shown in Table 59. This group includes one species of *Aleurites* (*A. moluccana*, candlenut or lumbang), *Antidesma*, *Bischofia*, *Hevea* (rubber seed), *Colliguaya*, three species of *Euphorbia* (*E. calycina*, *E. erythrææ*, and *E. marginata*), *Mercurialis* (dog's mercury), *Tetra-carpidium* (conophor) and also the otherwise exceptional seed oils of *Sapium* (Stillingia) and *Sebastiana*. In most of these the linolenic acid content falls between about 20 and 50 per cent. of the total fatty acids, but in four instances (*E. calycina*, *Mercurialis*, and *Tetracarpidium*) it is above 65 per cent.

It is curious that three isolated species of Euphorbiaceæ and three or four of the Labiatæ (Table 59) produce seed fats with this extremely high linolenic acid content, and which are also in other respects very similar in composition. Since such oils are superior to linseed oil in technical applications (paints, linoleum, etc.) it may be well to reproduce a summary of their component acids at this point:

		COMPONENT ACIDS (PER CENT. WT.)			
		SATD.	OL.	LIN.	LEN.
Euphorbiaceæ					
Euphorbia calycina		23	2	9	66
Mercurialis annuus		12	7	8	70
,, *perennis*	Dog's mercury	16	—	17	67
Tetracarpidium conophorum	Conophor	12	11	10	67
Labiatæ					
Hyptis spicigera	Black sesame	12	5	17	66
Ocimum kilimandscharicum		14	5	16	65
Perilla ocimoides	Perilla	7	14	16	63
Salvia hispanica	Chia	10	11	10	69

Candlenut (lumbang) oil and rubberseed oils have been the object of considerable study and the more recent determinations of their component acids are therefore given separately here (Table 61A) instead of in the general Table 61.

The linolenic acid contents recorded for the candlenut oils range from 23 to 35 per cent., but in nine of the twelve oils lie between 27 and 32 per cent. The linoleic and oleic acid contents are proportionately more variable, saturated acids remaining relatively constant at 10–14 per cent. The observed differences in the proportions of the three unsaturated acids are somewhat greater than those usually found in seed oils from the same species of plant, and the variations are not simple as between one unsaturated acid and another. It is possible, of course, that large-seeded fruits from trees may be subject to greater individual variations in component acid proportions than the smaller seeds of annual herbs.

TABLE 61A. *Component Acids (per cent. wt.) of Candlenut and Rubber Seed Oils*

	SATURATED							
	C_{16}	C_{18}	C_{20}	OL.	LIN.	LEN.	METHOD	OBSERVER
Candlenut (lumbang) oils (Aleurites moluccana *syn.* triloba)								
E. Indies	4·7	4·1	0·1	32	35	24	F,T	Jamieson and McKinney[132]
Ceylon	0·7	4·3	—	35	33	27	L,T	Child[133]
Ceylon	6·7	3·1	0·6	18·6	44·0	27·0	C,F,S	Hilditch and Weerakoon[134]
Queensland	5·5	6·7	0·3	10·5	48·5	28·5	,,	Gunstone and Hilditch[135]
Queensland	7·6	6·2	0·1	10·9	46·2	29·0	,,	Crossley and Hilditch[134]
Australasia	9·3	4·2	—	14·1	41·6	30·8	,,	Hilditch and Seavell[76b]
Hong Kong	8·6	5·2	—	26·7	36·5	23·0	,,	Hilditch and Seavell[76b]
Fiji	8·8	5·4	—	12·5	38·4	34·9	,,	Hilditch and Seavell[134]
Fiji	8·7	3·9	—	15·7	41·5	30·2	,,	Crossley and Hilditch[134]
Nigeria	7·7	5·4	—	14·2	42·0	30·7	,,	Hilditch and Seavell[134]
Uganda	8·3	6·3	—	16·1	36·9	32·4	,,	Crossley and Hilditch[134]
Kenya	7·5	6·5	—	18·3	36·8	30·9	,,	Crossley and Hilditch[134]
Rubber seed oils (Hevea brasiliensis)								
Brazil	7·5	9·5	—	29	33	21	F,H	Jamieson and Baughman[136a]
Brazil	9·5	8·6	0·3	30	30	21	F,T	Griffiths *et al.*[81b]
Brazil	←—— 14·8 ——→			29·5	41·3	14·4	?	Tuasan and Cruz[136b]
Ceylon	10·6	11·5	1·0	17·2	35·8	23·9	C,F,S	Gunstone and Hilditch[81c]
Ceylon	←—— 21·0 ——→			18·3	39·0	21·7	,,	Hilditch and Seavell[134]
Malaya	←—— 23·8 ——→			18·4	37·1	20·7	,,	Hilditch and Seavell[76b]
Siam	←—— 20·5 ——→			21·5	37·2	20·8	,,	Achaya and Hilditch[134]
Nigeria	8·8	10·3	1·3	19·9	38·4	21·3	,,	Gunstone and Hilditch[81c]
Nigeria	←—— 18·3 ——→			18·7	37·0	26·0	,,	Achaya and Hilditch[134]

The rubber seed oils exhibit less variation in composition than the candlenut oils. Except for a higher linolenic content in one of the Nigerian oils, linolenic acid ranges from 21 to 24 per cent., linoleic from 36 to 39 per cent., and oleic from 17 to 21 per cent. in the rubber seed oils examined spectrophotometrically by Hilditch *et al.*[76b, 81c, 134]

Variation in composition of oil from different individual candlenuts was studied by Crossley and Hilditch[134] in the case of candlenuts from a single tree grown at the Scott Agricultural Station, Nairobi, Kenya, with the following results:

	COMPONENT ACIDS (PER CENT. WT.)			
	SATD.	OL.	LIN.	LEN.
Individual nut 1	16·3	13·5	36·0	34·2
„ „ 2	14·8	14·0	40·5	30·7
„ „ 3	17·2	15·3	36·3	31·2
„ „ 4	16·1	18·8	36·1	29·0
„ „ 5	15·8	15·2	36·8	32·2
„ „ 6	17·1	13·3	40·9	28·7
Mean of 6 nuts	16·2	15·0	37·8	31·0
Bulk sample from tree	14·0	18·3	36·8	30·9

Since factors such as, for example, exposure to direct sun rays[119e] may have an appreciable effect on the rate of development of a seed, and therefore on the precise composition of its oil, differences of the order observed in oil composition from seed to seed are perhaps to be expected, although the average composition of the oilseed crop will conform to a regular pattern: it must be borne in mind that most studies of seed fat composition are based on the oil from many hundreds of nuts of the larger kind, and on many hundreds of thousands of seeds of small size such as those of poppy or tobacco plants. Similar behaviour to that seen above in candlenuts has been encountered in sunflower seeds,[119e] the oils from individual flower-heads of the same variety differing by 5–7 units per cent. in linoleic acid content, although the average composition of the oil from a number of flower-heads in each of five different varieties of sunflowers grown in the same area was practically identical (p. 227).

Euphorbiaceæ seed fats containing elæostearic acid. The seed fats of *Aleurites cordata*, *A. fordii*, *A. montana*, and *A. trisperma* contain substantial proportions of elæostearic glycerides, as also do those of *Garcia nutans* (pinonchillo) and *Ricinodendron africanum* (essang). The component acids of seed fats of all these species except *Aleurites fordii* and *A. montana* are listed in Table 61: the oils from *A. fordii* and *A. montana*, sources of the technically important China wood or tung oil, have been the subject of more study, and their component acids, as determined by the more modern techniques (especially spectrophotometric analysis) are illustrated in Table 61B.

TABLE 61B. *Component Acids of Tung (China Wood) Oils*
(*from* Aleurites fordii *or* A. montana)

SPECIES	SOURCE	SATD.	OL.	LIN.	ELÆO-STEARIC	METH-OD	OBSERVER
A. fordii	China	3	8	10	78	B, K "Diene"	Kaufmann and Baltes[137]
„	Russia	6	5	9	78	?	Taran[138a]
„	North Bengal	10·1	12·7	11·1	66·1	B, S	Chakrabarty[138b]
„	China	4	9	10	77	C, F, S	Hilditch and Riley[139]
„	Florida, U.S.A.	5	4	9	82	„	Hilditch and Riley[139]
„ (?)	Commercial	3·5	5·8	8·4	82·3	„	Hilditch and Mendelowitz[140]
„ (?)	„	4·8	8·6	8·7	77·9	„	Hilditch and Mendelowitz[140]
„ (?)	„	3·6	9·5	9·9	77·0	„	Hilditch and Mendelowitz[140]
„ (?)	„	6·0	8·5	10·6	75·9	„	Hilditch and Mendelowitz[140]
„	Darjeeling	5·1	18·4	11·7	64·8	„	Chakrabarty[138c]
A. montana	Hong Kong	4·2	3·5	11·7	80·6	„	Hilditch and Mendelowitz[140]
„	„ „	4·4	7·3	10·3	78·0	„	Hilditch and Mendelowitz[140]
„ (?)	Burma	5·1	6·9	13·9	74·1	„	Hilditch and Mendelowitz[140]
„	Nyasaland	4·9	8·7	14·8	71·6	„	Hilditch and Mendelowitz[140]
„	Darjeeling	6·5	18·2	10·7	64·6	„	Chakrabarty[138c]

α-Elæostearic acid forms from 82 per cent. to 72 per cent. of the total acids of tung oils, the most usual proportion being from 77 to 82 per cent. It has usually been considered that *A. montana* oils tend to possess lower proportions of elæostearic acid than *A. fordii* oils: but the figures for the *A. montana* oils from Hong Kong indicate that this species may also yield tung oils of the higher elæostearic acid content. It is therefore possible, but not certain, that differences in the proportions of elæostearic acid may be due to environmental conditions of growth of the tung trees, rather than to a species difference; this possibility, moreover, appears to receive support from Chakrabarty's figures[138c] for *A. fordii* and *A. montana* oils grown in plantations in India. Raymond and Ward[138d] state that *A. montana* nuts from Nyasaland yielded oil containing from 67 to 77 per cent. of elæostearic acid.

S. B. Davis *et al.*[141] observed traces (less than 0·1 per cent.) of an optically inactive 9,14-dihydroxy-octadec-10,12-dienoic acid in tung oil; this, as the authors suggest, is probably an artefact from autoxidation of elæostearic acid.

Japanese tung oil (from *A. cordata*) is very similar in elæostearic acid content to the other tung oils, whilst bagilumbang oil (from *A. trisperma*) contains less α-elæostearic glycerides (these however being still the chief components). The seed fat of the Mexican pinonchillo tree (*Garcia nutans*) may contain up to 90 per cent. of elæostearic acid and is probably closely similar to tung oil. The seed fatty acids of *Ricinodendron africanum* (essang oil) include about 50 per cent. of elæostearic acid with about 25 per cent. of linoleic acid and 10 per cent. each of oleic and saturated acids.

The most recent studies[139, 140] of the elæostearic acid group of fats indicate that the conjugated triene acid and the non-conjugated triene linolenic acid are not present together in any seed fats so far examined. In tung oils, the other acids are linoleic 9–14, oleic 4–9, and saturated (predominantly palmitic) 3–5 per cent. (wt.).

Euphorbiaceæ seed fats containing hydroxy-fatty acids. The seed fat of *Mallotus philippinensis* contains as its chief component a solid hydroxy-acid "kamlolenic acid", which Gupta *et al.*[142a] showed to be an 18-hydroxy-octadecatrienoic acid, and which Calderwood and Gunstone[142b] subsequently proved to be 18-hydroxy-octadeca-9,11,13-trienoic (18-hydroxy-α-elæostearic) acid. Much of the kamlolenic acid appears to be coupled concurrently with itself as well as with glycerol, so that this seed fat has exceptional features in its glyceride structure[142c,d,e] (*cf.* Chapter VI, p. 470).

The most important hydroxy-acid of seed fats, *ricinoleic* (12-hydroxy-octadec-9-enoic) acid, is that present in those of *Ricinus* species (*R. communis*, castor seed, and *R. zanzibarinus*), in which it forms about 90 per cent. of the total fatty acids. Castor oils also contain very small, but characteristic, proportions of dextrorotatory 9,10-dihydroxystearic acid.

In addition to the two earlier analyses of castor oil component acids given in Table 61, Gupta *et al.*[143a] examined in 1951 a wide range of castor oils from many regions: the method employed was to determine the acetyl value of the oil (Riley[143b]) and to liberate the fatty acids from another portion of the oil. These mixed fatty acids (after removal of unsaponifiable matter) were then (*a*) analysed spectroscopically after alkali-isomerisation in order to determine linoleic acid, and (*b*) a portion was crystallised from ethyl acetate at 0° to separate dihydroxystearic acid. Oleic acid was determined from the iodine value of the mixed acids (after allowing for the observed linoleic and ricinoleic acids) and the saturated acids (shown to be approximately 40 per cent. palmitic and 60 per cent. stearic) were obtained by difference.

The results are summarised in Table 61C.

TABLE 61C. *Component Acids (per cent. wt.) of Castor Oils*
(Gupta *et al.*[143a])

SOURCE	SATD.	OLEIC	LINOLEIC	RICINOLEIC	DIHYDROXY-STEARIC
India (Bombay)	1·0	—	4·3	94·0	0·7
South America (Brazil)	1·1	0·2	4·5	93·3	0·9
Africa:					
Nigeria (large)	1·3	—	4·8	93·2	0·7
Nigeria (medium)	2·1	1·2	4·7	91·4	0·6
Nigeria (small)	0·2	—	4·6	94·6	0·6
Uganda	—	—	4·4	94·9	0·7
Tanganyika (Eastern)	0·9	0·9	4·3	92·9	1·0
Tanganyika (Central)	0·4	0·1	4·2	94·4	0·9
Tanganyika (Lake)	1·1	0·1	5·0	93·0	0·8
Kenya (Witu)	2·3	0·1	4·7	92·2	0·7
Kenya (Meru, large)	0·5	0·6	4·0	94·0	0·9
Kenya (Meru, small)	2·5	6·8	3·9	85·9	0·9
Kenya (Nyeri)	2·2	0·6	4·2	92·0	1·0
South Africa (Transvaal)	1·3	1·8	4·5	91·8	0·6
West Indies:					
Tobago (Trinidad)	0·3	—	4·2	94·8	0·7

In spite of wide variation in the size of the castor seeds from different locations and to a less extent in the ratio of shell to kernel, the fatty acid compositions of the oils did not vary greatly. Except in one instance (Meru, small seeds – possibly immature) the ricinoleic acid content lay between 91·4 and 94·9 per cent. of the total fatty acids, the average being slightly over 93 per cent. These figures are slightly higher than those observed by earlier workers. Of the remaining acids linoleic accounted for about two-thirds, i.e. 4·5 to 5 per cent. of the total fatty acids; the amount of oleic acid was negligible, and of saturated (palmitic and stearic) acids between 1 and 2 per cent., with a relatively constant proportion of 0·6 to 1 per cent. of the optically active 9,10-dihydroxystearic acid (m.p. 141° C.).

Subsequently (1956) Sreenivasan *et al.*[143c] analysed castor oil component acids by a different procedure. The total acids were converted to methyl esters, which were heated with excess of succinic anhydride in toluene to produce the hydrogen succinates of the hydroxy-methyl esters present, which were extracted with alkali. Linoleic, oleic and saturated acids in the non-hydroxylated esters were determined spectrophotometrically after alkali isomerisation and from the iodine value in the usual manner. Ricinoleic acid was determined from the iodine value of the total mixed acids after allowing for the proportions of linoleic, oleic and saturated acids observed. The results for three samples of Indian castor oil from local mills were:

CROP	SATD.	OLEIC	LINOLEIC	RICINOLEIC	DIHYDROXY-STEARIC
1947	3·0	5·4	3·4	85·5	2·4
1949	3·5	5·1	3·5	86·0	1·9
1950	3·4	5·8	3·5	85·7	1·6

249

Still more recently (1962) Binder et al.[143d] determined by gas–liquid chromatography the component acids in castor oil from different regions, with the following results (per cent. wt.):

SOURCE	SATURATED		OLEIC	LIN.	LEN.	EICOSENOIC	RICINOLEIC	DIHYDROXY- STEARIC
	C_{16}	C_{18}						
Angola	1·0	0·7	2·9	4·3	0·6	0·5	89·4	0·6
Brazil	1·0	0·8	3·3	4·2	0·5	0·4	88·9	0·9
India	1·1	1·0	3·1	4·7	0·5	0·5	88·4	0·7
Texas	0·9	0·8	2·0	4·3	0·6	0·3	90·3	0·8

Ricinus seed fats are thus unique in their high content of ricinoleic acid, the presence of about 1 per cent. of *d*-9,10-dihydroxystearic acid, and the very small proportions of oleic, linoleic and saturated acids present.

Ricinoleic acid has elsewhere only been noted in quantity in the seed fat (ivory wood oil) of *Agonandra brasiliensis*, the latter belonging to the family Olacaceæ (*cf.* Table 60). The acid was formerly supposed to occur in some quantity in the oil of the grape seed (*Vitis vinifera*), but later work indicates that it is not a constituent, the earlier reports having been based on acetyl values of grape seed oils which had become partially hydrolysed into mono- and di-glycerides.[144] Similarly the presence (*cf.* Table 60) of 10 per cent. of ricinoleic acid (as also of 6 per cent. of hexadecenoic acid) in argemone oil (from a Papaveraceous plant) seems unusual, and confirmation of this observation is desirable.

Euphorbiaceæ seed fats (Stillingia oils) containing conjugated diene C_{10} (or C_{12}) acids. The fatty acids of Stillingia oil (the seed fat of *Sapium sebiferum*) were until about 1948 believed to be mixtures of linolenic, linoleic, oleic and saturated acids with about 25–30 per cent. of the first-named acid, and so to belong to the simple "linolenic-rich" type of oils (as in other Euphorbiaceæ and Rosaceæ, Table 61, and in other genera listed in Table 59). In 1938 Jamieson and McKinney[145] published figures of this nature, but noted that stillingia oils had lower saponification equivalents than were necessary to conform with the acid composition which these workers put forward. In 1946 Potts[146a] reported the presence of an acid with an abnormal ultra-violet spectrum among the components of stillingia oil, and later (1949) Potts et al.[146b] gave a more complete account of these observations without reaching a definite conclusion as to the nature of the acid. In 1948 a preliminary report appeared[147] of work carried out in two different laboratories which indicated that small proportions of a conjugated decadienoic acid, $C_{10}H_{16}O_2$, were present in stillingia oil and later Devine[148] and Crossley and Hilditch[149a] published more complete accounts of the studies in question, which established that about 5 per cent. (wt.) of the component acids of stillingia oil consisted of deca-2,4-dienoic acid, $CH_3.[CH_2]_4.CH:CH.CH:CH.COOH$. With the aid of low-temperature crystallisation, ester-fractionation, and spectrophotometric analyses these investigators obtained the data recorded in Table 61D for seed oils of *S. sebiferum* and *S. discolor*.

In these somewhat remarkable seed oils, therefore, linolenic and linoleic acids account for 70–75 per cent. of the total fatty acids, with linolenic ranging from 40–55 per cent. in those from *S. sebiferum*, and from 35–40 per cent. in

TABLE 61D. *Component Acids (per cent. wt.) of Stillingia Oils*

SPECIES	SOURCE	SATD.* C_{16}	C_{18}	DECADI-ENOIC	OLEIC	LINO-LEIC	LINO-LENIC	ELAEO-STEARIC	OBSERVER
Sapium	China	⌠←9→		5	20	25–30	40	Some	Devine.[148]
sebiferum	(commercial)	⌡8	5	5	10	26	44	1	Crossley and Hilditch.[149b]
,,	Hong Kong (1947)	7	3	5	7	24	54	—	Crossley and Hilditch.[149b]
,,	Hong Kong (1949)	9	5	5	10	30	41	—	Crossley and Hilditch.[149b]
,,	South Texas, U.S.A.	9	3	4	8	25	51	—	Crossley and Hilditch.[149b]
S. discolor	Hong Kong (1947)	6	4	5	8	35	40	2	Crossley and Hilditch.[149b]
,,	Hong Kong (1949)	8	5	4	6	42	34	1	Crossley and Hilditch.[149b]

* Traces of capric (decanoic) acid were present in most of the oils, and in three instances traces (up to 1 per cent.) of arachidic acid were recorded.

those of *S. discolor*. In all the oils there is about 5 per cent. of the conjugated deca-2,4-dienoic acid, which is present as mixed triglycerides with the other acids (*cf.* Chapter VI, p. 468), and in consequence stillingia oils are comparable with linseed oils in "drying" capacity. There is some evidence (in the *S. sebiferum* oils) of environmental influences on the seed fat composition, as well as indication of a species difference between the seed fats of *S. sebiferum* and *S. discolor* in regard to the proportions of linolenic and linoleic acids.

In another shrub of the Euphorbiaceæ family, *Sebastiana lingustrina* (from Texas, U.S.A.), Hanks and Potts[146c] found similar proportions (5 per cent.) of a conjugated unsaturated acid of the C_{12} series – probably dodeca-2,4-dienoic acid – accompanying the usual mixture of long-chain component acids (saturated 9, oleic 12, linoleic 39 and linolenic 35 per cent. wt.).

Cucurbitaceæ seed fats. These resemble those of Rosaceæ rather than those of Euphorbiaceæ in that nearly all species so far examined have seed fats whose component acids belong to the simple type of those in Table 60 – abundant oleic and linoleic acids with subordinate amounts of palmitic and stearic acids. In a few instances the saturated acids approach about 30 per cent. of the total acids, and sometimes stearic acid is equally prominent with palmitic acid.

In four genera only have differences from this common mixture of fatty acids yet been encountered. Whilst the seed fat of *Telfairia pedata* is derived from the usual mixture of saturated, oleic, linoleic, and linolenic acids, that of *T. occidentalis* contains fairly large amounts of α-elæostearic and no linolenic glycerides. Similarly, the seed fat of *Trichosanthes cucumeroides* contains, in its component acids, about 30 per cent. of an isomeric form of elæostearic acid (*trichosanic acid*, see Chapter IX, p. 635) in addition to oleic (20 per cent.), linoleic (42 per cent.), and saturated (8 per cent.) acids, although that of the related *T. Kadam* is apparently free from conjugated polyethenoid unsaturation. Ahlers and Dennison[150a] reported (1954) that the seed fat of *T. cucumeroides* (Japan) contained 37 per cent., and that of *T. anguina* (India) 41 per cent., of trichosanic acid. Certain wild gourds (*Cucurbita digitata* and *C. palmata*) indigenous to California and Arizona, U.S.A., have been found by Ault *et al.*[151a] to contain in their seed fats 10–12 per cent. of a conjugated triene C_{18} acid, apparently not identical with α-elæostearic acid (possibly "trichosanic" acid ?). Chakrabarty *et al.*[151b] and Varma and Aggarwal[151c] state that, contrary to earlier reports, the seed fats of *Momordica* species contain 40–50 per cent. of a conjugated triene acid, the structure of which was not given by the authors.

Yet another isomeride of elæostearic acid, denominated *punicic acid*, was isolated by Toyama and Tsuchiya[152a] from pomegranate seed oil (*Punica granatum*, family Punicaceæ or Lythrarieæ); Farmer and van den Heuvel[152b] confirmed (1936) the observation that punicic acid is a third naturally occurring isomeric form of elæostearic acid (see also Chapter IX, p. 635).

Infra-red spectroscopic studies (1954) by Ahlers *et al.*[150a,b,c] showed that trichosanic and punicic acid are identical, and that they are geometrical isomers of elæostearic acid in which the conjugated ethenoid bonds have the configuration *cis- cis- trans-* (instead of *cis- trans- trans-*, as in natural α-elæostearic acid).

TABLE 61. *Component Acids of Seed Fats of the Families Rosaceæ, Euphorbiaceæ and Cucurbitaceæ*

Major component acids: OLEIC, LINOLEIC, LINOLENIC (sometimes LINOLENIC, ELÆOSTEARIC or other conjugated polyene acid, RICINOLEIC).
Minor component acids: Palmitic and Stearic.

ROSACEÆ SEED FATS

COMPONENT FATTY ACIDS PER CENT. (WT.)

Species		HABITAT	PAL-MITIC	STEA-RIC	OLEIC	LINO-LEIC	OTHER UNSATURATED	METHOD	OBSERVERS
Cratægus oxyacantha	Hawthorn	Temperate	2	1	81	11	5 linolenic	L, H	Vasterling[1a] Earle *et al.*[1b]
" *mollis*	"	U.S.A.	6 →		38	50	—	S	
Cydonia vulgaris	Quince	Sub-tropics	9 →		43	47	1 linolenic	B, T	Steger and van Loon[2a]
Geum chiloense	Avens	U.S.A.	3 →		37	26	30 linolenic	S	Earle *et al.*[1b]
Licania arborea	Cacahua-nanche nut	Mexico	12 →		5	8	ca. 73 α-licanic*	Carbonyl, "Diene"etc.	Rose and Jamieson[3]
" *crassifolia*		E. Indies	8 →		5	22	ca. 65 α-licanic	"Diene" K	Sesseler and Rowaan[4]
" *rigida*	Oiticica nut	Brazil	8	4	?	?	88 others		van Loon and Steger[2b]
" "	"	"	10 →			16	74 α-licanic		Kaufmann and Baltes[5]
" "	"	"	11 →		6	—	78 α-licanic	B, K	McKinney and Jamieson[6]
" "	"	"	6	5	4	—	82 α-licanic		Machado[7]
" "	"	"	11 →		6	5	{ 61 α-licanic, 17 α-elæostearic }	S	Mendelowitz[8a]
" "	"	"	12 →		11	6	{ 55 α-licanic, 16 α-elæostearic }	S	Mendelowitz[8a]
" "	"	U.S.A.	9.9 →		18.1	—	{ 58 α-licanic, 14 α-elæostearic }	Paper C	Kaufmann *et al.*[9a]
" *venosa*	"	?	5.7	10.3	14.3	21.5	48.2 α-licanic	RPC	Crombie *et al.*[8b]
" "	—	British Guiana	?	?	?	?	50 α-licanic	S	Bennett *et al.*[9b]
Parinarium annamense		E. Indies	9.6 →		25.2	—	{ 22 α-licanic, 43 α-elæostearic }	Paper C	Kaufmann *et al.*[9a]
" *campestre*	Behurada	"	15 →		27	9	{ 49 α-elæostearic, 13 α-elæostearic }	"Diene"	Steger and van Loon[10a]
" *corymbosum*	Taritih	"	4	7	8	6	{ 62 α-licanic, 15 α-elæostearic }	"Diene"	Frahm[11]
" "	"	Java	12 →		10 →		63 α-licanic	"Diene"	Steger and van Loon[10b]
" *curatellifolia*	—	Sudan	?	?	?	?	{ some α-elæostearic, 70 α-licanic }	S	Grindley[12]
" *glaberrimum*	—	E. Indies	3	4	some	some	some α-elæostearic	"Diene"	Frahm[11]
" *laurinum*	Makita	Fiji	?	?	?	?	{ 46 α-parinaric†, 34 α-elæostearic }	S	Winter[13]
" "	"	Pacific Is.	4	1	10	4	{ 51 α-parinaric, 30 α-elæostearic }	C, F, S	Riley[14]
" "	"	"	3	1	6	3	{ 56 α-parinaric, 31 α-elæostearic }	C, F, S	Riley[14]

TABLE 61. Component Acids of Seed Fats of the Families Rosaceæ, Euphorbiaceæ and Cucurbitaceæ—continued

		COMPONENT FATTY ACIDS PER CENT. (WT.)						
	HABITAT	PALMITIC	STEARIC	OLEIC	LINOLEIC	OTHER UNSATURATED	METHOD	OBSERVERS
ROSACEÆ, continued.								
,, *macrophyllum* Neou	Sierra Leone	←—11—→		23	34	32 α-elæostearic		Steger and van Loon[15a]
,, ,, ,,	W. Africa	←—12—→		21	37	30 α-elæostearic		Ivanov[16]
,, ,, ,,	Nigeria	12	2	40	15	31 α-elæostearic	C, F, S	Hilditch and Riley[17]
,, *sherbroense* Po-Yoak	Sierra Leone	←—ca.12—→		ca.9–10	—	ca. 48 α-licanic / ca. 32 α-elæostearic / 45 α-licanic		Steger and van Loon[15b]
,, ,, ,,	W. Africa	←—13—→		6	←9→	33 α-elæostearic / 35 α-licanic	S	Steger and van Loon[15c]
,, ,, ,,	,,	←—15—→			7	37 α-elæostearic	S	Mendelowitz[8a]
Prinsepia utilis	India	15·2	4·5	32·6	43·6(a)	—	F	Puntambekar[18]
Prunus amygdalus Almond kernel	Temperate	←—3—→		77	20	—	L, H	Heiduschka and Weisemann[19]
,, ,, ,,	India	4·5	—	77·0	17·3(b)	—	F	Thompson[20a]
,, ,, ,,	,,	8·9	4·0	62·5	24·4	—	F	Achaya[20b]
,, var. *dulcis* ,,	English	9·8	2·1	43·8	44·3	—	C, S	Meara[21]
,, *armeniaca* Apricot kernel	Temperate	2·6	1·2	64·4	31·8	—	F	Jamieson and McKinney[22]
,, ,, ,,	Mongolia	←—8—→		60	32	—		Tutiya[23]
,, ,, Bitter apricot	India	4·5	1·1	69·2	22·0(c)	—	F	Dhingra and Shukla[24a]
,, *cerasus* Cherry kernel	Temperate	4·3	2·9	49·5	42·3(d)	—	F	Jamieson and Gertler[25]
,, *communis* Sloe	India	0·5	4·5	65·4	19·7(e)	—	F	Dhingra[24b]
,, *domestica* Plum kernel	Temperate	←—7—→		69	24	—		Delvaux[26]
,, *laurocerasus* Cherry laurel kernel	Sub-tropics	9·9	1·7	73·4	13·2(f)	—	B, T	(Miss) E. E. Jones[27]
,, *lusitanica* Portuguese laurel kernel	,,	6·6	2·2	57·9	32·0(g)	—	F	(Miss) E. E. Jones[27]
Rosa canina Wild rose	Russia	←—5—→		26	55	14 linolenic	B, T	Rusch and Ivanova[28]
,, ,, ,,	Holland	←—5—→		9	54	32 linolenic	B, K	Steger and van Loon[15d]
,, *rubiginosa* ,,	Brazil	1·6	1·5	6·6	73·6(h)	16·3 linolenic	F	Cattaneo et al.[29]
Rubus cæsius Blackberry seed	Temperate	5	—	16	76	3 linolenic	L	Krzizan[30]
Sanguisorba minor Burnet	U.S.A.	←—9—→		19	38	29 linolenic	S	Earle et al.[31a]
Spiræa ulmaria Meadowsweet	Temperate	←—8—→		29	16	47 linolenic	S	Nordstrom[31b]

* Licanic acid is 4-keto-octadeca-9,11,13-trienoic acid.
† Parinaric acid is octadeca-9,11,13,15-tetraenoic acid.

Minor component acids recorded as follows (per cent. wt.):

	MYRISTIC	ARACHIDIC	LIGNOCERIC
(a) *Prinsepia utilis*	1·8	—	0·9
(b) *Prunus amygdalus*	1·2	—	—
(c) ,, *armeniaca*	2·7	0·5	—

	MYRISTIC	ARACHIDIC
(e) *Prunus communis*	3·8	6·1
(f) ,, *laurocerasus*	1·8	—
(g) ,, *lusitanica*	1·3	—

EUPHORBIACEÆ SEED FATS

Species	Habitat	Name	COMPONENT FATTY ACIDS PER CENT. (WT.)					METHOD	OBSERVERS
			PALMITIC	STEARIC	OLEIC	LINOLEIC	OTHER UNSATURATED		
Aleurites cordata	Japan	Japanese tung seed	←7→		19		74 α-elæostearic	B, K	McKinney and Jamieson[32b]
" *fordii, montana*	China, E. Indies, U.S.A.	China wood or tung seed	←3-5→		4-10	8-15	71-82 α-elæostearic	—	(See text, p. 247)
" *moluccana* syn. *triloba*	E. Indies, Africa	Candlenut or lumbang	4-9	4-7	10-35	33-48	23-35 linolenic	—	(See text, p. 246)
" *trisperma*	E. Indies	Bagilumbang nut	←17→		13	—	67 α-elæostearic	B, K	McKinney and Jamieson[33]
"	Java	Bagilumbang nut	←18→		12	19	51 α-elæostearic	"Diene"	Frahm and Koolhaas[34]
Antidesma diandrum	E. Indies	—	←25.5→		13.1	13.9	47.5 linolenic	F	Chakrabarty and Sankar[32a]
Bischofia javonica	"	—	←13.8→		23.4	11.8	51 linolenic	F	Chakrabarty and Sankar[32a]
Cephalocroton cordofanus	Sudan	—	3.9	2.8	9.8	17.1(m)	62 epoxy-oleic	C, F	Bharucha and Gunstone[35b]
peuschelii	S. Africa	—	2.9	2.5	6.6	14.5(o)	72.4 epoxy-oleic	RPC	Gunstone and Sykes[35c]
Chrozophora plicata	Sudan	—	←24.0→		27.1	48.9	—	B, T	Grindley[36]
Cnidoscolus texanus	Southern U.S.	Bull nettle	9.0	13.2	24.6	52.1(a)	—	C, F, S	Barker et al.[37]
"	"		←12.4→		21.2	61.6	—		Cushing and Cirino[38a]
Colliguaya intergerrima	Argentine	Duraznillo	10.0	1.2	30.2	31.5(b)	20.1 linolenic	F, T	Cattaneo et al.[38b]
Croton texensis	U.S.A.	Skunkweed	←15→		8	46	28 linolenic	S	Earle et al.[31a]
tiglium	Asia	Croton seed	1.3	0.5	56	29(c)	Traces lower acids	?	Flaschenträger and Wolfersdorff[39a]
Daphniphyllum glaucescens	Japan	—	←10.2→		67.1	22.7	—	T	Koyama and Toyama[39b]
Daphniphyllum humile	U.S.A.	—	←14→		53	28	1 linolenic	S	Earle et al.[31a]
Emblica officinalis	India	—	3.4	2.5	32.5	50.4(d)	10.1 linolenic	F, T	Dhar and Shrivastava[40]
Euphorbia calycina	Sudan	—	←9→		19	12	60 linolenic	L, T	Henry and Grindley[35a]
" *erythraeæ*	Red Sea Hills	—	10.8	12.1	2.2	8.9	66.0 linolenic	C, F, S	Barker et al.[37]
" *erythraeæ*	"	—	←13→		7	39	41 linolenic	L, T	Henry and Grindley[35a]
" *heterophylla*	U.S.A.	Painted spurge	13.8	5.2	9.2	17.9(e)	53.4 linolenic	C, F, S	Barker et al.[37]
" *lathyris*	Temperate	Caper spurge	←8→		10	22	55 linolenic	S	Earle et al.[1c]
" *lathyris*	U.S.A.		←5.8→		92	2	—	?	Sobol et al.[41]
" *marginata*	U.S.A.		←3.1→		6.9	45.3	44.6 linolenic	?	Albertsma[42]
" *marginata*	U.S.A.		←8→		17	14	57 linolenic		Earle et al.[1c]
Garcia nutans	Mexico	Pinonchillo	←2→		?	—	93-95 α-elæostearic	"Diene"	Jamieson and Rose[43a]
"	Mexico	"	←2→		10	—	85 α-elæostearic; 1 linolenic	S	Madrazo and Sierra[43b]

TABLE 61. *Component Acids of Seed Fats of the Families Rosaceæ, Euphorbiaceæ and Cucurbitaceæ—continued*

EUPHORBIACEÆ SEED FATS

Species		HABITAT	COMPONENT FATTY ACIDS PER CENT (WT.)					METHOD	OBSERVERS
			PALMITIC	STEARIC	OLEIC	LINOLEIC	OTHER UNSATURATED		
Hevea brasiliensis	Rubber seed	Tropics	←16–24→		17–30	30–39	21–24 linolenic	T	(See text, p. 246)
Hura polyandra	Habilla	Mexico	←32→		16	52	—	T	Munguia et al.[44]
Jatropha curcas	Physic nut	Philippine Is.	11·9	5·1	63·4	18·8(f)	—	F	Cruz and West[45]
,, ,,	,, ,,	India	15·6	9·7	40·9	32·1(g)	—	F	Kartha and Menon[46a]
,, ,,	,, ,,	E. Indies	17·0	5·7	35·7	41·6	—	F	Steger and van Loon[47a]
,, ,,	,, ,,	,,	←14→		36	50	—	S	Popják and Tietz[46b]
,, glandulifera	,, ,,	Nigeria	16·4	6·6	40·3	36·7	—	RPC	Gunstone and Sykes[35c]
,, ,,	,, ,,	India	8	5	44	43	—	L	Alimchandani et al.[48a]
,, ,,	—	India	14·5	5·9	34·2	43·0(p)	—	F	Seth and Desai[48b]
Joannesia princeps	Anda-assu	Brazil	5·4	—	45·8	46·4(h)	—	F, H	Gurgel and Ramos[49]
,, ,,	,, ,,	,,	ca.14		43	43	—	?	Pereira[50]
Mallotus philippinensis	Kamala	India	←5→		29	2	{38 α-elæostearic	B	Puntambekar[51a]
,, ,,	,, ,,	,,	18		28	18	26 hydroxyelæostearic	S	Gunstone[51b]
,, ,,	,, ,,	,,	8·7	0·7	13·3	11·7(n) 58·5	36 hydroxyelæostearic	F,S	Gupta and Aggarwal[51c]
,, ,,	,, ,,	Bombay	←10·1→		7·2	5·2	{58·6 hydroxyelæostearic / 19·0 linolenic	S	Chakrabarty[51d]
,, ,,	,, ,,	,,	←9·1→		2·7	4·3	{66·2 hydroxyelæostearic / 17·7 linolenic	S	Chakrabarty[51d]
,, ,,	,, ,,	Calcutta		←9·1→		6·7	{66·1 hydroxyelæostearic / 18·1 linolenic	S	Chakrabarty[51d]
Mercurialis annuus	Herb mercury	U.S.A.	←12→		7	8	70 linolenic	S	Earle et al.[31a]
,, perennis	Dog's mercury	England	←15·7→		—	17·3	67 linolenic	S	Hilditch[52]
Omphalea diandra	Cavete	Central America	ca.20	—	ca.48	ca.32	—	?	Callier[53a]
,, queenslandiæ	—	Queensland Babinda	12·7	8·1	47·0	31·7	0·5 linolenic	C, F, S	Hatt and Szumer[53b]
,, ,,	—	Innisfail	←18·1→		39·7	41·3	0·9 linolenic	S	Hatt and Szumer[53b]
Phyllanthus sp.	—	U.S.A.	←10→	15	30	21	35 linolenic	S	Earle et al.[31a]
Putranjiva Roxburghii	—	India	8	15	56	18(i)	—	?	Dutt[54]
Ricinodendron africanum	Essang seed	W. Africa	←10·4→		17	12	{49 α-elæostearic / 11 linolenic	B, K	Steger and van Loon[47b]
,, viticoides	,, ,,	Nigeria	10	1	10	26	53 α-elæostearic	C, F, S	Hilditch and Riley[17]
,, ,,	,, ,,	Tanganyika	←13·7→		15·1	40·1	31·1 α-elæostearic	T	Raymond et al.[55]

Species	Source					Principal acid(s)	Code	Reference
Ricinus communis	Castor seed	—		7	4(j)	88 ricinoleic	L, K	Panjutin and Rapoport[56a]
"	"	0·3 →	2·4 →	7	3(k)	87 ricinoleic	B, K	Kaufmann and Bornhardt[56b]
"	" Sub-tropical	← 1–2 →	0·1–2	4–5(l)		91–94 ricinoleic	B, T	Gupta *et al.*[57a], Kane *et al.*[57b] (*See text*, p. 249)
" *zanzibarinus*	"	← 1 →	Traces	8		91 ricinoleic	B, T	Steger *et al.*[58]
Sapium sebiferum syn. *Stillingia sebifera*	Stillingia "China"	6–9	3–5	7–10	24–30	{ 41–54 linolenic 4–5 decadienoic		(*See text*, p. 251)
"	" U.S.A. India	2·8	1·0	9·4	53·4(q)	30 linolenic	F	Narang and Sadgopal[59a]
" *discolor*	" Hong Kong	6–8	4–5	6–8	35–42	{ 34–40 linolenic 4–5 decadienoic		(*See text*, p. 251)
" *sylvatica*	Queen's root Southern U.S.A.	3·5	1·9	18·9	25·7	50·0 linolenic	F, S	Batterson and Potts[59b]
Sebastiana lingustrina	— Southern U.S.A.	← 9·7 →	11·9	38·9		{ 34·9 linolenic 4·6 dodecadienoic	F, S	Hanks and Potts[60]
Tetracarpidium conophorum	Awusa, conophor Nigeria 1943	4	3	13	17	63 linolenic	C, F, S	Gunstone and Hilditch[61]
"	" 1944	3	6	15	11	65 linolenic	C, F, S	Gunstone and Hilditch[61]
"	" 1946	4	7	9	12	68 linolenic	C, F, S	Gunstone and Hilditch[61]
"	" 1949	← 12 →	11	10		67 linolenic	C, F, S	Hilditch and Seavell[62]
Trewia nudiflora	India	← 35·4 →	25·1			39·5 α-elæostearic	S	Chakrabarty[51e]

Minor component acids recorded as follows (per cent. wt.):

	MYRISTIC	ARACHIDIC	HEXA-DECENOIC	UNSATD. C₂₀₋₂₂			MYRISTIC	ARACHIDIC
(a) *Chrozophora plicata*	0·2	0·6	0·3	—	(e) *Euphorbia erythrææ*		0·1	0·4
(b) *Colliguaya intergerrima*	0·7	0·9	1·1	4·2	(f) *Jatropha curcas*		0·5	0·3
(c) *Croton tiglium*	11·3	2·3	—	—	(g) " *Joannesia princeps*		1·4	0·4
(d) *Emblica officinalis*	1·1	—	—	—	(h) " *Putranjiva*		2·4	—
					(i)		—	2

(j) *Ricinus communis* 1·1 per cent. dihydroxystearic acid.
(k) " " 0·6 " " "
(l) " " 0·5–1·0 " " "
(m) *Cephalocroton cordofanus* 0·7 per cent. arachidic and 3·7 per cent. *threo*-12,13-dihydroxyoleic acids.
(n) *Mallotus* 2·5 per cent. myristic and 4·5 per cent. conjugated diene acids.
(o) *Cephalocroton peuschelii* 0·2 per cent. lauric, 0·4 per cent. myristic and 0·5 per cent. arachidic acids.
(p) *Jatropha glandulifera* 2·4 per cent. myristic acid.
(q) *Sapium sebiferum* 1·5 per cent. octanoic, 1·0 per cent. decanoic, 0·9 per cent. myristic acids.

TABLE 61. Component Acids of Seed Fats of the Families Rosaceæ, Euphorbiaceæ and Cucurbitaceæ—continued

CUCURBITACEÆ SEED FATS

Species		Habitat	COMPONENT FATTY ACIDS PER CENT. (WT.)					Method	Observers
			Palmitic	Stearic	Oleic	Linoleic	Other Unsaturated		
Benincasa cerifera	—	India	15·8 →		21·9	62·3	1 linolenic	S	Chowdhury et al.[63a]
Cucumis Melo	Cantaloup (melon)	Tropics	10·5	5·8	20·0	62·4(n)	—	F	Seth and Aggarwal[63c]
"	var. "Sarda"	India	10·3	4·6	27·5	57·3(a)	—	F,H	Baughman et al.[63b]
"	"	"	7·3	0·2	43·2	45·2(b)	—	F	Dhingra and Narain[64a]
"	"	"	3·2	5·4	32·9	55·6(c)	—	F	Ahmad and Dhingra[64b]
" sativus	—	"	23·1 →		17·0	59·9	—	S	Chowdhury and Bagchi[63e]
" "	—	"	4·1	16·5	38·8	40·0(d)	—	L,F	Soni et al.[65a]
" "	—	"	13·0 →		35·0	52·0	—	S	Chakrabarty et al.[65b]
Cucurbita (Citrullus) colocynthis	—	Algeria	8·9	5·6	17·2	65·0(e)	1·6 linolenic	C,F,S	Abu-Nasr and Potts[66a]
" digitata	Gourd	India	9·6	6·6	21·1	59·2(o)	10·1 trichosanic*(?)	F,T	Sengupta et al.[66c]
" fistulosus	—	Arizona	1·7	11·5	39·3	37·4	—	B,S	Ault et al.[67]
" foetidissima	Buffalo gourd	India	5·7	12·5	33·9	47·3(p)	—	F	Dhingra et al.[64d]
" maxima	Hubbard squash	Texas	6·2	2·3	23·4	66·7(f)	0·7 trichosanic (?)	C,F,S	Shahani et al.[68]
" "	squash	Sun-tropics	12·9	6·3	36·7	44·1	—	F,H	Baughman and Jamieson[69]
" "	"	India	29·9 →		26·4	43·7	—	S	Chowdhury et al.[63a]
" palmata	Gourd	California	3·2	9·3	28·3	59·2	12·2 trichosanic (?)	F	Tewari and Gupta[63d]
" pepo	Pumpkin	Sub-tropics	1·5	8·4	34·4	43·5	—	B,S	Ault et al.[67]
" "	"	"	30 →		25	45	—	L	Power and Salway[70]
" "	"	"	5·9	7·1	40·9	46·1	—	F	Riebsomer and Nesty[71]
" "	"	"	12	7	24	57	—	L,T	Kaufmann and Fiedler[72]
" vulgaris	Water melon	U.S.A.	15 →		30	51	—	S	Earle et al.[31a]
" "	"	Tropics	12·6	15·2	43	26 (g)	—	L	Pieraerts[73]
" "	"	Russia	11·3	10·2	13·4	65·2	—	F	Rankov and Popov[74]
" "	"	"	11·4	10·1	14·7	63·7	—	F	Rankov and Popov[74]
" "	"	India	7·6	6·1	35·3	48·7(h)	—	F	Dhingra and Biswas[64c]
" "	"	India	22·7 →		18·7	58·6	—	S	Chowdhury et al.[63a]
" " (var. Cuban Queen)	"	Florida	9·2	5·8	13·5	70·8(i)	—	F	Nolte and von Loesecke[75]
" " (var. Tom Watson)	"	U.S.A.	10·1	11·1	7·2	71·0(q)	—	RPC	Crombie et al.[8b]

Species	Common name	Source	Satd.	C16 unsat.	Oleic	Linoleic	Other acids	Reference	Analysis
Cucurbita (Citrullus) vulgaris	Water melon	Senegal	5·5	20·6	28·9	45·0	—	Carrière et al.[76]	?
" " *vulgaris*	"	Sudan	4·0	22·3	6·2	67·5	—	Grindley[77]	F, T
" "	Green Citron	Texas	10·5	6·4	19·1	61·9(j)	1 linolenic	Tsao and Potts[66b]	C, F, S
" "	"	U.S.A.	← 16 →		12	67	1 linolenic	Earle et al.[1b]	S
Echinocystis fabacea	—	U.S.A.	← 19 →		28	48	—	Earle et al.[1b]	S
" *oregana*	Wild cucumber	U.S.A.	← 19 →		26	49	—	Earle et al.[1b]	S
Hodgsonia capniocarpa	Kepayang	Malaya	37·3	8·7	27·1	24·6(k)	—	Hilditch et al.[79]	F
Lagenaria vulgaris	Seringe	India	20	31	16	33	—	Aggarwal and Dutt[80]	L, F
" "	—	India	← 17·8 →		18·2	64·0	—	Chowdhury et al.[63a]	S
" "	—	Sudan	6·7	13·0	38·2	42·1	—	Grindley[77]	F, T
Luffa acutangula	—	India, W. Africa	← 30 →		28	42	—	Pieraerts and de Winter[81]	?
"	—	India	← 24 →		39	37	—	Chakrabarty et al.[65b]	S
" *ægyptiaca*	—	U.S.A.	← 24 →		21	51	1 linolenic	Earle et al.[1b]	S
"	Loofah	Africa, India	← ca. 20 →		ca. 35	ca. 45	1 linolenic	Pieraerts and de Winter[81]	?
"	—	India	← 19 →		30	51	—	Chakrabarty et al.[65b]	S
" *cylindrica*	"	Sudan	9·6	18·9	6·9	64·6	—	Grindley[77]	F, T
Marah gilensis	Bigroot	U.S.A.	← 16 →		33	46	—	Earle et al.[31a]	S
" *macrocarpa*	"	U.S.A.	← 21 →		24	50	—	Earle et al.[31a]	S
Momordica charantia	—	India	—	16·3	83·7		—	Airan and Shah[82]	?
"	—	India	—	29·8	15·8	7·7	46·7 conj. triene	Varma and Aggarwal[78a]	?
" (var. *muricata*)	—	India	← 30 →		12	9	48 conj. triene	Chakrabarty et al.[65b]	S
" (var. *proper*)	—	India	← 26 →	16·9	15	18	40 conj. triene	Chakrabarty et al.[65b]	?
" *dioica*	—	India			83·1	—	—	Airan and Shah[82]	S
Telfairia occidentalis	Krobanko	Nigeria	← 27·1 →		9·2	8·8	54·9 conj. triene	Chakrabarty et al.[78b]	C, F, S
" *pedata*	Koëme	E. Africa	16	3	23	23(m)	19 α-elæostearic	Hilditch and Riley[17]	F, T
" "	"	"	26·4	19·9	12	35	6 linolenic	Smit and van Loon[83]	F, T
" "	"	"	32·5	14·2	14	35·5(l)	3 linolenic	Hilditch and Meara[84]	F, T

TABLE 61. Component Acids of Seed Fats of the Families Rosaceæ, Euphorbiaceæ and Cucurbitaceæ—continued

CUCURBITACEÆ SEED FATS

	HABITAT	COMPONENT FATTY ACIDS PER CENT (WT.)					METHOD	OBSERVERS
		PAL-MITIC	STEA-RIC	OLEIC	LINO-LEIC	OTHER UNSATURATED		
Trichosanthes anguina	India	3·0	10·2	27·6	16·4	42·8 trichosanic*	"Diene"	Soni and Aggarwal[85a]
" cucumerina	"	←21→		32	21	26 conj. triene	S	Chakrabarty et al.[65b]
" cucumeroides	E. Indies	3·6	4·5	32·6	19·8(r)	35·5 conj. triene	F, S	Chakrabarty et al.[78b,c]
		←9→		20	42	29 trichosanic*	L.K and "Diene"	Toyama and Tsuchiya[86] Kaufmann et al.[87]
" dioica	India	←11·7→		27·1	33·4	—	"Diene"	Mathur and Aggarwal[85b]
" Kadam Kadam	Tropics	ca. 20	—	ca. 80	—	—	?	Sack[88]

* Trichosanic acid is a geometrical isomer of octadeca-9,11,13-trienoic (α-elæostearic) acid.

Minor component acids recorded as follows (per cent. wt.):

		SATURATED				UNSATURATED				
		C8	C10	C12	C14	C14	C16	C20	C22	
(a)	Cucumis Melo	—	—	—	0·3	—	—	—	—	
(b)	" " (Sarda)	1·0	2·0	—	1·1	—	—	0·9	—	
(c)	" " sativus	—	—	—	2·0	—	—	—	—	
(d)	" "	—	—	—	0·6	—	—	—	—	
(e)	Citrullus colocynthis	—	—	—	1·2	0·9	1·2	0·3	0·2	
(f)	" fœtidissima	—	—	—	0·2	—	—	—	—	
(g)	" vulgaris	—	—	2·5	—	—	—	—	—	
(h)	" "	0·2	1·1	0·8	0·2	—	—	—	—	
(i)	" "	—	—	—	—	—	—	0·7	—	
(j)	" "	—	—	—	—	—	—	—	—	
(k)	Hodgsonia capniocarpa	—	—	—	—	—	—	—	—	Also 16 per cent. resin acids.
(l)	Telfairia pedata	—	—	—	0·9	0·4	0·8	—	—	Also 0·3 per cent. arachidic.
(m)	" occidentalis	—	—	—	0·6	—	0·9	—	—	Also 1·9 per cent. arachidic.
(n)	Benincasa cerifera	—	—	—	0·6	—	—	0·8	—	Also 0·6 per cent. myristic.
(o)	Citrullus colocynthis	—	—	—	—	—	—	—	—	Also 0·6 per cent. arachidic.
(p)	" fistulosus	—	—	—	—	—	—	—	—	Also 0·6 per cent. arachidic.
(q)	" vulgaris	—	—	—	—	—	—	—	—	Also 4·0 per cent. arachidic.
(r)	Tricosanthes cucumerina	—	—	—	—	—	—	—	—	

References to Table 61

1. (*a*) P. Vasterling, *Arch. Pharm.*, 1922, **260**, 33; (*b*) F. R. Earle, I. A. Wolff *et al.*, *J. Amer. Oil Chem. Soc.*, 1960, **37**, 440; (*c*) *idem, ibid.*, 1960, **37**, 48.
2. A. Steger and J. van Loon, (*a*) *Rec. trav. chim.*, 1934, **53**, 24; (*b*) J. van Loon and A. Steger, *Chem. Umschau*, 1930, **37**, 337.
3. W. G. Rose and G. S. Jamieson, *Oil and Soap*, 1943, **20**, 227.
4. M. Sesseler and P. A. Rowaan, *Chem. Weekblad*, 1939, **36**, 208.
5. H. P. Kaufmann and J. Baltes, *Ber.*, 1936, **69**, [B], 2679.
6. R. S. McKinney and G. S. Jamieson, *Oil and Soap*, 1936, **13**, 10.
7. A. Machado, *Rev. Soc. Brasil, Quim.*, 1938, **7**, 73.
8. (*a*) A. Mendelowitz, Thesis, University of Liverpool, 1952 (pp. 156–160); (*b*) W. Mary L. Crombie, R. Comber and S. G. Boatman, *Biochem. J.*, 1955, **59**, 309.
9. (*a*) H. P. Kaufmann and R. K. Such, *Fette, Seifen, Anstrichm.*, 1960, **62**, 160; (*b*) H. Bennett, E. Brown and H. T. Islip, *Colon. Plant Anim. Prod.*, 1950, **1**, 232.
10. A. Steger and J. van Loon, (*a*) *Fette u. Seifen*, 1942, **49**, 769; (*b*) *Rec. trav. chim.*, 1941, **60**, 13.
11. E. D. G. Frahm, *De Ingénieur in Ned. Indie*, 1941, **7**, 92.
12. D. N. Grindley, *J. Sci. Food Agric.*, 1950, **1**, 152.
13. G. Winter, *Paint Notes (Australia)*, 1948, **3**, 393.
14. J. P. Riley, *J. Chem. Soc.*, 1950, 12.
15. A. Steger and J. van Loon, (*a*) *Rec. trav. chim.*, 1934, **53**, 197; (*b*) *ibid.*, 1938, **57**, 620; (*c*) 1940, **59**, 955; (*d*) *Fette u. Seifen*, 1943, **50**, 505.
16. N. Ivanov, *Bull. Soc. chim.*, 1944, (v), **11**, 404.
17. T. P. Hilditch and J. P. Riley, *J. Soc. Chem. Ind.*, 1946, **65**, 74.
18. S. V. Puntambekar, *J. Indian Chem. Soc.*, 1942, **19**, 183.
19. A. Heiduschka and C. Weisemann, *J. pr. Chem.*, 1930, **124**, 240.
20. (*a*) H. M. Thompson, 1933, unpublished observation (see B. G. Gunde and T. P. Hilditch, *J. Soc. Chem. Ind.*, 1940, **59**, 47); (*b*) V. V. R. Subramanian and K. T. Achaya, *J. Sci. Food Agric.*, 1957, **8**, 657.
21. M. L. Meara, *Chem. and Ind.*, 1952, 667.
22. G. S. Jamieson and R. S. McKinney, *Oil and Soap*, 1933, **10**, 147.
23. T. Tutiya, *J. Chem. Soc. Japan*, 1941, **62**, 286.
24. (*a*) D. R. Dhingra and U. K. Shukla, *Proc. Ann. Conv. Oil Technol. Assocn., India*, 1947, **3**, 2; (*b*) D. R. and S. B. Dhingra, *Indian Soap J.*, 1953, **18**, 187.
25. G. S. Jamieson and S. I. Gertler, *Oil and Fat Ind.*, 1930, **7**, 371.
26. E. Delvaux, *Fette u. Seifen*, 1936, **43**, 183.
27. (Miss) E. E. Jones, 1931, unpublished observations.
28. V. A. Rusch and G. A. Ivanova, *Compt. rend. Acad. Sci. U.S.S.R.*, 1940, **26**, 259.
29. P. Cattaneo and G. K. de Sutton, *Rev. Brasil Quim.*, 1951, **32**, 381; *Anales Asoc. Quim. Argentina*, 1951, **39**, 145; 1954, **42**, 108.
30. R. Krzizan, *Chem. Rev. Fett-Harz-Ind.*, 1908, **15**, 7, 29.
31. (*a*) F. R. Earle, I. A. Wolff *et al. J. Amer. Oil Chem. Soc.*, 1959, **36**, 304; (*b*) A. M. and C. G. Nordstrom, *Suom. Kem. Tiedskr.*, 1950, **59**, 11.
32. (*a*) S. Sankar and M. M. Chakrabarty, *Science and Culture*, 1956, **22**, 336; (*b*) R. S. McKinney and G. S. Jamieson, *Oil and Soap*, 1937, **14**, 2.
33. R. S. McKinney and G. S. Jamieson, *Oil and Soap*, 1935, **12**, 146.
34. E. D. G. Frahm and D. R. Koolhaas, *Rec. trav. chim.*, 1939, **58**, 277.
35. (*a*) A. J. Henry and D. N. Grindley, *J. Soc. Chem. Ind.*, 1944, **63**, 188; (*b*) K. E. Bharucha and F. D. Gunstone, *J. Sci. Food Agric.*, 1956, **7**, 606; (*c*) F. D. Gunstone and P. J. Sykes, *ibid.*, 1961, **12**, 115.
36. D. N. Grindley, *J. Soc. Chem. Ind.*, 1948, **67**, 230.
37. C. Barker, H. C. Dunn and T. P. Hilditch, *J. Soc. Chem. Ind.*, 1950, **69**, 71.
38. (*a*) E. C. Cushing and V. O. Cirino, *J. Amer. Oil Chem. Soc.*, 1957, **34**, 611; (*b*) A. R. Riganti, P. Cattaneo and G. Karman, *Anales Asoc. Quim. Argentina*, 1947, **35**, 21.

39. (a) B. Flaschentrager and R. von Wolffersdorff, *Helv. Chim. Acta*, 1934, **17**, 1444; (b) Y. Koyama and T. Toyama, *J. Japan Oil Chem. Soc.*, 1956, **5**, 359.
40. D. C. and N. L. Dhar, and D. L. Shrivastava, *J. Sci. Indust. Res., India*, 1951, **10**, B, 88.
41. B. Tiutiunnikov, A. Sobol and V. Erschova, *Maslob. Shir. Delo*, 1935, **11**, 132.
42. A. N. Albertsma, *Paint Manuf.*, 1949, **19**, 135.
43. (a) G. S. Jamieson and W. G. Rose, *Oil and Soap*, 1943, **20**, 202; (b) M. Madrazo, G. and E. Sanchez Sierra, *Ciencia (Mex.)*, 1954, **14**, 208.
44. R. R. Munguia, R. Millares, N. F. Gurley and W. R. Lloyd, *J. Amer. Oil Chem. Soc.*, 1949, **26**, 432.
45. A. O. Cruz and A. P. West, *Philippine J. Sci.*, 1937, **61**, 437.
46. (a) A. R. S. Kartha and K. N. Menon, *Proc. Indian Acad. Sci.*, 1943, **18**, A, 160; (b) G. Popják and A. Tietz, *Biochem. J.*, 1954, **56**, 46.
47. (a) A. Steger and J. van Loon, *Fette u. Seifen*, 1942, **49**, 770; (b) A. Steger and J. van Loon, *Rec. trav. chim.*, 1935, **54**, 988.
48. (a) R. L. Alimchandani, R. C. Badami and M. C. T. Katti, *J. Indian Chem. Soc.*, 1949, **26**, 523; (b) M. C. Seth and C. M. Desai, *J. Indian Chem. Soc.*, 1954, **31**, 407.
49. L. Gurgel and F. Ramos, *Mem. Inst. Chim. Rio de Janeiro*, 1929, No. **2**, 21.
50. M. V. Pereira, *Anal. Asoc. Quim. Brazil*, 1944, **3**, 147.
51. (a) S. V. Puntambekar, *Proc. Indian Acad. Sci.*, 1952, A, **35**, 57; (b) R. C. Calderwood and F. D. Gunstone, *Chem. and Ind.*, 1953, 436; *J. Sci. Food Agric.*, 1954, **5**, 382; (c) S. C. and S. S. Gupta, and J. S. Aggarwal, *J. Amer. Oil Chem. Soc.*, 1954, **31**, 287; (d) M. M. Chakrabarty and S. Bhattacharyya, *Naturwiss.*, 1957, **44**, 91; (e) M. M. Chakrabarty and S. Sankar, *Science and Culture (India)*, 1956, **21**, 473.
52. T. P. Hilditch, *Chem. and Ind.*, 1952, 981.
53. (a) A. Callier, *Chim. et Ind.*, 1930, **24**, 930; (b) H. H. Hatt and A. Z. Szumer, *J. Sci. Food Agric.*, 1954, **5**, 534.
54. I. R. Gambhir and S. Dutt, *Indian Soap J.*, 1946, **11**, 169.
55. P. L. K. Fairchild, W. D. Raymond and R. G. W. Spickett, *Col. Plant and Animal Products*, 1955, **5**, 158.
56. (a) P. Panjutin and M. Rapoport, *Chem. Umschau*, 1930, **37**, 130; (b) H. P. Kaufmann and H. Bornhardt, *Fette u. Seifen*, 1939, **46**, 444.
57. (a) S. S. Gupta, T. P. Hilditch and J. P. Riley, *J. Sci. Food Agric.*, 1951, **2**, 245; (b) B. Sreenivasan, N. R. Kameth and J. G. Kane, *J. Amer. Oil Chem. Soc.*, 1956, **33**, 61.
58. A. Steger, J. van Loon and C. Smelt, *J. Soc. Chem. Ind.*, 1936, **55**, 41T.
59. (a) S. A. Narang and Sadgopal, *J. Amer. Oil Chem. Soc.*, 1958, **35**, 68; (b) V. C. Batterson and W. M. Potts, *J. Amer. Oil Chem. Soc.*, 1951, **28**, 87.
60. D. P. Hanks and W. M. Potts, *J. Amer. Oil Chem. Soc.*, 1951, **28**, 292.
61. F. D. Gunstone, T. P. Hilditch and J. P. Riley, *J. Soc. Chem. Ind.*, 1947, **66**, 293.
62. T. P. Hilditch and A. J. Seavell, *J. Oil Col. Chem. Assocn.*, 1950, **33**, 24.
63. (a) D. K. Chowdhury, M. M. Chakrabarty and B. K. Mukherji, *Science and Culture (India)*, 1953, **19**, 163; *J. Amer. Oil Chem. Soc.*, 1955, **32**, 384; (b) W. F. Baughman, G. S. Jamieson and D. H. Brauns, *J. Amer. Chem. Soc.*, 1920, **42**, 2398; (c) S. C. Seth and J. S. Aggarwal, *J. Sci. Indust. Res. (India)*, 1954, **13B**, 853; (d) R. D. Tewari and P. C. Gupta, *J. Proc. Oil Tech. Assn., India*, 1954, **10**, 25; (e) D. K. Chowdhury and R. Bagchi, *Naturwiss.*, 1956, **43**, 350.
64. (a) D. R. Dhingra and P. Narain, *J. Indian Chem. Soc.*, 1945, **22**, 123; (b) S. A. Ahmad and D. R. Dhingra, *ibid.*, 1945, **22**, 237; (c) D. R. Dhingra and A. K. Biswas, *ibid.*, 1945, **22**, 119; (d) S. R. Agarwal, D. R. Dhingra and G. N. Gupta, *Indian Soap J.*, 1959, **24**, 257.
65. (a) P. Soni, S. C. Gupta and J. S. Aggarwal, *J. Sci. Indust. Res., India*, 1949, **8**, B, 210; (b) M. M. Chakrabarty, D. K. Chowdhury and B. K. Mukherji, *Naturwiss.*, 1955, **42**, 344.
66. (a) A. M. Abu-Nasr and W. M. Potts, *J. Amer. Oil Chem. Soc.*, 1953, **30**, 118; (b) C. M. Tsao and W. M. Potts, *ibid.*, 1952, **29**, 444; (c) A. Sengupta and M. M. Chakrabarty, *Science and Culture*, 1957, **22**, 581; *J. Sci. Food Agric.*, 1964, **15**, 74.

67. W. C. Ault, M. L. Swain and L. C. Curtis, *J. Amer. Oil Chem. Soc.*, 1947, **24**, 289.
68. H. S. Shahani, F. G. Dollear, K. S. Markley and J. R. Quimby, *J. Amer. Oil Chem. Soc.*, 1951, **28**, 90.
69. W. F. Baughman and G. S. Jamieson, *J. Amer. Chem. Soc.*, 1920, **42**, 152.
70. F. B. Power and A. H. Salway, *J. Amer. Chem. Soc.*, 1910, **32**, 346.
71. J. L. Riebsomer and G. A. Nesty, *J. Amer. Chem. Soc.*, 1934, **56**, 1784.
72. H. P. Kaufmann and H. Fiedler, *Fette u. Seifen*, 1939, **46**, 125.
73. J. Pieraerts, *Bull Soc. Pharmacol.*, 1917, **24**, 204.
74. G. Rankov and A. Popov, *Fette u. Seifen*, 1941, **48**, 489.
75. A. J. Nolte and H. W. von Loesecke, *J. Amer. Chem. Soc.*, 1939, **61**, 889.
76. M. Carrière and A. Coulier, *Compt. rend. Fac. Sci. Marseille*, 1947, **1**, 83.
77. D. N. Grindley, *J. Sci. Food Agric.*, 1950, **1**, 152.
78. (a) J. P. Varma and J. S. Aggarwal, *J. Indian Chem. Soc.*, 1956, **33**, 357; (b) M. M. Chakrabarty, S. Bhattacharyya, M. J. Desai and S. A. Patel, *Naturwiss.*, 1956, **43**, 523; (c) *idem, J. Indian Chem. Soc.*, 1958, **35**, 67.
79. T. P. Hilditch, M. L. Meara and W. H. Pedelty, *J. Soc. Chem. Ind.*, 1939, **58**, 26.
80. R. R. Aggarwal and S. Dutt, *Proc. Acad. Sci. Agra & Oudh*, 1934–35, **5**, 227.
81. J. Pieraerts and F. de Winter, *Ann. Mus. Colon. Marseille*, 1928, **36**, No. 6, 5.
82. J. W. Airan and S. V. Shah, *J. Univ. Bombay*, 1942, **11**, A, (iii), 105.
83. W. C. Smit and J. van Loon, *Fettchem. Umschau*, 1936, **43**, 71.
84. T. P. Hilditch and M. L. Meara, *J. Soc. Chem. Ind.*, 1944, **63**, 112.
85. (a) P. Soni and J. S. Aggarwal, *J. Sci. Indust. Res., India*, 1949, **8**, B, 150; (b) H. H. Mathur and J. S. Aggarwal, *ibid.*, 1953, **12**, B, 60.
86. Y. Toyama and T. Tsuchiya, *J. Soc. Chem. Ind. Japan*, 1935, **38**, 185B.
87. H. P. Kaufmann, J. Baltes and H. Büter, *Ber.*, 1937, **70** [B], 2535.
88. J. Sack, *Pharm. Weekblad*, 1903, **40**, 313.

III. Seed Fats in which Palmitic, as well as Oleic and Linoleic, Acid is a Major Component

Major component acids: PALMITIC, OLEIC, LINOLEIC (in a few cases stearic).
Minor component acids: (Myristic), stearic, (arachidic, lignoceric), linolenic.
(See Table 62, p. 268.)

There is a very large number of oils whose component fatty acids include oleic and linoleic in much the same amounts as those in Table 60, but in which palmitic acid is also prominent. No sharp line of demarcation falls, of course, between oils of "minor" and "major" palmitic acid content; for the present purpose, as explained in Chapter I (p. 7), an acid is deemed to be a "major component" of a fat when it forms about 10 per cent. or more of the whole of the mixed fatty acids. Families with seed fats in which palmitic acid, as well as oleic and linoleic acids, is an important constituent include many herbaceous and shrubby types, and these have a definite tendency to be more regularly natives of sub-tropical and tropical regions than those falling within the categories of Tables 59 and 60; recorded detailed analyses for seed fat component acids of this type are collected in Table 62 (pp. 268–276). Another important group of seed fats belonging to this class is that of the Gramineæ, which it is convenient, however, to discuss separately (Table 63, p. 282); the Gramineæ, of course, are represented by many genera indigenous to temperate, as well as warmer, climes.

In the seed fats falling in Table 62, oleic and linoleic acids almost always still form 70 per cent. or more of the mixed fatty acids, an amount which is not greatly inferior to that of the oils in Tables 59 and 60; but the balance is made up to a marked extent by palmitic acid. Of the unsaturated acids, again, sometimes linoleic and sometimes oleic is the more in evidence; in quite a number of instances, including the abundant and technically valuable cottonseed oil, linoleic acid amounts to about 50 per cent. of the total acids, and such oils are, of course, characteristic members of the "semi-drying" class. It is in relatively few instances that the linoleic acid content falls much below 25–30 per cent., the oleic acid figure then rising proportionately to 50–60 per cent. or even higher.

The palmitic acid content of this group of seed fats seems to fall into two or three classes, somewhat as follows:

(i) In the families belonging to the Malvales (Malvaceæ, Tiliaceæ, Bombacaceæ), it is frequently in the region of about 20 per cent. of the total acids, and sometimes rises to considerably more than this figure. It may be more than a coincidence that another seed fat belonging to the Malvales (that of *Theobroma cacao*, Sterculiaceæ) which has been studied in detail contains a similar proportion of palmitic acid (23 per cent.), although in this case stearic acid is present in still larger quantities (*cf.* Table 68, p. 325).

(ii) In contrast to this resemblance between the seed fats of many of the Malvales, it must be pointed out that other seed fats of similar high palmitic content belong to a variety of plant orders and, equally, that families belonging to one and the same order yield seed fats whose major components are fre-

264

quently quite different. The component acids of seed fats, in other words, are usually strongly specific with respect to the plant families, but not always in regard to the wider groups (orders) into which the families have been collected on botanical grounds.

Other families, in addition to those mentioned, in which palmitic acid usually forms about 20 per cent. or more of the seed fats, appear to include Menispermaceæ (Table 68 and Magnoliaceæ (Ranales), Rutaceæ and Burseraceæ (Table 68) (Geraniales), Caryocaraceæ (Parietales), Combretaceæ and perhaps Lecythidaceæ (Myrtifloræ), Rubiaceæ and Caprifoliaceæ (Rubiales) (Table 62). In practically all these instances the amount of any other saturated acid present is of quite a minor order. The palmitic acid content (48 per cent.) of piqui-a kernel fat (*Caryocar villosum*) is one of the highest yet observed in a seed fat.

(iii) Finally, in some of the families (Anacardiaceæ, Apocynaceæ, Anonaceæ, Martyniaceæ), the palmitic acid content of seed fats is somewhat variable and, in several of the examples, stearic acid is recorded in amounts approaching or even exceeding 10 per cent. of the total acids. Such seed fats are, more strictly speaking, intermediate between the class now under discussion and that (Table 68) in which, in a few tropical families, stearic acid becomes a prominent feature of the seed fat. It is rather obvious that decrease in linoleic acid does not necessarily accompany the appearance of stearic acid in such cases; indeed, although in some cases (e.g. cashew and shinia nuts) the proportion of linoleic acid is very low, in others it forms over half of the total acids in spite of the presence of 11 per cent. of stearic and 15 per cent. of palmitic acid. It is accordingly, at present, doubtful whether any correlation can be detected between the presence of stearic acid, and low proportions of linoleic acid, in these seed fats.

The seed fats in Table 62 include many which have not yet found technical applications, some which have very important uses (notably cottonseed oil), and some others which might well serve for similar purposes to cottonseed oil if they were grown on the necessary scale.

Cottonseed oil is on the whole remarkable for its constancy of composition, oils from different varieties of *Gossypium* and from different regions often showing extremely small variations in the amounts of their component acids, of which palmitic acid forms about 20–22 per cent. Stansbury and Hoffpauir[153a] have however shown that in specific environmental conditions the same variety of the cotton plant may yield seed oils with a fairly wide range of composition, the extreme variations which they record being saturated 21–29, oleic 22–36, and linoleic 56–34 per cent. (wt.). Similarly, in cottonseed oils from 39 commercial crops grown in different provinces of Argentina, Cattaneo *et al.*[153b] observed ranges of fatty acids, palmitic 20–27, stearic 1–4, oleic 16–25, and linoleic 53–43 per cent. (wt.); two typical analyses are included in Table 62 (p. 270). The seed oils of several mallow (*Hibiscus*) species, which seem to be attracting attention as suitable for extended cultivation, are practically identical in composition with cottonseed oil, especially okra seed (*H. esculentus*), and kenaph seed (*H. cannabinus*).

There are species in other families, members of which are grown for other purposes, with seeds which contain fats sufficiently closely resembling cotton-seed oil to make them of technical interest. The most notable are the seed oils of *Citrus* species (orange, grape fruit, lime, etc.): these closely resemble cottonseed oils except that they contain small proportions of linolenic acid in addition to 35–40 per cent. of linoleic acid. They are particularly easy to extract in a clean condition and, where citrus fruits are processed in large quantities (as in Florida and elsewhere), a considerable tonnage of oil could be recovered from the seeds.

Similarly, jute seed contains oil not very dissimilar in composition from that of cottonseed oil.

Unusual acids present in Malvaceæ seed fats and Strophanthus *seed fats* (*Apocynaceæ*). The unusual appearance of major amounts of vernolic acid, 12,13-epoxy-octadec-9-enoic acid in the seeds of *Vernonia anthelmintica* in the Compositæ, and of a cyclopropene (sterculic) acid,

$$CH_3.[CH_2]_7.C=C.[CH_2]_7.COOH,$$
$$CH_2$$

in seeds of *Sterculia fœtida* (Sterculiaceæ), is paralleled by four instances in the seed fats included in Table 62.

(i) "*Malvalic*" *acid* occurs in small proportions amongst the component acids of a number of species in the Malvaceæ,[154a] notably in those of *Gossypium* and *Hibiscus*. It is a cyclopropene acid containing one carbon atom less than sterculic acid, its structure being[154c,d]

$$CH_3.[CH_2]_7.C=C.[CH_2]_6.COOH.$$
$$CH_2$$

The cyclopropene group in malvalic and sterculic acids is responsible for the characteristic colour of the "Halphen" test.

Wilson *et al.*[154b,c] state (1961) that *Hibiscus syriacus* seed fat contains 16·3 per cent. of malvalic with 3 per cent. of sterculic acid, and that *Lavatera trimestris* seed fat contains 7·7 per cent. of malvalic and 0·6 per cent. of ster-culic acid; Shenstone and Vickery[154a] (1961) give figures of 0·7–1·5 per cent. of malvalic and 0·3–0·5 per cent. of sterculic acid in cottonseed oil; Cornelius and Shone[154f] (1963) found malvalic (5 per cent.) and sterculic (22 per cent.) acids in *Bombax oleagineum* seed fat, and de Bruin *et al.*[154g] (1963) observed 26·5 per cent. of cyclopropenoid acids in *Pachira aquatica* seed fat.

(ii) *Epoxy-acids*. Wilson *et al.*[154c] also refer to the presence of 1–3 per cent. of epoxy-acids in the seed fats of *Hibiscus syriacus* and of *Lavatera*, thus confirming the observations of Hopkins and Chisholm[154e] that seed fats of several species of *Hibiscus*, *Malva* and *Lavatera* include 1·5–3 per cent. of 12,13-epoxy octadec-9-enoic (vernolic) acid in their component acids. The latter authors state that other Malvaceæ seed oils (*Althea, Abutilon, Gossypium hirsutum*) appeared not to contain any epoxy-acid.

(iii) 9-*Hydroxy*-cis-*octadec*-12-*enoic acid*. Whilst most seed fats from the Apocynaceæ family apparently contain simple mixtures of oleic, linoleic, palmitic and stearic acids in their glycerides, those of the genus *Strophanthus* include with these familiar components about 6–14 per cent. of this hydroxy-octadecenoic acid (which is isomeric[155a] with the ricinoleic acid of castor oil) together with traces of an optically active 9,10-dihydroxystearic acid. Gunstone and co-workers[155b] give the following compositions for a range of seed fats from Strophanthus species:

	SATD.	OLEIC	LINOLEIC	9-HYDROXY-OCTADEC-*cis*-12-ENOIC
S. courmentii	21	39	30	10
S. sarmentosus				
Forest form	24	44	26	6
Savannah form	25	38	30	7
S. hispidus	21	35	29	15
S. nicholsonii	25	29	37	9
S. eminii	27	27	32	14
S. gratus	22	36	32	10
S. thollonii	25	37	28	10
S. intermedius	24	38	28	10
S. congœnsis	24	39	27	10
S. welwitschii	24	39	27	10
S. verrucosus	24	45	26	6
S. ambœnsis	24	43	24	9
S. schuchardtii	24	43	21	12

(iv) *Conjugated acids in some seed fats* (*Bignoniaceæ*). Hopkins and Chisholm[155c] (1962) have confirmed the observation of Markman and Bodnya[155e] (1957) that *Catalpa ovata* seed fat contains over 30 per cent. of a conjugated triene acid, the latter being, however, octadec-*trans*-9-*trans*-11-*cis*-13-trienoic acid, a hitherto unobserved isomer of elæostearic acid.

Hopkins and Chisholm[155d] (1962) have also found that the seed fat of *Chilopsis linearis* (desert willow) contains the following unusual conjugated unsaturated acids:

	Per cent. (approx.)
Octadeca-*trans*-10-*trans*-12-dienoic	12
Octadeca-*trans*-9-*trans*-12-dienoic	15
Octadeca-*trans*-9-*trans*-11-*cis*-13-octadecatrianoic	25

with 25 per cent. of linoleic acid and 5 per cent. of saturated acids in the total seed fatty acids.

TABLE 62. *Component Acids of Seed Fats*

Major component acids: PALMITIC, OLEIC, LINOLEIC (in a few cases, stearic).
Minor component acids: (Myristic), stearic, (arachidic, lignoceric), linolenic.

			COMPONENT FATTY ACIDS PER CENT. (WT.)					
		HABITAT	PALMITIC	STEARIC	OLEIC	LINOLEIC	METHOD	OBSERVERS
BERBERIDACEÆ								
Akebia lobata	Akebi seed	Japan	23	2	53	22	L	Komori and Ueno[1]
MAGNOLIACEÆ								
Illicium verum	Chinese star aniseed	China	—	7·9	63·3	24·4 (a)	F	Airan and Shah[2]
" religiosum	Japanese star aniseed	Japan	ca. 23·5	ca. 2·5	ca. 63·5	ca. 10·5	L,H	Bulir[3]
Michella champaca	—	E. Indies	ca. 30	←— 9 —→	ca. 70	—	?	Sack[4]
Schizandra chinensis	—	Russia	←— 9 —→		29–35	62–56	?	Balandin[5]
ANONACEÆ								
Anona muricata	Guanabana	Puerto Rico	17·6	6·0	63·5	12·6 (b)	F	Asenjo and Goyco[6]
" reticulata	Bull's heart	India	16·6	6·7	49·6	22·3 (c)	L,F	Naidu and Achaya[7]
" squamosa	Sirikaya	Tropics	14·8	10·7	55·4	18·2 (d)	F,H	Ghanekar and Ayyar[8]
Asimina triloba	Sugar apple	India	12·5	8·9	54·2	20·0 (e)	L,F	Naidu and Achaya[7]
Monodora myristica	Papaw seed	U.S.A.	2·5	2·0	65·3	28·6 (f)	F	Riebsomer et al.[9a]
Xylopia aethiopica	—	Tropics	3·8	5·3	37·2	49·7 (u'')	GLC	Mackie and Mieras[9b]
—	—	Tropics	38·6	9·1	41·6	3·2 (v'')	GLC	Mackie and Mieras[9b]
RUTACEÆ								
Ægle marmelos	Bael seed	Ceylon	16·6	8·8	30	39 (g)	F,T	Child[10]
Citrus aurantium	Orange seed	S. California	20·7	4·7	36·5	36·5 (h)	F,T	Van Atta and Dietrich[11a]
" "	—	India	14·2	19·0	8·0	54·2 (w'')	F	Dhingra et al.[11b]
" " dulcis	Sweet orange seed	Jamaica	23·8	8·3	24·8	37·1 (i)	C,F,S	Dunn et al.[12a]
" " "	" " "	Hyderabad	19·0	8·0	32·7	32·1 (x'')	F	Achaya et al.[12b]
" " "	" " "	Ceylon	21·8	6·4	27·4	34·2 (y'')	F	Weerakoon[12d]
" decumana	Grape fruit seed	Sub-tropics	20·2	7·5	20·7	51·4 (j)	F	Jamieson et al.[13]
" " var. Foster	" " "	Trinidad	28·9	2·1	25·1	36·6 (k)	C,F,S	Dunn et al.[12a]
" " var. Marsh	" " "	Trinidad	27·5	2·9	21·1	39·3 (l)	C,F,S	Dunn et al.[12a]
" "	Indian shaddock	India	20·7	15·3	55·4	8·1 (n)	?	Rao et al.[14]
" limetta	—	Trinidad	26·1	9·6	11·1	39·3 (n)	C,F,S	Dunn et al.[12a]
Fagara coco	Lime seed	Brazil	15·5	28	45·0	23·3 (o)	C,F,S	Cattaneo et al.[15a]

Species	Common name	Country						Type	Reference
Ptelea trifoliata	Water ash	U.S.A.		← 1 →	22	42	(z″)	S	Earle et al.[15b]
Skimmia japonica		U.S.A.		← 8 →	42	20	(A)	S	Earle et al.[15b]
ZYGOPHYLLACEÆ									
Balanites ægyptiaca	Lalob seed	Sudan		← 25·4 →	31·2	43·2	(p)	S	Hussein et al.[16]
" "	"	U.S.A.		32	23	37		S	Earle et al.[15b]
ANACARDIACEÆ									
Anacardium occidentale	Cashew nut	Tropics	11·3	6·4	74·1	7·7		F	Patel et al.[17]
" "	"	Tropics	5·8	4·1	68·2	21·7	(q)		Ichaporia[18]
Anthrocaryon nannani	Gonyo almond	Congo	10·5	13·5	45·5	24·5	(r)	L,H	Pieraerts and Ipatiev[19]
Buchanania latifolia	—	India	8·1	28·9	57·4	5·5	(s)	F	Gunde and Srivastava[20]
Mangifera indica	Mango	India	34·0	8·8	49·8	—	(t)	F	Pathak et al.[21]
" "	"	Jamaica	42·5	4·4	44·7	5·4	(u)	C,F,S	Dunn and Hilditch[22]
" "	"	India	31·2	11·2	43·8	4·1	(v)	GLC	Dhingra et al.[23]
" "	"	Tropics	47·8	6·5	38·2	4·4	(B)	?	Mackie and Mieras[9b]
Pistacia lentiscus	Shinia nut	Levant	13	27	53	7		L,H	Vodret[24]
" *vera*	Pistachio nut	Asia		19	60	21		F	Beythien[25]
" "	"	India	1·6	8·2	69·6	20·0	(w)	S	Dhingra and Hilditch[26]
Rhus radicans	Poison sumach	U.S.A.		← 62 →	10	24		S	Earle et al.[15d]
CAPPARIDACEÆ									
Capparis aphylla		India	7·7	21·1	57·2	11·4		F,S	Gupta et al.[29a]
" *rothii*		Sudan	24·5	15·5	38·0	22·0		T	Grindley[27a]
" *spinosa*		Russia	21·3	← 7–9 →	42–46	51–45		L	Zambrami et al.[28a]
" *tomentosa*		Sudan	9·5	23·4	29·2	26·1		T	Grindley[27b]
Cleome pentaphylla	Spider flower	India		9·6	32·0	39·0	(B′)	F	Misra and Dutt[28b]
" *pungens*	"	U.S.A.		← 19 →	32	41	(C)	S	Earle et al.[15c]
" *serrulata*	"	U.S.A.		← 8 →	21	38	(D)	S	Earle et al.[15b]
" *spinosa*	"	U.S.A.		← 16 →	36	40	(E)	S	Earle et al.[15b]
Courbonia virgata		Sudan	38·9	12·6	27·0	21·5		T	Grindley[27b]
Gynandropsis pentaphylla		India	8·1	18·4	15·4	53·8	(H)	F	Gupta and Chakrabarty[29a]
Isomeris arborea		U.S.A.		← 15 →	44	35	(F)	S	Earle et al.[15b]
Polanisia trachysperma	Clammyweed	U.S.A.		← 10 →	19	65	(G)	S	Earle et al.[15b]
" *viscosa*	"	U.S.A.		← 8 →	32	55		S	Earle et al.[15b]

TABLE 62. Component Acids of Seed Fats—continued

| | HABITAT | COMPONENT FATTY ACIDS PER CENT. (WT.) | | | | METHOD | OBSERVERS |
		PALMITIC	STEARIC	OLEIC	LINOLEIC		
HERNANDIACEÆ							
Hernandia ovigera —	Japan	8.7	7.1	39.6	44.6	?	Hatta[29b]
TILIACEÆ							
Corchorus capsularis	Jute seed	Tropics	←20→	37	43	L, H	Sen[30]
,, *olitorius* ,, ,,	India	12.0	4.6	28.7	41.3 (x)	C, F, S	Meara and Sen[31]
,, ,, ,, ,,	India	16.1	4.1	12.8	61.5 (y)	F, S	Chakravarti and Sen[32]
,, ,, ,, ,,	India	16.9	3.7	9.1	62.5 (z)	C, F, S	Meara and Sen[31]
Tilia parvifolia ,,	Lime seed	Temperate zones	←13→	29	58	B, T	Kaufmann and Fiedler[33]
MALVACEÆ*							
Abutilon theophrasti	Buttonweed	U.S.A.	12.8	0.9	14.8	60.9 (a')	F	Carmody et al.[34a]
,, ,,	Velvetweed	U.S.A.	←16→	16	63 (l')	S	Earle et al.[15b]
Althea officinalis	Mallow	Europe	←9.7→	30.8	52.9 (l')	?	Tropp[34b]
Gossypium arboreum	Cottonseed	India	19.9	1.3	29.6	45.3 (b')	F	Hilditch and Jones[35a]
,, *barbadense* ,,	U.S.A. Sea Is.	20.2	2.0	35.2	41.7 (c')	F, H	Jamieson and Baughman[36a]
,, *herbaceum*, etc. ,,	India	19.6	2.7	24.6	50.4 (d')	F	Hilditch and Rhead[35b]
,, ,, ,,	India	23.4	1.1	22.9	47.8 (e')	F	Hilditch and Maddison[35c]
,, ,, ,, (Indian seed)	Hyderabad	17.2	0.9	44.2	33.9 (p'')	L, F	Harwalkar et al.[37a]
,, ,, ,, (Indian seed)	Hyderabad	17.1	2.0	41.4	36.9 (q'')	L, F	Harwalkar et al.[37a]
,, ,, ,, (U.S. seed)	Hyderabad	19.5	0.9	34.8	41.7 (r'')	L, F	Harwalkar et al.[37a]
,, *hirsutum* ,,	U.S.A. Upland	21.9	1.9	30.7	44.9 (f')	F	Jamieson and Baughman[36b]
,, ,, ,,	U.S.A.	←27→	19	54	T	Mitchell et al.[37b]
,, ,, ,,	U.S.A.	←27→	18	55	S	Mitchell et al.[37b]
,, ,, ,,	U.S.A.	←26→	22	47	S	Earle et al.[15c]
,, ,, ,,	Azerbaijan	←21.6→	27.0	47.0	T	Artamonov[37c]
,, ,, ,,	Central Asia	←25.2→	22.6	47.6	T	Artamonov[37c]
,, ,, ,,	Argentina	24.8	2.0	19.6	50.9	L, F	Cattaneo et al.[37d]
,, ,, ,,	Argentina	21.6	2.4	23.7	47.4	L, F	Cattaneo et al.[37d]

270

Species	Material	Source							Reference
Hibiscus cannabinus	Kenaph seed	Egypt, India	15.8	6.8	51.0	26.4	(J)	?	Bauman[38a]
" "	"	U.S.A.	19	23	28	43	(K)	S	Earle et al,[15b]
" "	"	Cuba	15	2	30	41		F,S	Hopkins and Chisholm[38b]
" "	"	S. America		6	48	25		F	Ramos[38d]
" "	"	India	26.9	23.6	32.5	38.5	(K')	F,H	Mehta et al,[38e]
" *esculentus*	Okra seed	Tropics	23.0	2.7	43.7	26.6	(g')	L,F	Jamieson and Baughman[36c]
" "	"	India		5.0	49.2	22.1	(h')	F,S	Singh and Dutt[39]
" "	"	U.S.A.		33.5	27.2	39.3		F,S	Clopton et al,[40]
" "	"	U.S.A.	23.8	31.1	29.0	39.9		C,F,S	Hussein and Dollear[41]
" "	"	Sudan		7.4	27.1	41.7		F,T	Crossley and Hilditch[42]
" "	"	Canada	29	2	23	39			Chisholm and Hopkins[38c]
" " *moschata × H. coccineus.*	Rose mallow			16.5	42.5	41	(L)		Barkenbus and Thorn[43a]
" *moscheutos*	"	U.S.A.		13	36	46	(M)	S	Earle et al,[15b]
" *mutabilis*	"	Japan		15.0	25.4	59.4	(N)	S	Kato[43b]
" *syriacus*	Rose of Sharon	U.S.A.		11	42	43		S	Earle et al,[15b]
Lavatera trimestris	Tree mallow	U.S.A.		19	42	30		S	Earle et al,[15b]
Malva arborea	Mallow	Europe		8.0	39.2	50.0	(N')	?	Tropp[34b]
" *parviflora*		U.S.A.		13	29	53		S	Earle et al,[15d]
BOMBACACEÆ*									
Adansonia digitata	Baobab kernel	Rhodesia	34.0	6.2	36.7	21.7	(Y)	RPC	Cmelik[44a]
" *grandidieri*	"	Madagascar, India	37	2	42	10	(i')	L(?)	Thomas and Boiry[44b]
Bombax malabaricum	Kapok seed	India	23.6	—	64.9	7.5	(j')	F	Rao et al,[45]
" *oleagineum*	"	N. Rhodesia	58	21	—	8		GLC*	Cornelius and Shone[15e]
Ceiba acuminata	"	U.S.A.		4	51	23		S	Earle et al,[15c]
" *pentandra*, syn. *Eriodendron anfractuosum*	"	Tropics	26	—	44.5	29.5		L	Trevithick and Dickhart[46]
"	"	Tropics	16.1	2.3	50.6	29.7	(k')	F	Cruz and West[47a]
"	"	Java	10.5	8.5	46.1	33.6	(l')	F	Jamieson and McKinney[48]
Chorisia insignis	"	Japan		16.5	51	32.5		L	Mehlenbacher[49]
Pachira aquatica	Pachira kernel	Argentine	17.9	0.8	31.5	42.0	(m')	L,F	Cattaneo et al,[50]
" (syn. *Bombax sessile*)	"	Congo	46	—	43	11		T	Pieraerts et al,[51a]
"	"	Sudan		50.7	40.8	8.5		L	Grindley[51b]
"	"	S. America	56	3	7.5	5		GLC*	De Bruin et al,[51c]

Malvaceæ* and Bombacaceæ,* *cf.* also p.266 (presence of malvalic and sterculic acids)

271

TABLE 62. *Component Acids of Seed Fats—continued*

		HABITAT	COMPONENT FATTY ACIDS PER CENT. (WT.)					METHOD	OBSERVERS
			PALMITIC	STEARIC	OLEIC	LINOLEIC			
CARYOCARACEÆ									
Caryocar villosum	Piqui-a	Brazil	48·4	0·9	46·0	3·3 (n')		F	Hilditch and Rigg[52]
CARICACEÆ									
Carica papaya	Melon tree seed	S. America	12·0	5·5	80·0	2·0 (o')		F	von Loesecke and Nolte[53]
" "	Papaya seed	Florida	13·0	1·8	80·6	— (p')		H	Asenjo and Goyco[54a]
" "	" "	India	17·2	3·6	77·3	0·4 (O)		F	Achaya et al,[12c]
LECYTHIDACEÆ									
Bertholletia excelsa, nobilis	Brazil nut	Brazil	14·3	2·7	58·3	22·8 (q')		F, H	Schuette et al,[55a]
" " "	" "	Brazil	15·4	6·2	48·0	29·8 (r')		F, H	Schuette et al,[55b]
{ Solvent-extracted	" "	Brazil	16·2	10·4	31·0	41·6 (P)		GLC	} Elias and Brescani[55c]
Expressed		Brazil	13·8	10·3	30·5	44·9 (Q)		GLC	
COMBRETACEÆ									
Anogeissus schimperi	—	Tropics	1·4	6·8	15·4	38·6 (R)		GLC	Mackie and Mieras[9b]
Quisqualis indica	—	China	29·2	9·1	49·2	10·0 (s')		F, T	Kaufmann and King[56]
Terminalia belerica	—	India	22·4	15·7	28·1	33·0 (t')		F	Kartha et al,[57]
" "	—	India	11·3	15·5	43·7	29·5		F	Singh[58]
" *catappa*	Talisay seed	E. Indies	29·0	4·1	41·7	23·4 (u')		F	Cruz and West[47b]
" "	" "	W. Africa	34·0	9·7	27·3	28·6 (v')		F	Ichaporia[18]
" "	Tropical almond	Philippines	38·9	4·0	37·3	19·1 (w')		F	Asenjo and Goyco[54b]
" *chebula*	Myrobalan	India	←—— 18 ——→		59	23		L	Sunthankar and Jatkar[59]
" *kaernbachii*	Okari nut	Fiji	39·6	8·2	36·6	15·6		F	Clark et al,[60]
APOCYNACEÆ									
Apocynum carnabinum	Dogbane	U.S.A.	←—— 2 ——→		30	53 (S)		S	Earle et al,[15b]
Cerbera odollam	—	India, Pacific	30·1	9·9	42·6	16·5 (x')		F, H	Ghanekar and Ayyar[61a]
" "	—	India	32·0	10·8	38·8	18·4		F	Subbaram[61c]
Holarrhena antidysenterica	—	Tropical Asia	5·6	6·8	21·0	54·7 (y')		F, H	Ghanekar and Ayyar[61b]
Nerium thevetifolium	—	India	23	10	57	10		F	Kartha[62]
Strophanthus courmontii	—	Nigeria	13·4	4·5	38·6	30·4 (z')		C, F, S	Gunstone[63a]
" *hispidus*	—	Africa	15	7	62	16		L, H	Matthes and Rath[64]

272

Species	Common name	Source					Method	Reference
" sarmentosus	(forest form)	Nigeria	11·9	7·0	35·5	30·0 (a'')	C, F, S	Gunstone[63a]
" sarmentosus	(savannah form)	Nigeria	12·2	8·1	43·5	26·4 (b'')	C, F, S	Gunstone[63a]
Strophanthus species	—	Nigeria	11·9	9·2	38·3	29·8 (c'')	C, F, S	Gunstone[63b]
		Various	←21-27→		27-44	21-37		Gunstone and Morris[63c] (See text, p. 267)
(Also ca. 10 per cent of 9-hydroxy-octadec-12-enoic)								
Thevetia neriifolia	—	India	17·1	11·8	64·4	6·3 (d'')	F, H	Bhattacharya and Ayyar[65]
" thevetioides	—	U.S.A.	←17→		64	14	S	Earle et al.[15b]
" sp.	—	U.S.A.	←25→		54	17	S	Earle et al.[15b]
Wrightia tinctoria	—	India	8·9	17·8	34·3	32·9 (e'')	F	Parihar and Dutt[66]
AMARANTACEÆ								
Amaranthus gangeticus	—	S. India	20·8	2·2	43·7	27·3	?	Chidabaram and Iyer[67a]
" polygamus	—	India	←6·3→		56·2	37·5	T	Chowdhury and Bagchi[67b]
" retroflexus	Pigweed	India	8·5	7·5	35·0	43·0 (f'')	?	Kapoor and Dutt[68]
		Oregon, U.S.A.	18·9	1·9	51·3	27·9		Christensen and Miller[69]
Celosia argentea	—	Tropics	45·7	23·3	28·1	— (T)	GLC	Mackie and Mieras[9b]
MARTYNIACEÆ								
Martynia diandra	Unicorn seed	India	9·1	12·7	40·3	36·4 (g'')	F	Tayal and Dutt[70]
Proboscidea althæfolia	Devil's claw	India	10·5	8·5	74·5	5·5	F	Rege et al.[71]
		U.S.A.	←4→		55	36	S	Earle et al.[15a]
ACANTHACEÆ								
Blepharis edulis	—	India	←12→		73·5	14·5	L	Pendse and Lal[72]
Hygrophyla spinosa	—	India	18·3	5·3	←75·0→		F	Phalnikar et al.[73]
		India	5·4	11·9	9·8	71·5 (i'')	F	Godbole et al.[74]
BIGNONIACEÆ								
Catalpa bignonioides	—	Russia	←4·4→		10·1	38·8	S	Markman and Bodnya[75a]
(Also linolenic 16, conjugated trienoic 31 per cent.)								
		U.S.A.	←18→		14	36	S	Earle et al.[15b]
(Also conjugated trienoic 28 per cent.)								
" ovata	—	China	*(Major component octadeca-trans-9-trans-11-cis-trienoic acid)*				S	Hopkins and Chisholm[75b]
Chilopsis linearis	—	U.S.A.	←21→		14	28	S	Earle et al.[15b]
(Also conjugated dienoic 12, conjugated trienoic 21 per cent.)								
Crescentia alata	—	S. America	←16·6→		61·8	15·0 (U)	S	van Séveren[75c]
" cujete	Calabash seed	Honduras	←19·6→		58·8	19·3 (j'')	B, S	Smith and Dollear[75d]
Tabibenia palmeri	—	U.S.A.	←38→		39	18	S	Earle et al.[15a]

273

TABLE 62. Component Acids of Seed Fats—continued

Species	Name	HABITAT	COMPONENT FATTY ACIDS PER CENT. (WT.)				METHOD	OBSERVERS
			PALMITIC	STEARIC	OLEIC	LINOLEIC		
RUBIACEÆ								
Cinchona sp.	Cinchona	U.S.A.	28·2	12·7	43	42	S	Earle et al.[15b]
Coffea arabica	Coffee seed	Tropical Asia, America, etc.	←10→		17·3	35·8 (k'')	F	Schuette et al.[76a]
" "	"		24·3	1·1	20·8	38·7 (l'')	F	Heiduschka and Kühn[77]
" "	"	Brazil	←44→		31	25	B	Bauer and Neu[78a]
" "	"		←36→		35	39	B	Bauer and Neu[78b]
" "	"	America	31·8	7·0	22·9	32·1 (s'')	F	Bengis and Anderson[79a]
" "	"	America	32·0	7·6	8·2	46·3 (t'')	C, F, S	Khan and Brown[79b]
" "	"	S. India	28·8	4·5	18·9	44·0 (V)	F	Achaya et al.[12b]
" robusta	"	S. India	23·3	6·5	17·4	48·0 (W)	F	Achaya et al.[12b]
Gardenia jasminoides	Cape jasmine	U.S.A.	←11→		35	50	S	Earle et al.[15b]
Vanguera spinosa	—	India	18·8	9·0	32·5	39·7	L, F	Nadkarni et al.[80]
CAPRIFOLIACEÆ								
Lonicera tartarica	Honeysuckle	U.S.A.	←10→	2·8	18	68 (X)	S	Earle et al.[15b]
Sambucus canadensis	Elderberry	Canada	5·8		4	53 (m'')	F, T	Schuette et al.[76b]
" racemosa	"	General	23	1·3	45	25 (n'')	L, H	Matthes and Rossi[81]
Viburnum dentatum	Arrow wood	U.S.A.	5·4	←5→	65·5	23 (o'')	F	Schuette et al.[76c]
" opulus var. americanum	"	U.S.A.			74	16	S	Earle et al.[15b]
" "	Highbush cranberry	U.S.A.	←1·7→		60·8	37·5	L	Schuette and Korth[76d]
LOGANIACEÆ								
Buddleia davidii	Buddleia	U.S.A.	12·6		22	59 (Y)	S	Earle et al.[15b]
Strychnos nux vomica	Nux vomica	India	6·6	←13→	62·0	9·2 (Z)	F	Achaya et al.[12c]

Minor component acids recorded as follows (per cent. wt.):

	C14	SATURATED C20	C24	C26	UNSATURATED C16	LINO-LENIC	C20
(a) Illicium verum	4·4	—	—	—	—	—	—
(b) Anona muricata	0·3	—	—	—	—	—	—
(c) " reticulata	0·5	—	0·9	—	—	—	—
(d) " squamosa	—	—	—	—	—	—	—
(e) Asimina triloba	0·3	1·8	—	—	—	—	—
(f) Ægle marmelos	—	1·6	—	—	—	—	—
(g) Orange seed	—	—	—	—	4·3	—	—
(h) Sweet orange seed	—	—	—	—	—	6	—
(i) Grape fruit seed	—	0·9	—	—	2·3	Trace	—
(j) "	0·8	0·7	—	—	—	5·3	—
(k) "	1·2	0·6	—	—	—	5·9	—
(l) "	—	2·1	0·2	—	—	5·9	—
(m) "	0·3	—	—	—	—	0·5	—
(n) Lime seed	1·6	0·5	—	—	—	13·1	—
(o) Fagara coco	—	—	—	—	—	11·8	—
(p) Lalob	—	—	—	—	—	Trace	—
(q) Cashew nut	6·0	—	—	—	—	—	—
(r) Gonyo almond	0·1	0·2	—	—	—	—	—
(s) Buchanania	0·7	—	—	—	—	—	—
(t) Mango	—	6·7	—	—	—	—	—
(u) "	8·0	3·0	—	—	—	—	—
(v) "	—	1·7	—	—	—	—	—
(w) Pistachio	0·6	—	—	—	—	—	—
(x) Jute seed	—	2·2	0·9	1·2	—	4·7	4·4
(y) "	—	1·8	1·2	—	—	0·9	2·4
(z) "	Trace 10	1·8	1·1	—	—	Trace	4·0
(a') Abutilon	3·3	—	—	—	—	—	—
(b') Cottonseed	0·3	0·6	—	—	—	—	—
(c') "	0·3	0·6	—	—	—	—	—
(d') "	2·0	0·7	—	—	2·1	—	—
(e') "	1·4	1·3	—	—	—	—	—

	C14	SATURATED C20	C24	C26	UNSATURATED C16	LINO-LENIC	C20
(f') Cottonseed	0·5	0·1	—	—	—	—	—
(g') Okra seed	0·7	0·1	—	—	—	—	—
(h') "	—	—	—	—	—	—	—
(i') Baobab "	8·7	2·8	—	—	—	—	—
(j') Kapok seed	1·2	0·8	—	—	—	—	—
(k') "	0·5	1·3	—	—	—	—	—
(l') "	—	—	Trace	—	—	—	—
(m') Chorisia "	2·1	0·1	0·9	—	—	—	4·7
(n') Piqui-a seed	1·4	—	—	—	—	—	—
(o') Melon tree seed	—	0·3	—	—	—	—	—
(p') Papaya	4·6	—	—	—	—	—	—
(q') Brazil nut	1·9	—	—	—	—	—	—
(r') "	0·6	—	—	—	—	—	—
(s') Quisqualis	4·5	0·8	—	—	—	—	—
(t') T. belerica	1·0	0·8	—	—	—	—	—
(u') T. catappa	—	0·4	—	—	—	—	—
(v') "	0·7	—	—	—	—	—	—
(w') "	—	—	—	—	—	—	—
(x') Cerbera odollam	—	—	0·9	—	—	—	—
(y') Holarrhena	0·1	—	1·9	—	—	—	—
(z') Strophanthus courmontii	—	2·5	—	—	10·0 (10·2 9-hydroxy-octadec-12-enoic)	—	—
(a'') S. hispidus	0·1	2·0	—	—	(13·5)	—	—
(b'') S. sarmentosus: (Forest form)	0·2	3·1	—	—	(6·5)	—	"
(c'') (Savannah form)	0·2	4·0	—	—	(6·6)	—	"
(d'') Thevetia	—	0·4	—	—	—	—	—
(e'') Wrightia	0·1	6·0	—	—	—	—	—
(f'') Amaranthus polygamus	5·4	0·6	—	—	—	—	—
(g'') Martynia diandra	1·4	1·5	—	—	—	—	—

TABLE 62. *Component Acids of Seed Fats—continued*

Minor component acids recorded as follows (per cent. wt.)

		SATURATED			UNSATURATED		
	C_{14}	C_{20}	C_{24}	C_{26}	C_{16}	LINO-LENIC	C_{20}
(h'') Hygrophyla spinosa	1·4	—	—	—	—	—	—
(i'') " Cresentia cujete "	1·4	—	—	—	—	2·3	—
(j'') " Coffee seed	3·1	2·9	—	—	—	—	—
(k'') "	(0·4 decanoic acid and 14·7 "carnaubic")						
(l'') " Elderberry	—	—	—	—	—	34	—
(m'') "	—	—	—	—	—	7	—
(n'') "	—	Trace	—	—	—	—	—
(o'') Arrow wood	0·4	—	—	—	4·4	—	—
(p'') Cotton seed	1·3	—	—	—	2·5	—	—
(q'') " "	1·3	—	—	—	1·3	—	—
(r'') " " spinosa	2·3	—	—	—	0·8	—	—
(s'') Coffee seed	—	—	1·8	—	—	—	(Hydroxy un- saturated 4·0)
(t'') " "	0·2	1·4	—	—	0·9	—	5·0
(u'') Monodora myristica	0·3	(3·6 C_{21})	—	—	—	2·5	—
(v'') Xylopia aethiopica	0·7	1·2	—	—	—	3·3	—
(w'') Orange seed	0·5	0·8	—	—	0·8	6·1	—
(x'') Sweet orange seed	7·4	0·6	—	—	—	2·1	—
(y'') "	—	—	—	—	—	30	—
(z'') Ptelea trifoliata "	—	—	—	—	—	26	—
(A) Skimmia japonica	0·3	—	—	—	—	—	—
(B) Mango	—	2·7	—	—	—	0·5	—
(B') Cleome pentaphylla	—	0·4	—	—	—	—	—
(C) " pungens	—	—	—	—	—	4	—
(D) " serrulata	—	—	—	—	—	29	—
(E) " spinosa	—	—	—	—	—	4	—
(F) Isomeris arborea	—	—	—	—	—	1	—

		SATURATED			UNSATURATED		
	C_{14}	C_{20}	C_{24}	C_{26}	C_{16}	LINO-LENIC	C_{20}
(G) Polanisia trachy-sperma	—	—	—	—	—	2	—
(H) Gynandropsis pentaphylla	0·3	2·0	—	—	—	2·0	—
(I) Abutilon theophrasti	—	—	—	—	—	1	—
(I') Althea officinalis	—	—	—	—	—	2·5	—
(J) Kenaph seed	—	—	—	—	1	1	—
(K) " "	Trace						(also 5 per cent. 12,13-epoxy-oleic acid)
" "							(also 5·6 per cent. 12,13-epoxy-oleic acid)
(K') Okra seed	Trace	1	—	—	—	—	(also 3 per cent. 12,13-epoxy-oleic acid)
(L) " "	0·6	—	—	—	—	Trace	Trace
(M) Rose Mallow	—	—	—	—	—	1	—
(N) "	—	—	—	—	—	0·2	—
(N') Malva arborea	0·2	—	—	—	1·3	0·8	—
(O) Papaya	0·1	—	—	—	0·3	—	—
(P) Brazil nut	0·1	—	—	—	0·4	—	—
(Q) "	—	—	—	—	—	—	—
(R) Anogeissus	—	4·1	—	—	29·4	1·9	— (also 2·4 per cent. tetradecenoic acid)
(S) Apocynum	1·4	—	—	—	—	10	—
(T) Celosia argentea	—	—	—	—	1·6	—	—
(U) Crescentia alata	2·0	1·6	0·2	—	—	2·3	—
(V) Coffea arabica	2·3	2·9	—	—	—	—	—
(W) " robusta	—	—	—	—	—	—	—
(X) Buddleia davidii	—	—	—	—	—	1	—
(Y) Adansonia	1·4	7·0	—	—	—	—	—
(Z) Strychnos	0·9	1·7	1·7	—	—	—	—

References to Table 62

1. S. Komori and S. Ueno, *Bull. Chem. Soc. Japan*, 1938, **13**, 505.
2. J. A. Airan and S. V. Shah, *J. Indian Chem. Soc.*, 1942, **19**, 175.
3. J. Bulir, *Z. Nahr. Genussm.*, 1912, **24**, 309.
4. J. Sack, *Pharm. Weekblad*, 1903, **40**, 103.
5. D. A. Balandin, *Compt. rend. Acad. Sci. U.S.S.R.*, 1940, **26**, 584.
6. C. F. Asenjo and J. A. Goyco, *J. Amer. Chem. Soc.*, 1943, **65**, 208.
7. N. B. Naidu and K. T. Achaya, *J. Indian Chem. Soc. (Industr. News Ed.)*, 1951, **1**, 14.
8. R. V. Ghanekar and P. R. Ayyar, *J. Indian Inst. Sci.*, 1927, **10A**, 28.
9. (*a*) J. L. Riebsomer, J. Bishop and C. Rector, *J. Amer. Chem. Soc.*, 1938, **60**, 2853; (*b*) A. Mackie and D. G. Mieras, *J. Sci. Food Agric.*, 1961, **12**, 202.
10. R. Child, *J. Amer. Chem. Soc.*, 1935, **57**, 356.
11. (*a*) G. R. van Atta and W. C. Dietrich, *Oil and Soap*, 1944, **21**, 19; (*b*) D. R. Dhingra, G. N. Gupta and R. P. Agarwal, *Indian Soap J.*, 1957, **23**, 67.
12. (*a*) H. C. Dunn, T. P. Hilditch and J. P. Riley, *J. Soc. Chem. Ind.*, 1948, **67**, 199; (*b*) V. V. R. Subramaniam and K. T. Achaya, *J. Sci. Food Agric.*, 1957, **8**, 662; (*c*) *idem, ibid.*, 1957, **8**, 657; (*d*) A. H. Weerakoon, *ibid.*, 1960, **11**, 273.
13. G. S. Jamieson, W. F. Baughman and S. I. Gertler, *Oil and Fat Ind.*, 1930, **7**, 181.
14. C. J. D. Rao, T. R. Seshadri and J. Veeraraghaviah, *Proc. Indian Acad. Sci.*, 1940, **12, A**, 367.
15. (*a*) P. Cattaneo, G. K. de Sutton and M. M. Gonzalez, *Rev. Brasil Quim.*, 1951, **32**, 386; (*b*) F. R. Earle, I. A. Wolff, *et al.*, *J. Amer. Oil Chem. Soc.*, 1960, **37**, 440; (*c*) *idem, ibid.*, 1959, **36**, 304; (*d*) *idem.*, *ibid.*, 1962, **39**, 381; (*e*) J. A. Cornelius and G. Shone, *Chem. and Ind.*, 1963, 1246.
16. S. A. Hussein, F. G. Dollear and R. T. O'Connor, *J. Amer. Oil Chem. Soc.*, 1949, **26**, 730.
17. C. K. Patel, J. J. Sudborough and H. E. Watson, *J. Indian Inst. Sci.*, 1923, **6**, 111.
18. M. B. Ichaporia, unpublished observation, 1937.
19. J. Pieraerts and N. Ipatiev, *Mat. grasses*, 1927, **19**, 7974.
20. B. G. Gunde and P. D. Srivastava, *J. Indian Chem. Soc.*, 1941, **18**, 557.
21. S. P. Pathak, B. G. Gunde and N. N. Godbole, *J. Indian Chem. Soc.*, 1946, **23**, 407.
22. H. C. Dunn and T. P. Hilditch, *J. Soc. Chem. Ind.*, 1947, **66**, 209.
23. D. R. Dhingra, S. N. Kapoor and G. Chandra, *Proc. Ann. Convn. Oil Technol. Assocn., India*, 1948, **3**, 39.
24. F. L. Vodret, *Annali Chim. Appl.*, 1929, **19**, 76.
25. K. Beythien, *Pharm. Zentr.*, 1929, **70**, 551, 571.
26. D. R. Dhingra and T. P. Hilditch, *J. Soc. Chem. Ind.*, 1931, **50**, 9т.
27. D. N. Grindley, (*a*) *J. Sci. Food Agric.*, 1954, **5**, 92; (*b*) *ibid.*, 1950, **1**, 152.
28. (*a*) D. Zambrami, A. Ostchakovski and N. Petrova, *Maslob. Shir. Delo.*, 1940, No. 5–6, 57; (*b*) A. L. Misra and S. Dutt, *Proc. Nat. Inst. Sci. India*, 1937, **3**, 325.
29. (*a*) A. S. Gupta and M. M. Chakrabarty, *Science and Culture, India*, 1957, **23**, 306; *J. Sci. Food Agric.*, 1964, **15**, 69; (*b*) C. Hatta, *J. Chem. Soc. Japan*, 1942, **63**, 1540.
30. N. K. Sen, *J. Indian Chem. Soc.*, 1928, **5**, 759.
31. M. L. Meara and N. K. Sen, *J. Sci. Food Agric.*, 1952, **3**, 237.
32. J. K. Chakravarti and N. K. Sen, *J. Indian Chem. Soc.*, 1951, **28**, 390.
33. H. P. Kaufmann and H. Fiedler, *Fette u. Seifen*, 1938, **45**, 149.
34. (*a*) D. R. Carmody, W. de Jong and T. R. Smith, *Oil and Soap*, 1945, **22**, 263; (*b*) G. J. Tropp, *Pharmaz. J. Ukraine*, 1935, **8**, 134 (*Chem. Zent.*, 1936, I, 3426).
35. T. P. Hilditch, (*a*) with E. C. Jones, *J. Chem. Soc.*, 1932, 805; (*b*) with A. J. Rhead, *J. Soc. Chem. Ind.*, 1932, **51**, 198т; (*c*) with L. Maddison, *J. Soc. Chem. Ind.*, 1940, **59**, 162.
36. G. S. Jamieson and W. F. Baughman, (*a*) *J. Amer. Chem. Soc.*, 1920, **42**, 1197; (*b*) *Oil and Fat Ind.*, 1927, **4**, 131; (*c*) *J. Amer. Chem. Soc.*, 1920, **42**, 166.

37. (a) J. R. Halwarkar, K. T. Achaya and S. A. Saletore, *J. Indian Chem. Soc.* (*News Ed.*), 1953, **16**, 87; (b) J. H. Mitchell, H. R. Kraybill and F. P. Zscheile, *Ind. Eng. Chem.* (*Anal.*), 1943, **15**, 1; (c) P. A. Artamonov, *Maslo.-Zhir. Prom.*, 1959, **25**, (2), 8; (d) P. Cattaneo, G. K. de Sutton *et al.*, *Anales Asoc. Quim. Argentina*, 1961, **49**, 192.

38. (a) M. R. Bauman, *Chem. Abst.*, 1929, p. 3117; (b) C. Y. Hopkins and M. J. Chisholm, *Canad. J. Chem.*, 1959, **36**, 95; (c) idem, ibid., 1957, **35**, 358; (d) R. de Castro Ramos, *Grasas y Aceites*, 1958, **9**, 176; (e) T. N. Mehta and S. S. Lokras, *Indian J. Appl. Chem.*, 1960, **23**, 18.

39. R. Singh and S. Dutt, *Indian Soap J.*, 1947, **13**, 99.

40. J. R. Clopton, A. Roberts and H. A. Jeskey, *J. Amer. Oil Chem. Soc.*, 1948, **25**, 401.

41. S. A. Hussein and F. G. Dollear, *J. Amer. Oil Chem. Soc.*, 1950, **27**, 295.

42. A. Crossley and T. P. Hilditch, *J. Sci. Food Agric.*, 1951, **2**, 251.

43. (a) C. Barkenbus and S. T. Thorn, *J. Amer. Chem. Soc.*, 1935, **57**, 728; (b) A. Kato, *Yukagaku*, 1961, **10**, 174.

44. (a) S. H. W. Cmelik, *J. Sci. Food Agric.*, 1963, **14**, 287; (b) V. Thomas and F. Boiry, *Bull. Soc. chim.*, 1913, [iv], **13**, 827.

45. C. V. Rao, M. N. Rao and A. Venkateswarulu, *J. Indian Chem. Soc.*, 1943, **20**, 403.

46. H. P. Trevithick and W. A. Dickhart, *Cotton Oil Press*, 1921, **5**, 34.

47. A. O. Cruz and A. P. West, (a) *Philippine J. Sci.*, 1931, **46**, 131; (b) ibid., 1932, **48**, 13.

48. G. S. Jamieson and R. S. McKinney, *Oil and Soap*, 1936, **13**, 233.

49. V. C. Mehlenbacher, *Oil and Soap*, 1937, **14**, 118.

50. P. Cattaneo, G. Karman and L. Uberti, *Anales Asocn. Quim. Argentina*, 1946, **34**, 5.

51. (a) J. Pieraerts, N. Ipatiev and E. Simar, *Mat. grasses.* 1928, **20**, 8252; (b) D. N. Grindley and A. A. Akour, *J. Sci. Food Agric.*, 1955, **6**, 461; (c) A. de Bruin, J. E. Heesterman and M. R. Mills, ibid., 1963, **14**, 758.

52. T. P. Hilditch and J. G. Rigg, *J. Soc. Chem. Ind.*, 1935, **54**, 109т.

53. H. W. von Loesecke and A. J. Nolte, *J. Amer. Chem. Soc.*, 1937, **59**, 2565.

54. C. F. Asenjo and J. A. Goyco, (a) *Oil and Soap*, 1943, **20**, 217; (b) *J. Amer. Chem. Soc.*, 1943, **65**, 1417.

55. (a) H. A. Schuette, R. W. Thomas and M. V. Dutley, *J. Amer. Chem. Soc.*, 1930, **52**, 4114; (b) H. A. Schuette and W. W. F. Erz, ibid., 1931, **53**, 2756; (c) L. G. Elias and R. Brescani, *J. Amer. Oil Chem. Soc.*, 1961, **38**, 450.

56. H. P. Kaufmann and B. W. King, *Fette u. Seifen*, 1939, **46**, 387.

57. A. R. S. Kartha, T. A. Venkitasubramanian and K. N. Menon, *Proc. Indian Acad. Sci.*, 1946, **23**, A, 283.

58. B. K. Singh, *Proc. Indian Acad. Sci.*, 1946, **23**, A, 379.

59. S. R. Sunthankar and S. K. K. Jatkar, *J. Indian Inst. Sci.*, 1938, **21**, A, 149.

60. D. J. Clark, H. H. Hatt and W. J. Troyhan, *Australian J. Applied Sci.*, 1951, **2**, 378.

61. R. V. Ghanekar and P. R. Ayyar, (a) *J. Indian Inst. Sci.*, 1927, **10**, A, 20; (b) ibid., 1927, **10**, A, 24; (c) M. R. Subbaram, *J. Madras Univ.*, 1952, **22**, B, 223.

62. A. R. S. Kartha, Thesis, University of Madras, 1949.

63. F. D. Gunstone, (a) *J. Sci. Food Agric.*, 1953, **4**, 129; (with K. E. Bharucha), 1955, **6**, 373; (b) ibid., 1952, **3**, 185; (c) (with L. J. Morris), ibid., 1959, **10**, 522.

64. H. Matthes and L. Rath, *Arch. Pharm.*, 1914, **252**, 683.

65. R. Bhattacharya and P. R. Ayyar, *J. Indian Inst. Sci.*, 1927, **10A**, 15.

66. D. B. Parihar and S. Dutt, *J. Indian Chem. Soc.*, 1946, **23**, 307.

67. (a) N. Chidabaram and R. R. Iyer, *J. Indian Chem. Soc.*, 1945, **22**, 117; (b) D. K. Chowdhury and R. Bagchi, *Naturwiss.*, 1956, **43**, 558.

68. O. S. Kapoor and S. Dutt, *Indian Soap J.*, 1947, **13**, 120.

69. B. E. Christensen and L. S. Miller, *J. Amer. Chem. Soc.*, 1941, **63**, 2272.

70. J. N. Tayal and S. Dutt, *Proc. Nat. Acad. Sci., India*, 1939, **9**, 78.

71. A. V. Rege, J. W. Airan and S. V. Shah, *J. Univ. Bombay*, 1944, **12**, A, 31.

72. G. P. Pendse and J. B. Lal, *J. Indian Chem. Soc.*, 1937, **14**, 362; 1938, **15**, 471.

73. N. L. Phalnikar, K. S. Nargund and D. D. Kanga, *J. Univ. Bombay*, 1935, **4**, II, 146.

74. N. N. Godbole, B. G. Gunde and P. D. Srivastava, *Oil and Soap*, 1941, **18**, 206.

75. (*a*) A. L. Markman and M. D. Bodnya, *Zhur. Obshcheikhim.*, 1957, **27**, 2293; (*b*) C. Y. Hopkins and M. J. Chisholm, *J. Chem. Soc.*, 1962, 573; (c) M. L. van Sévéren, *J. Amer. Oil Chem. Soc.*, 1960, **37**, 402; (*d*) B. A. Smith and F. G. Dollear, *J. Amer. Oil Chem. Soc.*, 1947, **24**, 52.

76. (*a*) H. A. Schuette, M. A. Cowley and C. Y. Chang, *J. Amer. Chem. Soc.*, 1934, **56**, 2085; (*b*) H. A. Schuette, J. W. Brooks, H. A. Vogel and J. A. Bain, *Oil and Soap*, 1936, **13**, 314; 1943, **20**, 46; (*c*) H. A. Schuette, A. N. Pines and G. I. Krueger, *ibid.*, 1943, **20**, 158; (*d*) H. A. Schuette and J. A. Korth, *ibid.*, 1940, **17**, 265.

77. A. Heiduschka and R. Kühn, *J. pr. Chem.*, 1934, (ii), **139**, 269.

78. K. H. Bauer and R. Neu, (*a*) *Fette u. Seifen*, 1938, **45**, 229; (*b*) *ibid.*, 1943, **50**, 345.

79. (*a*) R. D. Bengis and R. J. Anderson, *J. Biol. Chem.*, 1934, **105**, 139; (*b*) N. A. Khan and J. B. Brown, *J. Amer. Oil Chem. Soc.*, 1953, **30**, 606.

80. M. N. Nadkarni, J. W. Airan and S. V. Shah, *J. Indian Chem. Soc.*, 1947, **24**, 25.

81. H. Matthes and W. Rossié, *Arch. Pharm.*, 1918, **256**, 284.

IIIA. SEED FATS OF THE GRAMINEÆ

Major component acids: OLEIC, LINOLEIC, PALMITIC.
Minor component acids: Stearic (occasionally myristic, arachidic, linolenic).
(*See Table* 63, p. 282.)

The available data in this class, which are shown in Table 63, are of interest not only because they include analyses of the oils present in the common and important cereals wheat, barley, rice, oats, and maize, but also because they afford instances in which endosperm fats have been examined separately from those of the embryo. The embryo or germ, in the Gramineæ, usually contains much more fatty matter than the corresponding endosperm; thus, in wheat the embryo contains 10–17 per cent. of fat, and the endosperm only 1–2 per cent., whilst for rye the respective figures are 8–11 per cent. and 1–3 per cent., and for rice, up to 35 per cent. and 8–12 per cent.

The respective embryo and endosperm fats, so far as can be judged from the analyses in Table 63, are not very different in any given species, but there seems to be a very definite distinction in the relative amounts of oleic, linoleic and linolenic acids present in the seed fats of the various genera. Linolenic acid is reported in the case of wheat, millet, rye and barley seed fats (especially in wheat germ fat) and the proportion of oleic acid in these fats (all of which are denizens of temperate climatic regions) is definitely lower than in those of the sub-tropical maize or the tropical rice; on the other hand, the embryo fat of the oat resembles the latter in being rich in oleic and lower in linoleic acid components. Any effect due to purely climatic influences is thus, as in previous cases, apparently obscured by some other influence of a specifically biological nature.

The content of saturated acids (almost all palmitic) of all Gramineæ seed fats is usually in the region of 10–15 per cent., but occasionally approaches or exceeds 20 per cent.

Variations in the component acids of maize oils have recently (1954) been studied in the cases of (*a*) a wide range of commercial samples from the United States 1950 crop (Quackenbush *et al.*[156a]), and (*b*) a group of individual and hybrid varieties of maize (Baldwin *et al.*[156b]). Linoleic acid contents ranging between extremes of 67 and 16 per cent. are recorded, with a corresponding range of oleic acid contents from 20 to 70 per cent. The proportions of saturated acids were less variable in most instances, although more marked in some cases than in those of other seed oils discussed earlier in this chapter (pp. 210, 211 ff.). Varietal differences seem to be involved in some of the data,[156b] whilst in others no details of growth conditions were reported, and no general conclusions can be drawn. A selection from these results is given in Table 63A.

After studying 22 varieties of maize grown in different parts of Argentina, Borquete,[156c] however, found that the oils from the colder regions had the highest contents of linoleic acid and correspondingly lower oleic acid. The extreme values ranged as follows: palmitic 9·5–18·7, stearic 0·1–3·2, *as* arachidic 0·9–1·5; hexadecenoic 0·5–2·0, oleic 25·6–45·5 and linoleic 35·1–53·4 per cent. Cattaneo *et al.*[156d] similarly found the following ranges in nearly fifty specimens of commercially grown Argentine maize oils: palmitic 10–19, stearic 1–3, arachidic 0·5–2, hexadecenoic 1–3, oleic 32–46, linoleic 35–49 per cent. (wt.).

TABLE 63A. *Component Acids (per cent. wt.) of Maize Oils*

IODINE VALUE OF OIL	COMPONENT ACIDS		
	SATURATED	OLEIC	LINOLEIC
(a) Lofland, Quackenbush and Brunson[156a]			
139·5	6·6	25·8	67·6
131·2	10·4	27·8	61·8
122·4	10·0	38·6	51·4
105·0	9·1	62·3	29·3
98·7	4·9	75·9	19·2
88·4	13·7	70·1	16·2
(b) Sniegowski and Baldwin[156b]			
130·6	10·9	23·0	66·1
126·0	10·8	32·9	56·3
121·0	12·2	35·7	52·1
113·2	14·9	39·3	45·8

Comprehensive analyses by gas–liquid chromatography of the glycerides and phosphatides in barley, oat and rye grains were made by Aylward and Showler[156e] (1962). In addition to the chief component acids (Table 63B) traces of lauric, myristic and stearic acids were usually also present.

TABLE 63B. *Component Acids (per cent. wt.) of Lipids in Barley, Oats and Rye*[156e]

	PALMITIC	OLEIC	LINOLEIC	LINOLENIC
BARLEY				
Glycerides	22·1	7·2	70·8	—
"Lecithins"	17·8	13·1	63·3	5·8
"Kephalins"	31·9	27·7	41·0	—
OATS				
Glycerides	15·9	40·4	43·7	Trace
"Lecithins"	21·8	22·6	55·6	Trace
"Kephalins"	31·9	27·2	41·0	—
RYE				
Glycerides	21·0	7·0	63·7	8·3
"Lecithins"	18·2	8·9	64·9	8·0
"Kephalins"	30·5	7·8	61·7	—

TABLE 63. Component Acids of Seed Fats of the Gramineæ

Major component acids: OLEIC, LINOLEIC, PALMITIC.
Minor component acids: Stearic (occasionally myristic, arachidic, linolenic).

			COMPONENT FATTY ACIDS PER CENT. (WT.)					
		HABITAT	PALMITIC	STEARIC	OLEIC	LINOLEIC	METHOD	OBSERVERS
Andropogon sorghum	Sorghum (seed)	U.S.A.	8·3	5·8	36·2	49·4 (a)	T	Kummerow[1]
" "	" "	U.S.A.*	6-10	3-6	35-47	41-53	T	Kummerow[1]
Avena sativa	Oat (germ)	Temperate zones	10 →	17·6 →	59	31	L, H	Amberger and Hill[2]
Coix lacrymæ	Job's tears	U.S.A.			59·6	22·8	S	Wiley and Wilken[3]
Euchlæna mexicana	Teosinte	U.S.A.	←	15·8 →	47·8	36·4	S	Wiley and Wilken[3]
Hordeum vulgare	Barley (seed)	Temperate zones	9	3	33	54 (b)	L, H	Täufel and Rusch[4]
" "	Barley (germ) (malt)	"	10	6	21	62 (c)	L, H	Täufel and Rusch[4]
Oryza sativa	Rice (meal)	Tropics	13·2	1·9	44·1	39·4 (d)	F	Jamieson[5]
"	Rice (bran)	Tropics	←	17·5 →	42·5	40	L	A.O.C.S.[6]
"	Rice (bran)	Philippine Islands	18·0	2·8	48·2	29·4 (e)	F	Cruz, West and Aragon[7]
"	Rice	Japan	←	13 →	52	35	L	Ueno and Ueda[8]
"	Rice (bran)	U.S.A.	←	18 →	47	34 (f)	B, S	Murti[9a]
"	Rice (bran)	Peru	14·2	2·5	45·8	36·2 (f')	F, S	Escribens and Freire[9b]
"	Rice (bran)	S. America	22·9	0·4	60·1	15·9 (f'')	F	Almarza and Ruiz[9c]
"	Rice (germ)	Sub-tropics	5·8	3·6	24·5	58 (g)	B, T	Steger and van Loon[10]
Panicum miliaceum	Millet	England	←	21 →	22·5	66·9 (h)	F, S	Bridge[11]
" "	Millet	Temperate zones	2·5	8·8	18	61	L, H	Croxford[12]
Secale cereale	Rye (seed)	Temperate zones	←	10 →	33	52·5 (i)	F	Stout and Schuette[13]
"	Rye (germ)	Manchuria	11·1	14·7	9	81	L	Mano, Yoshiketsu[14]
Setaria italica	Foxtail millet (bran)	India	←	3·2 →	21·8	38·2 (j)	F, L, H	Pargal and Dutt[15]
" "	Foxtail millet (seed)	U.S.A.	13·8	1·0	46·4	50·4	S	Wiley and Wilken[3]
Tripsacum dactyloides	Gama grass (seed)	Temperate zones	11·8	3·0	30	49 (k)	F, T	Jamieson and Baughman[16]
Triticum vulgare	Wheat (germ)	Temperate zones	←	15·5 →	39	30 (l)	F, T	Sullivan and Bailey[17]
" "	Wheat (germ)	"	16	6	25·5	53 (m)	B, T	Radlove[18]
" "	Wheat (germ)	"	←	18·9 →	12	57 (n)	C, F, S	Gunstone and Hilditch[19]
" "	Wheat (germ)	"	18·3	1·2	22·2	52·0 (o)	T	Iselin[20]
" "	Wheat (whole seed)	Argentina	17·3	0·9	22·1	42·2 (p)	C, F, S	de Fortunato[21]
" "	Wheat (whole seed)	England I	22·1	0·7	14·3	62·8 (w)	GLC	Fisher and Broughton[22]
" "	Wheat (whole seed)	" II	22·3	0·8	9·4	63·6 (x)	GLC	Fisher and Broughton[22]
" "	Wheat (whole seed)	" III			9·6	62·9 (y)	GLC	Fisher and Broughton[22]

* Range of fourteen varieties.

282

Zea Mays

Maize (germ)	Sub-tropics	7·8	3·5	46·3	41·8 (q)	F,H	Baughman and Jamieson[23]
„ „ Maize (germ)	U.S.A.	10·2	3·0	49·6	34·3 (r)	F	Longenecker[24]
„ „ Maize (germ)	U.S.A.	8·1	2·5	30·1	56·3 (s)	F,T	Baur and Brown[25]
„ „ Maize (germ)	U.S.A.	←——15·1——→		23·5	60·8 (t)	C,F,S	Doerschuk and Daubert[26]
„ „ Maize (germ)	Argentina	13·0	0·9	41·9	40·6 (u)	C,F,S	Fortunato[27]
„ „ Maize (germ)	India	8·0	3·5	46·2	42·0 (v)	F	Parikh[28]
„ „ Yellow dent		←——11·4——→		31·8	56·9	T	Takeda et al.[29]
„ „ White dent		←——15·4——→		36·3	48·4	T	Takeda et al.[29]
„ „ Maize (germ)	U.S.A.	12·7	2·7	30·7	53·5 (z)	GLC	Ahrens et al.[30]
„ „ Maize (germ)	Canada	12·0	2·3	28·3	56·6 (z')	GLC	Craig and Murti[31]

I: Petrol Soluble (1·8 per cent.); II: Petrol insoluble (1·7 per cent.); III: Petrol soluble but acetone insoluble (0·7 per cent. of dry seed).

Minor component acids recorded as follows:

	SATURATED			UNSATURATED		
	C14	C20	C24	C16	LINO-LENIC	C20
(a) Sorghum	0·2	—	—	0·1	—	—
(b) Barley (seed)	—	—	—	—	0·5	—
(c) „ (germ)	—	—	—	—	1·0	—
(d) Rice (meal)	0·3	0·6	0·5	—	—	—
(e) „ (bran)	0·1	0·5	1·0	—	1	—
(f) „ (bran)	—	—	—	—	0·8	—
(f') „ (bran)	—	—	0·5	—	—	—
(g) „ (germ)	0·7	—	—	—	5·5	—
(h) Millet	—	—	—	—	—	—
„	—	—	—	—	3·0	—
(i) Rye (germ)	—	1·2	—	—	—	—
(j) Setaria	—	0·2	1·2	—	6·4	—
(k) Wheat (germ)	—	6·6	0·3	—	6	—
(l) „ „	—	—	1·2	—	15	—
(m) „ „	—	—	—	—	6	—

	SATURATED			UNSATURATED		
	C14	C20	C24	C16	LINO-LENIC 9	C20
(n) Wheat (germ)	—	—	—	—	9	—
(o) „ „	—	—	—	—	7	—
(p) „ „	0·2	0·8	0·2	2·1	9·3	3·7
(q) Maize (germ)	—	0·4	—	—	—	—
(r) „ „	1·4	—	—	1·5	—	1·7
(s) „ „	0·1	—	—	1·2	0·6	—
(t) „ „	—	—	—	0·2	—	—
(u) „ „	0·2	1·5	0·2	—	—	1·5
(v) „ „	—	0·3	—	—	—	—
(w) Wheat (whole seed)	Trace	—	—	—	3·0	0·4
(x) „ „ „	Trace	—	—	—	2·5	1·1
(y) „ „ „	Trace	—	—	—	2·6	1·3
(z) Maize (germ)	—	—	—	—	—	—
(z') „ „	0·4	—	—	—	0·8	—

283

References to Table 63

1. F. A. Kummerow, *Oil and Soap*, 1946, **23**, 167, 273.
2. K. Amberger and E. W. Hill, *Z. Unters. Lebensm.*, 1927, **54**, 417.
3. R. H. Wiley and P. H. Wilken, *J. Org. Chem.*, 1951, **16**, 1536.
4. K. Taüfel and M. Rusch, *Z. Unters. Lebensm.*, 1929, **57**, 422.
5. G. S. Jamieson, *Oil and Fat Ind.*, 1926, **3**, 256.
6. American Oil Chemists' Society Committee, *Oil and Soap*, 1937, **14**, 215.
7. A. O. Cruz, A. P. West and V. B. Aragon, *Philippine J. Sci.*, 1932, **48**, 5.
8. S. Ueno and S. Ueda, *J. Soc. Chem. Ind. Japan*, 1938, **41**, 325B.
9. (*a*) K. S. Murti, *J. Amer. Oil Chem. Soc.*, 1948, **25**, 211; (*b*) M. R. Escribens and F. Freire, *Agronomia (Peru)*, 1952, **17**, 139; (*c*) A. Y. Almarza and A. S. Ruiz, *An. real. Soc. esp. Fis. Quim.*, 1954, **50**, **B**, 87.
10. A. Steger and J. van Loon, *Rec. trav. chim.*, 1934, **53**, 41.
11. R. E. Bridge, Thesis, University of Liverpool, 1951.
12. J. W. Croxford, *Analyst*, 1930, **55**, 735.
13. A. W. Stout and H. A. Schuette, *J. Amer. Chem. Soc.*, 1932, **54**, 3298.
14. Y. Mano, *J. Agric. Chem. Soc. Japan*, 1940, **16**, 1074; M. Yoshiketsu, *Rep. Inst. Sci. Res., Manchukuo*, 1940, **4**, 393.
15. H. K. Pargal and S. Dutt, *Indian Soap J.*, 1948, **14**, 81.
16. G. S. Jamieson and W. F. Baughman, *Oil and Soap*, 1932, **9**, 136.
17. B. Sullivan and C. H. Bailey, *J. Amer. Chem. Soc.*, 1936, **58**, 383, 390.
18. S. B. Radlove, *Oil and Soap*, 1945, **22**, 183.
19. F. D. Gunstone and T. P. Hilditch, *J. Soc. Chem. Ind.*, 1946, **65**, 8.
20. E. Iselin, *Mitt. Lebensm. Hyg.*, 1945, **36**, 377.
21. E. J. G. de Fortunato, *Industria y Quim.*, 1948, **10**, 127.
22. N. Fisher and M. E. Broughton, *Chem. and Ind.*, 1960, 869.
23. W. F. Baughman and G. S. Jamieson, *J. Amer. Chem. Soc.*, 1921, **43**, 2696.
24. H. E. Longenecker, *J. Biol. Chem.*, 1939, **129**, 13.
25. F. J. Baur and J. B. Brown, *J. Amer. Chem. Soc.*, 1945, **67**, 1899.
26. A. P. Doerschuk and B. F. Daubert, *J. Amer. Oil Chem. Soc.*, 1948, **25**, 425.
27. A. D. Fortunato, *Industria y Quim.*, 1949, **11**, 132.
28. V. K. Parikh, *Oils and Oilseeds J. (India)*, 1953, **5**, No. 10/12, 33.
29. M. Takeda, H. Takai, F. Ono and Y. Toyama, *J. Japan Oil Chem. Soc.*, 1957, **6**, 13.
30. E. H. Ahrens, Jr., W. Insull, Jr., W. Stoffel, H. J. Thomasson *et al.*, *Lancet*, 1959, (i), 315.
31. B. M. Craig and N. L. Murti, *J. Amer. Oil Chem. Soc.*, 1959, **36**, 549.

Seed Fats Containing characteristic acids other than, or in addition to, Oleic, Linoleic and Palmitic Acids

In passing from the fats in which oleic, linoleic (linolenic) and palmitic acids are the only major components to those in which one or more other acids are present in substantial proportions, the close connection between seed fat composition and the family to which the parent plant belongs becomes still more evident. Fatty acids which appear individually in quantity in certain seed fats include:

(i) unsaturated: petroselinic, tariric, octadecendiynoic, eicosenoic, erucic, hexacosenoic, triacontenoic, chaulmoogric and hydnocarpic, elæo-stearic, keto-elæostearic, parinaric, ricinoleic.

(ii) saturated: arachidic and lignoceric, stearic, myristic, lauric (or both of the latter together).

(i) Seed Fats Containing Specific Unsaturated Acids

The fats in which *elæostearic* acid and its natural isomeric forms, $CH_3.[CH_2]_3.[CH:CH]_3.[CH_2]_7.COOH$, 4-keto-elæostearic acid, $CH_3.[CH_2]_3.[CH:CH]_3.[CH_2]_4.CO.[CH_2]_2.COOH$, parinaric acid, $CH_3.CH_2.[CH:CH]_4.[CH_2]_7.COOH$, and ricinoleic acid, $CH_3.[CH_2]_5.CH(OH).CH_2.CH:CH.[CH_2]_7.COOH$, are present in large amounts have already received attention (*cf.* pp. 243ff, and Table 61). Other examples of unsaturated major components known up to the present include the mono-acetylenic *tariric* acid, $CH_3.[CH_2]_{10}.C:C.[CH_2]_4.COOH$, an acid $C_{18}H_{26}O_2$ with one ethenoid (terminal vinyl) group and two acetylenic linkings, and the following mono-ethylenic acids: *petro-selinic*, $CH_3.[CH_2]_{10}.CH:CH.[CH_2]_4.COOH$, an eicosenoic acid, $CH_3.[CH_2]_7.CH:CH.[CH_2]_9.COOH$, *erucic* acid, $CH_3.[CH_2]_7.CH:CH.[CH_2]_{11}.COOH$, *ximenic* acid, $CH_3.[CH_2]_7.CH:CH.[CH_2]_{15}.COOH$, *lumequic* acid, $CH_3.[CH_2]_7.CH:CH.[CH_2]_{19}.COOH$; and also the octadecenynoic (ximeny-nic, santalbic) acid of *Ximenia* and *Santalum* seed fats, the cyclopropene acids $C_{19}H_{34}O_2$ and $C_{18}H_{32}O_2$ present in small quantities in some Malvaceæ and *Sterculia* seed fats (in major proportions in that of *S. fœtida*), and *chaulmoogric* and *hydnocarpic* acids. The latter are cyclopentene derivatives of the formulæ:

$$\underset{\substack{|\\ \underset{H_2}{C}-\underset{H_2}{C}}}{\overset{\overset{H\;\;\;\;H}{C=C}}{}}\!\!\Big\rangle CH.[CH_2]_{12}.COOH \qquad\qquad \underset{\substack{|\\ \underset{H_2}{C}-\underset{H_2}{C}}}{\overset{\overset{H\;\;\;\;H}{C=C}}{}}\!\!\Big\rangle CH.[CH_2]_{10}.COOH$$

Each of these unsaturated acids is associated with the seeds of only one or two families of plants, as will be seen from the descriptions which follow.

SEED FATS WITH PETROSELINIC (OCTADEC-6-ENOIC) ACID AS MAJOR COMPONENT

Major component acids: PETROSELINIC, OLEIC, LINOLEIC.
Minor component acids: Palmitic.

(See Table 64, p. 287)

The occurrence of unsaturation in the 6:7 position of the C_{18} chain, in contrast to or accompanying the 9:10 ethylenic linking common to oleic, linoleic and linolenic acids, is comparatively uncommon, except in the seed fats of the Umbelliferæ and of ivy and one or two other species of plants. In umbelliferous plants, however, the octadec-6-enoic acid seems invariably to be a major component.

It may here be interpolated that the triethenoid C_{18} acid present in the seed fat of the evening primrose (*Œnothera*) is octadeca-6,9,12-trienoic acid,[157] and is thus related to the mono-ethenoid petroselinic acid in the same way that ordinary linolenic acid is to oleic acid. Again, the acetylenic tariric acid, octadec-6-ynoic acid, the occurrence of which is discussed below, is structurally related to petroselinic and not to oleic acid.[158]

The observation of Vongerichten and Köhler[159] in 1909 that parsley seed oil contained over 70 per cent. of octadec-6-enoic acid (petroselinic acid) was confirmed in 1927 by Hilditch and (Miss) Jones,[160a] and by van Loon.[160b] Subsequent examination of the seed fats from other species of Umbelliferous genera has disclosed the presence in every instance of petroselinic acid in amounts varying from 17 to 60 per cent. of the total fatty acids of the oils (*cf.* Table 64, p. 287). The other acids present are oleic and linoleic in varying proportions, together with minor amounts (usually 3–4 per cent.) of palmitic, the only saturated acid. Chervil seed oil appears peculiar in its high content of linoleic acid coupled with substantial absence of oleic acid, and this feature is perhaps worth further study. The seed fat of *Myrrhis odorata* (fern-leaved chervil, sweet cicely) appears to be exceptionally rich in petroselinic acid, since it contains considerable proportions of tripetroselinin, m.p. 29–30° (Clemo and Stevens[161]).

Petroselinic acid has thus been observed in quantity in every Umbelliferous seed fat so far analysed, but its presence has hitherto only been reported in the seeds of plants belonging to two other families, Araliaceæ (a closely allied Umbellate family, classified separately on account of the more succulent fruit) and one genus from the Simarubaceæ.

The fat of ivy (*Hedera helix*, Araliaceæ) seeds was stated to contain petroselinic acid by Palazzo and Tamburello[162] in 1914, and this observation was confirmed by the detailed analysis of Steger and van Loon[163] in 1928.

Tsujimoto and Koyanagi[164] have observed that the 77 per cent. of unsaturated acids from Nigaki seed fat (*Picrasma quassioides*, Simarubaceæ) consist for the greater part of petroselinic acid.

TABLE 64. *Component Acids of Seed Fats of the Umbelliferæ and Araliaceæ*

Major component acids: All unsaturated—OLEIC, LINOLEIC and PETROSELINIC.
Minor component acids: Palmitic.

		COMPONENT FATTY ACIDS PER CENT. (WT.)					
		PALMITIC	OLEIC	LINOLEIC	PETROSELINIC	METHOD	OBSERVERS
UMBELLIFERÆ*							
Ammi visnaga							
(from Sudan)		5	42	3	50	L, T	Grindley[1]
(from Argentina)		5†	30	19	44	L, F	Cattaneo et al.[2]
Angelica sylvestris	Angelica	4	44	33	19	F	Hilditch and (Miss) Jones[3]
Anthriscus cerefolium	Chervil	5	0·5	53·5	41	F	Christian and Hilditch[4]
Apium graveolens	Celery	3	26	20	51	F	Christian and Hilditch[4]
(from Argentina)	Celery	12‡	30	10	41	L, F	Farooq et al.[5a]
Carum carvi	Caraway	3	40	31	26	F	Christian and Hilditch[4]
" "		3·6	60·7	19·6	17·0	?	Zaraiskaya and Borisyuk[9a]
Carum copticum		2·6	34·8	20·7	41·8	?	Menon and Raman[12]
(from India)		5§	24	20	48	L, F	Farooq et al.[5b]
Coriandrum sativum	Coriander	8	32	7	53	F	Christian and Hilditch[4]
" "		9·7	37·8	14·0	38·5	?	Rankov et al.[10a]
Daucus carota	Carrot	4	14	24	58	F	Christian and Hilditch[4]
" "		6·9	22·8	14·8	55·5	?	Prakash et al.[11]
Fœniculum officinale	Fennel	4	22	14	60	F	Christian and Hilditch[4]
Heracleum sphondylium	Hogweed	4	52	25	19	F	Hilditch and (Miss) Jones[3]
Pastinaca sativa	Parsnip	1	32	21	46	F	Christian and Hilditch[4]
Petroselinum sativum	Parsley	3	15	6	76	F	Hilditch and (Miss) Jones[6]
" "	Parsley	3	9	18	70	L, H	van Loon[7]
Pimpinella anisum	Aniseed	3·3	56·0	17·2	23·6	?	Zaraiskaya and Borisyuk[9a]
" "		3·4	61·0	9·6	26·0	?	Borisyuk and Makarova[9b]
" "		14·0	43·5	25·0	17·5	?	Rankov et al.[10b]
ARALIACEÆ*							
Hedera helix	Ivy	5	20	13	62	L, H	Steger and van Loon[8]

* All the species mentioned (except *Ammi visnaga* and *Carum copticum*) grow in temperate or sub-tropical regions.
† 1·5 per cent. stearic and traces of arachidic and behenic acids also recorded.
‡ 7 per cent. "resin acids" also recorded.
§ 3 per cent. "resin acids" also recorded.

287

References to Table 64

1. D. N. Grindley, *J. Sci. Food Agric.*, 1950, **1**, 53.
2. P. Cattaneo, G. K. de Sutton and G. A. Robles, *Anales Asoc. Quim. Argentina*, 1951, **39**, 145.
3. T. P. Hilditch and (Miss) E. E. Jones, *Biochem. J.*, 1928, **22**, 326.
4. B. C. Christian and T. P. Hilditch, *Biochem. J.*, 1929, **23**, 327.
5. (*a*) M. O. Farooq, M. Kiamuddin and S. M. Osman, *Rec. trav. chim.*, 1953, **72**, 135; (*b*) M. O. Farooq, S. M. Osman and M. S. Ahmad, *J. Sci. Food Agric.*, 1953, **4**, 132.
6. T. P. Hilditch and (Miss) E. E. Jones, *J. Soc. Chem. Ind.*, 1927, **46**, 174т.
7. J. van Loon, *Rec. trav. chim.*, 1927, **46**, 492.
8. A. Steger and J. van Loon, *Rec. trav. chim.*, 1928, **47**, 471.
9. (*a*) E. N. Zaraiskaya and Y. G. Borisyuk, *Sbornik*, 1956, 185; (*b*) Y. G. Borisyuk and G. V. Makarova, *ibid.*, 1956, 179.
10. (*a*) G. Rankov, A. Iorcherand and L. Davidkova, *C.R. Bulgar. Sci.*, 1957, **10**, 133; (*b*) G. Rankov, D. Chobanov and G. Zagorski, *ibid.*, 1957, **10**, 185.
11. O. Prakash, A. Ram and J. C. Gupta, *J. Proc. Oil Technol. Assn., India.*, 1957, **13**, 42.
12. K. N. Menon and P. S. Raman, *Proc. Indian Acad. Sci.*, 1953, **38**, A, 128.

SEED FATS WITH TARIRIC ACID (OR OTHER ETHYNOID ACID) AS MAJOR COMPONENT

Tariric (octadec-6-ynoic) acid was first reported by Arnaud[158] in 1892 as a component of the seed fat of *Picramnia tariri* and was later observed in those of *P. camboita* and *P. carpinteræ*,[165a] these species being indigenous to Guatemala, Guiana, or Brazil. Grimme[165b] found that the component acids of the seed fat of *P. lindeniana* (Guatemala) consisted approximately of myristic 22, palmitic 33, stearic 3, oleic 22, and tariric 20 per cent., acids. The fatty acids from the seed fat of yet another species of *Picramnia*, *P. sow*, were, however, found by Steger and van Loon[165c] to consist almost wholly (nearly 95 per cent.) of tariric acid; these authors confirmed the structure of the acid as octadec-6-ynoic acid, $CH_3.[CH_2]_{10}.C \vdots C.[CH_2]_4.COOH$.

The occurrence of this acetylenic acid is at present confined to the one Central American genus *Picramnia*, a member of the family Simarubaceæ (sub-family Terebinthaceæ). The seed fats of other plants belonging to the Simarubaceæ are quite different, and somewhat variable, in their component acids (see Table 69A and pp. 333, 334).

Reference should again be made here to the rare di-unsaturated C_{18} acid, with two acetylenic and one ethylenic (terminal vinyl) linkings, isolated from the seed fat (boleko or isano oil) of species of *Onguekoa* (Olacaceæ) by Steger and van Loon and by other workers.[96] Steger and van Loon (1937) noted the presence in *Onguekoa* seed fat of an acid with one ethenoid and two ethynoid linkages which (following Hébert, who had first observed it in 1902) they termed "isanic" acid. Boekenoogen[96b] (1937) considered isanic acid to be the chief constituent of the fat, whilst Castille[96c] (1939), who independently had isolated it and termed it "erythrogenic" acid, showed that it was either octadec-17-en-9,15-diynoic or octadec-17-en-9,11-diynoic acid. Steger and van Loon (1940) proved that isanic acid has the latter structure, $CH_2:CH.[CH_2]_4.C \vdots C.C \vdots C.[CH_2]_7.COOH$. Nevertheless much of the *Onguekoa* seed fatty acids consist of a hydroxy-unsaturated acid, shown by Riley[96d] (1951) to be an 8-hydroxy-acid of the C_{18} series. Concurrently Kaufmann et al.[96e] showed that this hydroxy-acid (which they termed "isanolic" acid, and concluded, from its similar absorption spectrum to isanic acid, to be probably 8-hydroxy-isanic acid) was a major component amounting to 44 per cent. of the total fatty acids of the oil, the other constituents being largely isanic acid accompanied by small proportions of linolenic and saturated acids. The two chief component acids of *Onguekoa* seed fat are therefore 8-hydroxy-octadec-17-en-9,11-diynoic and octadec-17-en-9,11-diynoic acids. Two subsequent determinations[96f,g] of the groups of acids present gave the following results:

	Seher[96f]	Pouliquen[96g]
Saturated acids	3	2·5
Oleic acid	17	}8·8
Linoleic + linolenic	4	
Isanic	15	30–40
Isanolic (8-hydroxy-isanic)	45	40–50
"Undetermined"	16	—

Minor amounts of two other acetylenic acids are reported in this oil by Meade[96h] and Badami[96j]: "bolekic" (possibly octadec-cis-13-en-9,11-diynoic) and an 8-hydroxy-derivative of the latter.

A later study (Gunstone et al.[96i]) of isano oil (by reversed-phase chromatography and U.V. spectroscopy) indicated the following acids:

	Per cent.
Myristic	1
Palmitic	4
Stearic	1
Oleic	14
Linoleic	5
Octadeca-9-yn-11-enoic	1
Octadeca-9,11-diynoic	10
Octadeca-17-en-9,11-diynoic	32
Octadeca-cis-13-en-9,11-diynoic	2
Octadeca-cis-13,17-dien-9,11-diynoic	6
8-Hydroxy-octadeca-9,11-diynoic	4
8-Hydroxy-octadeca-17-en-9,11-diynoic	15
8-Hydroxy-octadeca-cis-13-en-9,11-diynoic	1
8-Hydroxy-octadeca-cis-13,17-dien-9,11-diynoic	2
Threo-9,10-Dihydroxystearic acid	2

Another genus of the Olacaceæ family, *Ximenia*, was shown (1952) by Ligthelm et al.[95c] to contain in its seed fats an octadec-11-en-9-ynoic acid ("ximenynic" acid). The presence of small proportions of monoethenoid acids of the C_{26} ("ximenic") and C_{30} ("lumequic") series had been previously observed[95a,b] in the seed fat of *Ximenia americana*, but Ligthelm et al.[95c] now recorded as follows the seed fat component acids of three South African species of *Ximenia* (*X. caffra*, *X. caffra natalensis*, *X. americana microphylla*): oleic (32–40 per cent.) and "ximenynic" (22–24 per cent.) acids are the chief components, accompanied by small proportions (totalling 25–33 per cent.) of monoethenoid C_{20}, C_{22}, C_{24}, C_{26}, C_{28} and C_{30} acids (all of which belong to the series $CH_3.[CH_2]_7.CH:CH.[CH_2]_x.COOH$); saturated acids (chiefly stearic and hexacosanoic) together amount to about 8–10 per cent. of the total fatty acids. Infra-red spectroscopic study of "ximenynic" acid indicates that the 11:12 ethenoid bond has the *trans*-configuration.[95d]

Another acid of previously undetermined identity, "santalbic" acid, which had been stated[167a] to form about half of the seed fatty acids of *Santalum album* (Santalaceæ), was found by Gunstone and McGee[167b] also to be octadec-11-en-9-ynoic acid. Hatt and Szumer[167c] state that the seed fats of the Australian species *Santalum acuminatum* and *S. Murrayana* include 40–43 per cent. of "santalbic" acid and confirm that this is identical with "ximenynic" acid. Hatt and Schoenfeld[167d] reported that nearly all the rest of the acids in *S. acuminatum* seed fat was oleic acid, except for 3–4 per cent. of palmitic acid. Hatt et al.[95e] also found that the seed fat of other shrubs of the Santalaceæ, *Exocarpus cupressiformis* and *E. stricta*, contained over 60 per cent. of ximenynic (santalbic) acid; these workers[44a,b] also noted the presence of ximenynic and other octadec-en-ynoic acids in the root and stem fats of *Ximenia* (Olacaceæ) and of *Santalum*, *Exocarpus* and *Leptomeria* (Santalaceæ) (*cf.* pp. 183, 185).

Seed fats of two other species of the family Santalaceae, *Comandra pallida* and *Osyris alba*, were observed by Mikolajczak *et al.*[167e] to contain respectively 43 and 57 per cent. of ximenynic acid, and 41 and 32 per cent. of oleic acid, with minor amounts of palmitic, stearic, linoleic and linolenic acids, but no acids containing more than eighteen carbon atoms.

SEED FATS WITH CYCLIC UNSATURATED ACIDS
(CHAULMOOGRIC, HYDNOCARPIC, GORLIC)
AS MAJOR COMPONENTS

Flacourtiaceæ Seed Fats (see Table 65, p. 293)

Chaulmoogric and hydnocarpic acids, the C_{16} and C_{18} acids containing a cyclopentene group, and whose structural formulæ were given on p. 285, are present in quantity in the seed fats of many members of this family; moreover, so far as at present known, they do not seem to occur elsewhere. These acids contain an asymmetric carbon atom and are thus capable of existence in optically active forms; actually, the naturally occurring chaulmoogric and hydnocarpic glycerides are strongly dextro-rotatory. The acids also possess marked therapeutic properties and are valuable medicinally, especially in the treatment of leprosy.

A diethenoid cyclopentene acid, gorlic acid, $C_{18}H_{30}O_2$, has been observed in some cases[168a] to accompany chaulmoogric acid in smaller quantities than the latter: in gorlic acid one ethylenic linking is in the cyclopentene ring (as in chaulmoogric acid), whilst the other is in the aliphatic chain (13-*cyclo*pent-2-enyl-tridec-6-enoic acid).[168b]

Members of this family are found in tropical regions in Asia, Africa, and Central and South America.

Formerly, quantitative methods for determination of chaulmoogric and hydnocarpic acids in admixture with oleic, linoleic, palmitic, etc., acids were unavailable, but Cole and Cardoso[169a] gave detailed figures for five of the Flacourtiaceæ seed fats of the chaulmoogric type. Table 65 in addition to these data, includes a summary of most of the Flacourtiaceæ seed fats which may serve to indicate in a general manner the extent to which the cyclic acids are present, and also to demonstrate their absence from some species (although other species, even of the same genus, may develop them in abundance in their seeds). Cole and Cardoso[169b] also established that very small quantities of lower homologues of the cyclopentenyl fatty acids accompany hydnocarpic and chaulmoogric acids in some of the fats of this group: they have identified and assigned names to these as follows: $C_6H_8O_2$ (aleprolic), $C_{10}H_{16}O_2$ (aleprestic), $C_{12}H_{20}O_2$ (aleprylic), and $C_{14}H_{24}O_2$ (alepric) acids.

Adriaens[170] has also published the fatty acid compositions of oils of *Hydnocarpus anthelmintica*, *H. wightiana*, *Caloncoba glauca*, *C. welwitschii*, and *Lindackenia dentata*, all of which are in general qualitative similarity to those given in Table 65: unfortunately the oils studied by Adriaens were from old seed and contained from 13–25 per cent. of oxidised oils, so that the actual figures obtained are unsuitable for comparison.

References to Table 65

1. S. G. Quinza and P. R. Anno, *Anales Fis. y. Quim.* (*Madrid*), 1946, **42**, 393.
2. H. I. Cole and H. T. Cardoso, (*a*) *J. Amer. Chem. Soc.*, 1938, **60**, 614, 617; (*b*) *ibid.*, 1939, **61**, 3442; (*c*) *ibid.*, 1939, **61**, 2351.
3. N. D. Nair and N. S. Varier, *Indian Soap J.*, 1954, **19**, 225.
4. A. S. Gupta, S. C. Mutha and A. P. Waghrey, *J. Sci. Food Agric.*, 1963, **14**, 457.

TABLE 65. Seed Fats of the Flacourtiaceæ

		HABITAT	IOD. VAL.	OPTICAL ROTATION [α]D	CHIEF COMPONENT ACIDS
Carpotroche brasiliensis	Sapocainha oil	Brazil	ca. 110	+53°	Chaulmoogric, hydnocarpic, gorlic
Hydnocarpus alcalæ		Philippine Islands	93	+50°	Chaulmoogric
" alpina		Ceylon	84	+49°	Chaulmoogric and hydnocarpic (oleic)
" anthelmintica	Lukrabo oil	Siam	90	+51–54°	Chaulmoogric and hydnocarpic (oleic)
" ilicifolia		Siam, Malaya	90	+51°	Chaulmoogric and hydnocarpic (oleic)
" kurzii	Chaulmoogra oil	East Indies	ca. 95	+44–51°	Chaulmoogric, hydnocarpic, gorlic, oleic
" odoratus	Gynocardia oil	East Indies, etc.	152	—	Linoleic, linolenic, oleic, etc.
" ovoidea		Philippine Islands	47	+1°	Chaulmoogric, etc., apparently not present
" wightiana	Maratti oil	East Indies	ca. 95	+54–64°	Chaulmoogric, hydnocarpic, gorlic
Oncoba echinata	Gorli seed oil	Central Africa	98	+56°	Chaulmoogric, gorlic
" spinosa		Central Africa	177	—	Linoleic, linolenic, oleic, etc.
Pangium edule	Pitjoeng oil	East Indies, etc.	113	+4°	Oleic and linoleic; chaulmoogric, etc., if present, only in minor quantities

Component Fatty Acids per cent. (wt.)

	PALMITIC	OLEIC	LOWER CYCLIC HOMOLOGUES $C_6H_8O_2$ to $C_{14}H_{24}O_2$	HYDNOCARPIC $C_{16}H_{28}O_2$	CHAULMOOGRIC $C_{18}H_{32}O_2$	GORLIC $C_{18}H_{30}O_2$
Caloncoba welwitschii[1]	6·8	0·8	?	?	75·0	17·4
Carpotroche brasiliensis[2a]	6·8	6·4	?	46·1	24·9	15·8
Hydnocarpus anthelmintica[2b]	7·7	12·6	0·1	69·3	8·9	1·4
(Taraktogenos) kurzii[2b]	4·0	14·8	0·4	35·3	22·7	22·8
" wightiana[2c]	1·8	6·5	3·4	48·9	27·1	12·3
" wightiana[3]	9·6	12·5	?	46·4	21·5	10·0
Oncoba echinata[2a]	7·8	2·2	?	nil	75·2	14·8
Taraktogenos kurzii[4]	5·8*	11·3	?	19·7	20·9	26·7

* (Also myristic 6·0, linoleic 4·3 per cent.)

293

SEED FATS WITH UNSATURATED ACIDS OF THE C_{20}, C_{22}
OR HIGHER SERIES AS MAJOR COMPONENTS

The only abundant unsaturated acid of greater molecular weight than oleic acid in the vegetable kingdom is erucic (docos-13-enoic) acid, $CH_3.[CH_2]_7.$ $CH:CH.[CH_2]_{11}.COOH$, which is the main component of seed glycerides in the large and important family Cruciferæ, and which forms, apparently, a very high proportion of the component acids of the seed fats of *Tropæolum* (Tropæolaceæ). Apart from these two families, it has not been detected with certainty in any other seed fats.

In 1946 Hopkins[171] noted the presence in hare's ear mustard seed oil of small proportions of a C_{20} mono-ethenoid acid, eicos-11-enoic acid, accompanying erucic acid, and in the following year Hilditch, Laurent and Meara[172] showed that erucic acid is also accompanied in rape oils by very small amounts of a diene C_{22} acid. Baliga and Hilditch[173a] (1949) confirmed the constitution of Hopkin's C_{20} unsaturated acid as eicos-11-enoic acid, and also showed that the C_{22} diene acid was docos-13,16-dienoic acid; they also showed that rape oils (like other seed fats) contain traces of unsaturated acids of the C_{16} series which consist mainly of the usual hexadec-9-enoic acid with minor proportions of polyethenoid C_{16} acids. These workers[173b] determined the proportions of these minor acids as well as the chief component acids in a number of rape and allied oils.

Eicos-11-enoic acid has been reported as a seed fat component (sometimes up to 10–11 per cent.) in several other instances, e.g., in the seed fats of *Delphinium* (Ranunculaceæ) and of milkweed (Asclepiadaceæ) (Table 60), and those of *Pongamia* and *Erythrina* (Papilionatæ, Table 67). In one of the Sapindaceæ seed fats (Table 67, p. 315), that of *Cardiospermum halicacabum*, and also in one Compositæ seed fat (*Marshallia cæspitosa*), eicos-11-enoic acid is exceptionally the major component, to the extent of 42 to 44 per cent. of the total fatty acids[166]; in seed fats of this family which contain large proportions of arachidic acid there is also evidence of the presence of small amounts of a related eicosenoic acid.[174] The unusual seed fats of *Ximenia* species (Olacaceæ) contain in their component acids monoethenoid acids of the C_{20}, C_{22}, C_{24}, C_{26}, C_{28}, and C_{30} series of the general formula

$$CH_3.[CH_2]_7.CH:CH.[CH_2]_x.COOH^{95,\,156b} \text{ (v. supra, p. 290)}$$

Finally, the lipid matter from the seeds of *Simmondsia californica*, which is unique in that it is a wax and not a fat, contains as principal acids eicos-11-enoic, $C_{20}H_{38}O_2$, and a docosenoic acid, $C_{22}H_{42}O_2$, which is probably erucic acid. This seed wax is further discussed below (p. 296).

SEED FATS WITH ERUCIC ACID AS A MAJOR COMPONENT

Major component acids: ERUCIC, OLEIC, LINOLEIC (LINOLENIC, EICOSENOIC).
Minor component acids: Palmitic, stearic, arachidic, behenic, lignoceric, hexadecenoic, docosadienoic.

(*See Table* 66, p. 298.)

Cruciferæ seed fats. There is every reason to think that most Cruciferous plants, which form a very large family widely distributed in many parts of the world, produce seeds in which erucic acid, $C_{22}H_{42}O_2$, is an important constituent.

The older procedures of simple ester-fractionation after lead salt separation of the mixed fatty acids were insufficient to cope with the complex mixtures of acids present in these oils, and the earlier studies made with the help of this method alone can now only be considered to give a rough outline of the component acids. The assistance of low-temperature crystallisation greatly facilitated the subsequent resolution of homologous esters by fractional distillation, whilst spectrophotometric analysis permitted accurate determinations of linoleic, linolenic and other "pentadiene" or "polyallylic"* acids which may be present. Latterly the acids in a number of Cruciferæ seed fats have been determined by gas–liquid chromatography.[175a] With very few exceptions all the data in Table 66 are based on analyses by one or other of the modern techniques.

The fatty acid compositions of seed fats from about 60 species of Cruciferous plants have so far been given. Erucic (docos-13-enoic) acid is present in all these except the genus *Lesquerella* and the following species: *Alyssum saxatile, Arabis alpina, Camelina sativa, Capsella bursa-pastoris, Hesperis matronalis* and two species of *Lepidium*. It forms 40 per cent. or more of the total acids of seed fats in *Arabis virginica*, most *Brassica* species, *Crambe* sp., *Eruca* sp., *Iberis umbellata, Lunaria* sp. and *Thlaspe arvense*, somewhat less in *Cheiranthus, Erysimum, Sisymbrium* and some other genera, and only 20 per cent. or less in woad, radish, watercress (*Nasturtium officinale*) and some species of cress (*Lepidium*).

The related docos-13,16-dienoic acid has been definitely detected in comparatively few of these seed fats, in which it only amounts to traces, or, at most, 1–2 per cent. of the total fatty acids.

Eicos-11-enoic acid is often present in larger amounts, usually of the order of 7–15 per cent. of the total acids, but its recorded appearance is erratic and in several species it may not be present. On the other hand, exceptionally large proportions of eicosenoic acid have been found in the seed fats of *Selenia grandis* (58), *Lepidium virginicum* (42), *Lobularia maritima* (42) and virginia stock (31 per cent.).

Lunaria sp. (Honesty) seed fats are exceptional in containing about 20 per cent. of a tetracosenoic acid, $C_{24}H_{46}O_2$.

The seed fats of 12 species of *Lesquerella* are still more unusual in their

---

* A term suggested by Hatt and Szumer[175c] for acids containing a repeated —$CH_2.CH:CH$— grouping.

major content of 45–74 per cent. of 14-hydroxy-eicos-*cis*-11-enoic acid, whilst two other species contain 44–50 per cent. of a hydroxy-oleic acid,[175b] and a major constituent of *Lesquerella densipila* seed fat acids is 12-hydroxy-octadeca-*cis*-9-*cis*-15-dienoic ("densipolic") acid.[175d]

Minor amounts (1·3 per cent.) of 15,16-epoxylinoleic acid (*cf.* Chapter IX, p. 618) were observed by Gunstone and Morris[175e] in the seed fat of *Camelina sativa*.

Saturated acids are only minor components of most Cruciferæ seed fats. Palmitic acid usually forms about 3–7 per cent., stearic not more than 2 or 3 per cent., whilst arachidic, behenic and lignoceric may account together for another 2–4 per cent.

Of the common unsaturated C_{18} acids, the more recent analyses indicate that linolenic acid is present in greater proportions in *Brassica* (and possibly other Cruciferæ) seed fats than was formerly supposed, with consequent reductions (compared with older records) in the amounts of oleic and linoleic acids. In the *Brassica* seed fats, speaking in very general terms, about 40 per cent. of the total acids belong to the unsaturated C_{18} series, made up of somewhere about 15 per cent. each of oleic and linoleic with up to 10 per cent. of linolenic acid. In other genera the relative proportions of the three C_{18} unsaturated acids, like those of erucic and eicosenoic, are much more variable.

Tropæolum seed fats. The seed fats of the nasturtium contain extremely high proportions of erucic acid. In 1899 Gadamer[176] stated that the seed fat of the giant nasturtium, *Tropæolum majus*, consists largely of trierucin, m.p. 30·5°, an observation confirmed by Sudborough *et al.*[177] in 1926.

In 1938 Hilditch and Meara[178] examined the liquid fat present to the extent of 8 per cent. in the seeds of the ordinary garden nasturtium (*Tropæolum minus* or *lobbianum* var.), and found component acids: erucic 81·8, oleic 16·0, linoleic 1·2, and saturated acids (chiefly palmitic and behenic) 1·0 per cent. This oil solidified on cooling to a mass of white stellate needles, which melted, after recrystallisation, at 31·5–32°, and were shown by X-ray spectrographic analysis to be trierucin. In 1953 Chisholm and Hopkins[179] reported that the 7 per cent. of oil in the seeds of Canadian nasturtiums had the following component acids: erucic 69, eicosenoic 20, oleic 7, linoleic 2, palmitic and stearic (each) 0·5, and arachidic 1 per cent.

In 1961 Earle *et al.*[175a] determined by gas–liquid chromatography the acids in *Tropæolum majus* seed fats to be palmitic 1, stearic *trace*, arachidic 0·3, behenic 0·2, unsaturated C_{18} 7, unsaturated C_{20} 21, unsaturated C_{22} 72 per cent.

The high proportion of erucic acid in the component acids of *Tropæolum* seed fats necessitates, of course, the presence of considerable amounts of the simple triglyceride, trierucin, therein, although it may be something of an exaggeration to say that they "consist largely" of trierucin.

The liquid seed wax of *Simmondsia californica*. The seeds of this sub-tropical North American shrub, belonging to the family Buxaceæ (formerly placed by botanists in the Box section of the Euphorbiaceæ), are exceptional, in their botanical group, in consisting wholly of embryo and cotyledons instead of endosperm. Their lipid content is equally exceptional, indeed at present unique, in that glycerides are completely absent: it is composed of a mixture of wax esters of higher unsaturated alcohols with higher unsaturated fatty acids.

Attention was first drawn to this unusual feature by Greene and Foster,[180] who pointed out that the seed lipids were waxes and not fats (glycerides), and likened the material to the sperm oil of the sperm whale. Concurrently, but independently, the nature of the seed wax was studied later in more detail by McKinney and Jamieson,[181] and by Green, Hilditch and Stainsby.[182] Neither group of workers could detect any glycerine in the products of hydrolysis, but both observed that the latter consisted of almost equal weights of higher aliphatic alcohols and acids. McKinney and Jamieson's fractionation figures led to the following percentage compositions for the alcohols and acids: *Alcohols*—eicosenol, $C_{20}H_{39}.OH$, 30 per cent.; docosenol, $C_{22}H_{43}.OH$, 70 per cent.; *Acids*—saturated 3·5, hexadecenoic 0·5, oleic 1·4, eicosenoic 64·4, and docosenoic 30·2 per cent. By disruptive oxidation, and by hydrogenation of the respective individual acids and alcohols to the corresponding saturated derivatives (which were submitted to X-ray spectrographic analysis), Green *et al.* established the structure of the alcohols as *n*-eicos-11-enol and *n*-docos-13-enol, and that of the main acid component as *n*-eicos-11-enoic acid; it is almost certain that the higher acid is docos-13-enoic (erucic) acid.

TABLE 66. *Component Acids of Seed Fats of Cruciferae*

Major component acids: All unsaturated—OLEIC, LINOLEIC, LINOLENIC, ERUCIC (LINOLENIC, EICOSENOIC).
Minor component acids: Saturated (C_{16} to C_{24}), hexadecenoic, docosadienoic (linolenic, eicosenoic).

| | | UNSATURATED COMPONENT ACIDS (PER CENT. WT.) | | | | | | | | |
| | | C_{16} MONO-ENE | C_{18} | | | C_{20} MONO-ENE | C_{22} | | METHODS | OBSERVERS |
	SOURCE		OL.	LIN.	LEN.		ERUCIC	DIENE		
Alyssum maritimum Sweet alyssum	U.S.A.	Trace	30.2	6.7	10.2	41.8	—	—	GLC	Mikolajczak et al.[23a]
" *saxatile* Yellow alyssum	U.S.A.	0.4	12	20	58	—	—	—	GLC	Earle et al.[1]
Arabis alpina White rock	U.S.A.	0.3	12	24	53	—	—	—	GLC	Earle et al.[1]
" *virginica*	U.S.A.	Trace	17	15	5	12	44	?	GLC	Earle et al.[1]
Brassica alba Yellow mustard	India	?	22.0	14.2	6.8	7.0	44.2	?	C,F,S	Kapur and Daubert[2a]
" *campestris* Rape, colza	Japan	?	14	24	2	?	55	?	F,K	Yamasaki et al.[2b]
" "	France	?	29	16	1	?	51	?	F	Rollet and Paquot[3]
" "	E. Indies	0.1	15.2	16.0	7.0	?	53.8	2.3	C,F,S	Hilditch et al.[4]
" "	U.S.A.	?	17.6	13.7	9.0	3.0	50.8	?	C,F,S	Kapur and Daubert[2a]
" "	India (Toria)	1.5	12.5	16	8.5	5	47.5	1.5	C,F,S	Baliga and Hilditch[5]
" "	India (Guzerat)	2.5	16.5	13.5	7	5	45	1	C,F,S	Baliga and Hilditch[5]
" "	Poland	3	14	12	7.5	3.5	52.5	1	C,F,S	Baliga and Hilditch[5]
" "	Argentina	0.5	16	12.5	10	6	47.5	1	C,F,S	Baliga and Hilditch[5]
" "	W. Canada	?	16.5	15	10	12	40	—	F	Youngs et al.[6]
" "	Poland	—	15–23	13–19	5–9	—	44–49	—	F	Budzynska[7a]
" "	U.S.A.	0.3	25	18	10	10	31	—	GLC	Earle et al.[1]
" "	U.S.A.	0.5	14	14	9	8	31	—	GLC	Earle et al.[1]
" *carinata* Ravison	Black Sea	0.5	15.5	21	14	4	39	1	C,F,S	Baliga and Hilditch[5]
" *carinata* Abyssinian mustard	U.S.A.	0.4	8	19	14	8	42	—	GLC	Earle et al.[1]
" *juncea* Mustard	U.S.A.	0.5	10	21	13	7	37	0.8	GLC	Earle et al.[1]
" *juncea* Mustard	India	?	31	17	3	?	42	?	F	Dutt[7b]
" *napus* Rape (Matador)	U.S.A.	0.4	22	24	10	13	22	—	GLC	Earle et al.[1]
" *napus* (Duro)	U.S.A.	0.5	14	15	8	8	44	—	GLC	Earle et al.[1]
" *nigra* Black mustard	U.S.A.	0.2	16	16	8	10	43	1	GLC	Earle et al.[1]
" *nigra* Black mustard	India	?	20.7	18.0	6.5	8.1	40.6	?	C,F,S	Kapur and Daubert[2a]
" *oleracea* Cabbage	U.S.A.	0.4	8	14	18	7	43	1	GLC	Earle et al.[1]
" *oleracea* Cabbage	U.S.A.	0.4	8	20	15	9	36	1	GLC	Earle et al.[1]
" *sinapis* Charlock	W. Canada	?	31	27	13	12	8.5	?	C,F,S	Hoffman et al.[8]

298

Species	Common name	Source								Method	Reference
Cakile edentula	Sea rocket	U.S.A.	0·2	23	26	18	7	17	Trace	GLC	Earle et al.[1]
Camelina sativa	—	Sweden	2·4	23·9	14·5	33·4	13·8	3·2	?	C,F,S	Holmberg and Sellman[9]
Capsella bursa-pastoris	Shepherd's purse	U.S.A.	—	9	19	38	18	—	—	GLC	Earle et al.[1]
Cheiranthus cheiri	Wallflower	U.S.A.	0·3	11	18	35	16	—	—	GLC	Earle et al.[1]
" "		England	?	10	32	16	?	38·5	?	F,T	Griffiths and Hilditch[10]
" "		Holland	?	8	21	23	?	43	?	B,T	Van Loon[11]
Conringia orientalis	Hare's ear mustard	U.S.A.	0·3	10	17	23	12	31	Trace	GLC	Earle et al.[1]
" "		W. Canada	?	20–30	15–20	?	ca. 10	35–45	?	L,F	Hopkins[12a]
Crambe abyssinica	Colewort	Europe	0·5	18·7	12·7	7	—	51·4	1	F	Niewiadomski et al.[12b]
" "		U.S.A.	0·3	18	11	4	2	59	—	GLC	Earle et al.[1]
" "		U.S.A.	0·5	18	9	6	3	59	—	GLC	Earle et al.[1]
Descurainia sophia	—	India	1·5	14	17	37	10	9	0·5	C,F,S	Balga and Hilditch[5]
Eruca sativa	Jamba rape	Bulgaria	—	35·7	12·2	6·3	11·5	40·5	0·5	?	Popov et al.[12c]
" "		U.S.A.	0·2	18	10	12	—	43	?	GLC	Earle et al.[1]
" "		Russia	0·4	44	2	2·5	8	29	?	?	Maslov et al.[13]
Erysimum canescens	—	U.S.A.	?	13	27	22	?	22	?	GLC	Earle et al.[1]
" *perowskianum*	—	Holland	1	11	35	46	?	?	?	B,K	Steger and van Loon[14a]
Hesperis matronalis	Rocket	U.S.A.	—	13	24	51	6	38	—	GLC	Earle et al.[1]
Iberis amara	Candytuft	U.S.A.	0·3	19	18	12	7	50	Trace	GLC	Earle et al.[1]
" *umbellata*	—	Holland	0·2	10	19	19	?	21	?	GLC	Earle et al.[1]
Isatis tinctoria	Woad	U.S.A.	?	27	19	24	13	20	Trace	F,K	Steger and van Loon[14b]
" "		India	—	16	12	28	—	32	?	GLC	Earle et al.[1]
Lepidium iberis	Cress	U.S.A.	—	13	48	5	15	8	—	F,T	Joshi and Tewari[21a]
" *lasiocarpum*	—	U.S.A.	0·8	17	8	40	0·6	—	—	GLC	Earle et al.[1]
" *montanum*	—	India	0·5	25	14	50	—	26·4	—	GLC	Earle et al.[1]
" *sativum*	—	Bulgaria	—	61·3	29·0	28·0	10	19	—	?	Vasudev[21b]
" "		U.S.A.	0·3	32·3	10	6·8	42	—	—	?	Popov et al.[12c]
" *virginicum*	—	U.S.A.	1	21	6	32	10	—	—	GLC	Earle et al.[1]
Lesquerella species (14)	—	U.S.A.	ca. 1	10–29	3–10	1–14	ca. 1	—	—	GLC	Earle et al.[1]
										GLC	Mikolajczak et al.[23a]

(45–74 per cent. 14-hydroxy-*cis*-eicos-11-enoic acid in 12 species, 44, 50 per cent. hydroxy-oleic acids in 2 species.) (See *text*, p. 295)

Species	Common name	Source								Method	Reference
Lobularia maritima	Honesty	U.S.A.	Trace	30	17	10	42	—	—	GLC	Earle et al.[1]
Lunaria annua	—	U.S.A.	0·3	26	7	0·6	2	48	—*	GLC	Earle et al.[1]
" *biennis*	—	U.S.A.	0·2	23	7	2	2	42	—*	GLC	Wilson et al.[23b]

* *Lunaria annua* seed fat also contained tetracosenoic acid 14 per cent.; *L. biennis*, 21 per cent.

TABLE 66. Component Acids of Seed Fats of Cruciferæ—continued

UNSATURATED COMPONENT ACIDS (PER CENT. WT.)

Species	Common name	SOURCE	C_{16} MONO-ENE	C_{18} OL.	C_{18} LIN.	C_{18} LEN.	C_{20} MONO-ENE	C_{22} ERUCIC	DIENE	METHODS	OBSERVERS	Lit. Ref. No.
Malcolmia maritima	Virginia stock	U.S.A.	0·4	6	15	21	31	15	0·4	GLC	Earle et al.[1]	
Matthiola bicornis	Night-scented stock	U.S.A.	0·8	14	12	63	—	—	—	GLC	Earle et al.[1]	
incana		Argentine	—	32·2	21·7	10·7	—	13·1	—	F, H	Rohman and Khan[22]	23a
Nasturtium officinale	Watercress	U.S.A.	Trace	34	23	0·5	11	18	—	GLC	Earle et al.[1]	1
Nerisyrenia camporum		U.S.A.	0·4	21	24	21	21	—	—	GLC	Earle et al.[1]	1
Pringlea antiscorbutica	Kerguelen cabbage	Antarctic	3·7	14·4	20·4	28·6	11·3	11·5	0·1	C, F, S	Hatt and Szumer[15]	
Raphanus sativus	Radish	India	?	60·8	4·5	3·6	?	22·0	?	C, F	Singh and Kumar[16]	
Selenia grandis		U.S.A.	0·4	26	13	11	9	30	—	GLC	Earle et al.[1]	
" "		U.S.A.	0·3	28	4	2	58	3	—	GLC	Earle et al.[1,23c]	
Sisymbrium altissimum	Tumbling mustard	U.S.A.	?	5	19	35	?	26	?	F, T	Goss and Ruckman[17]	
" irio	Wild mustard	India	?	27	35	8	?	17	?	L, F, H	Aggarwal et al.[18]	
Sophia ochroleuca		U.S.A.	0·8	19	13	33	8	6	—	GLC	Earle et al.[1]	
Stanleyella texana		U.S.A.	0·2	12	18	26	13	14	—	GLC	Earle et al.[1]	
Thlaspe arvense		U.S.A.	0·6	23	9	23	15	18	—	GLC	Earle et al.[1]	
"	Fanweed	W. Canada	?	12·5	33	0·5	?	49	?	F	Clopton and Triebold[19]	
"		U.S.A.	?	16	25	12	7	37	?	C, F, S	Hopkins and Chisholm[20]	
"		U.S.A.	0·2	10	20	14	11	38	—	GLC	Earle et al.[1]	

SATURATED COMPONENT ACIDS (PER CENT. WT.)

Species	Common name	SOURCE	C_{14}	C_{16}	C_{18}	C_{20}	C_{22}	C_{24}	Lit. Ref. No.
Alyssum maritimum	Sweet alyssum	U.S.A.	Trace	3·9	5·8	0·6	0·5	—	23a
" saxatile	Yellow alyssum	U.S.A.	2	5	1	—	—	—	1
Arabis alpina	White rock	U.S.A.	Trace	6	2	0·4	—	—	1
" virginica	—	U.S.A.	—	6	—	0·5	Trace	—	
Brassica alba	Yellow mustard	India	0·4	1·5	0·6	—	2·0	1·0	2a
" campestris	Rape, colza	Japan	—	4	0·4	—	1	—	2b
" "		France	—	1·5	—	—	—	1·5	3
" "		E. Indies	0·2	2·2	0·4	0·5	1·5	0·8	4
" "		U.S.A.	0·6	1·0	0·2	0·4	2·5	1·2	2a
" "		India (Toria)	—	2	—	←	5·5	→	5

Species	Common name	Source										Ref.
Brassica alba campestris	Rape, colza	India (Guzerat)	—	2		↑		↑		7·5	↑	5
" "	"	Poland	—	3						3·5		5
" "	"	Argentina	—	2·5						4·0		5
" "	"	W. Canada	—			6·5						6
" "	"	Poland	Trace	2	1	7–22	0·6		0·3		0·9	7a
" "	"	U.S.A.	—	3	1		1		0·7		0·7	1
" " *carinata*	Ravison	U.S.A.	—	4	2		1		1		2	1
" "	Abyssinian mustard	Black Sea	0·2	4	—	5	1		1		2	5
" " *juncea*	Mustard	India	0·5	—	0·5				4			7b
" "	"	U.S.A.	—	3	2		0·8		0·3		2	1
" " *napus*	Rape (Matador)	U.S.A.	—	3	1		0·6		0·2		2	1
" "	(Duro)	U.S.A.	—	2	1		0·3		Trace		0·5	1
" " *nigra*	Black mustard	India	0·8	0·7	—		0·5		2·3		0·6	2a
" "	"	U.S.A.	Trace	3	1		0·8		0·5		1·8	1
" " *oleracea*	Cabbage	U.S.A.	Trace	5	2				1		1	8
" " *sinapis*	Charlock	W. Canada	—	—		6·3						1
Cakile edentula	Sea rocket	Sweden	—	4	2		1		1			9
Camelina sativa	—	U.S.A.	Trace	5·2	1·8		1·2		0·6			1
Capsella bursa-pastoris	Shepherd's purse	England	—	6	3		2		1		0·5	10
Cheiranthus cheiri	Wallflower	Holland	—	9	6		3				0·5	11
" "	"	U.S.A.	—	3								12a
Conringia orientalis	Hare's ear mustard	W. Canada	4·7	5		2	0·5		0·7			12b
Crambe abyssinica	Colewort	Europe	0·1	3	0·8		0·5		0·7			1
" "	"	U.S.A.	—	2	—		2·7		0·1			1
" "	"	U.S.A.	0·1	9·7	0·5		1		1			1
Descurainia sophia	—	U.S.A.	—	2	0·7		1		1			5
Eruca sativa	Jamba rape	India	Trace	2	2	5	0·9		0·3		1	1
" " *Erysimum canescens*	—	U.S.A.	—	6	—							13
" " *perowskianum*	—	Russia	Trace	4·5	1		0·8		0·5			1
Hesperis matronalis	Rocket	Holland	—	4	—	8						14a
" "	"	U.S.A.	Trace	10·5								1
Iberis amara	Candytuft	U.S.A.	—	3								1
" " *umbellata*	"	U.S.A.	—	3	2							1

301

TABLE 66. Component Acids of Seed Fats of Cruciferæ—continued

			SATURATED COMPONENT ACIDS PER CENT. (WT.)						Lit. Ref. No.
			C_{14}	C_{16}	C_{18}	C_{20}	C_{22}	C_{24}	
Isatis tinctoria	Woad	Holland	—	4	3	2	2 →	→	14b
" "		U.S.A.	—	6	2	3	Trace	1	1
Lepidium iberis	Cress	India	—	6	2	3	—	—	21a
" *lasiocarpum*		U.S.A.	—	7	3	3	—	—	1
" *montanum*		U.S.A.	—	1·3	6·0	1·5	1·7	0·2	21b
" *sativum*		India	0·1	9	2	3	0·8	—	1
" "		U.S.A.	0·2	7	1·4	3	2	2	23a
" *virginicum*		U.S.A.	Trace	1·7	6	—	0·5	—	1
Lesquerella species		U.S.A.	Trace	4	0·3	0·6	—	—	1
Lobularia maritima		U.S.A.	—	1	0·4	0·4	—	—	23b
Lunaria annua	Honesty	U.S.A.	—	2	0·4	0·4	—	—	1
" *biennis*		U.S.A.	—	6	2	3	—	—	1
Malcolmia maritima	Virginia stock	U.S.A.	0·3	4·7	4·4	—	—	0·7	22
Matthiola bicornis	Night-scented stock	U.S.A.	2·6	9	2	2·6	0·5	—	1
" *incana*		Argentina	—	6	3	1	—	—	15
Nasturtium officinale	Watercress	U.S.A.	—	4·5	2·6	0·7	0·5	—	16
Nerisyrenia camporum		U.S.A.	—	1·3	1·4	3·0	3·4	—	1, 23c
Pringlea antiscorbutica	Kerguelen cabbage	Antarctic	—	6	2	2	—	Trace	17
Raphanus sativus	Radish	India	—	2	1	Trace	—	—	18
" "		U.S.A.	—	14	3	Trace	—	—	1
Selenia grandis		U.S.A.	—	8	3	3	0·5	—	1
Sisymbrium altissimum	Tumbling mustard	U.S.A.	—	14	1	2	0·6	—	1
" *irio*	Wild mustard	India	—	9	3	2	2	—	19
" "		U.S.A.	—	7	1	2	—	—	20
Sophia ochroleuca		U.S.A.	—	1·5	3	Trace	0·1	3·5	1
Stanleyella texana		U.S.A.	—		3	—	—	—	1
Thlaspe arvense	Fanweed	W. Canada	0·3	3	0·5	Trace	—	—	19
" "		U.S.A.							20
" "		U.S.A.							1

302

References to Table 66

1. F. R. Earle, I. A. Wolff *et al.*, *J. Amer. Oil Chem. Soc.*, 1961, **38**, 678.
2. (*a*) S. L. Kapur and B. F. Daubert, *J. Amer. Oil Chem. Soc.*, 1949, **26**, 472; (*b*) R. Yamasaki and K. Ichihara, *Bull. Chem. Soc. Japan*, 1936, **11**, 114.
3. M. Rollet and C. Paquot, *Bull. Soc. Chim.*, 1945, [v], **12**, 1048.
4. T. P. Hilditch, P. A. Laurent and M. L. Meara, *J. Soc. Chem. Ind.*, 1947, **66**, 19.
5. M. N. Baliga and T. P. Hilditch, *J. Soc. Chem. Ind.*, 1948, **67**, 258.
6. C. G. Youngs, T. M. Mallard, B. M. Craig and H. R. Sallans, *Canad. J. Chem.*, 1951, **29**, 871.
7. (*a*) J. Budzynska, *Roczniki Chem.*, 1956, **6**, 229; (*b*) S. Dutt, *Indian Soap J.*, 1939, **5**, 279.
8. W. F. Hoffman, A. Zuckerman and N. H. Grace, *J. Amer. Oil Chem. Soc.*, 1951, **28**, 522.
9. J. Holmberg and G. Sellman, *Svensk Kem. Tidskr.*, 1952, **64**, 270.
10. H. N. Griffiths and T. P. Hilditch, *J. Soc. Chem. Ind.*, 1934, **53**, 75т.
11. J. van Loon, *Rec. trav. chim.*, 1930, **49**, 745.
12. (*a*) C. Y. Hopkins, *Canad. J. Research*, 1946, **B**, **24**, 211; (*b*) H. Niewiadomski, B. Drozdowski and W. Zwierzykonski, *Fette, Seifen, Anstrichm.*, 1959, **61**, 897; (*c*) A. Popov and P. Mazhdrakov, *C. R. Acad. Bulg. Sci.*, 1958, **11**, 279.
13. N. Y. Maslov and A. E. Petrov-Speridonov, *Zhur. Priklad. Khim.*, 1952, **25**, 1326.
14. A. Steger and J. van Loon, (*a*) *Rec. trav. chim.*, 1942, **61**, 123; (*b*) *ibid.*, 1941, **60**, 947.
15. H. H. Hatt and A. Z. Szumer, *J. Sci. Food Agric.*, 1953, **4**, 273.
16. B. K. Singh and A. Kumar, *Proc. Indian Acad. Sci.*, 1948, **27**, **B**, 156.
17. W. H. Goss and J. E. Ruckman, *Oil and Soap*, 1944, **21**, 234.
18. J. S. Aggarwal and Karimullah, *J. Sci. Indust. Res., India*, 1946, **5**, **B**, 57.
19. J. R. Clopton and H. O. Triebold, *Ind. Eng. Chem.*, 1944, **36**, 218.
20. C. Y. Hopkins and M. J. Chisholm, *Canad. J. Chem.*, 1954, **32**, 1033.
21. (*a*) B. C. Joshi and J. D. Tewari, *Arch. Pharm.*, 1957, **290**, 215; (*b*) Vasudev, I. Chandra and K. L. Handa, *J. Sci. Indust. Res. (India)*, 1956, **15**, **B**, 725.
22. A. U. Rohman and M. S. Khan, *J. Amer. Oil Chem. Soc.*, 1961, **38**, 281.
23. (*a*) K. L. Mikolajczak, F. R. Earle and I. A. Wolff, *ibid.*, 1962, **39**, 78; (*b*) T. L. Wilson, C. R. Smith, Jr. and I. A. Wolff, *ibid.*, 1962, **39**, 104; (*c*) *idem, ibid.*, 1963, **40**, 294.

(*ii*) Seed Fats Containing Specific Saturated Acids

As in the case of the rarer unsaturated acids of vegetable origin which have just been discussed, the occurrence of saturated acids other than palmitic in quantity is of a very specific nature and is confined, broadly speaking, to the seed fats of members of the following families:

SPECIFIC SATURATED MAJOR COMPONENTS	FAMILIES
Arachidic (behenic, lignoceric)	Leguminosæ, Moringaceæ, Ochnaceæ, Sapindaceæ.
Stearic	Gnetaceæ, Meliaceæ, Menispermaceæ, Sterculiaceæ, Guttiferæ, Dipterocarpaceæ,Burseraceæ,Sapotaceæ, Convolvulaceæ, Verbenaceæ.
Myristic	Myristicaceæ (Vochysiaceæ).
Lauric	Lauraceæ.
Lauric and myristic (together)	Palmæ, Simarubaceæ (Salvadoraceæ).
Capric and lauric	Ulmaceæ.

SEED FATS OF WHICH ARACHIDIC (BEHENIC) OR LIGNOCERIC ACIDS ARE MAJOR COMPONENTS

Major component acids: OLEIC, LINOLEIC, ARACHIDIC, (BEHENIC), LIGNOCERIC.
Minor component acids: Palmitic, stearic (myristic, arachidic, lignoceric, linolenic).
(*See Table 67, p. 312*).

Leguminosæ seed fats. The figures for these are interesting from several points of view, and suggest that this family (perhaps especially its sub-division Mimosoideæ) may prove a very interesting field for further investigation of the component acids of seed fats. The *Adenanthera* fat was investigated by workers at the Indian Institute of Science, Bangalore, and the presence of 25 per cent. of lignoceric (*n*-tetracosanoic) acid was unequivocally established. *Pentaclethra* seed fats contain 10–15 per cent. of behenic and lignoceric acids as the major saturated components (arachidic acid, formerly believed to be present in quantity, only amounts to about 3 per cent. of the total acids). Behenic acid also seems to be the most abundant saturated acid in the seed fats of *Parkia* and *Xylia* species. In contrast, the saturated acids of seed fats of *Acacia* and *Albizzia* species consist largely of palmitic acid, but also include from 2 to 4 per cent. of arachidic, behenic and lignoceric acids – thus resembling many seed fats of the two other botanical sub-divisions of the pea family (*v. infra*).

It is interesting that Black *et al.*[183a] who found that the seed fatty acids of *Acacia cyclops* were similar to those of other *Acacia* species mentioned above, also examined the fat in the funicle (the short stalk attaching the seed to the pod) of this species, and give its component acids as palmitic 21·6, stearic 2·7, arachidic 0·4, hexadecenoic 7·3, oleic 61·7, linoleic 3·1, and unsaturated C_{20} acids 1·2 per cent. (wt.). Thus, the funicle fat is a typical *fruit-coat* fat (*cf.* pp. 189–200 and Table 57) with palmitic and oleic acids as the major components, and with no behenic or lignoceric, and only a fractional percentage of arachidic acid. Harrison and Hawke,[183b] on the contrary, found that the 1·2 per cent. of fat in the pods of *Acacia giraffæ* had a similar composition to the seed fat (Table 67, p. 312): myristic 0·8, palmitic 17·0, stearic 9·1, arachidic 8·3, behenic 0·1; unsaturated C_{16} 11·5, oleic 29·3, linoleic 19·0, unsaturated C_{20} 4·9 per cent. (wt.).

In the other botanical sub-divisions of the Leguminosæ (Cæsalpinioidæ and Papilionatæ) no striking instance of large proportions of arachidic or higher saturated acids has yet been encountered. There seem here to be, however, two types of seed fat component acid mixtures with no sharply defined boundary between them. In one group the saturated C_{20}, C_{22}, and/or C_{24} acids are present, albeit as minor components in these cases; together they may amount to nearly 15 per cent. of the total acids (as in tonka bean oil) or to 6–7 per cent. (as in groundnut and pongamia oils). In this type of seed fat there is also usually 5–8 per cent. of palmitic and a smaller amount of stearic acid. In the other group (which includes soya beans, alfalfa (lucerne), some pulses and vetches), palmitic and stearic acid contents are usually similar to those just mentioned, but the amount of higher saturated acids is almost negligible and is, as a matter of fact, no higher than has frequently been noted as arachidic or lignoceric acid in many of the liquid fats discussed in Tables 59, 60, 61 and 62.

It should be observed that, in one important respect, all the Leguminosæ seed fats resemble the simple "linoleic-oleic-palmitic" type dealt with in detail in Table 60: the chief components are oleic and linoleic acids, these together usually forming 60–80 per cent. of the total component acids. In many species the seed fats are "linoleic-rich", i.e., they may contain 40–50 per cent. or more of linoleic acid; in others the position is reversed and oleic is present in greater amount than linoleic acid.

Linolenic acid is absent from many leguminous seed fats, but in others it is present in small proportions (e.g. soya bean oil), and again in other species (e.g. *Lespedeza*, pulses (*Phaseolus, Vicia*), lucerne) it may appear as a major component and form 15 per cent. or more of the total fatty acids. This appears to obtain in small leguminous herbs such as the clovers, lucernes and vetches, but more detailed data are necessary before this can be accepted as a general feature.

It is not yet possible to correlate these variations with biological variations or with differences in temperature, although the former may at present appear on the whole more likely. Cooler temperatures of growth might be considered to account for the higher linoleic/oleic acid ratio in Spanish and Virginian groundnuts as compared with West African groundnuts, or for the higher linoleic/oleic acid ratio as between soya beans on the one hand, and groundnuts on the other. Contrariwise, however, the linoleic/oleic acid ratio is higher in the tropical Bonducella nut than in the sub-tropical soya bean or the Manchurian mungo bean.

Groundnut oils. As in other cases where the industrial importance of a fatty oil has afforded opportunity for detailed examination of specimens from many sources, the component acid data will be dealt with here (Table 67A) instead of in the general Table 67. All data quoted were obtained by the

TABLE 67A. Component Acids of Groundnut Oils

SOURCE	VARIETY, ETC.	PALMITIC	STEARIC	C$_{20}$, C$_{22}$ and C$_{24}$	OLEIC	LINOLEIC	METHOD	OBSERVERS
India		9·4	3·1	5·1	54·9	26·2 (a)	F	Longenecker[184]
"		8·3	3·1	6·6	56·0	26·0	F	Jasperson et al.[185a]
"		8·0	4·4	6·6	52·5	26·3 (b)	C, F	Hilditch and Riley[186]
"	Coromandel	17·9 →			63·5	18·6	T	Vizern[187a]
Philippines	var. Valencia	8·6	3·6	5·9	54·5	27·4	T	Cruz and West[188a]
China	var. Valencia	17·4 →			52·3	30·3	T	Vizern[187a]
United States	var. Virginia	6·3	4·9	5·9	61·1	21·8	F	Jamieson et al.[189a]
"	var. Spanish	8·3	6·3	7·1	53·4	24·9	F	Jamieson et al.[189a]
" (Georgia)	var. N.C. Runner	20 →			53	27	T	Higgins et al.[190]
"	var. Improved West Spanish	23 →			45	32	T	Higgins et al.[190]
"	var. Hybrid Spanish x Basse	23 →			50	27	T	Higgins et al.[190]
"	var. Basse x Dixie Giant	18 →			60	22	T	Higgins et al.[190]
West Africa Senegal		7·3	2·6	5·2	65·7	19·2	F	Armstrong and Allan[191]
Nigeria		8·2	3·4	6·1	60·4	21·9	F	Griffiths et al.[192]
"		8·7	3·1	6·6	64·8	16·8	F	Jasperson[185b]
"		17·9 →			64·0	18·1	T	Vizern[187a]
"		8·8	4·5	6·1	60·3	20·3	C, F	Crawford et al.[193]

								Method	Reference
Tanganyika (Kongwa)	Natal Common	9·7	5·6	8·0	40·8	35·9		C, F	Crawford et al.[193]
" "	Spanish Bunch	8·7	5·0	9·9	39·2	37·2		C, F	Crawford et al.[193]
" "	Valencia	10·8	4·2	7·6	39·2	38·2		C, F	Crawford et al.[193]
Argentina		11·4	2·8	7·3	42·3	33·4 (c)		C, F	Hilditch and Riley[186]
"		←——— 17·4 ———→			45·4	37·3		T	Vizern[187a]
Canada		11·4	3·3	3·8	54·7	25·7 (d)		GLC	Craig and Murti[187b]
United States (Florida)	Spanish	12·9	4·5	4·9	43·1	32·5 (e)		GLC	French[128b]
" "	N. Carolina	10·5	4·3	4·8	51·9	26·2 (f)		GLC	French[128b]
" "	Early Runner	9·7	3·1	5·2	55·6	24·7 (g)		GLC	French[128b]
" "	Dixie Runner	9·3	3·1	4·9	58·5	22·4 (h)		GLC	French[128b]
" "	Fla. 393—47	7·3	4·3	5·3	63·5	17·7 (i)		GLC	French[128b]
" " (Georgia)	Arachis pusilla	←——— 21·7 ———→			40·4	37·9		T	Pickett[187c]
" "	A. villosa var. correntina	←——— 16·7 ———→			56·9	26·4		T	Pickett[187c]

	SATURATED			UNSATURATED	
	C_{20}	C_{22}	C_{24}	C_{16}	C_{20}
	1·2	1·8	0·8	—	1·1
	0·7	3·1	1·1	0·2	—
	0·6	3·1	1·1	Trace	—
	1·0	3·1	1·1	—	—
	0·7	3·1	1·1	—	—
	1·1	3·1	1·1	—	—

Minor component acids recorded as follows:

		MYRISTIC	HEXADECENOIC
(a)	India (Longenecker)	0·4	0·9
(b)	" (Hilditch and Riley)	0·5	1·7
(c)	Argentina	0·4	2·4

(d) Canada
(e) Florida Spanish
(f) " N. Carolina
(g) " Early Runner
(h) " Dixie Runner
(i) " Fla. 393—47

(Literature references to Table 67A are in the general bibliography to Chapter IV, pp. 353 356.)

307

modern methods, and in nearly all instances ester-fractionation or gas–liquid chromatography was employed.

From the figures in Table 67A it would appear that perhaps three different types of groundnut oil fatty acids may be distinguished, differing somewhat as follows:

SATURATED	OLEIC	LINOLEIC
15–18	66–60	19–22
18–23	56–50	25–27
22–24	48–39	30–37

West African native grown groundnuts belong to the group with the lower linoleic acid contents, and seem not to vary much in their seed fat composition; Indian groundnuts on the whole tend to belong to the intermediate class (with about 26 per cent. of linoleic acid) as do several of those grown in the United States, but groundnut oils from China, Tanganyika and Argentina contain nearly twice as much linoleic acid as the Nigerian native oils. Such wide variations may have some effect on the relative suitability of different groundnut oils for edible fats (cf. Chapter VI, p. 449). The causes of the variable oleic and linoleic acid content are apparently not so simple as in the cases of some other oils such as those of linseed (p. 211), sunflower (p. 227) or soya beans (p. 309). The data of Jamieson et al.[189] and of Higgins et al.[190] suggest that different varieties or hybrids of the groundnut plant yield seed oils of somewhat different composition when grown in the same location: on the other hand, the Spanish and Valencia varieties of groundnuts, when grown in Tanganyika, produced oils of much higher linoleic acid content than the same varieties when grown in the United States or in the Philippine Islands.

The figures given by French[128b] for eleven varieties of groundnuts grown on the Florida Experimental Station in 1958 (of which five typical results are shown in Table 67A) suggest to this worker that "genetic factors may be of importance equal to that of environmental temperature." This conclusion is supported by the earlier work of Pickett[187c] on two other species of Arachis grown at the Georgia Experimental Station in the U.S.A., wherein differences similar to those between Argentine[186] and Indian[186] or West African[193] groundnut oils were observed. On the other hand, Cattaneo[187d] found that groundnut oils from different geographical areas in Argentina had similarly wide ranges of component acids: palmitic 8–13, stearic 2–4, saturated C_{20}, C_{22} and C_{24} 3–9, oleic 37–54, linoleic 26–40 per cent.

Although groundnut oils from the (possibly) somewhat cooler climates of China and Argentina also belong to the group richest in linoleic acid, the high linoleic acid figures for groundnut oils from Tanganyika suggest that, in this instance, cooler climates with slower development of the seeds are not the sole cause of the production of the more unsaturated groundnut oils. It may be concluded that, besides varietal differences and the influence of temperature during ripening of the nuts, other factors – as yet unclarified – contribute materially to the observed differences in composition of groundnut oils. The peculiarity of Arachis hypogæa in burying its fruits in the ground as they mature is an unusual factor which may enter into the matter.

Whatever may be the causes of these differences, it is noticeable that, as in cases where climatic (temperature) influences are the main factors in producing oils of different degrees of unsaturation from the same plant species, the most unsaturated groundnut oils also contain somewhat more of the saturated component acids than do the less unsaturated groundnut oils. It may therefore be concluded that, whatever the influences responsible, the relative effects on the synthesis of the unsaturated C_{18} acids and on that of the saturated acids in the developing groundnut are strictly similar in character to those in other seed oils (cf. biosynthesis of seed fats, Chapter VIII, pp. 537–539).

There was at one time some uncertainty as to whether the higher saturated acids (arachidic, behenic and lignoceric) in groundnut and other leguminous seed oils were in fact acids of the normal series, or whether possibly they were branched-chain acids. This was due to the difficulty of separating either of the three acids from the mixture of all three by the simple process of crystallisation from solvents. When separation by fractional distillation of simple esters of the mixed acids in efficient fractionation columns came into use, it was soon established that the three acids were respectively n-eicosanoic, n-docosanoic, and n-tetracosanoic acids. Jantzen and Tiedcke[194] were the first to succeed by this means in obtaining definite fractions of the methyl esters of each of the three acids from groundnut oil; Jasperson et al.[185a] give the proportions of these acids in an Indian groundnut oil as arachidic 2·4, behenic 3·1, and lignoceric 1·1 per cent. (wt.) of the total fatty acids.

Soya bean oils. Here again the somewhat numerous component acid records are given separately from the main Table 67 in Table 67B.

TABLE 67B. *Component Acids of Soya Bean Oils*

PALMITIC	STEARIC	C_{20}, C_{22} and C_{24}	OLEIC	LINOLEIC	LINOLENIC	OBSERVERS
6·8	4·4	0·8	34	52	2	Jamieson et al.[189b]
←	14	→	26	57	3	Heiduschka et al. [195]
7·0	5·5	0·3	23	60	3	Griffiths et al.[192]
9·0	3·9	0·6	30·5	54	2	Cruz and West[188b]
9·8	2·4	0·9	28·9	50·7	6·5(a)	Hilditch et al.[196a]
10·6	2·4	2·4	23·5	51·2	8·5(b)	Hilditch et al.[196b]
←	17·2	→	23·5	49·8	9·5	Hilditch et al.[196c]
←	15	→	22	53	10	Mitchell et al.[197]
←	15	→	23	55	7	Mitchell et al.[197]
←	17	→	22	56	5	Mitchell et al.[197]
10	3	—	30	53	4	Venkitasubramanian[198]
11·5	3·9	—	24·6	52·0	8·0(c)	Craig and Murti[187b]

(a) Also myristic 0·3, hexadecenoic 0·5 per cent. (wt.).
(b) Also myristic 0·4, hexadecenoic 1·0 per cent. (wt.).
(c) Analysis by gas–liquid chromatography (all other results in Table 67B by ester-fractionation and/or U.V. spectrophotometry).

The higher saturated acids in soya bean oil appear to consist mainly of arachidic acid. The general figures given for the oils in Table 67B are elaborated by a number of studies of soya beans grown under controlled conditions in the United States; the component acids (total saturated, oleic, linoleic, and linolenic) were determined in these further studies by lead salt separations (L) coupled with thiocyanometric determination (T) of the unsaturated acids.

In 1933, Jamieson, Baughman and McKinney[199] gave the component acids of soya bean oils from different varieties of seed, grown in various localities of the United States suitable for soya bean culture, as follows:

VARIETY	OIL I.V.	COMPONENT FATTY ACIDS			
		SAT.	OL.	LIN.	LEN.
Dunfield	131·4	13·5	32	44·5	10
Manchu	131·0	13	29	52	6
Haberlandt	131·0	13·5	28·5	51	7
Virginia	127·8	13·5	31·5	49	6
Chiquita	140·7	13	25	49	13
Mammoth Yellow	129·4	13	33	46	8

In 1938, Dollear, Krauczunas and Markley[200a] published figures for three oils from seeds of the Dunfield variety grown in Missouri and Indiana, one of which, grown in Missouri in a very abnormal (hot and dry) season in 1936, yielded an oil of exceptionally low iodine value. In 1940 the same workers[200b] gave similar data for four other varieties grown in Illinois and in New York State. They concluded that the abnormally low unsaturation of the 1936 Missouri crop was due to a combination of factors – varietal, climatic and soil; and that, although the relative influence of each environmental factor cannot be evaluated, in this instance the total effect resulted in a considerable lowering of the total unsaturation. These authors further pointed out that, as the total unsaturation of the oils varies, the proportions of saturated acids remain remarkably constant, whilst those of linolenic and linoleic acids increase more or less regularly with increasing iodine values of the oils, and those of oleic acid at the same time decrease progressively. These findings are borne out not only by their own figures (below), but also by other data in Table 67B.

VARIETY	GROWN IN	OIL I.V.	COMPONENT FATTY ACIDS			
			SAT.	OL.	LIN.	LEN.
Dunfield	Missouri, 1936	102·9	12	59	28	1
"	" 1937	124·0	13	33·5	50·5	3
"	Indiana, 1937	127·3	13	31	53	3
Illini	Illinois, 1936	131·6	13	27	56	4
Peking	" 1937	137·8	12	22	61	5
Seneca	New York, 1938	139·4	12	23	59	6
Wild beans	Illinois, 1938	151·4	13	10	66	10

Similar conclusions, based upon analyses of 95 specimens of soya bean oil of iodine values ranging from 99·6 to 147·6, were recorded by Scholfield and Bull[201a] (1944). Alderks[201b] (1949) examined thirteen specimens of soya bean oil from experimental strains of beans grown in Indiana, Illinois, Iowa and Ohio; the extremes of iodine values were 128·7–136·6, and of component acids: saturated 16–19, oleic 11–22, linoleic 49–58, and linolenic 6–8·5 per cent. (wt.). Similar trials (1961) on about 250 field samples by H. B. White et al.[201c] gave ranges of linoleic 36–53 and linolenic acid 5–9 per cent., and results for some 40 oils from about twenty of the varieties of soya bean grown most abundantly in the United States (1957, 1959) were given by Collins et al.[201d]

Moringaceæ, Ochnaceæ and Sapindaceæ seed fats. Ben oil (Moringaceæ) was the origin of the name behenic acid for n-docosanoic acid, but in fact the amount of this acid present therein is not large. The oil is an oleic-rich oil with about 75 per cent. of oleic acid in its component acids. The saturated acids include small proportions of the five even-numbered acids from palmitic to lignoceric, stearic and behenic or lignoceric being the more prominent.

The seed fats of two species of *Lophira* (the only members of the Ochnaceæ yet studied in detail) are remarkable in containing palmitic (27–37 per cent.) and linoleic (25–33 per cent.), together with *behenic* (15–35 per cent.) acid as the main components. Oleic and small proportions of lignoceric acid are also present, but neither stearic nor arachidic acid is present in detectable amounts.

Six out of the nine Sapindaceæ seed fats so far examined are known to contain substantial proportions (10–35 per cent.) of arachidic acid (identified in the fats from *Schleichera trijuga* and *Nephelium lappaceum* as n-eicosanoic acid by X-ray spectral analysis). In the seed fats of higher arachidic acid content small quantities of an eicosenoic acid, $C_{20}H_{38}O_2$, have also been found; oleic acid (40–60 per cent.) is the major component of most of the Sapindaceæ seed fats, linoleic acid being observed in only minor proportions in all but two instances.

Chisholm and Hopkins[166] found that the components of the seed fat of *Cardiospermum* were apparently exceptional for a Sapindaceous fat in that eicos-11-enoic acid was the major component (42 per cent.), with only 10 per cent. of arachidic acid (*see* Table 67).

311

TABLE 67. Component Acids of Seed Fats of Leguminosæ, Sapindaceæ, etc.

Major component acids: OLEIC, (ARACHIDIC, BEHENIC, LIGNOCERIC, LINOLEIC).
Minor component acids: Palmitic, stearic (myristic, arachidic, lignoceric, linolenic).

Plant	Common name	Habitat	COMPONENT FATTY ACIDS PER CENT. (WT.) SATURATED					UNSATURATED			METHOD	OBSERVERS
			C_{16}	C_{18}	C_{20}	C_{22}	C_{24}	OLEIC	LINO-LEIC	LINO-LENIC		
LEGUMINOSÆ												
Sub-family Mimosoideæ												
Acacia albida	—	Sudan	←19·8→			2·2	→	45	33	—	L,T	Grindley[1a]
" arabica	—	Sudan	←20·8→			1·2	→	42	36	—	L,T	Grindley[1a]
" cyclops	—	S. Africa	5·6	0·6	0·8	—	2·9 →	10·1	67·7	0·8(a)	C,F,S	Black et al.[2a]
" giraffæ	—	S. Africa	12·8	5·6	1·7	0·9	—	23·5	41·5	4·2(a')	C,F,S	Harrison and Hawke[2b]
" mellifera	—	Sudan	←30·6→			4·4	→	43	22	—	L,T	Grindley[1a]
" sieberiana	—	Sudan	←20·6→			4·4	→	31	44	—	L,T	Grindley[1a]
Adenanthera pavonina	Coral tree	India	9·0	1·1	—	0·6	25·5	49·3	14·7	(b)	F,H	Mudbidri et al.[3a]
Albizzia amara	—	India	7·6	4·3	2·2	0·6	0·4	31·3	45·6	(r)	F	Chandra et al.[3b]
" lebbek	—	India	←30·6→				→	10·3	57·6	1·5	F	Gupta and Chakrabarty[3c]
" odoratissima	—	India	←25·9→			3·1		43	28	—	L,T	Grindley[1a]
Entada phaseoloides	—	Uganda	7·3	9·6	10·9		→	39·3	32·9	—	F	Farooq et al.[4a]
Leucæna glauca	—	India	14·3	6·9	0·8		—	26·6	51·4	—	F	Farooq et al.[4b]
Mimosa pudica	—	India	←20·4→			8·5	—	40·5	30·6	—	L,T	Grindley[1c]
Parkia biglandulosa	Parkia	India	12·7	5·0			0·7	23·7	54·3	0·4	L,F	Farooq et al.[4c]
Pentaclethra eetveldeana	—	Congo	8·7	8·9				31·1	50·9	—	L,T	Aggarwal[5a]
" filamentosa	Paroacaxy	Brazil	8·8	13·3		7·9		30·6	39·4	—	F,H	Paranjpe[5b]
" macrophylla	Owala nut	W. Africa	3·7	4·8	5·4	13·9	2·8	53·3	16·1	—	C,F,S	Hilditch et al.[6]
" "	—	Congo	←ca. 28→			ca. 25 →		←ca. 47→		—	?	Margaillan et al.[7]
" "	—	W. Africa	←ca. 30 (? chiefly C_{20})→					←ca. 70→		—	?	Margaillan et al.[7]
" "	—	W. Africa	5·2	4·3	2·6	5·8	13·1	20·3	48·7	—	C,F,S	Hilditch et al.[6]
" "	—	W. Africa	4·0	2·1	3·8	5·9	11·0	18·7	54·5	—	C,F,S	Hilditch et al.[6]
Xylia xylocarpa	—	India	Trace	Trace		17·3	Some	67·5	12·5	—	?	Manjunath and Nagaraj[8]
Sub-family Cæsalpinoideæ												
Bauhinia purpurea	—	U.S.A.		34				13	48	—	S	Earle et al.[9]
" variegata	Kachnar	India	17	13·4			1	31·8	35·8	(c)	L,F	Puntambekar et al.[10]

312

Species	Common name	Source							Oleic	Linoleic		Analysis	Reference
Cæsalpinia bonducella	Bonducella	Tropics	10	6		1·5	0·2		22	62	1·7(s)	L,H	Godbole et al.[11a]
" digyna	—	India	20·4	8·2					30·3	37·1		F	Gupta et al.[11b]
" separia	—	India	5·6	7·3			0·5		23·5	63·1		?	Mhaskar et al.[11c]
Cassia absus	—	?	7·8	10·1			1·0		20·4	59·2	0·5(d)	F,H	Ahmad[12a]
" arereh	—	Sudan	←26·6→		4·4				29	40		L,T	Grindley[1b]
" fistula	—	Sudan	←23·2→		4·8				32	39		L,T	Grindley[1b]
" occidentalis	Wild coffee	India	16·0	—				5·2	30·7	48·1		F,T	Farooq et al.[12b]
" Tora	"	India	19·7	←22·5→					34	37	6·5	B,T	Steger and van Loon[13a]
" Tora	"	India	7·5	7·3				4·3	31·6	38·1	6·3	F,T	Farooq et al.[12b]
" Tora	"	India	23·5	—				9·7	38·4	37·1		F,T	Tewari and Gupta[12c]
Cercidium floridum	—	U.S.A.			24			3·4	28·1	45·0		F,T	Farooq et al.[12b]
Erythrophleon guineense	—	Sudan	←28·4→		1·6			↑	32	36	—(t)	S	Earle et al.[9]
Parkinsonia aculeata	—	Sudan	←22·0→		1·0			↑	27	43		L,T	Grindley[1b]
Tamarindus indica	—	Sudan	←19·2→		11·8			↑	21	56		L,T	Grindley[1b]
" indica	—	India	6·2	2·6	4·4	7·0			38·2	41·6		F	Tawakley et al.[13b]
Torresea cearensis	Amburana	Brazil	11·5	3·5	3·0	4·0		2·5	60·0	6·5	Trace(d′)	RPC	Badami and Gunstone[13c]

Sub-family Papilionatæ

Species	Common name	Source							Oleic	Linoleic		Analysis	Reference
Abrus precatorius	—	India	1·1	5·0	4·6			2·6	48·5	19·5	13·3	F,H	Dutt et al.[14a]
Arachis hypogæa	Groundnut	Sub-tropics	6-10	3-6	5-8			↑	40-64	18-38	—	—	(See text, p. 305)
Butea frondosa	Kino	India	21·2	9·1	5·7			4·4	25·7	27·9		F,H	Dutt et al.[14b]
Cajanus cajans	Indian pulse	India			36·7				6·3	51·4	5·6	F,T	Mitra and Chakrabarty[37a]
Caragana arborescens	—	Canada	3	6	1	3			16	67	2	F,S	Cole and Craig[37b]
Cicer arietinum	Pulse	Pakistan	12·7	1·5	Trace				19·3	62·9	3·3(u)	GLC	Baker et al.[38]
Clitorea ternatea	—	Queensland	←25·8→		5·2				52·3	16·7		L,T	Grindley[1c]
Cyamopsis psoraloides	Guar	India	6·9	6·6		16·4		10·0	34·1	35·1		L,T	Tewari and Gupta[12d]
Dipteryx odorata	Tonka bean	India							64·0	19·1	0·4	F	Mehta[39]
Erythrina christogalli	"	Malaya	5·1	5·9	14·8			↑	61·0	13·2		S	Hilditch and Stainsby[15]
" indica	"	Malaya	6·1	5·7	13·2			↑	59·6	15·4		F	Hilditch and Stainsby[15]
" christogalli	—	Argentine	11·4	3·9	3·2				50·9	18·9	(e)	F	Cattaneo[16]
" indica	—	India	9·3	8·1	4·0	11·3		0·5	46·8	7·3	(v)	F	Pathak and Dey[40a]
" rubrinervia	—	Mexico	12·8	10·5					58·0	14·7		F	Dominguez and Canalis[41]

TABLE 67. Component Acids of Seed Fats of Leguminosæ, Sapindaceæ, etc—continued

| | | | COMPONENT FATTY ACIDS PER CENT. (WT.) | | | | | | | | | |
| | | | SATURATED | | | | | UNSATURATED | | | | |
Species		Habitat	C_{16}	C_{18}	C_{20}	C_{22}	C_{24}	OLEIC	LINO-LEIC	LINO-LENIC	METHOD	OBSERVERS
LEGUMINOSÆ (Papilionatæ)												
Galega officinalis	Lagwort	Europe	20	25				9	46	—	L,H	Fink and Richter[17]
Lens esculenta	Pulse	Pakistan	23·2	4·6	2·3	2·7	1·7	36·0	20·6	1·6(w)	GLC	Baker et al.[38]
Lespedeza cuneata	—	Kentucky, U.S.A.	←		16·6			19·4	41·8	22·2	S	Wiley et al.[18a]
" stipulacea	—	Kentucky, U.S.A.	←		20·2			21·5	30·3	28·0	S	Wiley et al.[18a]
" striata	—	Kentucky, U.S.A.	←		7·5			42·9	26·5	23·1	S	Wiley et al.[18a]
" species	—	Kentucky, U.S.A.	←		14·0			27·0	46·5	12·5	C,S	Wiley et al.[18b]
Lupinus termis		Sudan	←11·3→			5·9		52·6	23·4	6·8	T	Grindley and Akour[1d]
Medicago sativa	Alfalfa	U.S.A.	9·5	4·5				7	71	11	L,T	Schuette et al.[19a]
"	"	Switzerland	←		10·3			11	43	32	F,T	Hilditch and Zaky[20]
" tribuloides		U.S.A.	←		20			30	22	24	S	Earle et al.[9]
Milletia ovalifolia		U.S.A.	←		18			45	33	—	S	Earle et al.[9]
Pachyrrhizus angulatus		India	←		38			34	28	—	L	Nag et al.[21]
" erosus	Yam bean	Malaya	26·7	5·7				33·4	34·2	Trace	GLC	Broadbent and Shone[21b]
Phaseolus lunatus	Lima bean	California	23·3	3·5	3			9·3	43·8	19·7	GLC	Korytnyk et al.[43]
" mungo	Mungo	Manchuria	28	8				18	40	3	?	Miki and Sera[22]
" "	Pulse	Pakistan	28·1	7·8	0·9	2·4	6·3	6·4	32·6	14·4(x)	GLC	Baker et al.[38]
" radiatus		Pakistan	14·1	4·3		9·3	3·8	20·8	16·3	35·7(y)	GLC	Baker et al.[38]
" sp.	Blackeye bean	California	32·5	4·6		2·5		7·2	31·2	22·0	GLC	Korytnyk et al.[43]
" "	Pinto bean	California	14·7	1·0				7·0	28·1	49·2	GLC	Korytnyk et al.[43]
" vulgaris	Kidney bean	California	13·4	0·7				8·3	26·9	50·6	GLC	Korytnyk et al.[43]
Pongamia glabra	Hongay	E. Indies	6·6	2·4	4·7		3·5	71·3	10·8	0·5(f)	F,H	Desai et al.[23a]
"		India	7·9	3·7	2·5	4·2	1·1	62·1	11·9	5·0(f')	F	Gupta and Mitra[23b]
"		India	6·3	8·9	2·2	5·3	2·0	46·5	18·2	(z)	F	Pathak and Dey[40b]
" pinnata		Philippine Is.	←		23			11	66	—	L	Soliven[24]
"		U.S.A.	←		19			56	19	1	S	Earle et al.[9]
Psoralea drupacea		Asia	←9→					←—91—→		—	L	Tsukervanik et al.[25]
Sesbania ægyptica		India	9·0	17·5				24·4	36·3	10·9	F,T	Farooq et al.[4d]
grandiflora		India	12	5			1·9	26	56	—	F	Tewari and Garg[12e]
Soja hispida	Soya bean	Asia, U.S.A.	7-10	2-5		1-3	→	22-30	50-60	5-9	—	(See text, p. 309)

Species	Country	Common name									Char.	Reference
Sophora japonica	Rumania	—	15·3	—	12·5	—	—	22·3	52·8	12·4	T	Cornea et al.[26]
" *secundiflora*	Mexico	—	—	9·2	—	—	—	52·8	16·3	—	F	Dominguez and Canalis[41]
Stylosanthes gracilis	U.S.A.	—	—	—	22	—	—	27	46	1	S	Earle et al.[9]
Tephrosia sp.	U.S.A.	—	—	—	29	—	—	40	25	1	S	Earle et al.[9]
Trifolium subterraneum	U.S.A.	Clover species	—	—	24	—	—	24	46	2	S	Earle et al.[9]
Trigonella fœnum græcum	U.S.A.	Fenugreek	8·4	2·7	1·0	0·7	—	11	70	6	F,T	Schuette et al.[19b]
" "	Egypt	"	9·6	4·9	2·0	0·9	—	35·1	33·7	13·8	F,T	Shahat[27]
Vicia faba	Canada	Horse bean	—	—	7·5	—	—	57·5	35	—		Labarre et al.[28]
" "	India	Pulse	2·0	8·2	1·1	0·1	—	45·9	30·0	12·7	F,T	Dutt et al.[14c]
Vigna sinensis	Pakistan	Pulse	33·4	7·1	0·9	4·0	1·1	12·2	27·4	12·3(a')	GLC	Baker et al.[38]

MORINGACEÆ

Species	Country	Common name									Char.	Reference
Moringa concanensis	India	—	6·0	5·2	3·0	6·1	3·3	74·2	0·9	(b')	F,S	Patel[29a]
" *oleifera*	Haiti	Ben seed	3·9	11·5	—	6·6	0·2	72·2	4·0	(g)	F	Jamieson[29b]
" "	Trinidad	" "	5·5	7·8	2·7	1·2	5·3	75·8	0·8	(h)	F,S	Dunn and Hilditch[30]

OCHNACEÆ

Species	Country	Common name									Char.	Reference
Lophira alata	W. Africa	Oyster, Niam	27·1	—	—	14·2	2·3	14·5	33·3	(i)	F	Hilditch and Meara[31]
" *procera*	Sierra Leone	" "	28·8	—	—	34·3	6·8	14·0	11·5	(j)	C,F,S	Hilditch et al.[6]
"	Sierra Leone	—	37·9	—	—	20·9	0·5	11·5	26·3	(k)	C,F,S	Hilditch et al.[6]

SAPINDACEÆ

Species	Country	Common name									Char.	Reference
Cardiospermum halicacabum	Holland	Balloon vine	3	2	10	5		22	8	8 (c')	F, GLC	Chisholm and Hopkins[42]
Koelreuteria formosana	U.S.A.	—	14·0	17·7	25			54	11	5	S	Earle et al.[9]
Dodonea viscosa	India	—	2·0	13·8	5·9	2·3	—	25·2	31·8	(l)	F,T	Dutt et al.[14d]
Nephelium lappaceum	Malaya	Rambutan tallow	2·0	13·8	34·7	—	—	45·3	—	(m)	F	Hilditch and Stainsby[15]
" *mutabile*	Malaya	Pulasan tallow	3·0	31·0	22·3	—	—	43·7	—	—	F	Hilditch and Stainsby[15]
Sapindus drummondii	Oklahoma	Western soapberry	—	—	23	—	—	57	20	—	L,T	Dermer and Crews[32]
" *mukorossi*	U.S.A.	Chinese soapberry	—	—	14	—	—	69	11	3	S	Earle et al.[9]
" *trifoliatus*	India	Soap nut	5·6	8·5	21·9	—	2·5	61·5	—	—	F,H	Paranjpe and Ayyar[33a]
" "	India	" "	5·4	8·5	20·7	2·1	—	55·1	8·2	—	F	Achaya et al.[33b]

315

TABLE 67. *Component Acids of Seed Fats of Leguminosæ, Sapindaceæ, etc—continued*

COMPONENT FATTY ACIDS PER CENT. (WT.)

	HABITAT	SATURATED					UNSATURATED			METHOD	OBSERVERS
		C_{16}	C_{18}	C_{20}	C_{22}	C_{24}	OLEIC	LINO-LEIC	LINO-LENIC		
SAPINDACEÆ											
Schleichera trijuga	Kusum, India	5.3	6.3	19.8	—	3.5	61.6	2.5	—(n)	F, H	Dhingra et al.[34]
" "	macassar India	8.7	1.7	22.6	—	2.2	59.2	4.5	—(o)	F, H	Dhingra et al.[34]
" "	India	7.9	—	31.1	—	—	57.6	—	—(p)	?	Patel[35]
" "	Kusum, Kon Ceylon	8.1	4.8	30.6	—	1.5	39.9	5.2	0.2(q)	C, F, S	Weerakoon[36]

Other minor component acids recorded as follows (per cent. wt.):

		SATURATED		UNSATURATED	
		C_{12}	C_{14}	C_{16}	C_{20}
(a)	*Acacia cyclops*	0.1	0.7	8.6	2.1
(a')	" *giraffæ*		Trace	8.4	1.4
(b)	Coral tree		0.4	—	—
(c)	*Bauhinia*		1	—	—
(d)	*Cassia absus*	(Also 1 per cent. hydroxy-acids)		9.0	
(e)	*Erythrina*	Traces	1.9	—	—
(f)	*Pongamia glabra*		0.2	—	—
(g)	Ben seed		1.6	—	—
(h)	" "		1.6	0.9	—

		SATURATED	UNSATURATED		
		C_{14}	C_{16}	C_{20}	C_{22}
(i)	*Lophira alata*	1.9	1.5	—	5.2
(j)	"	0.3	—	—	4.3
(k)	" *procera*	0.7	—	—	2.2
(l)	*Dodonea viscosa*	—	—	3.1	—
(m)	Rambutan tallow	—	—	4.2	—
(n)	Kusum	1.0	—	—	—
(o)	"	1.1	—	—	—
(p)	"	(*)—	—	—	—

		SATURATED	UNSATURATED		
		C_{14}	C_{16}	C_{20}	C_{22}
(q)					
(r)	*Albizzia amara*	0.8	—	8.9	—
(s)	*Cæsalpinia digyna*	1.5	—	—	—
(t)	*Cercidium floridum*	1.6	—	—	—
	(Also conjugated diene 3, hydroxy-acids 9 per cent.)				
(u)	*Cicer arietinum*	0.3	0.1	—	†
(v)	*Erythrina indica*		3.6	9.1	2.8†
(w)	*Lens esculenta*	1.1	0.3	1.9	†
(x)	*Phaseolus mungo*	0.4	0.1	—	†
(y)	" *radiatus*	0.6	0.9	—	0.4
(z)	*Pongamia glabra*		0.6	9.6	†
(a')	*Vigna sinensis*	0.3	0.3	—	†
(b')	*Moringa concanensis*	1.3			
(c')	*Cardiospermum halicacabum*	(Also 42 per cent. of eicos-11-enoic acid.)			
(d')	*Torresea cearensis*	(Also saturated C_{10} 0.5.)			

* Capric 1.1, lauric 2.3 per cent.
† Also traces of odd-numbered and iso-acids.

316

References to Table 67

1. D. N. Grindley, (*a*) *J. Soc. Chem Ind.*, 1945, **64**, 152; (*b*) *ibid.*, 1946, **65**, 118; (*c*) (with E. H. W. J. Burden and A. A. Akour), *J. Sci. Food Agric.*, 1954, **5**, 278; (*d*) (with A. A. Akour), *ibid.*, 1955, **6**, 461.

2. (*a*) M. M. Black, D. A. Harris and H. M. Schwartz, *J. S. Afr. Chem. Inst.*, 1949, **2**, 111; (*b*) G. S. Harrison and F. Hawke, *ibid,.* 1952, **5**, 1.

3. (*a*) S. M. Mudbidri, P. R. Ayyar and H. E. Watson, *J. Indian Inst. Sci.*, 1928, **11, A,** 173; (*b*) I. Chandra, R. P. Seed and K. L. Handa, *J. Sci. Indust. Res.* (*India*), 1956, **15, B,** 196; (*c*) A. S. Gupta and M. M. Chakrabarty, *Indian J. Appl. Chem.*, 1958, **21**, 227.

4. (*a*) M. O. Farooq and I. P. Varshneg, *Bull. Soc. chim. Fr.*, 1954, 739; (*b*) M. O. Farooq and M. S. Siddiqui, *ibid.*, 1954, 741; (*c*) *idem, J. Amer. Oil Chem. Soc.*, 1954, **31**, 8; (*d*) M. O. Farooq, M. S. Ahmad and M. A. Malik, *J. Sci. Food Agric.*, 1954, **5**, 498.

5. (*a*) J. S. Aggarwal and Karimullah, *J. Sci. Indust. Res. India*, 1945, **4**, 80; (*b*) D. R. Paranjpe, *J. Indian Chem. Soc.*, 1931, **8**, 767.

6. T. P. Hilditch, M. L. Meara and C. B. Patel, *J. Sci. Food Agric.*, 1951, **2**, 142.

7. L. Margaillan, A. Dupuis and J. Rosello, *Ann. Musée Colon. Marseille*, 1925, **3**, (4), 23, 26.

8. B. L. Manjunath and B. S. Nagaraj, *J. Mysore Univ.*, 1942, **3, B,** 105.

9. F. R. Earle, I. A. Wolff, *et al.*, *J. Amer. Oil Chem. Soc.*, 1960, **37**, 440.

10. S. V. Puntambekar and S. Krishna, *J. Indian Chem. Soc.*, 1940, **17**, 96.

11. (*a*) S. N. Godbole, D. R. Paranjpe and J. G. Shrikhande, *J. Indian Inst. Sci.*, 1929, **6**, 295; (*b*) D. K. Gupta, B. T. R. Iyengar and M. M. Chakrabarty, *J. Indian Chem. Soc.* (*News Edn.*), 1957, **20**, 112; (*c*) V. V. Mhaskar, B. V. Bhide and N. L. Phalnikar, *J. Univ. Bombay*, 1951, **19, A,** 16.

12. (*a*) Z. Ahmad, *Z. Unters. Lebensm.*, 1935, **70**, 166; (*b*) M. O. Farooq, M. A. Aziz and M. S. Ahmad, *J. Amer. Oil Chem. Soc.*, 1956, **33**, 21; (*c*) R. D. Tewari and P. C. Gupta, *J. Proc. Oil Technol. Assn.*, *India.*, 1954, **10**, 111; (*d*) *idem, ibid.*, 1957, **13**, 9; (*e*) R. D. Tewari and S. P. Garg, *ibid.*, 1960, **16**, 35.

13. (*a*) A. Steger and J. van Loon, *Rec. trav. chim.*, 1934, **53**, 28; (*b*) M. S. Tawakley and R. K. Bhatnagar, *Indian Soap J.*, 1953, **19**, 113; (*c*) R. C. Badami and F. D. Gunstone, *J. Sci. Food Agric.*, 1963, **14**, 479.

14. (*a*) M. R. Mandiratta and S. Dutt, *Indian Soap J.*, 1949, **14**, 195; (*b*) D. B. Parihar and S. Dutt, *ibid.*, 1946, **12**, 26; (*c*) I. R. Gambhir and S. Dutt, *ibid.*, 1950, **16**, 13; (*d*) R. K. Kochar and S. Dutt, *ibid.*, 1948, **14**, 132.

15. T. P. Hilditch and W. J. Stainsby, *J. Soc. Chem. Ind.*, 1934, **53**, 197т.

16. P. Cattaneo, *Anal. Asoc. Quim. Argentina*, 1945, **33**, 5.

17. F. Fink and A. F. Richter, *časop. českoslov. Lék.*, 1937, **17**, 69.

18. (*a*) R. H. Wiley, A. W. Cagle and P. H. Wilken, *J. Amer. Oil Chem. Soc.*, 1951, **28**, 459; (*b*) R. H. Wiley and J. P. Burns, *Trans. Kentucky Acad. Sci.*, 1953, **14**, 10.

19. (*a*) H. A. Schuette, H. A. Vogel and C. H. Wartinbee, *Oil and Soap*, 1938, **15**, 35; (*b*) H. A. Schuette, M. A. Cowley, H. A. Vogel and M. M. Meuller, *ibid.*, 1940, **17**, 122.

20. T. P. Hilditch and Y. A. H. Zaky, *J. Soc. Chem. Ind.*, 1944, **63**, 112.

21. (*a*) N. C. Nag, H. N. Banerjee and A. K. Pain, *Trans. Bose Res. Inst.*, 1935–36, **11**, 83; (*b*) J. H. Broadbent and G. Shone, *J. Sci. Food Agric.*, 1963, **14**, 524.

22. S. Miki and S. Sera, *J. Agric. Chem. Soc. Japan*, 1932, **8**, 1313.

23. (*a*) R. D. Desai, J. J. Sudborough and H. E. Watson, *J. Indian Inst. Sci.*, 1923, **6**, 93; (*b*) S. S. Gupta and C. R. Mitra, *J. Indian Chem. Soc.*, 1953, **30**, 781.

24. F. A. Soliven, *Philippine Agric.*, 1934, **23**, 576.

25. I. Tsukervanik and V. Bersutski, *Bull. Univ. Asie Centrale*, 1935, **21**, 49, 55.

26. I. Cornea and A. Rudenco, *Bull. Inst. Nat. Cercetari Technol.*, 1948, **3**, 48.

27. M. Shahat, *Proc. XIth Inst. Congr. Pure Appl. Chem.*, *London*, 1947, **3**, 569.

28. J. Labarre and S. Pfeffer, *Canad. Chem.*, 1945, **29**, 724, 736.

29. (*a*) K. C., R. D. and S. A. Patel, *Indian J. Appl. Chem.*, 1958, **21**, 85; (*b*) G. S. Jamieson, *Oil and Soap*, 1939, **16**, 173.

30. H. C. Dunn and T. P. Hilditch, *J. Soc. Chem. Ind.*, 1947, **66**, 209.

31. T. P. Hilditch and M. L. Meara, *J. Soc. Chem. Ind.*, 1944, **63**, 114.

32. O. C. Dermer and L. T. Crews, *J. Amer. Chem. Soc.*, 1939, **61**, 2697.

33. (*a*) D. R. Paranjpe and P. R. Ayyar, *J. Indian Inst. Sci.*, 1929, **12**, A, 179; (*b*) V. V. R. Subramanian and K. T. Achaya, *J. Sci. Food Agric.*, 1957, **8**, 657.

34. D. R. Dhingra, T. P. Hilditch and J. R. Vickery, *J. Soc. Chem. Ind.*, 1929, **48**, 281т.

35. S. M. Patel, Thesis, University of Bombay, 1930.

36. A. H. Weerakoon, Thesis, University of Liverpool, 1952.

37. (*a*) C. R. Mitra and M. M. Chakrabarty, *Indian Sci. J.*, 1956, **21**, 143; (*b*) L. N. Cole and B. M. Craig, *Canad. J. Technol.*, 1953, **31**, 196.

38. B. E. Baker, J. A. Papaconstantinou, C. K. Cross and N. A. Khan, *J. Sci. Food Agric.*, 1961, **12**, 205.

39. D. R. Mehta, *J. Amer. Oil Chem. Soc.*, 1957, **34**, 459.

40. S. P. Pathak and L. M. Dey, (*a*) *J. Sci. Food Agric.*, 1956, **7**, 200; (*b*) *J. Chem. Soc.*, 1957, 1917.

41. X. A. Dominguez and I. V. Canalis, *Rev. Quim. e Ing. Quim.* (*Monterrey*), 1954, **1**, (1), 23.

42. M. J. Chisholm and C. Y. Hopkins, *Canad. J. Chem.*, 1958, **36**, 1537.

43. W. Korytnyk and E. A. Metzler, *J. Sci. Food Agric.*, 1963, **14**, 841.

SEED FATS OF WHICH STEARIC ACID IS A MAJOR COMPONENT

Major component acids: OLEIC, STEARIC, PALMITIC.
Minor component acids: Linoleic, (myristic, arachidic).
(See Table 68, p. 324).

It was remarked on p. 265, in connection with Table 62, that as seed fats become less unsaturated, and palmitic acid makes its appearance in larger quantities, so in some instances there is also an increase in stearic acid content. We come now to a group of families in which stearic acid is nearly always present, in the seed fats, to the extent of over 10 per cent.; in some cases it becomes the chief component and forms over 50 per cent. of the mixed fatty acids of the glycerides. Its occurrence in quantity in seed fats has, however, only been observed in plants belonging to a few tropical families, and it cannot be too much emphasised that, in the vegetable kingdom, stearic acid is at least as rare as, for example, arachidic or elæostearic acid, and is probably produced in less abundance than lauric, erucic, or petroselinic acids, the respective characteristic components of the very large and widely distributed natural families Palmæ, Cruciferæ and Umbelliferæ.

There was some indication in the "drying" and "semi-drying" oils dealt with in Tables 59 and 60 (pp. 213–229) that the relative amounts of oleic, linoleic and linolenic acid in seed fats of related species alter in some measure correspondingly; that is to say, one does not often find cases in which a seed fat contains much oleic and linolenic with little linoleic acid. Progressive development of unsaturation from a "non-drying" to a "drying" oil is usually regular, in the sense that oleic acid content falls somewhat as the amount of linoleic acid increases, and may be still more reduced in cases where linolenic acid makes its appearance. This is suggestive, of course, of some kind of inter-relation between the three unsaturated acids or of their immediate precursors in the endosperm metabolism. Whilst such inter-conversion may or may not occur between the three unsaturated acids, it is, nevertheless, in the writers' opinion, most unlikely that any such process accounts for the appearance, in the fats under notice at the moment, of large amounts of stearic acid (*cf.*, this Chapter, pp. 211, 224, 310; Chapter VIII, pp. 537–539); for, were this the case, we should expect stearic acid to be at least as prominent a feature as palmitic acid of those oils in which the latter is only a minor component. The facts point in exactly the opposite direction; palmitic acid most frequently forms at least 6–10 per cent. of the less saturated seed fats and sometimes more, whilst (except in a very few families) the proportion of stearic acid is very small (often 1–2 per cent. or less) and on occasion it is completely absent. It appears more logical, therefore, for the time being to regard stearic acid, when present as a major component of seed fats, on the same footing as arachidic, lauric, erucic, petroselinic and other "specific" acids.

The above argument, of course, is intended to apply only to the stearic acid of vegetable fats. We saw that in the case of certain animal reserve fats (Chapter III, pp. 108, 112) there is a very different state of affairs, with strong

319

evidence of a very close inter-connection between the stearic and oleic acid content of such fats.

It will be observed that, even within the limits of a single family, there are various proportions in which stearic and palmitic acids are found. For example, there are several cases (e.g. *Azadirachta indica, Calophyllum inophyllum,* or *Calocarpum mammosum* fats) in which the palmitic content is of the order of not more than 15 per cent. and the stearic content only 20 per cent. or even less; in another group (e.g. *Theobroma cacao* and *Shorea aptera*) the stearic content reaches 35–40 per cent. and the palmitic content also rises to somewhat over 20 per cent.; whilst there is a third category marked by extremely high proportions of stearic acid (50 per cent. or thereabouts) with very small amounts of palmitic acid.

More often than not, linoleic acid is only present in quantity in cases where stearic acid forms 20 per cent. or less of the total acids; but, as indicated above, it is preferred to regard this as an instance of the usual state of things that, when the total proportion of saturated acids is relatively small and of unsaturated acids relatively great, the latter generally includes appreciable amounts of linoleic as well as oleic acid. The disappearance of linoleic acid when conditions are reversed, and saturated acids preponderate in the whole fat, is no more likely to connote conversion of linoleic into stearic acid in *Allanblackia* or *Shorea* seed fats than, for example, its conversion on similar but unlikely lines into lauric or myristic acids in those of *Cocos, Elæis,* or *Myristica* species (*cf.* Tables 69A and 69B).

Fats which are made up almost exclusively of stearic and oleic acids, with the former often predominating, are confined (according to the existing records) to seeds of certain genera of the Guttiferæ and Sapotaceæ. In addition to those for which quantitative data are given in Table 68 (pp. 325, 328) the following seed fats have also been stated to contain stearic acid as the chief saturated component acid, although definite figures were not given:

GUTTIFERÆ

Pentadesma kerstingii		Pacific Is.
Platonia insignis		S. America
Symphonia fasciculata	Hazina kernel	Madagascar
,, *globulifera*	Mani nut	Tropics
,, *lævis*		Madagascar

SAPOTACEÆ

Payena oleifera	Kansive nut	Burma

It is interesting to note, as pointed out earlier (p. 208), that the tropical gymnosperm *Gnetum scandens* produces a seed fat containing 56 per cent. of stearic acid and 14 per cent. of palmitic acid, thus possessing marked resemblances to the stearic-rich seed fats of the Sapotaceæ and Guttiferæ families.

Perusal of Table 68 suggests that, whilst within any of the families there may be considerable variation in the proportions of oleic, stearic and palmitic acids in the seed fats, there is a general tendency towards the following relations:

Guttiferæ and Sapotaceæ seed fats: Rich in stearic and oleic; often little palmitic and usually little linoleic.

Dipterocarpaceæ, Burseraceæ and Menispermaceæ seed fats: Rich in stearic and oleic, but also in palmitic acid, the latter frequently about 20 per cent. of the total acids; linoleic acid usually almost absent.

Meliaceæ, Convolvulaceæ and Verbenaceæ seed fats: Less rich in stearic, which is, however, still prominent; moderate proportions of palmitic acid; oleic acid prominent and linoleic acid a frequent component in variable proportions.

The "stearic-rich" nature of most of the seed fats in the eleven botanical families included in Table 68 is evident, but here and there exceptions will be noticed. In a few instances, e.g., *Carapa* (Meliaceæ), *Sterculia urens* (Sterculiaceæ), *Platonia* (Guttiferæ), *Canarium* (Burseraceæ), *Madhuca butyracea* (Sapotaceæ), the palmitic acid content is considerable whilst that of stearic acid is small, so that the fats in question belong more properly to the "palmitic-rich" seed fats already considered in Table 62 (pp. 268–276). In a few other instances, such as *Brachychiton* (Sterculiaceæ), and one or two others in Table 68, the proportions of both palmitic and stearic acids fall below 10 per cent. of the total acids, and these fats may be looked upon as borderline cases between the palmitic-rich fats of Table 62 and the stearic-rich fats of Table 68 on the one hand, and, on the other, the oleic-linoleic-rich fats with low saturated acid contents, which were included in Table 60 (pp. 229–239).

The seed fats of the genus *Madhuca* in the Sapotaceæ require a further reference. These have long been known to the technologists as "*Bassia* fats". The term *Bassia* was originally given to genera in two different orders, Chenopodiaceæ (1766) and Sapotaceæ (1771); the former having priority of date, Gmelin in 1791 assigned the term *Madhuca* to the Sapotaceæ genera concerned, and systematic botanists have since adopted this nomenclature, which is accordingly used here. It will be seen that *Madhuca* seed fats are more variable than those of some other genera in this family in their composition, the stearic and palmitic acid contents in *M. latifolia, longifolia* and *mottleyana* being of somewhat the same order, with each ranging from about 15 to 25 per cent. of the total acids.* The seed fat of *M. butyracea*, however, is a complete exception to the rest of this genus and of the Sapotaceæ seed fats as a whole; its fatty acids include 56 per cent. of palmitic acid, and only 3 per cent. of stearic acid (the remainder being nearly all oleic acid). From the point of view of its major component acids, it belongs to the large group dealt with in Table 62, in which palmitic and oleic acids are major components and stearic acid a minor component. Indeed, the palmitic acid content of *M. butyracea* seed fat is the second highest yet observed in any seed fat.

A very full account of the botanical varieties (with their geographical

---

* The analysis of *M. latifolia* seed fatty acids by Gill and Shah (Table 68, ref. 50) differs from all the other analyses in this group by including 16 per cent. of myristic acid with 27 per cent. of palmitic and only 2 per cent. of stearic acid.

distribution and seed fat composition) of *Butyrospermum parkii* (Sapotaceæ), whose seed fat, shea butter, is of some technical interest, has been given by André.[202a]

The six species belonging to the family Convolvulaceæ which have been examined all contain up to 10 per cent. of linolenic acid in their seed fat component acids: a feature which sets this family of plants apart from any of the others in Table 68. Their seed fat contents of linoleic (usually 15–20 per cent.) and oleic (30–60 per cent.) acids are also fairly high, but in addition they usually contain over 11 per cent. of stearic acid and thus belong to the "stearic-rich" group of seed fats. The presence of stearic, oleic, linoleic *and* linolenic acids in significant proportions in the same seed fat is a feature which, up to the present, has not appeared in any other botanical family.

In the seed fat of *Gmelina asiatica* (Verbenaceæ) Gunstone and Sykes[202b] observed 10 per cent. of eicos-11-enoic acid with traces of an eicosadienoic and erucic acid – apparently another instance of the occasional erratic appearance of the C_{20} monoene acid in seed fats (*cf.* pp. 294, 609–610).

Sterculiaceæ seed fats: On the present evidence, this is one of the comparatively few botanical families in which seed fats of different genera and even species are markedly dissimilar in their component acids. The most familiar seed fat of the family, cacao butter (from *Theobroma cacao*), is a solid fat containing component acids palmitic 24, stearic 35, oleic 39 and linoleic 2 per cent., and thus falls in the same general group as the stearic-rich seed fats of many members of the Guttiferæ, Sapotaceæ and Dipterocarpaceæ. It is interesting to note, from partial analyses by Bauer and Seber,[203] that the fat in the seed shells of the cacao bean contains 51–56 per cent. of saturated, 33–35 per cent. of oleic and 9–16 per cent. of linoleic acid; this suggests that, as in most other fruit-coat fats, the main component acids are palmitic, oleic and linoleic, with possibly in this instance stearic acid also as a major component.

On the other hand, *Brachychiton diversifolium* (but not *B. acerifolium*) has a seed fat low in palmitic and stearic acids, but with 73 per cent. oleic and 13 per cent. linoleic in its component acids, thus resembling a typical non-drying oil, whilst the *Herrania* species studied by MacLean[204] are remarkable for containing 75 per cent. of saturated (presumably palmitic and stearic) acids in their seed fatty acids, with about 20 per cent. or more of linoleic acid and almost negligible amounts of oleic acid (this curious composition, coupled with the statement that the fats are liquid at 25–29°C., may suggest that further confirmation of their composition is desirable).

The genus *Sterculia* (which gives its name to the family) has seed fats of radically varying types within its different species. The seed fats of *S. tomentosa* (Sudan) and *S. platonifolia* (Japan) are similar in composition, with about 25 per cent. of saturated (palmitic and stearic) acids, 45 per cent. oleic acid, and the relatively high content of about 30 per cent. of linoleic acid, but the seed fat of *S. urens* is stated to contain 66 per cent. of oleic and 18 per cent. of palmitic acid, with only minor proportions of stearic and linoleic acids. The seed fats of "Java olive oil" (*S. fœtida*) and *S. parviflora* are extremely peculiar in that they contain large amounts of glycerides which on heating to 250° suddenly polymerise with considerable evolution of heat. The component acids of the seed fat of *S. fœtida* consist[205] of about 15 per cent. of saturated (palmitic and myristic) acids, 13 per cent. of oleic acid, and over 70 per cent. of a very unusual unsaturated acid, $C_{19}H_{34}O_2$. This was at first thought to be possibly a methyl-octadecadienoic acid, but it was later shown by Nunn[206a] to have the constitution

$$CH_3.[CH_2]_7.C{=\!=}C.[CH_2]_7.COOH$$
$$\underset{CH_2}{\bigvee}$$

i.e., ω-(2-*n*-octyl*cyclo*prop-1-enyl) octanoic acid. "Sterculic acid" (the name suggested by Nunn for the above compound) forms about three-quarters of the total fatty acids in *S. fœtida* seed fat.

Sterculic acid has also been reported to be present in the seed fats of two other Sterculiaceæ seed fats, those of *Brachychiton acerifolius* and *Firmiana simplex*, which give the Halphen colour test characteristic of this acid.[206b]

Sterculic acid also accompanies in very small amounts the homologous cyclopropene malvalic acid which is present in small proportions in the seed fats of a number of species belonging to the family Malvaceæ (*cf.* p.)266[154a, b, c]. *Per contra*, small proportions of malvalic acid are reported to accompany sterculic acid in *Sterculia fœtida* seed fat.[154c]

TABLE 68. Component Acids of Seed Fats Frequently Rich in Stearic Acid

Major component acids: OLEIC, STEARIC, PALMITIC.
Minor component acids: Linoleic (myristic, arachidic).

		HABITAT	COMPONENT FATTY ACIDS (PER CENT. WT.)					METHOD	OBSERVERS
			PALMITIC	STEARIC	ARA-CHIDIC	OLEIC	LINO-LEIC		
GYMNOSPERM									
GNETACEÆ									
Gnetum scandens		India	14	56	—	27	3	L	Varier[1a]
" "		India	12·0	54·7	—	30·3	3·3	L, F	Nair and Varier[1b]
ANGIOSPERMS									
MELIACEÆ									
Amoora rohituka	Amoora	India, Africa	7·8	15·1	—	11·2	57·4(a)	F, H	Ayyar and Patwardhan[2]
Azadirachta indica	Neem, margosa	India	14·1	24·0	0·8	58·5	—(b)	?	Roy and Dutt[3]
" "	" "	Ceylon	13·6	19·1	2·4	49·1	15·8	F	Child and Ramanathan[4]
" "	" "	India	14·9	14·4	1·3	61·9	7·5	F	Hilditch and Murti[5a]
" "	" "	India	13·8	18·2	1·8	52·6	13·6	F	Rao and Seshadri[6]
" "	" "	India	16·2	14·6	3·4	56·6	9·0	C, F, S	Gupta and Mitra[7a]
" "	" "	India	15·9	17·7	2·1	52·9	10·5(y')	GLC	Skellon et al.[7b]
Carapa guyanensis	Andiroba	W. Indies	28·6	7·2	2·3	51·1	9·2(c)	C, F, S	Meara[8a]
" "	"	Brazil	9·3	—		58·9	9·2(j)	?	Pinto[11a]
" procera	"	W. Indies	21·0	11·0	0·2	47·6	18·1(d)	C, F, S	Meara[8a]
" "	"	W. Africa	31·3	5·0	0·9	49·3	11·9(w')	GLC	Mackie and Mieras[11b]
Melia azedarach	Greek laurel	Argentine	8·1	1·2	0·6	20·8	67·7(z')	L, F	Cattaneo et al.[11c]
Swietenia macrophylla	Mahogany	Mexico	←26·1→			24·8	49·1	T	Lloyd et al.[9a]
" "	"	India	12·5	16·4	0·6	25·3	33·9(i')	C, F, S	Chowdhury et al.[10a]
" mahogani	"	India	9·5	18·4	—	56·0	16·1	F	Shah et al.[10b]
Trichilia emetica	—	Sudan	←54→			43	3	L, T	Henry and Grindley[11d]
" hirta	—	Mexico	←33·2→			34·5	32·3	L	Lloyd et al.[9b]
MENISPERMACEÆ									
Anamirta cocculus		India	6·1	47·5	—	46·4	—	L, F	Kasturi and Iyer[12a]
Cocculus trilobus		Japan	←10·0→			32·3	57·7	T	Koyama and Toyama[12b]
Stephania tetranda	Hanfangchi	China	18·9	20·6	0·2	51	8 (e)	F, H	Hsii[12c]

324

STERCULIACEÆ

Species	Common name	Source							Reference
Brachychiton acerifolium	Flame tree	U.S.A.	8.5	→15	34	46 (*k*)		S	Earle et al.[13a]
" *diversifolium*	—	?		6.1	72.7	12.7		L	Labruto and de Angelis[13b]
Firmiana simplex		U.S.A.		→15	40	39 (*l'*)		S	Earle et al.[13a]
Herrania balænsis	—	S. America		→76	2	22		T	MacLean[14]
" *mariæ*	—	S. America		→74	7	26		T	MacLean[14]
"	—	S. America		→75		18		T	MacLean[14]
Sterculia foetida	Java olive	E. Indies	(Major component acid: $C_{19}H_{34}O_2$, see text, p. 323)					F	Hilditch, Meara and Zaky[15a]
" *parviflora*	—	E. Indies							Hilditch and Meara[15b]
" *platonifolia*	—	Japan (?)		25	45	30		?	Ueno and Ueda[16]
" *tomentosa*	—	Sudan		22	46	32		L,T	Henry and Grindley[11d]
" *urens*		India	18	2	1.5	66.5	2.5(*h'*)	L,H	Puntambekar and Batra[67b]
Theobroma cacao	Cacao butter	Tropics	24.4	34.5		39.1	2.0	F	Lea[17]
" "	"	Tropics	24.4	35.4		38.1	2.1	F	Hilditch and Stainsby[18a]
" "	"	Tropics	24.3	35.4		38.1	2.2	C,F	Meara[8b]

GUTTIFERÆ

Species	Common name	Source							Reference
Allanblackia floribunda	Bouandja	Nigeria	—	52-56		48-44	—	L	Pieraerts and Adriaens[19]
" "	"	Nigeria	2.1	57.1	0.7	38.7	1.4	F	Bushell[20]
" *klainei*	"	Nigeria	2.9	57.1	0.2	39.4	0.4	F	Meara and Zaky[21]
" *parviflora*	"	W. Africa	—	62.5		37.5	—	?	Adriaens[22]
" *stuhlmannii*	Mkanyi	Gold Coast	3.5	52.7		43.8	—	F	Meara and Zaky[21]
		E. Africa		ca. 55		ca. 45		L	Heise[23]
Calophyllum inophyllum	Indian laurel	E. Africa	3.1	52.6		44.1	0.2	F	Hilditch and Saletore[24]
" "	Dilo kernel	India	16.8	9.7		49.7	23.8	F	Dhingra and Hilditch[25]
" "	Dombo kernel	Fiji	15.6	12.2		53.1	15.8(*f*)	F	Glasgow[26a]
" *wightianum*	Indian laurel	Ceylon	14.8	19.9	0.2	36.2	28.5(*g*)	C,F,S	Weerakoon[26b]
Garcinia echinocarpa	Madol nut	India	20	13		60	—	L,F	Das and Pillay[26c]
		Ceylon, S. India		22	←78→			?	Nair and Varier[1c]
" *indica*	Kokum butter	India	3.7	43.7		52.6		F	Child[27]
" "		India	2.5	56.4		39.4	1.7	F	Hilditch and Murti[5b]
" *morella*	Gurgi nut	India	5.3	52.0		41.5	—(*h*)	F	Vidyarthi and Rao[28a]
" "	"	India	7.2	42.5	0.3	43.6	6.1(*i*)	F	Dhingra et al.[29]
" "	"	India	0.7	46.4	2.5	49.5	0.9	F	Hilditch and Murti[5b]

325

TABLE 68. *Component Acids of Seed Fats Frequently Rich in Stearic Acid—continued*

Species	Source	HABITAT	COMPONENT FATTY ACIDS (PER CENT. WT.) PALMITIC	STEARIC	ARACHIDIC	OLEIC	LINOLEIC	METHOD	OBSERVERS
GUTTIFERÆ									
Mesua ferrea	Iron wood nut	Bengal	8·5	10·4	1·8	66·5	11·2(*j*)	F	Dhingra and Hilditch[25]
"	"	Malabar	8·4	14·2	—	65·4	9·7(*k*)	F	Dhingra and Hilditch[25]
"	"	India	8·2	15·8	1·0	55·4	19·6	?	Chatterji and Gupta[30a]
"	"	India	13·6	13·2	—	59·1	13·9(*m'*)	L,F	Kasturi et al.[30b]
Pentadesma butyracea	Kanya butter	W. Africa	5·4	46·1	—	48·5	—	F	Hilditch and Saletore[24]
"	"	E. Indies	7·7	39·7	—	49·0	1·6	B	Frahm[31]
Platonia insignis	Bacury	Brazil	28	28	—	40	4	L	Chaves and Pechnik[32]
"	"	Brazil	55·1	6·4	0·3	31·7	2·3(*l*)	C,F	Hilditch and Pathak[33]
DIPTEROCARPACEÆ									
Shorea gysbertsiana	Borneo tallow	Sarawak	←	64·4	→	34·8	0·5(*n'*)	S	Raymond and Ward[34a]
"	"	Malaya	←	61	→	38·5	0·5	S	Raymond and Ward[34a]
" *palembanica*	"	Sarawak	←	65·1	→	33·9	0·7(*o'*)	S	Raymond and Ward[34a]
" *seminis*	"	Sarawak	←	65·3	→	34·1	0·4(*p'*)	S	Raymond and Ward[34a]
" *stenoptera*	"	Malaya	21·5	39·0		38·1	—(*m*)	F	Hilditch and Priestman[34b]
"	"	Borneo	18·0	43·3	1·1	37·4	0·2	S	Bushell and Hilditch[35a]
"	"	Sarawak		65·3		34·1	0·4(*q'*)	F	Raymond and Ward[34a]
" *robusta*	"	N. India	4·5	44·2	6·3	42·2	2·8	S	Hilditch and Zaky[36a]
"	"	India	8·3	34·7	12·3	41·9	2·8	L,F	Prakash et al.[36b]
Vateria indica	Dhupa, Malabar tallow	S. India	10·2	38·9	3·1	47·8	—	F	Hilditch and Jones[37]
"	"	S. India	13·0	43·1	0·4	42·5	0·1(*n*)	F	Venkatarao and Narasing-arao[38]
"	"	S. India	13·0	43·2	0·4	42·6	0·1(*o*)	F	Rao[39]
"	"	S. India	9·7	40·7	4·6	42·2	2·3(*p*)	C,F,S	Baliga and Meara[40]
BURSERACEÆ									
Canarium commune	Java almond	E. Indies	29·5	15	—	43	12·5	L,H	Pastrovich[41]
"	Canari seed	E. Indies	29·0	9·7	—	38·3	21·8(*q*)	F	Steger and van Loon[42]
"	"	E. Indies	30·5	10·2	—	39·9	18·7(*r*)	F	Steger and van Loon[42]

,, *ovatum* syn.	Pili nut	Philippine Is.	38·2	1·8	—	60	—	F	West and Balce[43]
pachyphyllum	,, ,,	Japan	33·6	21·9	0·4	43·3	0·7	F	Ueno and Man[44]
**Dacryodes rostrata*	Java almond	Borneo	10·7	40·3	2·1	43·6	3·3	F	Hilditch and Stainsby[18b]
,, ,,	,, ,,	Malaya	12·7	30·9	3·1	49·5	2·8(*s*)	F	Hilditch, Meara and Zaky[15a]
SAPOTACEÆ									
Acharas sapota	Sapota	India	12·6	12·0	—	66·2	1·4(*t*)	F	Vidyarthi and Mallya[28b]
Autranella congolensis	—	Congo	←	22	→	78	—	?	Adriaens[45a]
Butyrospermum parkii	Shea butter	W. Africa	8·5	35·9	—	49·9	5·3(*u*)	F	Hilditch and Saletore[24]
,, ,,	,, ,,	W. Africa	5·7	41·0	—	49·0	4·3	F	Green and Hilditch[46]
Calocarpum mammosum	Mammy apple	Honduras	10·0	22·3	—	54·3	13·4	F	Jamieson and McKinney[47]
,, ,,	,, ,,	Mexico	←	37·5	→	38·2	24·2	T	Lloyd *et al.*[9c]
Dumoria africana	—	W. Africa	—	46	—	54	—	L	Pieraerts *et al.*[48]
†*Madhuca butyracea*	Phulwara butter	India	54	—	—	46	—	L, H	Pelly[49]
,, ,,	,, ,,	India	56·6	3·6	—	36·0	3·8	F	Bushell and Hilditch[35b]
,, *latifolia*	Mowrah butter	Bengal	←	34	→	66	—	L, H	Pelly[49]
,, ,,	,, ,,	India	27·1	2·0	—	41·0	13·6(*v*)	F	Gill and Shah[50]
,, ,,	,, ,,	India	16·0	25·1	3·3	45·2	9·4(*w*)	F	Dhingra *et al.*[29]
,, ,,	,, ,,	India	23·7	19·3	—	43·3	13·7	F	Hilditch and Ichaporia[51]
,, *longifolia*	Illipé butter,	India, Ceylon	←	40	→	51	9	L, H	Pelly[49]
,, ,,	Mee oil	India, Ceylon	28·2	14·1	—	48·8	8·9	F	Child and Hilditch[52]
,, *mottleyana*	Katio kernel	Borneo	10	18·5	—	69	2·5	L	Zimmermann[53]
Mimusops elangi	—	India	11·0	10·1	0·4	64·0	14·5	F	Kartha and Menon[54]
,, *hexandra*	Rayan seed	N. India	19	14	1	63	3	L	Patel[55]
,, *heckelii*	Dumori butter	W. Africa	4·2	35·5	1·1	58·5	Trace(*x*)	F	Atherton and Meara[56]
,, *njave*	Njave	W. Africa	4·4	36·0	0·5	58·5	0·3(*y*)	F	Atherton and Meara[56]
,, ,,	Baku butter	W. Africa	3·7	35·4	2·1	57·4	1·4	C, F, S	Cama[57]
Omphalocarpum boyankombo	—	Congo	←	21	→	79	—	L	Adriaens[45b]
Palaquium formosanum	—	Formosa	—	60	Some	40	—	L	Kafuku and Hata[58]
,, *oblongifolium*	Njatuo tallow	Pacific Is.	6·5	57·5	—	36	—	L	de Jong and de Haas[59]
,, ,,	Taban merah	Malaya	5·9	54·0	—	39·9	—(*z*)	F	Hilditch and Stainsby[18b]
Payena lancifolia	Surin kernel	Malaya, Borneo	—	*ca.* 58	—	*ca.* 42	—	L	Lewkowitsch[60]

* This was originally published[18b] as the seed fat of *Sterculia fœtida*, but the fruits were subsequently found to be not those of this plant, but of *Dacryodes rostrata*, a plant known, with related *Canarium* sp., as "Java almond".

† Formerly classified as *Bassia*.

TABLE 68. *Component Acids of Seed Fats Frequently Rich in Stearic Acid—continued*

Species		HABITAT	COMPONENT FATTY ACIDS PER CENT. (WT.)					METHOD	OBSERVERS
			PALMATIC	STEARIC	ARACHIDIC	OLEIC	LINOLEIC		
SAPOTACEÆ									
Sideroxylon cinereum	Morocco ironwood	U.S.A.	←—14—→		→	62	24	L	Dickhart[61]
„ *ferrugineum*	Ironwood	Formosa	ca. 26	Some	—	57	17 (a')	L	Kafuku and Hata[58]
„ *tomentosum*	„	Japan (?)	29·5	Trace	—	56·5	14	L	Nobori[62]
„ —	—	India	11·0	17·9	—	57·8	13·3	L, F, H	Airan et al.[63]
CONVOLVULACEÆ									
Argyria speciosa	—	India	6·7	29·1	—	33·2	18·2 (b')	F	Bhide et al.[64a]
Cuscuta reflexa	—	India	10·5	1·9	—	26·6	51·7 (c')	F	Dutt et al.[65a]
„ „	—	India	12·6	29·7	—	28·0	18·9 (d')	F, H	Dutt et al.[65b]
Ipomæa angulata	—	Japan		33·6 →	7·8	11·5	43·7 (r')	T	Koyama and Toyama[12b]
„ *hederacea*	—	India	5·9	20·4	—	44·0	14·6 (e')	F	Dutt et al.[65c]
„ *muricata*	—	India	13·6	22·5	—	41·0	15·2 (f')	F	Bhide et al.[64b]
„ „	—	India	8·0	11·5	—	60·3	19·1 (g')	F	Misra et al.[66a]
„ *palmata*	—	India	8·3	11·4	3·0	24·5	32·7 (s')	F	Handa et al.[66b]
VERBENACEÆ									
Gmelina asiatica	—	Singapore	7·9	8·2	2·9	30·6	35·7 (t')	RPC	Gunstone and Sykes[68a]
Lantana sp.	—	India	9·6	19·7	—	33·6	25·8 (u')	?	Aggarwal and Soni[68b]
Lantana „	—	India	←—10—→		—	43·1	41·6 (v') →	T	Nigam and Kaul[68c]
Tectona grandis	Teak nut	India	6	19	—	←—75—→		L	Puntambekar and Krishna[67a]
„ „	„ „	India	11·0	10·2	2·3	29·5	46·4 (x')	F	Achaya et al.[67c]
ZINGIBERACEÆ									
Elettaria cardamomum	—	India	8·4	18·3	—	62·6	10·5	L, F	Kasturi and Iyer[30c]

Other minor component acids recorded as follows (per cent. wt.):

		SATURATED	UNSATURATED	
		C_{14}	C_{16}	LINOLENIC
(a)	Amoora	0·7	—	7·8
(b)	Neem	2·6	—	—
(c)	Andiroba	—	0·9	0·7
(d)	C. procera	0·2	1·1	0·8
(e)	Stephania	—	—	1
(f)	Dilo	Also 3·3 Erucic (?)		
(g)	Dombo	—	—	—
(h)	Garcinia indica	1·2	—	0·4
(i)	G. morella	0·3	—	—
(j)	Mesua ferrea	1·6	—	—
(k)	"	2·3	3·2	—
(l)	Bacury	1·0	—	—
(m)	Borneo tallow	1·4	—	—
(n)	Dhupa	0·9	—	—
(o)	"	0·7	—	—
(p)	"	—	—	0·5
(q)	Canari	—	—	1·2
(r)	"	—	—	0·7
(s)	Dacryodes	1·0	—	—
(t)	Sapota	6·2 (also 1·6 lauric)	—	—
(u)	Shea	0·4	—	—
(v)	Mowrah	16·3	0·7	—
(w)	Dumori	1·0	0·3	—
(x)	"	—	—	—
(y)	Baku	—	—	—
(z)	Taban merah	0·2	—	—

		SATURATED		UNSATURATED	
		C_{14}	C_{22}	C_{16}	LINOLENIC
(a')	Ironwood	Some	—	—	—
(b')	Argyria	—	6·6	—	6·2
(c')	"	—	—	—	9·3
(d')	Cuscuta	—	—	—	10·8
(e')	I. hederacea	—	1·3	—	6·0
(f')	I. muricata	—	3·8	—	3·9
(g')	"	—	—	—	1·1
(h')	Sterculia urens	4·5	—	(Also 5 per cent. resin acids)	—
(i')	Mahogany	14·1	—	—	11·3
(j')	Andiroba	—	—	—	—
(k')	Brachychiton	(Also 11 per cent. epoxy (?) acid)			—
(l')	Firmiana	(Also 16 per cent. epoxy (?) acid)			—
(m')	Mesua ferrea	0·2	—	—	—
(n')	Shorea gysbertsiana	—	—	—	0·3
(o')	" palembanica	—	—	—	0·3
(p')	" seminis	—	—	—	0·2
(q')	" stenoptera	—	—	—	0·2
(r')	Ipomœa angulata	—	—	—	11·2
(s')	" palmata	—	0·2	—	4·8
(t')	Gmelina asiatica	(Also 10·1 per cent. eicos-11-enoic, 0·8 per cent. each of eicosadienoic and erucic acid)			0·8
(u')	Lantana sp.	(Also 11·3 per cent. ricinoleic acid)			5·3
(v')	"	—	—	—	0·4
(w')	Carapa procera	0·2	—	—	1·0
(x')	Teak nut	0·2	—	—	0·4
(y')	Neem	0·1	—	1·0	—
(z')	Melia azedarach	0·1	0·5 (Also 0·3 lignoceric acid)	1·5	—

References to Table 68

1. (a) N. S. Varier, *Proc. Indian Acad. Sci.*, 1943, **17**, A, 195; (b) K. V. Nair and N. S. Varier, *Bull. Res. Inst. Univ. Travancore*, 1955, A, **4**, 13; (c) *ibid.*, 1954, **3**, 161; 1955, **4**, 19, 23.
2. P. R. Ayyar and V. A. Patwardhan, *J. Indian Inst. Sci.*, 1935, **18**, A, 19.
3. A. C. Roy and S. Dutt, *J. Soc. Chem. Ind.*, 1929, **48**, 333T.
4. R. Child and S. Ramanathan, *J. Soc. Chem. Ind.*, 1936, **55**, 124T; R. Child and W. R. N. Nathanael, *J. Indian Chem. Soc.*, 1944, **21**, 35.
5. T. P. Hilditch and K. S. Murti, (a) *J. Soc. Chem. Ind.*, 1939, **58**, 310; (b) *ibid.*, 1941, **60**, 16.
6. C. J. D. Rao and T. R. Seshadri, *Proc. Indian Acad. Sci.*, 1942, **15**, A, 161.
7. (a) S. S. Gupta and C. R. Mitra, *J. Sci. Food Agric.*, 1953, **4**, 44; (b) J. H. Skellon *et al.*, *J. Sci. Food Agric.*, 1962, **13**, 639.
8. M. L. Meara (a) privately communicated; (b) *J. Chem. Soc.*, 1949, 2154.
9. R. R. Munguia, R. Millares, N. F. Gurley and W. R. Lloyd, (a) *J. Amer. Oil Chem. Soc.*, 1949, **26**, 431; (b) *ibid.*, 1949, **26**, 433; (c) *ibid.*, 1949, **26**, 434.
10. (a) D. K. Chowdhury, M. M. Chakrabarty and N. K. Sen, *Science and Culture* (*India*), 1954, **20**, 52; M. M. Chakrabarty and D. K. Chowdhury, *J. Amer. Oil Chem. Soc.*, 1957, **34**, 489; (b) D. G. Pishawikar and S. V. Shah, *J. Univ. Bombay*, 1946, **15**, No. 3, 17.
11. (a) G. P. Pinto, *Bull. Tech. Inst. Agron.* (*Brazil*), 1956, **31**, 187; (b) A. Mackie and D. G. Mieras, *J. Sci. Food Agric.*, 1961, **12**, 202; (c) P. Cattaneo, G. K. de Sutton and M. H. Bertoni, *Anales Asoc. Quim. Argentina*, 1960, **48**, 101; (d) A. J. Henry and D. N. Grindley, *J. Soc. Chem. Ind.*, 1944, **63**, 188.
12. (a) T. R. Kasturi and B. H. Iyer, *J. Indian Chem. Soc.*, 1954, **31**, 623; (b) Y. Koyama and Y. Toyama, *J. Japan Oil Chem. Soc.*, 1956, **5**, 359; (c) C. F. Hsii, *J. Chinese Chem. Soc.*, 1937, **5**, 14.
13. (a) F. R. Earle, I. A. Wolff *et al.*, *J. Amer. Oil Chem. Soc.*, 1960, **37**, 440; (b) G. Labruto and E. de Angelis, *Annali Chim. Appl.*, 1939, **29**, 68.
14. J. A. R. MacLean, *Nature*, 1952, **169**, 589.
15. (a) T. P. Hilditch, M. L. Meara and Y. A. H. Zaky, *J. Soc. Chem. Ind.*, 1941, **60**, 198; (b) T. P. Hilditch and M. L. Meara, *ibid.*, 1944, **63**, 112.
16. S. Ueno and S. Ueda, *J. Soc. Chem. Ind. Japan*, 1938, **41**, 326B.
17. C. H. Lea, *J. Soc. Chem. Ind.*, 1929, **48**, 41T.
18. T. P. Hilditch and W. J. Stainsby, (a) *J. Soc. Chem. Ind.*, 1936, **55**, 95T; (b) *ibid.*, 1934, **53**, 197T.
19. J. Pieraerts and L. Adriaens, *Mat. grasses*, 1929, **21**, 8510, 8539.
20. W. J. Bushell, unpublished observation.
21. M. L. Meara and Y. A. H. Zaky, *J. Soc. Chem. Ind.*, 1940, **59**, 25.
22. L. Adriaens, *Mat. grasses*, 1933, **25**, 9931, 9961.
23. R. Heise, *Tropenpflanzer*, 1897, **1**, 10; 1899, **3**, 203.
24. T. P. Hilditch and S. A. Saletore, *J. Soc. Chem. Ind.*, 1931, **50**, 468T.
25. D. R. Dhingra and T. P. Hilditch, *J. Soc. Chem. Ind.*, 1931, **50**, 9T.
26. (a) K. W. R. Glasgow, *J. Soc. Chem. Ind.*, 1932, **51**, 172T; (b) A. H. Weerakoon, Thesis, University of Liverpool, 1952; (c) K. G. Das and P. P. Pillay, *Bull. Res. Inst. Univ. Travancore*, 1955, A, **4**, 1, 9.
27. R. Child, *Trop. Agric.*, 1941, **97**, 78.
28. (a) N. L. Vidyarthi and C. J. D. Rao, *J. Indian Chem. Soc.*, 1939, **16**, 437; (b) N. L. Vidyarthi and M. V. Mallya, *ibid.*, 1939, **16**, 443.
29. D. R. Dhingra, G. L. Seth and P. C. Speers, *J. Soc. Chem. Ind.*, 1933, **52**, 116T.
30. (a) N. G. Chatterji and A. C. Gupta, *Oil. Col. Trade J.*, 1937, **91**, 1656; (b) T. R. Kasturi, N. L. N. Murti and B. H. Iyer, *J. Sci. Indust. Res.* (*India*), 1954, **13**, A, 453; (c) T. R. Kasturi and B. H. Iyer, *J. India Inst. Sci.*, 1955, **37**, A, 106.
31. E. D. G. Frahm, *De Ingénieur in Ned. Indie*, 1941, **8**, 87.

32. J. M. Chaves and E. Pechnik, *Rev. Quim. Ind.*, 1945, **14**, No. 163, 18; 1946, **15**, No. 165, 16, 21.

33. T. P. Hilditch and S. P. Pathak, *J. Chem. Soc.*, 1949, Suppl. Issue, 87.

34. (*a*) W. D. Raymond and J. B. Ward, *Col. Plant and Animal Products*, 1956, **6**, 243; (*b*) T. P. Hilditch and J. Priestman. *J. Soc. Chem. Ind.*, 1930, **49**, 197T.

35. W. J. Bushell and T. P. Hilditch, (*a*) *J. Soc. Chem. Ind.*, 1938, **57**, 447; (*b*) *ibid.*, 1938, **57**, 48.

36. (*a*) T. P. Hilditch and Y. A. H. Zaky, *J. Soc. Chem. Ind.*, 1942, **61**, 34; (*b*) O. Prakash, A. C. Gupta and S. Rai, *J. Proc. Oil Technol. Assn., India*, 1956, **12**, 47.

37. T. P. Hilditch, (Miss) E. E. Jones and S. A. Saletore, *J. Soc. Chem. Ind.*, 1931, **50**, 468T.

38. C. Venkatarao and M. Narasingarao, *J. Indian Chem. Soc.*, 1943, **20**, 239, 298.

39. M. N. Rao, Thesis, Andhra University, 1946.

40. M. N. Baliga and M. L. Meara, *J. Soc. Chem. Ind.*, 1949, **68**, 52.

41. L. Pastrovich, *Chem.-Ztg.*, 1907, **31**, 781.

42. A. Steger and J. van Loon, *Rec. trav. chim.*, 1940, **59**, 168.

43. A. P. West and S. Balce, *Philippine J. Sci.*, 1923, **23**, 269.

44. S. Ueno and K. Man, *J. Agric. Chem. Soc. Japan*, 1944, **20**, 465.

45. L. Adriaens, (*a*) *Mat. grasses*, 1935, **27**, 10370; (*b*) *ibid.*, 1935, **27**, 10343.

46. T. G. Green and T. P. Hilditch, *J. Soc. Chem. Ind.*, 1938, **57**, 49.

47. G. S. Jamieson and R. S. McKinney, *Oil and Fat Ind.*, 1931, **8**, 255.

48. J. Pieraerts, J. Adriaens and J. Meulenberg, *Mat. grasses*, 1929, **21**, 8701; 1930, **22**, 8726, 8757, 8782.

49. R. G. Pelly, *J. Soc. Chem. Ind.*, 1912, **31**, 98.

50. A. H. Gill and C. C. Shah, *Oil and Fat Ind.*, 1925, **2**, 46.

51. T. P. Hilditch and M. B. Ichaporia, *J, Soc. Chem. Ind.*, 1938, **57**, 44.

52. R. Child and T. P. Hilditch, unpublished figures.

53. J. Zimmermann, *Chem. Weekblad*, 1933, **30**, 657.

54. A. R. S. Kartha and K. N. Menon, *Proc. Indian Acad. Sci.*, 1944, **19**, A, 1.

55. C. K. Patel, *J. Indian Inst. Sci.*, 1924, **7**, 71.

56. D. Atherton and M. L. Meara, *J. Soc. Chem. Ind.*, 1940, **59**, 95.

57. J. S. Cama, Thesis, University of Liverpool, 1952.

58. K. Kafuku and C. Hata, *J. Chem. Soc. Japan*, 1935, **56**, 1081.

59. A. W. K. de Jong and W. R. T. de Haas, *Chem.-Ztg.*, 1904, **28**, 780.

60. J. Lewkowitsch, *Analyst*, 1906, **31**, 2.

61. W. H. Dickhart, *Amer. J. Pharm.*, 1939, **111**, 293.

62. H. Nobori, *J. Soc. Chem. Ind. Japan*, 1940, **43**, 435B.

63. M. N. Nadkarni, J. W. Airan and S. V. Shah, *J. Univ. Bombay*, 1946, **14**, A, 23.

64. G. M. Kelkar, N. D. Phalnikar and B. V. Bhide, (*a*) *J. Indian Chem. Soc.*, 1947, **24**, 83; (*b*) *ibid.*, 1947, **24**, 87.

65. (*a*) B. Biwas, L. D. Tewari and S. Dutt, *Indian Soap J.*, 1947, **13**, 51; (*b*) R. R. Aggarwal and S. Dutt, *J. Indian Chem. Soc.*, 1936, **13**, 264; (*c*) Y. Kathpalia and S. Dutt, *Indian Soap J.*, 1947, **13**, 77.

66. (*a*) A. L. Misra and J. D. Tewari, *J. Indian Chem. Soc.*, 1951, **28**, 721; (*b*) K. L. Handa, V. Paul and Vasudev, *J. Sci. Indust. Res. (India)*, 1956, **15**, B, 727.

67. (*a*) S. V. Puntambekar and S. Krishna, *J. Indian Chem. Soc.*, 1933, **10**, 401; (*b*) S. V. Puntambekar and P. C. Batra, *Proc. Indian Acad. Sci.*, 1952, **36**, A, 284; (*c*) V. V. R. Subramaniam and K. T. Achaya, *J. Sci. Food Agric.*, 1957, **8**, 662.

68. (*a*) F. D. Gunstone and P. T. Sykes, *J. Sci. Food Agric.*, 1961, **12**, 115; (*b*) J. S. Aggarwal and P. Soni, *J. Sci. Indust. Res. (India)*, 1949, **8**, B, 49; (*c*) S. K. Nigam and K. N. Kaul, *ibid.*, 1958, **17**, B, 472.

SEED FATS OF WHICH MYRISTIC AND LAURIC ACIDS ARE MAJOR COMPONENTS

Major component acids: LAURIC, MYRISTIC, (CAPRIC), palmitic, oleic.
Minor component acids: Caprylic, capric, stearic, linoleic.
(*See Tables* 69A, p. 335, *and* 69B, p. 341.)

We come, in conclusion, to a number of families in which seed fats are characterised by low contents of palmitic acid and also, more often than not, of oleic and linoleic acid, but in which the chief component is lauric or myristic acid (or sometimes both of these). The unsaturated acid content in a few cases exceeds 50 per cent. of the total acids, but is usually much less, in quite a number of instances only amounting to about 10 per cent. or even less of the mixed fatty acids.

The available quantitative data are collected in Tables 69A and 69B. The relatively large proportions of saturated acids of molecular weight 228 or less, coupled with the presence of relatively small amounts of unsaturated acids, cause the mean saponification and iodine values of the fats to possess more significance than usual, and render it possible for the detailed data in the tables to be reinforced by others based only on saponification and iodine values.

A few notes are desirable with reference to each of the families included in Tables 69A and 69B.

Ulmaceæ. The peculiarities of the elm seed fats, when contrasted with those of the seeds of most of the large trees of temperate climates, were remarked when dealing with the latter group (Table 60, and pp. 219, 230). From the two analyses available it is evident that elm seed fats are characterised by the presence of very large proportions of glycerides of *n*-decanoic (capric) acid. The more recent studies of *Zelkova serrata* show that the seed fat of this member of the Ulmaceæ family is even richer than that of the elm in *n*-decanoic acid (over 70 per cent.). Since the seeds of at least four other shrubs or trees belonging to this family produce fats consisting of glycerides of only the four most common acids (linoleic, oleic, palmitic, stearic), further study of other species in the Ulmaceæ would be most interesting; apart from a more complete picture of which species produce capric-rich seed fats and which produce linoleic-rich, the possibility of correlating the two types with some biological factor might well arise.

The only species (*Cuphea*) of the family Lythrarieæ (loosestrife) which has yet been examined also produces a seed fat with over 80 per cent. of decanoic acid. This and the seed fat of *Sassafras albidum* (Lauraceæ) are the only other instances so far recorded of capric-rich seed fats.

Lauraceæ. This family, from the typical genus of which *n*-dodecanoic acid was originally named, elaborates seed fats which in many cases seem to consist very largely of lauric, admixed with a smaller proportion of oleic, glycerides. The more elaborate recent analyses usually show that the fats extremely rich in lauric acid also contain minor proportions of capric, myristic and palmitic acids. Although some of the earlier studies do not refer to any saturated acid other than lauric, the latter acid is probably accompanied in all cases by small proportions of, at all events, capric and myristic acids. Nevertheless, in all the Lauraceæ species (except *Laurus nobilis*) which have been examined lauric acid constitutes 80 per cent. or more of the total seed fatty acids. Small proportions of monoethenoid C_{12} and C_{14} acids have been observed in certain *Lindera* and *Tetradenia* seed fats (see Chapter IX, p. 623). Saponification values (260–280) and iodine values (3–40) of nine other Lauraceous seed fats belonging to the genera *Acrodiclidium*, *Lindera* and *Nectandra* (for which no component acid figures have yet been published) indicate general similarity to the lauric-rich seed fats in Table 69A (p. 335). The frequent substantial absence of other saturated acids renders the Lauraceæ seed fats extremely simple in composition, a feature which is reproduced in some of the Myristicaceæ.

Myristicaceæ. Here again the characteristic acid of the seed fats owes its common name to the nutmeg genus *Myristica*. The seed fats which have been studied come mainly from numerous species of the genus in question and of the allied *Virola*; they seem for the most part to be made up of relatively little oleic and palmitic acids with predominating amounts of myristic acid. As usual, fully quantitative analyses are few but there is no reason to doubt that myristic acid is the chief, often practically the only, saturated component of the seed fats of this family. There may be a minor difference in the component acids of seed fats of the genera *Myristica* and *Virola*: both seem to contain, as a rule, about 70 per cent. of myristic acid, but *Myristica* species usually have little or no lauric acid whilst *Virola* species may have 10–20 per cent. of lauric acid. Both types may have up to 10 per cent. or so of palmitic acid present in the seed fats. Four species of *Myristica* (other than those detailed in Table 69A), five other species of *Virola*, and two species from other genera of Myristicaceæ have been stated to have seed fats similar to nutmeg butter (*Myristica fragrans*) in saponification and iodine values, and their component acids may be supposed, in the absence of more satisfactory evidence, also to be generally similar to the characteristic myristic-rich fats of other members of the family given in Table 69A.

Two seed fats of the Myristicaceæ have so far been observed to present divergent features. That of *M. malabarica* has less myristic and more oleic acid than the other fats, and these acids are accompanied by considerable amounts of resinous acids which seem to enter into the glycerides of the fat. The seed fat of *Pycnanthus kombo* is another instance of complete departure from the usual mixture of seed fatty acids, since these include nearly 25 per cent. of the monoethenoid C_{14}, tetradec-9-enoic acid – which has not been observed in quantity elsewhere in the vegetable kingdom, although it is usually present as a minor constituent of aquatic animal and some other animal fats.

Simarubaceæ. It seems that, as in Euphorbiaceæ and one or two other families, this is a case in which seed fat composition is specific to various genera rather than to the order as a whole. The *Irvingia* seed fats for which we have data seem to consist of minor amounts of oleic with a mixture of myristic and lauric acids as the major component (and thus fall in the group listed in Table 69A). Those of the genus *Picramnia*, as we have seen earlier (p. 289), contain a mixture of acids in which the unusual acetylenic tariric acid appears, and those of *Picrasma* include petroselinic acid (p. 286) as a major component; whilst the analyses of *Ailanthus, Perriera, Samadera* and *Simaruba* fats place these in the large category of palmitic-oleic-linoleic seed fats which was dealt with in Tables 60 and 62 (pp. 229, 268).

Vochysiaceæ. The analyses of a seed fat from this family (Jaboty kernel fat) also place it in a class in which lauric, myristic and palmitic are the main saturated acids present in quantity.

Salvadoraceæ. The earlier data of Patel *et al.* (p. 337) seemed to show that *Salvadora* seeds (from India and N.W. Asia) contained fats remarkably similar to those of the Palmæ, from which, of course, they are far removed botanically. The later study of Gunde, carried out on material specially collected in the Punjab by the Indian Forestry Service, indicates, however, that both species examined contained almost identical fats, the component acids of which consisted of about 50 per cent. of myristic acid with about 20 per cent. each of lauric and palmitic acids, and about 5 per cent. of oleic acid.

TABLE 69A. *Component Acids of Seed Fats Frequently Rich in Lauric and/or Myristic Acids*
[For Palmæ seed fats, see Table 69B]

Major component acids: DECANOIC, LAURIC, MYRISTIC, palmitic, oleic.
Minor component acids: Octanoic, decanoic, stearic, linoleic.

	HABITAT	COMPONENT FATTY ACIDS PER CENT. (WT.)						METHOD	OBSERVERS
		SATURATED				OLEIC	LINOLEIC		
		DEC-ANOIC	LAURIC	MYRIS-TIC	PAL-MITIC				
ULMACEÆ									
Ulmus americana Elmseed	U.S.A.	61·3	5·9	4·6	2·9	11·0	9·0(a)	F	Schuette et al.[1]
" *montana* Elm	Sweden	65·2	4·7	3·4	6·4	←-16·7→	(a')	GLC	Sørensen and Søltoft[2]
Zelkova serrata	Japan	73	3	1	2	3	3 (w)	GLC	Hopkins and Chisholm[3a]
" "	U.S.A.	77	3	1	2	3	4 (x)	GLC	Earle et al.[3b]
LYTHRARIEÆ									
Cuphea llavea Loose-strife	Mexico	82·7	1·2	0·8	2·6	4·9	6·3(y)	GLC	Earle et al.,[3b] Wilson et al.[3c]
LAURACEÆ									
Actinodaphne angustifolia	India	—	ca. 90	—	—	ca. 10	—	?	Puntambekar[11a]
" *hookeri*	India	—	96	—	—	4	—	?	Puntambekar and Krishna[11b]
Cinnamomum camphora Cinnamon	India	—	95	—	—	5	—	?	Puntambekar[11a]
" "	India	10·1	83·9	—	—	4·6	—	?	Puntambekar[11c]
" *zeylanicum*	Ceylon	0·3	86·8	7·3	1·8	3·8	—(h)	C, F, S	Weerakoon[5]
Laurus nobilis Laurel, bay	S. Europe, India, etc.	—	35·0	—	9·7	36·6	18·7	F	Collin and Hilditch[4a]
" "	Yugoslavia	—	43·1	—	6·2	32·3	18·4	F	Collin[12a]
" "	East Indies	—	45·1	—	3·8	28·0	23·1	F	Krajčinović[12b]
Lepidadenia wightiana Tangkallak	India	—	87 (?)	—	—	13 (?)	—	?	Sack[13]
Litsea chinensis	India	—	93	—	—	7	—	?	Puntambekar[11a]
" *citrata*	India	—	ca. 95	—	—	ca. 5	—	?	Puntambekar[11a]
" *longifolia*	Ceylon	—	88·3	—	3·4	5·9	Trace(i)	F	Child and Nathanael[14]
" *zeylanica*	India	—	70	—	—	30 (?)	—	?	Puntambekar[11a]

335

TABLE 69A. Component Acids of Seed Fat Frequently Rich in Lauric and/or Myristic Acids—continued

			COMPONENT FATTY ACIDS PER CENT. (WT.)							
			SATURATED				OLEIC	LINOLEIC	METHOD	OBSERVERS
Species		HABITAT	DEC-ANOIC	LAURIC	MYRIS-TIC	PAL-MITIC				
LAURACEÆ										
Neolitsea involucrata	Dawul-Kurundu	Ceylon	3·0	85·9	3·8	—	4·0	3·3(j)	F	Gunde and Hilditch[15]
" *zeylanica*	Wild cinnamon	Ceylon	3·8	78·7	6·7	2·0	6·7	1·9(k)	C, F, S	Weerakoon[5]
Sassafras albidum	Sassafras	U.S.A.	59	17	1	—	5	—	GLC	Earle et al.[3b]
MYRISTICACEÆ										
Myristica fragrans syn. *officinalis*	Nutmeg	East Indies	—	1·5	76·6	10·1	10·5	1·3	F	Collin and Hilditch[4a]
" "		East Indies	—	—	60	32	8	—	?	Heiduschka and Häbel[4b]
" *iriya*		India	—	0·4	71·8	14·3	5·2	1·5(b)	F	Pathak and Ojha[4c]
" *malabarica*	Iriya	Ceylon	0·5	25·1	66·8	4·4	2·8	0·4	C, F, S	Weerakoon[5]
Pycnanthus kombo	Kombo nut	South India	—	—	39·2	13·3	44·1	1·0(c)	F	Collin and Hilditch[4a]
Virola(Myristica)bicuhyba	Ucuhuba nut	Sierra Leone	—	5·5	61·6	3·6	5·7	—(d)	F	Atherton and Meara[6]
" "		S. America	—	13·3	66·6	8·9	6·6	3·0(e)	F	Steger and van Loon[7]
" " *otobo*	Otobo nut	S. America	—	5	73	11	11	—	F	Ramos and de Nascimento[8]
" " *surinamensis*		Brazil	0·7	20·8	73·4	0·3	5·5	5·1(e')	F	Baughman et al.[9a]
" " *species*	Virola nut	S. America	0·5	13·0	69·7	3·0	7·7	—(f)	F	Pinto[9b]
" "		S. America	—	14·9	73·2	5·0	6·4	—	F	Atherton and Meara[6]
" "		S. America	—	13·3	66·6	8·9	6·6	3·0(g)	F	Verkade and Coops[10]
SIMARUBACEÆ										
Ailanthus altissima	Tree of heaven	U.S.A.	—	⟵——— 4 ———⟶		35	56	—	S	Earle et al.[3b]
" *glandulosa*		Transcaucasia	—	—	—	9·8	82·0	5·5(l)		Michelson[16]
Irvingia barteri	Dika nut	Nigeria	—	38·8	50·6	—	10·6	—	F	Collin and Hilditch[17]
" *gabonensis*	" "	Nigeria	—	19·5	70·5	—	10	—	F	Pieraerts[18]
" "	" "	Nigeria	3·1	58·6	33·4	2·0	1·8	—(m)	F	Bushell and Hilditch[19]
" *oliveri*	Cay-Cay nut	Indo-China	—	ca. 39	ca. 56	—	ca. 5	—	F	Bontoux[20]
" *species*	Dika "	W. Africa	1·6	43·0	46·4	6·2	2·6	0·2(n)	C, F, S	Meara and Patel[21]
Perriera madagascariensis	Kirondro seed	Madagascar	—	—	—	17·5	62·5	20	L, H	Volmar and Samdahl[22]

336

Species	Source	Sample	ca. 22	ca. 33		ca. 22		Reference
Picramnia lindeniana	Central America	Tariri	2 →			— (o)	?	Grimme[23]
" *pentandra*	U.S.A.					93, 1	S	Earle et al.[3b]
" *sow*	Central America		5 →			— (p)	?	Steger and van Loon[24]
Picrasma quassioides	Japan, China	Nigaki seed	23 →			←—77—→ (q)	?	Tsujimoto and Koyanagi[25]
Samadera indica	India			34 →	36	48	?	Kartha[26]
Simaruba glauca	Salvador	Aceituno		9	62	4	S	van Séveren[27]
Erisma calcaratum	Brazil	Jaboty kernel	—	43·6	28·0	25·0 (r)	?	Margaillan[28]
" "	Brazil	"	23·9	18·9	52·8	2·8 (s)	F	Steger and van Loon[29]
SALVADORACEÆ								
Salvadora oleoides	India, Persia	Khakan kernel	6·7 / 47·2	—	28·4	12·0 · 1·3 (t)	F	Patel et al.[30]
" *persica*	India	"	1·5 / 21·2	18·9	52·9	5·5 (u)	F	Gunde and Hilditch[31]
" "	India	"	1·0 / 19·6	19·5	54·5	5·4 (v)	F	Gunde and Hilditch[31]

(*Erisma calcaratum* falls under **VOCHYSIACEÆ**.)

Minor (or other) component acids recorded as follows (per cent. wt.):

		STEARIC	OTHER ACIDS
(a)	Elmseed	—	5·3 *n*-octanoic
(a')	*Ulmus* sp.	—	3·6 *n*-octanoic
(b)	Nutmeg	1·2	0·8 tetradecenoic, 4·8 hexadecenoic
(c)	*M. malabarica*	2·4	—
(d)	Kombo	—	23·6 Tetradec-9-enoic
(e)	Ucuhuba	1·6	—
(e')	*V. surinamensis*	0·9	—
(f)	Virola	1·6	—
(g)	"	—	—
(h)	Cinnamon	1·6	—
(i)	Litsea	2·4	—
(j)	Neolitsea	—	—
(k)	"	0·2	—

		STEARIC	OTHER ACIDS
(l)	Ailanthus	2·4	Traces linolenic
(m)	Dika	1·1	—
(n)	Tariri	3	20 Octadec-6-ynoic (tariric)
(o)	"	—	95 Octadec-6-ynoic (tariric)
(p)	Nigaki	3·4	Unsatd. chiefly octadec-6-enoic
(q)	Jaboty	—	—
(r)	*S. oleoides*	—	1·6 unspecified
(s)	"	—	4·4 *n*-octanoic
(t)	*S. persica*	—	—
(u)	"	—	—
(v)	Zelkova	1	8 *n*-octanoic (undetermined 6 per cent.)
(w)	*S. persica*	—	9 *n*-octanoic
(x)	"	—	—
(y)	*Cuphea*	0·5	0·8 *n*-octanoic, 0·1 linolenic

References to Table 69A

1. H. A. Schuette and C. M. Lunde, *Oil and Soap*, 1936, **13**, 12; R. G. Zehnpfennig and H. A. Schuette, *ibid.*, 1941, **18**, 189.
2. I. Sørensen and P. Søltoft, *Acta Chem. Scand.*, 1958, **12**, 814.
3. (*a*) C. Y. Hopkins and M. J. Chisholm, *J. Amer. Oil Chem. Soc.*, 1959, **36**, 210; (*b*) F. R. Earle, I. A. Wolff *et al.*, *ibid.*, 1960, **37**, 440; (*c*) T. L. Wilson, T. K. Miwa and C. R. Smith, Jr., *ibid.*, 1960, **37**, 675.
4. (*a*) G. Collin and T. P. Hilditch, *Biochem. J.*, 1929, **23**, 1273; *J. Soc. Chem. Ind.*, 1939, **49**, 141т; (*b*) A. Heiduschka and H. Häbel, *Arch. Pharm.*, 1933, **271**, 56; (*c*) S. P, Pathak and V. N. Ojha, *J. Sci. Food Agric.*, 1957, **8**, 537.
5. A. H. Weerakoon, Thesis, University of Liverpool, 1952.
6. D. Atherton and M. L. Meara, *J. Soc. Chem. Ind.*, 1939, **58**, 353.
7. A. Steger and J. van Loon, *Rec. trav. chim.*, 1935, **54**, 149.
8. F. Ramos and R. de C. A. de Nascimento, *Rev. Chim. Ind.*, 1938, **7**, 186.
9. (*a*) W. F. Baughman, G. S. Jamieson and D. H. Brauns, *J. Amer. Chem. Soc.*, 1921, **43**, 199; (*b*) G. P. Pinto, *Rev. Quim. Ind. (Brazil)*, 1954, **23**, 98.
10. P. E. Verkade and J. Coops, *Rec. trav. chim.*, 1927, **46**, 528.
11. (*a*) S. V. Puntambekar, *J. Indian Chem. Soc.*, 1938, **15**, 19; (*b*) S. V. Puntambekar and S. Krishna, *ibid.*, 1933, **10**, 395; (*c*) S. A. Narang and S. V. Puntambekar, *ibid.*, 1957, **34**, 143.
12. (*a*) G. Collin, *Biochem. J.*, 1931, **25**, 95; (*b*) M. Krajćinović and M. Filajdić, *Kem. i. Ind. (Zagreb)*, 1957, **6**, 141.
13. J. Sack, *Pharm. Weekblad*, 1903, **40**, 4.
14. R. Child and W. R. N. Nathanael, *J. Amer. Chem. Soc.*, 1942, **64**, 1079.
15. B. G. Gunde and T. P. Hilditch, *J. Chem. Soc.*, 1938, 1610.
16. L. A. Michelson, *J. Appl. Chem. Russia*, 1936, **9**, 2050.
17. G. Collin and T. P. Hilditch, *Biochem. J.*, 1929, **23**, 1273; *J. Soc. Chem. Ind.*, 1930, **49**, 138т.
18. J. Pieraerts, *Bull. Agric. Congo Belge*, 1922, **13**, 68.
19. W. J. Bushell and T. P. Hilditch, *J. Soc. Chem. Ind.*, 1939, **58**, 24.
20. E. Bontoux, *Bull. Sci. Pharmacol.*, 1910, **17**, 78.
21. M. L. Meara and C. B. Patel, *J. Sci. Food Agric.*, 1950, **1**, 48.
22. Y. Volmar and B. Samdahl, *J. Pharm. Chim.*, 1927, [viii], **6**, 295, 346.
23. C. Grimme, *Chem. Rev. Fett-Harz-Ind.*, 1912, **19**, 51.
24. A. Steger and J. van Loon, *Rec. trav. chim.*, 1933, **52**, 593.
25. M. Tsujimoto and H. Koyanagi, *Bull. Chem. Soc. Japan*, 1933, **8**, 161.
26. A. R. S. Kartha, Thesis, University of Madras, 1942.
27. M. L. van Séveren, *J. Amer. Oil Chem. Soc.*, 1953, **30**, 124.
28. L. Margaillan, *Ann. Musée Colon. Marseille*, 1925, **3**, (iv), 37.
29. A. Steger and J. van Loon, *Chem. and Ind.*, 1935, **13**, 1095.
30. C. K. Patel, S. N. Iyer, J. J. Sudborough and H. E. Watson, *J. Indian Inst. Sci.*, 1926, **9**, A, 117.
31. B. G. Gunde and T. P. Hilditch, *J. Chem. Soc.*, 1939, 1015.

SEED FATS OF THE PALMÆ FAMILY

The seed fats of the palms are perhaps more striking than those of any other natural order of plants, because on the one hand they contain an extremely unusual and varied mixture of saturated acids, and on the other hand this mixture persists with remarkably little quantitative variation throughout the whole family, with very few exceptions. (In the Batava and date palms, the endosperms contain only small quantities of fat, and the saponification and iodine values of the latter indicate more unsaturated acids and acids of higher molecular weight than in any other instances: this may, of course, be due to the presence of more testa fat than usual with the endosperm fat.)

Lauric acid forms 45–50 per cent. of the total fatty acids of most of the endosperm fats, whilst myristic acid amounts as a rule to about 20 per cent.; characteristic also is the presence, in smaller quantities, of capric and caprylic acids, $C_{10}H_{20}O_2$ and $C_8H_{16}O_2$, but the proportions of palmitic and stearic acids are respectively only about 7–9 and 2–3 per cent. The studies of Taylor and Clarke, Longenecker, Nobori and some others (for literature references see Table 69B, p. 343) show that coconut oil fatty acids also contain very small proportions (0·3–0·8 per cent. wt.) of n-hexanoic (caproic) acid, and probably also the customary traces of hexadecenoic acid. Witgert[207] carried out an intensive fractional distillation of the methyl esters of 25 kilograms of coconut oil fatty acids, and found that over 99·5 per cent. of the acids belonged to the even-numbered series of acids from C_8 upwards; he isolated, however, small amounts of nonanoic (0·3 g.), undecanoic (0·2 g.) and tridecanoic (0·4 g.) acids and considered that the existence of traces of these acids in coconut oil is established, but that their combined amount does not exceed 0·1 per cent. of that of the even-numbered acids.

Oleic acid forms not more than 10 per cent. of the total fatty acids in the seed fats of *Cocos nucifera, Attalea cohune, Astrocaryum murumuru* and *Manicaria saccifera*; in another group (*Elæis guineensis, Acrocomia sclero-carpa, Astrocaryum tucuma, Attalea excelsa, A. funifera*) it amounts to about 15–18 per cent. of the total acids, and in a very few other instances the proportion rises to 25–30 per cent. of the total acids. Linoleic acid rarely forms more than 1–2 per cent. of the acids in Palmæ seed fats.

The extent to which the characteristic acids of Palmæ seed fats are quantitatively reproduced in eleven out of the fourteen species listed in Table 69B (p. 341) is remarkable. Moreover, the saponification and iodine values of the kernel fats of eighteen other species from thirteen different genera of palms – for which only general analytical characteristics are available – are close either to those of coconut or palm kernel oils (saponification values 250–260 and 243–250, iodine values 8–10 and 15–18 respectively).

The above figures and discussion refer, of course, to the fats present in the endosperm of the seed. The thin testa of the seeds also contains fatty matter, and the composition of the testa fat is not the same as that of the endosperm. This was first noticed by Richardson[208] in the case of the testa fat of the coconut, whilst Allan and Moore[209a] subsequently found that the testa fats

339

of a number of other Palmæ seeds were similar in character. The fat content of the testa is less than that of the endosperm, and the testa fat contains more of the unsaturated, and less of the saturated, acids than that of the endosperm. Thus, Armstrong, Allan and Moore,[209b] and Carsten, Hilditch and Meara,[210] record the following component acids for testa and endosperm fats from, respectively, the coconut (*Cocos nucifera*) and the West African oil palm (*Elæis guineensis*):

COMPONENT ACIDS PER CENT.	COCONUT		PALM KERNEL	
	TESTA	ENDOSPERM	TESTA	ENDOSPERM
Caprylic	2 (?)	9·5	0·6	4·3
Capric	2	4·5	4·4	4·8
Lauric	28	51·0	35·7	51·3
Myristic	22	18·5	16·0	16·5
Palmitic	12	7·5	10·7	7·6
Stearic	1 (?)	3·0 (?)	1·5	1·7
Oleic	23	5·0	26·0	11·3
Linoleic	10	1·0	5·0	1·3

The fat content and the saponification and iodine values of the fats from the testa and endosperm of various seeds of the Palmæ, as given by Allan and Moore,[209a] are as follows:

SPECIES	COMMON NAME	TESTA FAT			ENDOSPERM FAT		
		PER CENT. FAT IN TESTA	SAP. VAL.	IOD. VAL.	PER CENT. FAT IN ENDOSPERM	SAP. VAL.	IOD. VAL.
Attalea funifera	Babassu	49	232·5	22·8	66	257·5	10·2
Attalea maripa	Ouricoury	56	241	30·4	70	261·7	10·5
Cocos nucifera	Coconut	22–58	221–241	21·5–59·7	55–75	255·5–262·5	5·7–9·3
Elæis guineensis	Oil palm	30–33	229·5–233·3	28·0–29·6	56	244	12·4

Thus testa fat, in seeds of the Palmæ, has a composition intermediate between those of the fruit-coat fat and the endosperm fat, but is distinctly more akin to the latter.

TABLE 69B *Component Acids of Seed Fats of the Palmæ*

Major component acids: LAURIC, MYRISTIC, palmitic, oleic.
Minor component acids: Caprylic, capric, stearic, linoleic.

COMPONENT FATTY ACIDS PER CENT. (WT.)

Species	Common name	Habitat	C_8	C_{10}	C_{12}	C_{14}	C_{16}	C_{18}	OLEIC	LINO-LEIC	METHOD	OBSERVERS
Acrocomia mexicana	Coyol nut	Mexico	—	6·2	44·0	10·5	11·9	1·9	20·2	5·3	F	Giral and Peralta[32a]
,, *sclerocarpa*	Grugru kernel	Brazil, W. Indies	*7·8	5·6	44·9	13·4	7·6	2·6	16·5	1·6	F	Collin[32b]
Areca catechu	Areca, betel nut	Bengal	—	0·2	16·6	44·9	13·8	2·0	7·4	6·4(l)	L, F	Pathak and Mathur[33a]
,, ,,	"Pinang mabuk"	Malaya	—	Trace	15·9	50·6	14·8	3·4	4·9	6·9(o)	GLC	Mackie and Mieras[33b]
Astrocaryum murumuru	Murumuru kernel	Brazil	1·1	1·6	42·5	36·9	4·6	2·1	10·8	0·4	F	Saraiva[34]
,, *tucuma*	Tucuma kernel	Brazil, W. Indies	1·3	4·4	48·9	21·6	6·4	1·7	13·2	2·5	F	Collin[32b]
Attalea cohune	Cohune nut	Honduras	*7·5	6·6	46·4	16·1	9·3	3·3	9·9	0·9	F	Hilditch and Vidyarthi[35]
,, *excelsa* (syn. *Syagrus coronata*)	Ouricoury nut	Central America, Brazil	*9·8	8·2	45·8	9·0	7·7	2·3	13·1	2·2	F	McKinney and Jamieson[36]
,, *funifera* (syn. *Orbignia speciosa*)	Babassu kernel	Brazil, Mexico, W. Africa	*6·5	2·7	45·8	19·9	6·9	—	18·1	—	F	Heiduschka and Agsten[37]
,, ,,	,,	Brazil	4·1	7·6	45·1	16·5	5·8	5·5	11·9	2·8	F	Nobori and Ono[38a]
,, ,,	,,	Brazil	*4·8	6·6	44·1	15·4	8·5	2·7	16·1	1·4(a)	F	Jackson and Longenecker[39]
Cocos nucifera	Coconut	Tropical coasts	9·5	4·5	51·0	18·5	7·5	3·0	5·0	1·0	F	Armstrong *et al.*[40a]
,, ,,	,,	Tropical coasts	*8·7	5·6	45·0	18·0	(← not estimated ──→)			((b)	F	Taylor and Clarke[41]
,, ,,	,,	Tropical coasts	*7·9	7·2	48·0	17·5	9·0	2·1	5·7	2·6	F	Collin and Hilditch[42]
,, ,,	,,	Tropical coasts	*7·8	7·6	44·8	18·1	9·5	2·4	8·2	1·5	F	Child and Collin[43]
,, ,,	,,	Tropical coasts	*9·0	6·8	46·4	18·0	9·0	1·0	7·6	1·6(c)	F	Lepkovsky *et al.*[44]
,, ,,	,,	Tropical coasts	*5·4	8·4	45·4	18·0	10·5	2·3	7·5	Trace(d)	F	Longenecker[45]
,, ,,	,,	Tropical coasts	*7·7	9·7	45·0	18·0	8·4	3·7	5·8	1·5(e)	C, F, S	Dale and Meara[46]

341

TABLE 69B Component Acids of Seed Fats of the Palmæ—continued.

COMPONENT FATTY ACIDS PER CENT. (WT.)

			SATURATED						OLEIC	LINO-LEIC	METHOD	OBSERVERS
		HABITAT	C_8	C_{10}	C_{12}	C_{14}	C_{16}	C_{18}				
Cocos nucifera	Coconut	S. China	8·7	8·1	51·3	13·1	7·5	2·0	5·5	2·3(f)	F	Nobori[38b]
"	"	South Sea Is.	*9·2	9·7	44·1	15·9	9·6	3·2	6·3	1·5(g)	F	Nobori and Kawabata[38c]
" *pulposa*		Uruguay	*10·4	14·4	37·1	7·1	1·8	1·3	23·7	2·6(h)	F	Jamieson and Rose[47]
Elæis guineensis	Palm kernel	W. Africa	3·0	3·0	52·0	15·0	7·5	2·5	16·0	1·0	F	Armstrong et al.[40b]
"	"	W. Africa	2·7	7·0	46·9	14·1	8·8	1·3	18·5	0·7	F	Collin and Hilditch[42]
"	"	W. Africa	4·3	4·8	51·3	16·5	7·6	1·7	11·3	1·3(i)	F,S	Carsten et al.[48]
"	"	W. Africa	3·9	6·3	51·2	17·5	6·5	2·0	10·5	1·2(j)	F,S	Carsten et al.[48]
"	"	W. Africa	2·4	3·7	45·2	18·6	8·5	2·5	15·1	2·1(k)	C,F,S	Dale and Meara[46]
"	"	W. Africa	4·3	4·7	46·0	17·1	9·9	2·7	13·3	1·0(m)	RPC	Crombie et al.[52a]
"	"	W. Africa	3·2	3·2	44·5	16·6	10·4	3·5	15·6	2·5(n)	RPC	Crombie and Boatman[52b]
Hyphaene thebaica	Doum palm nut	Tropical Africa	1·3	2·8	31·8	14·8	13·8	4·8	← 30·7 →		F	Ubaldini[49]
Manicaria saccifera	Turluru kernel	Brazil, W. Indies	*5·3	6·6	47·5	18·9	8·2	2·4	9·7	1·4	F	Collin[32b]
Palma campestris	Butia palm fruit	Tropics	—	30			25		32	13	B,T	Kaufmann and Baltes[50]
Roystonia oreodoxa	Cuban palmiche nut	Central America	—	5·0	32·2	16·1	7·5	1·0	28·7	9·5	F	Stillman and Reed[51]

* Traces of *n*-hexanoic (caproic) acid.

Other minor component acids recorded as follows (per cent. wt.):

	HEXANOIC	ARACHIDIC	HEXA-DECENOIC
(a) Coconut	—	0·2	—
(b) "	0·5	—	—
(c) "	0·5	—	1·3
(d) "	0·8	0·4	—
(e) "	0·2	1·5	—
(f) "	—	0·2	—
(g) "	0·3	—	—
(h) C. pulposa	1·6	—	—

	HEXANOIC	ARACHIDIC	HEXA-DECENOIC
(i) Palm kernel	—	0·6	0·6
(j) "	—	0·5	0·4
(k) "	—	1·9	—
(l) " Areca	—	Trace	7·8
(m) Palm kernel	1·0	Trace	—
(n) " Areca	0·1	0·4	—
(o) Areca	Also saturated C_{17} 0·3, C_{19} 3·1, C_{21} 4·9, linolenic 1·1 per cent.		

342

References to Table 69B

32. (*a*) F. Giral and C. Peralta, *Ciencia*, 1956, **16**, 7; (*b*) G. Collin, *Biochem. J.*, 1933, **27**, 1366.
33. (*a*) S. P. Pathak and S. S. Mathur, *J. Sci. Food Agric.*, 1954, **5**, 461; (*b*) A. Mackie and D. G. Mieras, *ibid.*, 1961, **12**, 202.
34. M. Saraiva, *Mem. Inst. Chim. Rio de Janeiro*, 1929, **2**, 5.
35. T. P. Hilditch and N. L. Vidyarthi, *J. Soc. Chem. Ind.*, 1928, **47**, 35T.
36. R. S. McKinney and G. S. Jamieson, *Oil and Soap*, 1938, **15**, 172.
37. A. Heiduschka and R. Agsten, *J. pr. Chem.*, 1930, **126**, 53.
38. H. Nobori and I. Ono, (*a*) *J. Soc. Chem. Ind. Japan*, 1940, **43**, 435B; (*b*) H. Nobori, *ibid.*, 1940, **43**, 199B; (*c*) H. Nobori and M. Kawabata, *ibid.*, 1940, **43**, 383B.
39. F. L. Jackson and H. E. Longenecker, *Oil and Soap*, 1944, **21**, 73.
40. E. F. Armstrong, J. Allan and C. W. Moore, (*a*) *J. Soc. Chem. Ind.*, 1925, **44**, 61T; (*b*) *ibid.*, 1925, **44**, 143T.
41. E. R. Taylor and H. T. Clarke, *J. Amer. Chem. Soc.*, 1927, **49**, 2829.
42. G. Collin and T. P. Hilditch, *J. Soc. Chem. Ind.*, 1928, **47**, 261T.
43. R. Child and G. Collin, 1931, unpublished observation.
44. S. Lepkovsky, G. V. Feskov and H. M. Evans, *J. Amer. Chem. Soc.*, 1936, **58**, 978.
45. H. E. Longenecker, *J. Biol. Chem.*, 1939, **130**, 167.
46. (Miss) A. P. Dale and M. L. Meara, *J. Sci. Food Agric.*, 1955, **6**, 162, 166.
47. G. S. Jamieson and W. G. Rose, *Oil and Soap*, 1940, **17**, 144.
48. H. A. Carsten, T. P. Hilditch and M. L. Meara, *J. Soc. Chem. Ind.*, 1945, **64**, 207.
49. I. Ubaldini, *Annali Chim. Appl.*, 1938, **28**, 191.
50. H. P. Kaufmann and J. Baltes, *Fette u. Seifen*, 1938, **45**, 176.
51. R. C. Stillman and R. M. Reed, *Oil and Soap*, 1934, **11**, 208.
52. (*a*) W. Mary L. Crombie, R. Comber and S. G. Boatman, *Biochem. J.*, 1955, **59**, 309; (*b*) W. Mary L. Crombie and S. G. Boatman, *J. W. Afr. Inst. Oil Palm Res.*, 1955, **1**, 64.

Component Acids of Seed Phosphatides

Seeds contain phosphatides as well as glycerides, but the amounts of phosphatides are usually very small, frequently only about 0·1–0·2 per cent. of that of the glycerides which are also present. Doubtless owing to this circumstance, the fatty acids present in combination in phosphatides from the vegetable kingdom have received less notice hitherto than those from animal sources. Until Levene and Rolf[211] published in 1925–26 the results of their study of soya bean phosphatides, plant phosphatides were usually supposed to be varieties of lecithin and the only acid components which had been reported were palmitic, stearic and oleic – in the "lecithins" respectively of leguminous seeds,[212] sugar cane,[213] and beet root.[214] Levene and Rolf,[211] in the case of soya bean phosphatides, showed that more than one type was present, including products less soluble in alcohol than "lecithin", and that the phosphatides sparingly soluble in alcohol and also the alcohol-soluble forms gave optically active barium glycerophosphate, indicating that the phosphoric acid was combined with an α-glyceryl hydroxyl group. They identified palmitic, stearic and (in the form of bromo-additive products) oleic, linoleic and linolenic acids in the mixed fatty acids; they concluded that in the alcohol-soluble phosphatides (choline compounds) the proportion of saturated acids was lower than in animal lecithin, whereas the alcohol-insoluble compounds (ethanolamine derivatives) showed no marked difference in this respect from animal kephalin.

Jamieson et al.[215] (1937) discussed the separation of the mixture of phosphatidic compounds present in soya beans, and put forward evidence that in the seed the phosphatides may be united with carbohydrates in compounds resembling glucosides.

The complexity of the phosphatidic compounds present in seeds has been more fully realised since 1939, when Klenk and Sakai[217] showed that derivatives of inositolphosphoric acids were present in the alcohol-insoluble portions of soya bean phosphatides. The presence of "phosphoinositides" was confirmed by other workers[218] in soya bean and in other phosphatides, notably those of the brain and spinal cord of animals.[219] In 1950, Hutt, Malkin and their co-workers[220a] commenced to publish the results of their studies of the phospholipids of groundnut oil and of other seed phosphatides: they showed that, in addition to "lecithin" (phosphatidyl-choline) and "kephalin" (phosphatidyl-ethanolamine), there was also present phosphatidyl-serine, both the ethanolamine and the serine derivatives being also in combination with inositol or with a galactoarabinoside.

The chemical constitution of the phospholipids is thus a subject – at present in process of more rapid development than formerly – which is sufficiently complex to require independent treatment. There are now several monographs dealing at length with the matter, which (including as it does phospholipids of animal as well as vegetable tissues) is a biochemical subject of considerable importance. Since the immediate object here is to discuss the fatty acids present as components of seed phosphatides – a topic which has not usually

344

received adequate attention – the reader must be referred to these more general biochemical monographs[220b] for a complete discussion of the non-fatty acid part of phospholipid compounds. A few instances only will be quoted here of the general proportions of alcohol-soluble and alcohol-insoluble phosphatides which have been reported in the case of vegetable phospholipids.

Rewald[216] gave the following proportions of "lecithin" (alcohol-soluble phosphatides) and "kephalin" (alcohol-insoluble) in the phosphatides of various seed endosperms:

	GROUNDNUT PER CENT.	COTTONSEED PER CENT.	LINSEED PER CENT.	SUNFLOWER PER CENT.	SESAME PER CENT.
"Lecithin"	35·7	28·8	36·2	38·5	52·2
"Kephalin"	64·3	71·2	63·8	61·5	40·6

Sesame seed phosphatides also contain 7·2 per cent. of a fraction soluble in hot but insoluble in cold alcohol.

Diemair, Bleyer and Schmidt[221a] examined the fatty acids from the phosphatides present in barley, wheat and oats to the respective extents of 0·16, 0·12 and 0·14 per cent. They separated the acids by the lead salt method into "solid" and "liquid" portions; the "solid" acids were mainly palmitic acid, whilst the crystalline tetrabromo-adduct (m.p. 114°) of seed fat linoleic acid was readily isolated from all the "liquid" acids. Their quantitative data included the following:

PHOSPHATIDES OF:	BARLEY	WHEAT		OATS
P:N ratio	1:1·01	1:1·06	1:1·03	1:1·02
Yield of fatty acids (per cent.)	69·1	59·0	62·4	62·5
"Solid" acids (per cent.)	14·8	16·7	16·5	12·2
"Liquid" acids (per cent.)	84·6	83·3	73·4	86·1
Iodine value of "liquid" acids	ca. 170	135·0	141·2	198·3

If these data are compared with those for the corresponding Gramineæ seed fats in Table 63 of this chapter, it will be seen that the proportion of saturated acids may be somewhat higher in the phosphatide than in the glyceride fatty acids, and that the phosphatide unsaturated fatty acids contain much more linoleic (and possibly linolenic) acids than the corresponding portions of the glyceride acids.

The phosphatides of the leaves of grasses, as distinct from the seed phosphatides, have been shown to resemble those of leaves of other plants in that they contain calcium and potassium salts of phosphatidic acids* in addition to the true phosphatides (choline or ethanolamine esters of these acids) (cf. Chibnall et al.[27, 30]). Smith and Chibnall[30] stated that in cocksfoot grass phosphatides the fatty acids present include higher proportions of unsaturated than of saturated acids. Shorland[31a, b] found 2·4 per cent. of total phosphatides in the lipids of mixed New Zealand pasture grasses, and also found that the phosphatide fatty acids of cocksfoot grass (Dactylis glomerata) resembled those of the corresponding glycerides in composition, except that the un-

* Current opinion leans to the view that these phosphatidic acids are probably artefacts resulting from the partial decomposition of phosphatides.

saturated C_{18} acids had a somewhat lower mean unsaturation ($-3\cdot7$ to $-4\cdot8H$) than in the case of the glycerides ($-5\cdot0$ to $-5\cdot3H$).

Diemair and Weiss[221b] observed that the proportions of "lecithin" and "kephalin" in the seed phosphatides of lupins are respectively about 74 and 26 per cent. The lupin "lecithin" fatty acids consisted of about 16 per cent. saturated (palmitic and traces of arachidic) and 84 per cent. unsaturated (oleic, linoleic and linolenic). Bleyer, Diemair and Weiss[221c] found that rape seed "lecithin" contained in its fatty acids about 16 per cent. saturated and 84 per cent. unsaturated components. Heiduschka and Neumann[222] reported 18 per cent. of palmitic, 25–28 per cent. of oleic and 45 per cent. of linoleic acid in rape seed phosphatides, but did not mention erucic or hexadecenoic acids (*cf.* below).

That linoleic acid is the most characteristic, and usually the most prominent, component of seed phosphatide fatty acids is also shown by detailed (ester-fractionation) analyses carried out by Hilditch, Pedelty and Zaky[223] on the acids of soya bean, rape seed, cottonseed, sunflower seed, groundnut and linseed phosphatides. Table 70 shows the weight percentages of the component acids in alcohol-insoluble and alcohol-soluble fractions of soya bean and rape seed phosphatides, and of the combined phosphatides from the other four seeds, together with those of the corresponding glycerides (*cf.* Tables 67B, ref. 196*a*; 66, ref. 4; 62, ref. 35*c*; 60B, ref. 119*b*; 67A, ref. 185*a*; 59A, ref. 81*a, b*, respectively).

A later ester-fractionation and thiocyanometric (T) analysis of the fatty acids of purified soya bean phosphatides (97 per cent. lecithin and 3 per cent. kephalin) by Thornton *et al.*[224] showed palmitic 16, stearic 6, oleic 13, linoleic 63 and linolenic 2 per cent. (wt.).

From the six instances in Table 70 (which cover a fairly wide range of botanical families) the following generalisations may be suggested tentatively:

(i) Acids of the saturated series form a greater proportion of seed phosphatide than of seed glyceride fatty acids; palmitic acid seems usually to amount to at least 12–15 per cent. of the phosphatide fatty acids.

(ii) All the acids present in any seed glyceride are also found in the corresponding seed phosphatide.

(iii) Linoleic acid is on the whole the most characteristic acid of seed phosphatides. Although, in two instances out of the six in Table 70, it amounts to only 20–25 per cent. of the total acids, in the others it forms 45–55 per cent. of the total phosphatide acids. The relative amounts of oleic and linoleic acid are also interesting. In soya beans and rape seed the ratio of linoleic to oleic acid is greater in the phosphatides than in the glycerides; in cottonseed and sunflower seed it is much the same in both lipids; whilst in groundnut and linseed it is definitely lower in the phosphatides than in the glycerides. In linseed, indeed, the relative proportions of oleic, linoleic and linolenic acids in the glycerides are reversed in the phosphatides.

(iv) Hexadecenoic acid, which is found as a minor component in all animal phosphatides, is also present in small quantities in some seed phosphatides, but in others (e.g. sunflower seeds and groundnuts) it appears to be absent.

(v) Seed phosphatides may contain characteristic, although minor, proportions of highly unsaturated C_{20} and C_{22} acids which are not present in the corresponding glycerides.

In proportions of saturated acids, and in the presence of highly unsaturated C_{20-22} acids, there is marked resemblance between the phosphatides of vegetable and animal fats, especially when these are compared with the corresponding glycerides. The vegetable phosphatides are perhaps distinguished in that they

TABLE 70. *Component Acids of Soya Bean and Rape Seed Glycerides and Phosphatides (per cent. wt.)*

	SOYA BEAN			RAPE SEED	
	GLYCERIDES	PHOSPHATIDES		GLYCERIDES	PHOSPHATIDES
		ALCOHOL-INSOLUBLE	ALCOHOL-SOLUBLE		ALCOHOL-INSOLUBLE
Myristic	Trace	—	—	—	1
Palmitic	10	12	19	2	8
Stearic	2	4	—	0·5	—
Arachidic	1	1	—	0·5	—
as Behenic	—	—	—	2	2
Hexadecenoic	0·5	9	6	Trace	2
Oleic	29	10	18	15	22
Linoleic	51	55	52	16	42
Linolenic	6·5	4	4	7	—
as Unsaturated C_{20}	—	5	1	1	—
Erucic	—	—	—	56	23

	COTTONSEED		SUNFLOWER		GROUNDNUT		LINSEED	
	GLYC.	PHOS.	GLYC.	PHOS.	GLYC.	PHOS.	GLYC.	PHOS.
Myristic	1·5	—	—	—	—	—	Trace	—
Palmitic	23	17	7	15	8	16	5	11
Stearic	1	7	3	5	3	3	3·5	11
Arachidic	1·5	3	1	10	—	—	0·5	—
as C_{20}, C_{22}, C_{24}	—	—	1	—	7	7	—	—
Hexadecenoic	2	2	—	—	—	—	—	4
Oleic	23	20	20	19	56	47	19	34
Linoleic	48	45	68	46	26	23	24	20
Linolenic	—	—	—	—	—	—	47	17
as Unsaturated C_{20-22}	—	6	—	5	—	4	—	3

contain all the fatty acids which occur in the corresponding seed glycerides, and by the general prominence of linoleic acid amongst the component fatty acids. Moreover, the linoleic acid of the plant phosphatides is the form present in seed glycerides, furnishing nearly 50 per cent. of the crystalline tetrabromo-additive product of m.p. 114°. Possibly linoleic acid has a specific function in the phosphatides of seeds, but in the absence of a much wider range of information this suggestion is only speculative.

It will, in general, be clear from the foregoing section that comparisons which have been made from time to time on the basis only of the iodine values of mixed fatty acids of phosphatides or glycerides are of little value without some form of detailed analysis – at the least, a determination of the proportions of saturated acids.

General Conclusions

It may be well to conclude this somewhat unwieldy chapter by summarising the main conclusions which have been reached:

(i) The almost exclusive fatty components of the leaf, stem, root and fruit-coat of all plants are palmitic, oleic, linoleic (and sometimes linolenic) acids; unsaturation is most evident in the C_{18} acids of the leaf, and least so in the storage fats of fruit-coat and roots.

(ii) These acids are also the main components of many seed fats; but, equally, one or more of a number of other acids, saturated and unsaturated, is frequently found in quantity in numerous seed fats.

(iii) The fatty (glyceride) components of seeds are specific and closely related to the families in which the parent plants have been grouped by botanists. It is, indeed, not an exaggeration to say that the component acids of seed fats could themselves be made the basis of a system of classification of plants.

(iv) Seed phosphatides have been relatively little studied. The few results available suggest that linoleic acid is often the most prominent fatty acid in these compounds; but any specific acids of the corresponding seed glycerides are also found, usually in relatively smaller proportions than in the latter. Seed phosphatides may resemble animal phosphatides in possessing an increased proportion of saturated acids as compared with the corresponding glycerides, the increase being in palmitic acid in the vegetable, as contrasted with increase in stearic acid in the animal kingdom; also, seed phosphatides may contain very minor amounts of unsaturated C_{20} acids, these being absent from the glycerides.

(v) Perusal of the tables included in this chapter will indicate the scope for further detailed information regarding the component acids of fats from all parts of plants. It is not beyond our province, it may be hoped, to point out that work of this nature is only useful when it is as quantitative as possible, when quantitative data are substantiated by careful evidence as to the individuality of at least the chief component acids, and, above all, when the identity of the species from which the fat is derived is known with certainty.

References to Chapter IV

1. (a) R. J. Anderson et al., J. Biol. Chem., 1929, **85**, 77; 1933, **101**, 499; 1936, **112**, 759; **113**, 637; **114**, 431; 1937, **121**, 649, 669; etc.; (b) W. B. Geiger and R. J. Anderson, J. Biol. Chem., 1939, **129**, 519; (c) R. J. Anderson, Chem. Reviews, 1941, **29**, 225; Yale J. Biol. and Med., 1943, **15**, 311; (d) F. H. Stodola, A. Lesuk and R. J. Anderson, J. Biol. Chem., 1938, **126**, 505; A. Lesuk and R. J. Anderson, ibid., 1940, **136**, 603.

2. (a) E. Chargaff and M. Levine, J. Biol. Chem., 1938, **124**, 195; (b) E. Chargaff, Z. Physiol. Chem., 1933, **218**, 223.

3. (a) J. Asselineau, C.R. Acad. Sci., Paris, 1949, **229**, 791; 1950, **230**, 1620; J. Asselineau and E. Lederer, ibid., 1949, **228**, 1892; 1950, **230**, 142; Nature, 1950, **166**, 782; Biochem. Biophys. Acta, 1951, **7**, 126; (with N. Choucroon), ibid., 1950, **5**, 197; (with H. Demarteau), Compt. rend., 1950, **230**, 877; (with E. Ganz), ibid., 1951, **232**, 2050; (b) H. Demarteau, ibid., 1951, **232**, 2494; (c) E. Lederer and J. Pudles, Bull. Soc. Chim. Biol., 1951, **33**, 1003; 1954, **36**, 759; Bull. Soc. Chim., 1954, 919; (with S. Barbezat and J. J. Trillat), Bull. Soc. Chim., 1952, (v), **19**, 93; (with A. Aebi), Bull. Soc. Chim. Biol., 1953, **35**, 661; (with A. Aebi and E. Vilkas), Bull. Soc. Chim., 1954, (v), **22**, 79; (with M. Barbier), Biochem. Biophys. Acta, 1954, **14**, 246; (d) E. Lederer, V. Portelance and K. Senck-Hanssen, ibid., 1952, (v), **19**, 413; (e) G. Michel, C. Bordet and E. Lederer, Compt. rend., 1960, **250**, 3518.

4. (a) J. Cason et al., J. Biol. Chem., 1953, **205**, 435; 1956, **220**, 391, 407, 893; 1959, **234**, 2555; J. Org. Chem., 1958, **23**, 1497; (b) N. Polgar, J. Chem. Soc., 1954, 1008, 1011; N. Polgar et al., J. Chem. Soc., 1955, 3851; 1957, 3779; 1962, 4262; (c) Chem. and Ind., 1961, 1958.

5. (a) K. Hofmann and R. A. Lucas, J. Amer. Chem. Soc., 1950, **72**, 4328; K. Hofmann, O. Jocker, W. R. Miller, A. C. Young Jr. and F. Tausig, ibid., 1954, **76**, 1799; (b) K. Hofmann, Record Chem. Progress, 1953, **14**, 7; K. Hofmann and S. M. Sax, J. Biol. Chem., 1953, **205**, 55; (c) K. Hofmann, G. J. Marco and G. H. Jeffrey, J. Amer. Chem. Soc., 1958, **80**, 5717; (d) K. Hofmann and F. Tausig, J. Biol. Chem., 1955, **213**, 415; (e) K. Hofmann, D. B. Henis and C. Panus, ibid., 1957, **228**, 349.

6. K. Täufel, H. Thaler and H. Schreyegg, Fette u. Seifen, 1937, **44**, 34.

7. M. S. Newman and R. J. Anderson, J. Biol. Chem., 1933, **102**, 219.

8. R. Reichert, Helv. Chim. Acta, 1945, **28**, 484.

9. T. P. Hilditch and R. K. Shrivastava, Biochem. Biophys. Acta, 1948, **2**, 80.

10. (a) J. Holmberg, Svensk Kem. Tidskr., 1948, **60**, 14; (b) L. Hartman, J. C. Hawke, F. B. Shorland and M. E. di Menna, Arch. Biochem. Biophys., 1959, **81**, 346.

11. A. Bass and J. Hospodka, Chem. Listy, 1952, **46**, 243.

12. B. Rewald, Oil and Soap, 1943, **20**, 151.

13. A. Kiesel, Z. physiol. Chem., 1925, **150**, 149; 1927, **164**, 103.

14. (a) G. E. Ward and G. S. Jamieson, J. Amer. Chem. Soc., 1934, **56**, 973; (b) T. P. Hilditch and M. L. Meara, J. Soc. Chem. Ind., 1944, **63**, 112; (c) Y. Abe, Proc. Fac. Eng. Keiogijuku Univ., 1949, **2**, 129.

15. H. P. Kaufmann and O. Schmidt, Vorratspflege u. Lebensmittelforsch., 1938, **1**, 166.

16. (a) J. Singh, S. Shah and T. K. Walker, J. Sci. Indust. Res. (India), 1956, **15**, C, 220; (b) idem, Biochem. J., 1956, **62**, 222; (c) J. Singh, S. E. Philip and T. K. Walker, J. Sci. Food Agric., 1957, **8**, 697; (d) I. R. Shiral, J. Singh and T. K. Walker, Biochem, J., 1959, **72**, 184; (e) J. Singh, T. K. Walker and M. L. Meara, ibid., 1955, **61**, 85; (f) J. Singh, J. Sci. Indust. Res. (India), 1957, **16**, C, 113; (g) J. Singh and T. K. Walker, Biochem. J., 1956, **62**, 286; Res. Bull. Panjab Univ., 1956, No. **92**, 135; J. Sci. Indust. Res. (India), 1956, **15**, C, 222; T. K. Walker et al., J. Sci. Food Agric., 1956, **7**, 233, 237; 1959, **10**, 597.

17. (a) K. Bernhard and H. Albrecht, Helv. Chim. Acta, 1948, **31**, 977; (b) D. Todd, D. Stone, O. Hochter and A. Nussbaum, J. Biol. Chem., 1957, **229**, 527; (c) L. Hartman, J. C. Hawke, I. M. Morice and F. B. Shorland, Biochem. J., 1960, **75**, 274; (d)

L. Hartman, I. M. Morice and F. B. Shorland, *ibid.*, 1962, **82**, 76; (*e*) H. B. White, Jr., F. S. Chu and F. W. Quackenbush, *J. Amer. Oil Chem. Soc.*, 1962, **39**, 123.

18. G. W. Fiero, *J. Amer. Pharm. Assoc.*, 1933, **22**, 608.
19. H. Van der Meulen, *J. Pharm. Belg.*, 1939, **21**, 195, 213, 237.
20. K. E. Bharucha and F. D. Gunstone, *J. Chem. Soc.*, 1957, 610.
21. J. Zellner, *Monatsh.*, 1910, **31**, 617.
22. W. Heinisch and J. Zellner, *Monatsh.*, 1904, **25**, 537.
23. R. L. Peck and C. R. Hauser, *J. Amer. Chem. Soc.*, 1939, **61**, 281.
24. A. Rathje, *Arch. Pharm.*, 1908, **246**, 692.
25. J. L. Riebsomer and J. R. Johnson, *J. Amer. Chem. Soc.*, 1933, **55**, 3352.
26. J. Maizite, *Latvij. Univ. Raksti*, 1939, **4**, 529.
27. A. C. Chibnall and H. J. Channon, (*a*), *Biochem. J.*, 1927, **21**, 233; (*b*) *ibid.*, 1927, **21**, 479; (*c*) A. C. Chibnall and P. N. Sahai, *Ann. Bot.*, 1931, **45**, 499.
28. J. P. Kass, W. O. Lundberg and G. O. Burr, *Oil and Soap*, 1940, **17**, 50; J. P. Kass, H. G. Loeb, F. A. Norris and G. O. Burr, *ibid.*, 118; T. P. Hilditch and K. S. Murti, *Analyst*, 1940, **65**, 437; N. L. Matthews, W. R. Brode and J. B. Brown, *Oil and Soap*, 1941, **18**, 182; R. W. Riemenschneider, C. E. Swift and C. E. Sando, *ibid.*, 203; E. P. Painter and L. L. Nesbitt, *Ind. Eng. Chem. (Anal.)*, 1933, **15**, 123; P. Desnuelle, J. Rouzier and M. Naudet, *Bull. Soc. Chim.*, 1947, (v), **14**, 325.
29. J. H. Mitchell, H. R. Kraybill and F. P. Zscheile, *Ind. Eng. Chem. (Anal.)*, 1943, **15**, 1; B. W. Beadle and H. R. Kraybill, *J. Amer. Chem. Soc.*, 1944, **66**, 1232; T. P. Hilditch, R. A. Morton and J. P. Riley, *Analyst*, 1945, **70**, 68; T. P. Hilditch, C. B. Patel and J. P. Riley, *Analyst*, 1951, **76**, 81; B. W. Beadle, *Oil and Soap*, 1946, **23**, 140; R. T. O'Connor and D. C. Heinzelman, *J. Amer. Oil Chem. Soc.*, 1947, **24**, 212; R. W. Riemenschneider *et al.*, *ibid.*, 1949, **26**, 37; 1950, **27**, 329; 1951, **28**, 55; B. A. Brice, M. L. Swain *et al.*, *J. Opt. Soc. Amer.*, 1945, **35**, 532; *Oil and Soap*, 1945, **22**, 219; *J. Amer. Oil Chem. Soc.*, 1949, **26**, 272; 1952, **29**, 279; etc.
30. J. A. B. Smith and A. C. Chibnall, *Biochem. J.*, 1932, **26**, 218, 1345.
31. F. B. Shorland, (*a*) *New Zealand J. Sci. Tech.*, 1941, **23**, 112A; (*b*) *Nature*, 1944, **153**, 168; (*c*) *Nature*, 1945, **156**, 269; (*d*) *Biochem. J.*, 1951, **49**, 503; (*e*) *J. Sci. Food Agric.*, 1961, **12**, 39; (*f*) R. O. Weenink, *New Zealand J. Sci.*, 1959, **2**, 273; (*g*) *J. Sci. Food Agric.*, 1961, **12**, 34; (*h*) S. Adhikari, F. B. Shorland and R. O. Weenink, *Nature*, 1961, **191**, 1301.
32. (*a*) H. Jasperson and F. Burke, privately communicated; (*b*) T. P. Hilditch and H. Jasperson, *J. Soc. Chem. Ind.*, 1945, **64**, 109.
33. G. A. Garton, *Nature*, 1960, **187**, 511.
34. S. M. Gordon, *Amer. J. Pharm.*, 1928, **100**, 433, 509.
35. J. H. Speer, E. C. Wise, M. C. Hart and F. W. Heyl, *J. Biol. Chem.*, 1929, **82**, 105, 111.
36. W. Menke and E. Jacob, *Z. physiol. Chem.*, 1942, **272**, 227.
37. M. Tsujimoto, *J. Soc. Chem. Ind. Japan*, 1940, **43**, 208.
38. T. H. Tang and C. W. Hsu, *J. Chinese Chem. Soc.*, 1940, **7**, 105.
39. (*a*) A. H. Jackson and F. A. Kummerow, *J. Amer. Oil Chem. Soc.*, 1949, **26**, 26; (*b*) C. F. Krewson, *ibid.*, 1952, **29**, 4.
40. J. Pieraerts, *Mat. grasses*, 1926, **18**, 7669.
41. V. Ruchkin, *Maslob. Shir. Delo*, 1929, No. **2**, 47.
42. H. Dieterle and O. Dorner, *Arch. Pharm.*, 1937, **275**, 428.
43. (*a*) Y. P. Kathpalia and S. Dutt, *Indian Soap J.*, 1952, **17**, 235; (*b*) P. N. Bhargava, *Proc. Indian Acad. Sci.*, 1946, A, **24**, 496; (*c*) U. Gerloff, *Planta*, 1936, **25**, 667 (*Chem. Abst.*, 1937, **31**, 131).
44. (*a*) H. H. Hatt, A. C. K. Triffett and P. C. Wailes, *Austral. J. Chem.*, 1960, **13**, 488; (*b*) *idem.*, *ibid.*, 1959, **12**, 190.
45. (*a*) N. L. Vidyarthi and M. Narasingarao, *J. Indian Chem. Soc.*, 1939, **16**, 135; (*b*) V. V. Mhaskar and A. B. Kulkarni, *J. Sci. Indust. Res. (India)*, 1957, **16**, B, 374; (*c*) D. E. Whyte and B. Hengeveld, *J. Amer. Oil Chem. Soc.*, 1950, **27**, 57; (*d*) D. H. S. Horn and M. Matic, *J. Sci. Food Agric.*, 1957, **8**, 571.

46. J. A. Lamberton and A. H. Redcliffe, *Chem. and Ind.*, 1959, 1627; *Austral. J. Chem.*, 1960, **13**, 261, 498; *Austral. J. Appl. Sci.*, 1960, **11**, 473.

47. J. A. Wallach, *Soap*, 1937, **13**, 31, 73.

48. C. Becher, *Chem.-Ztg.*, 1936, **60**, 373.

49. H. Niesen, *Fette u. Seifen*, 1937, **44**, 426.

50. R. H. Anderson and D. H. Wheeler, *Oil and Soap*, 1945, **22**, 137.

51. (*a*) W. H. Jennings, *Paper Trade J.*, 1945, **120**, *TAPPI* Sect., 185; (*b*) G. N. B. Burch *et al.*, *Pulp Paper Mag.*, *Canada*, 1947, **48**, 127.

52. (*a*) R. P. Hansen, *New Zealand Sci. Review*, 1960, **17**, 114; (*b*) R. P. Hansen and N. J. Cooke, *J. Sci. Food Agric.*, 1957, **8**, 482; *New Zealand J. Sci.*, 1959, **2**, 366; *Chem. and Ind.*, 1959, 1516.

53. W. F. Baughman and G. S. Jamieson, *J. Agric. Res.*, 1923, **26**, 77.

54. (*a*) F. Josephs, *Fette u. Seifen*, 1938, **45**, 292; (*b*) F. R. Earle, I. A. Wolff, *et al.*, *J. Amer. Oil Chem. Soc.*, 1959, **36**, 304.

55. S. W. Goldstein and G. L. Jenkins, *J. Amer. Pharm. Assoc.*, 1936, **25**, 636.

56. A. Neville, *J. Chem. Soc.*, 1912, **101**, 1101.

57. A. Schröder, *Arch. Pharm.*, 1905, **243**, 628.

58. A. J. Henry and D. N. Grindley, *J. Soc. Chem. Ind.*, 1949, **68**, 9.

59. Y. A. Dranitsyna, *Trudy Botan. Inst. Acad. Nauk. U.S.S.R.*, 1955, **5**, 85.

60. B. Rewald, *Oil and Soap*, 1944, **21**, 93.

61. L. Schmid and W. Hasse, *Mikrochemie*, 1939, **26**, 59; L. I. H. Dieterle and K. Fay, *Arch. Pharm.*, 1939, **277**, 65.

62. D. B. Panihar and S. Dutt, *Indian Soap J.*, 1950, **15**, 161.

63. C. Mitra, P. N. Rao *et al.*, *J. Sci. Indust. Res. India*, 1947, **6**, **B**, 19.

64. N. A. Sörensen, (*a*) with J. Stene, *Annalen.*, 1941, **549**, 80; with R. T. Holman, *Acta Chem. Scand.*, 1950, **4**, 416; (*b*) with K. Stavholt, *ibid.*, 1950, **4**, 1080; (*c*) *ibid.*, 1950, **4**, 1567; (*d*) *ibid.*, 1950, **4**, 1575; (*e*) with T. Bruun and C. M. Haug, *ibid.*, 1950, **4**, 850; *see also*, with T. Bruun and D. Holme, *ibid.*, 1954, **8**, 26, 34, 1741, 1763, 1769; Chap. IX, ref. 233 (p. 657); F. Bohlmann, *Fortschr. Chem. Org. Naturstoffe*, 1957, **14**, 1.

65. S. Takei, Y. Sakato, M. Ono, Y. Kuraiwa and T. Takahata, *J. Agric. Chem. Soc. Japan*, 1938, **14**, 709, 717; 1949, **15**, 193; 1940, **16**, 772; L. Ruzicka, H. Schinz and B. P. Suss, *Helv. Chim. Acta*, 1944, **27**, 1561.

66. L. Crombie and S. H. Harper, *J. Chem. Soc.*, 1950, 873; F. Sondheimer, *ibid.*, 1950, 877.

67. L. E. Eberhardt, *Dissertation*, Strassburg, 1888.

68. A. C. Geitel and G. van der Want, *J. pr. Chem.*, 1900, (2–3), **61**, 151.

69. (*a*) M. Tsujimoto, *Bull. Chem. Soc. Japan*, 1931, **6**, 325, 337; (*b*) Y. Toyama and H. Hirai, *Res. Rept. Nagoya Ind. Sci. Res. Inst.*, 1954, **No. 7**, 46; H. Takai and Y. Toyama, *Nagoya Inst. J.*, 1957, **10**, 62.

70. F. M. Dyke, *African World, Suppl.*, 1928, August 25, p. 25.

71. O. A. Roels and L. Thuriaux, *Bull. Inst. Roy. Col. Belge*, 1950, **21**, 730.

72. V. Brandonisio, *Chem. e. Ind.*, 1936, **18**, 14.

73. (*a*) G. S. Jamieson, R. M. Hann and W. F. Baughman, *Oil and Fat Ind.*, 1927, **4**, 63; (*b*) M. R. Fuhrmann, *Rev. francaise des Corps Gras*, 1955, **2**, 237; (*c*) B. G. Gunde and T. P. Hilditch, *J. Soc. Chem. Ind.*, 1940, **59**, 47.

74. (*a*) C. R. Smith, Jr., M. O. Bagby, T. K. Miwa, R. L. Lohmar and I. A. Wolff, *J. Org. Chem.*, 1960, **25**, 1770; 1961, **26**, 1261; T. K. Miwa and I. A. Wolff, *J. Amer. Oil Chem. Soc.*, 1962, **39**, 320; (*b*) R. A. Peters and R. J. Hall, *Biochem. Pharmacol.*, 1958, **2**, 25; R. A. Peters, R. W. Wakelin and A. J. P. Martin, *Biochem. J.*, 1959, **71**, 245; R. A. Peters, R. J. Hall, P. F. V. Ward and N. Sheppard, *ibid.*, 1960, **77**, 17; R. A. Peters and R. J. Hall, *J. Sci. Food Agric.*, 1960, **11**, 608; (*c*) F. L. M. Pattison and R. E. A. Dear, *Nature*, 1961, **192**, 1284.

75. (*a*) P. Cattaneo, *Anales Asoc. Quim. Argentina*, 1950, **38**, 83; (*b*) P. Cattaneo, G. K. de Sutton and J. Schmidt, *ibid.*, 1950, **38**, 268; (*c*) F. Crespo and P. Cattaneo, *ibid.*, 1958, **46**, 368; (*d*) P. Cattaneo and G. K. de Sutton, *Rev. Argentina Grasas y Aceites*, 1959, **1**, 1.

76. (a) C. Barker and T. P. Hilditch, *J. Oil Col. Chem. Assocn.*, 1950, **33**, 6; (b) T. P. Hilditch and A. J. Seavell, *ibid.*, 1950, **33**, 24.

77. S. Ivanov, *Ber. deut. Bot. Ges.*, 1926, **44**, 31; *Z. Angew. Chem.*, 1929, **42**, 292; *Chem. Umschau*, 1931, **38**, 96; *Allgem. Oel-Fett-Ztg.*, 1932, **29**, 149; S. Juschkevitsch, *Fettchem. Umschau*, 1933, **40**, 197.

78. (a) C. R. Smith, Jr., M. O. Bagby, I. A. Wolff *et al.*, *J. Org. Chem.*, 1960, **25**, 218; (b) F. R. Earle, I. A. Wolff *et al.*, *J. Amer. Oil Chem. Soc.*, 1959, **36**, 304; (c) B. G. Gunde and T. P. Hilditch, *J. Chem. Soc.*, 1938, 1980.

79. H. P. Kaufmann and M. Keller, *Z. angew. Chem.*, 1929, **42**, 76.

80. P. J. Gay, *J. Soc. Chem. Ind.*, 1932, **51**, 126T.

81. H. N. Griffiths, T. P. Hilditch and E. C. Jones, (a) *J. Soc. Chem. Ind.*, 1934, **53**, 13T; (b) *ibid.*, 75T; (c) F. D. Gunstone and T. P. Hilditch, *J. Soc. Chem. Ind.*, 1946, **65**, 8.

82. H. R. Sallans and G. D. Sinclair, *Canad. J. Research*, 1944, **22**, 132.

83. (a) W. Mary L. Crombie, R. Comber and S. G. Boatman, *Biochem. J.*, 1955, **59**, 309; (b) B. M. Craig and N. L. Murti, *J. Amer. Oil Chem. Soc.*, 1959, **36**, 549; (c) F. R. Earle, I. A. Wolff, *et al.*, *ibid.*, 1960, **37**, 48.

84. W. G. H. Edwards and A. J. D. Robb, *J. Sci. Food Agric.*, 1951, **2**, 429.

85. T. P. Hilditch, with (a) M. M. Chakrabarty, (b) J. P. Riley, (c) R. E. Bridge, (d) A. J. Seavell, *J. Sci. Food Agric.*, 1951, **2**, 543.

86. F. N. Woodward, *Analyst*, 1939, **64**, 265.

87. W. G. Rose and G. S. Jamieson, *Oil and Soap*, 1941, **18**, 173.

88. E. P. Painter and L. L. Nesbitt, *Ind. Eng. Chem.* (*Anal.*), 1943, **15**, 123; *Oil and Soap*, 1943, **20**, 208; E. P. Painter, *Oil and Soap*, 1944, **21**, 343.

89. A. C. Dillman, *U.S. Dept. Agric.*, *Tech. Bulletin* No. 844 (1943).

90. (a) R. E. Bridge and T. P. Hilditch, *J. Chem. Soc.*, 1950, 2396; (b) P. Cattaneo, G. K. de Sutton, R. R. Brenner *et al.*, *Anales Asoc. Quim. Argentina*, 1962, **50**, 1; (c) A. Mackie and D. G. Mieras, *J. Sci. Food Agric.*, 1961, **12**, 202.

91. (a) H. A. Schuette and C. M. Lunde, *Oil and Soap*, 1936, **13**, 12; R. G. Zehnpfennig and H. A. Schuette, *ibid.*, 1941, **18**, 189; (b) M. A. Pawlenko, *Chem. Rev. Fett-Harz-Ind.*, 1912, **19**, 43; (c) A. Beythien, H. Hempel, P. Pannwitz and E. Spreckels, *Z. Unters. Nahr. Genussm.*, 1916, **32**, 305; (d) I. Sørensen and P. Søltoft, *Acta Chem. Scand.*, 1958, **12**, 814; (e) C. Y. Hopkins and M. J. Chisholm, *J. Amer. Oil Chem. Soc.*, 1959, **36**, 210; F. R. Earle, I. A. Wolff *et al.*, *ibid.*, 1960, **37**, 440.

92. N. L. Vidyarthi, *Patna Univ. J.*, 1945, **1**, 51.

93. (a) F. D. Gunstone, *J. Chem. Soc.*, 1954, 1611; (b) C. R. Smith, Jr., M. C. Bennett, T. L. Wilson, R. L. Lohmar and I. A. Wolff, *J. Amer. Oil Chem. Soc.*, 1960, **37**, 320; (c) C. R. Smith, Jr., I. A. Wolff *et al.*, *J. Org. Chem.*, 1960, **25**, 218; (d) A. J. Morris, R. T. Holman and K. Fontell, *J. Amer. Oil Chem. Soc.*, 1960, **37**, 323; (e) M. J. Chisholm and C. Y. Hopkins, *Canad. J. Chem.*, 1957, **35**, 358; C. R. Smith, Jr., T. L. Wilson, E. H. Melvin and I. A. Wolff, *J. Amer. Chem. Soc.*, 1960, **82**, 1417; (f) M. J. Chisholm and C. Y. Hopkins, *Canad. J. Chem.*, 1960, **38**, 2500; (g) idem, *ibid.*, 1956, **34**, 459; (h) idem, *J. Amer. Oil Chem. Soc.*, 1957, **34**, 477; (i) idem, *Canad. J. Chem.*, 1960, **38**, 805; *Canad. J. Biochem. Physiol.*, 1961, **39**, 829; (j) R. C. Badami and F. D. Gunstone, *J. Sci. Food Agric.*, 1963, **14**, 481; (k) T. K. Miwa, F. R. Earle, G. C. Miwa and I. A. Wolff, *J. Amer. Oil Chem. Soc.*, 1963, **40**, 225; W. E. Scott, C. F. Krewson and R. W. Riemenschneider, *Chem. and Ind.*, 1962, 2038; *J. Amer. Oil Chem. Soc.*, 1963, **40**, 587.

94. L. Gurgel and T. F. de Amorim, *Mem. Inst. Chim. Rio de Janiero*, 1929, No. **2**, 31.

95. (a) S. V. Puntambekar and S. Krishna, *J. Indian Chem. Soc.*, 1937, **14**, 268; (b) H. A. Boekenoogen, *Fette u. Seifen*, 1939, **46**, 717; (c) S. P. Ligthelm, D. H. S. Horn, H. M. Schwartz and M. M. van Holdt, *J. Chem. Soc.*, 1952, 1088; *J. Sci. Food Agric.*, 1954, **5**, 281; (d) N. H. E. Ahlers and S. P. Ligthelm, *J. Chem. Soc.*, 1952, 5039; (e) H. H. Hatt, A. C. K. Triffett and P. C. Wailes, *Australian J. Chem.*, 1959, **12**, 190; 1960, **13**, 488.

96. (a) A. Steger and J. van Loon, *Fette u. Seifen*, 1937, **44**, 243; *Rec. trav. chim.*, 1940, **59**,

1156; 1941, **60**, 342; (*b*) H. A. Boekenoogen, *Fette u. Seifen*, 1937, **44**, 344; (*c*) A. Castille, *Annalen*, 1939, **543**, 104; (*d*) J. P. Riley, *J. Chem. Soc.*, 1951, 1346; (*e*) H. P. Kaufmann, J. Baltes and H. Herminghaus, *Fette u. Seifen*, 1951, **53**, 537; (*f*) A. Seher, *Arch. Pharm.*, 1954, **287**, 548; (*g*) F. Pouliquen, *Bull. Soc. Chim.*, 1957, 1495; *Oléagineux*, 1959, **14**, 453; (*h*) E. M. Meade, "Progress in the Chemistry of Fats and other Lipids," 1957, p. 50: Pergamon Press; (*i*) F. D. Gunstone (with A. J. Sealy), *J. Chem. Soc.*, 1963, 5772; (*j*) (with R. C. Badami), *J. Sci. Food Agric.*, 1963, **14**, 863.

97. D. L. Sahasrabuddhe and N. P. Kale, *J. Univ. Bombay*, 1932, **1**, (ii), 37.

98. N. L. Vidyarthi and M. V. Mallya, *J. Indian Chem. Soc.*, 1940, **17**, 87.

99. (*a*) M. M. Chakrabarty, Thesis, University of Liverpool, 1951; (*b*) S. R. and M. M. Chakrabarty, *Indian Sci. J.*, 1954, **19**, 165; (*c*) *J. Indian Chem. Soc., Ind. News Edn.*, 1957, **20**, 17.

100. C. R. Pye, *Paint Tech.*, 1945 ,**10**, 113.

101. T. P. Hilditch, with I. C. Sime, *J. Soc. Chem. Ind.*, 1944, **63**, 112; with R. K. Shrivastava, *Analyst*, 1947, **72**, 527.

102. H. C. Dunn and T. P. Hilditch, *J. Soc. Chem. Ind.*, 1950, **69**, 13.

103. C. Venkatarao, M. Narasingarao and A. Venkateswarulu, *J. Indian Chem. Soc.*, 1943, **20**, 374.

104. S. D. Mahant and P. N. Pandit, *J. Sci. Indust. Res. India*, 1948, **7**, A, 229.

105. R. V. Crawford and T. P. Hilditch, *J. Sci. Food Agric.*, 1950, **1**, 230.

106. A. O. Cruz and A. P. West, *Philippine J. Sci.*, 1937, **61**, 161.

107. W. L. Roberts and H. A. Schuette, *J. Amer. Chem. Soc.*, 1934, **56**, 207.

108. L. F. Salisbury, *J. Biol. Chem.*, 1937, **117**, 21.

109. R. W. Riemenschneider, R. M. Speck and E. G. Beinhart, *Oil and Soap*, 1945, **22**, 120.

110. R. E. Bridge, (*a*) 1951 (privately communicated); (*b*) Thesis, University of Liverpool, 1951.

111. (*a*) J. D. Langawankar, N. L. Phalnikar and B. V. Bhide, *J. Univ. Bombay*, 1943, **12**, A, 71; (*b*) T. N. Mehta and S. B. Dabhade, *J. Amer. Oil Chem. Soc.*, 1958, **35**, 501.

112. N. L. Vidyarthi, *J. Indian Chem. Soc.*, 1943, **20**, 45.

113. G. S. Jamieson and S. I. Gertler, *Oil and Fat Ind.*, 1929, **6**, (4), 11.

114. J. van Loon, *Verfkroniek*, 1937, **10**, 80.

115. H. P. Kaufmann and H. Fiedler, *Fette u. Seifen*, 1937, **44**, 420.

116. J. D. Bickford, G. E. Mann and K. S. Markley, *Oil and Soap*, 1943, **20**, 85.

117. (*a*) R. T. Milner, J. E. Hubbard and M. B. Wiele, *Oil and Soap*, 1945, **22**, 304; (*b*) B. M. Craig, *Canad. J. Technol.*, 1953, **31**, 202.

118. A. T. Pugsley and G. Winter, *Munitions Supply Lab., Australia*, Report No. 171 (1947); G. Winter, *J. Amer. Oil. Chem. Soc.*, 1950, **27**, 82.

119. C. Barker and T. P. Hilditch, (*a*) *J. Soc. Chem. Ind.*, 1950, **69**, 15; (*b*) *idid.*, 1950, **69**, 16; (*c*) *J. Sci. Food Agric.*, 1950, **1**, 118; (*e*) *ibid.*, 1950, **1**, 140; (*d*) R. E. Bridge, A. Crossley and T. P. Hilditch, *ibid.*, 1951, **2**, 472.

120. (*a*) B. M. Craig and N. L. Murti, *J. Amer. Oil Chem. Soc.*, 1959, **36**, 549; (*b*) F. R. Earle, I. A. Wolff *et al.*, *ibid.*, 1960, **37**, 440; (*c*) S. Ueno and P. H. Wan, *J. Agric. Chem. Soc. Japan*, 1943, **19**, 735.

121. H. Nobori, *J. Soc. Chem. Ind. Japan*, 1941, **44**, 705, 720.

122. G. Rankoff, *Fette u. Siefen*, 1937, **44**, 465.

123. (*a*) W. F. Baughman and G. S. Jamieson, *J. Amer. Chem. Soc.*, 1922, **44**, 2952; (*b*) R. Viollier and E. Iselin, *Mit. Geb. Lebensm. Hyg.*, 1942, **33**, 295.

124. J. Pieraerts, *Mat. Grasses*, 1925, **17**, 7280, 7340.

125. B. Horowitz and G. Winter, *Nature*, 1957, **179**, 582.

126. R. V. Crawford, 1952, privately communicated.

127. D. N. Grindley, *J. Sci. Food Agric.*, 1952, **3**, 82.

128. (*a*) B. K. Singh and A. Kumar, *Proc. Indian Acad. Sci.*, 1947, **26**, A, 205; (*b*) R. B. French, *J. Amer. Oil Chem. Soc.*, 1962, **39**, 176.

129. (a) A. Mendelowitz and J. P. Riley, *Analyst*, 1953, **78**, 704; (b) A. Mendelowitz, unpublished observations.

130. T. Tutiya, *J. Chem. Soc., Japan*, 1940, **61**, 717.

131. (a) H. P. Kaufmann and M. Keller, *Chem. Ber.*, 1948, **81**, 152; (b) H. P. Kaufmann, *ibid.*, 1948, **81**, 159; (c) S. Sarkar and M. M. Chakrabarty, *Science and Culture*, 1956, **21**, 616; (d) H. P. Kaufmann and R. K. Such, *Fette, Seifen, Anstrichm.*, 1960, **62**, 160.

132. G. S. Jamieson and R. S. McKinney, *Oil and Soap*, 1937, **14**, 203.

133. R. Child, *Oil and Soap*, 1941, **18**, 224.

134. T. P. Hilditch, with K. T. Achaya, A. Crossley, A. J. Seavell and A. H. Weerakoon, *J. Sci. Food Agric.*, 1951, **2**, 543.

135. F. D. Gunstone and T. P. Hilditch, *J. Soc. Chem. Ind.*, 1947, **66**, 205.

136. (a) G. S. Jamieson and W. F. Baughman, *Oil and Fat Ind.*, 1930, **7**, 419, 437; (b) A. M. Tuasan and A. O. Cruz, *Philippine J. Sci.*, 1953, **82**, 341.

137. H. P. Kaufmann and J. Baltes, *Ber.*, 1936, **69**, **B**, 2676.

138. (a) E. N. Taran, *J. Appl. Chem. Russia*, 1941, **14**, 239; (b) D. K. Chowdhury and M. M. Chakrabarty, *Science and Culture (India)*, 1953, **19**, 260; (c) S. R. and M. M. Chakrabarty, *ibid.*, 1955, **21**, 326; (d) W. D. Raymond and J. B. Ward, *Col. Plant and Animal Products*, 1956, **6**, 120.

139. T. P. Hilditch and J. P. Riley, *J. Soc. Chem. Ind.*, 1946, **65**, 74.

140. T. P. Hilditch and A. Mendelowitz, *J. Sci. Food Agric.*, 1951, **2**, 548.

141. S. B. Davis, E. A. Conroy and N. E. Shakespeare, *J. Amer. Chem. Soc.*, 1950, **72**, 124.

142. (a) S. C. Gupta, V. N. Sharma and J. S. Aggarwal, *J. Sci. Indust. Res., India*, 1951, **10**, **B**, 76; S. C. and S. S. Gupta and J. S. Aggarwal, *J. Amer. Oil Chem. Soc.*, 1954, **31**, 287; (b) R. C. Calderwood and F. D. Gunstone, *Chem. and Ind.*, 1953, 436; (c) J. D. von Mikusch, *Deutsch-Farb.-Zeitsch.*, 1954, **5**, 166; (d) L. A. O'Neill, A. C. Dennison and N. H. E. Ahlers, *Chem. and Ind.*, 1954, 756; (e) S. C. and S. S. Gupta and J. S. Aggarwal, *J. Amer. Oil Chem. Soc.*, 1954, **31**, 287; V. H. Kapadia and J. S. Aggarwal, *J. Sci. Indust. Res. (India)*, 1958, **17**, **B**, 117; K. T. Achaya and J. S. Aggarwal, *Chem. and Ind.*, 1962, 1616.

143. (a) S. S. Gupta, T. P. Hilditch and J. P. Riley, *J. Sci. Food Agric.*, 1951, **2**, 245; (b) J. P. Riley, *Analyst*, 1951, **76**, 40; (c) B. Sreenivasan, N. R. Kameth and J. G. Kane, *J. Amer. Oil Chem. Soc.*, 1956, **33**, 61; (d) R. G. Binder, T. H. Applewhite, G. O. Kohler and L. A. Goldblatt, *ibid.*, 1962, **39**, 513.

144. L. Margaillan, *Bull. Soc. d'Encour*, 1927, **126**, 560; *Brit. Chem. Abst.*, **B**, 1927, 945.

145. G. S. Jamieson and R. S. McKinney, *Oil and Soap*, 1938, **15**, 295.

146. (a) W. M. Potts, *Paint Oil Chem. Rev.*, 1946, **109**, 16; (b) P. T. Huang, R. T. Holman and W. M. Potts, *J. Amer. Oil Chem. Soc.*, 1949, **26**, 405; (c) D. P. Hanks and W. M. Potts, *ibid.*, 1951, **28**, 292; 1955, **32**, 356.

147. T. P. Hilditch, *J. Oil Col. Chem. Assocn.*, 1949, **32**, 5.

148. J. Devine, *J. Sci. Food Agric.*, 1950, **1**, 88.

149. A. Crossley and T. P. Hilditch, (a) *J. Chem. Soc.*, 1949, 3353; (b) *J. Sci. Food Agric.*, 1950, **1**, 292.

150. N. H. E. Ahlers, (a) with A. C. Dennison, *Chem. and Ind.*, 1954, 603; (b) with A. C. Dennison and L. A. O'Neill, *Nature*, 1954, **173**, 1045; (c) with N. G. McTaggart, *J. Sci. Food Agric.*, 1954, **5**, 75.

151. (a) W. C. Ault, M. L. Swain and L. C. Curtis, *J. Amer. Oil Chem. Soc.*, 1947, **24**, 289; (b) M. M. Chakrabarty, D. K. Chowdhury and B. K. Mukherji, *Naturwiss.*, 1955, **42**, 344; M. M. Chakrabarty, S. Bhattacharyya, M. J. Desai and S. A. Patel, *ibid.*, 1956, **43**, 523; (c) J. P. Varma and J. S. Aggarwal, *J. Indian Chem. Soc.*, 1956, **33**, 357.

152. (a) Y. Toyama and T. Tsuchiya, *J. Soc. Chem. Ind. Japan*, 1935, **38**, 182B; (b) E. H. Farmer and F. A. van den Heuvel, *J. Chem. Soc.*, 1936, 1809.

153. (a) M. F. Stansbury and C. L. Hoffpauir, *J. Amer. Oil Chem. Soc.*, 1952, **29**, 53; 1953, **30**, 120; (b) P. Cattaneo, G. K. de Sutton *et al.*, *Anales Asoc. Quim. Argentina*, 1961, **49**, 192.

154. (a) F. S. Shenstone and J. R. Vickery, *Nature*, 1956, **177**, 94; 1957, **179**, 830; 1961, **190**, 168; (b) C. R. Smith, Jr., T. L. Wilson and K. L. Mikolajczak, *Chem. and Ind.*, 1961, 256; (c) *idem.*, *J. Amer. Oil Chem. Soc.*, 1961, **38**, 696; (d) F. S. Shenstone and J. R. Vickery, *Poultry Science*, 1959, **38**, 1055; (e) C. Y. Hopkins and M. J. Chisholm, *J. Amer. Oil Chem. Soc.*, 1960, **37**, 682; (f) J. A. Cornelius and G. Shone, *Chem. and Ind.*, 1963, 1246; (g) A. de Bruin, J. E. Heesterman and M. R. Mills, *J. Sci. Food Agric.*, 1963, **14**, 758.

155. F. D. Gunstone, (a) *J. Chem. Soc.*, 1952, 1274; *J. Sci. Food Agric.*, 1952, **3**, 185; (b) *idem.*, *ibid.*, 1953, **4**, 129; (with K. F. Bharucha) *ibid.*, 1955, **6**, 373; (with L. J. Morris) *ibid.*, 1959, **10**, 522; (c) C. Y. Hopkins and M. J. Chisholm, *J. Chem. Soc.*, 1962, 573; (d) *idem.*, *Chem. and Ind.*, 1962, 2064; *Canad. J. Chem.*, 1963, **41**, 1888; *J. Amer. Oil Chem. Soc.*, 1964, **41**, 42; (e) A. L. Markman and M. D. Bodnya, *Zhur. Obschei Khim.*, 1957, **27**, 2293.

156. (a) H. B. Lofland, F. W. Quackenbush and A. M. Brunson, *J. Amer. Oil Chem. Soc.*, 1954, **31**, 412; (b) M. S. Sniegowski and A. R. Baldwin, *ibid.*, 1954, **31**, 414; (c) J. A. Borquete, *Rev. Fac. Cienc. Quim., Univ. Nac. La Plata*, 1956, **29**, 61; (d) P. Cattaneo, G. K. de Sutton *et al.*, *Anales Asoc. Quim. Argentina*, 1960, **48**, 169; (e) F. Aylward and A. J. Showler, *J. Sci. Food Agric.*, 1962, **13**, 492.

157. A. Eibner and E. Schild, *Chem. Umschau*, 1927, **34**, 312, 339; J. P. Riley, *J. Chem. Soc.*, 1949, 2728.

158. A. Arnaud, *C. R. Acad. Sci., Paris*, 1892, **114**, 79; *Bull. Soc. chim.*, 1902, (iii), **27**, 484.

159. E. Vongerichten and A. Köhler, *Ber.*, 1909, **42**, 1638.

160. (a) T. P. Hilditch and (Miss) E. E. Jones, *J. Soc. Chem. Ind.*, 1927, **46**, 174т; (b) J. van Loon, *Rec. trav. chim.*, 1927, **46**, 492.

161. G. R. Clemo and R. Stevens, *J. Chem. Soc.*, 1952, 4684.

162. F. C. Palazzo and A. Tamburello, *Atti. R. Acad. Lincei*, 1914, (v), **23**, (ii) 352.

163. A. Steger and J. van Loon, *Rec. trav. chim.*, 1928, **47**, 471.

164. M. Tsujimoto and H. Koyanagi, *Bull. Chem. Soc. Japan*, 1933, **8**, 161.

165. C. Grimme, (a) *Chem. Rev. Fett.-Harz-Ind.*, 1910, **17**, 158; (b) *ibid.*, 1912, **19**, 51; (c) A. Steger and J. van Loon, *Rec. trav. chim.*, 1933, **52**, 593.

166. M. J. Chisholm and C. Y. Hopkins, *Canad. J. Chem.*, 1958, **36**, 1537; see also K. L. Mikolajczak, C. R. Smith, Jr. and I. A. Wolff, *J. Amer. Oil Chem. Soc.*, 1963, **40**, 294.

167. (a) M. K. Madhuranath and B. L. Manjunath, *J. Indian Chem. Soc.*, 1938, **15**, 389; (b) F. D. Gunstone and M. A. McGee, *Chem. and Ind.*, 1954, 1112; (c) H. H. Hatt and A. Z. Szumer, *ibid.*, 1954, 962; (d) H. H. Hatt and R. Schoenfeld, *J. Sci. Food Agric.*, 1956, **7**, 130; (e) K. L. Mikolajczak, F. R. Earle and I. A. Wolff, *J. Amer. Oil Chem. Soc.*, 1963, **40**, 342.

168. (a) R. Wrenshall and A. L. Dean, *U.S. Pub. Health Service Bulletin*, 1924, **141**, 12; (b) E. André and D. Jouatte, *Bull. Soc. chim.*, 1928, (iv), **43**, 347; H. I. Cole and H. T. Cardoso, *J. Amer. Chem. Soc.*, 1938, **60**, 612.

169. H. I. Cole and H. T. Cardoso, (a) *J. Amer. Chem. Soc.*, 1938, **60**, 614, 617; 1939, **61**, 2351, 3442; (b) *ibid.*, 1939, **61**, 2349.

170. L. Adriaens, *Bull. Soc. Chem. Belge*, 1945, **54**, 101.

171. C. Y. Hopkins, *Canad. J. Research*, 1946, **B**, **24**, 211; C. Y. Hopkins and H. J. Chisholm, *Canad. J. Chem.*, 1954, **32**, 1033.

172. T. P. Hilditch, P. A. Laurent and M. L. Meara, *J. Soc. Chem. Ind.*, 1947, **66**, 19.

173. M. N. Baliga and T. P. Hilditch, (a) *J. Chem. Soc.*, 1949, *Suppl. Issue* 1, 91; (b) *J. Soc. Chem. Ind.*, 1948, **67**, 258.

174. T. P. Hilditch and W. J. Stainsby, *J. Soc. Chem. Ind.*, 1934, **53**, 197т.

175. (a) F. R. Earle, I. A. Wolff *et al.*, *J. Amer. Oil Chem. Soc.*, 1961, **38**, 678; (b) K. L. Mikolajczak, F. R. Earle and I. A. Wolff, *ibid.*, 1962, **39**, 78; (c) H. H. Hatt and A. Z. Szumer, *J. Sci. Food Agric.*, 1953, **4**, 273; (d) C. R. Smith, Jr., T. Wilson, R. Bates and C. R. Scholfield, *J. Org. Chem.*, 1962, **27**, 3112; (e) F. D. Gunstone and L. J. Morris, *J. Chem. Soc.*, 1959, 2127.

176. J. G. Gadamer, *Arch. Pharm.*, 1899, **237**, 471.

177. J. J. Sudborough, H. E. Watson, P. R. Ayyar and N. R. Damle, *J. Indian Inst. Sci.*, 1926, **9, A,** 65.
178. T. P. Hilditch and M. L. Meara, *J. Chem. Soc.*, 1938, 1608.
179. M. J. Chisholm and C. Y. Hopkins, *Canad. J. Chem.*, 1953, **31,** 1131.
180. R. A. Greene and E. O. Foster, *Bot. Gaz.*, 1933, **94,** 826.
181. R. S. McKinney and G. S. Jamieson, *Oil and Soap*, 1936, **13,** 289.
182. T. G. Green, T. P. Hilditch and W. J. Stainsby, *J. Chem. Soc.*, 1936, 1750.
183. (*a*) M. M. Black, D. A. Harris and H. M. Schwartz, *J. S. African Chem. Inst.*, 1949, **2,** 111; (*b*) G. S. Harrison and F. Hawke, *ibid.*, 1952, **5,** 13.
184. H. E. Longenecker, *J. Soc. Chem. Ind.*, 1937, **56,** 199т.
185. (*a*) T. P. Hilditch, M. B. Ichaporia and H. Jasperson, *J. Soc. Chem. Ind.*, 1938, **57,** 363; (*b*) H. Jasperson, Thesis, University of Liverpool, 1938.
186. T. P. Hilditch and J. P. Riley, *J. Soc. Chem. Ind.*, 1945, **64,** 204.
187. (*a*) J. Vizern, *Oléagineux*, 1947, **2,** 442; (*b*) B. M. Craig and N. L. Murti, *J. Amer. Oil Chem. Soc.*, 1959, **36,** 549; (*c*) T. A. Pickett, *ibid.*, 1955, **32,** 521; (*d*) P. Cattaneo and G. K. de Sutton, *Anales Asoc. Quim. Argentina*, 1958, **46,** 96.
188. A. O. Cruz and A. P. West, (*a*) *Philippine J. Sci.*, 1931, **46,** 199; (*b*) *ibid.*, 1932, **48,** 77.
189. (*a*) G. S. Jamieson, W. F. Baughman and D. H. Brauns, *J. Amer. Chem. Soc.*, 1921, **43,** 1372; (*b*) W. F. Baughman and G. S. Jamieson, *ibid.*, 1922, **44,** 2947.
190. H. B. Higgins, K. T. Holley, T. A. Pickett and C. D. Wheeler, *Georgia Expt. Station*, 1941, Bulletin No. 213, 3.
191. E. F. Armstrong and J. Allan, *J. Soc. Chem. Ind.*, 1924, **43,** 216т.
192. H. N. Griffiths, T. P. Hilditch and E. C. Jones, *J. Soc. Chem. Ind.*, 1934, **53,** 13т, 75т.
193. R. V. Crawford and T. P. Hilditch, *J. Sci. Food Agric.*, 1950, **1,** 372.
194. E. Jantzen and C. Tiedcke, *J. pr. Chem.*, 1930, (2), **127,** 277.
195. A. Heiduschka and H. Eger, *Chem. Umschau*, 1931, **38,** 129.
196. (*a*) T. P. Hilditch and H. Jasperson, *J. Soc. Chem. Ind.*, 1939, **58,** 187; (*b*) T. P. Hilditch, J. Holmberg and M. L. Meara, *J. Amer. Oil Chem. Soc.*, 1947, **24,** 321; (*c*) T. P. Hilditch and A. J. Seavell, *J. Oil Col. Chem. Assocn.*, 1950, **33,** 24.
197. J. H. Mitchell, H. R. Kraybill and F. P. Zscheile, *Ind. Eng. Chem. (Anal.)*, 1943, **15,** 1.
198. T. A. Venkitasubramanian, *J. Sci. Indust. Res. India*, 1952, **11, B,** 132.
199. G. S. Jamieson, W. F. Baughman and R. S. McKinney, *J. Agric. Res.*, 1933, **46,** 57.
200. F. G. Dollear, P. Krauczunas and K. S. Markley, (*a*) *Oil and Soap*, 1938, **15,** 263; (*b*) *ibid.*, 1940, **17,** 120.
201. (*a*) C. R. Scholfield and W. C. Bull, *Oil and Soap*, 1944, **21,** 87; (*b*) O. H. Alderks, *J. Amer. Oil Chem. Soc.*, 1949, **26,** 126; (*c*) H. B. White, Jr., F. W. Quackenbush and R. H. Probst, *ibid.*, 1961, **38,** 113; (*d*) F. I. Collins (with R. W. Howell), *ibid.*, 1957, **34,** 491; (with V. E. Sedgwick), *ibid.*, 1959, **36,** 641.
202. (*a*) E. André, *Oléagineux*, 1947, **2,** 546, 599; (*b*) F. D. Gunstone and P. J. Sykes, *J. Sci. Food Agric.*, 1961, **12,** 115.
203. K. H. Bauer and L. Seber, *Fette u. Seifen*, 1938, **45,** 293.
204. J. A. R. MacLean, *Nature*, 1952, **169,** 589.
205. T. P. Hilditch, M. L. Meara and Y. A. H. Zaky, *J. Soc. Chem. Ind.*, 1941, **60,** 198; *see also* A. Steger and J. van Loon, *Fette u. Seifen*, 1943, **50,** 305; J. P. Varma, S. Dasgupta, B. Nath and J. S. Aggarwal, *J. Amer. Oil Chem. Soc.*, 1957, **34,** 452; F. R. Earle, I. A. Wolff *et al.*, *ibid.*, 1959, **36,** 304; 1960, **37,** 440.
206. (*a*) J. R. Nunn, *J. Chem. Soc.*, 1952, 313; (*b*) F. R. Earle, I. A. Wolff *et al.*, *J. Amer. Oil Chem. Soc.*, 1960, **37,** 440.
207. H. Witgert, *Dissertation*, Aachen, 1933.
208. W. D. Richardson, *J. Ind. Eng. Chem.*, 1911, **3,** 574.
209. (*a*) J. Allan and C. W. Moore, *J. Soc. Chem. Ind.*, 1925, **44,** 61т; (*b*) E. F. Armstrong, J. Allan and C. W. Moore, *ibid.*, 1925, **44,** 67т.
210. H. A. Carsten, T. P. Hilditch and M. L. Meara, *J. Soc. Chem. Ind.*, 1945, **64,** 207.
211. P. A. Levene and I. P. Rolf, *J. Biol. Chem.*, 1925, **62,** 759; **65,** 545; 1926, **68,** 285.

212. E. Schulze and A. Likiernik, *Z. Physiol. Chem.*, 1891, **15**, 405; V. Njegovan, *ibid.*, 1911, **76**, 1.
213. E. C. Shorey, *J. Amer. Chem. Soc.*, 1898, **20**, 113.
214. V. Grafe and V. Horvat, *Biochem. Z.*, 1925, **159**, 449.
215. G. S. Jamieson, R. S. McKinney and W. B. Holton, *Oil and Soap*, 1937, **14**, 126.
216. B. Rewald, *Biochem. J.*, 1942, **36**, 822.
217. E. Klenk and R. Sakai, *Z. physiol. Chem.*, 1939, **258**, 33.
218. D. W. Woolley and A. G. C. White, *J. Biol. Chem.*, 1943, **147**, 581.
219. J. Folch and H. A. Schneider, *J. Biol. Chem.*, 1941, **137**, 51; J. Folch, *ibid.*, 1941, **139**, 973; 1942, **146**, 35; J. Folch and D. W. Woolley, *ibid.*, 1942, **142**, 963; J. Folch and F. N. Le Baron, *Canad. J. Biochem.*, 1956, **34**, 305; J. N. Hawthorne, *Nature*, 1959, **184**, 790; T. Malkin and A. G. Poole, *J. Chem. Soc.*, 1953, 3470; J. H. Davies and T. Malkin, *Nature*, 1959, **184**, 789; *Chem. and Ind.*, 1959, 1155; etc., etc.
220. (*a*) H. H. Hutt, T. Malkin, A. G. Poole and P. R. Watt, *Nature*, 1950, **165**, 314; T. Malkin and A. G. Poole, *J. Chem. Soc.*, 1953, 3470; (*b*) T. Malkin, "The Synthesis of Phospholipids", in "*Progress in the Chemistry of Fats and Other Lipids*" (Pergamon Press, London), 1957, vol. IV, 97–139; "Recent Work in the Phospholipid Field", *Chem. and Ind.*, 1961, 605–611; J. N. Hawthorne, "Inositol Phospholipids", *J. Lipid Research*, 1960, **1**, 255.
221. (*a*) W. Diemair, B. Bleyer and W. Schmidt, *Biochem. Z.*, 1935, **275**, 242; 1937, **294**, 353; (*b*) W. Diemair and K. Weiss, *ibid.*, 1939, **302**, 112; (*c*) B. Bleyer, W. Diemair and K. Weiss, *ibid.*, 1939, **302**, 167.
222. A. Heiduschka and W. Neumann, *J. pr. Chem.*, 1938, (ii), **151**, 1.
223. T. P. Hilditch and W. H. Pedelty, *Biochem. J.*, 1937, **31**, 1964; T. P. Hilditch and Y. A. H. Zaky, *ibid.*, 1942, **36**, 815.
224. M. H. Thornton, C. S. Johnson and M. A. Ewan, *Oil and Soap*, 1944, **21**, 85.
225. A. R. S. Kartha, *J. Sci. Food Agric.*, 1963, **14**, 515.

CHAPTER V

The Component Glycerides of Natural Fats: General Survey

In the course of the three preceding chapters it will have become clear how greatly varied are the specific mixtures of component acids found in different natural organisms, yet within a given biological family there are usually marked resemblances, qualitative and often quantitative, in the characteristic kinds of fatty acids common to such botanical or zoological groups. The manner in which these fatty acid mixtures are woven into molecules of mixed triglycerides is however much the same in all cases: very broadly speaking, wherever they occur – in vegetable or animal, in depot (reserve) or tissue (organ) fats, and whatever may be the particular nature of the component acids, similar general principles seem to apply over wide ranges of natural fats.

It is therefore better in the first place to deal with the structure of natural glycerides as a whole, rather than in relation to their different natural sources – aquatic, land fauna and land flora. Descriptions of the component glycerides of a number of specific vegetable and animal fats will then be given in the chapters (VI and VII) which follow.

We shall give first a brief review of the earlier, mainly qualitative studies of glyceride structure prior to 1927, and then proceed to the subsequent more quantitative investigations based at first on chemical methods (chiefly determination of trisaturated glycerides), but, latterly and increasingly, on physical methods of partial resolution of the natural fats into simpler mixtures of mixed glycerides. By 1952 the later techniques had been developed and used sufficiently to permit approximate statements of the chief constituent glycerides of many fats, and to establish clearly the main features of the arrangement of their component acids in the mixed glycerides of natural fats.

The different modern methods, chemical and physical, which have so far been adapted to the study of mixed glycerides in natural fats will be outlined in more or less detail, in the first instance, without much discussion as to the views on glyceride structure which have developed concurrently with the advances in technique. These views will later receive full consideration in the section of this chapter entitled "Present knowledge of glyceride structure of natural fats" (p. 389).

For what seems an unnecessarily long time after Chevreul had discovered in 1823 that the natural fats were glycerol esters of palmitic, stearic, oleic and other acids, it was more or less tacitly assumed that they were necessarily mixtures of *simple* triglycerides such as tripalmitin, tristearin, triolein in varying proportions; even though already in 1860, when the trihydroxylic structure of glycerol had become recognised, Berthelot[1] had pointed out the possibility that fats might contain mixed triglycerides.

This tacit assumption is somewhat amusingly illustrated by an incident which occurred just before 1900: in 1897 Heise[2] announced that mkanyi (*Allanblackia stuhlmannii*) fat yielded by simple crystallisation from an appropriate solvent considerable amounts of an oleodistearin, and Henriques and Künne,[3] in view of what they termed this "unusual" observation, repeated the work and confirmed his conclusions. A very few years later, the work of Klimont, Bömer, and others on the resolution of fats by systematic crystallisation from different media presented ample, if somewhat negative, evidence that the vast majority of natural fats do *not* contain any significant amount of simple triglycerides, and at the present time it would be considered very "unusual" if a seed fat of the fatty acid composition of that of *Allanblackia* (*cf.* p. 436) were found to contain more than extremely small proportions of a simple triglyceride, i.e., G(X)₃. As early as 1902, indeed, Guth[4] defined natural fats as "mixtures of mixed glycerides", whilst twenty years later Leathes and Raper[5] stated "the probability is that as a rule they" (glycerides in natural products) "are mixed".

Early attempts to isolate natural glycerides by crystallisation. In 1901 Holde and Stange[6] separated a small amount of solid glycerides from olive oil by crystallising it from ether at −40°: presumably the first occasion on which "low-temperature crystallisation" was applied to a fat. After recrystallisation the solid glycerides had m.p. 30–31° and iodine value 29·8: they were clearly mono-oleo-disaturated glycerides, chiefly oleodipalmitin.

Cacao butter and the physically similar Borneo tallow and stillingia ("Chinese vegetable") tallows were, soon after, subjected to crystallisation from solvents such as chloroform or ether-alcohol at or above 0°. In 1902 Fritzweiler[7] thus obtained 6 per cent. of oleodistearin (m.p. 44·5–45°) from cacao butter, and this glyceride as well as oleodipalmitin (m.p. 37–38°) was separated in small quantities from the same fat in 1901–02 by Klimont,[8a] who also isolated the same oleodistearin and oleodipalmitin from Borneo[8b] and stillingia[8c] tallows. Curiously, although Klimont rightly interpreted the presence in quantity in these fats of oleodistearin and oleodipalmitin as the cause of their special physical qualities, he finally concluded that oleopalmitostearin (actually the chief component of cacao butter and Borneo tallow) was absent; but from the iodine values of the most soluble fractions which he obtained he correctly deduced the absence of any significant amount of triolein. In 1909 Klimont[8d] showed that stearodipalmitin, m.p. 59–60°, was a minor component of duck and goose fats and that duck fat contained some triolein; and in 1912[8e] he was able to isolate the simple triglyceride tripalmitin (m.p. 61·5°) by fractional crystallisation of rabbit fat.

From about 1907 onwards Bömer and his co-workers were occupied with similar systematic crystallisations of various animal and vegetable fats; in Bömer's hands the method was elaborated to an extraordinary degree, and in some cases many hundreds of crystallisations were involved in the examination of a single fat. Although in many cases the quantitative results obtained were perhaps hardly a recompense for the enormous amount of tedious manipulation which must have been involved, they served to prove that the natural fats were built up for the most part of mixed glycerides, and that the old conception of fats as mixtures of simple triglycerides was in no case even approached; moreover, in some cases, it was found possible to give an approximate estimate of the amount of some of the higher melting and more sparingly soluble components present.

Thus Bömer and his collaborators record the isolation of some 2 to 4 per cent. each of tristearin, palmitodistearin and dipalmitostearin from mutton tallow,[9a] and of the two palmitostearins from lard[9b] and from goose fat[9c] (Hansen[10a] and Kreis and Hafner[10b] had earlier isolated small amounts of palmitodistearin from beef and mutton tallows). Amberger and his students meantime made similar studies of a few animal fats: from butter[11a] small amounts of the palmitostearins, oleodipalmitin, and butyropalmito-olein were isolated, whilst about 2 per cent. of triolein and some butyrodiolein were concluded to be present. In 1923 Amberger and Wiesehahn[11b] obtained results with lard similar to Bömer's of ten years earlier, but in addition isolated 2 per cent. of oleodistearin and 11 per cent. of oleopalmitostearin, whilst Amberger and Bromig,[11c] like Bömer, studied goose fat and detected therein dipalmitostearin, oleodipalmitin, palmitodiolein, and possibly triolein.

In 1920, with Baumann,[12a] Bömer studied coconut fat, from which he failed to isolate any trilaurin, but obtained evidence of much dilauromyristin (m.p. 33°) with smaller amounts of laurodimyristin (m.p. 38°) and dimyristopalmitin (m.p. 45°), and traces of dipalmitostearin (m.p. 55°). In 1924 Bömer and Schneider[12b] published similar results for palm kernel fat, again finding considerable amounts of dilauromyristin (m.p. 33°), with less laurodimyristin (m.p. 40°), dimyristopalmitin (m.p. 45°), and myristodipalmitin (m.p. 51°) and, again, no evidence of trilaurin; as in coconut fat, the greater part of the fat remained as a most-soluble residue. In 1928 Bömer and Ebach[12c] demonstrated that when trilaurin or trimyristin is present in appreciable quantity in a fat their isolation by crystallisation presents no difficulty: for about 30 per cent. of trilaurin was thus separated from the seed fat of *Laurus nobilis* and about 40 per cent. of trimyristin from nutmeg butter. Bömer's last study[12d] of this kind, published posthumously in 1938, dealt with the similar fractional crystallisation of the glycerides of babassu fat, another Palmæ seed fat which was shown to contain much dilauromyristin, some quantity of laurodimyristin, and small amounts of dimyristopalmitin.

Prior to Bömer's studies, Krafft[13] had separated trilaurin from laurel kernel fat, and trimyristin from nutmeg butter, by partial distillation of the fats in high vacuum. Similarly, Caldwell and Hurtley[14] had attempted to isolate some of the supposed simpler glycerides present in coconut fat or in butter fat by partial fractional distillation of these fats in the vacuum of the cathode light. In his work on coconut and babassu fats, and also on laurel kernel fat and nutmeg butter, Bömer also employed partial distillation in a vacuum as a preliminary means of separating the constituents of smallest molecular size, thus facilitating the subsequent application of the fractional crystallisation procedure.

It appears from more recent work published by other investigators that evaporation of natural fatty glycerides at the very low pressure of the "molecular still", whilst affording some separation of mixed glycerides, does not lead to anything approaching a complete separation of such frequent components of fats as, for instance, oleopalmitostearin and palmitodiolein. On the other hand, crystallisation of solid or liquid fats from acetone (at moderate or very low temperatures according to circumstances) has become a most useful method of resolving fats into mixtures of less complexity than the original fat, which are more amenable than the latter to quantitative examination (see pp. 372–376).

Isolation of chemically modified natural glycerides by simple crystallisation. Between 1920 and 1930 several studies were made, on analogous lines to those already discussed, of crystallisation of natural fats which had first been transformed into more crystalline derivatives by (a) hydrogenation to completely saturated glycerides or (b) conversion into fully-brominated adducts of the unsaturated glycerides originally present.

(a) The first resort to hydrogenation was by Amberger,[15a] who in 1920 submitted completely hydrogenated rape oil to fractional crystallisation and isolated stearodibehenin in quantity, thus indicating the presence of corresponding amounts of oleo- (linoleo- or linoleno-) dierucin in the original oil. In 1924, with Bauch,[15b] he similarly studied hydrogenated cacao butter. In 1929, Bömer and Engel[16] isolated much dihydrochaulmoogrodidihydrohydnocarpin and less dihydrohydnocarpo-didihydrochaulmoogrin by fractional crystallisation of hydrogenated chaulmoogra oil.

Very much later (1934–1941), after the quantitative determination of fully-saturated glycerides in a fat had become possible (cf. pp. 363–372), methods for estimating the content of tri-unsaturated glycerides in liquid (unsaturated) fats were employed for a short time which depended upon investigation of the mixture of glycerides produced when such fatty oils were completely or partly hydrogenated. Systematic crystallisation from ether of a completely hydrogenated oil concentrated tristearin and palmitodistearin into the least soluble fractions, from the equivalent of which the approximate content of tristearin (corresponding to the original tri-C_{18}-unsaturated glycerides) was estimated; this method was used to assess the tri-C_{18}-glycerides in cottonseed, soya bean and linseed oils.[17a, b]

A probably somewhat more accurate, but also more tedious, procedure is to prepare a series of progressively hydrogenated fats from the natural liquid fat and to determine the proportion of tri-saturated glycerides, and the component acids therein, for each partly-hydrogenated fat. The glyceride structure of a number of seed fats (cottonseed,[17a] groundnut,[17c] sesame,[17c] teaseed,[17d] rape,[17e] cocoa butter [17f] and of olive[17d] and palm[17g] oils, pig fats,[17h] whale[17i] and cod liver[17j] oils) were estimated by this means.

These methods (which were described in detail in the 2nd Edition of this work, 1947, pp. 238–240) are not likely to be employed in the future in view of the improved methods for segregation of fatty glycerides by physical means (cf. pp. 372, 383) and are therefore only mentioned here for historical completeness.

(b) Another modification of the crystallisation method, adopted in 1927–1929 with some success, was the bromination of unsaturated fats in light petroleum, followed by isolation of various individual bromo-glycerides by crystallisation from various solvents. This procedure which, again, gave results mainly qualitative in character, nevertheless threw considerable light on the types of glycerides present in a wide variety of drying oils.

In the important case of linseed oil, Eibner,[18] with Widenmayer, Schild and Brosel, isolated the bromo-adducts of linoleo-dilinolenins and oleodilinolenin. Eibner suggested that the last-named may account for all the oleic acid in the oil, whilst linoleo-dilinolenin is probably the chief drying principle; he also pointed out the probability that all oleic acid present is linked with linoleic or linolenic acids, thus disposing of the view that its presence in linseed oil is necessarily a deterrent to the drying qualities of the oil.

Suzuki and Yokoyama[19a] reported (1927) the isolation from linseed oil of brominated glycerides derived from dilinoleo-linolenin, linoleo-dilinolenins, linoleo-dioleins, oleo-dilinolein, oleo-linoleo-stearin and oleo-linoleno-stearin; in soya bean oil they similarly obtained evidence of the presence of dilinoleo-linolenin, linoleo-dilinolenin, oleo-dilinolein, linoleo-diolein and oleo-linoleno-stearin. Hashi[20] arrived at similar conclusions, identifying in addition the presence of oleodipalmitin and oleo-dilinolein. Simple triglycerides were not reported.

Suzuki and Masuda[19b] applied the fractional crystallisation process of brominated glycerides to marine animal oils, including whale oil and cod liver, herring, sardine, salmon, shark liver, sand eel and cuttlefish oils. In all these cases the results disclosed a most complex mixture of unsaturated glycerides (ten or more different bromo-derivatives having been isolated from some of the fats); hexadecenoic, oleic, linoleic, and the unsaturated acids of the C_{20} and C_{22} series are linked, two or three at a time, in numerous combinations, but simple triglycerides appeared to be absent.

Nearly all the investigations referred to above – whether of natural solid fats, of hydrogenated natural fats, or of the bromo-additive products of natural fats – were based essentially upon attempted separation of triglycerides by the physical method of crystallisation. The results obtained were almost wholly qualitative in character, and in only a few instances led to even an approximate statement of the proportion of any individual mixed triglyceride present. Nevertheless they are in themselves sufficient to demonstrate conclusively the generalisation that seed fats are mixtures of mixed triglycerides, and that the occurrence of simple triglycerides is quite exceptional.

Modern Quantitative Studies of Glyceride Structure

From about 1927 onwards, more definitely chemical methods of attack upon the problem of glyceride structure commenced to be employed in place of, or in conjunction with, the partial separation of triglycerides by crystallisation from solvents. These methods, developed for the most part at the University of Liverpool, usually lead to more or less quantitative statements of the different component glycerides present in natural fats, or at least define the proportions of different groups of component glycerides. In a number of instances it became possible to give approximate figures for the proportions of each of the main component mixed glycerides present in natural fats, whilst in a few cases the configuration of individual mixed glycerides such as for example β-oleodistearin was ascertained. Both vegetable (seed and fruit-coat) and animal (depot and milk) fats have been studied quantitatively or semi-quantitatively by these methods; the number of fats so investigated naturally falls far short of that of the fats whose component acids have been quantitatively determined (Chapters II, III and IV), but is sufficient to define clearly any modifications in glyceride structure which are characteristic of different groups of natural fats.

The modern methods of investigation have developed somewhat as follows:

I. Determination of the proportion of fully saturated glycerides present in natural fats (pp. 363–372).

II. (*a*) More detailed examination of the component glycerides in solid seed or animal fats by separating the latter into fractions varying in solubility in acetone, each fraction being examined separately for its fatty acid composition and, if desired, its fully saturated glyceride content, content of tri-unsaturated C_{18} glycerides, etc.

(*b*) Similar examination of liquid vegetable or animal fats by systematic crystallisation from acetone or ether at suitable temperatures down to $-70°$, each fraction being then examined separately for its fatty acid composition (pp. 372–382).

III. Separation of the glycerides in a fat by counter-current distribution between two immiscible solvents (pp. 383–385).

IV. Separation of glycerides by chromatographic adsorption (thin-layer chromatography, paper chromatography, p. 385).

V. Selective hydrolysis of triglycerides by pancreatic lipase, whereby the acids in combination with the primary (1- or α-) glyceryl hydroxyl groups are removed preferentially to those attached to the secondary (2- or β-) hydroxyl group (pp. 385–388).

Of these techniques method I was formerly of outstanding utility and served to establish the main outlines of natural glyceride structure in so far as the less unsaturated types of natural fats are concerned. Although still of frequent use, it has become subordinate to the more recently developed procedures of preliminary resolution of a fat by systematic crystallisation (method II), or by counter-current distribution between two solvents (method III). The greater part of the results to date on quantitative glyceride structure have been obtained with method II, only a few having so far been provided by method III; the latter has mainly been applied to seed oils with high proportions of linoleic and linolenic acids in their glycerides, with results which raise some doubt as to how far the low-temperature crystallisation method II is valid for linoleic-linolenic-rich oils (p. 373).

Method IV (chromatographic adsorption) has not yet (1963) been used very much in quantitative glyceride composition studies, but is included because some of the techniques may well become important aids in the near future.

Method V (selective lipase hydrolysis) is not an aid to complete analysis of mixed glycerides, but is mentioned here because of its great utility in showing which acyl groups are attached to the outer (primary) and central (secondary) hydroxyl groups of a glycerol molecule.

I. DETERMINATION OF FULLY-SATURATED GLYCERIDES

In 1927 Hilditch and Lea[21] showed that when a fat is oxidised in acetone solution with powdered potassium permanganate all glycerides containing one or more unsaturated acyl radicals are ultimately converted into the corresponding azelao-glycerides (in the case of oleo-, linoleo-, linoleno-, or elæostearo-glycerides), whilst the completely saturated glycerides remain unattacked. If the possible combinations of glycerol with a saturated fatty acid $(S.CO_2H)$ and an unsaturated (e.g. oleic) acid $(U.CO_2H)$ be considered, it will be seen that the following products may arise:

	ORIGINAL GLYCERIDE	GLYCERIDE PRODUCT OF OXIDATION
Fully saturated	$C_3H_5(O.CO.S)_3$	$C_3H_5(O.CO.S)_3$
Mono-oleo-derivative	$C_3H_5\langle\!\!\!{}^{(O.CO.S)_2}_{(O.CO.U)}$	$C_3H_5\langle\!\!\!{}^{(O.CO.S)_2}_{(O.CO.[CH_2]_7.CO_2H)}$
Dioleo-derivative	$C_3H_5\langle\!\!\!{}^{(O.CO.S)}_{(O.CO.U)_2}$	$C_3H_5\langle\!\!\!{}^{(O.CO.S)}_{(O.CO.[CH_2]_7.CO_2H)_2}$
Triolein	$C_3H_5(O.CO.U)_3$	$C_3H_5(O.CO.[CH_2]_7.CO_2H)_3$

The acid azelaic glycerides usually form a complex mixture which is extremely difficult to separate from the unchanged fully saturated glycerides, because the alkali salts of the azelao-glycerides are very strong emulsifying agents (especially those of the monoazelao-derivatives, which in addition are soluble in ether as well as in water). By taking suitable precautions during the removal of the acid azelao-glycerides by washing with alkali it is, however, quite possible to recover quantitatively the unchanged fully-saturated glycerides.

If the component glycerides of a fat are considered with respect to the two groups of fatty acids, saturated (S) and unsaturated (U), it is evident that the following types of triglyceride (G = glyceryl residue) may be present:

$$GS_3, \ GS_2U, \ GSU_2, \ GU_3.$$

The proportion of fully saturated glycerides (GS_3) leaves three possible group components to be estimated. If the component acids of the original fats and of the fully saturated portion are known, the amounts of the saturated acids linked in mixed glycerides with unsaturated acids can be deduced. If it were practicable to isolate and recover quantitatively either the monoazelao-glycerides, diazelao-glycerides, or triazelain (produced as hydrogen esters of glycerol in the oxidation of unsaturated C_{18} acids) the proportions of mono-, di-, and tri-unsaturated glycerides in a fat under examination could be determined; but after exhaustive study of this separation Hilditch and Saletore[22] concluded that quantitative isolation of either of the three groups of azelao-glycerides, after oxidation of a fat with permanganate in acetone, could not be effected.

In 1950 Begemann, Keppler and Boekenoogen[23] showed that when the oxidation of a fat is carried out in solution in acetic acid, instead of acetone, secondary side reactions are much reduced and, in 1951, Kartha[24a] suggested that when acetone alone is used as solvent considerable hydrolysis of azelao-glycerides is caused by alkali liberated from the permanganate used up in oxidising the unsaturated part of the fat. Kartha found that addition to the acetone solvent of sufficient acetic acid to maintain slight acidity throughout the oxidation suppresses hydrolysis and enables all the mono-azaleo-glycerides to be recovered (in admixture with some diazelao-glycerides). This procedure therefore leads to determination of the amount of monoazaleo-glycerides which in turn gives the molar percentage of mono-unsaturated glycerides in the fat. The amount of trisaturated glycerides having also been ascertained the proportions of di- and tri-unsaturated glycerides can be calculated from the fatty acid composition of the whole fat.

Kartha's proposed method requires considerably smaller quantities of fat than are needed for examination by the older oxidation procedure or by the modern crystallisation techniques, and its further examination and confirmation by other workers in this field seems desirable. Eshelman and Hammond[25a] (1958) studied both the Hilditch-Lea and the Kartha procedures, concluding that neither was a very reliable method for studying glyceride structure. Lakshminarayana and Rebello[25b] (1960) also made a critical study of both methods and found that the Hilditch-Lea method gave slightly lower values for tri-saturated glycerides than that of Kartha; these workers however found that, owing to considerable hydrolysis of diazaleo-glycerides during subsequent procedure, Kartha's results for the proportions of mono-, di- and tri-unsaturated glycerides were liable to serious error.

We ourselves remain of the opinion that the quantitative determination of mono- and di-azaleo glycerides resulting from the controlled oxidation of fats is unreliable, whereas the differences in the amounts of fully saturated glycerides obtained by the two methods are actually of a very minor order, rarely exceeding one unit per cent. We consider that such differences fall within the normal experimental error to which an analytical procedure of this nature is liable.

Hilditch and Lea[21] stated in 1927 that cottonseed oil, with 25 per cent. of saturated acids in its total fatty acids, contained negligible amounts of fully saturated glycerides; and that the respective fully saturated glyceride contents of cacao butter and a specimen of mutton tallow were 2 per cent. and 26 per cent., although their component fatty acids were very similar, namely, about 25 per cent. palmitic, 35 per cent. stearic, and 30 per cent. oleic (including 1–2 per cent. of linoleic) acids. The much higher content of fully saturated components (relative to the proportion of saturated acids in the total acids of the whole fat) in the case of the sheep depot fat was subsequently found to be characteristic for the depot fats, and also for the milk fats, of most of the common herbivorous ruminant mammals (oxen, buffalo, sheep, goats).

Trisaturated glyceride contents of vegetable seed and fruit-coat fats. Similar studies of coconut and palm kernel oils, and of other seed fats of high total saturated acid content, were next made (1928–9) by Collin and Hilditch[26]. Out of a total of eleven seed fats examined, in all but two fully saturated glycerides did not appear in quantity unless the proportion of saturated acids in the total fatty acids exceeded about 60–65 per cent. Since then, the fully saturated glyceride contents of very many other seed and fruit-coat fats have been determined; the results of most of these studies are expressed graphically in Fig. 2 and a summary of the quantitative data on which the graph is based is given in Table 71.

It will be seen from Fig. 2 and Table 71 that, until the saturated acids in a seed fat amount to about 60 per cent. of the total fatty acids, the proportion of fully saturated triglycerides is insignificant. In Fig. 2, the broken line represents the relationship between the fully saturated glyceride content and the proportion of saturated to unsaturated acids in the whole fat which would obtain if the acids were distributed (when the proportion of saturated acids exceeds about 58 per cent.) so that as great an amount as possible of the triglycerides contained an average proportion of 1·4 mols. of saturated to 1 mol. of unsaturated acid in combination, the excess above this ratio of saturated acids appearing, of course, in the form of fully saturated triglycerides. (This ratio corresponds with a mixture of about 3–4 mols. of mono-unsaturated-di-saturated glycerides with 1 mol. of di-unsaturated-monosaturated glycerides.)

The general regularity with which the experimental findings approximate to this relationship in the seed fats indicates the strikingly uniform manner in which the constituent acids are assembled in these natural triglycerides, and also illustrates very well the operation of what came to be termed the "rule of even distribution" in glyceride structure.

In the fruit-coat (pericarp, etc.) fats the generalisation appears not to hold

TABLE 71

NUMBER ON FIG. 2	SPECIES	FAT	SATURATED ACIDS IN TOTAL FATTY ACIDS PER CENT. (MOL.)	FULLY-SATURATED GLYCERIDES PER CENT. (MOL.)	"ASSOCIATION RATIO"* IN MIXED SATURATED-UNSATURATED GLYCERIDES
		SEED FATS			
1	*Cocos nucifera*	Coconut oil	93·9	86	1·3–1·4
2	„ „	Coconut oil	92·9	84	1·4
3	*Irvingia barteri*	Dika fat	91·7	81	1·3
4	*Manicaria saccifera*	—	91·6	82	1·2
5	*Myristica fragrans*	Nutmeg butter	90·2	73	1·6
6	*Astrocaryum tucuma*	Tucuma fat	88·0	73	1·25
7	*Acrocomia sclerocarpa*	Gru-gru fat	86·3	69	1·3
8	*Elæis guineensis*	Palm kernel oil	85·3	66	1·3–1·4
9	*Shorea stenoptera*	Borneo tallow	62·9	5·1	1·6
10	„ „	Borneo tallow	62·8	4·5	1·5
11	*Madhuca butyracea*	Phulwara butter	62·4	*8*	*1·4*
12	*Palaquium oblongifolium*	Taban Merah fat	60·2	1·8	1·5
13	*Theobroma cacao*	Cacao butter	59·8	2·5	1·4
14	*Garcinia indica*	Kokum butter	59·0	1·5	1·4
15	*Myristica malabarica*	—	59·2	*19*	*1·0*
16	„ „	—	56·2	*16*	*1·0*
17	*Laurus nobilis*	Laurel kernel	58·5	*40·5*	*0·4*
18	*Allanblackia stuhlmannii*	Mkanwi fat	55·6	1·5	1·2
19	*Nephelium mutabile*	Pulasan fat	55·3	1·5	1·2
20	*Dacryodes rostrata*	Java almond fat	53·4	1·8	1·1
21	*Caryocar villosum*	Piqui-a	53·1	2·5	1·1
22	*Pentadesma butyracea*	—	51·6	3·0	1·0
23	*Garcinia morella*	Gamboge butter	50·5	2·7	1·0
24	„ „	Gamboge butter	49·4	2·0	0·9
25	*Nephelium lappaceum*	Rambutan fat	49·0	1·4	0·9
26	*Hodgsonia capniocarpa*	—	47·8	2·7	0·9
27	*Butyrospermum parkii*	Shea fat	46·3	4·5	0·8
28	„ „	Shea fat	45·1	2·5	0·8
29	*Madhuca latifolia*	Mowrah fat	43·4	1·2	0·8
30	*Schleichera trijuga*	Kusum fat	34·6	1·2	0·6
31	*Azadirachta indica*	Neem oil	32·0	0·6	0·6
32	*Gossypium hirsutum*	Cottonseed oil	27·3	less than 1	0·3
33	*Arachis hypogæa*	Groundnut oil	15·5	„ „ 1	0·2
34	*Sesamum indicum*	Sesame oil	14·9	„ „ 1	0·2
35	*Thea sinensis*	Teaseed oil	10·0	„ „ 1	0·1
36	*Brassica campestris*	Rape oil	3·6	„ „ 1	—
		FRUIT-COAT FATS			
a	*Sapium sebiferum*	Stillingia tallow	72·5	28·4	1·6
b	„ „	Stillingia tallow	68·4	23·9	1·4
c	*Elæis guineensis*	Palm oil, Congo	50·9	*10·3*	*0·8*
d	„ „	Palm oil, Sumatra	51·2	2·0	1·0
e	„ „	Palm oil, Congo	49·6	*6·5*	*0·8*
f	„ „	Palm oil, Malay	49·2	*9·5*	*0·8*
g	„ „	Palm oil, Cameroons	49·1	*8·3*	*0·8*
h	„ „	Palm oil, Drewin	46·6	*7·4*	*0·7*
i	„ „	Palm oil, Cape Palmas	41·5	3·4	0·7
j	*Caryocar villosum*	Piqui-a pericarp	45·9	2·3	0·8
k	*Dacryodes rostrata*	Pericarp	38·7	1·0	0·6
l	*Laurus nobilis*	Laurel berry	25·4	3·0	0·3
m	*Olea europæa*	Olive oil	13·8	2·0	0·1

* "Association ratio": Mols. saturated acid associated with one mol. unsaturated acid in mixed saturated-unsaturated glycerides.

In Table 71, numbers in italics indicate fats with abnormal trisaturated glyceride contents (*cf.* p. 393).

so completely as in the seed fats. In the fruit-coat or pericarp fats of *Caryocar* and *Stillingia* the data accord with the "even distribution" rule, but in olive, laurel berry and palm oils there is usually a somewhat higher content of fully saturated triglycerides (in these cases tripalmitin, since palmitic forms almost the whole of the saturated acids present) than is consistent with the operation of this principle to the extent usually observed in the seed fats. Relatively few examples of fruit-coat fats have yet been available for study, and it is hardly

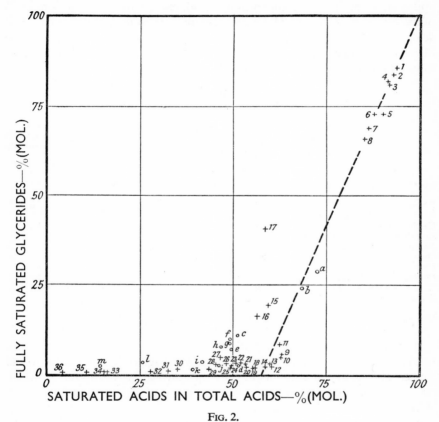

Fig. 2.

possible to say, on the evidence at present to hand, whether the strictly "evenly distributed" type is more common, or not, in this group of vegetable fats.

It has already been said that glyceride structure appears to be quite independent of the particular acids which are present. This is particularly well shown by the seed fats quoted in Table 71 which contain from 43 to 63 per cent. of saturated acids in the total fatty acids, and which also, it so happens, include several different saturated acids amongst their major component acids. It is therefore interesting to consider these fats in somewhat greater detail (Table 72).

In the group of fats illustrated in Table 72, the amount of fully saturated glycerides is for the most part insignificant, irrespective of whether the 43–63 per cent. of saturated acids in the whole fat consists very largely of one acid

367

(either palmitic or stearic), or of a mixture of two saturated acids in quantity (either palmitic and stearic, or stearic and arachidic). Similarly, of the fats numbered 1–8 in Table 71 the predominating saturated acids are lauric (45–50 per cent.) and myristic (about 20 per cent.) in the Palmæ seed fats, myristic (about 75 per cent.) in nutmeg fat, and myristic and palmitic in dika fat.

The general picture of glyceride structure exhibited by the relatively more saturated seed fats is thus that fully saturated glycerides do not appear in appreciable amounts until the saturated acids exceed about 60 per cent. or so of the total fatty acids. Put in the converse manner, so long as the unsaturated acids form somewhat more than one-third of the total fatty acids, at least one oleic group occurs in nearly every triglyceride molecule, i.e., the amount of fully saturated glycerides is negligible.

TABLE 72

SEED FAT	COMPONENT SATURATED ACIDS PER CENT. (MOL.)				SATURATED ACIDS IN TOTAL ACIDS PER CENT. (MOL.)	FULLY-SATURATED GLYCERIDES IN FAT PER CENT. (MOL.)
	C_{14}	C_{16}	C_{18}	C_{20}		
Borneo tallow	—	19·5	42·4	1·0	62·9	5·1
,, ,,	1·8	23·3	37·5	—	62·6	4·5
Phulwara butter	1·6	57·4	3·4	—	62·4	8·0
Palaquium oblongifolium	0·2	6·5	53·5	—	60·2	1·8
Cacao butter	—	24·3	35·5	—	59·8	2·5
Allanblackia stuhlmannii	—	3·4	52·2	—	55·6	1·5
Nephelium mutabile	—	3·3	31·4	20·6	55·3	1·5
Dacryodes rostrata	—	11·7	39·8	1·9	53·4	1·8
Caryocar villosum	1·6	50·7	0·8	—	53·1	2·5
Pentadesma butyracea	—	5·9	45·7	—	51·6	3·0
Nephelium lappaceum	—	2·3	14·2	32·5	49·0	1·4
Shea butter	—	6·3	40·0	—	46·3	4·5
,, ,,	—	9·3	35·4	—	44·7	2·5
Mowrah fat	—	24·1	19·3	—	43·4	1·2

It should be noted that formation of mixed glycerides by a process of *random distribution* of fatty acids amongst the triglyceride molecules would lead to quite different amounts of fully saturated glycerides in fats in which saturated acids form from about 30 to 70 per cent. of the total fatty acids. With "random" distribution, the amount of fully saturated triglycerides would be proportional to the cube of the proportion of saturated acids in the total fatty acids: with 50 per cent. saturated acids the amount of fully saturated glycerides would be 12·5 per cent. of the fat, with 63 per cent. of saturated acids it would reach 25 per cent. (whereas fully saturated glycerides are still negligible at this fatty acid composition).

Trisaturated glyceride contents of land animal depot and milk fats. It has been indicated (p. 365) that the proportions of fully-saturated glycerides in many animal depot and milk fats are markedly greater (in relation to the proportion of saturated acids in the total acids of the fats) than is the case in vegetable fats such as those considered in Table 71 and Fig. 2. Corresponding data for the trisaturated glycerides in a range of such animal fats are therefore next given in tabular and graphical form (Table 73, pp. 369, 370, and Fig. 3). For the animal

TABLE 73. *Trisaturated Glycerides in Animal Fats*

| | | DEPOT FATS | SATURATED ACIDS IN TOTAL FATTY ACIDS | | | | FULLY SATURATED PER CENT. (MOL.) |
			MYRISTIC	PALMITIC	STEARIC	TOTAL PER CENT. (MOL.)	
H	*Birds*	Domestic fowl (hen)	0·1	27·1	6·8	34·0	2·5
R	*Rodents*	Wild rabbit	5·4	24·5	3·8	33·7	6·0
R		Rat (low fat diet)	6·0	25·5	3·0	34·5	2·5
R		Rat (low fat diet)	5·4	29·7	1·9	37·0	3·5
P	*Herbivora* *Pigs*	Sow, outer back fat	4·6	21·7	7·6	33·9	2·2
P		Sow, inner back fat	2·8	27·3	14·4	44·5	5·6
P		Sow, inner back fat	4·6	27·7	10·6	42·9	6·7
P		Sow, perinephric fat	4·7	29·4	16·9	51·0	11·4
P		Hog, perinephric fat	2·0	27·4	17·5	46·9	13·2
P		Hog, perinephric fat	4·4	30·2	20·5	55·1	17·7
O	*Oxen*	Beef tallow, North American	7·5	29·1	13·4	50·0	13·9
O		Shorthorn bullock, perinephric fat	3·9	26·5	23·8*	54·2	15·8
O		Shorthorn heifer, perinephric fat	2·7	33·4	22·7*	58·8	17·4
O		Shorthorn cow, perinephric fat	3·5	31·0	20·4*	54·9	18·4
O		Shorthorn heifer, perinephric fat	2·5	28·7	26·5*	57·7	18·6
O		Beef tallow, South American	5·3	32·9	18·2	56·4	22·8
O		Beef tallow, South American	9·5	29·2	23·2	61·9	25·8
O		Beef tallow, South American	6·9	25·5	27·4	59·8	26·0
S	*Sheep*	Mutton tallow	5·5	26·2	29·3	61·0	26·6
G	*Goat*		7·2†	27·0	28·9*	63·1	29·2
U	*Buffalo*	Indian	3·9	33·4	32·2*	69·5	32·5
		Indian	8·8‡	45·6	19·5*	73·9	37·2

369

TABLE 73. *Trisaturated Glycerides in Animal Fats—continued.*
SATURATED ACIDS IN TOTAL FATTY ACIDS

	MILK FATS	C_4–C_{14}	PALMITIC	STEARIC	TOTAL	FULLY SATURATED
	Herbivora					
	Cows					
B	English, stall-fed, 1934 (cod liver oil in diet)	21·7	22·4	6·5*	50·6	14·6
B	English, stall-fed, 1934 (cod liver oil in diet)	22·9	22·8	7·8*	53·5	17·2
B	English, stall-fed, 1934 (linseed oil in diet)	32·7	20·0	8·6*	61·3	24·8
B	English, stall-fed, 1934 (rape oil in diet)	30·3	17·0	12·1*	59·4	25·3
B	English, spring pasture, 1929	32·2	24·3	5·4	61·9	27·2
B	English, autumn-fed, 1928	28·8	27·1	7·1*	63·0	29·1
B	New Zealand, market sample, 1927	32·0	26·2	7·9*	66·1	31·5
B	Indian, pasture-fed, 1930	35·6	26·8	5·5	67·9	33·7
B	New Zealand, market sample, 1927	30·9	25·7	10·7*	67·3	33·8
B	English, stall-fed, 1934	33·1	25·2	10·8*	69·1	34·2
B	English, stall-fed, 1929 (soya bean cake in diet)	38·7	23·7	7·6*	70·0	38·2
B	New Zealand, spring pasture, 1928	35·2	25·0	10·0*	70·2	39·6
B	English, stall-fed, 1934	40·3	20·5	10·6*	71·4	40·4
U	English, stall-fed, 1929 (coconut cake in diet)	44·4	24·1	3·9	72·4	41·3
	Buffalo					
	Indian, pasture-fed, 1930	31·4	28·7	10·0*	70·1	34·3
	Indian, mainly pasture-fed, 1945	30·4	31·9	12·6*	74·9	41·7
	Indian, heavy cottonseed feed, 1945	17·7	25·1	20·1*	62·9	24·3
S	*Sheep* Indian, winter diet, 1932	47·5	20·4	6·7*	74·6	36·8
G	*Goat* Indian, winter diet, 1932	45·7	21·5	7·4*	74·6	39·3
C	*Camel* Indian, pasture, 1933	24·6	28·3	9·7	62·6	25·6
	Omnivora					
	Human English, 1944	18·8	23·6	7·4	49·8	9·1

* Includes small amounts (up to about 1 per cent.) of arachidic acid.
† Includes 4·7 per cent. lauric acid.
‡ Includes 1·4 per cent. lauric acid.

370

fats, however, it will be well to give, in addition to the total percentage of saturated acids in the component acids of each fat, separate figures for the proportions of palmitic and stearic acids, and of acids of lower molecular weight than palmitic. Also, since in the milk fats the range of molecular weight of the saturated acids is very wide, it is desirable to give all quantitative data in this group in the form of molar proportions.

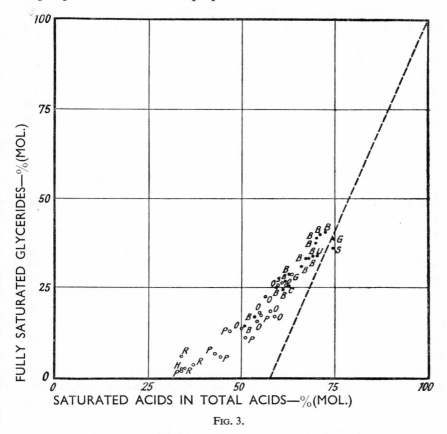

Fig. 3.

Fig. 3 should be compared with Fig. 2 (p. 367) showing similar data for vegetable seed and fruit-coat fats. In Fig. 3 the "evenly distributed" types of mixed glycerides which are almost universally the rule in seed fats would fall on the horizontal axis as far as about 58 per cent. of saturated acids in the total fatty acids of a fat, and would thereafter follow the broken line inserted on the graph. It is clear that only those animal depot fats containing less than about 35 per cent. of saturated acids in the total fatty acids conform with this generalisation; with increasing contents of saturated acids the proportions of fully saturated glycerides increase steadily, whether in depot or milk fats, and the relationship between content of fully saturated glycerides and of total saturated acids is obviously fundamentally different from that encountered in nearly all the vegetable fats (Fig. 2). The significance of these differences will

371

be dealt with in the course of the general discussion of the glyceride structure of animal fats on pp. 403–416.

Consideration of tri-saturated glyceride contents, as indicated by the oxidation procedure, thus enabled a number of important general similarities and differences to be discerned in different kinds of natural fats, and represented a marked advance beyond that available before 1927. With the aid of various assumptions, the tri-saturated glyceride contents of fats have also been made the basis of means for computing the proportions of mono-, di- and tri-unsaturated glycerides also present, as will be described later (pp. 419–508).

Sole consideration of tri-saturated glyceride content, inevitable before more adequate experimental methods for glyceride study had been worked out, is fortunately no longer necessary, and the chemical determination of fully saturated glycerides will probably be confined in future to special problems.

II. PARTIAL RESOLUTION OF MIXED GLYCERIDES OF NATURAL FATS BY CRYSTALLISATION FROM SOLVENTS

Since about 1935 there has been a return to the use in glyceride structure studies of fractional crystallisation of fats from solvents. The aim has differed from that of Bömer and the earlier workers in this field, however, since no attempt is now made to isolate individual mixed glycerides, but merely to effect so much simplification of the original fat that the constitution of each fraction obtained by the crystallisation procedure adopted can be approximately deduced from its fatty acid composition. Repeated and systematic crystallisation of a fat or fatty oil from a suitable solvent (usually acetone), first at a low temperature ($-60°$C. or lower for liquid fats), and thereafter at successively higher temperatures (with appropriate recrystallisation of intermediate fractions as may be found necessary), leads ultimately to the production of a number of final fractions, each of which represents a much simpler mixture of glycerides than that in the whole fat. Determination of the component acids present in each of these simpler mixtures permits an approximate estimate to be made of the component mixed glycerides therein, and thus to obtain similar data for the original fat. When the fatty acids present are relatively few in number, the individual component glycerides of a fat can be stated with some degree of precision. In the more frequent cases where the major component acids exceed three or four the results are often less definite, but it is nevertheless possible by this means to arrive at the approximate proportions of the main classes of glycerides present and, to some extent, of the chief individual mixed glycerides concerned.

It should at once be made clear that, although the crystallisation procedure is believed to give an accurate statement* of glyceride composition in the cases

* E.g., to a probable accuracy of ± 2 units per cent. for each glyceride category in fats not containing very high proportions of linoleic or linolenic acids. Only in fats containing as few as two or three component acids is a higher order of accuracy likely to be possible in component glyceride determination.

of the more saturated kinds of fats and of fats which do not contain excessive proportions of polyethenoid acids, the more recent use of segregation by counter-current distribution between two immiscible solvents (*see* III, p. 383) has shown that the contents of simple tri-unsaturated glycerides such as trilinolein or trilinolenin in linoleic – or linolenic-rich fatty oils as determined by the crystallisation procedure are often considerably below the true values. It would appear that mixtures of, e.g., dioleolinoleins, oleodilinoleins and trilinolein resist segregation by low temperature crystallisation much more than was at first believed, and results obtained by this process for highly unsaturated oils such as linseed, safflower, or sunflower seed oils must now be considered with reserve. The exact point at which the crystallisation method commences to be ineffective is not at present clear, but it seems at the moment reasonable to consider it quite satisfactory so long as a fat does not contain more than 50 per cent. linoleic (or total polyethenoid) acids.

The general principles which operate in the separation of various groups of mixed glycerides by crystallisation are illustrated in Table 74. This indicates the four main types of glycerides (from fully saturated to completely un-saturated) and some typical individual components of each group, together with a rough diagrammatic representation of the chief components present in hard solid, soft solid, and liquid fats. It includes similar diagrammatic indica-tions of the general composition of the various fractions into which a fat may be separated (i) in the cases of solid or semi-solid fats crystallised from acetone at not lower than 0° or − 10°, and (ii) in liquid fats for which the temperatures employed in crystallisation from solvents may range from about 0° down to − 60° or lower.

TABLE 74. *General Separation of Component Glycerides Effected by Crystallisation from Acetone*

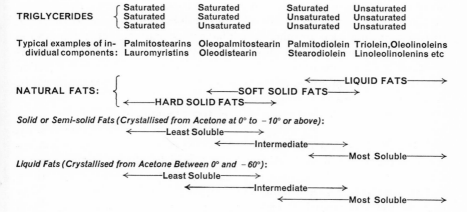

The crystallisation procedure thus divides the natural fat into a number of portions (from three or four to ten or more, according to the complexity of the original fat), in each of which the component acids are determined. If neces-sary, determination of trisaturated glycerides by the oxidation procedure may be applied to individual fractions. Occasionally, also, it may be found useful to study the products of hydrogenation of individual fractions.

In the cases of many solid fats it has by these means been possible to give with some confidence a detailed, approximately quantitative statement of the component glycerides in each portion of the fat, and therefrom to deduce that of the original fat. In the more unsaturated, liquid fats (from which fully saturated glycerides are usually absent) reliance must in general be placed solely on the component acid analyses for each portion obtained by crystallisation, and it is thus the more important in these cases to effect as complete a separation as possible into mixtures of mixed glycerides which include only two of the unsaturated group-types. Here the final quantitative statement of component glycerides may vary from a fairly detailed picture to one in which the fat is described in terms of groups of glycerides, rather than individuals.

The crystallisation procedure is rather complicated, varies in detail with the nature of the fat studied, and, naturally, the best conditions for a given fat or fatty oil must be worked out to suit each individual case. The experimental technique is further explained and illustrated in Chapter XI (pp. 701–705), but the crystallisation scheme used in the case of a horse mesenteric fat[27] is given here (Fig. 4) in order to assist the discussion which follows. In such fractional crystallisations it is convenient always to letter the final least soluble (and most saturated) fraction "A", and to list successive fractions "B", "C", etc., in increasing order of unsaturation – although, of course, the *first* fraction isolated is actually the material (I in Fig. 4 and Table 75) left in solution in the *initial* crystallisation at the lowest temperature used.

The compositions of the glyceride fractions A–I shown in Fig. 4 are given in Table 75. The calculation of the various glyceride types in each fraction from its component acid data depends on the assumption that, as a result of the crystallisation procedure, no fraction contains more than *two* contiguous members of the four possible categories of components (e.g., tri-, di- and mono-saturated, and tri-unsaturated; or glycerides containing respectively no, one, two, or three oleo, or other individual acid group). No other assumption as regards the distribution of fatty acid groups in the glyceride molecules is involved, but it is evidently important to scrutinise carefully how far resolution into solely binary mixtures of the respective different glyceride types can be reasonably presumed.

Considering, in the first place, the relative amounts of saturated and un-saturated acids in the glycerides of segregated fractions (e.g., of the horse fat in Table 75), it is clear that the most saturated glycerides have been concentrated in the least soluble fractions *A* and *B*, which indeed contain some tri-saturated glycerides in addition to mono-unsaturated disaturated glycerides. In fraction *C*, di- as well as mono-unsaturated glycerides are present; in view of the very small proportion of trisaturated glycerides in the preceding fraction *B*, it is reasonable to suppose that the latter are not present in *C*. In the remaining fractions, tri-unsaturated glycerides are evidently present in increasing proportions; it is possible that fraction *D* may also contain some mono-unsaturated glycerides, but in view of the drastic crystallisation procedure

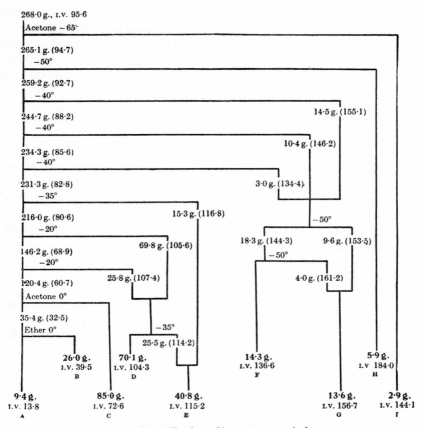

FIG. 4. Crystallisation of horse mesenteric fat.

TABLE 75. *Horse Fat Fractions*[27] *Obtained by Crystallisation*

	A	B	C	D	E	F	G	H	I	TOTAL
Iodine value	13·8	39·5	72·6	104·3	115·2	136·6	156·7	184·0	144·1	95·6
Glycerides (Per cent. mol.)	3·7	10·0	32·1	25·9	15·0	5·3	5·0	2·1	0·9	100·0
COMPONENT ACIDS (PER CENT. MOL.)										
Palmitic	55·5	45·6	34·1	18·2	17·4	6·6	5·5	10·3	18·5	25·9
Other saturated	30·0	22·9	11·0	8·5	4·2	5·8	4·7	—	—	10·3
Oleic	14·5	22·1	32·5	39·3	42·1	39·1	29·5	24·1	31·8	34·0
Linolenic	—	4·8	9·5	16·6	22·8	27·9	38·4	53·0	40·0	16·1
Other unsaturated	—	4·6	12·9	17·4	13·5	20·6	20·9	12·6	9·7	13·7
COMPONENT GLYCERIDE CATEGORIES (INCREMENTS PER CENT. MOL.)										
I Trisaturated	2·1	0·5	—	—	—	—	—	—	—	2·6
Disatd. mono-unsatd.	1·6	9·5	11·3	—	—	—	—	—	—	22·4
Monosatd. di-unsatd.	—	—	20·8	20·7	9·7	2·0	1·5	0·7	0·5	55·9
Tri-unsaturated	—	—	—	5·2	5·3	3·3	3·5	1·4	0·4	19·1
II Dipalmito-	2·5	3·7	0·7	—	—	—	—	—	—	6·9
Monopalmito-	1·2	6·3	31·4	14·1	7·8	1·1	0·8	0·7	0·5	63·9
III Di-oleo-	—	—	—	4·6	4·0	0·9	—	—	—	9·5
Mono-oleo-	1·6	6·6	31·3	21·3	11·0	4·4	4·4	1·5	0·8	82·9
IV Dilinoleno-	—	—	—	—	—	—	0·8	1·2	0·2	2·2
Monolinoleno-	—	1·4	9·2	12·9	10·2	4·4	4·2	0·9	0·7	43·9

375

applied, and of the fact that glycerides such as oleopalmitostearin are relatively insoluble in comparison with the di- and tri-unsaturated glycerides present, it is unlikely that any appreciable proportion of mono-unsaturated glycerides has been left in fraction D, and still less so in the later fractions. Similarly, it is almost certain that no di-unsaturated glycerides have been retained in the least soluble fractions A and B. Thus, when care has been taken to pursue the original crystallisation of the fat to a point at which little or no change takes place on further recrystallisation of intermediate glyceride fractions, it can be assumed with considerable certainty that any one glyceride group contains only binary mixtures of tri- and di-saturated, di- and mono-saturated, or mono-saturated and tri-unsaturated glycerides. The proportions of such binary mixtures can be calculated from the component acid data (Table 75, I).

The probable proportions of mono-, di-, and tri-palmitoglycerides (Table 75, II), mono- and di-oleoglycerides (Table 75, III), and mono- and di-linoleno-glycerides (Table 75, IV), in each glyceride group can be deduced on similar lines, although it should be borne in mind that the degree of segregation of the unsaturated glycerides, at all events, cannot be postulated with so much certainty as in the case of the various categories of saturated-unsaturated triglycerides.

The proportions of the remaining acids (myristic, stearic, unsaturated C_{20-22} acids) in all the groups of glycerides are small enough to indicate that each will contribute only one acyl group to any triglyceride in which it is present.

The above example serves to illustrate the limitations of the quantitative interpretation of the final analytical data for the segregated glyceride fractions. If the crystallisation procedure has been pushed so far that no further appreciable resolution occurs on recrystallisation of a segregated fraction, it is considered that, although subject to some degree of minor error, the final figures are reasonably near to the truth. The validity of the final results depends essentially and ultimately upon the efficiency of the crystallisation–segregation procedure. This should in every case be pursued until the investigator is satisfied that no further perceptible resolution can be obtained by recrystallisation of intermediate fractions.

Indirect evidence of the general accuracy (within the limits just given) of the methods employed in studying glyceride structure is afforded by the facts that the graphs relating contents of trisaturated glycerides, triolein, trilinolein, or other simple tri-unsaturated glycerides to the proportion of such acid in the total acids of fats obtained by the crystallisation procedure (Figs. 5, 6, 7, 8) are of exactly the same form as those for trisaturated glycerides obtained by the older and entirely different chemical method of permanganate–acetone oxidation (Figs. 2, 3). Again, the graphs showing similar relationships of the contents of mono-, di-, and tri-glycerides of any given acid to the proportion of that acid in the total acids of the fats (Figs. 5–8) are also broadly of identical form, with maxima in each case of mono-glycerides at 33 per cent. content and of di-glycerides at 65–67 per cent. content of the respective acids in the total acids.

376

The accuracy of the crystallisation procedure was examined[28] by preparing concentrates of a number of individual mixed glycerides (oleodistearin, oleopalmitostearin, palmito- and stearo-dioleins, trilinolein with oleodilinolein, etc.) by intensive crystallisation of suitable natural fats, and making up from these concentrates various mixtures to simulate the composition of various fats and fatty oils. These mixtures were then submitted to the crystallisation procedure. It was found that the proportions of tri-, di-, and mono-saturated

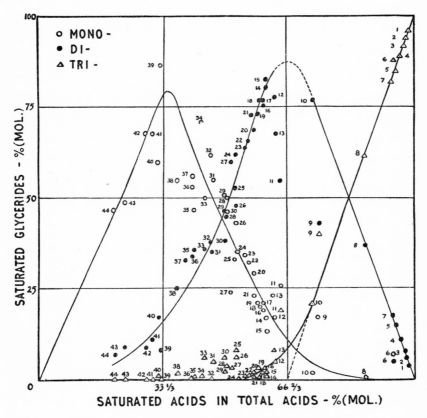

FIG. 5. Mono-, di-, tri-saturated glycerides in vegetable fats.

glycerides determined from these analyses were close to those known to be present from the composition of the mixtures selected. The accordance between the observed and the known proportions of specific unsaturated glycerides was also reasonably good in some, but not all, instances.

The large amount of data obtained with the aid of crystallisation-segregation by the Hilditch school at Liverpool and by other investigators in America and in India has been collected and analysed so as to show the proportions of glycerides containing three, two, or one group of various acids (saturated in vegetable fats, saturated in animal fats, oleic, linoleic) in relation to the

377

TABLE 76. *Distribution of Saturated Acids in Vegetable Fats*
(Crystallisation Procedure)

| Seed or fruit-coat Fats | SATURATED FATTY ACIDS | | | | | | GLYCERIDES | | |
	C_{12} (or below)	C_{14}	C_{16}	C_{18}	C_{20} (or above)	TOTAL	TRI-SATD.	DI-SATD.	MONO-SATD.
1. Dika	65·4	30·8	1·6	0·8	—	98·6	96	4	—
2. Dika	48·6	44·1	5·2	—	—	97·9	94	6	—
3. *Cinnamomum zeylanicum*	91·2	5·2	1·0	—	—	97·4	92	8	—
4. *Myristica iriya*	23·8	67·2	5·4	—	—	96·4	89	11	—
5. *Virola surinamensis*	17·6	72·9	4·4	—	—	94·9	85	15	—
6. *Neolitsea zeylanica*	90·4	3·4	—	—	—	93·8	88	5	7
7. Coconut	66·7	16·8	8·0	2·5	—	94·0	82	18	—
8. Palm Kernel	60·7	16·8	6·8	2·5	—	86·8	62	37	1
9. *Pycnanthus kombo*	8·9	63·6	2·0	—	—	74·5	40	43	17
10. *Sapium sebiferum* (fruit-coat)	—	0·6	65·4	7·1	—	73·1	21	77	2
11. *Platonia insignis*	—	1·2	57·2	6·0	0·2	64·6	19	55	26
12. Borneo tallow	—	—	19·5	42·4	1·0	62·9	5	78	17
13. *Madhuca butyracea*	—	1·6	57·4	3·4	—	62·4	8	69	23
14. *Allanblackia floribunda*	—	—	2·2	58·3	0·2	60·7	1	81	17
15. Cacao butter (1949)	—	—	26·2	34·4	—	60·6	2	83	13
16. *Lophira procera*	—	0·8	41·8	—	17·7	60·3	3	76	19
17. Cacao butter (1936)	—	—	24·3	35·4	—	59·7	2	77	21
18. *Garcinia indica*	—	—	3·1	56·1	—	59·2	1	77	20
19. *Garcinia indica*	—	1·2	5·3	52·0	—	58·5	3	73	21
20. *Vateria indica*	—	0·7	13·0	43·3	0·4	57·4	2	69	29
21. *Vateria indica*	—	—	12·2	42·4	2·7	57·3	1	73	23
22. *Allanblackia parviflora*	—	1·3	2·2	52·7	—	56·2	1	66	32
23. *Shorea robusta*	—	—	4·6	44·2	6·3	55·1	1	64	34
24. *Sapium discolor* (fruit-coat)	—	2·0	49·0	1·9	—	52·9	—	62	35
25. Palm oil (Cameroons) (fruit-coat)	—	1·3	47·3	3·9	—	52·5	8	53	32
26. Palm oil (N'Dian) (fruit-coat)	—	2·8	43·8	5·8	—	52·4	6	48	43
27. *Hodgsonia capniocarpa*	—	—	41·7	9·3	—	51·0	3	60	24
28. *Garcinia morella*	—	0·3	7·2	42·5	0·3	50·3	3	45	50
29. *Garcinia morella*	—	—	1·2	48·2	—	49·4	2	46	51
30. Palm oil (fruit-coat)	—	2·8	43·4	3·4	—	49·6	6	38	48
31. Shea butter	—	—	6·3	40·0	—	46·3	5	35	55
32. *Lophira alata*	—	2·4	29·9	—	13·6	45·9	—	38	62
33. Palm oil (Bassa) (fruit-coat)	—	0·7	39·8	3·6	—	44·1	6	36	50
34. Mowrah (*Madhuca latifolia*)	—	—	24·1	19·3	—	43·4	1	28	71
35. Kusum (*Schleichera trijuga*)	—	1·5	6·9	6·0	27·0	41·4	1	36	47
36. *Mimusops heckelii* (Baku fat)	—	—	4·6	35·3	1·2	41·1	1	34	53
37. *Mimusops heckelii* (Baku fat)	—	—	4·1	35·1	1·9	41·1	—	34	56
38. Lime seed (*Citrus limetta*)	—	—	29·7	6·2	1·0	36·9	2	25	55
39. Sapota	1·6	6·2	12·6	12·0	—	32·4	—	8	87
40. Neem (*Azadirachta indica*)	—	—	16·3	14·5	1·2	32·0	1	17	60
41. *Pentaclethra macrophylla*	—	—	5·0	7·5	17·8	30·3	—	11	68
42. *Pentaclethra eetveldeana*	—	—	4·5	5·3	18·9	28·7	—	9	68
43. Groundnut (Valencia)	—	—	11·7	3·1	7·9	22·7	—	9	49
44. Groundnut (West African)	—	—	9·2	5·5	5·6	20·3	—	7	47

All other seed fats with 25 per cent. or less of saturated acids so far recorded contained no trisaturated glycerides.

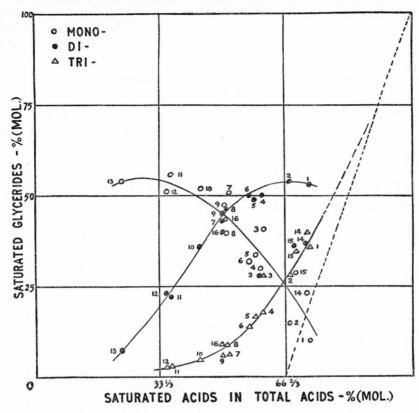

FIG. 6. Mono-, di-, tri-saturated glycerides in animal fats.

TABLE 77. *Distribution of Saturated Acids in Land Animal Fats*
(Crystallisation Procedure)

	SATURATED FATTY ACIDS						GLYCERIDES		
	C_{12} (or below)	C_{14}	C_{16}	C_{18}	C_{20} (or above)	TOTAL	TRI-SATD.	DI-SATD.	MONO-SATD.
Depot Fats									
1. Cow, Indian (Bombay)	0·1	5·8	40·8	25·5	0·7	72·9	36	53	10
2. Cow, Indian (Calicut)	0·5	5·2	33·4	27·9	0·5	67·5	28	54	15
3. Sheep, Indian	—	2·9	30·9	25·3	1·5	60·6	28	28	41
4. Elephant, Indian	1·1	7·6	45·3	6·1	—	60·1	18	50	30
5. Cow, English	0·2	2·4	33·4	21·4	1·3	58·7	17	49	34
6. Sheep, English, perinephric	0·3	2·7	27·1	25·6	1·5	57·2	14	50	32
7. Tiger, Indian	—	0·8	25·1	24·5	1·0	51·4	6	43	51
8. Pig, perinephric	0·5	1·3	31·1	17·6	—	50·5	9	46	40
9. Sheep, English, back	—	3·8	31·5	14·5	0·4	50·2	6	45	47
10. Pig, back	—	1·3	29·0	13·8	—	44·1	5	36	52
11. Horse, English	0·3	5·0	26·0	4·7	0·2	36·2	3	22	56
12. Badger, English	—	7·5	20·1	7·5	—	35·1	3	23	51
13. Neat's foot oil	—	0·8	18·4	3·5	0·1	22·8	—	7	54
Milk Fats									
14. Buffalo, Indian	21·2	11·1	27·5	11·1	1·4	72·3	40	37	23
15. Cow, Indian	21·4	10·3	26·5	9·6	1·1	68·9	35	36	29
16. Human	9·8	9·0	23·6	6·5	0·9	49·8	9	40	43

proportion of the acid in question in the total acids of each fat. The results are given in Tables 76–79, and shown graphically in Figs. 5–8. In these tables are included data ranging from the earlier crystallisation studies of such solid

TABLE 78. *Distribution of Oleic Acid in Vegetable Fats*
(Crystallisation Procedure)

SEED OR FRUIT-COAT FAT	OLEIC ACID CONTENT (PER CENT. MOL.)	GLYCERIDES		
		TRI-OLEIN	DI-OLEO	MONO-OLEO
1. Olive, Palestine (fruit-coat)	76·4	29	71	—
2. Olive, Italian (fruit-coat)	66·8	5	91	4
3. Sapota	66·2	1	91	8
4. Neem *(Azadirachta indica)*	60·3	—	81	19
5. Groundnut (West African)	59·1	6	65	29
6. *Mimusops heckelii* (Baku fat)	58·3	10	52	37
7. *Mimusops heckelii* (Baku fat)	57·5	7	58	35
8. *Pentaclethra eetveldeana*	54·5	4	56	40
9. *Garcinia morella*	49·7	1	48	51
10. Palm oil (Bassa) (fruit-coat)	49·7	—	46	51
11. Sunflower (I.V. 113·8)	44·2	—	33	67
12. *Sapium discolor* (fruit-coat)	44·1	1	31	68
13. *Allanblackia parviflora*	43·8	—	32	66
14. Mowrah *(Madhuca latifolia)*	43·4	—	31	67
15. Palm oil (fruit-coat)	43·1	—	37	49
16. *Vateria indica*	42·5	—	29	69
17. *Shorea robusta*	42·4	—	28	72
18. *Schleichera trijuga* (Kusum)	42·4	—	32	63
19. *Vateria indica*	40·5	—	23	76
20. Groundnut (Valencia)	40·5	—	30	62
21. *Garcinia indica*	39·4	1	19	78
22. *Allanblackia floribunda*	38·6	—	16	82
23. Cacao butter (1936)	38·2	—	14	86
24. Palm oil (N'Dian) (fruit-coat)	38·1	—	23	68
25. Palm oil (Cameroons) (fruit-coat)	37·6	—	23	66
26. Cacao butter (1949)	37·3	Trace	12	85
27. Borneo tallow	36·9	—	16	79
28. Sunflower (I.V. 121·1)	36·7	—	18	74
29. Sesame	36·5	—	15	79
30. *Madhuca butyracea*	34·5	—	11	81
31. *Platonia insignis*	33·2	—	16	58
32. Sunflower (I.V. 125·1)	33·1	—	7	86
33. Okra *(Hibiscus esculentus)*	27·2	—	2	78
34. Candlenut, Hong Kong	26·4	—	3	72
35. Orange seed *(Citrus aurantium dulcis)*	25·5	—	1	74
36. *Sapium sebiferum* (fruit-coat)	25·5	—	—	76
37. *Hodgsonia capniocarpa*	25·5	—	—	76
38. Cottonseed	25·0	—	—	75
39. Sunflower (I.V. 130·0)	23·8	—	—	71
40. Maize *(Zea mais)*	23·5	—	8	55
41. *Chrozophora plicata*	23·3	—	—	70
42. Soya bean oil	22·0	—	—	66
43. Soya bean oil	21·8	—	—	65
44. *Pentaclethra macrophylla*	20·0	—	—	60

Other seed fats with 25 per cent. or less of oleic acid so far recorded contain only mono-oleo-glycerides.

fats as cacao butter, etc., which were described at some length in the Second Edition of this book, and also all subsequent studies of solid and liquid fats, including of course the more unsaturated vegetable oils to which the method (with the aid of very low temperatures) was later applied.

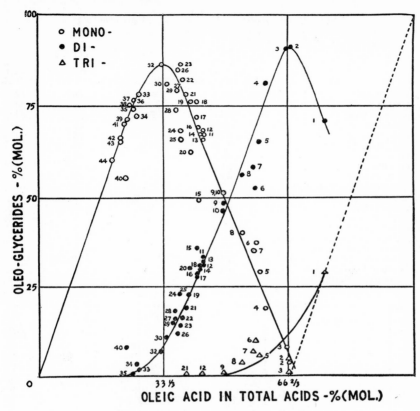

FIG. 7. Mono-, di-, tri-oleo-glycerides in vegetable fats.

TABLE 79. *Distribution of Linoleic Acid in Vegetable Fats*
(Crystallisation Procedure)

FAT	LINOLEIC ACID CONTENT (PER CENT. MOL.)	GLYCERIDES		
		TRILINOLEIN	DI LINOLEO-	MONO- LINOLEO-
1. Safflower seed	76·5	31*	67	2
2. Niger seed	74·4	31*	61	8
3. Poppy seed, English	73·2	27*	66	7
4. Sunflower seed (I.V. 137·6)	72·4	24*	69	7
5. Tobacco seed, Indian	70·9	19*	74	7
6. Poppy seed, Indian	70·2	21*	69	10
7. Sunflower seed (I.V. 132·2)	67·3	8*	86	6
8. Sunflower seed (I.V. 130·0)	63·2	7*	76	17
9. Jute seed	61·1	8*	68	23
10. Maize seed	60·8	1*	83	14
11. Sunflower seed (I.V. 125·1)	56·3	Trace	68	31
12. Hemp seed	53·8	—	61	39
13. *Chrozophora plicata* seed	52·6	3	56	37
14. Sunflower seed (I.V. 121·1)	51·1	Trace	56	42
15. *Pentaclethra macrophylla* seed	49·7	1	46	53
16. Soya bean	49·3	—	48	52

* These figures for trilinolein are probably lower than the true values (*cf.* pp. 373, 383).

TABLE 79. *Distribution of Linoleic Acid in Vegetable Fats*
(Crystallisation Procedure) – continued

			GLYCERIDES	
FAT	LINOLEIC ACID CONTENT (PER CENT. MOL.)	TRILINOLEIN	DI-LINOLEO-	MONO-LINOLEO-
17. Soya bean	49·2	—	48	52
18. Cottonseed	47·8	—	46	48
19. Sesame seed	46·7	Trace	43	53
20. Sunflower seed (I.V. 113·8)	44·0	—	39	53
21. Candlenut (Australian)	41·5	—	25	74
22. Candlenut (Australian)	41·2	—	25	73
23. Okra seed	40·2	1	32	53
24. Groundnut (Valencia)	36·8	—	19	73
25. Rubber seed	36·6	—	15	79
26. Candlenut (Hong Kong)	36·4	—	14	81
27. Orange seed	34·8	—	15	74
28. Lime seed	34·5	—	15	73
29. *Lophira alata* seed	33·6	—	9	82
30. *Lophira procera* seed	26·5	—	4	72
31. *Hodgsonia capniocarpa* seed	23·5	—	—	71
32. *Sapium sebiferum* seed	22·3	—	—	67
33. Groundnut (West African)	20·6	—	6	50
34. *Pentaclethra eetveldeana*	16·8	—	—	50
35. Tung (Nyasaland)	15·7	—	1	45

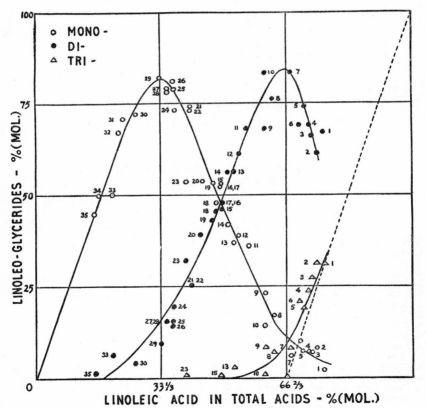

FIG. 8. Mono-, di-, tri-linoleo-glycerides in vegetable fats.

III. SEPARATION OF THE GLYCERIDES IN A FAT BY COUNTER-CURRENT DISTRIBUTION BETWEEN TWO IMMISCIBLE SOLVENTS

An alternative method to crystallisation from solvents for segregation of natural fat glycerides was first put forward by Dutton *et al.*[29a] in 1950. This consists in continuous counter-current distribution of an oil between two immiscible solvents in a semi-automatic apparatus of the kind described by Craig *et al.*[30] Dutton, Scholfield *et al.*[29b–f] employed an instrument possessing 200 tubes each of 80 ml. solvent capacity and used as solvents either a pentane–hexane fraction with furfural, or a mixture of 2 vols. pentane–hexane:1 vol. furfural:1 vol. nitroethane; they determined by this means some of the chief glycerides present in linseed, soya bean, safflower and maize (corn) oils and in cocoa butter. With the more unsaturated oils they thus achieved more complete segregation than had been effected by low-temperature crystallisation, and observed considerably more simple triglycerides (trilinolenin or trilinolein) than the latter procedure had indicated; but with the less unsaturated cocoa butter their results were similar to those obtained by crystallisation by other workers.

In 1956 Dutton and Cannon[29b] studied linseed oil, from which after 800 "transfers" in the Craig apparatus they isolated various (combined) samples of similar iodine value; spectrophotometric analyses in conjunction with the iodine values indicated the presence of trilinolenin 18, linoleodilinolenin 12, oleodilinolenin 20 and dilinoleolinolenin 4 per cent. (the component acids of the oil were saturated 8·5, oleic 24·3, linoleic 14·9 and linolenic 52·3 per cent.). The efficiency of the counter-current segregation was shown by the iodine values of the isolated fractions, e.g., trilinolenin fractions 255·1–257·9 (theory 261·6), linoleodilinolenin 230·5–233·0 (theory 232·0). The remaining mixed glycerides of the oil (46 per cent.) were not characterised, but from the results given it was concluded that the linseed oil glycerides were essentially "randomly" distributed. In 1957 Scholfield and Hicks[29c] similarly studied soya bean oil, and observed the presence of trilinolein 14, oleodilinolein 25, oleodilinolenin 5 per cent. (component acids of oil: saturated 13·7, oleic 30·5, linoleic 49·1, linolenic 6·7 per cent.); about 40 per cent. of the oil was not characterised, but the figures indicated that "the acids in soya bean oil approached a random type of distribution".

Scholfield and Dutton[29d] (1958) examined two samples of safflower seed oil of slightly different fatty acid composition by the same method. The component acids (per cent. wt.) of the oils were:

	Saturated	Oleic	Linoleic	Linolenic
(a)	10·7	12·6	76·6	0·1
(b)	11·2	9·3	79·2	0·3

and the glycerides observed:

	Trilinolein	Oleodilinolein	Palmitodilinolein	Monolinoleoglycerides
(a)	47	26	8	13
(b)	51	15	12	15

About 92–93 per cent. of these oils was accounted for by the counter-current distribution analyses, and again the distribution of the glycerides seemed to be random in character. This was confirmed by interesterifying or "randomising" one of the oils with sodium methoxide, which caused little or no change in the component glycerides. During this work, also, in order to ensure that no acyl interchange takes place during the lengthy progress of counter-current distribution, a 50/50 mixture of safflower seed oil and olive oil was fractionated by the procedure; and the observed amount of trilinolein (25 per cent.) was little different from that (23·5 per cent.) in the original mixture of the oils. In 1961 they gave results[29e] for maize (corn) oil, the component acids of which (by GLC) were palmitic 10·0, stearic 2·7, oleic 26·7, linoleic 60·3 and linolenic 0·3 per cent., the observed values for trilinolein 21, dilinoleo-glycerides 37 and monolinoleo-glycerides 30 per cent. again corresponding with a "random" distribution.

This marked tendency for the major polyethenoid acid in linolenic- or linoleic-rich seed oils to be assembled on a random basis was not observed (at least, not to anything like this extent) in similar studies on the same oils segregated by low-temperature crystallisation. The latter method (as already mentioned, p. 373) thus appears to be inadequate for the resolution of mixed linoleo- and/or linoleno-glycerides in the different combinations in which they may be present, but its validity was confirmed for a solid fat containing substantially only oleic, palmitic and stearic acids when Scholfield and Dutton[29f] studied the glycerides of cocoa butter by the counter-current distribution process. The mono-oleo-disaturated glycerides found in two separate analyses were 75 and 81 per cent. (consisting respectively of oleodistearin 22, 27; oleopalmitostearin 41, 39; and oleodipalmitin 12, 15 per cent.); in the second analysis 19 per cent. of monosaturated diunsaturated glycerides was also recorded.* The figures for the respective mono-oleo- and di-oleo-glycerides are closely similar to those obtained by crystallisation by other workers (cf. Chapter VI, p. 434, for a more detailed discussion of cocoa butter glycerides) but the values for individual mixed glycerides differ somewhat from the latter (as indeed these do also in the results of the earlier workers). In a subsequent communication Dutton et al.[29g] submitted cocoa butter after interesterification with sodium methoxide to examination by the counter-current procedure, finding that the composition of the product was, as expected, completely "random".

Unfortunately, cocoa butter is the only less unsaturated fat which has so far been studied both by the low-temperature crystallisation and the counter-current distribution methods. It is much to be desired that further studies by the latter method of a suitable range of fats (e.g., palm oils, cottonseed oil, citrus seed oils, whale and fish oils, etc.) should be undertaken in the near future to ascertain at what point of relative unsaturation the crystallisation procedure commences to lose accuracy so far as the more unsaturated component

---

* In the first analysis the glycerides unaccounted for (25 per cent. of the fat) would have contained increments of 14 oleic and 11 saturated acids, corresponding with at least a further 8 per cent. of mono-oleo-disaturated glycerides.

glycerides are concerned. Meanwhile we consider that, used as described in the foregoing pages, its results may safely be regarded as trustworthy for all fats solid or semi-solid at room temperature (and relatively less unsaturated), and probably also for liquid fats in which polyethenoid acids do not predominate markedly over oleic acid.

The marked tendency to "random" distribution observed in one linolenic-rich and three linoleic-rich seed fats investigated by Dutton et al.[29b-e] will be considered further in the general discussion of our present knowledge of glycerides in natural fats (p. 394).

IV. SEPARATION OF GLYCERIDES BY CHROMATOGRAPHIC ADSORPTION

Some brief reference should be made to the possibility of adsorption methods of separation, or at least partial segregation, of mixed glycerides. The use of "column chromatography", usually with silicic acid columns, has occasionally been attempted with some partial success, and a few references to publications on this subject are given.[31] It seems very probable that, with further advances in chromatographic technique, separations of this kind will prove efficacious aids to the study of glyceride structure and for this reason the directions in which progress seems at present to be most likely may be indicated. The two most promising paths appear at the time of writing to be:

(a) "Thin layer" chromatography (cf. Chapter XI, p. 707), usually with silica gel as adsorbent, may be expected to become of increasing assistance in separating mixtures of triglycerides.[32a] The use of silica gel impregnated with silver nitrate[32b] shows excellent promise in this respect (Barrett et al.[32c]).

(b) Paper chromatographic separations of glycerides are also currently the subject of considerable study.[33]

V. SELECTIVE HYDROLYSIS OF TRIGLYCERIDES BY PANCREATIC LIPASE

Advances in the study of glyceride structure, after the (chemical) method of determination of fully saturated glycerides was first put forward in 1927, were confined to physical aids to segregation of natural fats into simpler mixtures of mixed glycerides (discussed in the preceding Sections II–IV of this chapter) for nearly thirty years. About 1952, however, it was noticed[34a, 35a] that pancreatic lipase effects partial hydrolysis of triglycerides in a highly selective manner: acyl groups attached to the 1-(α-) and 3-(α'-) hydroxyl groups of the glyceryl radical are hydrolysed before those attached to the central (2- or β-) hydroxyl group are attacked. In 1955 Desnuelle, Savary et al.[34b] and Mattson and co-workers[35b] submitted a number of natural fats to hydrolysis with pancreatic lipase and determined the composition of the acids in the isolated 2-monoglycerides. Thus, after an interval of twenty-nine years, a new chemical (or, more strictly, biochemical) means of attack on the problem of glyceride structure was at length achieved. It led immediately to most important findings, namely, that the acids removed by this hydrolysis from vegetable fats are very largely saturated, or are unsaturated acids containing more than 18 carbon atoms; the results with some animal fats were different in some respects (*cf.* below for details). This established beyond doubt that, in vegetable glycerides at all events, the arrangement of fatty acyl groups, far from being random, is extraordinarily specific or selective, and thus made a profound addition to our knowledge of the structure of natural triglycerides.

Mattson and Volpenhein[35d] (1961) generalised this behaviour in seed fat glycerides as exclusive attachment of saturated acids and C_{20} and C_{22} saturated acids to the 1- and 3-glyceryl hydroxyl groups, with the result that the central (2-) position contained a high proportion of the unsaturated C_{18} acids; it is equally correct, and perhaps more logical, to say that oleic, linoleic (and perhaps linolenic) acids are preferentially attached at the 2-position (in so far as their proportion permits), allowing any excess of unsaturated C_{18} acids and also saturated or other unsaturated acids to find attachments to the 1- or 3-hydroxyl positions of the glycerol molecule.*

As in the preceding descriptions of other experimental techniques which have been employed in the study of glyceride structure, the use which has been made of the selective hydrolysis technique in the elucidation of the modes of combination of component acids in the natural fats will receive attention later (pp. 396–402). At this point a selection of the data will serve to indicate the general nature of the results so far obtained (Table 80).

---

* It has been known for some time that, with phosphatides, an enzyme (phospholipase A) present in snake venom selectively removes acyl groups from one of the two acylated glyceryl hydroxyl groups, and that the hydrolysed acids were predominantly unsaturated (oleic). It was, however, originally believed that acyl groups were split off by this means from the 1-(α-)glyceryl position, so that saturated acids were supposed to be attached predominantly to the 2-(or β-)position; but later it was established that the snake venom enzyme removes acyl groups from the 2-(β-)position (Hanahan *et al.*[35e] (1960), Tattrie[35f]), so that, since oleic acid is the acid liberated by snake venom, it follows that (as in seed fat glycerides) the 2-(β)-glyceryl position in phosphatides is also selectively occupied by (oleic or linoleic acid.

Tattrie[35f] (1960) also showed that, when egg lecithin (phosphatidylcholine) was hydrolysed by phospholipase D to the corresponding 1,2-diglycerides and the latter hydrolysed by pancreatic lipase (which, as above, attacks acyl groups in the 1-(α-)position) the resulting mono-(2- or β-)glycerides were completely unsaturated, and consequently saturated acids were preferentially present in the 1-(α-)positions in the glycerol molecules.

TABLE 80. *Component Acids (per cent. wt.) in the 2-Position in Various Natural Fats*

	TOTAL FATTY ACIDS				ACIDS IN 2-MONO-GLYCERIDES			
	SATD.		UNSATD.		SATD.		UNSATD.	
	C_{16}	C_{18}	C_{20-22}	C_{18}	C_{16}	C_{18}	C_{20-22}	C_{18}
(a) Seed Fats								
Borneo tallow[36b]	17	46	—	37	2	2	—	96
„ „ [35c]	68		—	32	15		—	85
Cocoa butter[35c]	60		—	40	10		—	90
„ „ [35d]	62		—	38	2	2	—	96
„ „ [36b]	26	36	—	38	2	1	—	97
Shea butter[36b]	4	41	—	55	—	3	—	97
Cotton seed[35c]	30		—	70	11		—	89
Groundnut[35c]	21		—	79	1		—	99
„ [35d]	18		—	81	1		—	99
Soya bean[35c]	13		—	87	—		—	100
„ „ [36b]	18		—	82	5		—	95 (linoleic 64, oleic 31)
Rape[35d]	6		43	51	1	—	1	97
„ [35d]	5		50	45	1	1	3	95
Mustard[35d]	3		56	40	—	—	1	99
Cabbage[35d]	7		48	45	1	1	2	96
Radish[35d]	11		39	49	1	—	1	97
(b) Fruit Coat Fats								
Palm[35c]	49		—	51	13		—	87
„ [36b]	44	6	—	50	17	2	—	81
Olive[35c]	15		—	85	1		—	99
„ [36b]	15		—	85	1		—	99 (oleic 89, linoleic 10)

	Palmitic	Stearic	C_{18} unsatd.	Palmitic	Stearic	C_{18} unsatd.
(c) Animal Depot Fats						
Birds						
Chicken[36b]	32	6	62	17	5	78
Pheasant[36b]	26	5	69	9	3	88
Pigeon[36b]	23	9	68	9	5	86
Rodents						
Rabbit[36b]	36	8	56	36	3	61
Rat[35c]	15		85	17		83
Mammals						
Non-ruminants						
Dog[35c]	34		66	29		71
Horse[35c]	39		61	21		79
Pig[35c]	22		78	44		56
„ [35c]	36		64	71		29
„ [36b]	24	10	66	66	4	30
„ [36b]	27	14	59	67	4	29
„ [36b]	31	18	51	75	4	21
„ [36b]	28	21	51	73	4	23
„ [36b]	31	22	47	77	4	19
Human[35c]	33		67	19		81
Ruminants						
Sheep[35c]	58		42	33		67
Ox[35c]	54		46	29		71
„ [36b]	34	34	32	28	19	53

Some subsequent results (Barrett *et al.*[32c]) in which details of the acids present in some whole fats and in their 2-monoglycerides left after selective enzyme hydrolysis are included may be quoted here (Table 80A); the experimental figures are quoted to the nearest unit per cent.

TABLE 80A. *Component Acids in some Whole Fats and in their 2-Monoglycerides*

	SATURATED			UNSATURATED		
	C_{14}	C_{16}	C_{18}	C_{16}	Oleic	Linoleic
Cacao butter:						
Whole fat	—	27	36	—	35	2
2-Monoglycerides	—	1	2	—	90	7
Shea butter:						
Whole fat	—	3	41	1	47	7
2-Monoglycerides	—	—	4	—	81	15
Palm oil (Malayan):						
Whole fat	1	45	5	1	41	7
2-Monoglycerides	1	17	1	1	67	13
Lard I:						
Whole fat	2	27	11	4	51	5
2-Monoglycerides	4	71	3	7	14	1
Lard II:						
Whole fat	2	32	18	3	43	2
2-Monoglycerides	4	78	5	4	9	—

Present Knowledge of Glyceride Structure of Natural Fats

Although much scope remains for further intensive study of the mixed glycerides which constitute natural fats, sufficient data are now available to present a broad general picture of the nature of these compounds. Before discussing the present position of our knowledge in this field, however, it is well to consider again the degree of precision likely to be available in experimental studies of glyceride structure.

(i) It has been mentioned already (p. 372) that the determined values of specific categories of mixed glycerides, or of any individual triglyceride may be subject to an experimental error of perhaps ±2 units per cent. When, for example, the ultimate determination of glyceride categories depends on component acid analyses of the segregated glyceride fractions, possible analytical errors in the fatty acid determinations will be magnified threefold in the derived figures for glycerides. Whilst, therefore, the available methods of procedure should lead to figures of the order of accuracy suggested, it must be borne in mind that no greater approach to absolute precision is very likely, unless in exceptional cases. It is therefore unprofitable to base any argument or hypothesis on unduly small differences in the observed content of particular glycerides or glyceride categories. On the other hand, the general trend of the results illustrated in the preceding pages of this chapter amply suffice to show the character of the glyceride structure of the fats studied; furthermore, they serve to define clearly the major component glycerides and glyceride types present in each particular fat.

(ii) The calculation of glyceride categories (e.g., tri-, di- and mono-saturated and tri-unsaturated; or glycerides containing respectively no, one, two, or three oleo-, linoleo- or other individual acid groups) from the component acid data for a glyceride fraction obtained by crystallisation is only valid if such fraction contains not more than *two* of the four possible types of components. The extent to which this condition obtains has been critically considered earlier (pp. 374–376).

(iii) Attention may also be directed to a matter of quite a different kind, namely, that studies of natural fats really concern the examination of material which is made up of the fatty products from many individual seeds, in the case of plants, or of tissues (e.g., livers or adipose tissues) from a number of animals. The composition of a particular seed fat, for example, may vary within small but nevertheless significant degrees from one seed to the next. Thus the sunflower seed oils from individual ripe heads of sunflowers of the same variety grown in the same plot[37a] were found to vary over a range of about 5 units per cent. of linoleic acid; minor variations of the same order have been found[37b] in the linoleic and linolenic acid contents of the oil in six individual candlenut fruits taken from the same tree. Again, it has been shown (Kartha,[37c] 1963) that within the endosperm there may be appreciable differences, both in fat content and in the mean unsaturation of the seed fat, between the interior and the periphery of the seed. Hence, although a fat from a given part of a particular species consists of a specific "mixture of mixed glycerides", the composition of this mixture may vary to a minor degree within certain limits: the fat actually examined is in most cases an average sample, possibly drawn from many hundreds or even thousands of individual fruits, and its composition must be the average of a large mixture of "mixtures of mixed glycerides".

Another possible complication is that, whereas a study is made of the composition of a fat taken, for instance, from a mature fruit, the fatty acids and glycerides synthesised at one stage of the developing fruit may differ in proportions from those produced at another stage. It is conceivable, again, that in some instances fats of different composition might be produced concurrently in different cells of the endosperm or embryo of a seed. Possibilities of this nature may call for occasional consideration when endeavouring to interpret the results of studies of glyceride structure.

With the above factors in mind, let us proceed to survey the features of glyceride structure which have emerged as a direct consequence of the various developments in *experimental* techniques which have been made since the time when observation of tri-saturated glyceride content was the only available approach.* Even here it is difficult at present to maintain a reasonable perspective, because the range of species examined is very uneven. Most of the work has been done on seed and fruit-coat fats, and on the depot and milk fats of the more common ruminant animals, but detailed survey of similar fats of a wide range of animals other than ruminants (in which it has now been demonstrated that a very specific process of metabolic change of ingested fat takes place) is very much lacking. For this reason, and still more because the synthesis of glycerides in living vegetable tissues from carbohydrates (or the products of its breakdown) is an as yet little understood biochemical process of fundamental importance, the glyceride structure of vegetable fats will be dealt with in the first instance.

Glyceride structure of vegetable fats. The chemical (Table 71, Fig. 2) and physical (crystallisation, Table 76, Fig. 5) methods of investigation agree in showing (subject to the very few exceptions discussed below, p. 393) that no significant amount of trisaturated glycerides appears until saturated acids form 60 per cent. or more of the total acids of a seed fat. The crystallisation analyses of seed fatty oils containing oleic or linoleic acids (Tables 78, 79, Figs. 7, 8) show similar relationships with regard to the proportions of triolein or trilinolein. Rigid adherence to complete "even distribution" would of

---

* During the long period which elapsed in the gradual introduction of fresh experimental methods, a vast amount of discussion based upon the proportions of tri-saturated, mono-, di- and tri-unsaturated glycerides in natural fats has taken place, and very divergent views have been expressed as to whether the distribution of fatty acids therein is "random", "restricted random", "partial random", "widest", "even", and so on. These communications will be considered fully and (it is hoped fairly) later in this chapter, but owing to their multiplicity, and the different classes of natural fats which have to be taken into account, it has been felt preferable to present the story first in the light of the facts as ascertained by experimental work. An account of the prolonged discussions referred to, which have been largely concerned with attempts (some of them markedly successful) to compute the proportions of the glycerides in natural fats, will be found on pp. 417–420.

course demand absence of a simple triglyceride until its constituent acid formed 66·7 per cent. of the total acids.

A great advantage of the crystallisation procedure is that it also gives the approximate proportions of glycerides containing one or two (as well as three) groups of a particular acid. The graphs in Figs. 5, 7 and 8 illustrate this for saturated, oleic and linoleic glycerides. It is seen in each case that:

(i) Glycerides containing *one* (mono-) group of a particular acid persist in small quantities until the acid in question forms about 75 per cent. of the total acids (not 66·7 per cent. as demanded by complete even distribution). In all cases, however, the content of glycerides containing one group of the particular acid reaches a maximum when that acid forms 33 per cent. of the total acids.

(ii) Glycerides containing *two* (di-) groups of a particular acid commence to appear when the acid in question forms from 20 to 25 per cent. of the total acids (not 33·3 per cent. as demanded by arithmetically complete even distribution). In all cases, however, the content of glycerides containing two groups of a particular acid reaches a maximum when that acid forms 66–67 per cent. of the total acids.

Following examination of the fully saturated glycerides in a number of relatively saturated seed fats Collin and Hilditch[26b] in 1929 were the first to remark upon the "*pronounced tendency to even distribution of the fatty acids throughout the glycerides of seed fats*". Much later, in 1947, this "principle of even distribution" was defined by Hilditch[38a] in terms of the occurrence of glycerides containing one, two, or three groups of a given acid in relation to the proportion of that acid in the total fatty acids of a fat (this definition is repeated in Chapter I, p. 19, of the present edition). The primary object of Hilditch and co-workers was to define and classify the general pattern of glyceride structure rather than to attempt to find any numerical formula which would fit all instances. Such a formula, by nature of the case, appears most unlikely to exist. Some workers, however, have insisted on taking "even distribution" in its most literal interpretation (e.g., that until a given acid forms over two-thirds of the total acids in a fat, no simple glyceride with three radicals of that acid must be present; or, that when it forms 66·7 per cent. of the total acids all the glycerides must contain two radicals of the acid; and so on). Thus Dutton *et al.*[29a] make the following criticism: "Hilditch would have the rule of even distribution applied as a generalisation which covers 'the general trend of the observed facts more or less accurately'. In defining the rule, the limits are so broadly drawn as to make evaluation of its validity impossible in many instances...." They add that, in their own communication on the structure of soya bean glycerides,[29a] "even distribution will be defined in strict stoichiometric algebraic terms". It can only be repeated that such strict stoichiometric interpretation has little relation to the facts of natural glyceride structure, except in so far as it represents a limiting state towards which the glycerides of seed fats and other fats approach, sometimes closely, but rarely with complete exactitude. Similarly, Norris and Mattil[38b] complain that "the rather qualitative nature of Hilditch's 'rule of even distribution' has hampered a reliable evaluation of its validity".

It would be very remarkable if a mathematical formula could be reached which conformed accurately with the results of a sequence of natural operations leading to so complex a mixture as a natural fat. The most that can be expected is to reach generalisations which cover the general trend of the observed facts more or less adequately, and in this sense any explanation is

TABLE 81. *Component Glycerides (per cent. mol.) of some Seed Fats*

	Allanblackia floribunda[40a]	Garcinia indica[40b]	Cocoa butter[40d]	Mowrah[40e]	Neem[40c]
Component acids:					
Palmitic (and lower)	2·2	3·1	26·2	24·2	16·3
Stearic (and higher)	58·5	56·1	34·4	19·3	15·7
Oleic	38·6	39·1	37·3	43·3	60·3
Linoleic	0·7	1·7	2·1	13·2	7·7
Component glycerides:					
Trisaturated	2	2	2	Trace	1
"Oleo"-dipalmitin	—	—	4	Trace	5
"Oleo"-palmitostearin	5	8	57	27	12
"Oleo"-distearin	76	68	22	Trace	—
Palmitodi-"olein"	1	—	8	41	26
Stearodi-"olein"	16	20	6	30	34
Tri-"olein"	—	2	1	Trace	22

"Oleo" indicates oleo- with linoleo-glycerides.

	Chrozophora plicata[41a]	Sesame[41b]	*Cottonseed[41c]	*Okra seed[41d]
Component acids:				
Palmitic (and lower)	10·0	10·7	26·3	26·3
Stearic (and higher)	13·5	6·1	2·1	6·3
Oleic	24·6	36·5	24·9	27·2
Linoleic	51·9	46·7	46·7	40·2
Component glycerides:				
Trisaturated	—	—	Trace	—
Oleodisaturated	4	3	4	5
Linoleodisaturated	9	1	10	18
Saturated diolein	—	—	2	9
Saturated oleo-linolein	28	37	26	21
Saturated dilinolein	19	4	30	22
Triolein	—	—	1	2
Dioleolinolein	—	15	9	10
Oleodilinolein	37	39	17	12
Trilinolein	3	1	—	1

* Component glycerides as recalculated by Gunstone.[39]

bound to be "rather qualitative" in that it is not to be expected to afford a rigidly quantitative picture. As a matter of fact, chemists concerned with fats may find legitimate satisfaction that no other group of complex natural organic products is as yet so susceptible to quantitative generalisation, even when it is admitted that the discussion of natural fats has perforce to be largely on broad and general lines.

Other investigators (e.g., Doerschuk and Daubert[38c]) whilst similarly at pains to emphasise that seed fat and other glycerides do not rigidly follow strict stoichiometric or arithmetical "even distribution", have pointed out that they do not conform either to a "random distribution" pattern.

Gunstone[39] (1962) proposes to reserve the term "even distribution" for the generalised "tendency" as intended originally by Hilditch, and the term "widest distribution" for the strict arithmetical rule. It is unfortunate that some such differentiation was not made much earlier, and some confusion thus perhaps avoided. Actually very few seed fats come fairly close to conformity with "widest distribution", and the great majority do not; on the other hand most of them exhibit a notable tendency to "even distribution", using both terms in the Gunstone sense.

Some typical instances of this tendency in seed fats are illustrated in Table 81, and others will be found among the individual seed fats discussed in Chapter VI.

Seed fats with high proportions of simple saturated triglycerides. A very few seed fats have been noticed in which the content of tri-saturated glycerides is much greater than is normally found with seed fats containing similar proportions of saturated acids in their total component acids (*cf.* Table 71, Nos. 15, 17; Table 76, Nos. 9, 11):

Seed fat	Component acids (per cent. mol.)		Trisaturated glycerides (per cent. mol.)	
	Total saturated	Chief component	Total	Chief component
Laurus nobilis	49·0	Lauric 43·0	40	Trilaurin *ca.* 35
Myristica malabarica	52·0	Myristic 32·0	16–19	Trimyristin
Pycnanthus kombo	74·5	Myristic 63·6	40	Trimyristin *ca.* 21
Platonia insignis	64·6	Palmitic 57·2	19	Tripalmitin *ca.* 15

The reasons for these departures from the regularities in glyceride structure which characterise the overwhelming majority of seed fats are obscure. In the case of *Laurus nobilis* seed fat it has been observed[42] that, whilst the tri-saturated glycerides are substantially trilaurin, the rest of the fat (consisting of lauric, palmitic and oleic glycerides) is constituted in the usual "mixed" fashion and, for example, contains little or no triunsaturated glycerides. It could be that these fats represent cases in which the component acids are synthesised in different proportions at different stages of development of the fruit.

To a much smaller extent some palm oils and also the seed fat of *Madhuca butyracea* (Table 71, Nos. *c, e, f, g,* 11; Table 76, Nos. 25, 26, 30, 33, 13) contain minor amounts (up to 8–10 per cent.) of trisaturated glycerides (chiefly tripalmitin), although their content of palmitic acid (45–55 per cent. of the total acids) is well below that at which significant quantities of trisaturated glycerides are usually found. At first it was supposed that fruit-coat glycerides, of which palm oils are examples, might be less regularly constituted than the seed fats, but the majority of fruit-coat fats which have now been investigated (including several other palm oils), conform to the same type of even distribution as that most common in seed fats. This statement holds for several fruit-coat fats (*Sapium sebiferum, Caryocar villosum, Dacryodes rostrata*) which contain as much, or much more than, the proportion of palmitic acid in palm oil fatty acids. Similarly, whilst *Madhuca butyracea* seed fat, with 59 per cent. of palmitic acid, contains 8 per cent. of trisaturated glycerides, other seed fats (e.g., Table 76, Nos. 14–23) with from 55 to 60 per cent. of total saturated acids show insignificant proportions of trisaturated glycerides.

Again, small or even moderately large proportions of disaturated glycerides are often observed in seed oils in which the proportion of saturated acids does not exceed 30 per cent. of the total acids, as illustrated in Table 82.

TABLE 82. *Disaturated Glycerides in Cottonseed Oil, etc.*

	OKRA SEED OIL[41d]	COTTONSEED OIL[41c]	GROUNDNUT OIL[41e]	*Chrozophora plicata*[41a] SEED OIL
Component acids (per cent. mol.)				
Myristic	—	1·6	—	0·2
Palmitic	26·3	24·7	9·7	9·8
Stearic	6·3	1·0	5·6	13·0
Arachidic (or higher)	—	1·1	8·0	0·5
Oleic	27·2	24·9	40·8	24·6
Linoleic	40·2	46·7	35·9	51·9
Disaturated glycerides (per cent. mol.)	23	14	11	13

This appearance of somewhat more glycerides containing two saturated acyl groups than might be expected from the total saturated acid content of the fat is met with in fats which include more than one saturated acid in their component acids. It is seen to a less extent in such oils as soya bean, sunflower, sesame, maize, and others in which both palmitic and stearic acids are present, albeit in smaller proportions than in the instances quoted in Table 82. It is probably connected with the circumstance, already referred to above, that each acid seems to behave as far as possible individually in its entrance into glyceride molecules. When more than one saturated acid is present, two different saturated acids may occasionally be found in a comparatively small number of molecules, although the proportion of each in the total acids of the fat may be quite small. It will be seen that, in each example in Table 82, the amounts of disaturated glycerides can be nearly or wholly accounted for as mixed glyceride combinations of palmitic or other saturated acid.

Seed fats with high proportions of simple triglycerides of polyethenoid C_{18} *acids.* The application of the counter-current distribution (CCD) method of mixed glyceride segregation by Dutton, Scholfield *et al.*,[29b–f] described on p. 383, has shown that seed oils in which linolenic or linoleic acid forms more than about 50 per cent. of the total acids may contain trilinolenin or trilinolein in amounts comparable with those which would result from completely random distribution of the acid amongst the three glycerol hydroxyl groups. This behaviour was also observed when low-temperature crystallisation (LTC) was applied to makita oil, in which triparinarin was found in quantity. These results are summarised in Table 83.

The importance of the newer observations by the Dutton school has already been mentioned (p. 383). The collected results in Table 83 suggest, in fact, that these multi-ethenoid seed fat acids tend to form their simple triglycerides in

TABLE 83. Content of Simple Tri-unsaturated Glycerides in Some Mainly Unsaturated Seed Oils

	MAJOR COMPONENT ACID		METHOD	SIMPLE TRI-UNSATURATED GLYCERIDES		
		PER CENT.			FOUND PER CENT.	CALC. FOR "RANDOM" DISTRIBUTION
Linseed[29b]	Linolenic	52·3	CCD	Trilinolenin	18	14
Makita (Parinarium laurinum)[43a]	Parinaric	55·8	LTC	Triparinarin	22*	18
Safflower[29d]	Linoleic	79·2	CCD	Trilinolein	51	49
"	"	76·6		"	47	45
Vernonia anthelmintica[43d]	Vernolic	76·0	LTC	Trivernolin	55*	44
Maize (corn)[29e]	Linoleic	60·3	CCD	Trilinolein	21	22
Soya bean[29c]	"	49·1	LTC	"	14	12
Tung oil[43b]	Elaeostearic	82·3	LTC	Trielaeostearin	56*	56
" " [43b]	"	79·0	"	"	45*	49
" " [43b]	"	71·1	"	"	23*	36
(Castor oil[43c])	Ricinoleic	91·6	"	Triricinolein	75*	77)

* These figures may also give some indication of the point at which the LTC method commences to be ineffective with liquid polyethenoid acids. It evidently works quite well with the relatively insoluble and high melting (85°C.) parinarin, but is probably not so reliable in the separation of the more soluble trielaeostearin (m.p. 48°) of tung oils.

Calculated figures for oils in which the content of the major unsaturated acid exceeds 90 per cent. will in any case show little difference between "random" and "widest" distribution (e.g., castor oil, "random" 77, "widest" 75 per cent.).

395

excess of the proportions calculated from purely "random" (probability) distribution. It is also interesting to note that the low-temperature crystallisation procedure gives similar results in the case of triparinarin, although it becomes less marked with the trielaeostearin of tung oils as the proportion of elaeostearic acid therein progressively diminishes.

Selective attachment of oleo- and linoleo-groups in vegetable fats to the 2-(β-) glyceryl hydroxyl group. The above outline (pp. 391–395) covers the chief results obtained by experimental observations on vegetable fat glyceride structure made prior to the outstanding discovery, resulting from experiments on selective hydrolysis with pancreatic lipase (p. 385), that in seed fats oleic and linoleic acids differ essentially from all the other natural fatty acids in their preferential attachment to the central (2- or β-, secondary alcoholic) group of the glycerol molecule. Results from the publications of Mattson *et al.*,[35c, d] of Coleman,[36b] and of Barrett *et al.*,[32c] showing the distribution of unsaturated and saturated acids at the central or 2-position of a number of vegetable fats were given in Tables 80 and 80A (pp. 387–388).

Mattson and Volpenhein[35d] visualised the nearly exclusive attachment of saturated acids and unsaturated acids containing more than 18 carbon atoms to the 1- and 3-glyceryl positions, so that in consequence the 2-positions contained a high proportion of the unsaturated C_{18} acids. It is surely more rational to express this in the alternative form, namely, that oleic and linoleic acids are preferentially attached to the 2-position, leaving any excess of these acids together with all other fatty acids present to be distributed at the 1- and 3-positions. This not only gives more emphasis to the specificity with which oleic and linoleic acids take up the 2-position, but is a matter which might eventually turn out to be connected with the rather special relations which seem to be involved in the biosynthesis of oleic and linoleic acids and their assemblage into glycerides in seed fats – a subject to be considered in Chapter VIII (p. 539).

The implications of this selectivity were quickly appreciated. In 1960 Vander Wal,[44a] who had contributed much to earlier discussions of Kartha's calculations on "restricted random" distribution of glycerides in natural fats (described in some detail on pp. 417–418), assumed (*a*) that whatever proportions of saturated (S) or unsaturated (U) acyl groups are present at the respective 1-, 2- and 3-positions of the triglycerides, they are distributed therein at random; and (*b*) that the 1- and 3-positions are occupied by identical proportions of S and U. Then, from the percentages of saturated acids S in the whole fat and in the acyl groups in the 2-positions (revealed by pancreatic lipase hydrolysis) he was able to obtain calculated values for the types GS_3, GS_2U, GSU_2 and GU_3, and also for the isomeric types SSU, SUS, SUU and USU, in good accordance with experimental values observed in a number of fats by Mattson and Lutton.[35c] Youngs[36a] (1961) confirmed that Vander Wal's calculations gave good accordance for lard, chicken and rat fats, linseed oil and cocoa butter, for which he had determined experimental values by a combination of modern methods, including the lipase hydrolysis. In 1961, also, Coleman[36b] determined the component acids of the whole fats and of the

2-monoglycerides left after pancreatic lipase hydrolysis in five animal and seven vegetable fats (*cf.* Table 80); therefrom, in each case, he deduced the acids which had been in combination at the 1- and 3-positions and distributed the latter "random"-wise at the 1- and 3-positions, with results in most instances in fair agreement with the experimental values.

A very comprehensive survey, original in several aspects, of the distribution of fatty acids in natural vegetable fats was published by Gunstone[39] in 1962, in the course of which he described methods of calculation of the various glyceride categories present in a vegetable fat based on the following assumptions:

(*a*) "The secondary hydroxyl of glycerol is acylated only by oleic, linoleic or linolenic acids unless there is not enough of these acids to achieve this" (this of course assumes 100 per cent. selectivity with regard to the 2-position).

(*b*) The subsequent distribution of acyl groups at the 1- and 3-positions is postulated in three ways:

> *MODE I.* The $C_{(1)}$ and $C_{(3)}$ hydroxyl groups are acylated subsequently by all remaining acids and by any C_{18} unsaturated acid not required at $C_{(2)}$. Within these limits the distribution of acyl groups at each position is statistical.

> *MODE II.* One of the primary hydroxyl groups reacts preferentially with unsaturated C_{18} acids, and finally the other primary hydroxyl group reacts with the acids that remain. Within these limits the distribution of acyl groups at each position is statistical.

> *MODE III.* One of the primary hydroxyl groups reacts preferentially with acids other than unsaturated C_{18} acids, and finally the other primary hydroxyl group reacts with the acids that remain. Within these limits the distribution of acyl groups at each position is statistical. (Since there is no known means of distinguishing between $C_{(3)}$ and $C_{(1)}$ Modes II and III give the same arithmetical results.)

By means of arithmetical calculations (detailed in an Appendix to his paper) Gunstone obtained values for (i) trisaturated (S_3), disaturated (S_2U), mono-saturated (SU_2), and triunsaturated (U_3) glycerides; (ii) mono-, di-, and tri-oleo- or linoleo-glycerides; (iii) individual triglycerides (e.g., trilinolein, oleopalmitostearin, palmitodiolein, etc., etc.). It will suffice here to quote his results for the general (saturated–unsaturated) types (Tables 84A, 84B, 84C, pp. 399, 400), and for the unsaturated seed oils studied by Dutton *et al.*[29] (Table 84D, p. 401). Before doing so it is useful to reproduce from his publication two figures (9*a* and 9*b*, p. 398) which illustrate the pattern of glyceride distribution between saturated (S) and unsaturated (U) acids in different circumstances. Figure 9*a* shows the curves for "widest" and "random" distribution, Fig. 9*b* those corresponding with "Mode I" and "Modes II and III": "Modes II and III" (which give the same numerical results) both lead to the pattern of "widest" distribution, while "Mode I" gives results which lie between "widest" and "random" distribution. (The experimentally determined values (from low-temperature crystallisation studies) in Figs. 5, 7 and 8 (pp. 377, 381, 382) accord fairly well with the "Mode I" graph for glycerides of the type $S_2 U$, but not so well for those of type SU_2.)

We are of the opinion that Gunstone's contribution is outstanding. Its greatest service is that it brings together in a comprehensive generalisation most of the previous, often apparently divergent views on "even", "widest" and the various varieties of "random" distribution in seed fat glycerides. Moreover, it points to a probable feature of the secondary stages of triglyceride biosynthesis, namely, that both the external (1- and 3-) glyceryl hydroxyls are esterified concurrently and indiscriminately, and not in sequence; this follows from the better accordance with observed data of his "Mode I" calculations than those based on Modes II or III. As Gunstone himself points out (*v. infra*.) his calculations assume complete selectivity of the initial esterification of the central (2-) position by oleic or linoleic acids, whereas the experimental figures from selective hydrolysis point to a very high degree, but not 100 per

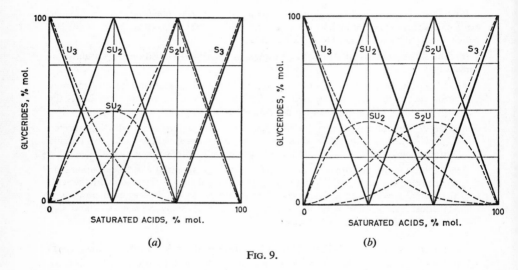

(*a*) (*b*)

FIG. 9.

cent., of selectivity. To this extent, therefore, Gunstone's views are still concerned with a *tendency* (not a total condition), albeit a much more pronounced tendency than that defined by the older concept of "even distribution". His conclusions are worth quoting more or less in his own words:

"It follows from this distribution pattern that fats containing high proportions of C_{18} unsaturated acids will appear to follow the random distribution pattern as found by Scholfield, Dutton et al.[29] Fats having a very low content of C_{18} unsaturated acids may also approximate to this pattern though this cannot be stated with certainty until more is known about the behaviour of saturated acids other than palmitic and stearic. The principles of even distribution elaborated by Hilditch and his collaborators are also incorporated into these new ideas, for fully saturated glycerides (GS_3) are not expected until the content of unsaturated C_{18} acids falls below about 35%. In many other aspects also, but not in all, many fats will approximate to the widest distribution pattern. The views of Kartha,[24] Vander Wal[44a] and Coleman[36b] also fit into the pattern elaborated here for their calculations 'correct' the present ones, in an empirical manner, for the slight discrepancies which occur in nature such

TABLE 84A. *Vegetable Fats Containing 20–45 per cent. (mol.) of Saturated Acids*

Fat	SATD. ACIDS (per cent.)	OBSERVED			"RANDOM"			"MODE I"			"MODES II, III" "WIDEST"		
		U_3	U_2S	US_2	U_3	U_2S	US_2	U_3	U_2S	US_2	U_3	U_2S	US_2
Groundnut[41e]	20	46	47	7	51	38	10	49	42	9	40	60	0
Niger seed[45a]	20	46	47	7	51	38	10	49	42	9	40	60	0
Groundnut[41e]	23	41	50	9	46	41	12	43	45	12	31	69	0
Chrozophora plicata[41a]	23	40	47	13	46	41	12	43	45	12	31	69	0
Pentaclethra macrophylla[45b]	24	36	56	8	44	42	13	41	46	13	28	72	0
Groundnut[41e]	25	36	53	11	42	42	13	39	47	14	25	75	0
Terminalia belerica[45c]	27	18	82	0	39	43	14	35	49	16	19	81	0
Pentaclethra eetveldeana[45b]	29	23	68	9	36	44	16	32	49	19	13	87	0
Jute[45d]	29	25	64	11	36	44	18	32	49	19	13	87	0
Cottonseed[41c]	29	28	59	13	36	44	18	32	49	19	13	87	0
Pentaclethra macrophylla[45b]	30	21	68	11	34	44	18	30	50	20	10	90	0
Neem seed[40c]	32	23	60	17	31	44	19	27	50	23	4	96	0
Okra seed[41d]	33	25	52	23	30	44	21	25	50	25	1	99	0
Sapota seed[45e]	34	5	87	8	29	44	22	24	50	26	0	98	2
Neem seed[46a]	35	17	61	22	28	44	23	22	50	28	0	95	5
Orange seed[45f]	35	23	50	27	28	44	24	22	50	28	0	95	5
Indian Laurel seed[46b]	36	17	56	25	26	44	24	21	50	29	0	92	8
Lime seed[45f]	37	18	55	25	25	44	25	20	49	31	0	89	11
Andiroba[46c]	40	13	50	36	22	43	26	16	48	36	0	80	20
Baku seed[46d]	41	12	53	34	21	42	29	15	47	38	0	77	23
Mowrah seed[40e]	44	0	71	28	18	41	30	12	44	44	0	68	32
Shea butter[46e]	44	0	65	30	18	41	32	12	44	44	0	68	32
Shea butter[46f]	46	5	55	35	16	40	34	10	42	48	0	62	38

399

TABLE 84B. Vegetable Fats Containing 55–80 per cent. (mol.) of Saturated Acids

	OBSERVED			"RANDOM"			"MODE I"			"MODES II, III" "WIDEST"		
SATD. ACIDS (per cent.)	U2S	US2	S3	U2S	US2	S3	U2S	US2	S3	U2S	US2	S3
Shorea robusta[47a] — 55	34	64	1	33	41	17	29	68	0	35	65	0
Allanblackia parviflora[40o] — 56	32	66	2	33	41	18	26	71	0	32	68	0
Vateria indica[47b] — 57	22	73	1	32	41	19	25	73	0	29	71	0
Garcinia indica[40b] — 59	20	76	2	30	42	21	21	78	0	23	77	0
Lophira procera[45b] — 60	19	76	3	29	43	22	18	81	0	20	80	0
Allanblackia floribunda[40a] — 61	17	81	2	28	43	23	15	84	0	17	83	0
Cocoa butter[40d] — 61	14	83	2	28	43	23	15	84	0	17	83	0
Madhuca butyracea[47c] — 62	23	69	8	27	44	24	13	87	0	14	86	0
Borneo tallow[47d] — 63	13	83	3	26	44	25	11	89	0	11	89	0
Platonia insignis[47e] — 63	25	55	20	26	44	25	11	89	0	11	89	0
Sapium sebiferum[47f] — 73	2	77	21	16	43	39	0	81	19	0	81	19

TABLE 84C. Vegetable Fats Containing 20–45 or 55–80 per cent. (mol.) of Saturated Acids

	OBSERVED (Kartha[24c])				"RANDOM"				"MODE I"				KARTHA'S THEORY			
SATD. ACIDS (per cent.)	U3	U2S	US2	S3	U3	U2S	US2	S3	U3	U2S	US2	S3	U3	U2S	US2	S3
Groundnut — 20	49	42	9		51	38	10	1	49	42	9	0	50	40	10	
Fenugreek seed — 20	51	38	11		51	38	10	1	49	42	9	0	50	40	10	
Almond kernel — 22	42	47	11		48	40	11	1	45	44	11	0	45	42	13	
Maize (corn) — 22	45	43	12		48	40	11	1	45	45	11	0	45	42	13	
Cottonseed — 23	43	44	13		46	41	12	1	43	45	12	0	45	41	14	
Calophyllum — 23	46	39	15		46	41	12	1	43	45	12	0	45	41	14	
Pongamia glabra — 26	37	48	15		40	44	15	2	37	48	15	0	39	45	18	
Thevetia neriifolia — 33	27	47	26		30	44	22	4	26	50	24	0	28	44	27	
Terminalia catappa — 38	20	46	34		24	44	27	5	18	49	33	0	21	44	35	
Terminalia belerica — 40	20	41	39		22	43	29	6	16	48	36	0	19	43	39	
Neem seed — 40	20	41	39		22	43	29	6	16	48	36	0	19	43	39	
Mowrah seed — 43	17	36	47		19	41	32	8	13	45	42	0	16	39	45	
Vateria indica — 57		18	76	1		32	41	19		25	73	0		23	73	1
Garcinia cambogia — 58		18	78	1		31	42	20		22	76	0		18	78	2
Garcinia indica — 61		13	84	1		28	43	23		15	84	0		15	82	2

TABLE 84D. Unsaturated Seed Oils (Studied by Counter-Current Distribution)

GLYCERIDE	OBSERVED	"RANDOM"	"MODE I"	"MODES II, III"
Linseed oil[29b]				
Trilinolenin	18	14	14	14
Linoleodilinolenin	12	12	12	12
Dilinoleolinolenin	4	3	3	3
Oleodilinolenin	20	20	20	19
Soya bean oil[29c]				
Trilinolenin	14	12	12	11
Oleodilinolenin	25	22	22	21
Oleolinoleolinolenin	9	6	6	6
Dioleolinolenin	4	2	2	2
Dilinoleolinolenin	5	5	5	4
Saturated linoleolinolenin	2	3	3	4
Safflower oil[29a]				
Trilinolein	51	50	50	48
Oleodilinolein	15	18	18	17
Palmitodilinolein	12	11	12	14
Diaplmito-, dioleo- and oleopalmito-linolein	15	16	16	20

as the unexpected amount of GS_3 (Kartha) or the presence of saturated acids at the $C_{(2)}$ position (Vander Wal). The conflicting views of widest distribution, random distribution, and variants of this latter are thus brought together into a single distribution pattern which should cover the whole range of vegetable fats."

It is perhaps of interest to interpolate here a prediction made in 1957 by A. S. Richardson[44b] in the course of correspondence on plant triglycerides with Vander Wal,[44a] who quotes from his letter as follows: "Even distribution, to the extent that it really occurs, will some day be found to be in large measure the result of preferential attachment of unsaturated acid at the 2-position of the glyceryl residue. Chance distribution, to the extent that it really prevails, will be found to be confined mainly to the 1- and 3-positions." This prediction crystallises in two sentences the synthesis which now appears to have been reached between the counter-currents of "widest" and "random" distribution views of vegetable fats.

Whilst the glyceride structure of seed fats can thus be discussed more adequately than in previous editions of this book, it would be erroneous to suppose that finality has been reached. The need for further intensive experimental research on the structure of natural triglycerides remains. In the vegetable kingdom it is to be desired that eventually such research (probably increasingly biochemical in nature) may lead to better understanding of the biosynthesis of triglycerides in the ripening seed. As regards animal fats, far more experimental study is needed of fats from a much wider range of animal species, terrestrial and aquatic, then the pitifully few whose glyceride structure has been adequately investigated to date.

In this connection attention may again be drawn to the work of Barrett, Dallas and Padley[32c] who, by a combination of a specialised thin-layer chromatographic technique with selective enzyme hydrolysis, coupled with gas–liquid chromatographic analyses of the separated glyceride fractions, have shown that it may soon be possible to give a reasonably quantitative and detailed account of the glycerides in a natural fat without recourse to any assumptions of the kinds which have hitherto been necessary.

A few other matters in connection with glyceride structure in seed and fruit-coat fats remain to receive brief consideration.

Configuration of seed and fruit-coat glycerides. In consequence of the evidence lately afforded by the selective enzyme hydrolysis of natural fats to 2-monoglycerides (p. 387), it has become clear that oleic or linoleic groups are normally attached to the central (2-) glyceryl hydroxyl group. Formerly the apparently exclusive occurrence of 2-oleoglycerides in such component glycerides of seed fats as oleodistearin or oleodipalmitin had been remarked over many years. At first such findings were based upon the melting point of carefully isolated and purified individual mixed glycerides – evidence not too certain in view of the polymorphic nature of glycerides. Later, more precise knowledge of the polymorphic forms, especially their melting and transition points and their X-ray and infra-red spectra, permitted the subject to be further studied and the earlier observations often confirmed. As a matter of history it may be of interest to include a brief summary of the earlier observations.

2-Oleodistearin, abundant in certain seed fats of the families Guttiferæ and Sapotaceæ, was defined by its melting point in the seed fats of *Allanblackia* sp. (1897[2]), *Garcinia indica* (1897[2]), cocoa butter (1902[7]), Borneo tallow (1904[8b]), Njatuo tallow[48a] and *Garcinia morella*[40b]; later surveys of melting and transition points[48b, c] and of X-ray data,[48c] have confirmed these observations.

2-*Oleodipalmitin* is the only isomer in the glycerides of piqui-a and stillingia fruit-coat fats,[48d,e] but in palm oil Meara[48f] found that both 1- and 2-oleodipalmitins were present.

Similarly, both 1- and 2-oleo-(linoleo-)dierucins may be present in rape oil.[48g]

The chief constituent of cocoa butter, 2-*oleopalmitostearin*, was erroneously believed to be the 1-palmito isomer[17f, 49a] for a long period, but study of transition points, X-ray examination and enzymic hydrolysis by Lutton,[49b] and in addition infra-red spectral investigation by Chapman *et al.*,[49c] has established that the oleo-group is in the central (2-) position of the glycerol molecule.

Optical rotatory power in natural fats. When natural organic compounds possess molecular asymmetry, they most frequently, as is well known, occur in one of the optically active, enantiomorphic forms, the presence of an inactive or racemic mixture of enantiomorphs being quite unusual. It is only necessary to mention naturally occurring sugars, terpenes, or alkaloids as examples. The most abundant naturally occurring derivatives of glycerol, the triglycerides, have never been found to possess optical rotatory power, although other natural glycerol derivatives, such as the α-glyceryl higher acyl ethers (e.g. batyl alcohol) possess small but definite rotatory powers. Again, natural α-glycerophosphoric acid, closely related to the phosphatides and phosphatidic acids, is optically active.

Of course, in symmetrical triglycerides of the type of 2-oleodistearin or 2-palmitodistearin, mentioned in the preceding section, in which two identical acyl groups are attached to the terminal hydroxyl groups of the glycerol molecule and a different acyl group to the central (2-) hydroxyl group, no molecular asymmetry and therefore no optical activity is present. On the other hand, when the central (2-) carbon atom of the glycerol carbon-chain is united with four *different* groups, it becomes asymmetric and there is a possibility of optical activity. This happens in the case of an unsymmetrically arranged triglyceride which contains only two fatty acids (e.g., 1-palmitodistearin), and also in the case of triglycerides (very many of which occur in nature) in which three different fatty acids are present in the same molecule.

The synthetical work of H. O. L. Fischer and E. Baer[50] has, in fact, opened up the possibility that such natural triglycerides may after all be confined to one enantiomorphic form, and not be racemic compounds. These investigators showed that, whilst synthetic mono- or di-glycerides of higher fatty acids had a slight but definite rotatory power ($[\alpha]_D -2°$ to $-4°$), unsymmetrical triglycerides such as 1-laurodistearin or 1-stearodipalmitin had no measurable optical activity, although glyceryl 1-*p*-nitrobenzoyl-di-benzoate had $[\alpha]_D -20°$ (*cf.* also, Chapter X, p. 665). They pointed out that lack of observable rotation in the synthetic unsymmetrical long-chain aliphatic triglycerides suggests that the same may apply in the natural compounds, and that natural unsymmetrical triglycerides, though they do not show measurable optical rotation, are not necessarily racemic. They further remarked that the slight evanescent rotation which has sometimes been recorded in the case of fats which have developed hydrolytic rancidity may be due to the presence therein of small amounts of optically active monoglycerides (produced in the course of partial enzymic hydrolysis).

The component acids of trisaturated glycerides present in small proportions in vegetable fats. When the proportion of oleic acid, and therefore of oleoglycerides, in a seed fat is small (e.g. the Palmæ seed fats, nutmeg butter, dika fats), the component acids of the fully saturated, major portion of the fat are present in much the same proportion as in the whole fat (*cf.* pp. 424–429). In cases where the ratio of saturated to unsaturated acids in the whole fat falls within the range of 1–1·7:1, on the other hand, there is, more often than not, a marked tendency for the saturated acid of lower molecular weight to concentrate in the small amounts of fully saturated components present in such fats. The reason for this is at present obscure, and this state of affairs does not hold in every case; but it is sufficiently usual to deserve notice here, and is illustrated by the data collected in Table 85 (p. 404).

Glyceride structure of animal fats.

Studies of animal fats have up to now been relatively few in comparison with those of seed fats. Moreover, attention has been mostly concentrated on fats from a single group of animals, the ruminants, and unfortunately (as is now realised) the processes of fat metabolism and synthesis in ruminants are affected by the specific action of enzymes in rumen bacteria and protozoa, with the consequence that ruminant fat structure differs in important respects from that in the many other groups of animals (whose species *in toto* must amount to many more than those in the Ruminantia). This disproportionate attention to ruminant fats is perhaps natural

TABLE 85. *Comparison of the (molar) Composition of the Saturated Acids in the Whole Fat and the Fully Saturated Components of Seed Fats containing 1–1·7 mols. Saturated Acid per mol. Unsaturated Acid*

| | PERCENTAGE COMPOSITION OF SATURATED ACIDS IN THE WHOLE FAT | | | | FULLY SATURATED COMPONENTS | | |
| | | | | | PER CENT. (MOL.) | SATURATED ACIDS PRESENT (PER CENT.) | |
SEED FAT	C_{14}	C_{16}	C_{18}	C_{20}		C_{16}	C_{18}	C_{20}
Borneo tallow	2	35	63	—	4·5	57	43	—
„ „	—	31	67	2	5·1	56	44	—
Njatuo tallow	—	10	90	—	1·8	13	87	—
Cacao butter	—	41	59	—	2·5	66	34	—
Allanblackia stuhlmannii	—	6	94	—	1·5	32	68	—
Pentadesma butyracea	—	10	90	—	3·0	25	75	—
Garcinia morella	1	14	84	1	2·7	39	61	—
„ *indica*	—	5	95	—	1·5	33	67	—
Dacryodes rostrata	—	22	75	3	1·8	17	83	—
Pulasan fat	—	5	55	40	1·5	—	81	19
Rambutan tallow	—	4	27	69	1·4	—	41	59
Shea butter	—	12	88	—	4·5	55	45	—
„ „	1	19	80	—	2·5	50	50	—
Mowrah fat	—	53	47	—	1·2	67	33	—
Neem oil	—	49	47	4	0·6	33	67	—
Hodgsonia capniocarpa	1	78	20	1	2·7	92	8	—

because of their importance to man as foods, and also because of their relative accessibility; but these factors should not have been permitted to restrict scientific examination of the fats of the diverse and numerous species which make up the animal kingdom. It is interesting to contrast the approximate number of experimental studies made on land animal fats with the very much larger range of seed fats which have been similarly examined:

		Number of species	Approximate number of glyceride studies
Animal depot fats	Non-ruminants	8	*ca.* 15
	Ruminants	4	*ca.* 20
Animal milk fats	Non-ruminants	2	*ca.* 4
	Ruminants	4	*ca.* 20
Seed fats		80–100	probably over 150

The species of vegetable fats whose glyceride composition have been investigated form only a minute fraction of the number known to botanists, but the position as regards animal fats is far worse and, as has been said, an altogether disproportionate number of experimental studies has been confined to a few species of one group, the ruminants. All that can be done here, therefore, is to review the experimental data in the sectors in which it is available and to bear in mind that experimental evidence is virtually non-existent over very wide regions of amphibia, reptiles, birds and (to a great extent) the mammals.

Nearly forty depot or milk fats of land animals have been studied by means of the older chemical method which serves primarily to define the contents of fully-saturated glycerides: the results have already been summarised in Table 73 and Fig. 3 (pp. 369, 371). Up to the present, less than half as many of such fats have been subjected to the later and more detailed crystallisation procedure which permits also the evaluation of other glyceride categories (Table 77 and Fig. 6, p. 379).

Land animal depot fats. As pointed out in Chapter I (p. 12) a most characteristic feature of land animal fats is the presence of major proportions of palmitic acid – about 25–30 per cent. (mol.) of the total acids in depot fats, and somewhat less in milk fats. When the amounts of other saturated acids are small in comparison with that of palmitic acid (as in hen and rat fats, pig back fat, or neat's foot oil), the proportion of fully saturated components is insignificant, and such fats are quite similar in this respect to, for example, vegetable fats with similar mixtures of saturated and unsaturated component acids.

Divergence from the general glyceride pattern is only seen in those animal depot fats in which the content of saturated acids rises well above 30 per cent. of the total acids. In practically all such instances so far studied (an Indian cow fat and an Indian elephant fat are exceptional in higher contents of palmitic acid), the palmitic acid content remains in the region of 30 per cent. of the total acids, and the excess is substantially wholly *stearic acid*. It is in these cases (conveniently termed *stearic-rich animal depot fats*) that the trisaturated glyceride contents become much larger than usual. Thus in extreme cases the amount of stearic acid may approach that of palmitic acid and a depot fat with a total content of about 60 per cent. of saturated acids may contain 25 per cent. or more of trisaturated glycerides. In such fats the content of *trisaturated glycerides* approaches more or less to that calculated on the basis of probability ("random" distribution). This coincidence is not however maintained for the remaining categories of mixed saturated-unsaturated glycerides. The later crystallisation studies have permitted approximate determinations of these groups also to be made, and the examples given in Table 86 (p. 406) show that there is little or no correlation between the observed values and those calculated on a "random" basis in these categories. Indeed the amounts of *triunsaturated glycerides* are in all cases insignificant, even in those fats where probability considerations would indicate the presence of up to 15 per cent. or more of this group.*

Much earlier (1930–1931), the increasing proportions of trisaturated glycerides present in animal fats which contained more than 30 per cent. of saturated acids (the *stearic-rich* animal fats, which were seen to be those in *ruminant* animals) had already been discerned by the use of the chemical

---

* In a pig fat investigated by Riemenschneider *et al.*[68a] the presence of 17·6 per cent. of triunsaturated glycerides was recorded. This fat, however, contained 12·8 per cent. of linoleic and 1·2 per cent. of other polyethenoid acids as well as 49·6 per cent. of oleic acid – a total unsaturated acid content of 63·6 per cent. The amount of triunsaturated glycerides indicated by probability or "random" distribution is therefore about 25 per cent. – approximately half as much again as that actually found.

(oxidation) method for their determination.[52] It was noticed at the time by Hilditch and co-workers[52a,b] that in such cases the observed amounts of trisaturated glycerides were not very different from those calculated on the basis of "random" or "statistical" rather than "even" distribution.* Even at this comparatively early stage of glyceride structure study, however, it was observed that in these stearic-rich fats (in contrast to fats synthesised by heat treatment *in vacuo**) the content of triunsaturated glycerides, instead of being comparable with random distribution, was small or even non-existent. For this and other reasons, the view taken by some workers (e.g., Longenecker,[53] Norris and Mattil[38b] and others) that animal fats are wholly constituted on

TABLE 86. *Observed and Calculated (Probability) Contents of Glyceride Categories in Animal Depot Fats (per cent. mol.)*

	COMPONENT ACIDS		COMPONENT GLYCERIDES				
	SATD.	UNSATD.	TRI-SATD.	DI-SATD.	MONO-SATD.	TRIUN-SATD.	
Pig, back[51a]	44·1	55·9	5	36	52	7	Found
			8	33	41	18	Calc.
Sheep, English, back[51b]	50·2	49·8	6	45	47	2	Found
			13	38	37	12	Calc.
Pig, perinephric[51a]	50·5	49·5	9	46	40	5	Found
			13	38	37	12	Calc.
Sheep, English, perinephric[51b]	57·2	42·8	14	50	32	4	Found
			19	42	31	8	Calc.
Cow, English[51c]	58·7	41·3	17	49	34	0	Found
			20	43	30	7	Calc.
Sheep, Indian[51e]	60·6	39·4	28	28	41	3	Found
			22	43	29	6	Calc.
Cow, Indian (Calicut)[51d]	67·5	32·5	28	54	15	3	Found
			31	44	21	4	Calc.

"random" lines seemed to overlook the restriction of "random" distribution to the single category of trisaturated components, and this only in the stearic-rich (ruminant) fats.

Indeed, in 1931 Banks and Hilditch[52b] put forward the hypothesis that *in stearic-rich animal depot fats* the final mixture of component glycerides is the consequence of a bio-hydrogenation process operating indiscriminately upon preformed mixed glycerides of palmitic and oleic (linoleic) acids, these precursor glycerides having been assembled on the usual "evenly"-distributed lines. Various facts in consonance with this idea were noted from time to time (a brief summary is given below), but the strongest evidence for its validity rests in the experimental work of Reiser,[54a] Shorland,[54b] Holmberg,[54c] Garton[54d] and their respective co-workers, who (from 1951 onwards) showed that in ruminants and certain quasi-ruminants, but in no other mammals, ingested unsaturated fats undergo hydrogenation by enzymes in the bacteria

* It was also found[52a] that, when triglycerides or glycol di-esters were synthesised by heating either alcohol in a vacuum at 140–150° C. with mixtures of saturated and unsaturated acids, the proportions of trisaturated and of triunsaturated glycerides produced also closely resembled those calculated on a probability or statistical basis.

and protozoa of the rumen (further details of these studies have already been given in Chapter III, p. 112).

Whilst confirmation of a hypothesis by independent experimental evidence is the only satisfactory proof of its correctness, the arguments put forward earlier in support of the bio-hydrogenation mechanism in the elaboration of stearic-rich ruminant depot fats may be of interest:

(i) When the trisaturated glyceride contents of animal depot and milk fats are plotted against the proportions of saturated acids in the total fatty acids (Fig. 3, p. 371, shown on an enlarged scale in Fig. 10, below) they lie on a band which, when extrapolated to zero tri-

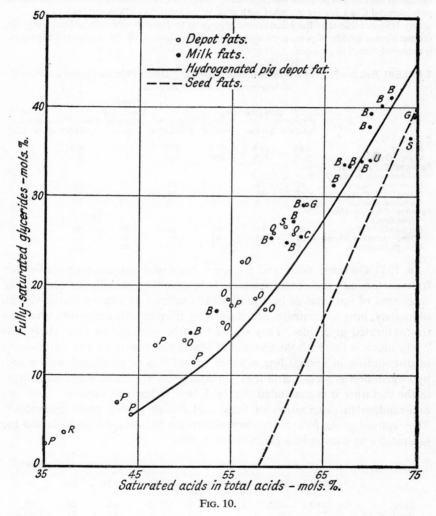

FIG. 10.

saturated glycerides, intersects the horizontal axis at about 30–35 per cent. of saturated acids (the normal figure[52b,d] for palmitic acid in animal depot fats. Thus an animal fat which contains little or no stearic acid has negligible proportions of trisaturated glycerides; further, increase in trisaturated glyceride content takes place *pari passu* with increasing proportions of *stearic* acid in the total fatty acids. Also, with approximate constancy of palmitic acid content, the amount of oleic acid must diminish as stearic acid augments.

(ii) The resemblance of these relationships to that caused by a hydrogenation process may be seen by the curve in Fig. 10 showing the progressive increase in trisaturated glycerides when a pig depot fat of low stearic acid content is progressively hydrogenated in presence of nickel catalyst under laboratory conditions.[17h]

(iii) If, in the series of animal body fats quoted in Table 86, the changes in the relative proportions of palmitodioleins, oleopalmitostearins, and palmitodistearins are compared (Table 87), it is seen that the dioleoglycerides fall steadily as the amount of stearic acid increases, the mono-oleoglycerides increase equally steadily, and the percentage of palmito-distearins rises from a very low figure to nearly 20 per cent. (In Table 87 the minor amounts of polyethenoid C_{18} acids are included with oleic in the term "oleo"-glycerides.)

(iv) It is notable that the trisaturated glycerides in these stearic-rich animal body fats consist almost wholly of palmitodistearins and dipalmitostearins: the amount of tripalmitin is extremely small in all cases.

TABLE 87. *Relative Proportions of Palmitodi-"Oleins," "Oleo"-Palmitostearins and Palmito-distearins in Animal Depot Fats*

	PIG[51a] BACK	SHEEP[51b] ENGLISH BACK	PIG[51a] PERINE- PHRIC	COW[51c] ENGLISH	SHEEP[51b] ENGLISH PERINE- PHRIC	SHEEP[51e] INDIAN	COW[51d] INDIAN (CALICUT)
C_{18} *fatty acids*:							
Stearic	13·8	14·5	17·6	21·4	25·6	26·8	27·9
Oleic + Octadecadienoic	51·1	47·9	45·9	38·7	40·4	35·1	30·5
Palmitodi-C_{18} *glycerides (increments per cent.)*:							
Palmitodi-"oleins"	53	46	40	23	25	26	17
"Oleo"-palmitostearins	27	28	34	32	41	27	38
Palmitodistearins	2	2	5	6	10	11	12
Palmitodi-C_{18} *glycerides (per cent.)*:							
Palmitodi-"oleins"	65	61	51	38	33	40	25
"Oleo"-palmitostearins	33	37	43	52	54	43	57
Palmitodistearins	2	2	6	10	13	17	18

In 1953 Quimby, Wille and Lutton[55] employed intensive crystallisation from acetone at varying temperatures to resolve the glycerides of commercial specimens of lard and of beef and mutton tallows into many fractions and, ultimately, into concentrates of trisaturated, disaturated, monosaturated and triunsaturated glycerides. They stated that the evidence of their study was "very much in line with the views of Hilditch with regard to non-randomness of distribution in animal fats whether or not this is associated with a bio-hydrogenation process", and that "in contrast with certain other statements in the literature it is concluded that lard, beef tallow and mutton tallow are non-random in distribution of fatty acid chains among their glycerides". They arrived at the following compositions for the component acids and the saturated and unsaturated glyceride categories:

	Component acids (per cent.)				Glyceride categories (per cent.)			
	Satd.	Oleic	Linoleic	Linolenic, etc.	S_3	S_2U	SU_2	U_3
Lard	37·8	45·6	10·6	1·7	2	28	40	30
Beef tallow	57·1	35·8	1·8	0·9	18	41	41	Trace
Mutton tallow	50·2	40·8	1·6	2·9	15	42	38	5

They further made detailed thermal and X-ray diffraction studies of hydro-genated glycerides from the purest concentrates isolated from each fat, finding that the pig fat was composed largely of 2-palmityl glycerides, but in both ox and sheep fats 1-palmityl glycerides were probably the most prominent; these findings applied both to the trisaturated and the mono- and di-unsaturated glycerides in the respective fats.

Whilst the depot glycerides of oxen, sheep and to some extent buffaloes and goats have been extensively studied those of the pig are the only representatives of non-ruminant mammals to have received similar attention. The slight data for chicken, rabbit, rats, horse and badger, all of which contain but little stearic acid, indicate absence of more than about 3 per cent. of trisaturated glycerides.

Again, the very modern technique of selective enzyme hydrolysis, leading to the isolation of 2-monoglycerides, has as yet been less used with animal than with vegetable fats. It is hoped that this will soon receive more application, for such results as are available suggest considerable differences in the acids attached to the 2-glyceryl hydroxyl groups as compared with seed fats (Table 80, p. 387).

Some depot fats of birds, rabbit, rats, dog, horse, sheep and human beings have been examined and the proportion of oleic (or unsaturated) acid combined at the 2-position varies from 53 to 88 per cent. (the mean figure being 75–80 per cent.), thus indicating that on the average saturated acyl groups form 20–25 per cent. of those at the 2-position – markedly more than in the vegetable fats. In contrast, 70–80 per cent. of the pig fat 2-acyl groups are those of palmitic acid, and pig fat has been said to be unique in its content of 2-palmityl glycerides.

This statement is at present, however, not justified. A much wider range of depot fats from all kinds of animals needs to be studied before any generalisations can be usefully made. All that can be deduced from the few instances yet investigated is that the almost total selectivity of attachment of oleo-(linoleo-) groups at the 2-position of vegetable glycerides may not be maintained in animal fats.

Marine animal depot fats. The quantitative (or, more strictly, semi-quantitative) information on the glycerides of this class of fats rests on progressive hydrogenation studies of cod liver oil[56a] and of whale oil,[56b] and of more recent use of the low-temperature crystallisation procedure in the cases of herring,[56c] seal,[56d] Antarctic whale,[56e] and sea lion[56f] oils (the results of these are given in more detail in Chapter VII, pp. 483–488). The number of major component acids in these oils is probably at least seven or eight, each of which may contribute from about 12 per cent. upwards to their total fatty acids.

No indication has been found of any simple triglyceride in any marine animal oil so far studied. The low-temperature segregation studies have permitted estimates of the distribution of saturated, unsaturated C_{16}, unsaturated C_{18}, unsaturated C_{20-22} acids in the glycerides, and these show that to a very large extent each group only appears once in any triglyceride molecule. Minor amounts of glycerides containing two acids of the same group are however frequently observed (and occasionally very small proportions of trisaturated glycerides); in these cases it is quite possible that the acids concerned, although from the same group, are not identical. The nature of the distribution of the acyl groups in the glycerides, in relation to the proportions of these acids in the total component acids, may be illustrated from Hilditch and Maddison's later data[56e] for an Antarctic whale oil (Table 88).

TABLE 88. *Distribution of Acids and Glyceride Groups in Whale Oil (per cent. mol.)*

PROPORTIONS IN TOTAL FATTY ACIDS	ACYL GROUPS	GLYCERIDE MOLECULES CONTAINING				
		0	1	2	3	GROUPS
30·2	Saturated	31	50	17	2	
18·0	Unsaturated C_{16} (+ C_{14})	46	54	—		
35·4	Unsaturated C_{18}	9	76	15	—	
16·4	Unsaturated C_{20} and C_{22}	54	42	4	—	

The presence of numerous component acids in comparable proportions automatically leads to closer similarity than usual between the proportions of the different categories of mixed glycerides and those calculated arithmetically according to probability ("random" distribution). This is illustrated for the mixed saturated-unsaturated glycerides of herring, seal blubber, and whale blubber fats in Table 89.

TABLE 89. *Component Glycerides of Marine Animal Oils*
(a) Observed, (b) Calculated on "Random" Basis

	SEA LION[56f]		SEAL[56d]		HERRING[56c]		WHALE[56e]	
Saturated acids in total acids, per cent. (mol.)	12·9		18·9		22·8		30·2	
	FOUND	CALC.	FOUND	CALC.	FOUND	CALC.	FOUND	CALC.
Glycerides, per cent. (mol.)								
Trisaturated	—	—	—	1	—	1	2	3
Disaturated-mono-unsaturated	—	4	4	9	6	12	17	19
Monosaturated-diunsaturated	39	30	61	37	45	41	50	44
Triunsaturated	61	66	35	53	49	46	31	34

Land animal milk fats. The position in regard to glyceride structure is unfortunate in that, apart from studies of human milk glycerides, and horse and sow milk fatty acids, attention has so far been concentrated wholly on the milk fats of ruminant herbivora. Moreover, investigations by low-temperature crystallisation have so far only been carried out on two cow milk fats, a buffalo milk fat, and human milk fat. Work based on the determination of fully-saturated glycerides by the older procedure has been recorded in the cases of the milk fats of fourteen cows, three buffaloes, a sheep, a goat, and a camel. In milk fats which contain important proportions of saturated acids (C_4 to C_{12}) of lower molecular weight than myristic, as in the similar case of stearic-rich animal depot fats, the content of trisaturated glycerides increases disproportionately as the amount of saturated acids in the milk fats increases. It will be seen in Fig. 10 that the relationships for these milk fats fall in exactly the same category as those for stearic-rich depot fats: indeed, the two series of fats overlap on the graph, the most unsaturated butter fats containing a smaller proportion of saturated acids than the most saturated depot fats.

There are very few detailed analyses available for even the *component milk fatty acids* of animals other than ruminants, but the data given in Table 90 suggest that the lower saturated acids are by no means invariable constituents of mammalian milk fats (the figures quoted are from analyses already discussed in Chapter III on milk fat component acids). The sow milk fat component acids closely resemble pig depot fatty acids (*cf.* Chapter III, p. 160) and, like the latter, contain notable proportions of ordinary linoleic acid. The human milk fat also has considerable resemblance to human depot fat but contains somewhat less oleic and linoleic acid, with rather more myristic and some lauric acid but no lower saturated acids other than a very small amount of decanoic. The milk fat of the mare contains rather more of the lower saturated acids (but much less C_4 and C_6 acids than ruminant milk fats) and, like horse depot fat, is remarkable for its content of linolenic acid. Lower saturated acids (especially butyric and hexanoic) only attain prominence in the milk fats of the ruminants.

TABLE 90. *Proportions (per cent. mol.) of Saturated Acids in Different Milk Fats*

MILK FAT	SATURATED								UNSATURATED		
	C_4	C_6	C_8	C_{10}	C_{12}	C_{14}	C_{16}	C_{18}	OLEIC	OCTADECA-DIENOIC	C_{16} and C_{20-22}
Pig	←		2	→		2	29	6	35	14	12
Human	—	—	—	2	8	9	23	9	34	7	8
Horse	1	2	4	8	7	7	15	3	16	21*	16
Camel	6	2	1	2	6	8	28	10	34	3	—
Sheep	8	5	3	6	5	10	22	11	22	4	4
Goat	7	5	4	13	7	12	24	5	17	3	3
Cow (English)	10	3	1	2	3	9	21	11	31	5	4
Cow (Indian)	11	4	2	3	2	13	28	7	23	3	4
Buffalo (Indian)	12	4	1	2	3	11	27	12	21	2	5

* Linoleic 7 and linolenic 14 per cent.

There is plain evidence that lower saturated acids are also not present in the milk fats of the dog, mouse, rat and cat, since the Reichert and Polenske values of these (which give a measure of steam-volatile fatty acids present in a fat) are insignificant (*cf.* Chapter III, p. 144). Thus the milk fats of marine mammals and of more land mammals than is sometimes realised are all characterised by absence of any acids of lower molecular weight than those in their body fats; moreover, in those instances where detailed knowledge of the component acids is available, such milk fats have been found to be closely similar in composition to the respective depot fats of the animals.

In milk fats which contain lower saturated fatty acids similar conditions operate to those in stearic-rich depot fats:

(i) The palmitic acid content is roughly constant at 24–28 per cent., and the proportions of lower saturated acids bear an inverse relationship to those of oleic acid.

(ii) The proportions of trisaturated glycerides, plotted against those of saturated acids in the total acids, fall close to a curve which intersects the horizontal axis at a point corresponding with a molar content of about 30 per cent. of saturated acids in the total acids (Fig. 10). These proportions of trisaturated glycerides resemble more or less those deducible from considerations of probability or random distribution; but Table 91A indicates that, as in stearic-rich depot fats (Table 86), this resemblance does not extend to the mixed saturated-unsaturated glycerides.

TABLE 91A. *Observed and Calculated (Probability) Contents of Glyceride Categories in Animal Milk Fats (per cent. mol.)*

MILK FAT	COMPONENT ACIDS		COMPONENT GLYCERIDES				
	SATD.	UNSATD.	TRISATD.	DISATD.	MONO-SATD.	TRIUN-SATD.	
Human	51	49	9	40	43	8	Found
			12	37	38	13	Calc.
Cow (Indian)	70	30	35	36	29	0	Found
			34	44	19	3	Calc.
Buffalo (Indian)	72	28	40	37	23	0	Found
			37	44	17	2	Calc.

(iii) Further, the proportions of monopalmito- and dipalmito-glycerides which have been observed in milk and depot fats, in relation to the content of palmitic acid in their total fatty acids, are of the order characteristic of the usual "evenly distributed" type of a fatty acid through the glyceride molecules of a fat (Table 91B).

TABLE 91B. *Distribution of Palmitic Acid in Animal Milk and Depot Fats*

ANIMAL	PER CENT. (MOL.) OF TOTAL ACIDS		DISTRIBUTION IN GLYCERIDES			
			MONOPALMITO-		DIPALMITO-	
	Milk	Depot	Milk	Depot	Milk	Depot
Pig	28	30	—	75–80	—	7–13
Human	23	28	60	—	6	—
Sheep	22	27–30	—	75	—	9–16
Cow (English)	23–24	27–30	65	70	5	13
Cow (Indian)	28	31–33	64	—	8	—
Buffalo (Indian)	27	31	70	—	6	—

As in stearic-rich depot fats, therefore, so in milk fats which contain important proportions of lower saturated acids the observed glyceride structure is explicable if it arises from subsequent alteration of pre-formed palmito-oleo- (or linoleo-) glycerides which had been previously synthesised on the lines of "even distribution". It is important to notice at this point that, during passage through the lactating gland, the glycerides in the blood are largely reduced in quantity, the amount which disappears being probably sufficient to account for the glycerides which appear in the milk as milk fat[57a, b, c]. Further, as a result of feeding to a lactating goat stearic acid "labelled" with tritium (^{3}H) in the 9 and 10 positions in the C_{18} chain, Duncombe and Glascock[57d] (1954) showed that glycerides with ingested "labelled" stearic acid rapidly appeared in the blood stream and also in the milk lipids; they estimated from their results that "approximately 70 per cent. of the long-chain acids in milk fat must be derived from dietary fat (presumably transported as blood lipids)".

It is evident, however, that the conversion of an oleo- or linoleo-group in a glyceride into a short-chain acyl group would be a much more complex transformation than the simple hydrogenation of an oleo- into a stearo-glyceride. There are two ways in which the postulated conversion of an oleo-group in a glyceride to a short-chain acyl group might conceivably be effected: by chemical transformation of the oleo-radical itself, or by replacement of the oleo-group by a short-chain acyl group which had been separately synthesised in the mammary gland. Either process might be expected to take place by random attack on oleo-groups in the pre-formed glycerides present in the gland.

It is now known that the *short-chain saturated acids* in milk fats are actually synthesised from carbohydrate or from C_2 units in the lactating gland. The production in the gland of short-chain milk fat acids from carbohydrate was first explicitly suggested by Graham et al.[58] in 1938, and by Reineke et al.[59] in 1941. A few years later Bloch and Rittenberg[60] established by tracer experiments (with radioactive carbon in the carboxyl acetate group) that the effective unit from which synthesis thus proceeds is acetate, or a more reactive derivative of the acetate (C_2) unit. Much work by Popják, Folley, and their co-workers has shown conclusively that a great part, at all events, of the saturated short-chain acids of cow and goat milk fats is synthesised in the lactating gland from acetate, or from hexose which is first converted to acetate or pyruvate. Comprehensive reviews of these researches have been given by Popják[61a] and by Folley.[61b] In 1951 Popják et al.[61c] injected goats intravenously with radioactive (carboxy-^{14}C) acetate and found that radioactive saturated fatty acids up to palmitic were present in their milk fat; the oleic and stearic acids in the latter however possessed negligible radioactivity. By oxidative degradation of the goat milk fat butyric, hexanoic and octanoic acids it was found that the radioactive carbon atoms were confined to the alternate carbon atoms 1 (carboxyl), 3, 5 and 7 of the acids, thus proving that the synthesis of the short-chain acids proceeds by attachment of an "acetate" (C_2) unit to the carboxyl end of a preformed fatty acid.

The large extent to which synthesis of short-chain milk fat glycerides is thus now known to take place in the lactating gland of a ruminant must be considered concurrently with observations that oleic glycerides do not seem to be produced in this synthesis,[61c] and that during passage through the gland the blood glycerides disappear in quantities commensurate with the milk fat formed, and also with the fact that milk fat glyceride structure involves the presence of short-chain groups where oleo- (or linoleo-) groups would be found in analogous (blood or depot) glycerides of the animal. Although the possibility was at first overlooked, it was pointed out later by Hilditch[62] that replacement of an oleic (linoleic) group in pre-formed blood glycerides by a short-chain acid synthesised in the gland – by the mechanism of acyl interchange – represents a "conversion" of an oleo-group into a short-chain acyl group which is more likely than chemical degradation or shortening of the long-chain unsaturated group. The interchange of acyl groups in mixed glycerides is known to proceed readily under various conditions *in vitro*, and conceivably may equally take place in living tissues by enzyme action.

If the incorporation of short-chain saturated acids into pre-formed blood glycerides takes place by acyl interchange, i.e., displacement of a long-chain acyl group, the groups preferentially displaced are those of the unsaturated (oleic) acids; yet it may be further supposed that, to a much smaller degree, palmitoyl groups may be similarly involved, thus accounting for the small but consistent drop in palmitic acid content of milk fats as compared with that of corresponding depot fats. The fate of the displaced long-chain acids is not obvious, unless they are catabolised and thus serve to provide some of the energy necessary for the many changes which take place in the lactating gland.

That, to a very small extent, oleic groups (combined as oleo-glycerides) are also broken down in the lactating gland by oxidation and reduction processes to shorter (unsaturated) groups is strongly suggested by the invariable presence in ruminant milk fats (in addition to short-chain saturated acids) of smaller proportions (decreasing as the chain shortens) of mono-ethenoid acids of the C_{16}, C_{14}, C_{12} and C_{10} series (but not below C_{10}), in which the ethenoid bonds occupy the same position $-CH:CH.[CH_2]_7.CO_2-$ relative to the carboxyl groups, as in oleic acid. The molar percentages of these acids present in the total acids of a typical cow milk fat were found by Hilditch and Longenecker[63] to be as follows:

ACID		PER CENT. (MOL.)
Oleic	$CH_3.[CH_2]_7.CH:CH.[CH_2]_7.COOH$	24·8
Hexadec-9-enoic	$CH_3.[CH_2]_5.CH:CH.[CH_2]_7.COOH$	3·7
Tetradec-9-enoic	$CH_3.[CH_2]_3.CH:CH.[CH_2]_7.COOH$	1·7
Dodec-9-enoic	$CH_3.CH_2.CH:CH.[CH_2]_7.COOH$	0·5
Dec-9-enoic	$CH_2:CH.[CH_2]_7.COOH$	0·4

The occurrence of this series of minor unsaturated (-9-enoic) acids is peculiar to milk fats in which lower saturated acids are also prominent, and is consistent with the presence of small amounts of transformed oleo-glycerides which have escaped complete saturation to lower saturated glycerides. The formation of shorter chain products could of course be visualised from either oleic or linoleic acyl groups in the blood glyceride molecules.

Some further points which are consistent with the foregoing views of the probable mechanism of production of the characteristic glyceride pattern of ruminant milk fats may be mentioned.

(i) The molar proportions of the short-chain acids in ruminant milk fats (cf. Table 90) are greatest in butyric acid (C_4) and fall steadily as the chain length increases through hexanoic (C_6) to the C_8, C_{10} and C_{12} members (apart from the specific occurrence of decanoic acid C_{10}) in goat and sheep milk fats). This sequence might be expected for short-chain acids synthesised from acetate in the lactating gland.

(ii) Pathological conditions such as the effects of starvation (Smith and Dastur[64a]) or ketosis (Shaw et al.[64b]) cause very marked reduction in the proportions of short-chain constituents and a corresponding increase in the oleic content; the milk fat composition of the affected cows rapidly reverts to normal on recovery from ketosis, or when normal feeding is resumed after fasting.

(iii) While inclusion of linoleic- or linolenic-rich seed oils in the diet of cows has little effect on the milk fat composition, similar ingestion of cod liver oil is followed by the appearance of several per cent. of the highly unsaturated C_{20} and C_{22} acids of the oil in the milk fat, coupled with large reduction in the proportions of the short-chain acids (Hilditch and Thompson[65]).

This explanation of ruminant milk glyceride structure thus takes account of short-chain acid synthesis from C_2 units in the ruminant lactating gland, of the specific presence in trace quantities of dec-9-enoic and dodec-9-enoic glycerides, of the specific glyceride pattern of these milk fats, and of the production of milk fat from blood glycerides which, on this view, serve as it were to absorb the synthesised shorter-chain acids into pre-formed glycerides during passage of the latter through the udder. Haphazard or random transformation of oleo- (linoleo-) groups in the blood glycerides by either mechanism – acyl interchange or chemical shortening of the long-chain groups – satisfies the condition that disproportionately large proportions of trisaturated glycerides (in relation to total saturated acid contents) are met with in these particular milk fats. Failure to detect radioactive oleic groups in milk fats produced in presence of labelled acetate or glucose is a further indication that the oleic acid (incidentally the preponderating acid) of milk fats enters the mammary gland entirely as preformed glyceride.

The results of studies of physiological or pathological conditions of animals in relation to the composition of their milk fats have proved very fruitful and enlightening, and further work on these lines must be eagerly awaited: indeed, ultimate proof of the chemical processes involved can only be looked for from physiological investigations. Deduction of possible or probable metabolic changes from examination of their end products can never lead to rigorous justification of theoretical explanations which may be propounded. It is, in fact, likely that this method of approach has now been explored almost to the limits in which it can be of service as a guide to the possible metabolic processes involved: although further advances may well be made in the direction of still more precise statements of component glycerides by further development of the experimental methods of separation and analysis, and also in compiling more exact component glyceride data for fats (both milk and depot) covering a much wider range of animal species than has yet been investigated.

In this connection it should be mentioned that selective hydrolysis by pancreatic lipase (p. 385) has not at the time of writing been used in the study of milk fats. This procedure, in conjunction with detailed analyses of the component acids present in the resulting 2-monoglycerides of milk fats, is bound to give much further insight into the problems which have been considered in the preceding pages.

Marine animal milk fats. No study of the component glycerides of the milk fat of any *marine mammal* has yet been made, but the component acids of several marine mammalian milk fats have been determined. In all instances examined there are complete qualitative, and extensive quantitative, resemblances between the proportions of the component acids of milk and blubber fats from the same species (for fuller details see Chapter II, pp. 68, 71). Schmidt-Nielsen and Frog[66a] noted in 1933 that the proportions of the homologous groups of acids in finner whale milk fat are similar to those of the blubber fat, and in 1935 Klem[66b] gave similar data for the milk fat of a blue Arctic whale; in 1953 Cama and Meara[66c] determined the component acids in four specimens of finner whale milk fat as follows (per cent. wt.): palmitic 14–17, unsaturated C_{16} 6–8 (-2 to -2.9H), unsaturated C_{18} 26–30 (-2.4 to -3.3H), unsaturated

C_{20} 18–26 ($-6{\cdot}0$ to $-8{\cdot}5$H) and unsaturated C_{22} 13–15 (-10 to -11H). The close resemblance to whale blubber fatty acids is evident, whilst it is noteworthy that acids below the C_{14} series have not been recorded (the small proportions of C_{14} saturated and unsaturated acids are similar to those of whale blubber fats). Similarly, studies[67] so far made of seal milk fats show qualitative identity and general quantitative resemblance, in component acid proportions and in the mean unsaturation of the various homologous groups, to those of seal blubber fats. These similarities between respective milk and body fats of different marine mammalian species justify the belief (in the absence of direct evidence as to their glyceride structure) that the milk glycerides are constituted similarly to the marine animal depot fats discussed on pp. 409, 483 ff.

AN ALTERNATIVE VIEW OF THE GLYCERIDE STRUCTURE
OF NATURAL FATS (KARTHA)

An approach to the problem of glyceride structure in all natural fats, based originally on a method of determining by the oxidation procedure (p. 364) not only trisaturated glycerides, but also mono-azelao-disaturated and di-azelao-monosaturated glycerides, has been the subject of a number of publications by Kartha.[24] Since Kartha's views differed considerably at different times and in different respects from those which have formed the basis of the work dealt with earlier in this chapter, it has been deemed better, for the sake of clarity, to devote a separate section to an account of them.

In his earliest publication (1951) Kartha[24a] inclined to the opinion that the acids in all natural fats were assembled into triglycerides on a completely random basis, and contradicted somewhat aggressively any idea of "even distribution" (by which he doubtless meant "widest", strictly arithmetical distribution). Since, obviously, completely random distribution demands in very many fats the presence of much more trisaturated material than is actually present, Kartha[24c] devised a modified form of glyceride pattern which he termed "restricted random distribution", which he described as follows: "The glyceride-type composition of any natural fat is that obtained by interchange, according to chance, of one-third of the saturated acids represented by the difference between the GS_3 content required by chance and that actually present with the unsaturated acids in the fat, without allowing the formation of any further GS_3" (this he refers to as the "Glyceride-Type-Distribution (G.T.D.) Rule"). This, in effect, postulates an initial tendency to completely "random distribution" which is modified (and converted to a wider distribution) by inclusion of extra unsaturated material into the potentially maximum "random" amount of trisaturated material. Subsequently he[24d] suggested that trisaturated glycerides cannot be present in natural fats "in excess of the quantity which can exist in the fluid state *in vivo*", and that "deviations from the completely random pattern may be due to inability of the plant or animal to produce GS_3 in excess of" that amount.

Kartha compared the values for the four categories trisaturated, mono- and di-unsaturated, and triunsaturated glycerides (obtained by his "G.T.D." Rule with a large number of plant and some animal fats) with the experimental values as observed by other workers using fractional crystallisation, and as observed by his own procedure of azelao- as well as trisaturated glycerides determination by his modification of the oxidation method (p. 364). He found excellent agreement between his own calculated and observed values, but wide differences in many instances between the former and the results obtained by fractional crystallisation.

The possibility of errors inherent in either of the experimental techniques employed cannot be ruled out, and in 1954 Luddy, Fertsch and Riemenschneider[68b] studied the glycerides in four fats (lard, chicken fat, palm oil, cottonseed oil) by Kartha's oxidation procedure[24b] and by systematic low temperature crystallisation from acetone. The experimental figures for the four categories of saturated and/or unsaturated glycerides were in fair agreement by

14

either method, but did not agree well (except in the chicken fat) either with those calculated on the basis of random distribution or with those calculated by Kartha's "G.T.D." formula. On the other hand, Lakshminaryana and Rebello[25b] obtained inaccurate results by the Kartha oxidation procedure, and in their opinion the "restricted random distribution" view (for which the procedure forms the experimental basis) requires re-examination.

Vander Wal has been – at all events until recently – a supporter of Kartha's general thesis. In 1958 he summarised[44c] the position by saying that "the evidence points to the conclusion that the proportions of the glyceride types in many fats are, at least approximately, in agreement with theoretical values based on the restricted-random distribution theory", adding, however, that it is likely that "in some or all fats the fatty acids are not distributed within the individual mixed glyceride molecules at random"; he further noted Lutton's suggestion[49b] that triglycerides of specific constitution are characteristic of natural fats rather than triglycerides formed by random fatty acid distribution. In 1960, following the developments in selective hydrolysis of fats by pancreatic lipase (*cf.* p. 385), Vander Wal[44a] devised a new form of calculation based on the proportion of saturated acids (*a*) in the whole fat, and (*b*) attached to the 2-glyceryl position, thereby arriving at computed values according with those of Kartha for the total categories S_3, S_2U, SU_2 and U_3, but showing great differences from the latter for the glyceride "isomers" SUS, SSU, USU and UUS. Vander Wal's later mode of computation is, indeed, more akin to that used by Gunstone[39] (p. 397).

It should be pointed out that Kartha himself noted that the "restricted random distribution" calculations point to a maximum proportion of about 45 per cent. for diunsaturated glycerides and up to 80 per cent. for mono-unsaturated glycerides, figures which are similar to those based upon selective attachment of oleic (or linoleic) groups to the 2-glyceryl hydroxyl.

We hope it is not too severe a judgment on Kartha's many contributions on this subject to say that computations necessarily (at the time) based on a single experimental determination (of trisaturated glycerides) coupled with a number of pure assumptions must be regarded more critically than those based on simpler and more secure foundations. However, Kartha eventually reached a formula which would appear to be a reliable guide to glyceride *computation* (*cf.* Appendix to this chapter, p. 419), since it yields data reasonably similar to those now available from the experimentally proved fact of selective esterification at the central (2-) glyceryl position coupled with the single assumption of indiscriminate (random) attachment of other acyl groups to the 1- and 3-positions.

The present chapter has been concerned entirely with general aspects of glyceride structure in natural fats, the general relationships which obtain throughout all natural mixtures of mixed glycerides, and the more specific characteristics which differentiate one class of fats from another. The succeeding chapters will be devoted to descriptive accounts of individual fats, vegetable (Chapter VI) and animal (Chapter VII).

Appendix to Chapter V

COMPUTATION OF COMPONENT GLYCERIDES IN A FAT
FROM ITS COMPONENT ACIDS

As may be gathered from several isolated references in preceding pages of this chapter, a variety of methods has been proposed from time to time whereby the main glyceride composition of a fat can be more or less satisfactorily indicated by empirical calculations based upon the proportions of its component acids. Such computations do not necessarily have any implication concerning the glyceride structure of natural fats, nor throw light on the processes operative in the synthesis of natural glycerides. In consequence of the lengthy investigation necessary to establish the constitution of a fat experimentally, and especially when comparatively few fats had thus been studied, it seemed desirable to seek arithmetical means whereby at least the chief constituents of a fat could be indicated from its fatty acid composition. It is likely that, with increasing precision and adaptability in new experimental methods for the study of component glycerides in natural fats the utility of these computations will progressively decrease. In this Edition, therefore, their general discussion is restricted to a summary of the chief proposals, with full references to the literature in which they appeared; somewhat fuller accounts are available, however, in the 2nd (1947) and 3rd (1956) Editions of this book. It should be borne in mind that these methods of computation are to a very large degree empirical and tentative.

It was noticed[17h] in 1935 that the observed amounts of palmitodiolein and stearodiolein in cocoa butter[17i] could be approximately simulated by calculation if the unsaturated acid in the whole fat were divided in arithmetical proportion to the palmitic and stearic acid contents, and then each portion combined with the latter so as to give mixtures of monopalmito-oleins and dipalmito-oleins, monostearo-di-oleins and distearo-oleins. The results obtained for dioleo glycerides were almost exactly those found by analysis, but did not account for the oleopalmitostearin which accompanies dipalmito- and distearo-oleins. In 1942 Hilditch and Meara[69] reviewed and extended the application of the computation method suggested above. It became evident that the choice of the particular acid to be "proportioned" amongst the rest of the component acids of a fat is strictly limited; almost always it was necessary to partition *oleic acid* amongst the rest. Although the basis of the computations under discussion was completely empirical, and had no obvious bearing on the manner in which glycerides are assembled by natural processes, it was wondered whether to a certain extent, this necessity for partitioning oleic amongst the other acids might point to some special feature which conditions the general glyceride structure of natural fats.

In fats (e.g., stearic-rich animal depot fats) which contain significant amounts of trisaturated glycerides, the amount of the palmitic and stearic acids present in the latter must be deducted from the total amounts of these acids present in the whole fats, and the oleic acid then "proportioned" between the remaining palmitic and stearic acids, when figures in fairly close agreement with the observed values were obtained for the various mixed oleosaturated triglycerides (*cf.* p. 508). Detailed examples of all these calculations were quoted in the 2nd Edition of this book (pp. 251–255, 259, 267–269, 282, 323–324). The procedure was found most reliable for fats which contain not more than two saturated acids with oleic acid in major proportions.

In 1948 Doerschuk and Daubert,[38c] having separated maize (corn) oil into nineteen fractions by intensive crystallisation and recrystallisation from acetone at low temperatures, were able to arrive at a numerical formula which accorded remarkably closely with their experimental findings, and which they describe as based on "partial random distribution". The calculations depend primarily on the assumption that each of the sixteen fractions into which the oil had been resolved is a binary mixture of glycerides containing respectively 1 and 2, 2 and 3, 3 and 4, 4 and 5, or 5 and 6 double bonds. The possible glyceride forms represented by each double bond category, e.g., (for glycerides containing three double bonds) linoleno-disaturated, linoleo-oleo-saturated, trilinolein, are then considered, and the glyceride constituents of each fraction evaluated from calculations based upon the contents of saturated, oleic, linoleic, and linolenic acids and the iodine values of the fractions. There are thus five equations possible, but the number of possible glycerides usually, sometimes considerably, exceeds this. When the system is thus indeterminate, the most probable composition is arrived at by an "approximate method".

Doerschuk and Daubert's mode of computation does not appear to have been used so far in the case of other fats.

From 1951 onwards Kartha[24] developed the methods of computation of glycerides present in many natural fats according to "restricted random distribution" by his "glyceride-type-distribution (G.T.D.) rule". This has been considered already (p. 417), as also have the contributions of Vander Wal (1958)[44c] in support of Kartha's findings, and later (1960)[44a] by a new formula which takes account of fatty acids attached specifically to the central (2-) hydroxyl group in the molecule of glycerol. The latest form of glyceride computation (at the time of writing) is that of Gunstone[39] for vegetable fats, in which preferential attachment of oleo-groups at the 2-glyceryl position is postulated, with random attachment of saturated (and any excess of oleic or linoleic) acids at the 1- and 3-glyceryl hydroxyl groups.

The sequence of computation methods may perhaps not unfairly be summed up as, originally, attempts to simulate the observed compositions on the basis of several purely empirical assumptions; the latest methods however (Vander Wal's publication of 1960, and Gunstone's of 1962) are based primarily on the observed phenomenon of specific esterification at the 2-position coupled with the single arbitrary assumption of random attachment of acyl groups to the 1- and 3-positions. It may well be that further use of computational methods will lie in the latter direction, rather than as a means to prediction of glyceride structure in place of experimental verification (which is, after all, the only sure method whereby the true facts may be ultimately discerned).

References to Chapter V

1. M. Berthelot, "Chimie organique fondée sur la synthèse", 1860, **2**, 31.
2. R. Heise, *Tropenpflanzer*, 1897, **1**, 10; 1899, **3**, 203; *Arb. Kais. Ges.-Amt*, 1897, **13**, 302.
3. R. Henriques and H. Künne, *Ber.*, 1899, **32**, 387.
4. F. Guth, *Z. biol. Chem.*, 1902, **44**, 78.
5. J. B. Leathes and H. S. Raper, "The Fats", Longmans, Green & Co., 1925, 2nd Edition, p. 38.
6. D. Holde and M. Stange, *Ber.*, 1901, **34**, 2402.
7. R. Fritzweiler, *Arb. Kais. Ges.-Amt*, 1902, **18**, 371; *Chem. Zentr.*, 1902, (i), 1113; *Z. Unters. Nahr. Genussm.*, 1902, **5**, 1164.
8. (a) J. Klimont, *Ber.*, 1901, **34**, 2636; *Monatsh.*, 1902, **23**, 51; 1905, **26**, 563; *Z. Unters. Nahr. Genussm.*, 1906, **12**, 359; (b) *Monatsh.*, 1904, **25**, 929; (c) *ibid.*, 1903, **24**, 408; (d) (with E. Meisels), *ibid.*, 1909, **30**, 341; (e) *ibid.*, 1912, **33**, 441.
9. (a) A. Bömer, A. Schemm and F. Heimsoth, *Z. Unters. Nahr. Genussm.*, 1907, **14**, 90; A. Bömer, *ibid.*, 1909, **17**, 353; (b) A. Bömer, *ibid.*, 1913, **25**, 321; (c) A. Bömer and H. Merten, *ibid.*, 1922, **43**, 101.
10. (a) W. Hansen, *Arch. Hyg.*, 1902, **42**, 1; (b) H. Kreis and A. Hafner, *Ber.*, 1903, **36**, 1123.
11. C. Amberger, (a) *Z. Unters. Nahr. Genussm.*, 1913, **26**, 65; 1918, **35**, 313; (b) (with A. Wiesehahn), *ibid.*, 1923, **46**, 276; (c) (with K. Bromig), *ibid.*, 1921, **42**, 193.
12. A. Bömer (a) (with J. Baumann), *ibid.*, 1920, **40**, 97; (b) (with K. Schneider), *ibid.*, 1924, **47**, 61; (c) (with K. Ebach), *Z. Unters. Lebensm.*, 1928, **55**, 501; (d) (with H. Hüttig), *ibid.*, 1938, **75**, 1.
13. F. Krafft, *Ber.*, 1903, **36**, 4339.
14. K. S. Caldwell and W. H. Hurtley, *J. Chem. Soc.*, 1909, **95**, 853.
15. C. Amberger, (a) *Z. Unters. Nahr. Genussm.*, 1920, **40**, 192; (b) (with J. Bauch), *ibid.*, 1924, **48**, 371.

16. A. Börner and H. Engel, *Z. Unters. Lebensm.*, 1929, **57**, 113.

17. T. P. Hilditch (*a*) (with E. C. Jones), *J. Soc. Chem. Ind.*, 1934, **53**, 13T; (*b*) (with D. Atherton), *J. Chem. Soc.*, 1941, 527; (*c*) (with M. B. Ichaporia and H. Jasperson), *J. Soc. Chem. Ind.*, 1938, **57**, 363; (*d*) (with H. M. Thompson), *ibid.*, 1937, **56**, 434T; (*e*) (with H. Paul), *ibid.*, 1935, **54**, 331T; (*f*) (with W. J. Stainsby), *ibid.*, 1936, **55**, 95T; (*g*) (with A. Banks and H. K. Dean), *ibid.*, 1935, **54**, 77T; (*h*) (with W. J. Stainsby), *Biochem. J.*, 1935, **29**, 90; (*i*) (with J. T. Terleski), *J. Soc. Chem. Ind.*, 1937, **56**, 315T; (*j*) (with D. A. Harper), *ibid.*, 1937, **56**, 322T.

18. A. Eibner, L. Widenmayer and E. Schild, *Chem. Umschau*, 1927, **34**, 312; A. Eibner and F. Brosel, *ibid.*, 1928, **35**, 157.

19. (*a*) B. Suzuki and Y. Yokoyama, *Proc. Imp. Acad. Tokyo*, 1927, **3**, 526, 529; 1929, **5**, 265; (*b*) B. Suzuki and Y. Masuda, *ibid.*, 1927, **3**, 531; 1928, **4**, 165; 1929, **5**, 268.

20. K. Hashi, *J. Soc. Chem. Ind., Japan*, 1927, **30**, 849, 856; 1928, **31**, 117.

21. T. P. Hilditch and C. H. Lea, *J. Chem. Soc.*, 1927, 3106.

22. T. P. Hilditch and S. R. Saletore, *J. Soc. Chem. Ind.*, 1933, **52**, 101T.

23. P. H. Begemann, J. G. Keppler and H. A. Boekenoogen, *Rec. Trav. Chim.*, 1950, **69**, 439.

24. (*a*) A. R. S. Kartha, "Studies on the Natural Fats", Thesis, University of Madras, 1951; (*b*) *J. Amer. Oil Chem. Soc.*, 1953, **30**, 280; (*c*) *ibid.*, 1953, **30**, 326; (*d*) *ibid.*, 1954, **31**, 85.

25. (*a*) L. R. Eshelman and E. G. Hammond, *J. Amer. Oil Chem. Soc.*, 1958, **35**, 230; (*b*) G. Lakshminarayana and D. Rebello, *ibid.*, 1960, **37**, 274; 1963, **40**, 300; *see also* A. R. S. Kartha and R. Narayanan, *J. Sci. Food Agric.*, 1962, **13**, 411.

26. G. Collin and T. P. Hilditch, (*a*) *J. Soc. Chem. Ind.*, 1928, **47**, 261T; (*b*) *Biochem. J.*, 1929, **23**, 1273.

27. S. S. Gupta and T. P. Hilditch, *Biochem. J.*, 1951, **48**, 137.

28. J. S. Cama, M. M. Chakrabarty, T. P. Hilditch and M. L. Meara, *J. Sci. Food Agric.*, 1953, **4**, 321.

29. H. J. Dutton (*a*) (with C. R. Lancaster and O. L. Brekke), *J. Amer. Oil Chem. Soc.*, 1950, **27**, 25 (*see also*, review by C. R. Scholfield, *ibid.*, 1961, **38**, 562); (*b*) (with J. A. Cannon), *ibid.*, 1956, **33**, 46; (*c*) C. R. Scholfield and M. A. Hicks, *ibid.*, 1957, **34**, 77; (*d*) C. R. Scholfield and H. J. Dutton, *ibid.*, 1958, **35**, 493; (*e*) *idem* (with J. Nowakowska), *ibid.*, 1961, **38**, 175; (*f*) *idem*, *ibid.*, 1959, **36**, 325; (*g*) *idem* (with T. L. Mounts), *ibid.*, 1961, **38**, 96; *cf. also*, D. G. Thierriault, *ibid.*, 1963, **40**, 395.

30. L. C. Craig, W. Hausmann, E. H. Ahrens, Jr. and C. J. Harfenist, *Analyt. Chem.*, 1951, **23**, 1236.

31. F. T. Walker and M. R. Mills, *J. Soc. Chem. Ind.*, 1942, **61**, 125; C. L. Reinbold and H. J. Dutton, *J. Amer. Oil Chem. Soc.*, 1948, **25**, 117; M. R. Sahasrabudhe and D. G. Chapman, *ibid.*, 1961, **38**, 88; B. C. Black and E. G. Hammond, *ibid.*, 1963, **40**, 575.

32. (*a*) See, *for example*, L. J. Morris, R. T. Holman and K. Fontell, *J. Lipid Res.*, 1960, **1**, 412; H. K. Mangold (general review), *J. Amer. Oil Chem. Soc.*, 1961, **38**, 708; O. S. Privett and M. L. Blank, *J. Lipid Res.*, 1961, **2**, 37; *J. Amer. Oil Chem. Soc.*, 1963, **40**, 70; (with W. O. Lundberg), *ibid.*, 1961, **38**, 312; H. P. Kaufmann, Z. Makus and B. Das, *Fette, Seifen, Anstrichm.*, 1961, **63**, 807; 1962, **64**, 214; C. Michalec *et al.*, *Nature*, 1962, **193**, 63; (*b*) P. L. Nichols, *J. Amer. Chem. Soc.*, 1952, **74**, 1091; (*c*) B. de Vries, *Chem. and Ind.*, 1962, 1049; C. B. Barrett, M. S. J. Dallas and F. B. Padley, *ibid.*, 1962, 1050; *J. Amer. Oil Chem. Soc.*, 1963, **40**, 580; F. D. Gunstone, F. B. Padley and M. I. Quyeshi, *Chem. and Ind.*, 1964, 483.

33. H. P. Kaufmann and Z. Makus, *Fette, Seifen, Anstrichm.*, 1959, **61**, 631; 1961, **63**, 125; O. Hirayama, *J. Agric. Chem. Soc. Japan*, 1961, **35**, 441; G. Rouser *et al.* (general review), *J. Amer. Oil Chem. Soc.*, 1961, **38**, 565.

34. (*a*) P. Desnuelle and M. J. Constantin, *Int. Colloq. Biochem. Problems of Lipids*, 1953, 174; (*b*) P. Savary and P. Desnuelle, *Compt. Rend.*, 1955, **240**, 2571; *Biochim. Biophys. Acta*, 1956, **21**, 349; 1959, **31**, 26; 1961, **50**, 319; (with J. Flanzy), *ibid.*, 1957, **24**, 414; *Rev. Français Corps Gras*, 1958, **5**, 493.

35. (a) F. H. Matsson et al., J. Nutrition 1952, **48**, 335; (b) F. H. Mattson and L. W. Beck, J. Biol. Chem., 1955, **214**, 115; 1956, **219**, 735; (c) F. H. Mattson and E. S. Lutton, ibid., 1958, **233**, 868; (d) F. H. Mattson and R. A. Volpenhein, ibid., 1961, **236**, 1891; J. Lipid Research, 1961, **2**, 58; 1962, **3**, 58; 1962, **3**, 281; 1963, **4**, 392; (e) D. J. Hanahan, H. Brockerhoff and E. J. Barron, J. Biol. Chem., 1960, **235**, 1917; (f) N. H. Tattrie, J. Lipid Research, 1960, **1**, 60.

36. (a) C. G. Youngs, J. Amer. Oil Chem. Soc., 1959, **36**, 664; 1961, **38**, 62; (b) M. H. Coleman, ibid., 1961, **38**, 685; see also, ibid., 1963, **40**, 568.

37. (a) C. Barker and T. P. Hilditch, J. Sci. Food Agric., 1950, **1**, 140; (b) A. Crossley and T. P. Hilditch, ibid., 1951, **2**, 545; (c) A. R. S. Kartha, ibid., 1963, **14**, 515.

38. (a) T. P. Hilditch, "The Chemical Constitution of Natural Fats", 2nd Edition 1947: Chapman and Hall, Ltd.; (b) F. A. Norris and K. F. Mattil, J. Amer. Oil Chem. Soc., 1947, **24**, 274; (c) A. P. Doerschuk and B. F. Daubert, ibid., 1948, **25**, 425.

39. F. D. Gunstone, Chem. and Ind., 1962, 1214.

40. (a) M. L. Meara and Y. A. H. Zaky, J. Soc. Chem. Ind., 1940, **59**, 25; T. P. Hilditch and K. S. Murti, (b) ibid., 1941, **60**, 16; (c) ibid., 1939, **58**, 310; (d) M. L. Meara, J. Chem. Soc., 1949, 2154; (e) T. P. Hilditch and M. B. Ichaporia, J. Soc. Chem. Ind., 1938, **57**, 44.

41. (a) C. Barker, privately communicated; (b) M. M. Chakrabarty and T. P. Hilditch, J. Sci. Food Agric., 1951, **2**, 255; T. P. Hilditch (c) (with L. Maddison), J. Soc. Chem. Ind., 1940, **59**, 162; (d) (with A. Crossley) J. Sci. Food Agric., 1951, **2**, 251; (e) (with R. V. Crawford), ibid., 1950, **1**, 372.

42. G. Collin, Biochem. J., 1931, **25**, 95.

43. (a) J. P. Riley, J. Chem. Soc., 1951, 291; (b) T. P. Hilditch and A. Mendelowitz, J. Sci. Food Agric., 1951, **2**, 548; (c) S. S. Gupta, T. P. Hilditch and J. P. Riley, ibid., 1951, **2**, 245; (d) C. F. Krewson, J. S. Ard and R. W. Riemenschneider, J. Amer. Oil Chem. Soc., 1962, **39**, 334.

44. (a) R. J. Vander Wal, J. Amer. Oil Chem. Soc., 1960, **37**, 18; (b) A. S. Richardson, footnote 3 in preceding paper, p. 18; (c) R. J. Vander Wal, ibid., 1958, **35**, 483.

45. (a) C. Barker and T. P. Hilditch, J. Oil Col. Chem. Assocn., 1950, **33**, 6; (b) T. P. Hilditch, M. L. Meara and C. B. Patel, J. Sci. Food Agric., 1951, **2**, 142; (c) B. K. Singh and A. Kumar, Proc. Indian Acad. Sci., 1946, **23**, A, 379; (d) M. L. Meara and N. K. Sen, J. Sci. Food Agric., 1952, **3**, 237; (e) N. L. Vidyarthi and M. V. Mallya, J. Indian Chem. Soc., 1939, **16**, 443; (f) H. C. Dunn, T. P. Hilditch and J. P. Riley, J. Soc. Chem. Ind., 1948, **67**, 199.

46. (a) S. S. Gupta and C. R. Mitra, J. Sci. Food Agric., 1953, **4**, 44; (b) A. H. Weerakoon, Thesis, University of Liverpool, 1952; (c) A. P. Dale and M. L. Meara, privately communicated; (d) J. S. Cama, Thesis, University of Liverpool, 1952; (e) T. P. Hilditch and S. R. Saletore, J. Soc. Chem. Ind., 1931, **50**, 468T; 1933, **52**, 101T; (f) T. G. Green and T. P. Hilditch, ibid., 1938, **57**, 49.

47. (a) T. P. Hilditch and Y. A. H. Zaky, J. Soc. Chem. Ind., 1942, **61**, 34; (b) M. N. Baliga and M. L. Meara, ibid., 1949, **68**, 52; (c) W. J. Bushell and T. P. Hilditch, ibid., 1938, **57**, 48; (d) M. L. Meara, privately communicated; (e) T. P. Hilditch and S. P. Pathak, J. Chem. Soc., 1949, Supp. I, 87; (f) S. S. Gupta and M. L. Meara, ibid., 1950, 1337.

48. (a) T. P. Hilditch and W. J. Stainsby, J. Soc. Chem. Ind., 1934, **53**, 197T; (b) M. L. Meara, J. Chem. Soc., 1945, **22**; 1949, 2154; (c) E. S. Lutton, J. Amer. Chem. Soc., 1946, **68**, 675; (d) (with F. L. Jackson) ibid., 1950, **72**, 3254; (e) M. L. Meara, J. Chem. Soc., 1947, 773; (with S. S. Gupta), ibid., 1950, 1337; (f) M. L. Meara, ibid., 1948, 722; (g) T. P. Hilditch and H. Paul, J. Soc. Chem. Ind., 1935, **54**, 331T.

49. (a) M. L. Meara, J. Chem. Soc., 1945, 23; (b) E. S. Lutton, J. Amer. Oil Chem. Soc., 1957, **34**, 521; (c) D. Chapman, A. Crossley and A. C. Davies, J. Chem. Soc., 1957, 1502.

50. E. Baer and H. O. L. Fischer, J. Biol. Chem., 1939, **128**, 475; Chem. Rev., 1941, **29**, 287.

51. T. P. Hilditch (a) (with W. H. Pedelty), Biochem. J., 1940, **34**, 971; (b) (with Y. A. H, Zaky) ibid., 1941, **35**, 940; (c) (with S. Paul), ibid., 1938, **32**, 1775; (d) (with K. S. Murti). ibid., 1940, **34**, 1301; (e) (with R. K. Shrivastava), J. Amer. Oil Chem. Soc., 1949, **26**, 1.

52. T. P. Hilditch (*a*) (with R. Bhattacharya), *Proc. Roy. Soc.*, 1930, A, **129**, 468; *J. Chem. Soc.*, 1931, 901; (*b*) (with A. Banks), *Biochem. J.*, 1931, **25**, 1168; 1932, **26**, 298; (*c*) (with J. J. Sleightholme), *ibid.*, 1931, **25**, 507; (*d*) (with H. E. Longenecker), *ibid.*, 1937, **31**, 1805.

53. H. E. Longenecker, *Chem. Rev.*, 1941, **29**, 201.

54. (*a*) R. Reiser, *Fed. Proc.*, 1951, **10**, 236; (with N. B. Willey *et al.*), *J. Anim. Sci.*, 1952, **11**, 705; (with H. G. R. Reddy), *J. Amer. Oil Chem. Soc.*, 1956, **33**, 155; (with R. E. Leighton), *ibid.*, 1959, **36**, 129; (*b*) F. B. Shorland, R. O. Weenink, *et al.*, *Nature*, 1955, **175**, 1129; *Biochem. J.*, 1957, **67**, 328; (*c*) S. Hofland, J. Holmberg and G. Sellmann, *Cornell Vet.*, 1956, **46**, 53; (*d*) G. A. Garton, A. K. Lough *et al.*, *Nature*, 1958, **182**, 1511; *J. Gen. Microbiol.*, 1961, **25**, 215.

55. O. T. Quimby, R. L. Wille and E. S. Lutton, *J. Amer. Oil Chem. Soc.*, 1953, **30**, 186.

56. T. P. Hilditch (*a*) (with D. A. Harper), *J. Soc. Chem. Ind.*, 1937, **56**, 322T; (*b*) (with J. T. Terleski), *ibid.*, 1937, **56**, 315T; (*c*) O. B. Bjarnason and M. L. Meara, *ibid.*, 1944, **63**, 61; T. P. Hilditch (*d*) (with S. P. Pathak) *ibid.*, 1947, **66**, 421; (*e*) (with L. Maddison), *ibid.*, 1942, **61**, 169; 1948, **67**, 253; (*f*) A. Cardin, Thesis, University of Liverpool, 1952, p. 53.

57. (*a*) W. R. Graham, T. S. G. Jones and H. D. Kay, *Proc. Roy. Soc.*, 1936, **B**, **120**, 330; (*b*) L. A. Maynard, C. M. McKay, G. H. Ellis, A. Z. Hodson and G. K. Davis, *Cornell University Agric. Expt. Stn.*, 1938, Memoir 211; (*c*) J. C. Shaw and W. E. Petersen, *J. Dairy Sci.*, 1938, **21**, 122; 1940, **23**, 1045; *Amer. J. Physiol.*, 1938, **123**, 183; (*d*) E. G. Duncombe and R. F. Glascock, *Biochem. J.*, 1954, **57**, *Proceedings*, xi.

58. W. R. Graham, O. B. Houchin, V. E. Peterson and C. W. Turner, *Amer. J. Physiol.*, 1938, **122**, 150.

59. E. P. Reineke, W. D. Stonecipher and C. W. Turner, *ibid.*, 1941, **132**, 535.

60. K. Bloch and D. Rittenberg, *J. Biol. Chem.*, 1942, **143**, 297; 1945, **160**, 417.

61. (*a*) G. Popják, *Nutrition Abstracts and Reviews*, 1951–52, **21**, 535; *Biochem. Soc. Symposia*, 1952, No. **9**, 37; (*b*) S. J. Folley, *Biol. Rev.*, 1949, **24**, 316; *Biochem. Soc. Symposia*, 1952, No. **9**, 52; (*c*) G. Popják, T. H. French, G. D. Hunter and A. J. P. Martin, *Biochem. J.*, 1951, **48**, 612.

62. T. P. Hilditch, *Biochem. Soc. Symposia*, 1952, No. **9**, 63; *see also* S. Hoflund and J. Holmberg, *Nordiska Veterinärmötet*, 1951, **6**, 321.

63. T. P. Hilditch and H. E. Longenecker, *J. Biol. Chem.*, 1938, **122**, 497.

64. (*a*) J. A. B. Smith and N. N. Dastur, *Biochem. J.*, 1938, **32**, 1868; J. A. B. Smith, *J. Dairy Res.*, 1941, **12**, 94; (*b*) J. C. Shaw, *J. Dairy Sci.*, 1941, **24**, 502; J. C. Shaw, R. C. Powell and C. B. Knodt, *ibid.*, 1942, **25**, 909.

65. T. P. Hilditch and H. M. Thompson, *Biochem. J.*, 1936, **30**, 677.

66. (*a*) S. Schmidt-Nielsen and F. Frog, *Kong. Norske Vidensk. Selsk. Forhandl.*, 1933, **6**, 127; (*b*) A. Klem, *Hvalradets Skr.*, 1935, No. **11**, 5–48; (*c*) J. S. Cama and M. L. Meara, *Biochem. J.*, 1953, **55**, 365.

67. M. L. Meara, *Biochem. J.*, 1952, **51**, 190.

68. (*a*) R. W. Riemenschneider, F. E. Luddy, M. L. Swain and W. C. Ault, *Oil and Soap*, 1946, **23**, 276; (*b*) F. E. Luddy, G. R. Fertsch and R. W. Riemenschneider, *J. Amer. Oil Chem. Soc.*, 1954, **31**, 266.

69. T. P. Hilditch and M. L. Meara, *J. Soc. Chem. Ind.*, 1942, **61**, 117.

CHAPTER VI

The Component Glycerides of Individual Vegetable Fats

Some account will now be given of the glyceride composition of a fairly large number of seed and fruit-coat fats which have been studied in greater or less detail by the quantitative techniques described in the preceding chapter. For convenience, these vegetable fats will be considered in roughly decreasing order of their content of saturated acids: that is to say, in both seed and fruit-coat fats, those of highest melting point and most saturated character will be discussed first, and those of most unsaturated character last.

Seed Fats

(a) SEED FATS CONTAINING OVER 80 PER CENT. OF SATURATED ACIDS IN THEIR TOTAL COMPONENT FATTY ACIDS

Seed fats of the Palmæ. The very striking similarity in the component fatty acids of this group, which was pointed out in Chapter IV, Table 69B (p. 341), is accompanied by close similarity in their general glyceride structure.

We need only consider in detail coconut,[1a] palm kernel,[1a] babassu[2a] and areca[2b] fats. From the quantitative results of the oxidation process, it was found that the content of fully saturated glycerides is in each case of an order which leaves the ratio of saturated to unsaturated acids in the remaining part of the fat at approximately 1·4:1 (see Chapter V, Table 71, p. 366). Since there is no evidence of any triolein in any of the fats, their general composition (per cent. wt.) may be summarised as follows:

	COCONUT[1a]	PALM KERNEL[1a]	BABASSU[2a]	ARECA[2b]
Fully saturated glycerides	84	63	63	56
Mono-oleo-disaturated glycerides	12	26	30	30
Dioleo-monosaturated glycerides	4	11	7	14

The fully saturated components, which form the greater part of the fats, apparently contain the various acids in much the same proportions in which they occur in the whole fats, as will be seen from the data on page 425.

The similarity in the proportions of saturated acids in the fats as a whole and in their fully saturated components is not by any means a general phenomenon, but appears to be confined to those fats in which unsaturated (oleic) acid is a very minor component, and in which, consequently, the fully saturated glycerides form a very large proportion of the fat. In other groups, in which the fully saturated components only amount to a few per cent. of the whole fat,

Percentage (wt.) of individual acids (i) in the saturated acids of the whole fats and (ii) in the component acids of the fully saturated glycerides of Palmæ Seed Fats

	COCONUT (1)		COCONUT (2)		PALM KERNEL		BABASSU		ARECA	
	WHOLE FAT	FULLY SATU- RATED PART	WHOLE FAT	FULLY SATU- RATED PART	WHOLE FAT	FULLY SATU- RATED PART	WHOLE FAT	FULLY SATU- RATED PART	WHOLE FAT	FULLY SATU- RATED PART
Caprylic	9	8	9	9	3	2	6	7	—	—
Capric	8	9	8	10	9	8	8	9	—	—
Lauric	52	51	50	52	58	60	53	48	24	19
Myristic	19	19	20	17	17	20	19	25	58	55
Palmitic	10	11	10	10	11	6	10	9	16	19
Stearic	2	2	3	2	2	4 (?)	3	1	2	7

the major component saturated acid of lowest molecular weight is usually found to be relatively concentrated in the fully saturated glycerides (*cf.* p. 404).

The fractional crystallisation of the fully saturated components[1a] of coconut and palm kernel fats and of the fats as a whole[3] has uniformly failed to reveal the presence of any simple trilaurin but, on the other hand, has indicated that in both fats dilauromyristins are present in considerable quantity. From the point of view of interpretation of glyceride structure it is unfortunate that there are so many saturated acids other than lauric also present in these fats, thus making any investigation by fractional crystallisation methods exceedingly difficult. A re-examination of the glycerides of coconut and palm kernel fats was made by Dale and Meara[4a] with the aid of the full crystallisation techniques described in Chapter V. Each fat, after extensive crystallisation and re-crystallisation of some intermediate fractions, was finally divided into nine or ten fractions, in each of which the component acids were determined. It was deduced that the probable component mixed glycerides of the fats were approximately as indicated by the figures given in Table 92 (p. 426); (it was necessary to group the C_8 and C_{10} acids together as "capro"-glycerides, and the small amounts of stearic with palmitic acid as "palmito"-glycerides, whilst the unsaturated acids were similarly taken together as "oleo"-glycerides). Whilst these results can still only be taken as approximate and indicative, they serve to illustrate the very complex nature of the Palmæ seed fats. In these analyses the proportions of diunsaturated glycerides appear even smaller than in the earlier studies quoted above: none of this category was observed in the coconut fat, and only about one per cent. in the palm kernel fat. Neither the laurodimyristin nor the dimyristopalmitin reported by Bömer[3] was in evidence in these studies; trilaurin was not detected in the coconut fat, and was present to the extent of less than one per cent. in the palm kernel fat.

Seed fats of Lauraceæ and Myristicaceæ. The glyceride structures of a few seed fats with very low unsaturated acid contents from these families (*cf.* Chapter IV, Table 69A, p. 335) have been studied in detail.

Puntambekar and Krishna[5] state that the seed fat of *Actinodaphne hookeri* consists very largely of trilaurin, its component acids being 96 per cent. lauric and 4 per cent. oleic acid. Gunde and Hilditch[6] found that the seed fat of another Lauraceous shrub, *Neolitsea involucrata*, contained 87 per cent. of fully saturated glycerides, trilaurin forming about 66 per cent. of the whole fat; the component acids of the whole fat were *n*-decanoic 3, lauric 86, myristic 4, oleic 4 and linoleic 3 per cent., whilst those of the fully saturated components were *n*-decanoic 5, lauric 90 and myristic 5 per cent. The proportions of the saturated acids in the fully saturated components and in the fat as a whole are thus, as in the Palmæ seed fats, not very different; and in the 13 per cent. of mixed saturated-unsaturated glycerides the "association ratio" of saturated

TABLE 92. *Component Glycerides (per cent. mol.) of Coconut and Palm Kernel Fats*

(Dale and Meara[4a])

	COCONUT	PALM KERNEL
Component acids:		
Caproic	0·5	—
Caprylic	9·1	3·6
Capric	12·0	6·5
Lauric	45·1	50·6
Myristic	16·8	16·8
Palmitic	8·0	6·8
Stearic	2·5	2·5
Oleic	5·2	11·6
Linoleic	0·8	1·6
Probable component glycerides:		
Di-"capro"-laurin	6	—
"Capro"-dilaurin	15	10
"Capro"-lauromyristin	17·5	5
Trilaurin	—	1
"Capro"-lauro-"palmitin"	8	3
Dilauromyristin	15	27
Dilauro-"palmitin"	7	8
"Capro"-myristo-"palmitin"	0·5	—
Lauromyristo-"palmitin"	13	7
Di-"capro"-"olein"	0·5	—
"Capro"-lauro-"olein"	9	12
Dilauro-"olein"	0·5	6
"Capro"-myristo-"olein"	1	—
Lauromyristo-"olein"	4	11
"Capro"-"palmito"-"olein"	1	—
Lauro-"palmito"-"olein"	2	9
Laurodi-"olein"	—	1

to unsaturated acids is 1·2:1. The glycerides of this fat therefore conform closely with the "rule of even distribution". Similarly, Child and Nathanael[7a] found the seed fat of *Litsea longifolia* to contain as component acids: lauric 91, palmitic 3, stearic 2 and oleic 4 per cent., with 75–80 per cent. of trilaurin in its component glycerides. Tsuchiya and Tanaka[7b] have noted the occurrence of trilaurin in the seed fats of *Tetradenia glauca* and *Lindera obtusifolia*.

The seed fats of two other species of the Lauraceæ, *Neolitsea zeylanica* and *Cinnamomum zeylanicum*, were later submitted to the full crystallisation procedure (from acetone at $-40°$C. to $+15°$C.) by Weerakoon[8] with the results shown in Table 93. The *Cinnamomum* fat, with over 97 per cent. of saturated acids, consists wholly of trilaurin and glycerides with two lauric and one other acyl group, whilst the *Neolitsea zeylanica* fat, with 91·5 per cent. of saturated acids, contains 7 per cent. of di-unsaturated glycerides (mainly oleo-linolein derivatives). The contents of trilaurin, in relation to the proportions of lauric acid in the total acids, accord closely with the graphs shown in Figs. 5, 7, 8 (Chapter V, pp. 377, 381, 382) and all the glycerides in both of these seed fats are typically "evenly distributed".

TABLE 93. *Component Glycerides of Lauraceæ Seed Fats*[8]

	Neolitsea zeylanica SEED FAT PER CENT. (MOL.)	Cinnamomum zeylanicum SEED FAT PER CENT. (MOL.)
Component acids:		
Capric	5·6	0·8
Lauric	84·8	90·4
Myristic	3·4	5·2
Palmitic	—	1·0
Oleic	4·6	2·6
Linoleic	1·6	—
Component glycerides:		
Capro-dilaurin	15	2·5
Trilaurin	63	71
Dilauromyristin	10	15·5
Dilauropalmitin	—	3
Capro-lauro-olein	0·5	—
Dilauro-olein	3·5	8
Lauro-myristo-olein	Trace	—
Dilauro-linolein	0·5	—
Capro-oleo-linolein	1	—
Laurodiolein	2·5	—
Lauro-oleo-linolein	3	—
Myristo-oleo-linolein	Trace	—

Nutmeg butter, the seed fat of *Myristica fragrans*, was examined by the oxidation method by Collin and Hilditch[1b]; it contained 73 per cent. of fully saturated glycerides, whilst its component acids were lauric 1·5, myristic 76·6, palmitic 10·1, oleic 10·5 and linoleic 1·3 per cent. The percentage proportions of the *saturated* acids in the whole fat were accordingly lauric 1·7, myristic 86·8 and palmitic 11·5 per cent., whilst those in the fully saturated part were lauric 2·2, myristic 91·1 and palmitic 6·7 per cent. – again showing little dissimilarity. Owing to the large proportion of myristic acid in the fully saturated glycerides, it necessarily follows that the simple glyceride trimyristin should be present in quantity. Actually Bömer and Ebach[9] isolated 40 per cent. of trimyristin by crystallisation from a sample of nutmeg butter.

Atherton and Meara[10a] studied the component glycerides of virola fat (from *Virola surinamensis*) and of kombo fat (from *Pycnanthus kombo*). In each fat oleic acid is only a minor component but, whereas virola fat resembles many other Myristicaceæ fats in containing a very high proportion of myristic acid, kombo fat contains in addition about 20 per cent. of tetradec-9-enoic (myristoleic acid) and in this respect is at present unique (*cf.* Chapter IV, pp. 333, 337). Both fats were examined by the acetone crystallisation procedure, as was also at a later date[8] the seed fat of *Myristica iriya*, which is very similar to virola fat in its fatty acid composition. The component fatty acids and probable

427

component glycerides of these three fats which have been submitted to the crystallisation technique are quoted from the results of the respective authors in Table 94. The glyceride structure of these Myristicaceæ fats, whilst qualitatively resembling that of the majority of seed fats, differs quantitatively in so far as the proportions of trimyristin appear to approach those of completely "random" rather than "even" distribution.

TABLE 94. *Component Glycerides of Myristicaceæ Seed Fats*

	Virola surinamensis SEED FAT[10a] PER CENT. (MOL.)	*Myristica iriya* SEED FAT[8] PER CENT. (MOL.)	*Pycnanthus kombo* SEED FAT[10a] PER CENT. (MOL.)
Component acids:			
Capric*	0·7	0·5	—
Lauric	16·9	23·4	8·9
Myristic	72·9	67·2	63·6
Palmitic	4·4	5·4	2·0
Tetradecenoic	—	—	20·8
Oleic	5·1	3·2	4·7
Linoleic*	—	0·3	—
Component glycerides:			
Dilauromyristin	1	7	—
Laurodimyristin	31	50	17
Trimyristin	43	19	21
Lauromyristopalmitin	10	2	—
Dimyristopalmitin	—	12	—
Lauromyristo-olein	12	5	—
Dimyristo-olein	3	3	—
Myristopalmito-olein	—	2	—
Lauromyristo-tetradecenoin	—	—	10
Dimyristo-tetradecenoin	—	—	33
Myristopalmito-tetradecenoin	—	—	3
Myristo-ditetradecenoin	—	—	7
Myristo-tetradeceno-olein	—	—	9

* The small amounts of capric and linoleic acids are included respectively with lauric and oleic acids in the component glyceride figures.

Two particularly well-marked exceptions to the "rule of even distribution" in seed fats also belong to the botanical families now under review, and may be briefly considered at this point.

Myristica malabarica seed fat. The endosperm of *M. malabarica* contains large quantities (nearly 50 per cent.) of resinous, non-fatty matter in addition to glycerides, and it is evident that these, since they must be completely separated from the glycerides, increase the difficulties of investigation to a considerable extent. The investigation of the fats obtained from the seeds by extraction with petrol ether and with carbon tetrachloride[1c, 11a] showed that much less resinous material is extracted by means of petrol ether, but the amount of fully saturated glycerides in either case was 16–19 per cent. The component acids of the whole fat are also abnormal for a *Myristica* seed fat, since myristic only forms 32 per cent., whilst in addition there is 17 per cent. of palmitic and 3 per cent. of stearic acid, with 48 per cent. of oleic acid. The great majority of other seed fats of the Myristicaceæ (*cf.* Chapter IV, Table 69A, p. 336) are very rich in saturated acids and thus resemble nutmeg butter rather than the fat of *M. malabarica*; the latter is also exceptional in its abundant content of resinous material, some of which may be actually in combination in the form of mixed glycerides. The fat thus appears to be abnormal in more than one respect.

Laurus nobilis (Lauraceæ) seed fat. This fat[11b] contained 34 per cent. (wt.) or 40·5 per cent. (mol.) of fully saturated glycerides, although its component fatty acids were made up of lauric 43, palmitic 6, oleic 32 and linoleic 19 per cent. (wt.). By hydrogenating the fat and submitting the product to fractional crystallisation from ether, Collin showed that there was extremely little tristearin present, so that the content of fully unsaturated glycerides in the original fat must have been very small. Further, of the lauric acid combined in the whole fat, fully 75 per cent. is present in the fully saturated glycerides, whereas only 25 per cent. of the total palmitic acid is therein represented. If, therefore, the lauric acid be considered separately, the rest of the component acids (oleic, linoleic, palmitic and a little lauric) are apparently built into glycerides on the usual lines met with in so many other seed fats. Whether the two groups of acids occur, in *Laurus nobilis,* in different parts of the seed, or whether they arrive or develop in the seed at different periods, it is not possible to say at present.

Collin's data (34 per cent. of fully saturated glycerides containing 95 per cent. of lauric acid) suggest the presence of about 31–32 per cent. of trilaurin in the whole fat; Bömer and Ebach[9] actually isolated 30 per cent. of trilaurin by fractional crystallisation of laurel fat.

Dika fats (Simarubaceæ). It will be seen from the table of component acids (Chapter IV, Table 69A, p. 336) that there is more than one variety of dika fats (from species of *Irvingia*). The seed fats of *I. barteri* (Nigeria) and *I. olivieri* (cay-cay fat, Cochin China) appear to be closely similar, their component acids including about 40 per cent. of lauric and 55 per cent. of myristic acid. There seem to be two varieties of *I. gabonensis* (Sierra Leone): in one the fatty acids include about 10 per cent. of oleic acid, with 70 per cent. of myristic acid and 20 per cent. of lauric acid, but in the other there is only about 2 per cent. of oleic acid, with nearly 60 per cent. of lauric and about 33 per cent. of myristic acid.

Dika fat from *I. barteri* was examined by Collin and Hilditch[1d] by isolation and analysis of its fully saturated glycerides. Dika fats of the almost saturated type were later examined by systematic crystallisation from acetone by Bushell

TABLE 95. *Component Glycerides of Dika Fats*

	COLLIN AND HILDITCH[1d] PER CENT. (WT.)	BUSHELL AND HILDITCH[12a] PER CENT. (MOL.)	MEARA AND PATEL[13] PER CENT. (MOL.)
Component acids:			
Capric	—	3·8	2·0
Lauric	38·8	61·6	46·6
Myristic	50·6	30·8	44·1
Palmitic	—	1·6	5·2
Stearic	—	0·8	—
Oleic	10·6	1·4	1·9
Linoleic	—	—	0·2
Component glycerides:			
Caprolauromyristin	—	ca. 11	5
Trilaurin	—	?	7
Dilauromyristin	ca. 31	ca. 65	33
Laurodimyristin	ca. 48	ca. 13	29
Trimyristin	—	—	5
Lauromyristopalmitin	—	ca. 5	13
Dimyristopalmitin	—	—	2
Lauromyristo-olein*	ca. 18	ca. 6	6
Lauro- or myristo-dioleins	ca. 3	—	—

* Including possible traces of caprolauro-olein and lauro-palmito-olein.

429

and Hilditch[12a] (a specimen from *I. gabonensis*) and by Meara and Patel[13] (a specimen (species unknown) from West Africa). The data for the *I. barteri* and *I. gabonensis* fats were less completely defined than those of Meara and Patel (Table 95). The chief constituents in these fats are dilauromyristin and laurodimyristin, with smaller proportions of capro-, palmito-, and oleo-lauromyristins. Meara and Patel also observed the presence of 5–7 per cent. each of trilaurin and tri-myristin, a result which suggests that dika fats may to some extent not conform with the usual even distribution.

The widely varying proportions of lauric and myristic acids in different dika fats is of course reflected in still greater variations in the proportions of dilauro-myristins and laurodimyristins, the chief component glycerides.

(b) SEED FATS CONTAINING 30–65 PER CENT. OF SATURATED ACIDS IN THEIR COMPONENT FATTY ACIDS

This group has received considerable attention in recent investigations for, although only two or three of these fats possess any intrinsic technical importance, they form a particularly interesting section in the following respects:

(i) They include the small number of tropical seed fats in which stearic acid is a prominent component.

(ii) Where the proportion of saturated acids in the whole fat approaches but does not exceed 60–65 per cent., there are just sufficient unsaturated acids to link up in mixed triglycerides with all the saturated acids, 1·3 to 1·5 mols. of saturated acid being therein associated with each mol. of unsaturated (oleic) acid; and in each of these cases the fully saturated glyceride content is very small or almost negligible and supports the general rule. Indeed, the extent to which the generalisation holds over this, the most critical, range of relative proportions of saturated and unsaturated acids is probably the strongest evidence so far put forward of the marked tendency to "even distribution" in seed fats.

At first sight it might be thought that complete even distribution should demand the presence of more than small proportions of palmitostearins, in cases where seed fats such as cacao butter, Borneo tallow, and some others contain nearly as much palmitic and stearic acids as they do oleic acid; but in such fats oleic acid always forms about 40 per cent. or more of the total acids so that, according to the definition of "even distribution" given in Chapter I (p. 19), nearly all the triglyceride molecules of these fats will contain at least one oleo-group, i.e. few will include three saturated acyl groups.

Moreover, it is now experimentally established that, in seed fats containing these proportions of oleic acid, practically all the central (2- or β-) hydroxyl groups of the glycerol molecules are selectively esterified with oleic acid (*cf.* Chapter V, p. 387). This not only defines the generalisation in the preceding paragraphs more precisely, but also supplies the reason why earlier studies of this group of fats indicated that specific forms of 2-oleoglycerides (e.g., 2-oleodistearin) are favoured in the natural synthesis of seed fats (*cf.* p. 402).

(iii) A further consequence of the operation of "even distribution" in these fats is that linoleic acid, even when it forms only two or three per cent. of the total fatty acids, is present almost wholly in diunsaturated glycerides. For, although linoleic acid (as a very minor component acid) will only occur once in any triglyceride molecule, the latter in any case contains at least one oleic group, so that the triglycerides containing a linoleo-group will be diunsaturated. These, therefore, form the part of the fat most soluble in acetone or other solvent: Table 96 illustrates the manner in which linoleo-glycerides are segregated into the most soluble fractions on crystallisation from acetone.

TABLE 96. *Concentration of Linoleo-Glycerides in most soluble Fractions (from Acetone) of Solid Seed Fats*

	WHOLE FAT PER CENT. (MOL.)	LEAST SOLUBLE PER CENT. (MOL.)	INTER-MEDIATE PER CENT. (MOL.)	MOST SOLUBLE PER CENT. (MOL.)
CACAO BUTTER				
Glycerides	100	26·7	48·8	24·5
Component acids:				
Palmitic	24·3	8·6	32·3	32·9
Stearic	35·4	55·1	31·2	18·5
Oleic	38·2	34·8	36·0	42·5
Linoleic	2·1	1·5	0·5	6·1
BORNEO TALLOW				
Glycerides	100	54·0	32·5	13·5
Component acids:				
Palmitic	19·5	12·5	30·2	21·8
Stearic	42·4	53·4	31·7	24·1
Arachidic	1·0	1·1	1·0	1·1
Oleic	36·9	33·0	37·1	51·4
Linoleic	0·2	—	—	1·6
SHEA BUTTER				
Glycerides	100	49·3	—	50·7
Component acids:				
Palmitic	6·3	5·5		7·1
Stearic	40·0	57·1		23·2
Oleic	49·8	36·5		62·8
Linoleic	3·9	0·9		6·9
PHULWARA BUTTER				
Glycerides	100	72·4	—	27·6
Component acids:				
Palmitic	59·4	65·0		44·9
Stearic	2·4	2·3		2·5
Oleic	34·5	31·7		41·6
Linoleic	3·7	1·0		11·0

(iv) This group of fats is rich in mono-unsaturated-disaturated glycerides which, in the course of the oxidation process, yield corresponding monoazelao-disaturated glycerides in quantities sufficient to permit their isolation and further examination.

(v) Most of these fats contain either palmitic and stearic, or stearic and arachidic, acids as the major component saturated acids, and it is interesting to observe how the acid of lower molecular weight tends to concentrate in the fully saturated glycerides (*cf.* Chapter V, Table 85, p. 404).

*Seed Fats of Sterculiaceæ and Dipterocarpaceæ (in which Palmitic
and Stearic are the major Saturated Component Acids)*

Cacao butter (Sterculiaceæ). The extensive use of this fat in chocolates and other confectionery has naturally caused much attention to be paid to its glyceride structure, which has been the subject of many investigations. Its special suitability in confectionery lies in the fact that it possesses a comparatively low melting point (about 30°) which is nevertheless much sharper than that of most fats, whilst in the solid state the material is comparatively brittle and not very greasy to the touch. These physical properties are, again, the result of the particular glyceride structure of this fat which, owing to the relative proportions of the few component acids of the fat and its conformity with the general rules of seed fat glyceride structure, is made up for the greater part of mono-oleo-disaturated glycerides, chiefly oleo-palmitostearin.

The qualitative crystallisation studies of Klimont (*cf.* Chapter V, p. 359) indicated the absence of simple triglycerides and the presence of oleodistearin and oleopalmitostearin. In 1924 Amberger and Bauch[14a] studied, more quantitatively, the fractional crystallisation of cacao butter which had been hydrogenated until its iodine value was reduced to 5·9, and stated that in their opinion the main components were 1-palmitodiolein 55, 1-oleodistearin 25 and 2-palmito-oleostearin 20 per cent. These figures did not tally with the component acid proportions in the whole fat, but Dr E. Lewkowitsch[14b] subsequently showed that by adopting a legitimate alternative assumption in the calculations involved, and by taking into account the components in 17·5 per cent. of the fat which was not recovered in Amberger and Bauch's crystallisation, the resulting data (1-palmito-oleostearin 56, 2-oleodistearin 26·5, 2-palmitodiolein 17·5 per cent.) accorded well with the component acid percentages for the whole fat and also with the work to be mentioned below. (It is now known,[15a] however, that a hydrogenated cacao butter of iodine value 6 still contains about 20 per cent. of oleo-disaturated glycerides which, being relatively soluble, probably account for the "loss" of 17·5 per cent. recorded by Amberger and Bauch.)

In 1927 Hilditch and Lea studied cacao butter by the oxidation method[16a] and showed that it contained about 2·5 per cent. of fully saturated glycerides (mainly dipalmitostearins); it is almost certain that the amount of triolein present is negligible, and consequently the remainder of the fat consists of about 73 per cent. of mono-oleo-disaturated glycerides and about 24·5 per cent. of dioleo-monosaturated glycerides. Lea[16b] actually isolated monoazelao-glycerides from the oxidation products of cacao butter corresponding with about 53 per cent. of mono-oleo-disaturated glycerides therein, and obtained a further 15–20 per cent. of monoazelao-glycerides in a less pure condition; so that to this extent the suggested proportion of mono-oleo-disaturated glycerides in the whole fat has been confirmed by chemical analysis.

In 1936 Hilditch and Stainsby[15a] separated cacao butter into three fractions by systematic crystallisation from acetone and therefrom deduced the approximate proportions of each of the mixed glycerides present; in 1949 Meara[17a] undertook a more complete resolution of the same fat, separating it finally into ten fractions by systematic crystallisation from acetone. The results of these two studies are summarised in Table 97 (in which the small proportion of linoleic acid is included with oleic acid in the statements of "oleo"-glycerides).

TABLE 97. *Component Glycerides of Cacao Butter*

	HILDITCH AND STAINSBY[15a] PER CENT. (MOL.)	MEARA[17a] PER CENT. (MOL.)
Component acids:		
Palmitic	26·2	26·2
Stearic	34·4	34·4
Oleic	37·3	37·3
Linoleic	2·1	2·1
Component glycerides:		
Palmitostearins	2	2·5
Oleodipalmitin	6	4
Oleopalmitostearin	52	57
Oleodistearin	19	22
Palmitodiolein	9	7·5
Stearodiolein	12	6
Triolein	—	1

In 1959 Scholfield and Dutton[18a] examined glycerides of cacao butter by the counter-current distribution technique (Chapter V, p. 384), and found 75 per cent. of oleodisaturated glycerides* (41 oleopalmitostearin, 22 oleo-distearin and 12 oleodipalmitin). In 1961 these workers, with Mounts,[18b] made a further and more complete analysis which indicated 81 per cent. of oleodisaturated glycerides (39 oleopalmitostearin, 27 oleodistearin, 15 oleo-dipalmitin) and 19 per cent. of dioleo-monosaturated glycerides.

In 1961 Jones and Hammond[19a] separated cacao butter into 43 fractions by "crystallisation in a thermal gradient" and found trisaturated 1, oleodi-saturated 84 and dioleo-monosaturated glycerides 15 per cent.; Steiner and Bonar[19b] used paper chromatography to determine the relative proportions of the three mono-oleodisaturated glycerides.

In 1963 Barrett, Dallas and Padley,[19c] by means of thin-layer chromato-graphy on silica impregnated with silver nitrate (*cf.* Chapter V, p. 385; Chapter XI, p. 707), found 2-oleodisaturated 73·5, 2-linoleodisaturated 6, mono-saturated-dioleins 17, and saturated-oleolinoleins and triolein 3·5 per cent. By selective enzyme hydrolysis they observed trisaturated 3, 2-oleodisaturated 80, 2-linoleodisaturated 6, monosaturated-dioleins and -oleolinoleins 11 per cent.

The glyceride constitution of cacao butter has thus been established more exactly than that of most natural fats, not only in regard to the proportions of individual mixed glycerides present but also with respect to the specific isomeric forms in which they occur (*cf.* below). The results of the earlier as well as the more recent attempts to determine the components of this fat are collected in the statement on page 434.

* The glycerides not accounted for (25 per cent. of the fat) would have contained increments of 14 oleic and 11 saturated acids, corresponding to at least a further 8 per cent. of oleo-disaturated glycerides.

GLYCERIDE TYPES

	FULLY SATURATED	MONO-OLEO-DISATURATED	DI-OLEO-MONO-SATURATED
Amberger and Bauch[14a] (as re-interpreted by Dr E. Lewkowitsch[14b]).	Traces (tristearin and palmitodistearin).	80 per cent. (55 per cent. 1-palmito-oleostearin, 25 per cent. oleodistearin).	20 per cent. (2-palmitodiolein).
Lea[16a,b]	2·5 per cent. (palmitostearins).	73 per cent.* (at least 50–60 per cent. oleopalmitostearins).	24·5 per cent.
Hilditch and Stainsby[15a]	2 per cent. (palmitostearins).	77 per cent. (52 per cent. oleopalmito-stearin, 19 per cent. oleo-distearin, 6 per cent. oleodipalmitin).	21 per cent. (9 per cent. palmito-diolein, 12 per cent. stearodiolein).
Meara[17a]	2·5 per cent. (palmitostearins).	83 per cent. (57 per cent. oleopalmito-stearin, 22 per cent. oleo-distearin, 4 per cent. oleodipalmitin).	13·5 per cent. (7·5 per cent. palmito-diolein, 6 per cent. stearodiolein).
Scholfield and Dutton[18a]	Trace.	75 per cent. (41 per cent. oleopalmito-stearin, 22 per cent. oleo-distearin, 12 per cent. oleodipalmitin).	?
Dutton, Scholfield and Mounts[18b]	Trace.	81 per cent. (39 per cent. oleopalmito-stearin, 27 per cent. oleo-distearin, 15 per cent. oleodipalmitin).	19 per cent.
Jones and Hammond[19a]	1 per cent.	84 per cent.	15 per cent.
Barrett et al.[19c] (T.L.C.)	—	80 per cent.	20 per cent.
(S.E.H.)	3 per cent.	86 per cent.	11 per cent.

* Monoazelao-glycerides (i) corresponding with 53 per cent. of mono-oleo-glycerides isolated as pure sodium salts, and (ii) corresponding with about 70 per cent. of mono-oleo-glycerides by separation as lithium salts.

Of the total mono-oleo-glycerides, about half to two-thirds is oleopalmito-stearin, the remainder consisting of either oleodistearin or oleodipalmitin. Half, or somewhat more, of the fat is made up of binary combinations in which stearic and oleic, or palmitic and oleic, acids are concerned, but similar combinations with palmitic and stearic acid occur in insignificant quantities, as is natural since an oleoyl group is present (in the 2-glyceryl position) in practically every molecule.

On the basis of selective attachment of oleic acid to the 2-glyceryl position, and random combination of the remaining acids with the (primary) 1- and 3-glyceryl groups, Vander Wal[20a] and Gunstone[20b] have computed the various component glycerides of cacao butter. The results are in very fair accordance with the relative proportions of mono-oleoglycerides (75–84 per cent.) and di-oleoglycerides (14–20 per cent.) as found in the above table, and also with the amounts of individual mono-oleoglycerides as determined by Dutton et al.,[18a,b] but the latter values as determined by the earlier methods are more divergent.

Configurational forms of the mono-oleodisaturated glycerides of cacao butter. Whilst the 2-oleodistearin of cacao butter was correctly identified from the melting and transition points of its polymorphic forms,[17a] similar studies[15a, 17d] of palmitodistearins obtained by the catalytic hydrogenation of appropriate concentrates of the oleopalmitostearin, oleodipalmitin or palmitodiolein led to the conclusion, now proved erroneous, that these respective cacao butter glycerides were made up of 2-palmito-glycerides. In 1957, infra-red spectroscopic analysis (Chapman et al.[21f]) showed conclusively that the major component glyceride in cacao butter is 2-(β-)oleo-palmito-stearin, whilst selective enzyme hydrolysis of oleopalmitostearin fractions (Savary et al.,[21a] Lutton,[21b] Mattson,[21c,d] Coleman[21e]) indicated that the resulting 2-mono-glycerides contained 96–97 per cent. of 2-mono-olein; these results were also confirmed by thermal (transition-points) and X-ray diffraction studies of these fractions (Lutton[21b]).

Borneo tallow (Dipterocarpaceæ). Hilditch and Priestman[22a] found that a specimen of this fat (component acids: myristic 1·5, palmitic 21·5, stearic 39·0, oleic 38·0 per cent. wt.) contained 4·5 per cent. of fully saturated palmito-stearins, and (no triolein being detected) 17·5 per cent. of dioleo-mono-saturated glycerides with 78 per cent. of mono-oleo-disaturated glycerides. The acetone crystallisation procedure was applied to Borneo tallow byBushell and Hilditch,[12b] and, later and more thoroughly, by Meara.[17b] The fat in the nuts of *Shorea robusta*, a tree of North India related botanically to the East Indian *S. stenoptera* (the source of Borneo tallow) was similarly examined by Hilditch and Zaky[22c]; the saturated acids in this fat differ from those of Borneo tallow in being largely stearic acid.

Selective enzyme hydrolysis of Borneo tallow led to the production of 2-mono-glycerides in which oleic acid formed 96 per cent. of the component acids.[21c]

Dhupa fat (Dipterocarpaceæ). This fat, also known as Malabar tallow, some-what resembles *Shorea* fat in its component acids; it is obtained from the seeds of *Vateria indica*, a large evergreen common in southern India. It was examined in 1943 by Venkatarao and Narasingarao,[23a] and in 1949 by Baliga and Meara[23c] by the crystallisation procedure.

The results of these glyceride studies of *Shorea* and *Vateria* fats are collected in Table 98.

TABLE 98. *Component Glycerides of Seed Fats of Dipterocarpaceæ Species*

| | S. stenoptera | | S. robusta | Vateria indica | |
	BUSHELL AND HILDITCH[12b] PER CENT. (MOL.)	MEARA[17b] PER CENT. (MOL.)	HILDITCH AND ZAKY[22c] PER CENT. (MOL.)	VENKA-TARAO ET AL.[23a] PER CENT. (MOL.)	BALIGA AND MEARA[23c] PER CENT. (MOL.)
Component acids:					
Palmitic	19·5	19·5	4·6	13·7	12·2
Stearic	42·4	42·4	44·2	43·1	42·4
Arachidic	1·0	1·0	6·3	0·4	2·7
Oleic	36·9	36·9	42·1	42·5	40·5
Linoleic	0·2	0·2	2·8	0·1	2·2
Component glycerides:					
Palmitostearins	5	3	1	—	1
Oleodipalmitin	8		—	7	—
Oleopalmitostearin	31	83	8	17	27
Oleodistearin	40		42	45	46
Oleodiarachidin	—		14	—	—
Palmitodiolein	3		5	13	8
Stearodiolein	13	13	25	16	14
Arachidodiolein	—		4	—	—
Triolein	—	1	1	—	4

In all three fats the observed proportions of the dioleo-glycerides are fairly closely simulated[20c] when the component glycerides are computed (from the component acids in each fat) by the method[20b] employed by Gunstone (cf. Chapter V, p. 397); this also holds for oleopalmitostearin and oleodistearin in S. robusta and Vateria fats, but in Borneo tallow the accordance in some cases (notably oleopalmitostearin and stearodiolein) is less close, whilst the amount (3–5 per cent.) of fully saturated glycerides is somewhat greater than usual for a fat with this mixture of saturated and unsaturated acids.

With more stearic and less palmitic acid in Borneo tallow and Dhupa fat than in cacao butter, these fats contain more oleodistearin and less oleopalmitostearin than the latter, and are in consequence somewhat harder and of higher melting point. The higher palmitic acid content of cacao butter (and correspondingly reduced stearic acid content, that of oleic acid being similar to Dipterocarp seed fats) greatly affects the glyceride structure, with the result that in cacao butter 2-(β-)oleopalmitostearin greatly predominates over the remainder of the constituent glycerides. This in turn not only lowers the "melting point" of the fat but also narrows the range over which it softens and melts. These factors, of importance in the confectionery industry, are not possessed in so marked a degree by the Dipterocarpaceæ seed fats, which are, therefore, less popular than cacao butter in the industry.

The seed fat of another denizen of Borneo, Dacryodes rostrata, a member of the Burseraceæ, was studied by Hilditch and Stainsby[15b] (the results were published erroneously as referring to the seed fat of Sterculia fœtida). The fat had as component acids: palmitic 11·7, stearic 39·8, arachidic 1·9, oleic 43·3 and linoleic 3·3 per cent. (mol.) and contained less than 2 per cent. of fully saturated glycerides. The main components are probably mono-oleo-disaturated glycerides about 57, and stearo- or palmito-dioleins about 41 per cent.; monoazelao-disaturated glycerides were isolated in the form of sodium salts from the oxidised glycerides in amount corresponding to 43 per cent. of mono-oleo-disaturated glycerides in the original fat.

Seed Fats of Guttiferæ and Sapotacæ (in which stearic acid is frequently the most prominent saturated acid, whilst palmitic acid is also present)

Allanblackia seed fats (Guttiferæ). These are of little technical importance but have been exceptionally useful in the study of glyceride structure, because they are built up almost wholly from stearic and oleic acids. It will be recalled that it was in the seed fat of A. stuhlmannii that Heise[24] first demonstrated in 1897 the presence of oleodistearin in quantity in a natural fat; moreover, it has later been possible to isolate this main component almost quantitatively in the pure condition, and to show that it is entirely 2-oleodistearin.

A. stuhlmannii seed fat (component acids: palmitic 3, stearic 52, oleic 45 per cent.) was studied quantitatively in 1931–1933 by Hilditch and Saletore,[25a] who found it contained only 1·5 per cent. of fully saturated components, and that it could be separated by crystallisation from acetone into nearly 70 per cent. of a solid glyceride (m.p. 42·5–44°, iod. val. 28·5) and a soluble liquid portion of iodine value 56·7 from which no fraction of higher iodine value could be obtained by further crystallisation. The main components are therefore about 66 per cent. of mono-oleo-glycerides (chiefly oleodistearin) and about 33 per cent. of stearo- (with perhaps a little palmito-) diolein. The melting point of the main component is that of 2-oleodistearin; the azelaodistearin obtained during oxidation of the fat melted at 63–64° (unchanged on admixture with 2-azelaodistearin prepared by oxidation of synthetic 2-oleodistearin).

Meara[17c] recorded in 1945 the transition and melting points of the four polymorphic forms of oleodistearins isolated from *Allanblackia stuhlmannii, floribunda,* and *parviflora;* these were in each instance 23–24°, 29–36°, 36–37·5°, and 43·0–43·6°, identical with those of synthesised 2-oleodistearin.

The seed fats of *A. floribunda* and *A. parviflora* have component acids, and also component glycerides, very similar to those of *A. stuhlmannii*. The molar percentages of component acids and component glycerides observed[25b] in these two fats were as follows (Table 99):

TABLE 99. *Component Glycerides of* Allanblackia *Seed Fats*[25b]

	A. floribunda PER CENT. (MOL.)	A. parviflora PER CENT. (MOL.
Component acids:		
Myristic	—	1·8
Palmitic	2·2	2·5
Stearic	58·3	51·6
Arachidic	0·2	0·2
Oleic	38·6	43·9
Linoleic	0·7	—
Component glycerides:		
Palmitostearins	2	2
Oleopalmitostearin	5	6
Oleodistearin	76	60
Palmitodiolein	1	3
Stearodiolein	16	29

Garcinia seed fats (Guttiferæ). These seed fats are also exceptionally rich in stearic acid and, as in *Allanblackia* fats, oleodistearin is the chief constituent glyceride present. It has been shown, in the case of *G. indica,* to be exclusively 2-oleodistearin by the transition and melting point data of Meara[17a] for its four polymorphic forms, and by thermal and X-ray data published by Lutton.[26]

The seed fat (kokum butter) of *G. indica* has been studied by the crystallisation method by Vidyarthi and Rao,[27a] and also by Hilditch and Murti,[28a] whilst that of *G. morella* was similarly examined by Dhingra *et al.,*[28c] and by Hilditch and Murti.[28a] These results are summarised in Table 100 (p. 438) and, again, are in most cases close to those computed by Gunstone's procedure.[20b,c]

Kanya butter (Pentadesma butyracea, Guttiferæ). Hilditch and Saletore[25a] give the probable composition of this fat (component acids: palmitic 5·4, stearic 46·1, oleic 48·5 per cent. wt.) as 3 per cent. of palmitodistearins and about equal proportions (47–50 per cent.) of oleodisaturated and dioleo-monosaturated glycerides. The monoazelao-glycerides obtained on oxidation of the fat consisted largely of monoazelaodistearin, m.p. 61°, connoting the presence of 2-oleodistearin, and later Meara[17c] showed from the transition and melting

TABLE 100. *Component Glycerides of* Garcinia *Seed Fats*

	G. indica		G. morella	
	VIDYARTHI AND RAO[27a] PER CENT. (MOL.)	HILDITCH AND MURTI[28a] PER CENT. (MOL.)	DHINGRA ET AL.[28c] PER CENT. (MOL.)	HILDITCH AND MURTI[28a] PER CENT. (MOL.)
Component acids:				
Myristic	1·5	—	0·3	—
Palmitic	5·8	3·1	7·9	1·2
Stearic	51·4	56·1	42·0	46·2
Arachidic	—	—	0·3	2·0
Oleic	41·3	39·1	43·3	49·7
Linoleic	—	1·7	6·2	0·9
Component glycerides:				
Palmitostearins	2	2	3	2
Oleopalmitostearin	15	8	} 45 {	—
Oleodistearin	58	68		46
Palmitodioleins	2	—	} 50 {	4
Stearodiolein	21	20		47
Tri-"oleins"	1	2	—	1

point data of the oleodistearin isolated from the fat by crystallisation that it consisted entirely of the symmetrical 2-oleodistearin.

Bacury seed fat (Platonia insignis, Guttiferæ). This is another of the few outstanding exceptions to the generally evenly distributed glyceride structure of solid seed fats. Chaves and Pechnik[29a] reported in 1945 that it had the unusually high melting point of 51–52° and contained 24 per cent. of fully saturated glycerides, although its component acids were approximately 56 per cent. saturated (palmitic and stearic) with 39 per cent. oleic and 4 per cent. linoleic acid. Subsequently Hilditch and Pathak[29b] submitted bacury fat to crystallisation from ether at −20° and at 0° and confirmed these observations: the component acids were found to be myristic 1·0, palmitic 55·1, stearic 6·4, arachidic 0·3, hexadecenoic 3·2, oleic 31·7 and linoleic 2·3 per cent. (wt.), and the component glycerides: fully saturated 20 (tripalmitin 15), oleodipalmitin 38, oleopalmitostearin 17, palmitodiolein 19, stearodiolein 6 per cent. (mol.).

Apart from the fully saturated glyceride content, the rest of the fat is constituted on the usual lines, and bacury fat thus resembles laurel kernel fat[11b] (*cf.* p. 429) in that it is only the fully saturated glycerides which are abnormal. It is possible, but of course not in any way proven, that such departures from the normal are caused by certain acids (in this instance, palmitic) being produced in the seed at some stage of its development in much greater proportions than the average content of the acid in the total seed fat at maturity; if so, the departure from normality would be more apparent than real.

In bacury fat, values for the three classes of trisaturated, mono- and di-oleo glycerides computed by Gunstone[20b] are widely different from those observed. **Indian laurel (Dilo, Dombe) kernel fat (Calophyllum inophyllum, Guttiferæ).** This is the seed fat of an evergreen tree common to parts of India, Ceylon and Indonesia. The saturated acids of this fat consist of about equal proportions of palmitic and stearic acids, amounting in all to about 35 per cent. of the total acids. Its component glycerides were investigated by the acetone crystallisation procedure by Weerakoon,[30] who found that (with component acids: myristic 1·2, palmitic 17·8, stearic 17·1, oleic 35·4 and linoleic 28·5 per cent. mol.) the chief constituents were oleopalmitostearin 16, linoleopalmitostearin 9, palmito-oleo-linolein 26, stearo-oleo-linolein 20, linoleodiolein 8 and oleo-dilinolein 9 per cent. (mol.), with about 4 per cent. each of palmito- and stearo-dioleins and about 1 per cent. each of palmito- and stearo-dilinoleins.

Shea butter (Butyrospermum parkii, Sapotaceæ). This somewhat important seed fat has also been examined by crystallisation methods. Hilditch and Saletore[25a] (1931) found that a specimen (component acids: palmitic 8·5, stearic 35·9, oleic 49·9, linoleic 5·3 per cent. wt.) contained only 2·3 per cent. of fully saturated glycerides and, assuming that triolein was present only in negligible propor-tions, concluded that it contained about 30 per cent. of oleo-disaturated glycerides and about 65 per cent. of dioleo-mono-saturated glycerides. Green and Hilditch,[25c] (1938) after applying the acetone crystallisation method to another specimen of the fat (component acids: palmitic 5·7, stearic 40·4, oleic 50·0, linoleic 3·9 per cent. wt.), gave the probable approximate com-position as stearodi-"oleins" 45, oleodistearin 35 and palmitodi-"oleins" 10 per cent., with minor amounts of palmitostearins (4·5 per cent.), tri-"olein" (4·5 per cent.) and possibly oleopalmitostearin. Apart from slightly higher proportions than usual of trisaturated and tri-unsaturated components, the fat conformed to the usual "evenly distributed" type.

Barrett et al.[19c] (1963) determined the glycerides in shea butter by their thin-layer chromatography procedure ("T.L.C.", cf. p. 433) and also by selective enzyme hydrolysis ("S.E.H.") with the following results:

	Trisaturated	2-oleodi-saturated	2-linoleo-disaturated	Saturated dioleins	Saturated-oleo-linoleins (with triolein)	"GU⁴"	"GU⁵"
T.L.C.	Trace	43	9	29	13	3	3
S.E.H.	1·5	41·5	7·5	32	14·5	2·5	Trace

"GU⁴": Triglycerides with 4 double bonds.
"GU⁵":   „   „ 5 „   „

Computed values by Gunstone's "Mode I" procedure[20b] (cf. Chapter V, p. 397) for the general glyceride structure of shea fat are mono-unsaturated-disaturated 44–48, diunsaturated-monosaturated 44–42, triunsaturated 12–10 per cent.

Njatuo tallow, Taban merah fat (Palaquium oblongifolium, Sapotaceæ). This fat was found by Hilditch and Stainsby[15b] to possess component acids: myristic 0·2, palmitic 5·9, stearic 54·0, oleic 39·9 per cent. (wt.), and to contain only 1·8 per cent. of fully saturated glycerides. Crystallisation from acetone yielded nearly 50 per cent. of a crystalline solid, m.p., 42·5–44°, evidently 2-oleodi-stearin, whilst the most soluble fractions did not exceed in iodine value that of stearodiolein (57·3). Triolein is therefore not present, and the chief component of the fat is about 77 per cent. of oleo-disaturated glycerides (mainly 2-oleo-distearin), whilst about 21 per cent. of stearo- (with a little palmito-) diolein is also present. Meara[17c] confirmed by transition and melting-point data that 2-oleodistearin is the only form of this glyceride present.

Sapota oil (Acharas sapota, Sapotaceæ). This fat (component acids: lauric 2·2, myristic 7·4, palmitic 13·7, stearic 11·0, oleic 64·2, linoleic 1·5 per cent. mol.), examined by Vidyarthi and Mallya,[27b] resembles neem oil somewhat in its general fatty acid composition. Resolution by crystallisation from acetone, coupled with determination of fully saturated glycerides, indicated that the component glycerides were mainly palmitodiolein 36, stearodiolein 28, myristodiolein 23 per cent. (mol.), with minor amounts of the following: tri-"olein" 5, oleopalmitostearin 5, and mono-oleo-glycerides with two of the lower saturated acyl groups 3 per cent. (mol.). The tri-"olein" is probably mainly linoleodiolein, and di-"oleo"-glycerides thus form about 90 per cent. of the whole fat.

Baku (Njave, Dumori) fat [Mimusops (Dumori) heckelii (Njave)], Sapotaceæ. This fat was examined by Atherton and Meara,[10b] who resolved it into three fractions by a simple form of the acetone crystallisation procedure, and later by Cama[31a] who used a more elaborate form of the technique and separated the fat into six portions. The earlier analyses gave less detailed information than that of Cama: in Table 101, in which the data are collected, the small amounts of linoleic acid are included with the oleic acid as "oleo"-glycerides.

TABLE 101. *Component Glycerides of Baku Fat*

	ATHERTON AND MEARA[10b]		CAMA[31a]
	SPECIMEN 1 PER CENT. (MOL.)	SPECIMEN 2 PER CENT. (MOL.)	PER CENT. (MOL.)
Component acids:			
Palmitic	4·8	4·8	4·1
Stearic	35·1	35·6	35·1
Arachidic	0·9	0·4	1·9
Oleic	59·2	58·9	57·5
Linoleic	Trace	0·3	1·4
Component glycerides:			
Palmitodistearin	1	1	—
"Oleo"-palmitostearin	7–3	8–2	5
"Oleo"-distearin	} 27–31	26–32 {	26
"Oleo"-stearo-arachidin			3
Palmito-di-"olein"	9–14	6–12	8
Stearo-di-"olein"	} 46–41	47–41 {	46
Arachidodi-"olein"			2
Tri-"olein"	10	12	10

Baku fat is an instance in which the principle of even distribution is not completely followed so far as the unsaturated acids are concerned, since it contains 10–12 per cent. of tri-"oleins", the chief components however being stearodiolein 41–47 per cent. and oleodistearin 26–32 per cent.

The fatty oil from another species of *Mimusops*, the Indian *M. elangi*, contains 64 per cent. of oleic and 14·5 per cent. of linoleic acid, with about 10 per cent. each of palmitic and stearic in its component acids. This fat also appears to diverge somewhat in its glyceride structure from the normal for Kartha and Menon,[31b] using the acetone-crystallisation procedure, found that

4 per cent. of fully saturated and 14 per cent. of mono-unsaturated disaturated glycerides were present, in spite of the high content of unsaturated acid in the whole fat.

Madhuca (Bassia) seed fats (Sapotaceæ). Mowrah fat, Illipé butter or mee oil, and phulwara butter, are seed fats of this genus grown in India and the East Indies, and have been usually known to the technologist as "*Bassia* seed fats" (*vide* Chapter IV, p. 321). The components of mowrah fat and phulwara butter have been determined by the modern methods, employing preliminary partial resolution by crystallisation from acetone.

Mowrah fat (from *M. latifolia*; component acids: palmitic 24·2, stearic 19·3, oleic 43·3, linoleic 13·2 per cent. mol.) was found by Hilditch and Ichaporia[32] to contain 1·2 per cent. of fully saturated dipalmitostearin. The main components are palmitodi-"oleins" 41, stearodi-"oleins" 30 and "oleo"-palmitostearins 27 per cent.; there may also be about 1 per cent. of "oleo"-dipalmitins or similar small quantities of "oleo"-distearin and of tri-unsaturated glycerides (oleolinoleins). This composition follows closely the prevailing rule in seed fats.

Phulwara butter (from *M. butyracea*; component acids: palmitic 59·4, stearic 2·4, oleic 34·5, linoleic 3·7 per cent. mol.) is remarkable amongst the other *Madhuca* seed fats or, indeed, those of the Sapotaceæ in general, in that stearic acid is a very minor component and that the only major component acids are oleic and palmitic, the latter in unusually large proportions (one of the highest yet recorded for any seed fat). Bushell and Hilditch[12c] showed the chief glycerides present to be "oleo"-dipalmitins 62 and palmitodi-"oleins" 23 per cent. The fully saturated components (8 per cent., substantially tripalmitin) are more abundant than is usual in a seed fat with the observed proportions of saturated and unsaturated acids. "Oleo"-palmitostearins may amount to about 7 per cent. of the fat. This fat is thus somewhat out of the common in several respects, but it may be added that triolein is not present in detectable quantities. By crystallisation from acetone, 72 per cent. of the fat was obtained as a crystalline solid which contained (calculated to the original fat) 58 per cent. of oleodipalmitin admixed with 8 per cent. of tripalmitin and 6 per cent. of palmitodi-"oleins"; it may thus prove to be a convenient source for the preparation of a natural oleodipalmitin.

Piqui-a kernel fat (Caryocar villosum). This fat, from a member of the family Caryocaraceæ, may be mentioned here because, like that of *Madhuca butyracea*, it is unusually rich in palmitic acid, its component acids being myristic 1·6, palmitic 50·6, stearic 0·9, oleic 43·7 and linoleic 3·2 per cent. (mol.). According to Hilditch and Rigg,[33] it contains 2·5 per cent. of fully saturated glycerides (tripalmitin), and the fat is almost certainly chiefly made up of about 50 per cent. of oleodipalmitin with about 40 per cent. of palmitodiolein.

It will be noticed that this fat, in contrast to that of *Madhuca butyracea*, conforms with the usual evenly distributed type of glycerides of which numerous instances have been mentioned in the immediately preceding pages, although its content of palmitic acid is unusually large and approaches that of phulwara butter.

Seed fats of the Sapindaceæ

These are of special interest because, in contrast to those with which we have just dealt, they contain two major component saturated acids which are in this case stearic and arachidic, instead of palmitic and stearic. Some of the seed fats of this family also contain appreciable quantities of a monoethenoid C_{20} (eicosenoic) acid.

Two seed fats from Malayan species of the genus *Nephelium* were studied by the older methods by Hilditch and Stainsby,[15b] and that of *Schleichera trijuga* (a shrub indigenous to India and Ceylon) has been more recently examined by the intensive crystallisation technique by Weerakoon.[30]

Pulasan fat (from *Nephelium mutabile*; component acids: palmitic 3·4, stearic 31·4, arachidic 20·6, oleic 44·6 per cent. mol.) contains about 63 per cent. of oleo-disaturated glycerides (including apparently both oleostearoarachidin and oleodistearin) and about 35 per cent. of dioleo-saturated glycerides, with only 1·5 per cent. of fully saturated glycerides and no detectable triolein. Direct crystallisation of the fat from acetone yielded 48 per cent. of a solid (iodine value 29·0, equivalent 300·5) which was evidently a mixture of oleo-stearoarachidin and oleodistearin.

Rambutan tallow (from *N. lappaceum*; component acids: palmitic 2·3, stearic 14·2, arachidic 32·5, oleic 47·0, eicosenoic (?) 4·0 per cent. mol.) contains about 43 per cent. of oleo-disaturated glycerides (probably oleostearoarachidin with some oleodiarachidin) and about 55 per cent. of dioleo-saturated glycerides (stearo- or arachido-diolein and probably some oleo-eicoseno-saturated glycerides). Only 1·4 per cent. of fully saturated glycerides are present, and triolein is absent.

The purest azelao-disaturated glycerides isolated by crystallisation from the oxidation products of the fat had an equivalent of 835 and melted at 65·5° (azelaostearoarachidin 822, azelaodiarachidin 850); direct crystallisation of the fat from acetone yielded 25 per cent. of a solid (m.p. 46°, iod. val. 27·4, equivalent 309·4) which evidently contained both oleodiarachidin and oleo-stearoarachidin.

Kusum or kon oil (from *Schleichera trijuga*; component acids: myristic 1·5, palmitic 6·8, stearic 6·0, arachidic 26·0, lignoceric 1·0, oleic 42·4, linoleic 4·3, and eicosenoic 12·0 per cent. mol.) differs from the preceding in its wider range of component acids, and in the larger proportions of eicosenoic acid which, with arachidic and oleic acids, makes up 80 per cent. of the total acids. Its glyceride structure, according to a detailed study by Weerakoon,[30] is as follows: "oleo"-disaturated glycerides 35, eicoseno-disaturated 2, saturated di-"oleins" 31, saturated-"oleo"-eicosenoins 16 per cent. (mol.), with 15 per cent. of triunsaturated glycerides (chiefly eicosenodi-"oleins") and only 1 per cent. of trisaturated glycerides.

Other Seed Fats in this Group

Some other seed fats with 30–50 per cent. of saturated acids in their total fatty acids have been studied, with results which are of interest as regards the general subject of glyceride structure.

Neem (Margosa) oil (Azadirachta indica, syn. Melia indica, Meliaceæ). In this fat the saturated acids form somewhat less than a third of the total fatty acids, with palmitic and stearic acids present in very similar proportions. It has been examined by the acetone crystallisation procedure by Hilditch and Murti[28b] and by Gupta and Mitra,[28d] with results summarised in Table 102.

TABLE 102. *Component Glycerides of Neem (Margosa) Oil*

	HILDITCH AND MURTI[28b] PER CENT. (MOL.)	GUPTA AND MITRA[28d] PER CENT. (MOL.)
Component acids:		
Palmitic	16·3	17·9
Stearic	14·5	14·4
Arachidic	1·2	3·0
Oleic	60·3	55·8
Linoleic	7·7	8·9
Component glycerides:		
Palmitostearins	0·5	Trace
"Oleo"-dipalmitin	5	—
"Oleo"-palmitostearin	12	20
"Oleo"-distearin	—	2
Palmitodi-"olein"	26	33
Stearodi-"olein"	34	28·5
Tri-"oleins"	22·5	16·5

Both studies show that the neem oil glycerides are constituted on the plan of widest distribution of the component fatty acids in the triglyceride molecules. Diunsaturated glycerides form nearly two-thirds of the fat, and about 20 per cent. of triunsaturated glycerides are present, these consisting almost entirely of linoleodiolein. In Table 102 arachidic has been included with stearic acid, and linoleic with oleic acid, in the summary of component glycerides. The observed proportions of the chief components, oleopalmitostearin, palmitodi-"oleins", stearodi-"oleins" and tri-unsaturated glycerides (linoleodiolein) are closely simulated if the oleic acid observed in the total fatty acids is arithmetically proportioned between the contents of palmitic, stearic and linoleic acids (*cf.* Chapter V, Appendix, p. 419); computation by the method[20b] of Gunstone in this instance gives only moderate accordance with the observed results.[20c]

Andiroba oil (Carapa guyanensis, Meliaceæ). This fat (component acids: palmitic 30·7, stearic 6·9, arachidic 2·0, hexadecenoic 1·0, oleic 49·7, linoleic 9·0 and linolenic 0·7 per cent. mol.) was found by Dale and Meara[4b] to contain the following glycerides: oleodipalmitin 14, oleopalmitostearin 18, oleo-palmito-arachidin 4, palmitodiolein 29, palmito-oleo-linolein 13, stearodiolein 7, arachidodiolein 1 and linoleodioleins 13 per cent. (mol.); only traces of fully saturated glycerides (palmitostearins) were present.

Mango kernel fat (Mangifera indica, Anacardiaceæ). This fat (component acids: myristic 0·9, palmitic 9·7, stearic 33·7, arachidic 6·0, oleic 49·7 per cent. mol.) was separated into fractions by Pathak, Gunde and Godbole,[34a] who deduced the presence of 14 per cent. of fully saturated glycerides (palmitodistearin 9, tristearin 5) with stearodiolein 54, oleopalmitostearin 16, oleodistearin 8 and palmitodiolein 7 per cent. (mol.). The proportion of trisaturated components

443

is considerably larger than usual for a fat in which saturated acids form only half of the total acids.

Buchanania latifolia seed-fat (Anacardiaceæ). This was found by Godbole, Gunde and Shrivastava[34b] to contain, as component acids, palmitic 31·0, stearic 7·8, oleic 55·8 and linoleic 5·4 per cent. (mol.). With a fully saturated glyceride content of only 5 per cent. mol. (*ca.* 2 per cent. tripalmitin and 3 per cent. dipalmitostearin), it is probable that the fat consists mainly of mono-saturated di-"oleins", but the more detailed crystallisation procedure was not applied in this instance.

Pentaclethra seed fats (Leguminosæ, sub-family, Mimosoidæ). The seed fats of two different specimens of *P. macrophylla* (owala or atta seed oil) which differed somewhat in their contents of stearic and linoleic acids, and of *P. eetveldeana*, which contained more oleic and less linoleic acid than the first-named fats, have been studied by the modern crystallisation technique by

TABLE 103. *Component Glycerides of* Pentaclethra *Seed Fats*

	Pentaclethra macrophylla		P. eetveldeana
	I	II	
	PER CENT. (MOL.)	PER CENT. (MOL.)	PER CENT. (MOL.)
Component acids:			
Palmitic	5·0	4·6	4·5
Stearic	7·5	2·2	5·3
Arachidic	2·6	3·6	5·1
Behenic	5·9	5·0	10·9
Lignoceric	9·3	8·7	2·9
Oleic	20·0	19·3	54·5
Linoleic	49·7	56·6	16·8
Probable component glycerides:			
Disaturated-oleins	—	—	9
Disaturated-linoleins	11	8	—
Saturated-dioleins	—	—	37
Saturated-oleo-linoleins	41	26	31
Saturated-dilinoleins	27	30	—
Triolein	—	—	4
Dioleolinoleins	—	—	19
Oleodilinoleins	19	32	—
Trilinolein	2	4	—

Hilditch, Meara and Patel,[35a] with the results summarised in Table 103. Their glyceride structures afford a good illustration of the even manner of distribution of fatty acids throughout seed fat glycerides with, at the same time, wide differences in the proportions of individual mixed glycerides consequent upon alterations (even of a relatively slight order) in the proportions of any one component acid. Thus, whilst linoleic acid forms about 50 per cent. of the total acids in *P. macrophylla* seed fat, whereas oleic acid forms a similar proportion of those in *P. eetveldeana* seed fat, the respective amounts of trilinolein or triolein are minimal; but, whilst the proportions of triunsaturated glycerides are not dissimilar, these are mainly oleo-dilinoleins in the *P. macrophylla* fats, but linoleodioleins in that from *P. eetveldeana*.

Lophira seed fats (Ochnaceæ). The seed fats of the two species of this genus which have so far been studied are peculiar (*a*) in containing major proportions of behenic acid in their saturated acids and minor proportions of a docosenoic acid in their unsaturated acids, (*b*) in containing more than twice as much linoleic as oleic acid – an unusual feature in seed fats in which approximately one-half of the component acids belong to the saturated series, and (*c*) in the apparent absence of any stearic or arachidic acids. The seed fat (niam fat) of *L. alata* and that of *L. procera* have been examined by the acetone crystallisation procedure,[35a, b] and the general nature of the constituent glycerides elucidated (Table 104). The acidic components of these fats being somewhat more complex than in many of those discussed above, the individual distribution of the major component saturated acids palmitic and behenic could not be

TABLE 104. *Component Glycerides of* Lophira *Seed Fats*

	L. alata[35b] PER CENT. (MOL.)	*L. procera*[35a] PER CENT. (MOL.)
Component acids:		
Myristic	2·4	0·8
Palmitic	29·9	41·8
Behenic	11·8	17·4
Lignoceric	1·8	0·3
Oleic	16·2	11·4
Linoleic	33·6	26·5
Docosenoic	4·3	1·8
Component glyceride categories:*		
Trisaturated	—	3
Mono-saturated	38	76
Diunsaturated	62	19
Triunsaturated	—	2
Containing 2 palmitic groups	3	27
Containing 1 palmitic group	91	71
Containing no palmitic groups	6	2
Containing 2 linoleic groups	9	4
Containing 1 linoleic group	83	72
Containing no linoleic group	8	24

* No indication was observed of glycerides containing more than *one* behenic, oleic, or docosenoic group in either of the fats. In computing the glyceride categories, the minor amounts of myristic and lignoceric acids were respectively included with palmitic and behenic acids.

followed very far, but it was observed that each was present in quantity in most of the fractions into which the fats were separated by crystallisation from acetone. It therefore appears that the behenic acid behaves in the same way as the palmitic and stearic acids more commonly present in other seed fats which have been investigated. The *Lophira* fats thus form a very interesting example of the manner in which glyceride structure seems to be largely independent of the particular component acids which may be present.

The relative proportions of monosaturated and disaturated glycerides observed suggest that the usual principles of "even distribution" are followed fairly closely in *Lophira* fats.

Hodgsonia capniocarpa seed fat (Cucurbitaceæ). This fat (component acids: myristic 0·6, palmitic 38·2, stearic 9·0, arachidic 0·3, hexadecenoic 2·9, oleic 25·5, linoleic 23·5 per cent. mol.) is interesting because it contains about equal proportions of saturated and unsaturated acids, whilst the latter in turn consist of nearly equal amounts of oleic and linoleic acids. This has the consequence that the mono-unsaturated as well as the di-unsaturated glycerides are found to contain both oleic and linoleic acids in corresponding proportions, whereas when linoleic is a minor, and oleic a major, component acid, the former is almost wholly present in the di-unsaturated glycerides alone. A further consequence is the presence of substantial amounts of tri-unsaturated glycerides, as shown by Hilditch, Meara and Pedelty[36] in a study of the fractions obtained by crystallisation of the fat from acetone: "oleo"-dipalmitin 33, "oleo"-palmitostearins 27, palmitodi-"oleins" 24 and tri-"oleins" 13 per cent. The tri-unsaturated glycerides are almost certainly mixed oleo-linoleins, and the specific mixture of glycerides encountered in this fat is the consequence of the combination of *four* major component acids (palmitic, stearic, oleic and linoleic) into mixed triglycerides, whereas in other cases only the *three* acids, palmitic, stearic and oleic, have been major components.

(*c*) SEED FATS IN WHICH UNSATURATED ACIDS PREDOMINATE (LIQUID SEED FATS: SATURATED ACIDS LESS THAN 25–35 PER CENT. OF TOTAL ACIDS)

At one time the glyceride structure of the more unsaturated (liquid) fatty oils could only be studied by indirect methods, such as the qualitative examination of crystalline bromo-glycerides from unsaturated oils (Chapter V, p. 361), the determination of tristearin after complete hydrogenation of the oils (p. 361), or the investigation of a series of incompletely hydrogenated products of an oil (p. 361). With the aid of crystallisation from solvents at low temperatures, and later of counter-current distribution between solvents, a considerable number of liquid fatty oils have however been studied since about 1945, and much fresh information has in consequence resulted in regard to the types of constituent glycerides, and in many instances the proportions of individual mixed glycerides, present.

In very many of these fatty oils the unsaturated acids are confined to oleic and linoleic, and it is interesting to note the wide variations in the proportions of the component glycerides which result from comparatively small alterations in the relative proportions of the two acids. Moreover, by reason of the general operation of "even distribution" it is needful for a given acid, e.g., oleic or linoleic, to form 65 per cent. or more of the total fatty acids of an oil before the corresponding simple triglyceride (e.g., triolein or trilinolein) is present in it in any quantity.

Thus it will be seen from references to individual fats that olive and teaseed oils are almost the only ones which contain triolein in quantity – and these to a much smaller degree than was formerly supposed, owing to the presence of maximal amounts of saturated dioleins and of linoleodioleins. Again, although groundnut oil differs from olive oil only in its higher proportions of linoleic acid in the unsaturated C_{18} acids, and in the presence of a few per cent. of higher saturated acids, the difference is amply sufficient to result in the absence of triolein from groundnut oil. Many of the well-known differences in appearance and properties between oils such as olive and groundnut are, in fact, obviously the consequence of these somewhat profound differences in the nature and proportions of their chief component glycerides.

In the discussion of individual liquid seed fats which follows, the order of treatment is from the less unsaturated ("non-drying") oils to the most unsaturated of the "drying" oils. It is of some interest to observe how the glyceride structure of these seed fats, and their relative contents of oleic, linoleic and linolenic acids, aligns itself with the old classification of "non-drying", "semi-drying" and "drying" oils.

(i) *Oleic-rich Seed Fats* ("*Non-drying*" *Oils*)

The number of fatty oils in this group whose glyceride structure has been studied in more or less detail is fewer than in the more unsaturated groups: groundnut oils, castor oil, rape oil and the fruit-coat fat olive oil (discussed later on p. 477) are the only instances in which modern techniques have yet been applied.

Tea seed oil (Thea sinensis, Theaceæ). This is very similar to the fruit-coat olive oil in its component acids (palmitic 7·6, oleic 83·3, linoleic 7·4 per cent., with fractional percentages of myristic, stearic and arachidic acids). It contains only traces of fully saturated components, whilst its content of tri-C_{18} glycerides is close to the minimum possible.[37a,b] It therefore consists of about 70 per cent. of tri-unsaturated glycerides (probably about 50 per cent. triolein and 20 per cent. linoleodioleins), the remainder being almost wholly monopalmitodi-"oleins" with subordinate amounts of other monosaturated-di-"oleins" and of dipalmito-"olein".

Almond oil (Prunus amygdalus, Rosaceæ). Gunde and Hilditch,[38] employing an unusual modification of the earlier acetone-crystallisation techniques, isomerised ("elaidinised") almond oil with selenium at 220° before separating the semi-solid product into several fractions by crystallisation from acetone. With component acids myristic 1, palmitic 5, oleic 77 and linoleic 17 per cent., the component glycerides appeared to consist approximately of palmito-diolein 17, linoleodiolein 52 and triolein 31 per cent.

Elaidinisation with selenium at high temperatures is not, however, a very desirable method, especially in presence of linoleic acid in any quantity in the glycerides, and the procedure is not recommended: nor is it any longer necessary now that direct crystallisation of liquid fatty oils from solvents at low temperatures is available.

Groundnut oils (Arachis hypogæa, Leguminosæ, sub-family Papilionatæ). The component acids usually lie in the ranges oleic *ca.* 50–65, linoleic *ca.* 18–30, palmitic *ca.* 8–10, and stearic, arachidic, behenic and lignoceric acids amounting together to about 10–12 per cent. Containing negligible proportions of fully saturated glycerides, groundnut oil was shown by the progressive hydrogenation method[39] to include the minimum proportion of tri-C_{18} glycerides. The low-temperature crystallisation technique was used by Crawford and Hilditch[40] with three groundnut oils of varying unsaturated composition with the results summarised in Table 105, which confirm earlier conclusions[38, 39] that ground-nut oil glycerides belong to the usual or "evenly-distributed" type of glycerides so characteristic of most seed fats. When the percentages of monolinoleo- and dilinoleo-glycerides, or of mono-oleo- and dioleo-glycerides, are plotted against the respective proportions of linoleic or oleic acid in the total acids of the oil, points are obtained which lie very close to the curves shown in Fig. 7 (oleo-glycerides, Nos. 5 and 20) and Fig. 8 (linoleo-glycerides, Nos. 24 and 33) in Chapter V (pp. 381, 382). The approximate amounts of these various categories of glycerides present in any groundnut oil can therefore be deduced directly from its contents of linoleic and oleic acids.

TABLE 105. *Component Glycerides of Groundnut Oils*

	WEST AFRICAN	TANGANYIKA	
		var. NATAL COMMON	*var.* VALENCIA
Iodine value of oil	86·8	95·5	99·2
Component acids:	PER CENT. (MOL.)	PER CENT. (MOL.)	PER CENT. (MOL.)
Palmitic	9·2	14·0	11·7
Stearic	5·5	3·9	3·1
Arachidic-lignoceric	5·6	7·2	7·9
Oleic	59·1	39·3	40·5
Linoleic	20·6	35·6	36·8
Component glycerides:			
Disaturated-oleins	7	5	1
Disaturated-linoleins	—	6	8
Saturated-dioleins	31	7	7
Saturated-oleo-linoleins	16	45	43
Saturated-dilinoleins	—	1	—
Oleodilinoleins	6	18	18
Dioleolinoleins	34	18	23
Triolein	6	—	—
Glyceride categories present:			
Containing 3 unsaturated groups	46 (49)	36 (39)	41 (43)
Containing 2 unsaturated groups	47 (42)	53 (47)	50 (45)
Containing 1 unsaturated group	7 (9)	11 (14)	9 (12)
Containing 3 oleic groups	6	—	—
Containing 2 oleic groups	65	25	30
Containing 1 oleic group	29	68	62
Containing no oleic group	—	7	8
Containing 2 linoleic groups	6	19	18
Containing 1 linoleic group	50	69	74
Containing no linoleic group	44	12	8

The observed values quoted in Table 105 for glycerides in which, respec-tively, one, two or three unsaturated acyl groups (oleic + linoleic) are present accord fairly well with those computed[20b] by Gunstone's "Mode I" (which are shown between brackets beside the corresponding experimental figures in Table 105).

By special thin-layer chromatographic technique ("T.L.C.") and also by selective enzyme hydrolysis ("S.E.H.") Barrett *et al.*[19c] (1963) obtained the following figures for groundnut oil glyceride categories:

	2-oleodisatd.	2-linoleodisatd. +monosatd.-dioleins	Oleolinoleo- satd.+triolein	"GU⁴"	"GU⁵"
T.L.C.	3	26	39	23·5	7·5
S.E.H.	4	24·5	46·5	21·5	3·5

"GU⁴": Triglycerides with 4 double bonds.
"GU⁵":   ,,   ,,   5   ,,   ,,

The presence of up to 10 per cent. of glycerides containing two saturated groups (although saturated acids do not form more than about 20 per cent. of the total component acids of groundnut oils) is probably in consequence of the number of saturated acids present as minor components, so that, to a certain extent, two different saturated acids may be found in a single triglyceride molecule (*cf.* this Chapter, p. 452).

The groundnut oils illustrated in Table 105 provide an excellent example of the profound effect of moderate alterations in fatty acid content upon the nature of the constituent glycerides. In one oil, the acids include about 60 per cent. of oleic and 20 per cent. of linoleic, whilst in the other two oleic forms about 40, and linoleic about 35 per cent. of the total acids. In the oil with 60 per cent. of oleic acid, the latter occurs in all triglyceride molecules, mainly as dioleoglycerides (65 per cent.), with in addition a small amount (6 per cent.) of triolein: in the oils with 40 per cent. of oleic acid, nearly 10 per cent. of the glycerides contain no oleic group, triolein is absent, and the proportions of mono- and di-oleo-glycerides are reversed, only 25–30 per cent. of dioleoglycerides being accompanied by 60–70 per cent. of mono-oleo-glycerides. Similarly, nearly half of the groundnut oil with only 20 per cent. of linoleic acid is made up of glycerides from which linoleic is absent, and only about 6 per cent. of the glycerides contain two linoleic groups: whereas, in a groundnut oil with 35 per cent. of linoleic acid, the latter is present in all but about 10 per cent. of the triglyceride molecules, and nearly 20 per cent. of the glycerides contain two linoleo-groups. Alterations of this order in glyceride constitution may have a more important bearing on the industrial use to which an oil is put than might be supposed from mere inspection of the component fatty acid percentages alone.

Castor oil (Ricinus communis, Euphorbiaceæ). The glyceride structure of a typical castor oil (component acids: saturated 2·4, oleic 0·8, linoleic 4·5, ricinoleic 91·6, dihydroxystearic 0·7 per cent. mol.) has been investigated by the detailed crystallisation technique (from acetone solutions at temperatures progressively increasing from − 50° to − 30°C.) by Gupta, Hilditch and Riley.[41] It proved to be a relatively simple mixture built up according to complete or "arithmetical" even distribution of the acids amongst the glycerides, 75 per cent. of which consisted of triricinolein and the remainder of diricinoleo-glycerides with the third acyl group from one of the minor component acids. It should be noted, however, that on this basis the percentages of triricinolein in castor oils will vary, more than may appear at first sight, with any variation of the ricinoleic content of the total fatty acids: thus, an oil with 95 per cent. of ricinoleic acid in its total acids may be expected to contain about 85 per cent. of triricinolein; one with 90 per cent. would contain about 70 per cent. of triricinolein; and one with only 85 per cent. of ricinoleic acid, perhaps only about 60 per cent. of triricinolein.

Rape seed oil and other seed oils of the Cruciferæ. In rape and mustard seed oils, the component acids include 40–50 per cent. of erucic, the remainder being a mixture of oleic, linoleic, linolenic and eicosenoic acids with very small proportions (3–4 per cent. in all) of palmitic and higher saturated acids. From crystallisation studies of the completely hydrogenated oil, Amberger[42a] deduced the absence of triolein or trierucin, and the probable presence of considerable amounts of oleodierucin. Hilditch and H. Paul,[42b] as a result of examination of the oil by progressive hydrogenation, confirmed and extended Amberger's work, and concluded that, apart from about 6 per cent. of mixed palmito-oleo- (or linoleo-) erucins, the rape oil investigated contained about 50 per cent. of di-C_{18}-erucin and about 44 per cent. of mono-C_{18}-dierucin (the C_{18} acid being either oleic, linoleic, or linolenic); they considered that both 1- and 2-"oleo"-dierucins and 1- and 2-erucodi-"oleins" were probably present but, by means of selective enzyme hydrolysis, Mattson and Volpenhein[21d] showed that 95–99 per cent. of the acyl groups attached in the 2-position are unsaturated acids of the C_{18} series. In other words, practically all of the higher (C_{22} and C_{20}) unsaturated homologues, as well as saturated acids present, are combined with the 1- or 3-hydroxyl groups of glycerol.

Hilditch, Laurent and Meara[42c] separated a specimen of rape seed oil into three fractions by crystallisation from acetone at $-20°$C. and then from ether at $-30°$C. The component acids of the oil were: palmitic 3·0, stearic, arachidic, behenic and lignoceric 2·9, oleic 16·9, linoleic 17·9, linolenic 7·8, erucic 49·4 and docosadienoic 2·1 per cent., and the chief classes of glycerides present were estimated to be:

	PER CENT. (MOL.)
Monosaturated-mono-C_{18}-unsaturated-mono-C_{22}-unsaturated	18
Mono-C_{18}-unsaturated-di-C_{22}-unsaturated	54
Di-C_{18}-unsaturated-mono-C_{22}-unsaturated	28

Unsaturated C_{18} and unsaturated C_{22} acyl groups were present throughout the whole of the glycerides; only very minor amounts of dilinoleo-glycerides and no trilinolein or trierucin were observed in the oil.

Dodder seed oil (from *Camelina sativa*, component acids: palmitic 5·2, stearic, arachidic and behenic 3·6, hexadecenoic 2·4, oleic 23·9, linoleic 14·5, linolenic 33·4, eicosenoic 13·8 and erucic 3·2 per cent. wt.) has been studied by Holmberg and Sellman.[43a] It differs from the seed oils of *Brassica* species in its higher content of linoleic and oleic acids and in its low percentage of erucic acid, which is partly compensated by an unusually large amount of eicosenoic acid (accompanied by some di- and tri-ethenoid C_{20} acids). Crystallisation of the oil from acetone at $-60°$C. and $-45°$C. yielded four fractions, from the component acids of which Holmberg and Sellmann deduced the presence in the dodder seed oil of the following classes of mixed glycerides:

PER CENT. (MOL.)

Polyethenoid C_{18} groups per mol.:

1 Linoleic	4
1 Linolenic	54
1 Linoleic + 1 linolenic	40
2 Linolenic	2

Dodder seed oil, like rape seed oil, is thus of the usual "evenly-distributed" type. Linolenic acid, the chief component acid, is present in 96 per cent. of the glycerides, whilst 42 per cent. contains two polyethenoid C_{18} groups, but no tripolyethenoid glycerides were detected. The presence of nearly 50 per cent. of linoleic and linolenic acids in the component acids of course causes dodder oil to be more akin to the "drying" than to the "non-drying" class of oils, but its content of dipolyethenoid glycerides is insufficient to make its drying properties of much technical value.

Seed fat of Vernonia anthelmintica (Compositæ). This fat is exceptional in containing over 70 per cent. of epoxyoleic (vernolic) acid in its component acids. Riemenschneider et al.[43b] have reported the isolation (by low-temperature crystallisation) of 55 per cent. of the simple triglycerides of epoxyoleic acid, "trivernolin", from a specimen of the oil in which vernolic acid formed 76 per cent. of the total fatty acids.

(ii) *Seed Fats rich in both Oleic and Linoleic Acids ("Semi-drying" Oils)*

Many seed fatty oils contain from about 25 to 45 per cent. each of oleic and linoleic acids in varying proportions and the constituent glycerides of a number of these have now been explored with the aid of low-temperature crystallisation techniques. As usual, no hard and fast line can be drawn between one group of seed fats and another, and it will have been noticed that the Cruciferæ oils mentioned above already commence to partake of the mixed oleic-linoleic acid content characteristic of the fatty oils whose glyceride structure is about to be described.

The glycerides of fatty oils of this general acid composition have been studied by the crystallisation procedures by Hilditch et al. in the cases of cottonseed oil[44a] and the botanically related okra seed[44b] oil, sesame oil,[44c] two seed fats of *Citrus* species[44d] (sweet orange and lime seed), and the seed fat of *Chrozophora plicata*,[44e] whilst Singh and Kumar have given other data for the seed fats of *Carthamus oxyacantha*,[45a] *Solanum nigrum*,[45b] and *Terminalia belerica*.[45c] The general results obtained are summed up in Tables 106A, B, C, following which notes are added, where necessary, in regard to the individual oils.

In the Tables 106 the computed values for the general categories (S_3, S_2U, SU_2 and U_3) of glycerides, as determined by Gunstone[20b] according to his "Mode I" (cf. Chapter V, p. 397), are shown, where available, in parentheses. Rather close accordance is noticeable, except in the case of *Terminalia belerica* seed fat, the figures for which appear very abnormal (in relation to the component acid data) in the absence of any disaturated glycerides, the very high figure recorded for saturated-oleo-linoleins, and the recorded presence of as much as 9 per cent. of the simple triglyceride triolein.

451

The experimental data for the various glycerides in cottonseed and okra seed oils (Table 106A) have been recalculated on a different basis by Gunstone,[20b] whose figures accord better with those computed by him than those as originally calculated by the respective investigators.

Of the fatty oils shown in Tables 106A, B, C the chief components are saturated-oleo-linoleins and oleodilinoleins, with saturated-dilinoleins (or -linoleolinolenins) also fairly prominent. These oils, in which appreciable proportions of other saturated acids accompany palmitic acid (which often forms over 25 per cent. of the total acids), include appreciable amounts of glycerides with two saturated acyl groups, although the saturated acids together form not much more, and often much less, than one-third of the total fatty acids. It is quite probable that these are largely glycerides with a stearic or other saturated acyl group present in addition to a palmitic group, but this cannot wholly explain the observed disaturated glyceride contents of okra, orange and lime seed oils, which evidently must contain definite amounts of di-palmito-glycerides. The Tables 106A, B, C, are a good illustration of the generally mixed character of liquid seed-fat glycerides; the proportions of mono- and di-oleo-glycerides, and of mono- and di-linoleo-glycerides, usually accord closely with the graphs relating glyceride content to fatty acid composition shown in Figs. 7 and 8 (Chapter V, pp. 381, 382).

Cottonseed oil (Gossypium sp., Malvaceæ). Hilditch and Lea[16a] showed in 1927 that, in spite of the presence of 25 per cent. of saturated acids in the total acids,

TABLE 106A. *Component Glycerides of Seed Fats Rich in Both Oleic and Linoleic Acids*

	COTTONSEED[44a]			OKRA SEED[44b]		
Component acids (per cent. mol.):						
Myristic	1·6			—		
Palmitic	25·0			26·3		
Stearic	1·0			6·3		
Arachidic	1·1			—		
Oleic	22·3			27·2		
Linoleic	46·7			40·2		
Component glyceride categories (per cent. mol.):						
Trisaturated (S₃)	—	—*	(—)	—	—*	(—)
Disaturated-monosaturated (S₂U)	13	13	(19)	23	23	(25)
Monosaturated-diunsaturated (SU₂)	59	59	(49)	52	52	(50)
Tri-unsaturated (U₃)	28	28	(32)	25	25	(25)
Component glycerides (per cent. mol.):						
Trisaturated	—	Trace*	(—)	—	—*	(—)
Disaturated-oleins	6	3	(6)	14	5	(10)
Disaturated-linoleins	7	10	(12)	9	18	(14)
Saturated-dioleins	—	2	(6)	—	9	(8)
Saturated-oleo-linoleins	41	26	(22)	42	21	(24)
Saturated-dilinoleins	18	31	(21)	10	22	(18)
Triolein	—	1	(1)	—	2	(2)
Dioleolinoleins	—	9	(8)	2	10	(8)
Oleodilinoleins	28	18	(15)	22	12	(11)
Trilinolein	—	—	(9)	1	1	(5)

* Alternative calculation by Dr F. D. Gunstone[20b] of the experimental results.

TABLE 106B. *Component Glycerides of Seed Fats Rich in Both Oleic and Linoleic Acids*

			Citrus SPECIES	
	Chrozophora plicata[44e]	SESAME[44c]	SWEET ORANGE[44d]	LIME[44d]
Component acids (per cent. mol.):				
Myristic	0·2	0·9	—	—
Palmitic	9·8	9·8	28·4	29·7
Stearic	13·0	5·3	4·8	6·2
Arachidic	0·5	0·8	1·5	1·0
Oleic	24·6	36·5	25·5	16·0
Linoleic	51·9	46·7	34·8	34·5
Linolenic	—	—	5·0	12·6
Component glyceride categories (per cent. mol.):				
S_3	— (—)	—	— (—)	2 (—)
S_2U	13 (12)	4	27 (28)	25 (31)
SU_2	47 (45)	41	50 (50)	55 (49)
U_3	40 (43)	55	23 (22)	18 (20)
Component glycerides (per cent. mol.):				
Trisaturated	—	—	—	2
Disaturated-oleins	4	3	27	25
Disaturated-linoleins	9	1	—	—
Saturated-oleo-linoleins	28	37	43	30
Saturated-dilinoleins	19	4	1	2
Saturated-linoleo-linolenins	—	—	6	23
Dioleolinoleins	—	15	1	—
Oleodilinoleins	37	39	15	8
Oleolinoleolinolenins	—	—	7	5
Dilinoleolinolenins	—	—	—	5
Trilinolein	3	1	—	—

TABLE 106C. *Component Glycerides of Seed Fats Rich in Both Oleic and Linoleic Acids*

	Carthamus oxyacantha[45a]	*Solanum nigrum*[45b]	*Terminalia belerica*[45c]
Component acids (per cent.):			
Myristic	0·7	—	—
Palmitic	3·1	1·8	11·3
Stearic	3·6	1·9	15·5
Oleic	55·8	49·7	43·7
Linoleic	36·8	46·3	29·5
Component glyceride categories (per cent. mol.):			
S_3	—	—	— (—)
S_2U	—	3	— (16)
SU_2	23	6	82 (49)
U_3	77	91	18 (35)
Component glycerides (per cent.):			
Disaturated oleins	—	3	—
Saturated-dioleins	—	—	3
Saturated-oleo-linoleins	23	6	79
Triolein	1	—	9
Dioleolinoleins	63	46	9
Oleodilinoleins	11	45	—
Trilinolein	2	—	—

less than 1 per cent. of fully saturated glycerides occurred in cottonseed oil (component acids: myristic 3, palmitic 20, stearic 1, arachidic 1, oleic 30, linoleic 45 per cent. wt.). By crystallisation of the completely hydrogenated oil,[37a] and later as the result of progressive hydrogenation of the oil,[37b] it was established that the tri-C_{18} glyceride content is only 25 per cent., a figure which indicates that the remaining 75 per cent. of the glycerides contained at least one acyl group of palmitic (myristic or arachidic) acid.

In Hilditch and Maddison's crystallisation analysis[44a] in 1940, the two most soluble of the six glyceride fractions into which the oil was separated (iodine values 134·0 and 124·7) only contained 65·0 and 59·8 per cent. of linoleic acid. Thus, in the most unsaturated part of the oil (further crystallisation of which failed to produce a product of higher iodine value), less linoleic acid was present than that which would necessitate the presence of any trilinolein. It should be pointed out, perhaps, that this study was made in the early days of the systematic use of crystallisation from solvents at low temperatures, but the results are however in line with those obtained much later for okra and sesame seed oils (of somewhat similar fatty acid composition). It was nevertheless possible that the triunsaturated glycerides were not wholly oleodilinoleins (as given), but included minor proportions of dioleolinoleins and perhaps trilinolein.

Concentrates of palmito-diunsaturated glycerides obtained in the course of the crystallisations were hydrogenated at a low temperature (65°), and by crystallisation of the product a pure specimen of 2-palmitodistearin was obtained,[44a] a result later confirmed[17d] by study of the transition points of the purified hydrogenated concentrates. Mattson and Lutton[21c] found by selective enzyme hydrolysis in 1958 that of the acids attached to the 2- (or central) hydroxyl group in the glycerides of cottonseed oil, 11 per cent. were saturated; this proportion of 2-saturated glycerides (exceptionally large for a seed fat) tends to support the previous finding that 2-palmito-glycerides are present to some extent in cottonseed oil.

By special thin-layer chromatographic technique ("T.L.C.") and also by selective enzyme hydrolysis ("S.E.H.") Barrett et al.[19c] (1963) observed mixed saturated-unsaturated glycerides of the following categories in a cottonseed oil:

	2-oleodisatd.	2-linoleodisatd. + monosatd.- dioleins	Oleolinoleosatd. + triolein	"GU⁴"	"GU⁵"	"GU⁶"
T.L.C.	5·5	22·5	22·5	30	12·5	6·5
S.E.H.	7·5	21	18·5	27	13	15

"GU⁴", "GU⁵", "GU⁶": Triglycerides with, respectively, 4, 5 or 6 double bonds.

Okra seed oil (Hibiscus esculentus, Malvaceæ). The okra plant grows freely in the Sudan and in other parts of Africa, and its cultivation in the United States and in India has been considered. The study (Table 106A) by Crossley and Hilditch[44b] in 1951 shows how closely the constituent glycerides resemble those of cottonseed oil, for which okra seed oil could thus if needed be substituted in edible fats or for other industrial uses.

Sesame oil (Sesamum indicum, Pedaliaceæ). Prior to its examination by crystallisation in 1951 by Chakrabarty and Hilditch,[44c] progressive hydrogenation studies[39] in 1938 had shown that in sesame oil (which contains no fully saturated components) the saturated acids must be present almost wholly as monosaturated-di-"oleins", and that consequently over half of the fat will consist of mixed oleo-linoleins. The later, more detailed examination[44c] in fact indicated the presence in the specimen studied of 39 per cent. of oleodilinoleins with 15 per cent. of dioleolinoleins and 37 per cent. of saturated-oleo-linoleins as the chief constituent glycerides.

Sesame oil thus differs from cottonseed oil mainly in its larger contents of oleolinoleins and in lower proportions of saturated-dilinoleins, the saturated-oleo-linoleins being of much the same order in both oils. On the other hand, sesame oil probably contains over 40 per cent. of glycerides in which two linoleic groups are present, a feature which *prima facie* would suggest some degree of proneness to oxidative rancidity, the onset of which is attributable to the presence of the reactive pentadiene grouping in linoleic glycerides.[46a] Sesame oil, however, has a good reputation in this respect, no doubt due (as Budowski[46b] has pointed out) to the antioxidant properties of small proportions of sesamol liberated from the glycoside sesamolin which occurs in the unsaponifiable fractions of this oil.

Citrus seed oils (Rutaceæ). The component glycerides of the seed oil of this important genus (*C. aurantium dulcis*, sweet orange, and *C. limetta*, lime) from the West Indies were studied by the crystallisation procedure in 1948 by Dunn, Hilditch and Riley.[44d] The component fatty acids of *Citrus* fats have a marked general resemblance to those of cottonseed oil, with a slightly higher proportion of palmitic acid; up to 10 per cent. or somewhat more of the triene linolenic acid is also however present, with corresponding reduction in the proportions of linoleic, and sometimes oleic, acid. Like cottonseed oil, the *Citrus* seed fats conform closely with the usual manner of distribution of individual fatty acids amongst seed fat glycerides, and consequently their glyceride constituents are not dissimilar so far as the monosaturated-diunsaturated and triunsaturated glycerides, taken as a whole, are concerned; the amount of disaturated-monounsaturated glycerides is greater than in cottonseed oil. At the same time the presence of definite proportions of linolenic acid involves that of about 10 per cent. or more of saturated-linoleo-linolenins, with reduced proportions of oleodilinoleins which, however, are made up for by the presence of up to 10 per cent. of oleolinoleolinolenins and/or dilinoleolinolenin. Consequently the *Citrus* oils should be good substitutes for cottonseed oil except for increased liability to oxidative rancidity. *Citrus* oils, after hydrogenation until linoleno-glycerides have disappeared, would on the other hand appear to be practically equivalent in composition to cottonseed oil hydrogenated to a similar iodine value.

(iii) *Linoleic-rich Seed Fats* (*"Drying" or "Semi-drying" Oils*)

We now pass to a group of seed fatty oils in which the linoleic acid content usually very much exceeds that of oleic acid, whilst that of the saturated acids

TABLE 107. *Component Glycerides of Linoleic-Rich Seed Oils.*

	MAIZE		JUTE SEED	TOBACCO SEED	POPPY SEED		PASSION FRUIT SEED
	U.S.A.[47]	U.S.A.[48a]	INDIAN[49]	INDIAN[50a]	INDIAN[50b]	ENGLISH[50b]	S. AFRICA
Preliminary segregation	L.T.C.	C.C.D.	L.T.C.	L.T.C.	L.T.C.	L.T.C.	L.T.C.
Iodine value of oil:	126·5	126·3	119·2	141·1	137·1	138·8	139·6
Component acids (per cent. mol.):							
Myristic		—	0·2	—	—	0·8	—
Palmitic	15·1	10·0	23·0	7·0	11·3	11·5	12·3
Stearic		2·7	4·6	2·9	4·4	1·7	3·3
Arachidic		—	1·0	0·8	0·4	0·4	0·4
Oleic	23·5	26·7	6·5	17·2	13·7	12·4	8·7
Linoleic	60·8	60·3	61·1	70·9	70·2	73·2	75·3
Linolenic	0·6*	0·3	1·6*†	1·2*	—	—	—
Component glyceride categories (per cent. mol.):							
Disaturated (S₂U)	2 (5)	?	11 (19)	3 (3)	1 (6)	1 (5)	4 (6)
Monosaturated (SU₂)	41 (35)	?	64 (49)	27 (27)	46 (37)	41 (34)	40 (36)
Triunsaturated (U₃)	57 (60)	?	25 (32)	70 (70)	53 (57)	58 (61)	56 (58)
Component glycerides (per cent. mol.):							
Disaturated-oleins	— (1)	?	1 (2)	— (1)	— (1)	— (1)	— (1)
Disaturated-linoleins	2 (4)	§	10 (17)	3 (2)	1 (5)	1 (4)	4 (5)
Saturated-di-oleins	1 (3)	?	— (1)	— (1)	— (1)	— (1)	—(—)
Saturated-oleo-linoleins	6 (14)	§	11 (10)	4 (8)	9 (10)	6 (8)	6 (7)
Saturated-dilinoleins	34 (18)	13 (10)	53 (38)	23 (18)	37 (25)	35 (25)	34 (29)
Triolein	— (1)	—	—(—)	— (1)	—(—)	—(—)	—(—)
Dioleolinoleins	7 (10)	§	— (1)	— (6)	— (4)	— (3)	— (2)
Oleodilinoleins	49 (26)	24 (30)	14 (9)	51 (26)	32 (20)	31 (20)	20 (14)
Trilinolein	1 (23)	22 (23)	11 (22)	19 (37)	21 (34)	27 (38)	36 (42)
Total di- and tri-linoleo glycerides:	84 (67)	59 (63)	78 (69)	93 (81)	90 (80)	93 (83)	90 (85)

* The small proportions of linoleno-glycerides are included with the linoleo-glycerides.
† Also 2·0 per cent. of eicoseno-glycerides (included with the oleo-glycerides).

(mainly palmitic and stearic) rarely exceeds 20 per cent. of the total acids, and is often much less. Here again there is no well-defined boundary between such fatty oils and those discussed in the preceding section: broadly speaking an oil whose component acids contain 60 per cent. or more of linoleic acid may be considered to belong to this group, but the term "linoleic-rich" oils should be further restricted, for certain technical uses, to those which contain from 67 per cent. upwards of linoleic acid.

A further complication in defining this group of fatty oils is that a somewhat large number of species which can produce seed fats very rich in linoleic acid seem particularly susceptible to environmental conditions, and only yield such fats when grown in cool climates or when the development of fat in the seed is relatively prolonged. Such species, grown in different (hotter) climatic conditions may produce seed fats of relatively low linoleic acid content. An outstanding example is the seed of the sunflower, *Helianthus annuus*, where the proportion of linoleic acid in the total fatty acids of its seed oil may be anything between about 70 and 30 per cent. according to the conditions of growth. Similar variations, but less marked in extent, have been recorded in the linoleic

(Over 60 per cent. (mol.) of linoleic acid)

SUNFLOWER SEED			SAFFLOWER SEED				NIGER SEED
TANGAN-YIKA[50d]	KENYA[50d]	SOUTHERN RHODESIA[50d]	INDIAN[27c]	KENYA[50d]	U.S.A.[48b]	U.S.A.[48b]	SOUTHERN RHODESIA[50d]
L.T.C.	L.T.C.	L.T.C.	C.B.A.	L.T.C.	C.C.D.	C.C.D.	L.T.C.
129·8	132·3	136·9	?	142·5	143·8	146·6	134·9
—	—	0·2	2	—	—	—	—
4·7	7·7	7·6	3	5·2	7·3	5·8	11·7
5·5	1·8	3·8	1	3·8	3·4	5·4	5·3
2·8	5·6	2·8	—	1·7	—	—	3·4
23·8	17·6	13·2	32	12·8	12·6	9·3	4·6
63·2	67·3	72·4	61	76·5	76·6	79·2	74·4
—	—	—	1*	—	0·1*	0·3*	0·6*
2 (4)	— (5)	1 (5)	— (1)	— (3)	?	?	7 (9)
35 (31)	45 (35)	41 (34)	33 (16)	32 (27)	?	?	47 (43)
63 (65)	55 (60)	58 (61)	67 (83)	68 (70)	?	?	46 (48)
— (1)	— (1)	— (1)	—(—)	— (1)	?	?	—(—)
2 (3)	— (4)	1 (4)	— (1)	Trace (2)	‡	‡	7 (9)
— (2)	— (2)	— (1)	— (2)	—(—)	?	?	—(—)
15 (12)	6 (11)	6 (9)	{18 }(7)(7)	2 (7)	‡	‡	1 (5)
20 (17)	39 (22)	35 (24)		30 (20)	8 (14)	12 (12)	46 (38)
— (1)	— (1)	—(—)	— (3)	—(—)	—(—)	—(—)	—(—)
— (11)	— (6)	— (4)	15 (19)	— (4)	‡	‡	— (1)
56 (28)	47 (23)	34 (20)	64 (37)	37 (22)	26 (22)	15 (18)	13 (7)
7 (25)	8 (30)	24 (37)	3 (24)	31 (44)	47 (45)	51 (50)	33 (40)
83 (70)	94 (75)	93 (81)	75 (68)	98 (86)	81 (81)	78 (80)	92 (85)

§ The monolinoleo-glycerides found in this analysis apparently amounted in all to *ca.* 41 (37) per cent.
‡ The monolinoleo-glycerides in these analyses amounted together to 13 (15) and 15 (18) per cent. respectively.

acid contents of safflower, Niger seed, poppy seed and some other oils (*cf.* Chapter IV, pp. 220–228). Whilst species which are capable of producing linoleic-rich seed oils will therefore be considered together in this section, the possibility that seed fats from some of the plants in question may vary rather widely in their relative proportions of linoleic and oleic acids must not be overlooked.

It is in this and the following section (linolenic-rich oils) that great advances in knowledge of glyceride constitution have been made following preliminary segregation of the oils into relatively simple glyceride mixtures by their systematic crystallisation at very low temperatures from acetone (or, sometimes, ether), or, more recently, by counter-current distribution of an oil between two immiscible solvents (*cf.* Chapter V, p. 383).

Summarised results of various studies of linoleic-rich seed oils are given in Tables 107 (oils containing over 60 per cent. of linoleic acid) and 108 (oils containing less than 60 per cent. of linoleic acid). The greater number of these studies were effected with the aid of low-temperature crystallisation ("L.T.C."), in four Indian studies preliminary resolution was effected by crystallisation of

TABLE 108. Component Glycerides of Linoleic-rich Seed Oils
(Seed fats of species in Table 107 with less than 60 per cent. of linoleic acid)

Preliminary segregation:	ZANZIBAR[50e]	SUNFLOWER SEED INDIAN[51]	TANGANYIKA[50d]	ZANZIBAR[50d]	NIGERIAN[50d]	NIGER SEED INDIAN[27d]	TOBACCO SEED INDIAN[23b]
	L.T.C.	C.B.A.	L.T.C.	L.T.C.	L.T.C.	C.B.A.	C.B.A.
Iodine value of oil:	94·7	111·6	113·8	121·1	126·7	?	?
Component acids (per cent. mol.):							
Myristic	}10·2	0·4	0·1	0·6	0·1	1·7	1·8
Palmitic		4·3	6·5	5·1	5·9	5·0	7·8
Stearic		5·4	3·0	2·9	2·7	2·3	5·6
Arachidic		—	2·2	3·6	1·9	—	—
Oleic	71·0	49·4	44·2	36·7	33·1	39·4	30·2
Linoleic	18·8	40·5	44·0	51·1	56·3	51·6	54·6
Component glyceride categories (per cent. mol.):							
Disaturated (S_2U)	— (2)	— (2)	1 (3)	1 (3)	— (2)	— (2)	— (5)
Monosaturated (SU_2)	31 (26)	31 (26)	34 (29)	35 (30)	31 (27)	28 (23)	44 (35)
Triunsaturated (U_3)	69 (72)	69 (72)	65 (68)	64 (67)	69 (71)	72 (75)	49 (60)
Component glycerides (per cent. mol.):							
Disaturated oleins	— (2)	— (1)	1 (2)	1 (1)	— (1)	— (1)	— (2)
Disaturated linoleins	— (—)	— (1)	— (1)	— (2)	— (1)	— (1)	— (3)
Saturated-di-oleins	27 (16)	— (8)	7 (7)	2 (5)	Trace (4)	— (4)	— (4)
Saturated-oleo-linoleins	4 (9)	31 (13)	27 (15)	25 (15)	24 (12)	18 (12)	29 (16)
Saturated-dilinoleins	— (1)	— (5)	Trace (7)	8 (10)	7 (11)	10 (7)	15 (15)
Triolein	26 (36)	— (12)	— (9)	— (5)	— (3)	— (6)	— (3)
Dioleolinoleins	34 (28)	45 (29)	26 (26)	16 (20)	7 (18)	30 (24)	7 (15)
Oleodilinoleins	9 (7)	24 (24)	39 (25)	48 (29)	62 (31)	40 (31)	35 (26)
Trilinolein	— (1)	— (7)	— (8)	Trace (13)	— (18)	2 (14)	7 (16)
Total di- and tri-linoleo glycerides:	9 (9)	24 (36)	39 (40)	56 (52)	69 (60)	52 (52)	57 (57)

458

the bromo-adducts of the oils ("C.B.A.") and in three more recent investigations (maize and safflower seed oils) counter-current distribution ("C.C.D.") between two solvents was employed in the separation of the glycerides; unfortunately the "C.C.D." analyses do not give a complete account of all the glycerides or glyceride groups present.

Where not already published[20b], Dr F. D. Gunstone has kindly supplied us[20c] with estimated values for all the oils in Tables 107 and 108 as computed on the basis of his "mode I" theory described in Chapter V (p. 397). The computed figures are in good accordance with those observed for specific types (e.g., trilinolein, oleodilinoleins, etc.) in the three studies made by counter-current distribution (C.C.D.), but vary from those found by low-temperature crystallisation (L.T.C.) in many of the oils most rich in linoleic acid.

Gunstone's computed values[20b,c] are in very fair agreement with the observed results by the L.T.C. procedure for relatively saturated fats such as cacao butter, borneo tallow, *Allanblackia* and *Garcinia* fats (pp. 434, 435–438), and for liquid seed fats such as groundnut oils (Table 105, p. 448), cottonseed, okra seed and other oils (Table 106, pp. 452, 453), in which the proportion of linoleic acid does not much exceed 40 per cent. of the total acids and is comparable with or less than that of the oleic acid. It is therefore perhaps reasonable, at the present state of development of glyceride structure investigation, to accept computation by the Gunstone or Vander Wal[20a] methods as an empirical guide to the general accuracy of published experimental data. In particular, scrutiny by this means of the results in Tables 107 and 108 appears to indicate the probable point at which the L.T.C. procedure commences to be defective in its segregation of the more unsaturated glycerides such as saturated-oleo-linoleins and saturated-dilinoleins, dioleolinoleins, oleo-dilinoleins and trilinolein.

To commence with the relative proportions of the general glyceride categories S_2U, SU_2 and U_3, the observed results are in fair agreement with the computed values in eleven of the fifteen analyses in which low-temperature crystallisation of the seed oils was employed, and in two of the four studies in which the bromo-adducts of seed oils were segregated by crystallisation. This suggests strongly that the crystallisation procedures have effected fairly complete separation of the three groups of disaturated-mono-unsaturated, monosaturated-di-unsaturated and triunsaturated groups, irrespective of the relative proportions of linoleic and oleic acids in the fats (the discrepant figures in one L.T.C. and two C.B.A. studies may possibly be ascribed to imperfect preliminary segregation).

It is equally clear that in oils containing large proportions of linoleic acid the crystallisation procedure does not give an adequate separation of the different groups of oleo-linoleo glycerides and trilinolein, if the computed figures are to be accepted as a guide. Moderately good agreement for individual tri-unsaturated groups of glycerides is occasionally present when the linoleic content of the component acids does not exceed about 50 per cent., but here, and in the oils richer in linoleic acid, there is poor accordance in many instances. For the total content of di- and tri-linoleo glycerides together (which is probably the determinant of the utility of this class of oil in paints) both experimental and computed values are very similar in most of the oils which contain less than 60 per cent. of linoleic acid, but the computed figures are usually several units lower than those observed with the L.T.C. procedure for oils very rich in linoleic acid.

In spite of the discrepancies between observed and calculated values which have been pointed out, both sets of figures respectively show regular progressive changes in the relative amounts of mono- or di-oleo-glycerides, mono- and di-linoleo-glycerides and trilinolein, which are dependent upon the relative proportions of linoleic and oleic acids in the total fatty acids of the oil. With the aid of the data in Tables 107 and 108 it should therefore now, at all events, be possible to obtain a good idea of the contents of the various categories of glycerides in a linoleic-rich oil directly from the content of linoleic, oleic and saturated acids in the total acids of the oil.

The proportions of di-linoleo-glycerides and trilinolein present in oils of this group have an important bearing upon their use in certain classes of paints, where "drying" capacity is an essential need. At one time some of these oils were variously reported as suitable or as quite inferior for use in paints, and in consequence the whole group was frequently relegated to the intermediate class of "semi-drying" oils, i.e., oils which were susceptible to atmospheric oxidation but did not produce a hard, non-tacky film. The cause of this uncertainty has become clear since the tendency of several of the plant species concerned to produce seed fats of differing linoleic-oleic acid contents under different climatic conditions became apparent. Subsequently, comparative tests of film-forming capacity have been carried out on linoleic-rich oils of varying linoleic acid content, and it has been ascertained that such oils are not fully effective in paints or in alkyd resins to be used in surface coatings unless at least 80–90 per cent. of the glycerides contain either two or three linoleic groups in the molecule.[50d] This criterion implies that these oils, to be efficient as "drying" oils, must contain not less than 70 per cent. (preferably more) of linoleic acid in their total fatty acids. Oils of lower linoleic acid content are more properly considered as belonging to the "semi-drying" class.

A further inference from these glyceride studies is that, considered as chemical entities and for technical applications, the botanical origin of linoleic-rich fatty oils is of no great significance. An oil with 70 per cent. of linoleic acid in its total acids, for example, will consist of the same mixture of glycerides whether it originates in the seeds of tobacco, sunflowers, Niger seed, poppies, safflowers or other plants. It has been pointed out[52] that, at least for industrial purposes, such oils should be classified by their fatty acid composition rather than by the species in whose seeds they are produced.

A few notes may be added on some of the individual oils included in Tables 107 and 108.

Maize oil (Zea mays, Gramineæ). This is the only seed oil of the cereal family of which the glyceride structure has yet been investigated. The general build of the glycerides is similar to that in other seed fats of like fatty acid composi-

460

tion, and it may be supposed, in the absence of direct evidence, that this may hold also for other Gramineæ seed oils. The experimental study of maize oil, undertaken by Doerschuk and Daubert,[47] involved its segregation into nineteen glyceride fractions by a very thorough scheme of over thirty crystallisations from acetone at temperatures between $+12°$ and $-78°$ C. The composition of each fraction was deduced from its component acids by means of calculations and certain assumptions which differ from those used by the Hilditch school. "Computed" values for this oil analysis accord as regards the total proportions of di- and mono-saturated, and triunsaturated glycerides, but differ widely for specific glyceride groups and for the total content of di- and tri-linoleo-glycerides.

The later study of maize oil by the counter-current distribution procedure (Scholfield et al.[48a]) gave figures (trilinolein 22, oleodilinoleins 24, saturated-dilinoleins 13 per cent.) which differed considerably from those of Doerschuk and Daubert, but were close to Gunstone's or Vander Wal's computed values[20]; data for other glyceride types were not included in this analysis.

Jute seed oil (Corchorus sp., Tiliaceæ). The seed fat examined by Meara and Sen[49] was from *C. olitorius*, the fatty acids of which differ from those of the fat from the related *C. capsularis* seeds in containing more linoleic and less oleic acid (*cf.* Chapter IV, Table 62, p. 270). Both oils contain small proportions of saturated acids of the C_{22}, C_{24}, or C_{26} series and also of a mono-ethenoid acid with 20 carbon atoms in the molecule. With nearly 30 per cent. of saturated acids (23 per cent. palmitic) in the total acids, disaturated glycerides occur to the extent of over 10 per cent. of the oil, as in other similar cases (*cf.* section (ii), p. 452); otherwise the general glyceride structure is in line with that of similar linoleic-rich seed oils.

Tobacco seed oil (Nicotiana tabacum, N. rustica, Solanaceæ); Poppy seed oil (Papaver somniferum, Papaveraceæ); Sunflower seed oil (Helianthus annuus, Compositæ); Safflower seed oil (Carthamus tinctorius, Compositæ); Niger seed oil (Guizotia abyssinica, Compositæ). These five seed oils can be considered together, since all of them are frequently characterised by high linoleic acid contents while, at the same time, all these species are capable, in some circumstances of growth, of producing seed fats with much reduced linoleic acid, and much increased oleic acid, contents. As already pointed out, and as will be seen from Tables 107 and 108, the nature of the glycerides present depends wholly on the relative proportions of oleic and linoleic acids in the oils: when the proportion of linoleic acid reaches 70 per cent. of the total fatty acids, 80–90 per cent. of the glycerides contain either two or three linoleic groups per molecule. Trilinolein commences to appear at a linoleic acid content of about 50 per cent., and forms about 30 per cent. of the glycerides when the total fatty acids include about 70 per cent. of linoleic acid.

The Indian *tobacco seed oils* quoted in Tables 107 and 108 include one with 70 per cent. linoleic acid[50a] and one with 55 per cent. linoleic acid[23b]; the latter type has appeared less frequently than those of high linoleic acid content. Similarly, the two *poppy seed oils* whose glyceride composition has been studied belong to the high linoleic acid type, but component acid analyses (*cf.* Chapter

IV, Table 60, p. 231) have sometimes indicated a content of not much over 60 per cent. in some poppy seed oils.

Of the three Compositæ seed oils, *sunflower seed oil* is the most sensitive to variation in composition owing to different conditions of growth. A linoleic acid content of about 58–67 per cent. is the most common, when the oils contain about 70–80 per cent. of di- (and tri-) linoleo-glycerides, but the more linoleic-rich type with up to 90 per cent. of more of these glycerides is frequently encountered. On the other hand, sunflower seed oils with only about 20 per cent. of linoleic acid (thus resembling groundnut oils in their component unsaturated acids) have been produced in very hot climates (*cf.* Chapter IV, p. 227).

Safflower seed oils appear most frequently to contain about 75 per cent. of linoleic acid in their total fatty acids, and in consequence 80–90 per cent. of the glyceride molecules contain two or three linoleic groups, trilinolein forming about 45 per cent. of the oil. Winter[53] has stated that Australian-grown safflower seed contains oil with 72–79 per cent. of linoleic acid. In a few instances, however, Indian safflower seed oils with much lower (*ca.* 60 per cent.) linoleic acid contents have been reported (in one of which the glyceride composition was determined by Vidyarthi[27c]).

Similarly, Indian and African *Niger seed oils* with over 70 per cent. of linoleic acid have been recorded, but at least one instance has been reported of an Indian Niger seed oil with only 53 per cent. of linoleic acid.[54]

(iv) *Seed Fats containing Linolenic Acid* ("*Drying*" *Oils*)

As usual, no sharp line can be drawn between seed oils containing no linolenic acid and those containing appreciable proportions, and it will be noticed that, amongst the oils discussed in the "linoleic-rich" section (iii), tobacco seed and Niger seed oils contain up to 1 per cent. of this acid. In the six oils for which component glyceride figures are available, linolenic acid occurs to the extent of about 6–9 per cent. in soya bean oil, 18–20 per cent. in hemp seed oil, 20–25 per cent. in rubber seed oil, 23–30 per cent. in candlenut oil, 52–57 per cent. in linseed oil, and 63–65 per cent. in conophor oil (and some other seed oils). The results of glyceride studies carried out with the aid of crystallisation from solvents at temperatures down to $-70°C$. are summarised in Table 109. In these oils, with four groups of major component acids, the individual mixed glycerides probably present are uncertain, and the composition is therefore indicated only by the proportions of glycerides containing different numbers of acyl categories – disaturated, monosaturated, triunsaturated; mono- or di-linoleo-glycerides; mono- or di-linoleno-glycerides and trilinolenin; di- and tri-polyethenoid glycerides (i.e. including both linoleic and linolenic groups). In this group, also, the saturated acids (which are in all cases mainly palmitic and stearic, accompanied by very small proportions of arachidic or higher acids, and sometimes myristic acid) are given in the table without differentiation.

As in the linoleic-rich seed oils illustrated in Tables 107 and 108, Dr F. D. Gunstone[20c] has supplied us with values for the linolenic-rich seed oils in

Table 109 as computed on his "mode I" theory (Chapter V, p. 397); these values are given in parentheses after the respective observed figures in Table 109. These computed values depend primarily on the observations that in seed fats oleic and linoleic acids are selectively attached at the central 2-position in the glycerol molecule coupled with the assumption that any excess of these

TABLE 109. *Component Glycerides of Seed Oils Containing Linolenic Acid*

(i) *Seed oils with less than 50 per cent. (mol.) of linolenic acid*

	SOYA BEAN		HEMP	RUBBER	CANDLENUT		
	I[55]	II[56]	SEED[56]	SEED[56]	I[56]	II[56]	III[57a]
Iodine value of oil	132·6	131·5	152·0	134·5	145·3	163·3	164·3
Component acids (per cent. mol.):							
Saturated	19·2	19·6	16·6	24·0	14·2	14·2	12·4
Oleic	21·8	22·0	10·9	18·7	26·4	14·0	15·1
Linoleic	49·3	49·2	53·8	36·6	36·4	41·2	41·5
Linolenic	9·7	9·2	18·7	20·1	23·0	30·6	31·0
Component glycerides (per cent. mol.):							
(a) Disaturated (S₂U)	— (8)	2 (8)	— (6)	7 (13)	1 (4)	2 (4)	— (4)
Monosaturated (SU₂)	58 (41)	55 (42)	50 (37)	58 (46)	40 (34)	39 (34)	37 (30)
Triunsaturated (U₃)	42 (51)	43 (50)	50 (57)	35 (41)	59 (62)	59 (62)	63 (66)
(b) Mono-linoleo-	45 (34)	52 (34)	39 (31)	79 (39)	81 (43)	73 (41)	75 (41)
Di-linoleo-	52 (38)	48 (37)	61 (41)	15 (26)	14 (25)	25 (30)	25 (30)
Trilinolein	— (12)	— (11)	— (15)	— (5)	— (5)	— (7)	— (7)
(c) Mono-linoleno-	29 (23)	28 (22)	56 (36)	62 (36)	67 (40)	74 (43)	78 (43)
Di-linoleno-	— (3)	— (2)	— (9)	— (10)	1 (12)	9 (20)	7 (20)
Trilinolenin	— (—)	— (—)	— (1)	— (1)	— (1)	— (3)	— (3)
(d) Mono-polyethenoid	27 (30)	28 (25)	9 (11)	29 (23)	29 (27)	11 (13)	15 (14)
Di-polyethenoid	68 (44)	68 (43)	64 (45)	65 (43)	63 (47)	62 (45)	53 (44)
Tri-polyethenoid	5 (20)	4 (18)	27 (37)	4 (18)	8 (21)	27 (36)	32 (37)
(e) Di + Tri-polyethenoid	73 (64)	72 (61)	91 (82)	69 (61)	71 (68)	89 (81)	85 (81)

(ii) *Seed oils with over 50 per cent. (mol.) of linolenic acid*

	LINSEED OIL		CONOPHOR
	ARGENTINE[56]	INDIAN[56]	OIL[56]
Iodine value of oil:	176·1	182·0	201·6
Component acids (per cent. mol.):			
Saturated	17·7	15·7	12·3
Oleic	15·2	13·7	10·8
Linoleic	14·9	14·4	11·2
Linolenic	52·2	56·2	65·7
Component glycerides (per cent. mol.):			
(a) Disaturated (S₂U)	5 (7)	3 (5)	1 (3)
Monosaturated (SU₂)	43 (39)	41 (36)	35 (30)
Triunsaturated (U₃)	52 (54)	56 (59)	64 (67)
(b) Mono-linoleo-	45 (31)	43 (31)	33 (26)
Di-linoleo-	— (6)	— (5)	— (3)
Trilinolein	— (—)	— (—)	— (—)
(c) Mono-linoleno-	43 (32)	35 (29)	13 (21)
Di-linoleno-	56 (39)	59 (42)	77 (44)
Trilinolenin	Trace (14)	5 (17)	10 (28)
(d) Mono-polyethenoid	24 (16)	18 (14)	6 (9)
Di-polyethenoid	51 (46)	53 (45)	58 (42)
Tri-polyethenoid	25 (29)	29 (34)	36 (45)
(e) Di + Tri-polyethenoid	76 (75)	82 (79)	94 (87)

463

acids and the other fatty acids present in the oil are distributed at random in the 1- and 3-positions (Vander Wal,[20a] Gunstone[20b]).

It has become evident that, as in the linoleic-rich seed oils (Tables 107 and 108), the low-temperature crystallisation procedure is not capable of effective resolution of mixed glycerides of oleic, linoleic and linolenic acids. If we assume that the computed values are at all events a rough approximation to the truth, it is evident from Table 109 that the L.T.C. procedure again gives a fair measure of the disaturated (S_2U), monosaturated (SU_2) and triunsaturated (U_3) types present and (in most instances) also of the total amounts of di- + tri-polyethenoid glycerides; but there is little accordance in the cases of individual glyceride types (e.g., mono-linoleo-, etc.), as is again the case in the linoleic-rich oils. The observed and computed data in Table 109, however, together afford as much evidence as can be offered by low-temperature crystallis-ation studies on the general pattern of the glycerides in these linolenic-rich oils.

Only two of the oils in this group have yet been studied by the counter-current distribution procedure, and here, unfortunately, results were only given for some of the more unsaturated mixed glycerides. Scholfield and Hicks[48c] examined soya bean oil, and Dutton and Cannon[48d] investigated linseed oil, with the following results:

Soya bean oil. Component acids: Saturated 13·7, oleic 30·5, linoleic 49·1, linolenic 6·7 per cent.

Component glycerides: Saturated-linoleo-linolenin 2 (3), saturated-dilinolenin 1 (—), dioleo-linolein 4 (2), oleo-dilinolein 25 (22), oleo-linoleo-linolenin 9 (6), oleo-dilinolenin 1 (—), trilinolein 14 (12), dilinoleo-linolenin 5 (5), linoleo-dilinolenin 1 (1) per cent. (leaving 38 (49) per cent. of the oil undetermined).

Linseed oil. Component acids: Saturated 8·5, oleic 24·3, linoleic 14·9, linolenic 52·3 per cent.

Component glycerides: Oleo-dilinolenin 20 (20), dilinoleo-linolenin 4 (3), linoleo-dilinolenin 12 (12), trilinolenin 18 (14) per cent. (leaving 46 (51) per cent. of the oil undetermined).

The experimental and computed[20b] figures for both oils, so far as they go, are in very good general accordance.

In this group of oils, in which either linoleic or linolenic acid, or both of them, may be prominent, the proportions of the technically important glycer-ides in which two or three polyethenoid acids are present depend upon the relative amounts of linoleic and linolenic acids in the total fatty acids. Whilst each individual acid (saturated, oleic, linoleic or linolenic) follows the usual mode of distribution in the triglyceride molecules (as shown in Chapter V, pp. 380–382), the consequent amounts of dipolyethenoid glycerides (dilinoleo-, linoleolinoleno-, or dilinoleno-) and tripolyethenoid glycerides (dilinoleo-linolenins, linoleo-dilinolenins, trilinolenin) are affected by the different proportions of linoleic and linolenic acid in the various oils, and the picture is in this respect somewhat complicated.

The oils (conophor and linseed) which contain 55 per cent. or more of linolenic acid in their total acids have from 80 per cent. upwards of di- and tri-polyethenoid components, the latter largely linoleodilinolenins and trilinolenin, whilst dilinoleno-glycerides constitute most of the dipolyethenoid glycerides present. Hemp seed and some candlenut oils also contain 80 per cent. or so of di- and tri-polyethenoid glycerides, but in these oils linoleic acid much exceeds linolenic acid in its contribution to the total fatty acids: in consequence dilinoleo-linolenins are the chief components of the tripolyethenoid groups, and linoleo-linoleno-glycerides the main contributors to the dipolyethenoid glycerides.

In another type of oil, illustrated by rubber seed and candlenut oil in Table 109, linoleic acid forms only about 35 per cent., and linolenic acid about 20–30 per cent., of the total fatty acids: in consequence the total amount of di- and tri-polyethenoid components may fall to about 70 per cent. of the oil, which consists mainly of saturated or oleo-linoleo-linolenins with small proportions of dilinoleo-linolenin. Finally, linolenic acid is only a minor component acid in soya bean oil, the main component acid being linoleic acid (*ca.* 50 per cent. of the total acids): in this oil, although the total amount of di- and tri-polyethenoid glycerides is still about 70 per cent., linolenic acid is only present in about 25–30 per cent. of the glycerides, and almost wholly as monolinoleno-glycerides.

It is natural that the widely different proportions of the various combinations of linoleic and linolenic acids in the mixed glycerides of oils in this group should be reflected in their differing specific properties, especially in regard to their "drying" qualities when used in surface coatings. We have seen (p. 460) that a good "linoleic-rich" oil for paint purposes should contain 80–90 per cent. of di- and tri-linoleo-glycerides (corresponding with a content of at least 70 per cent. of linoleic acid in the total fatty acids). A similar criterion for a good "drying" oil of the linseed type appears to be[56] that it should contain not less than 80 per cent. of di-+tri-polyethenoid glycerides, about 30 per cent. or more of the whole oil containing three polyethenoid groups (linoleodilinolenin or trilinolenin), whilst almost all the rest of the glycerides should contain one linolenic group. This corresponds to a content, in the total fatty acids of the oil, of not less than 70 per cent. of linolenic+linoleic acids, and linolenic acid should form at least 50 per cent. of the total fatty acids.

Technical evaluation of linseed oils has shown that an oil with a linolenic acid content below 55 per cent. gives unsatisfactory paint films on "drying", and that with increasing linolenic acid content above 55 per cent. a corresponding increase in the quality of the film becomes apparent. Similarly, paint films from oils of the conophor, perilla, etc., type (with over 65 per cent. of linolenic acid) "dry" more quickly and are superior in final properties to those from linseed oil.

It should be noted that it is, of course, possible, by low-temperature crystallisation from solvents or by the equivalent technical processes of solvent segregation, to obtain fractions from a linolenic-containing fatty oil which are richer in dipolyethenoid glycerides than the original oil.[57b] Thus from soya bean oils a fraction similar in composition to hemp seed oil may be obtained, and similarly linseed oils will yield fractions comparable in composition with conophor oil.

Soya bean oil. The approximate constitution of this oil has been given in Table 109 and discussed above. Earlier it had been shown that the completely hydrogenated oil contains the minimum possible amount of tristearin,[37a] whilst examination of the bromo-additive products of soya bean oil glycerides by Suzuki and Yokoyama[58b] and by Hashi[58c] had revealed no evidence of any simple tri-unsaturated glyceride, but indicated the presence of mixed glycerides such as oleodilinolein, dioleolinolein, oleolinoleo-linolenin and linoleo-linolenins.

Technical solvent-segregation of soya bean oil may produce about 40 per cent. of an extracted fraction, the acids in which include about 60 per cent. of linoleic and about 15 per cent. of linolenic acid.[57b] Such a fraction resembles hemp seed oil in composition.

Hemp seed oil. The glyceride composition given in Table 109 suggests that hemp seed oil might prove a serviceable "drying" oil of the linoleic-rich type, but with somewhat accelerated drying qualities in view of the presence of a linolenic group in some 40 per cent. of the glycerides (25 per cent. of the oil being dilinoleolinolenins).

Rubber seed and candlenut oils. It was pointed out above that in these oils linoleic and linolenic acids occur in comparable proportions, the former predominating. In consequence there is no great amount of dilinoleo-or dilinoleno-glycerides, and little if any trilinolein or trilinolenin present in oils of this type: the dipolyethenoid glycerides (probably 50 per cent. of the whole oils) are mainly linoleo-linoleno compounds, and the small proportions of tripolyethenoid glycerides are almost wholly dilinoleo-linolenins. This arrangement of glycerides thus differs specifically from that in linseed and other linolenic-rich oils, and the properties of this group of oils must also differ. They will not necessarily simulate linseed oil in technical applications, although they may find use as diluents or "extenders" with the more strongly "drying" oils of the linseed or conophor and perilla type. Moreover, although the linoleo-linoleno-(dipolyethenoid) glycerides and the dilinoleo-linolenins may be concentrated by processes such as solvent-segregation, the products so obtained will still not resemble linseed oil very closely, since the latter is rich in dilinoleno-glycerides which are probably only minor components of oils with the fatty acid compositions of rubber seed or candlenut oils.

Linseed oil. Qualitative information obtained by crystallisation of the bromo-adducts of linseed oil glycerides by Eibner[59] and his colleagues enabled these workers to identify two linoleodilinolenins and an oleodilinolenin in linseed oils from India, Riga, and Argentina; whilst Suzuki and Yokoyama,[58a] using similar methods, reported the presence in linseed oil of two linoleodilinolenins, a dilinoleo-linolenin and an oleodilinolein.

Selective adsorption on a column of activated alumina was employed in 1942 by Walker and Mills[60] to effect a separation of the mixed glycerides into simpler mixtures of varying mean unsaturation, the more unsaturated components being adsorbed preferentially in the upper parts of the column. By this means, these investigators were able, for the first time, to determine approximately the proportions in linseed oil of triglycerides which contained respectively 7, 6, 5, or 4 ethenoid groups. For typical oils of La Plata or Calcutta origin, they found about 63–64 per cent. of glycerides containing 7 ethenoid groups, 15–20 per cent. with 6, 9–10 with 5, and 5–8 with 4 ethenoid groups. The possible combinations of acids in each of these classes are as follow – 7:oleodilinolenin, dilinoleolinolenin; 6:monosaturated-dilinolenin, trilinolein, oleo-linoleo-linolenin; 5:monosaturated-linoleo-linolenin, dioleolinolenin, oleodilinolein; 4:monosaturated-dilinolein, monosaturated-oleolinolenin, dioleolinolein. Later, these workers showed that, by repeated adsorption on fresh columns of alumina of the 63–64 per cent. of primarily separated glycerides with a mean unsaturation of 7 ethenoid groups, it was possible to isolate some material with an average content of 8 ethenoid groups per triglyceride molecule (linoleodilinolenin), and a very small proportion of glycerides with 9 ethenoid groups per molecule (trilinolenin); whilst no evidence of glycerides with less than 4 ethenoid groups per molecule was forthcoming from the 5–8 per cent. of least unsaturated primary fractions.

This work, which is of interest as the first attempt to use adsorption methods of separation in quantitative studies of glyceride constitution, thus suggested that at least two-thirds of linseed oil glycerides contain two, and frequently three, di- or tri-ethenoid acyl groups per molecule. The later crystallisation studies[56] of Hilditch and Seavell in 1950, the results of which have already been given in Table 109, also indicate the preponderance of di- and tri-polyethenoid glycerides, but suggest that their actual proportion is higher than that found by Walker and Mills, namely, about 50 per cent. of dipolyethenoid, with 25–30 per cent. of tripolyethenoid glycerides.

Conophor oil. This is the only instance so far in which the component glycerides of an oil with 65 per cent. of linolenic acid in its total fatty acids have been examined in detail, this being effected by the low-temperature crystallisation method of preliminary segregation. Here again the results for individual categories of glycerides differ from those as "computed",[20c] but accord reasonably with the latter for the various combinations of the different types. Either method indicates that conophor oil contains about two-thirds of triunsaturated glycerides, the remainder being almost wholly diunsaturated; it contains, very roughly, about 40 per cent. of tripolyethenoid glycerides (ca. 25 per cent. trilinolenin and ca. 15 per cent. of linoleo-dilinolenin), with similar proportions of dipolyethenoid glycerides (containing two linolenic, or one linolenic and one linoleic group). Nearly all the glycerides (at least 95 per cent.) contain at least one linolenic group.

Conophor oil is the seed fat in the fruits of *Tetracarpidium conophorum*, a vine or rambling perennial which grows in parts of Nigeria and central Africa. Its cultivation in Nigeria and elsewhere was considered during and after the 1939–45 war, when linseed oil was scarce. Meanwhile it is of interest to note that a number of other seed oils have been reported, the fatty acids of which include about 65 per cent. of linolenic acid and 15–20 per cent. of linoleic acid. The glyceride constitution of these, in the absence of direct experimental evidence, may be supposed to be closely similar to that of conophor oil, and their properties more or less the same as those of conophor oil. The oils in question include the seed fats of perilla (*Perilla ocimoides*), *Hyptis spicigera*, and some species of *Ocimum* (all members of the family Labiatæ), and those of *Euphorbia calycina* and *Mercurialis* species (dog's mercury) of the Euphorbiaceæ (*cf.* Chapter IV, Tables 59 and 61, pp. 214, 215, 245).

Since growth of a new oilseed crop on a scale sufficient to counterbalance any shortage of a normally more abundant oil is a project which may require at least 10–20 years, it may be pertinent to remark that it is rather optimistic to wait until the shortage occurs before taking practical steps to develop an alternative crop. In the case of the conophor-perilla oil group there is the further circumstance that in the surface-coating industry these oils are technically superior to linseed oil.

Stillingia oil. The seed oils of *Sapium sebiferum* (stillingia oil) and of *S. discolor*, sub-tropical plants of the family Euphorbiaceæ, are unusual since their component acids include about 5 per cent. by weight (or 8 per cent. mol.) of the short-chain conjugated deca-2:4-dienoic acid, $CH_3.[CH_2]_4.CH:CH.CH:CH.COOH$; the remaining acids include linolenic 51, linoleic 22, oleic 6, palmitic 9 and stearic 4 per cent. (mol.).

The glycerides of stillingia oil were studied by Crossley and Hilditch[61] by the crystallisation technique, the oil being resolved into eight fractions for component acid analyses. It was found that the decadienoic acid was combined in mixed glycerides with the other, more usual, fatty acids, and that it occurred only once in any glyceride molecule in which it was present; two linolenic groups were present in 66 per cent. of the oil, 25 per cent. of the oil consisted of linoleodilinolenins and 70 per cent. of dilinoleno- or linoleo-linoleno-glycerides (the remaining group being saturated, oleic or deca-2:4-dienoic).

The conjugated diene acid undoubtedly confers additional "drying" properties, and, if this is included with the two C_{18} polyethenoid acids, the oil contained 50 per cent. of tripolyethenoid and 45 per cent. of dipolyethenoid glycerides. Its glyceride constitution thus indicates that it should be superior to linseed oil as a surface coating medium, a conclusion which is confirmed by industrial users of stillingia oil.

A concentrate of the stillingia oil glycerides rich in decadieno-diunsaturated C_{18} glycerides was completely hydrogenated[61] and yielded 2-decanodistearin, melting points 45–46° (α-), 53° (β'-) and 57° (β-form), so that symmetrical or 2-decadienoic di-C_{18}-unsaturated glycerides are the only forms present. This was the first occasion on which the configuration of a natural triunsaturated glyceride had been determined.

(v) *Seed Fats rich in Conjugated Tri- or Tetra-ene Acids*

These include tung (China wood) oil (*Aleurites fordii*, *A. montana*, Euphorbiaceæ) with 70–80 per cent. of elæostearic (octadeca-9:11:13-trienoic) acid, oiticica oil (*Licania rigida*, Rosaceæ) with about 60 per cent. of licanic (4-keto-octadeca-9:11:13-trienoic) and some elæostearic acid, kamala oil (*Mallotus philippinensis*, Euphorbiaceæ) with 40–50 per cent. of kamlolenic (18-hydroxyelæostearic) acid, and makita oil (*Parinarium laurinum*, Rosaceæ) which contains about 55 per cent. of parinaric (octadeca-9:11:13:15-tetraenoic) acid and about 30 per cent. of elæostearic acid. The glycerides of tung oils and of makita oils have been studied (1951) by the crystallisation technique.

Much earlier, in 1936, Morrell and Davis[62] converted tung and *oiticica oils* into their crystalline isomeric "β"-forms and attempted to isolate tri-"β"-elæostearin and tri-"β"-licanin by crystallisation. They found that the product from *tung oil* (which contained about 80 per cent. of α-elæostearic acid) was almost pure tri-"β"-elæostearin, whereas that from *oiticica oil* (which contained about 70 per cent. of α-licanic with some α-elæostearic acid) yielded little if any tri-"β"-ketoelæostearin, and was mainly a mixture of glycerides in which two conjugated triene groups were associated with one saturated, or non-conjugated unsaturated, acyl group. These observations accord with the view that the glycerides in either oil are assembled on the usual principles. The 70 per cent. of conjugated acid (now known to be not wholly licanic acid) in the oiticica oil would give rise to little or no trilicanin, whereas trielæostearin is now (*v. infra*) known to form about 45 per cent. of the glycerides in a tung oil with 80 per cent. of elæostearic acid in its component acids.

Tung (China wood) oil. Four tung oils (in which the elæostearic acid content varied from 71 to 82 per cent. of the total fatty acids) were studied by the crystallisation procedure by Hilditch and Mendelowitz,[63] each oil being resolved by crystallisation from petroleum ether and from acetone at $-65°$ and at $-50°$C. into four fractions. The results of this examination are summarised in Table 110.

TABLE 110. *Component Glycerides of Tung Oils*

	OIL I	OIL II	OIL III	OIL IV
Component acids (per cent. mol.):				
Saturated	5·7	4·9	3·7	3·5
Oleic	7·5	5·8	6·1	5·8
Linoleic	15·7	10·3	11·1	8·4
α-Elæostearic	71·1	78·9	79·0	82·3
Component glycerides (per cent. mol.):				
Monoelæostearo-	10	5	8	4
Dielæostearo-	67	53	47	40
Trielæostearin	23	42	45	56

Tung oil glycerides, therefore, closely follow the pattern which prevails in most seed fats. It is important to notice that, in consequence of the operation of "even distribution", variation in elæostearic acid content in the range of 70–80 per cent. of the total fatty acids of tung oils causes very wide changes in the proportion of trielæostearin present. It will be seen from Table 110 that an oil with 82 per cent. elæostearic acid will contain over twice as much trielæostearin as one with only 71 per cent. of elæostearic acid in its total acids. Commercial specimens of genuine tung oil may vary within the ranges indicated, the oils of higher elæostearic acid content being most often (but not always) derived from *Aleurites fordii*, and those of lower elæostearic content from *A. montana* trees. There is however some reason to believe that environment may also contribute to these differences in the elæostearic acid content of tung oils.

Kamala oil. The seed fat of *Mallotus philippinensis* is unique in that its chief component acid is 18-hydroxy-octadeca-9,11,13-trienoic ("kamlolenic") acid (*cf.* Chapter IV, Table 61 and p. 248). It is apparently also quite unusual in its constitution, for O'Neill *et al.*[64a] found that it contains only about one-third of the normal glycerol content of a fat and that the hydroxyl value of the oil is also only about one-third of that to be expected from the amount of "kamlolenic" acid known to be contained in it. These authors suggested that, to a considerable extent, the kamlolenic groups are present as "poly-esters" or lactide-like condensation products of the acid, either *per se* or linked with glycerol molecules to form complex glycerides of the poly-"kamlolenic" esters; these findings were supported by Mikusch.[64b]

Concurrently (1954) Aggarwal *et al.*[64c] segregated kamala oil into two approximately equal fractions, one with 37 per cent. and the other with 82 per cent. of kamlolenic acid. Subsequently these workers[64d] segregated kamala oil more thoroughly by low-temperature crystallisation into six fractions, some of which Achaya and Aggarwal[64e] showed to include glycerides containing one or more acyl groups of a dilactide of kamlolenic acid, $(OH).CH_2.[R].CO.O.CH_2.[R].COOH$ (where R represents the system $—[CH_2]_3.[CH=CH]_3.[CH_2]_7—$). They estimated the proportions and the probable structure of these groups to be as follows ("K" being a kamlolenic group, and "F" an acyl group of the more ordinary fatty acids elæostearic, linoleic, oleic or saturated):

Fraction	Per cent. (wt.)	Per cent. (mol.)	Possible composition
1	54	40	K—K—⎡K—K—F ⎣K—K—F
2	21	18	K—⎡K—K—F ⎣K—K—F
3	12	17	K—K—⎡F ⎣F
4, 5, 6	13	25	K—⎡F ⎣F

Makita oil. The glycerides in the seed fat of *Parinarium laurinum* have been investigated by Riley[65] after separating the fat into seven fractions by systematic crystallisation from petroleum ether or ether at temperatures between 0° and −70°. The component acids in the makita oil were parinaric 55·8, elæostearic 27·0, linoleic (and conjugated dienoic) 3·5, oleic 7·6 and saturated 6·1 per cent. (mol.). The principal glycerides were found to be triparinarin 22, diparinaro-elæostearin 27, parinarodielæostearin 7, and oleo- or saturated-parinaro-elæostearins each about 16 per cent. (mol.).

Although the mixed acids of the fat contain only 54 per cent. of parinaric acid, there is present in its glycerides 22 per cent. of triparinarin. At first glance this appears abnormally high but if, like linolenic or linoleic acid in the linolenic-rich or linoleic-rich oils, parinaric acid behaves like these and like saturated acids in being randomly attached at the 1- and 3-glyceryl positions, an oil of this parinaric acid content is computed[20c] to contain about 18 per cent. of triparinarin (cf. Chapter V, Table 83, p. 395). Elæostearic and the minor component acids of the oil appeared to be arranged in the usual manner (not occurring more than once in any one triglyceride molecule).

It is of interest that, with the relatively insoluble triparinarin, the low-temperature crystallisation procedure led to results of the same character as those obtained by counter-current distribution with oils rich in linolenic or linoleic acid.

Fruit-Coat Fats

It was shown in Chapter IV (p. 189) that the outstanding characteristic of fruit-coat fats is that their major component acids are confined to palmitic, oleic and linoleic acids, irrespective of the component acids of the corresponding seed fats or of the botanical families to which the parent plants belong. The data in Tables 71 and 76 and Figures 2 and 5 in Chapter V (pp. 366, 367, 377, 378) indicate that, so far as content of fully saturated glycerides (in these cases always substantially tripalmitin) is concerned, some fruit-coat fats follow the same course as almost all seed fats, i.e. fully saturated glycerides only appear in excess of the proportions of saturated acid required to associate with unsaturated acids (ca. 1·5:1) in the form of mixed saturated-unsaturated triglycerides. This holds for Stillingia tallow, piqui-a pericarp fat, the fruit-coat of Dacryodes rostrata (Java almond), and some palm oils.

On the other hand, the fruit-coat fats which happened first to be studied by the oxidation method – palm oils, olive oil, laurel berry pericarp fat – showed definitely higher (albeit still small) contents of fully saturated components than would be expected according to the usual generalisation. This led at first to the belief that the mixed glycerides of fruit-coat fats were constituted essentially differently from those typified by the seed fats; subsequently, not only were the above-mentioned instances of conformity with the usual habit encountered, but study of the mixed saturated-unsaturated glycerides of olive and palm oils showed that, apart from the observed somewhat abnormal proportions of tripalmitin, the whole of each of these fats is assembled on the usual, "evenly distributed" lines. Whilst, therefore, it is hardly possible to say at present whether the "evenly distributed" type, or the slightly abnormal type, of fruit-coat fat is the more common, it may perhaps be suggested that the occasional presence in a fruit-coat fat of more tripalmitin than would be expected may be somewhat analogous to the production, in certain seed fats, of small quantities of saturated components in which palmitic acid is frequently concentrated to a greater extent than in the saturated acids of the bulk of the fats in question.

Some account will now be given of the few instances of fruit-coat fats, the glyceride structure of which has been investigated in detail.

Sumach berry fat. The fat present in the exterior of berries of *Rhus* species is technically called "Japan wax", owing to its hardness, which is due to the presence of much tripalmitin. It is a mixture of glycerides of the following component acids (Tsujimoto[66]): palmitic 77, stearic 5, oleic 12 and saturated dicarboxylic acids of the C_{22} and C_{23} series, 5–6 per cent. (wt.). The content of tripalmitin is a consequence of its fatty acid composition, whilst the long-chain dicarboxylic acid components confer certain specific physical properties on the fat (*cf.* p. 198).

Stillingia tallows. The pericarp of seeds of *Sapium sebiferum* Roxb. and of some other species of this genus (formerly known to botanists as *Stillingia*) is accompanied by a solid fatty deposit known technically as Stillingia tallow or Chinese vegetable tallow: the seed fats themselves are liquid unsaturated oils (*v. supra*, Stillingia oil, p. 468).

Klimont[67a] concluded in 1905, after fractional crystallisation of the fat at room temperature, that oleodipalmitin, m.p. 37°, was an important component, together with tripalmitin.

Hilditch and Priestman[22b] examined two specimens of the tallow from *S. sebiferum* in 1930 by isolating and determining the component acids of the fully-saturated glycerides present. Gupta and Meara[67b] in 1950 made a more complete study of the component glycerides of the tallows from *S. sebiferum* and *S. discolor* by use of the more recent systematic crystallisation procedure; these workers also established the configuration of the oleodipalmitin and palmitodiolein present. The results of both studies are summarised in Table 111.

TABLE 111. *Component Glycerides of* Stillingia *Tallows*

	Sapium sebiferum			S. discolor
	CHINA[22b]	UNITED STATES[22b]	HONG KONG[67b]	HONG KONG[67b]
Component acids (per cent. mol.):				
Lauric	3·2	1·6	—	—
Myristic	4·1	3·3	0·6	2·0
Palmitic	59·0	64·6	65·4	49·0
Stearic	1·7	3·0	7·1	1·9
Oleic	32·0	27·5	25·5	44·1
Linoleic	—	—	1·4	3·0
Component glycerides (per cent. mol.):				
Tripalmitin	}24	28 {	8 (14)	— (—)
Dipalmitostearin			13 (5)	— (—)
"Oleo"-myristopalmitin			2 (1)	6 (4)
"Oleo"-dipalmitin	}56	62 {	67 (64)	51 (54)
"Oleo"-palmitostearin			8 (15)	5 (4)
Palmitodi-"olein"	20	10	2 (—)	35 (31)
Tri-"olein"	—	—	—	3 (4)

(Linoleic and oleic taken together as "oleo"-glycerides).

The chief components of *S. sebiferum* fruit-coat fat are thus oleodipalmitin, dipalmitostearin and tripalmitin, whilst those of the more unsaturated fat from *S. discolor* fruits are oleodipalmitin and palmitodiolein. The fruit-coat fats from both species are constituted very closely on the evenly-distributed pattern which is found in most seed fats; the values (shown in parentheses in Table 111) computed for the individual glycerides present by the Vander Wal[20a] or Gunstone procedures[20c] (*cf.* Chapter V, pp. 396, 397) are in good agreement with the observed figures (except that, curiously, the results for tripalmitin and dipalmitostearin are interchanged). Gupta and Meara[67b] also determined the configuration of the dipalmitostearin and oleodipalmitin from the *S. sebiferum* fruits and showed that in each case the symmetrical form was exclusively present: 2-oleodipalmitin and 2-stearodipalmitin.

Palm oils. Most of those who make technical use of the red palm oils of *Elæis guineensis* have long since realised that the statement – still occasionally found in the literature – that these oils contain tripalmitin in abundance is far from the truth. Nevertheless, some of them contain more of this simple triglyceride than would be expected from their fatty acid composition, if the palm oil glycerides were entirely of the "evenly distributed" type which is so characteristic of seed fats (and of some fruit-coat fats). From crystallisation of a palm oil and of the same oil after it had been hydrogenated, Brash[68a] concluded that there was about 10 per cent. of tripalmitin present, and also, probably, about the same proportion of triolein. Hilditch and (Miss) E. E. Jones[68b] isolated and examined the fully saturated glycerides from Congo and Malaya plantation oils and from Cameroons and Drewin (Ivory Coast) native oils with the following results:

	COMPONENT ACIDS OF THE OIL					FULLY SATURATED GLYCERIDES	COMPONENT ACIDS		
	MYR-ISTIC PER CENT.	PAL-MITIC PER CENT.	STEARIC PER CENT.	OLEIC PER CENT.	LIN-OLEIC PER CENT.	PER CENT.	MYR-ISTIC PER CENT.	PAL-MITIC PER CENT.	STEARIC PER CENT.
Congo	1·2	43·0	4·4	40·2	11·2	9·9	3	86	11
Malaya	2·5	40·8	3·6	45·2	7·9	9·1	5	90	5
Cameroons	1·4	40·1	5·5	42·7	10·3	7·9	7	81	12
Drewin	1·4	32·7	7·5	51·7	6·7	7·0			

Steger and van Loon[69a] found only 2 per cent. of fully saturated glycerides (m.p. 54–55° – impure tripalmitin and/or palmitostearins) in a Sumatra plantation palm oil of the "Buitenzorg" variety, the component acids of which were myristic 1·3, palmitic 42·9, stearic 4·7, oleic 39·8 and linoleic 11·3 per cent. (wt.).

Later, Banks, Dean and Hilditch[69b] determined the tristearin content of completely hydrogenated palm oils, and also studied their progressive hydrogenation in the cases of a Congo plantation oil and a Cape Palmas native oil (component acids, respectively: myristic 1·3, 1·6; palmitic 41·4, 32·3; stearic 4·7, 5·5; oleic 42·9, 52·4; linoleic 9·7, 8·2 per cent. wt.). They estimated the chief component glycerides of the two palm oils to be as shown (p. 474 top).

Subsequent glyceride studies of palm oils from 1940 onwards have been made by the later crystallisation procedure from acetone or ether. Hilditch

COMPONENT GLYCERIDES	CONGO PLANTATION OIL PER CENT. (MOL.)	CAPE PALMAS NATIVE OIL PER CENT. (MOL.)
Fully Saturated	6·5	3·5
(including tripalmitin	ca. 5·5	ca. 2)
"Oleo"-dipalmitins	29·5	16·5
Palmitodi-"oleins" (together with any "oleo"- palmitostearin)	58	66
Tri-C$_{18}$ glycerides (tri-"oleins" or stearodi- "oleins")	6	14

and Maddison[70a] resolved native Bassa and Cameroons plantation oils into three fractions by crystallisation from acetone at 0° and room temperature; Hilditch, Meara and Roels[71] separated an N'Dian palm oil into six fractions by similar crystallisations between 0° and −50°C., whilst Meara[17e], mainly in order to obtain sufficiently individual fractions to permit determination of the configuration of some of the mixed glycerides present, carried out a still more exhaustive crystallisation of a Congo oil, employing acetone and ether as solvents at temperatures between +15° and −55°, and resolving the original oil into thirteen fractions, each of which (as in the previous cases) was separately examined for component acids, etc. A summary of the results obtained by these workers is given in Table 112.

TABLE 112. *Component Glycerides of Palm Oils*

	BASSA[70a] NATIVE	CAMEROONS[70a] PLANTATION	N'DIAN[71] PLANTATION	CONGO[17e] PLANTATION
Component acids (per cent. mol.):				
Myristic	0·7	1·3	2·8	2·8
Palmitic	39·8	47·3	43·8	43·4
Stearic	3·6	3·9	5·8	3·4
Hexadecenoic	1·5	0·8	1·9	—
Oleic	48·2	36·8	36·2	43·1
Linoleic	6·2	9·9	9·5	7·3
Component glycerides (per cent. mol.):				
Tripalmitin	3	5	5	5
Dipalmitostearin	3	3	1	1
"Oleo"-myristopalmitin	—	—	5⎫	
"Oleo"-dipalmitin	31	43	32⎬	38
"Oleo"-palmitostearin	10	11	11⎭	
Palmito- (and Myristo-) di- "olein"	41	32	37	48
Stearodi-"olein"	—	—	6	—
Linoleodiolein	12	6	3	8

The data in Table 112 may be taken as characteristic for palm oils of their respective fatty acid compositions, and a general statement of the glycerides present in commercial palm oils may be made as follows:

The chief components of palm oils are "oleo"-dipalmitin and palmitodi-"olein", in amounts which vary according to the proportions of palmitic, oleic and linoleic acids in the whole fats. Together, these two groups of glycerides usually amount to 70–75 per cent. of palm oil, "oleo"-dipalmitin preponderating in oils with high palmitic acid content, and conversely. The other (minor) components are about 10–12 per cent. of "oleo"-palmitostearin; linoleo-diolein (with possibly a very little triolein), 3–12 per cent., according to the oleic and linoleic acid content of the palm oil; and about 3–9 per cent. of tripalmitin+dipalmitostearin, varying with the palmitic acid content of the palm oil.

The most common types of plantation or of native Lagos, Nigeria, Cameroons, etc., palm oils will usually be composed of about 40 per cent. "oleo"-dipalmitins, about 30–40 per cent. palmitodi-"oleins", about 10 per cent. of "oleo"-palmitostearins, and about 6–8 per cent. each of linoleo-diolein and fully saturated glycerides (tripalmitin+dipalmitostearin). The semi-solid nature of palm oil at ordinary European temperatures is due to the presence of the solid mono-"oleo"-glycerides (with the small amount of fully saturated components) dispersed through the palmitodi-"oleins" (mainly still liquid at this temperature).

Meara[17e] selected certain glyceride fractions, obtained by crystallisation of the Congo oil, which were very rich respectively in oleodipalmitins or palmitodioleins and converted them into the corresponding palmitostearins by hydrogenation. Crystallisation of the products led to the isolation of the various positional isomerides present, the identity of which was proved by transition and melting-point data. Contrary to the findings in a number of other natural fats, both the symmetrical and unsymmetrical forms of oleodipalmitin were present in approximately equal amounts in the palm oil, whilst 2-palmito-diolein formed only 5–7 per cent. of the di-unsaturated glycerides, the rest being the unsymmetrical 1-palmitodiolein. This is markedly different from the position in piqui-a fruit-coat fat (*v. infra*) which contains not dissimilar propor-tions of palmitic and unsaturated acids in its total fatty acids. Meara's con-clusions as regards saturated acyl groups attached at the central or 2-position of the glycerides of palm oil are supported to some extent by more recent studies of the production of 2-monoglycerides from palm oils by selective lipase hydrolysis. In one study[21c] the acids attached to the 2-positions were found to be made up of 87 per cent. unsaturated and 13 per cent. saturated; and in another investigation,[21e] of 81 per cent. unsaturated (oleic) with 19 per cent. saturated (palmitic 17, stearic 2). Thus, in contrast to nearly all seed fats so far examined by this method (Chapter V, Table 80, p. 387), and to the fruit-coat fat olive oil,[21c, e] in which 95–99 per cent. of the 2-mono-glyceride acids are unsaturated (oleic, linoleic), palm oils contain up to nearly 20 per cent. of saturated (palmitic) acid in the central 2-position of the glyceride molecules.

In 1963, Barrett *et al.*[19c] gave further confirmation of the findings in the preceding paragraph in the case of a Malayan (plantation) palm oil:

COMPONENT ACIDS	SATURATED				UNSATURATED		
	C_{12}	C_{14}	C_{16}	C_{18}	C_{16}	Ol.	Lin.
Whole fat	Trace	1·0	45·5	4·5	0·5	41·5	7·0
2-monoglycerides	0·5	1·0	16·5	1·5	0·5	67·0	13·0

These workers also determined the various categories of saturated and unsaturated glycerides in the oil by their thin-layer chromatography technique

(T.L.C.) and by selective enzyme hydrolysis (S.E.H.) with results which are in good general accordance with those obtained by crystallisation methods (Table 112):

	Trisaturated	2-oleodisatd.	1-oleodisatd.	2-linoleo-disatd.	Monosatd.-dioleins	Oleolinoleo-satd.	Dioleo-linoleins
T.L.C.	8	35·5	3	8	29	9	7·5
S.E.H.	10	32·5	8	7·5	26	13	3

Piqui-a pericarp fat. The fruit-coat fat of *Caryocar villosum* is interesting because its fatty acids closely resemble those of palm oils, namely: myristic 1·8, palmitic 47·3, stearic 1·7, oleic 47·3, linoleic 1·9 per cent. (mol.). Hilditch and Rigg[33] found that it contained only 2 per cent. of fully saturated components (tripalmitin), thus differing somewhat from palm oils of similar fatty acid composition. No tristearin was detected in the completely hydrogenated fat and the components of the fat (in addition to 2 per cent. of tripalmitin) were therefore 42 per cent. of oleodipalmitins and 56 per cent. of palmitodioleins – an instance of pronounced "even distribution".

Meara[17f] later subjected piqui-a fruit-coat fat to intensive crystallisation and obtained five fractions very rich in oleodisaturated glycerides and three more soluble fractions which consisted largely of diunsaturated glycerides. Oleodipalmitin was isolated separately from each of the five fractions and agreed in its transition and melting-points with 2-oleodipalmitin, whilst the hydrogenated products in each case were 2-stearodipalmitin. The symmetrical form of oleodipalmitin was thus exclusively present. Similar examination of the palmitodistearins obtained by hydrogenation of the palmitodioleins in the three more soluble fractions showed, in contrast, that the latter were present in both the symmetrical and the unsymmetrical configuration, the amounts of each positional isomeride being probably of the same order.

Fruit-coat fat of Java almond (*Dacryodes rostrata*). This fat, examined by Hilditch and Stainsby,[15b*] is also of the evenly distributed type. Its component acids are similar to those of the more unsaturated variety of palm oil (e.g., the Cape Palmas oil above), and comprise palmitic 33·9, stearic 2·7, oleic 59·3 and linoleic 4·1 per cent. (wt.). Palmitodi-"oleins" probably form nearly 85 per cent. of the fat, which further contains about 14 per cent. of "oleo"-dipalmitins and less than 1 per cent. of fully saturated glycerides (palmitostearins).

Laurel pulp oil (*Laurus nobilis*). This liquid fruit-coat fat (component acids: lauric 2·7, palmitic 20·3, oleic 63·0, linoleic 14·0 per cent. wt.) was found by Collin[11b] to contain 3 per cent. of fully saturated glycerides (substantially tripalmitin). It may be contrasted with cottonseed oil, which has somewhat the same quantity of combined palmitic acid, but which yields no appreciable quantity of fully saturated components. The high content of trilaurin in the corresponding laurel kernel fat (p. 429) is much more exceptional than the tripalmitin content of the pulp fat, which is in line with fruit-coat fats of the palm and olive oil type.

---

* Published erroneously as the fruit-coat fat of *Sterculia fœtida*.

Olive oil. This important fruit-coat fat, the component acids of which include about 12 per cent. of saturated acids (mainly palmitic), nearly 80 per cent. of oleic acid, and about 8 per cent. of linoleic acid (wt.), contains 2 per cent. of fully saturated glycerides[72] (tripalmitin); this amount is definitely larger than is usually observed in a seed fat of similarly low saturated acid content. Progressive hydrogenation studies[37b] have shown, in Tuscany and Palestine olive oils, that the tri-C_{18} glyceride content is very near the minimum consistent with the fatty acids present.

It has been mentioned (Chapter IV, p. 201) that two types of olive oil occur. In the most common variety, oleic acid forms 75 per cent. or somewhat more of the component acids with about 10 per cent. of palmitic and somewhat less linoleic acid; in the other, apparently rarer, type the component acids include about 15 per cent. each of palmitic and linoleic with 65 per cent. or less of oleic acid. Hilditch and Maddison[70b] have investigated, by separating each oil into six fractions by crystallisation from acetone at temperatures down to $-30°$, the component glycerides of a Turkish olive oil of the normal type, and an unusual Italian olive oil of the less common type, with the following results. *Turkish olive oil.* Component acids: myristic 0·5, palmitic 10·0, stearic 3·3, arachidic 0·1, hexadecenoic 1·0, oleic 76·5, linoleic 8·6 per cent. (wt.). Chief component glycerides (approximate): monosaturated-dioleins 45, triolein 30 and monolinoleo- (or hexadeceno-) dioleins 25 per cent. (mol.).
Italian olive oil. Component acids: myristic 1·2, palmitic 15·6, stearic 2·0, hexadecenoic 1·6, oleic 64·6 and linoleic 15·0 per cent. (wt.). Chief component glycerides (approximate): monosaturated-dioleins 55, monolinoleo- (or hexa-deceno-) dioleins 35, monosaturated-oleo-linoleins 5 and triolein 5 per cent. (mol.).

The content of fully saturated glycerides in both these olive oils was found to be lower than that stated above (less than 0·5 per cent. in the Turkish oil, and only traces in the Italian oil).

The frequent statement that olive oil consists almost entirely of triolein is thus by no means accurate; it is unlikely that the simple triglyceride triolein ever forms much more than half of the glycerides present in olive oil. Perhaps more important than the actual content of triolein is the proportion of the olive oil made up of glycerides in which a linoleic group is present. Linoleo-glycerides are far more susceptible than oleo-glycerides to atmospheric oxidation, and the content of these glycerides in an olive oil is therefore significant in relation to its suitability either for edible purposes (e.g., salad oil or packing oil for fish, etc.) or for use in the textile industries. The olive oils of the more common type will contain about 25 per cent. of linoleo-glycerides, whereas these may form 40 per cent. or more of the alternative, but less common, variety of genuine olive oil.

References to Chapter VI

1. G. Collin and T. P. Hilditch, (a) *J. Soc. Chem. Ind.*, 1928, **47**, 261T; (b) *ibid.*, 1930, **49**, 141T; (c) *Biochem. J.*, 1929, **23**, 1273; (d) *J. Soc. Chem. Ind.*, 1930, **49**, 138T.
2. (a) F. L. Jackson and H. E. Longenecker, *Oil and Soap*, 1944, **21**, 73; (b) S. P. Pathak and S. S. Mathur, *J. Sci. Food Agric.*, 1954, **5**, 461.
3. A. Bömer and J. Baumann, *Z. Unters. Nahr. Genussm.*, 1920, **40**, 97; A. Bömer and K. Schneider, *ibid.*, 1924, **47**, 61.
4. (Miss) A. P. Dale and M. L. Meara, (a) *J. Sci. Food Agric.*, 1955, **6**, 162, 166; (b) privately communicated.
5. S. V. Puntambekar and S. Krishna, *J. Indian Chem. Soc.*, 1933, **10**, 395.
6. B. G. Gunde and T. P. Hilditch, *J. Chem. Soc.*, 1938, 1610.
7. (a) R. Child and W. R. N. Nathanael, *J. Amer. Chem. Soc.*, 1942, **64**, 1079; (b) T. Tsuchiya and A. Tanaka, *J. Chem. Soc. Japan*, 1954, **75**, 1091.
8. A. H. Weerakoon, Thesis, University of Liverpool, 1952 (pp. 12–76).
9. A. Bömer and K. Ebach, *Z. Unters. Lebensm.*, 1928, **55**, 501.
10. D. Atherton and M. L. Meara, (a) *J. Soc. Chem. Ind.*, 1939, **58**, 353; (b) *ibid.*, 1940, **59**, 95.
11. G. Collin, (a) *J. Soc. Chem. Ind.*, 1933, **52**, 100T; (b) *Biochem. J.*, 1931, **25**, 95.
12. W. J. Bushell and T. P. Hilditch, (a) *J. Soc. Chem. Ind.*, 1939, **58**, 24; (b) *ibid.*, 1938, **57**, 447; (c) *ibid.*, 1938, **57**, 48.
13. M. L. Meara and C. B. Patel, *J. Sci. Food Agric.*, 1950, **1**, 48.
14. (a) C. Amberger and J. Bauch, *Z. Unters. Nahr. Genussm.*, 1924, **48**, 371; (b) E. Lewkowitsch, *J. Soc. Chem. Ind.*, 1933, **52**, 236T.
15. T. P. Hilditch and W. J. Stainsby, (a) *J. Soc. Chem. Ind.*, 1936, **55**, 95T; (b) *ibid.*, 1934, **53**, 197T.
16. (a) T. P. Hilditch and C. H. Lea, *J. Chem. Soc.*, 1927, 3106; (b) C. H. Lea, *J. Soc. Chem. Ind.*, 1929, **48**, 41T.
17. M. L. Meara, (a) *J. Chem. Soc.*, 1949, 2154; (b) privately communicated; (c) *J. Chem. Soc.*, 1945, 22; (d) *ibid.*, 1945, 23; (e) *ibid.*, 1948, 722; (f) *ibid.*, 1947, 773.
18. C. R. Scholfield and H. J. Dutton, (a) *J. Amer. Oil Chem. Soc.*, 1959, **36**, 325; (b) (with T. L. Mounts), *ibid.*, 1961, **38**, 96.
19. (a) G. V. Jones and E. G. Hammond, *J. Amer. Oil Chem. Soc.*, 1961, **38**, 69; (b) E. H. Steiner and A. R. Bonar, *J. Sci. Food Agric.*, 1961, **12**, 247; (c) C. B. Barrett, M. S. J. Dallas and F. B. Padley, *J. Amer. Oil Chem. Soc.*, 1963, **40**, 580.
20. (a) R. J. Vander Wal, *J. Amer. Oil Chem. Soc.*, 1960, **37**, 18; (b) F. D. Gunstone, *Chem. and Ind.*, 1962, 1214; (c) *idem*, privately communicated.
21. (a) P. Savary, J. Flanzy and P. Desnuelle, *Biochem. Biophys. Acta*, 1957, **24**, 414; (b) E. S. Lutton, *J. Amer. Oil Chem. Soc.*, 1957, **34**, 521; (c) F. H. Mattson (with E. S. Lutton), *J. Biol. Chem.*, 1958, **233**, 868; (d) (with R. A. Volpenhein), *ibid.*, 1961, **236**, 1891; (e) M. H. Coleman, *J. Amer. Oil Chem. Soc.*, 1961, **38**, 685; (f) D. Chapman, A. Crossley and A. C. Davies, *J. Chem. Soc.*, 1957, 1502.
22. T. P. Hilditch and J. Priestman, (a) *J. Soc. Chem. Ind.*, 1930, **49**, 197T; (b) *ibid.*, 1930, **49**, 397T; (c) T. P. Hilditch and Y. A. H. Zaky, *J. Soc. Chem. Ind.*, 1942, **61**, 34.
23. C. Venkatarao and M. Narasingarao, (a) *J. Indian Chem. Soc.*, 1943, **20**, 298; (b) *ibid.*, 1944, **21**, 249; (c) M. N. Baliga and M. L. Meara, *J. Soc. Chem. Ind.*, 1949, **68**, 52.
24. R. Heise, *Tropenpflanzer*, 1897, **1**, 10; 1899, **3**, 203.
25. (a) T. P. Hilditch and S. R. Saletore, *J. Soc. Chem. Ind.*, 1931, **50**, 468T; 1933, **52**, 101T; (b) M. L. Meara and Y. A. H. Zaky, *J. Soc. Chem. Ind.*, 1940, **59**, 25; (c) T. G. Green and T. P. Hilditch, *ibid.*, 1938, **57**, 49.
26. E. S. Lutton, *J. Amer. Chem. Soc.*, 1946, **68**, 676.
27. (a) N. L. Vidyarthi and C. J. Daso Rao, *J. Indian Chem. Soc.*, 1939, **16**, 437; (b) N. L. Vidyarthi and M. V. Mallya, *ibid.*, 1939, **16**, 443; (c) N. L. Vidyarthi, *ibid.*, 1943, **20**, 45; (d) N. L. Vidyarthi and M. V. Mallya, *ibid.*, 1940, **17**, 87.

28. T. P. Hilditch and K. S. Murti, (*a*) *J. Soc. Chem. Ind.*, 1941, **60**, 16; (*b*) *ibid.*, 1939, **58**, 310; (*c*) D. R. Dhingra, G. L. Seth and P. C. Speers, *J. Soc. Chem. Ind.*, 1933, **52**, 116T; (*d*) S. S. Gupta and C. R. Mitra, *J. Sci. Food Agric.*, 1953, **4**, 44.

29. (*a*) J. M. Chaves and E. Pechnik, *Rev. Quim. Ind.*, 1945, **4**, No. 163; 1946, **15**, No. 165; (*b*) T. P. Hilditch and S. P. Pathak, *J. Chem. Soc.*, 1949, Supp. **1**, 87.

30. A. H. Weerakoon, Thesis, University of Liverpool, 1952 (pp. 77–148).

31. (*a*) J. S. Cama, Thesis, University of Liverpool, 1952 (pp. 182–211); (*b*) A. R. S. Kartha and K. N. Menon, *Proc. Indian Acad. Sci.*, 1944, **19**, A, 1.

32. T. P. Hilditch and M. B. Ichaporia, *J. Soc. Chem. Ind.*, 1938, **57**, 44.

33. T. P. Hilditch and J. G. Rigg, *J. Soc. Chem. Ind.*, 1935, **54**, 109T.

34. (*a*) S. P. Pathak, B. G. Gunde and N. N. Godbole, *Indian Soap Journal*, 1946; (*b*) N. N. Godbole, B. G. Gunde and P. D. Shrivastava, *J. Indian Chem. Soc.*, 1941, **18**, 557.

35. (*a*) T. P. Hilditch, M. L. Meara and C. B. Patel, *J. Sci. Food Agric.*, 1951, **2**, 142; (*b*) T. P. Hilditch and M. L. Meara, *J. Soc. Chem. Ind.*, 1944, **63**, 114.

36. T. P. Hilditch, M. L. Meara and W. H. Pedelty, *J. Soc. Chem. Ind.*, 1939, **58**, 26.

37. T. P. Hilditch, (*a*) (with E. C. Jones), *J. Soc. Chem. Ind.*, 1934, **53**, 13T; (*b*) (with H. M. Thompson), *ibid.*, 1937, **56**, 434T.

38. B. G. Gunde and T. P. Hilditch, *J. Soc. Chem. Ind.*, 1940, **59**, 47.

39. T. P. Hilditch, M. B. Ichaporia and H. Jasperson, *J. Soc. Chem. Ind.*, 1938, **57**, 363.

40. R. V. Crawford and T. P. Hilditch, *J. Sci. Food Agric.*, 1950, **1**, 372.

41. S. S. Gupta, T. P. Hilditch and J. P. Riley, *J. Sci. Food Agric.*, 1951, **2**, 245.

42. (*a*) C. Amberger, *Z. Unters. Nahr. Genussm.*, 1920, **40**, 192; (*b*) T. P. Hilditch and H. Paul, *J. Soc. Chem. Ind.*, 1935, **54**, 331T; (*c*) T. P. Hilditch, P. A. Laurent and M. L. Meara, *J. Soc. Chem. Ind.*, 1947, **66**, 19.

43. (*a*) J. Holmberg and G. Sellmann, *Svensk Kem. Tidskrift*, 1952, **64**, 270; (*b*) C. F. Krewson, J. S. Ard and R. W. Riemenschneider, *J. Amer. Oil Chem. Soc.*, 1962, **39**, 334.

44. (*a*) T. P. Hilditch and L. Maddison, *J. Soc. Chem. Ind.*, 1940, **59**, 162; (*b*) A. Crossley and T. P. Hilditch, *J. Sci. Food Agric.*, 1951, **2**, 251; (*c*) M. M. Chakrabarty and T. P. Hilditch, *J. Sci. Food Agric.*, 1951, **2**, 255; (*d*) H. C. Dunn, T. P. Hilditch and J. P. Riley, *J. Soc. Chem. Ind.*, 1948, **67**, 199; (*e*) C. Barker, private communication.

45. B. K. Singh and A. Kumar, (*a*) *Proc. Indian Acad. Sci.*, 1948, **27**, B, 147; (*b*) *ibid.*, 1945, **22**, A, 310; (*c*) *ibid.*, 1946, **23**, A, 379.

46. (*a*) F. D. Gunstone and T. P. Hilditch, *J. Chem. Soc.*, 1946, 1022; T. P. Hilditch, *Nature*, 1950, **166**, 558; (*b*) P. Budowski, *J. Amer. Oil Chem. Soc.*, 1950, **27**, 264.

47. A. P. Doerschuk and B. F. Daubert, *J. Amer. Oil Chem. Soc.*, 1948, **25**, 425.

48. C. R. Scholfield and H. J. Dutton (*a*) (with J. Nowakowska), *J. Amer. Oil Chem. Soc.*, 1961, **38**, 175; (*b*) *ibid.*, 1958, **35**, 493; (*c*) C. R. Scholfield and M. A. Hicks, *ibid.*, 1957, **34**, 77; (*d*) H. J. Dutton and J. A. Cannon, *ibid.*, 1956, **33**, 46.

49. M. L. Meara and N. K. Sen, *J. Sci. Food Agric.*, 1952, **3**, 237.

50. (*a*) R. V. Crawford and T. P. Hilditch, *J. Sci. Food Agric.*, 1950, **1**, 230; (*b*) R. E. Bridge, M. M. Chakrabarty and T. P. Hilditch, *J. Oil Col. Chem. Assocn.*, 1951, **34**, 354; (*c*) A. Crossley, 1950 (privately communicated); C. Barker and T. P. Hilditch (*d*) *J. Oil Col. Chem. Assocn.*, 1950, **33**, 6; (*e*) *J. Sci. Food Agric.*, 1950, **1**, 118.

51. B. K. Singh and A. Kumar, *Proc. Indian Acad. Sci.*, 1947, **26**, A, 205.

52. T. P. Hilditch, *Chem. and Ind.*, 1951, 846.

53. G. Winter, *J. Amer. Oil Chem. Soc.*, 1950, **27**, 82.

54. D. L. Sahasrabuddhe and N. P. Kale, *J. Univ. Bombay*, 1932, **1**, (ii), 37.

55. T. P. Hilditch, M. L. Meara and J. Holmberg, *J. Amer. Oil Chem. Soc.*, 1947, **24**, 321.

56. T. P. Hilditch and A. J. Seavell, *J. Oil Col. Chem. Assocn.*, 1950, **33**, 24.

57. (*a*) F. D. Gunstone and T. P. Hilditch, *J. Soc. Chem. Ind.*, 1947, **66**, 205; (*b*) T. P. Hilditch and A. J. Seavell, *J. Oil Chem. Assocn.*, 1950, **33**, 49.

58. B. Suzuki and Y. Yokoyama, (*a*) *Proc. Imp. Acad. Tokyo*, 1927, **3**, 526; (*b*) *ibid.*, 529; (*c*) K. Hashi, *J. Soc. Chem. Ind. Japan*, 1927, **30**, 849, 856.

59. A. Eibner, L. Widenmayer and E. Schild, *Chem. Umschau*, 1927, **34**, 312; A. Eibner and F. Brosel, *ibid.*, 1928, **35**, 157.

60. F. T. Walker and M. R. Mills, *J. Soc. Chem. Ind.*, 1942, **61**, 125; 1943, **62**, 106.

61. A. Crossley and T. P. Hilditch, *J. Sci. Food Agric.*, 1953, **4**, 38.

62. R. S. Morrell and W. R. Davis, *J. Oil Col. Chem. Assocn.*, 1936, **19**, 264.

63. T. P. Hilditch and A. Mendelowitz, *J. Sci. Food Agric.*, 1951, **2**, 548.

64. (*a*) L. A. O'Neill, A. C. Dennison and N. H. E. Ahlers, *Chem. and Ind.*, 1954, 756; (*b*) J. D. von Mikusch, *Deutsch. Farb.-Zeitsch.*, 1954, **5**, 166; (*c*) J. S. Aggarwal (with S. C. and S. S. Gupta), *J. Amer. Oil Chem. Soc.*, 1954, **31**, 287; (*d*) (with V. H. Kapadia), *J. Sci. Indust. Res., India*, 1955, **17**, B, 117; (*e*) (with K. T. Achaya), *Chem. and Ind.*, 1962, 1616.

65. J. P. Riley, *J. Chem. Soc.*, 1951, 291.

66. M. Tsujimoto, *Bull. Chem. Soc., Japan*, 1931, **6**, 325, 337; 1935, **10**, 212.

67. (*a*) J. Klimont, *Monatsh.*, 1903, **24**, 408; 1905, **26**, 567; (*b*) S. S. Gupta and M. L. Meara, *J. Chem. Soc.*, 1950, 1337.

68. (*a*) W. Brash, *J. Soc. Chem. Ind.*, 1926, **45**, 438т; (*b*) T. P. Hilditch and (Miss) E. E. Jones, *J. Soc. Chem. Ind.*, 1930, **49**, 363т.

69. (*a*) A. Steger and J. van Loon, *Rec. trav. chim.*, 1935, **54**, 284; (*b*) A. Banks, H. K. Dean and T. P. Hilditch, *J. Soc. Chem. Ind.*, 1935, **54**, 77т.

70. T. P. Hilditch and L. Maddison, (*a*) *J. Soc. Chem. Ind.*, 1940, **59**, 67; (*b*) *ibid.*, 1941, **60**, 258.

71. T. P. Hilditch, M. L. Meara and O. A. Roels, *J. Soc. Chem. Ind.*, 1947, **66**, 284.

72. T. P. Hilditch and E. C. Jones, *J. Chem. Soc.*, 1932, 805.

CHAPTER VII

The Component Glycerides of Individual Animal Fats

Detailed research into the glyceride structure of animal fats has been so far chiefly concerned with depot and milk fats of the herbivorous land animals, especially those of ox, sheep and pig depots and cows' milk. Depot and milk fats of a small number of other animals (terrestrial and marine) have been similarly investigated but, as emphasised in Chapter V (p. 404) the range of study has been far less wide than is the case with vegetable seed fats and, moreover, is completely out of perspective in the disproportionate attention paid to the fats of the common ruminants and the lack of information for a comprehensive range of the many animal species belonging to other sectors of fauna.

Up to the present, two methods of study have been followed: (*a*) study of the proportions and compositions of the fully saturated glycerides in different animal fats, and (*b*) preliminary segregation of the fats, by systematic crystallisation from solvents at different low temperatures, into groups of varying unsaturation, followed by determination of the component acids (and, where applicable, fully saturated glycerides) in each group. To these may now hopefully be added (*c*) the use of thin layer chromatography as a means of segregation, and (*d*) the isolation of the 2-monoglycerides present in a fat by selective enzyme hydrolysis – either procedure to be coupled with detailed analysis of the component acids present in the segregated groups – or 2-monoglycerides – thus produced; at the time of writing, however, these procedures are in a very early stage of development.

We shall consider in sequence the available data regarding the component glycerides of individual marine and land animal depot and milk fats.

Marine Animal Fats

The great majority of fish oils and of ordinary whale, seal and similar oils contain only about 15–20 per cent. of saturated fatty acids, and consequently most of them possess no detectable quantity of fully saturated components. The oxidation method of investigation is therefore not of great service when applied to these fats, although it has given useful information with regard to the rather special case of the sperm whale oils (or rather waxes), to which further reference is made later.

The structure of the glycerides of many marine animal oils was nevertheless well illustrated, from a qualitative point of view, by the studies in 1927–1930 of Suzuki and his co-workers.[1] They established the presence of a sufficient number of mixed glycerides in these oils to justify the conclusions that the distribution of the numerous component acids of a fish or whale oil amongst the glycerol molecules of the fat is profoundly heterogeneous and that, whilst simple triglycerides are either absent or very rare, the most common form is a triglyceride containing three different acids, although sometimes two radicals of the same fatty acid are observed in a single glyceride molecule. The following examples of glycerides isolated in the form of their bromo-addition products by Suzuki and co-workers from various oils will serve by way of illustration:

Cod liver oil: stearidono-diclupanodonin, diarachidono-clupanodonin, hexadeceno-stearidono-clupanodonin, hexadeceno-arachidono-clupanodonin, dihexadeceno-linolenin and -linolein, etc.

Herring oil: hexadeceno-diarachidonin, gadoleo-diarachidonin, linoleno-gadoleo-clupanodonin, linoleo-digadolein and -dihexadecenoin, dicetoleo-gadolein, etc.

Sardine oil: some of the foregoing, with dicetoleo-olein, dicetoleo-arachidonin, triolein, triarachidonin, etc.

Shark liver oil: linoleno-diclupanodonin, arachidono-diclupanodonin, linoleno-arachidono-clupanodonin, linoleno-digadolein, dihexadeceno-linolein, palmitodiolein, triolein, etc.

Whale oil: oleo-arachidono-clupanodonin, oleo-diclupanodonin, oleo-diarachidonin, dihexadeceno-olein, etc.

Confirmatory evidence of the very mixed character of whale oil glycerides is afforded by the work of Greitemann[2] who in 1925 isolated specimens of the following mixed glycerides from hydrogenated whale oil: myristo-palmito-arachidin (m.p. 49·5°), palmito-stearo-arachidin (m.p. 57·3°), distearo-arachidin (m.p. 62·3°), stearo-arachido-behenin (m.p. 65°) and traces of diarachido-behenin and arachido-dibehenin.

The glycerides of *cod liver oil* and of an *Antarctic whale oil* were studied in 1937 by means of catalytic hydrogenation to varying stages by Harper and Hilditch[3a] and by Hilditch and Terleski.[3b] In the earlier stages of hydrogenation of these oils the highly unsaturated (C_{20} and C_{22}) acyl groups undergo partial reduction, but subsequently palmitic and stearic groups are formed from the corresponding monoethenoid glycerides whilst a certain proportion of di- or tri-ethenoid C_{20} and C_{22} compounds is still present. Even at low iodine values, e.g. 20–30, of the hydrogenated fats, some of the C_{20} and C_{22} acids are still more highly unsaturated than monoethenoid. The rate of production of fully saturated glycerides is slow until the final stages of the reduction (below iodine value 40–50). In both the fish oil and the marine mammal blubber oil the fully hydrogenated triglycerides at first produced by hydrogenation contain chiefly palmitic and stearic (and myristic) acids, arachidic and behenic acids being present only in small proportions. Subsequently saturated glycerides containing the latter are produced in quantity, whilst palmitic and stearic glycerides are being formed at the same time. This is further evidence that the original oils consist of a complex mixture of mixed triglycerides in which many combinations of the component acids are present, and in which there are always at least two, and usually three, different acids in each triglyceride.

In cod liver oil, which contains 45 per cent. of unsaturated acids of the C_{20} and C_{22} series, most of the glyceride molecules will contain at least one acyl group from these series. In the whale oil, the mixture of glycerides is probably almost as complex but, owing to the presence of only 16–20 per cent. of unsaturated C_{20} and C_{22} acids, almost half of the oil probably consists of glycerides containing only acids of the C_{18}, C_{16} and C_{14} series.

A hydrogenated whale oil of similar iodine value to beef or mutton tallow contains about the same proportion of fully saturated glycerides as the latter, and, in consequence, of the relative lack of C_{20} or C_{22} saturated acids at the earlier stages of hydrogenation, the component acids of such fully saturated glycerides are more similar to those of the corresponding components of tallows than might at first be expected. The (liquid) components of the rest of the fat (mixed saturated-unsaturated glycerides) are of course entirely different from those of tallow, owing to the presence of C_{20} and C_{22} unsaturated acids and of the "*iso*"-unsaturated acids of hydrogenation.

STUDY OF MARINE ANIMAL OIL GLYCERIDES BY THE LOW-TEMPERATURE CRYSTALLISATION PROCEDURE

In 1938 and following years the glycerides of several marine animal oils were investigated by separating them into a number of fractions by systematic crystallisation from acetone at temperatures from $-70°$ upwards and determining the component acids in each fraction. The complexity of the fatty acid mixtures prevents elucidation of the proportions of any one individual mixed glyceride, but the distribution of the various types of fatty acids in the glycerides of the oils can be roughly indicated by this very lengthy and tedious procedure, leading to fairly definite indications as to the chief classes of glycerides present in these complex fats of aquatic origin.

Before discussing in some detail the results of study of some individual marine animal oils by this procedure, it should be mentioned that the selective hydrolysis of any of these fats by pancreatic lipase, leading to the isolation of the 2-monoglycerides present, has not yet been applied to a marine animal oil. It is evident that this process, coupled with determination of the component acids attached to the 2-hydroxyl group of glycerol, will shed much further light on the constitution of such oils; it is to be hoped that information by this means will be sought at an early date.

Whale oil. In view of the technical importance of whale oil, application of the low-temperature crystallisation procedure to this oil will be reviewed somewhat more fully than in the cases of other marine animal oils which have so far received similar study. In 1942 Hilditch and Maddison[4a] separated an Antarctic whale oil into four fractions by crystallisation from acetone, first at $-10°$ and subsequently down to $-30°$, with results given in the 2nd Edition (1947) of this book. Later work showed the advantage of commencing crystallisations at the *lowest* temperature and working at successively higher temperatures, and also of segregating the oil into a larger number of fractions. In 1948, therefore, these authors[4b] repeated their study of the same whale oil in greater detail: the main results of the earlier investigation were confirmed, but a greater degree of precision was achieved in some of the quantitative aspects of the results.

The Antarctic whale oil (504g.) and the separated insoluble fractions were crystallised successively from 10 per cent. solutions in acetone at $-60°$, $-40°$, $-20°$, and $-10°$. Several recrystallisations of the solids, deposited at $-40°$ and $-10°$, were carried out at these respective temperatures, until the glycerides left in solution showed an iodine value definitely lower than that of the preceding solute. The following is a summary of the various fractions obtained and the manner in which they were combined to give six final fractions, the component acids in each of which were determined as in the case of the total mixed acids of the whale oil:

	FRACTIONS SEPARATED			FRACTIONS ANALYSED		
	g.	IODINE VALUE	No.	g.	PER CENT.	IODINE VALUE
Soluble at $-60°$	89·9	215·2	F	89·9	17·8	215·2
,, ,, $-60°$ (a)	31·2	192·9	E	31·2	6·2	192·9
,, ,, $-40°$	95·8	120·1				
,, ,, $-40°$ (a)	44·3	117·1	D	152·5	30·2	118·3
,, ,, $-40°$ (b)	12·4	109·5				
,, ,, $-20°$	109·7	82·7	C	109·7	21·8	82·7
,, ,, $-10°$	29·5	67·6				
,, ,, $-10°$ (a)	11·5	63·8	B	48·2	9·6	63·2
,, ,, $-10°$ (b)	7·2	51·6				
Insoluble at $-10°$	72·5	29·1	A	72·5	14·4	29·1

(a) 1st recrystallisation.   (b) 2nd recrystallisation.

The molar percentages and mean unsaturation of the acids determined in each of the glyceride fractions A to F are given in Table 113.

TABLE 113. *Component Acids of Antarctic Whale Oil and of fractions separated by Low-Temperature Crystallisation (per cent. mol.)*

	C_{12}	C_{14}	C_{16}	C_{18}	C_{20}	C_{22}
I. *Whole fat*						
Saturated	0·4	11·0	16·5	2·2	0·1	—
Unsaturated	—	3·2	14·8	35·4	10·8	5·6 ⎫
Mean unsaturation	—	−2·0	−2·1	−2·4	−7·0	−9·8 ⎭
II. *Fractions separated by crystallisation*						
A. *Insoluble at* $-10°$ (14·4 per cent.)						
Saturated	0·1	24·5	41·9	4·7	1·0	—
Unsaturated	—	1·3	4·4	17·5	4·0	0·6 ⎫
Mean unsaturation	—	−2·0	−2·0	−2·1	−2·7	−4·0 ⎭
B. *Soluble at* $-10°$ (9·6 per cent)						
Saturated	0·2	18·1	24·8	4·2	—	—
Unsaturated	—	2·1	11·6	30·6	6·4	2·0 ⎫
Mean unsaturation	—	−2·0	−2·0	−2·2	−4·9	−6·2 ⎭
C. *Soluble at* $-20°$ (21·8 per cent.)						
Saturated	Trace	11·4	18·0	2·8	—	—
Unsaturated	—	2·4	15·2	40·6	8·1	1·5 ⎫
Mean unsaturation	—	−2·0	−2·1	−2·2	−7·4	−9·7 ⎭
D. *Soluble at* $-40°$ (30·2 per cent.)						
Saturated	1·2	6·8	9·5	1·5	—	—
Unsaturated	—	4·2	19·0	44·4	9·1	4·3 ⎫
Mean unsaturation	—	−2·0	−2·1	−2·4	−7·0	−9·2 ⎭
E. *Soluble at* $-60°$ (6·2 per cent.)						
Saturated	—	5·1	5·8	—	—	—
Unsaturated	—	4·3	17·4	36·0	17·7	13·7 ⎫
Mean unsaturation	—	−2·0	−2·3	−2·7	−8·4	−10·3 ⎭
F. *Soluble at* $-60°$ (17·8 per cent.)						
Saturated	—	4·1	3·1	—	—	—
Unsaturated	—	4·2	16·8	31·7	23·3	16·8 ⎫
Mean unsaturation	—	−2·0	−2·3	−2·7	−8·3	−10·3 ⎭

In spite of the much improved segregation of the mixed glycerides in this study[4b] as compared with the earlier one[4a], no indication was forthcoming in any of the fractions A to F of the presence of any simple triglycerides, or of any triglyceride in which all the acyl groups have the same carbon content: this confirms earlier conclusions[1,3b] that whale oil mixed glycerides are an extremely heterogeneous mixture assembled on the lines of even (or widest) distribution of the many fatty acids present amongst the glycerol molecules (cf. Chapter V, p. 409).

Although the component acids in each fraction were still too complex to permit of any definite allocation of component glycerides, an estimate of the proportions present of various glyceride categories was possible. The distribution of saturated and homologous groups of unsaturated acids was estimated to be as follows, showing the number of mols. (per 100 mols. of total whale oil glycerides) which contained three, two, one, or none of each type of fatty acid:

Acyl groups present in a triglyceride molecule:	3	2	1	ABSENT
Saturated acyl groups	2·5	16·5	50	31
Unsaturated C_{16} (and C_{14}) acyl groups	Nil	Nil	54	46
Unsaturated C_{18} acyl groups	Nil	15	76	9
Unsaturated C_{20} and C_{22} acyl groups	Nil	3·5	42	54·5

These figures suggest that the general composition of the whale oil was somewhat as follows:

PER CENT. (MOL.)	ACID GROUPS PRESENT
2·5	3 Saturated (mainly myristopalmitins)
10	2 Saturated, 1 unsaturated C_{18}
6·5	2 Saturated, 1 unsaturated C_{14}, C_{16}, C_{20}, or C_{22}
50	1 Saturated, 1 unsaturated C_{18}, 1 unsaturated C_{14}, C_{16}, C_{20}, or C_{22}
15	2 Unsaturated C_{18}, 1 unsaturated C_{14}, C_{16}, C_{20}, or C_{22}
15	1 Unsaturated C_{18}, 2 unsaturated C_{14}, C_{16}, C_{20}, or C_{22}

Thus about 75 per cent. of the whale oil glycerides contained one unsaturated C_{18} (mainly oleic) acid group, whilst two of these groups were present in a further 15 per cent. of the oil. About half of the oil consisted of glycerides containing one saturated acid, one unsaturated C_{18} acid, and one of the other homologous unsaturated acids. There was a further 30 per cent. of triunsaturated glycerides, composed in about equal proportions of "oleo"-di-unsaturated (C_{14}, C_{16}, C_{20}, or C_{22}) glycerides and of glycerides containing two "oleo"-groups with one of the other homologous unsaturated acids. About 16 per cent. of the oil consisted of disaturated glycerides with only one unsaturated acyl group (oleic predominating), and a very small proportion (2·5 per cent.) of fully-saturated glycerides, probably myristo-palmitins, was detected in the whale oil.

About half of the whale oil glycerides contained no acids of higher molecular weight than the C_{18} series. This is the least unsaturated part of the oil, made up of oleopalmitohexadecenoin, oleomyristohexadecenoin, some palmitodiolein, oleomyristopalmitin, and similar glycerides. In the remaining half of the oil, the glycerides include one, or (in very small amounts – about 3 or 4 per cent.) two of the mainly polyethenoid C_{20} and C_{22} acids. Glycerides with three polyethenoid groups in the same molecule were not detected in the 30 per cent. of tri-unsaturated glycerides in the whale oil.

Herring oil, seal blubber oil and sea lion blubber oil. Three other marine animal oils have been studied in a similar manner to whale oil, namely, an Icelandic herring oil by Bjarnason and Meara,[5] blubber oil from a Grey (Atlantic) Seal (*Halichærus grypus*) by Hilditch and Pathak,[6] and the blubber fat from a California sea-lion (*Zalophus californianus*) by Cardin.[7] The general results of these investigations are summed up in Table 114.

TABLE 114. *Component Glycerides of Herring Oil, Grey Seal Oil, Sea-Lion Oil*

	ICELANDIC HERRING[5]	GREY SEAL[6]	SEA-LION[7]
Component acids (per cent. mol.):			
Myristic	8·8	4·7	3·8
Palmitic	13·0	12·1	6·7
Stearic	0·9	2·0	2·1
Arachidic	0·1	0·1	0·4
Unsaturated C_{14}	1·5(−2·0H)	3·3(−2·0H)	1·7(−2·0H)
,, C_{16}	13·3(−2·4H)	19·2(−2·2H)	9·5(−2·1H)
,, C_{18}	20·0(−3·5H)	31·8(−2·6H)	26·5(−2·4H)
,, C_{20}	24·0(−5·2H)	12·9(−6·2H)	25·6(−3·3H)
,, C_{22}	18·3(−4·3H)	13·4(−10·0H)	23·3(−6·8H)
,, C_{24}	0·1(−3·8H)	0·5(−11·0H)	0·4(−7·0H)
Glyceride Categories (per cent. mol.):			
(a) Disaturated mono-unsaturated	4	6	—
Monosaturated di-unsaturated	61	45	39
Tri-unsaturated	35	49	61
(b) Containing 1 unsaturated C_{16} (or C_{14})	44	68	33
Containing 2 unsaturated C_{16} (or C_{14})	—	—	—
(c) Containing 1 unsaturated C_{18}	60	89	76
Containing 2 unsaturated C_{18}	—	3	2
(d) Containing 1 unsaturated C_{20} or C_{22}	73	67	52
Containing 2 unsaturated C_{20} or C_{22}	27	6	48

The fatty acids of the oils in Table 114, with those of the whale oil (Table 113), provide typical examples of the variations in amounts of the various acid groups which are encountered in marine animal oils. The effect on the glyceride structure is also well illustrated by these four oils; the differences in amounts of the various fatty acids in different oils cause profound differences in the proportions of the glyceride categories.

Thus in the *whale oil* (with only 16·4 per cent. of C_{20-22} acids) over 50 per cent. of the glycerides contain neither C_{20} nor C_{22} acyl groups, and in the *seal oil* (with 26·8 per cent. of C_{20-24} acids) over 25 per cent. of the glycerides contain no acyl groups above the C_{18} series; but all the glycerides of the *herring* and *sea-lion* oils contain C_{20-22} acids, two C_{20-22} acyl groups being present in 27 per cent. and 48 per cent. of the respective oils. Conversely, over 90 per cent. of the *whale oil* and *seal oil* glycerides contain unsaturated C_{18} acids (which in these instances form over 30 per cent. of the total fatty acids of the oils); but 40 per cent. of the *herring oil* (in which there is only 20 per cent. of unsaturated C_{18} acids) is made up of glycerides which contain no unsaturated C_{18} acyl group.

It is well again to emphasise here that, as in some of the vegetable oils (Chapter VI, pp. 449, 469), alterations in the proportions of one or other of the component acids of fats may result in apparently disproportionate changes in the nature of their component mixed glycerides – and these, in turn, may have considerable bearing upon the properties of an oil, or of its hydrogenated products.

In the Icelandic *herring oil*[5] (as in other herring oils, *cf.* Chapter II, p. 46) no acid occurs in outstanding proportions. The three groups of unsaturated acids of the C_{18}, C_{20}, and C_{22} series respectively form 20, 24, and 18 per cent. of the total, with saturated and unsaturated C_{16} acids somewhat less (about 13 per cent. each), 9 per cent. of myristic acid, about 1 per cent. each of stearic and tetradecenoic acids, and traces of lauric, arachidic and tetracosenoic acids. There are moreover considerable, and, curiously, approximately equal proportions of monoethenoid acids in each homologous group of unsaturated acids. About one-third of the *herring oil* was made up of triunsaturated glycerides, nearly all of which may have contained both mono- and poly-ethenoid acids (including members of each homologous series). Apart from the small proportion of disaturated glycerides (probably myristo-palmito derivatives), the rest of the oil was nearly equally divided between monosaturated glycerides in which both a monoethenoid and polyethenoid acyl group was also present, and those in which both unsaturated groups belonged to homologous members of the monoethenoid series. In contrast to whale oil, about 40 per cent. (mol.) of the glycerides contained no unsaturated acid of the C_{18} series, whilst nearly all the triglycerides appeared to contain at least one C_{20} or C_{22} acyl group although none appeared to contain three.

It may be mentioned here that, in consequence of the marked differences in detail between the glyceride structure of whale and herring oils, the glyceride composition of these oils after being hydrogenated to similar iodine values will also differ essentially in many respects.

A less extended study of *menhaden oil* (*Brevoortia tyrannus*) by Baldwin and Parks[8] serves to give partial corroboration of the extremely mixed glyceride structure in oils from the herring family. These workers found that about 12·5 per cent. of the oil, with an iodine value of 92·9, was insoluble in acetone at −15°, whilst a further 75 per cent. (iodine value 179·0) separated from acetone at −60°, leaving in solution at −60° a residual 12·5 per cent., with an iodine value of 264·2. A very small portion of the original menhaden oil, separated on long standing at 15°, had iodine value 5·9, and contained chiefly myristic, palmitic and stearic acids.

The *grey* (*Atlantic*) *seal oil*[6] is made up of about equal parts of triunsaturated glycerides and of glycerides in which a saturated acyl group (and in a few per cent. two saturated groups) are present. Its fatty acids include about the same percentage of unsaturated C_{18} acids as the whale oil (Table 113), but somewhat larger amounts of unsaturated C_{16} and of unsaturated C_{20} and C_{22} acids. Consequently each of these latter acid categories is present in about 70 per cent. of the glycerides of the oil, but otherwise the seal oil glycerides are not dissimilar from those of the Antarctic whale oil.

The component acids of seal oils are liable to vary in their individual proportions according to the species and to other somewhat ill-defined factors (*cf.* Chapter II, p. 67), and it should be pointed out that the component glyceride features of the grey seal will not necessarily be the same in other specimens of seal blubber oils.

The *sea-lion oil*[7] is rather remarkable in that unsaturated C_{18}, unsaturated C_{20} and unsaturated C_{22} acids each contribute about 25 mols. out of every 100 mols. of total fatty acids. Each of these groups therefore appears singly in about 75 per cent. of the oil, whilst minor amounts of the glycerides may contain two groups of the same type of acid. Taken together, unsaturated C_{20} and C_{22} acids occur in all the glycerides of sea-lion oil, about half of which contains two of the C_{20-22} groups in the same triglyceride molecule. About 60 per cent. of the oil was made up of tri-unsaturated glycerides.

The data discussed above refer to various marine animal oils which are composed entirely of glycerides of the ordinary range of "aquatic" fatty acids. A few observations have been made with reference to the components of sperm whale oils (a mixture of glycerides and wax esters with the latter predominating) and of porpoise body fats (which contain the unusual *iso*valeric acid as a component, and are mainly glycerides with a small proportion of wax esters).

Sperm whale oils. The head and blubber oils of the sperm whale, the unusual acid and alcohol components of which have already received notice (Chapter II, pp. 72, 73), were examined by Hilditch and Lovern[9] by means of the oxidation method; it was found that in both oils the fatty acids are united in the usual heterogeneous and complex manner both with glycerol and with the higher alcohols. The head oil contains about 26 per cent. and the blubber oil about 34 per cent. of glycerides, the rest in each case being wax esters of the higher alcohols. Much more detailed information would result if the sperm oils were re-examined with the aid of the later crystallisation techniques or, possibly, by thin-layer chromatography.

Sperm head oil. Semi-quantitative examination of the saturated portions of the head oil revealed that in 100 parts of the original oil there were present about 3 parts of fully saturated glycerides, together with about 26 parts of wax esters built up entirely from saturated alcohols and acids; there was a marked tendency for the fatty acids of lower molecular weight (capric, lauric) to associate predominantly with the three saturated alcohols (tetradecyl, octadecyl and cetyl, the last in much greater proportion than the first two). Further, about 24 parts of the oil were composed of esters of saturated acids with unsaturated alcohols, and about 18 parts of esters of unsaturated acids with saturated alcohols; the remainder of the oil (about 29 parts) consisted of esters of unsaturated acids and alcohols and of mixed saturated-unsaturated glycerides. There can be no marked proportion of cetyl palmitate present, since although cetyl alcohol is the major alcoholic component of the wax, palmitic acid is combined with it to a far less degree than lauric, myristic and capric acids; the chief saturated wax esters present are undoubtedly cetyl laurate and myristate.

Sperm blubber oil. Although the blubber oil was not amenable to similar detailed treatment, the data obtained indicated that its general structure is not dissimilar from that of the head oil, and that it is a heterogeneous mixture of various wax esters (mainly liquid, owing to the more unsaturated character of both the alcohols and the acids present) and mixed triglycerides. Since oleyl alcohol is the chief alcoholic component, and oleic and hexadecenoic acids comprise the greater part of the fatty acids present, it is clear that both oleyl oleate and hexadecenoate are present in abundance.

Porpoise body fat. Lovern[10] observed that the body fat (almost wholly glycerides) of a porpoise contained 10·5 per cent. by weight (12·9 per cent. mol.) of fully saturated glycerides. The molar percentages of the acids present in the whole fat and in the fully saturated glycerides were as follows:

	IN WHOLE FAT PER CENT. (MOL.)	IN FULLY SATURATED PART PER CENT. (MOL.)
Saturated:		
*iso*Valeric	28·7	43·6
Lauric	3·8	16·8
Myristic	11·4	31·5
Palmitic	3·9	8·1
Unsaturated:		
C_{14}	4·5(−2·0H)	—
C_{16}	23·0(−2·0H)	—
C_{18}	12·8(−2·8H)	—
C_{20}	7·4(−4·8H)	—
C_{22}	4·5(−4·9H)	—

The glyceride structure of this fat appears somewhat curious in several respects. There is sufficient unsaturated acid present to produce a complete mixture of mixed saturated-unsaturated glycerides, but in fact about 13 mols. of triglycerides out of every 100 are fully saturated. In this respect, however, porpoise body oil falls in line with sperm head oil and with the depot fat of the amphibian green turtle[12]; both of these fats are also notable for the presence of unusual proportions of low molecular weight acids (*n*-decanoic, lauric, myristic).

The proportion of each of the total saturated fatty acids of porpoise body fat present in the form of fully saturated glyceride is *iso*valeric 20, lauric 60, myristic 36, and palmitic 27 per cent. This is in accordance with the corresponding features of sperm head oil in that larger proportions of the acids of lower molecular weight are combined as fully saturated material, except that the *iso*valeric acid is an outstanding exception. Only 20 per cent. of it is so combined, the remaining 80 per cent. being combined in glycerides which also contain at least one unsaturated acyl group. Whilst this is perhaps surprising, it nevertheless demonstrates very definitely that the abnormal *iso*valeric acid is interwoven with the more usual higher fatty acids into mixed glycerides of the customary type.

Depot fat of the Indian land crab. The crustacean *Birgus latro* (the Seychelles or Indian land crab) deposits a somewhat large proportion of fat in its tissues. The fat from specimens taken in the Seychelles Islands was examined by Hilditch and Murti,[11] and found to have a marked resemblance, in its general composition and its content of fully saturated glycerides, to coconut oil. The component acids of the whole fat, and of the 66·3 per cent. (mol.) of fully saturated glycerides which it contained, were: "(p. 490)."

Birgus latro, which is common on the shores of islands in the Indian Ocean from Zanzibar to the East Indies, is well known to make fallen coconuts its

	WHOLE FAT (PER CENT. MOL.)	FULLY SATURATED PART PER CENT. (MOL.)
Octanoic	1·5	3·2
Decanoic	5·3	7·1
Lauric	47·5	54·8
Myristic	19·0	20·5
Palmitic	13·1	12·7
Stearic	1·7	1·7
Unsaturated C_{14}	0·7	—
,, C_{16}	2·2	—
,, C_{18}	6·8	—
,, C_{20-22}	2·2	—

chief food, and it would appear that its fat is one of the instances in which the fat depots are supplied largely by assimilation from the diet, rather than by synthesis in the animal. The lauric and myristic acid contents of the land crab fat are very similar to those of coconut oil (Chapter IV, Table 69B, p. 341), and the lesser proportions of decanoic and, especially, of octanoic acid in the land crab fat further support the view that the main source of this depot fat is assimilated coconut fat, since it has been generally found that, when a fat containing glycerides of acids with less than 12 carbon atoms in the molecule is ingested by an animal, these lower fatty acids are not stored to any extent in the fat depots.

From the fully saturated glyceride content, it might be concluded that about 80 per cent. of the land crab fat was substantially derived from coconut fat; if this were so, the remaining 20 per cent. would have been composed of glycerides of saturated (myristic and palmitic), unsaturated C_{16}, unsaturated C_{18}, and unsaturated C_{20-22} acids in the respective proportions of about 30, 15, 35, and 15 per cent., and would thus be broadly similar to those of some amphibious animals (*cf.* Chapter III, p. 85), and also to those of some types of marine animal fat.

Green turtle depot fat. The fat of the amphibian *Chelone mydas* may be included here, since its glyceride structure appears from the work of Green and Hilditch[12] to be more akin to those of the marine animals just dealt with than to that of land animals. The component acids of the original fat were *n*-decanoic 0·3, lauric 16·9, myristic 11·9, palmitic 17·0, stearic 3·7; unsaturated C_{14} 1·5, C_{16} 7·8 (−2·0H), C_{18} 35·8 (−2·2H) and C_{20} 5·1 (−6·3H) per cent. (mol.). Examination of fractions of the fat obtained by the acetone-crystallisation procedure showed the presence of 9·6 per cent. (mol). of fully saturated glycerides and about 9 per cent. (mol.) of tri-C_{18} glycerides. The acids in the fully saturated components were in the same proportions as those in which they occurred in the whole fat, and consisted of mixed glycerides of lauric, myristic, palmitic and a little stearic acid. There is sufficient unsaturated acid (50 per cent. mol.) to permit the turtle fat to be made up wholly of mixed saturated-unsaturated glycerides, whilst little more than a third of its acids are of the unsaturated C_{18} series; yet it contains nearly 10 per cent. (mol.) each of fully saturated and of tri-C_{18} glycerides. The remaining 80 per cent. of the fat, on the other hand, contains a mixture of acids very similar to those in the whole of the fat.

The food of the green turtle is mainly herbivorous but they sometimes eat shell-fish, including young crabs. Since the specimen whose fat was examined came from the Seychelles Islands, it is possible that its fat owes some of its peculiar composition to assimilation of land crab fat (*cf.* preceding paragraphs) but this is of course no more than a speculation.

Land Animal Fats

DEPOT FATS

Bird and rodent depot fats

The glyceride structures of the depot fats of the rat and the rabbit have only been defined in so far as their relatively small contents of fully saturated components (mainly tripalmitin) are concerned (*cf.* Table 73, Chapter V, p. 369), but Mattson and Lutton[13a] and Coleman[13b] examined the acids in the 2-monoglycerides left after selective hydrolysis of rat and rabbit fat by pancreatic lipase with the following results:

	WHOLE FAT			2-MONOGLYCERIDES		
	Palmitic	Stearic	Unsatd. C_{18}	Palmitic	Stearic	Unsatd. C_{18}
Rat[13a]	15		85	17		83
Rabbit[13b]	36	8	56	36	3	61

If these two isolated observations are characteristic (rather than coincidental) for rodent fats it would suggest (i) that in contrast to vegetable seed fats the acyl groups at the 2-glyceryl positions are by no means wholly oleic (linoleic), but that considerable proportions of 2-palmitoglycerides are also present; and (ii) that in contrast to all the other land animal depot fats which have so far been studied by this procedure, there is little difference in composition between the acyl groups in the 2-position and those in the 1- and 3-positions of the glycerol molecules.

The abdominal and gizzard fats of *Light Sussex hens* have been studied in somewhat greater detail by Hilditch and Stainsby.[14] The component acids of the mixed fats included: myristic 0·1, palmitic 27·1, stearic 6·7, hexadecenoic 7·9, oleic 36·2, linoleic 21·5 and C_{20-22} unsaturated 0·5 per cent. (mol). Fully saturated glycerides formed only 2·5 per cent. of the fat (mainly tripalmitin with some palmitostearins).

Hilditch and Stainsby concluded from further analyses of the partly and the completely hydrogenated hen fat that the probable components of the original hen fat were somewhat as follows:

GENERAL TYPE		PER CENT (MOL.)
Fully saturated	Mainly tripalmitin with small amounts of palmitostearins.	2
Di-C_{16}-mono-C_{18} glycerides	Probably largely palmito-hexadeceno-"oleins," but might include up to 20 per cent. of palmito-hexadecenostearins.	28–29
Monopalmitodi-C_{18} glycerides	Palmitodi-"oleins" (but including up to 20 per cent. of "oleo"-palmitostearins).	41
Tri-C_{18} glycerides	Tri-unsaturated, probably oleo-linoleins (but might include up to 20 per cent. of stearodi-"oleins").	28–29

Chicken, pheasant and pigeon depot fats have also been submitted to the selective enzyme hydrolysis procedure, when it was observed[13b] that the acids in combination with the 2-(central) hydroxyl group of glycerol were made up of only 78–88 per cent. of oleic (linoleic), the remainder being predominantly palmitic acid. In these fats the proportions of the component acids at the 2-position were quite different from those in the 1- and 3-positions, and also the ratio of palmitic to stearic acid in the 2-acyl glycerides (*ca.* 3 : 1) was markedly less than that for the 1- and 3-acylglycerides (*ca.* 5 : 1):

	WHOLE FAT			2-MONOGLYCERIDES		
	Palmitic	Stearic	Unsatd. C_{18}	Palmitic	Stearic	Unsatd. C_{18}
Chicken[13b]	32	6	62	17	5	78
Pheasant[13b]	26	5	69	9	3	88
Pigeon[13b]	23	9	68	9	5	86

As in the rodent fats (above) the number of species at present examined is much too small to indicate whether these features are characteristic for all species of birds.

Hen body fats are differentiated from the corresponding fats of pigs, sheep, cows and some other animals (*vide infra*) by their unusually large proportions of tri-C_{18} (unsaturated) glycerides and, especially, of the mixed semi-unsaturated di-C_{16}-mono-C_{18} glycerides. The result is a more heterogeneous mixture of mixed triglycerides than in fats of the lard type. This is reflected in the physical consistency of the fats. A pig fat of similar mean unsaturation and not very different palmitic, stearic, oleic and linoleic acid contents forms a thin, semi-solid, almost homogeneous paste at atmospheric temperature; but the hen body fats separate into two well-marked phases – a clear liquid fat with a lower layer of solid glycerides (so-called "stearin").

Depot Fats of the Larger Mammals

As indicated in Chapter III (p. 99), a broad distinction can be drawn between those animal body fats which contain relatively little stearic acid, and those which are "stearic-rich", i.e., wherein stearic acid may form from about 10–15 per cent. up to nearly 30 per cent. of the total component acids. In general the glycerides of stearic-rich fats depart from the comparatively simple and "evenly-distributed" pattern, and are characterised notably by disproportionately large amounts of fully-saturated glycerides in comparison with "evenly-distributed" fats of corresponding saturated acid contents. Stearic-rich fats are met with most frequently, but not exclusively, in the adipose depots of ruminants: the component glycerides of such fats (so far as they have yet been studied) will be discussed later in this Chapter (pp. 497–510) after depot fats in which stearic acid is not so prominent have been considered.

It is not possible to be precise as to the content of stearic acid which defines approach to the "stearic-rich" depot fats. For the present purpose a fat which contains over 10 per cent. of stearic acid in its total acids has not been included in the "stearic-rich" group if its content of fully-saturated glycerides is insignificant (not above 2–3 per cent.); on the other hand all pig body fats are included with "stearic-rich" fats because, although some contain less than 10 per cent. of stearic acid, others contain as much as 20 per cent. of stearic acid in their total fatty acids.

Depot Fats of the Herbivora

Apart from the "stearic-rich" depot fats of ruminants and pigs, the glyceride constitution of only five fats from animals whose diet is predominantly vegetable in character has yet been investigated in detail with the aid of the low-temperature acetone crystallisation procedure. In two cases – kangaroo[16] and baboon[16] fats – the procedure was inadequate owing to shortage of experimental material, but the depot fat of a Ceylon bear[16] was resolved into five fractions, that of a horse mesenteric fat[15] into nine fractions, and that of an Indian elephant[17] into eight fractions for further examination and determination of component acids.

The component acids, and the proportions of various types of mixed glycerides indicated by these studies of glyceride structure in the five fats from herbivorous animals, are shown in Table 115.

TABLE 115. *Component Glycerides of Herbivorous Animal Fats (per cent. mol.)*

	HORSE[15]	KANGAROO[16]	CEYLON BEAR[16]	BABOON[16]	ELEPHANT[17]
Component acids:					
Lauric	0·3	0·2	0·5	—	2·2
Myristic	5·0	5·6	4·4	2·7	9·2
Palmitic	25·9	27·1	28·0	18·4	44·0
Stearic	4·7	13·5	2·4	7·6	4·9
Arachidic	0·2	1·3	—	—	0·5
Tetradecenoic	—	0·5	2·0	1·2	0·9
Hexadecenoic	6·3	2·9	11·8	6·8	2·8
Oleic	34·0	44·0	49·1	50·1	28·8
Linoleic	6·0	2·5	1·1	12·5	3·9
Linolenic	16·1	—	—	—	0·4
Unsaturated C_{20-22}	1·4	2·4	0·7	0·7	2·4
Component glyceride categories:					
(a) Trisaturated	3	1	2	Trace	17
Disaturated	22	51	16	—	51
Monosaturated	56	48	68	79	30
Tri-unsaturated	19	—	14	20	2
(b) Monopalmito-	64	88	73	64	49
Dipalmito-	7	10	13	Trace	38
Tripalmitin	2	—	—	—	2
(c) Mono-oleo-	83	...	...	...	58
Di-oleo-	9	...	...	...	20
(d) Mono-unsaturated C_{18}-	...	51	44	24	...
Di-unsaturated C_{18}-	...	48	54	75	...

It will be noticed that the distribution of individual acids, or of related groups of acids, in the glycerides of these fats in most instances follows that characteristic of individual acids in vegetable fats as illustrated in Chapter V (Figures 5, 7, 8, pp. 377, 381, 382). The greater number of component acids in these animal fats renders it difficult as a rule to give very precise estimates of the proportions of individual mixed glycerides present.

Horse fat. Horse body fats are unusual in that linolenic acid is a major component, and they also contain more hexadecenoic acid than is common in the depot fats of the larger land animals (*cf.* Chapter III, p. 102). The chief glyceride components of the horse mesenteric fat were about 30 per cent. of palmito-oleo-linolenins and about 19 per cent. of triunsaturated glycerides with one oleic group and two other (usually different) unsaturated groups. The rest of the fat is made up of about 5–7 per cent. each of oleodipalmitin, oleo-myristopalmitin, oleopalmitostearin, palmitodiolein, palmitohexadeceno-olein and palmito-oleo-linolein, with still smaller amounts of other mixed glycerides, but including only about 2–3 per cent. of tri-saturated glycerides. The glycerides of horse depot fat (semi-liquid at room temperature) are thus a complicated mixture of mixed glycerides built up on the usual lines of approx-imation to even distribution of each fatty acid amongst the glycerol molecules.

Mattson and Lutton[13a] state that a horse fat containing 39 per cent. of saturated and 61 per cent. of unsaturated acids in its total fatty acids had 21 per cent. of saturated and 79 per cent. of unsaturated acids attached to the 2-(central) position of the glyceride molecules.

Kangaroo fat.[16] A small specimen of the fat from the adipose tissues of a young adult Great Grey Kangaroo (*Macropus major*) was separated into two fractions by crystallisation from acetone at −10°, from which a rough idea of its com-ponent glycerides was obtained. In spite of the somewhat high content (13·5 per cent.) of stearic acid, the glycerides appeared to contain less than 1 per cent. of palmito-stearins, the main components being given as 47 per cent. palmitodi-"oleins" and 42 per cent. "oleo"-palmitostearins, with about 9 per cent. of "oleo"-dipalmitins and 2 per cent. of stearodi-"oleins". (It should, however, be noted that these figures were obtained only from the component acids in each crystallised fraction, lack of material preventing actual determina-tion of the fully-saturated glycerides in either fraction.)

Ceylon bear fat.[16] This liquid fat contained an unusually large proportion of hexadecenoic acid, so that important amounts of glycerides containing both hexadecenoic acid and unsaturated C_{18} acids were undoubtedly present. Nearly 15 per cent. of the fat consisted of triunsaturated glycerides containing two oleic groups with either a hexadecenoic or an octadecadienoic group; nearly 70 per cent. was made up of diunsaturated glycerides (either palmitodi-olein or palmito-oleo-hexadecenoin); and about 16 per cent. of the bear fat glycerides contained, in addition to an unsaturated (mainly oleic) group, two saturated (mainly palmitic) groups.

Baboon fat.[16] This liquid fat from a Ceylon sacred baboon was only available in small quantity, and only a cursory account of its components is possible. It contained less palmitic and more linoleic acid than is usual in an animal fat, and its main components were probably about 20 per cent. of linoleo- (and some hexadeceno-) diolein with over 70 per cent. of glycerides containing one saturated and two unsaturated acid groups (palmitodiolein and palmito-oleo-linolein probably forming the greater part of this portion of the fat.)

Elephant fat.[17] The component acids of elephant adipose tissue consisted of nearly 30 per cent. of oleic acid accompanied by very small amounts of other unsaturated acids together with about 60 per cent. of saturated acids. The latter are unusual in the high content (44 per cent.) of palmitic acid; myristic (9 per cent.) and stearic (5 per cent.) made up most of the remaining saturated fatty acids. The exhaustive separation of the glycerides undertaken by Cama[17] revealed the presence of 17 per cent. of trisaturated glycerides but not more than about 2 per cent. of tripalmitin, the remaining 15 per cent. being dipalmito-glycerides in which myristic or stearic acid formed the third acyl group. In spite of the exceptionally high proportion of palmitic acid in the total fatty acids, the amount of tripalmitin was thus very small, and much nearer to that demanded by strictly arithmetical even distribution (*nil*) than that corresponding to completely random distribution of palmitic acid (9 per cent.). Apart from the moderately large proportion of fully saturated glycerides the rest of the fat appeared to be constituted on the customary "evenly distributed" pattern, the main components indicated being somewhat over 20 per cent. each of oleodipalmitin and oleo-palmito-glycerides containing one other saturated group, and a similar quantity of palmitodioleins. The distribution of the fatty acids in the glycerides may be summarised as follows:

ACYL GROUPS	PER CENT. (MOL.)
Tripalmitin	2
2 Palmitic, 1 other saturated acid	15
2 Palmitic, 1 oleic	23
1 Palmitic, 1 oleic, 1 other saturated acid	22
1 Palmitic, 1 polyethenoid, 1 other saturated acid	5
1 Palmitic, 2 oleic	17
1 Palmitic, 1 oleic, 1 polyethenoid acid	6
1 Other saturated, 2 oleic	1
1 Other saturated, 1 oleic, 1 polyethenoid acid	7
2 Oleic, 1 polyethenoid acid	2

("Other saturated" acids include all saturated acids other than palmitic; minor monoethenoid acids are included with oleic; "polyethenoid acids" include octadecadienoic, octadecatrienoic, and unsaturated acids of the C_{20} and C_{22} series.)

It should be observed that the elephant body fat, although rich in total saturated acids in consequence of its very high palmitic acid content, is not one of the "stearic-rich" depot fats, and its glyceride structure is different in character from that of the "stearic-rich" group.

Depot Fats of Carnivora and Omnivora

The body fats of only one animal from each of these groups have yet been studied in detail by the crystallisation procedure. Gupta, Hilditch and Meara[18] separated the mixed back and mesenteric fat of a badger into seven fractions for component acid analysis, and Pathak and Agarwal[19] examined four fractions similarly obtained by crystallisation from acetone from the adipose tissues of a tiger. Fats from flesh-eating animals are probably more liable than those of many herbivorous animals to include directly assimilated glycerides in addition to those synthesised from carbohydrate by the animal, and consequently this may affect the nature of the mixed glycerides in the fats deposited in the adipose tissues. A much wider range of observations is therefore desirable in this group of animal fats and no general conclusions can be drawn from the studies of two individual fats from animals of widely diverse habits and diet. **Badger fat.**[18] The badger is said to feed mainly on roots, acorns, and other fruits, on insects, and on small animals such as mice, frogs, lizards and snakes. The component acids of the specimen examined by Gupta *et al.* included myristic 7·5, palmitic 20·1, stearic 7·5, hexadecenoic 8·5, oleic 31·2, octadeca-dienoic 8·7, octadecatrienoic 4·2 and unsaturated C_{20} acids 12·3 per cent. (mol.). Ordinary linoleic and linolenic acids were present in the C_{18} di- and tri-ene acids, whilst the mean unsaturation of the C_{20} acids was $-5 \cdot 4H$. This is a somewhat unusual composition for the fat of a land mammal, especially in its contents of unsaturated C_{20} and C_{16} acids, which resemble those of fats of the amphibia or even wholly aquatic animals.

The detailed study of the badger fat glycerides showed that the main glyceride categories present were as follows:

		PER CENT. (MOL.)
(a)	Trisaturated	3
	Disaturated-monounsaturated	23
	Monosaturated-diunsaturated	51
	Triunsaturated	23
(b)	Monopalmito-	53
	Dipalmito-	4
(c)	Mono-oleo-	81
	Di-oleo-	6
(d)	Mono-unsaturated C_{20}	37
	Di-unsaturated C_{20}	Trace

About half of the badger fat contained one saturated and two unsaturated acyl groups; the rest (except for a very small proportion – 3 per cent. – of trisaturated glycerides) was a mixture in about equal proportions of glycerides with two saturated and one unsaturated group, or with three unsaturated groups. Of the two major component acids, oleic groups occurred twice in 5–6 per cent., and once in over 80 per cent., of the triglyceride groups; palmitic groups occurred twice in about 4 per cent., and once in about 52 per cent. of the fat. The remaining component acids contributed only one acyl group to any triglyceride in which they were present. A large proportion (perhaps nearly half) of the fat contained both an oleic and a palmitic group in its glycerides, whilst the 23 per cent. of triunsaturated glycerides probably contained at least one oleic group associated with acyl groups of other unsaturated acids. Palmito-oleo-unsaturated C_{20}-glycerides were probably the most abundant individual mixed glycerides, and the di- and tri-saturated glycerides contained for the most part one palmitic group in association with other saturated acyl groups.

The badger fat thus exhibited the usual tendency towards very wide distribution of the component acids in the glycerides: no individual acid formed more than one-third of the total fatty acids, and only in the cases of oleic acid (31 per cent.) and palmitic acid (20 per cent.) was there evidence of the presence of small proportions of dioleo- or dipalmito-glycerides.

Tiger fat.[19] The fat of the Indian tiger examined by Pathak and Agarwal contained the following component acids: myristic 0·8, palmitic 25·0, stearic 24·5, arachidic 1·1, hexadecenoic 6·7, oleic 38·6, linoleic 3·3 per cent. (mol.). Apart from slightly higher proportions of hexadecenoic acid, these figures are very similar to those of some stearic-rich oxen or sheep depots fats of similar stearic acid contents.

The glyceride studies indicated the presence of about 6 per cent. of trisaturated glycerides with 42 per cent. of disaturated and 52 per cent. of monosaturated glycerides, triunsaturated glycerides not being detected. The proportion of fully saturated glycerides (which may have been somewhat under-estimated, according to the investigators) is below that which is present in a ruminant depot fat of similar composition; only traces of tripalmitin were present, the rest being mixed palmito-stearins. The other component glycerides present, were oleopalmitostearin *ca.* 35, stearodiolein *ca.* 21, palmitodiolein *ca.* 18, saturated hexadeceno-oleins *ca.* 13 and hexadecenopalmitostearin *ca.* 7 per cent. (mol.).

The composition of this fat shows both resemblances to and some differences from that of ruminant depot fats of similar fatty acid composition; since the diet of a wild tiger normally includes ruminant animals such as deer, goats and sheep, a significant part of its fat will be derived from the latter.

Human body fat. This fat contains only 5–8 per cent. of stearic acid in its component acids (*cf.* Chapter III, Table 45A, p. 128), and thus belongs to the large group of animal fats which are not "stearic-rich".

No study of its component glycerides has yet appeared, but Mattson and Lutton[13a] state that, in a specimen which contained 33 per cent. of saturated and 67 per cent. of unsaturated C_{18} acids in the whole fat, 81 per cent. of the acids in combination at the 2-(central) position of the glycerol molecules consisted of unsaturated C_{18} acids (largely oleic).

It is apparent that similar studies of the glycerides from a much wider range of carnivorous animals would prove of great interest and value.

"Stearic-rich" Animal Depot Fats

This group has received much investigation, especially in the cases of fats of the pig, and of the ruminants ox and sheep. After many earlier observations based on the content and composition of the fully saturated glycerides in these fats, or in their partly hydrogenated products, had been recorded, the more elaborate acetone crystallisation procedure was applied to three ox, three sheep, and two pig fats, the component acids of which formed a progressive series with increasing stearic and diminishing oleic acid content. This series, taken together, presents a rather complete picture of the progressive changes in glyceride structure consequent upon the alterations in the proportions of the two acids mentioned, and it is therefore preferable to discuss this group as a whole, rather than in terms of the various animals concerned.

Before dealing with these later observations, however, it will be well to review the main results of the earlier, less detailed, work which was carried out on the fully saturated glycerides present in the fats of the different animals or of their partly hydrogenated products.

Study of Fully Saturated Glycerides in Pig, Ox, Sheep and Goat Fats

Pig depot fats. Partial quantitative studies of pig depot fats included examination of the proportions and composition of their fully saturated glycerides,[20a] and study of the products formed during progressive hydrogenation of a pig back fat.[20c] Banks and Hilditch[20a] studied five pig fats: the outer and the inner layers of the back fat and the perinephric or leaf fat from an individual sow, and two perinephric fats from members of the same litter which had been fed respectively on a fat-free diet and on the same diet with the addition of 3 per cent. of groundnut oil.[20d] The data obtained in this series are summarised in Table 116.

TABLE 116. *Pig Depot Fats*

(i) *Component Fatty Acids of the Whole Fat (Molar Percentages)*

	MYRISTIC	PALMITIC	STEARIC	OLEIC	LINOLEIC	UNSATD. C_{20-22}
Outer back (sow)	4·6	21·7	7·6	52·6	12·7	0·8
Inner back (sow)	4·6	27·7	10·6	42·6	13·2	1·3
Perinephric (sow)	4·7	29·4	16·9	34·5	13·3	1·2
Perinephric (pigs, control diet)	4·4	30·2	20·5	39·9	5·0	—
Perinephric (pigs, control diet + 3 per cent. groundnut oil)	2·0	27·4	17·5	43·0	10·1	—

(ii) *Fully saturated Glycerides present in the Whole Fats (Molar Percentages)*

	IODINE VALUE OF FAT	TOTAL SATURATED ACID CONTENT	FULLY SATURATED GLYCERIDES	COMPONENT ACIDS		
			PER CENT.	MYRISTIC	PALMITIC	STEARIC
Outer back (sow)	72·6	33·9	2·2	0·3	54·7	45·0
Inner back (sow)	64·6	42·9	6·7	1·6	57·5	40·9
Perinephric (sow)	59·0	51·0	11·4	1·1	58·0	40·9
Perinephric (pigs, control diet)	45·7	55·1	17·7	1·9	61·5	36·6
Perinephric (pigs, control diet + 3 per cent. groundnut oil)	55·1	46·9	13·2	2·5	48·4	49·1

The component acids of the fully saturated glycerides (Table 116 (ii)) show more approach to constancy in composition than the saturated acids in the whole fats. Whilst the ratios of palmitic (plus the small amounts of myristic) to stearic acid in the whole fats lie between the extremes of about 3·5 : 1 and 1·5 : 1, the corresponding ratios of these acids in the fully saturated components vary only from about 1·5 : 1 to 1 : 1.

In the fully saturated components of pig depot fats the content of myristic acid is distinctly lower than in those of ox depot fats (*cf.* Table 118), and, correspondingly, the melting points (60·5°) of the pig fat fully saturated glycerides containing about 40 per cent. (mol.) of stearic acid are several degrees higher than those (54–54·5°) of ox depot fully saturated glycerides of similar stearic acid content. The latter may contain, in addition to dipalmitostearin and palmitodistearins, from 12–30 per cent. or even more of myristopalmitostearins, whereas those of pig fats will contain only about 3–6 per cent. of myristopalmitostearins. This typical difference in the fully saturated components of the respective fats is probably also the cause of the characteristic difference in the crystalline forms of the sparingly soluble solid constituents of ox and pig depot fats which is utilised in the Belfield test[21a] for distinguishing between beef tallows and lards; it probably also underlies the differences between the respective melting and solidifying points of the solid constituents of lards and tallows (as utilised by Polenske[21b]) and the corresponding characteristic differences between the melting points of these saturated glycerides and of the mixed fatty acids contained therein, which were proposed by Bömer[21c] as a further means of discrimination between pig and ox depot fats.

Hilditch and Stainsby[20c] prepared a series of progressively hydrogenated fats from the inner back fat of a sow (component acids: myristic 2·8, palmitic 27·3, stearic 14·4, oleic 40·9, linoleic 13·5, unsaturated C_{20-22} 1·1 per cent. mol.). The relation between the fully saturated glyceride and the total saturated acid contents of these fats gave the curve in Fig. 10 (p. 407) which closely follows the observations on the fully saturated glyceride contents of the whole series of natural depot and milk fats. The original inner back fat contained 5·6 per cent. (mol.) of fully saturated components (component acids: palmitic 54·0, stearic 46·0 per cent. mol.).

Crystallisation of the fully saturated glycerides produced in the hydrogenated fats gave 2-palmitodistearin (m.p. 67–67·5°), in amounts corresponding with 80 per cent. or more of the total palmitodistearin present in these fully saturated portions of the fat. That the original pig fat therefore contained 2-monopalmitoglycerides unaccompanied by any appreciable quantities of 1-monopalmitoglycerides was confirmed later by Meara[22a] and by Quimby et al.,[22b] who compared the melting points of the four polymorphic forms of the products mentioned with those of synthetically prepared 1- or 2-palmitodistearins.

Pig fats have so far been more extensively studied than other animal fats by

TABLE 117. *Component Acids in Pig, Ox and Sheep Body Fats and in the 2-Monoglycerides Isolated therefrom*

	IN WHOLE FATS			IN 2-MONOGLYCERIDES		
	Saturated		Unsaturated	Saturated		Unsaturated
	C_{16}*	C_{18}	C_{18}†	C_{16}*	C_{18}	C_{18}†
Pig (1958)[13a]	22		78	44		56
„ „	36		64	71		29
Pig (1961)[13b]	24	10	66	66	4	30
„ „	27	14	59	67	4	29
„ „	31	18	51	75	4	21
„ „	28	21	51	73	4	23
„ „	31	22	47	77	4	19
Pig (1963)[13c]	29	11	60	76	3	21
„ „	34	18	48	82	5	13
Ruminants:						
Sheep (1958)[13a]	58		42	33		67
Ox (1958)[13a]	54		46	29		71
„ (1961)[13b]	34	34	32	28	19	53

* Includes very small amounts of C_{14} (myristic)
† Includes small amounts of C_{16} (hexadecenoic)

isolating their 2-acyl glycerides after selective hydrolysis of the 1- and 3-acyl groups in the fats by pancreatic lipase, and comparing the composition of the acids attached at the 2-positions with those in the whole fats. The results so obtained by Mattson and Lutton (1958),[13a] and Coleman (1961),[13b] and by Barrett *et al.* (1963)[13c] by thin-layer chromatography, are summarised in Table 117 (for convenience, the few similar data available for ox and sheep fats (to be discussed in the following subsection) are also included in Table 117, p. 499).

The data in Table 117 show that in pig depot fats the central (2-) hydroxyl groups of glycerol are occupied to the extent of 70–80 per cent. with palmitic acid (whereas in seed fats they are almost wholly combined with oleic (linoleic) acid). This, of course, fully confirms the earlier observations (above) on the melting and transition points of palmitodistearin from the hydrogenated fats.[20c,22a,b]

In the ox and sheep body fats, on the other hand, the acids combined at the 2-positions of the glycerol are a mixture of palmitic, stearic and oleic acids in which the last predominates (forming apparently from about 55 to 70 per cent. of the 2-glycerides); in these ruminant body fats, therefore, it would appear that up to 20–30 per cent. of oleo-groups may occupy the 1- or 3-positions, as well as palmito- or stearo-groups.

Ox (sheep, goat) depot fats. Data for the amounts and component acids of the fully saturated glycerides have been given for beef tallows,[20b,23] for a mutton tallow,[24] for an Indian (Punjab) he-goat depot fat,[25] and for Indian buffalo depot fats[26]. These are summarised in Table 118 (p. 501).

Banks and Hilditch[20b] found evidence that the total C_{18} acid content of ox and sheep depot fats amounted to 62–70 per cent. of the mixed fatty acids, but at the time (1932) of their work the minor proportions of hexa-and tetra-decenoic acids present were not taken into account, with the result that their recorded figures for myristic and oleic acids are somewhat higher than the truth, at the expense of palmitic and tetra- and hexa-decenoic acids. Hilditch and Longenecker, in their 1937 communication,[23] recalculated the earlier figures (*cf.* Chapter III, p. 108), and as a result reached the conclusion that relative constancy of the total C_{18} acids of ox and sheep depot fats at about 60–65 per cent. of the total fatty acids is a strongly marked feature, any increase in stearic acid being closely balanced by diminution of oleic acid. At the same time, and largely independently of the amount of unsaturated acids present, the palmitic acid content of nearly all ox depot fats so far examined lies within the relatively constant limits of 30 ($\pm$ 3) per cent. mol.

These relationships are, of course, exactly similar to those which hold in the case of pig depot fats. The only differences are that ox and sheep depot fats are generally more saturated (i.e., contain less oleo-glycerides) than those of the pig, and that they also contain definitely more myristic acid in combination as a minor component.

The composition of the fully saturated glycerides of ox and sheep depot fats also resembles that of the corresponding parts of pig depot fats (except for higher myristic acid contents). Palmitic and myristic acids bear a ratio to stearic acid varying between 2 : 1 and 1 : 1 in the fully saturated components.

TABLE 118

(i) *Component Fatty Acids of the Whole Cattle Fats (Molar Percentages)*

	SATURATED				UNSATURATED				
					C_{14}	C_{16}	C_{18}		C_{20-22}
	C_{14}	C_{16}	C_{18}	C_{20}			OLEIC	DIENOIC	
Ox depot fat, South American[20b]	9·5	29·2	23·2	*	*	*	37·1	1·0	*
Ox depot fat, South American[20b]	6·9	25·5	27·4	*	*	*	40·2	—	*
Ox depot fat, South American[20b]	5·3	32·9	18·2	*	*	*	40·7	2·9	*
Ox depot fat, North American[20b]	7·5	29·1	13·4	*	*	*	47·6	2·4	*
Shorthorn bullock, perinephric[23]	3·9†	26·5	23·1	0·7	0·5	2·6	40·4	1·8	0·5
Shorthorn cow, peri-nephric[23]	3·5	31·0	20·1	0·3	0·7	2·8	39·6	1·8	0·2
Shorthorn heifer, peri-nephric[23]	2·5†	28·7	25·4	1·1	0·5	2·0	38·0	1·7	0·1
Buffalo, Indian[26]	3·9	33·4	31·7	0·5	0·4	2·0	27·8	—	0·3
Buffalo, Indian[26]	9·2§	45·6	19·2	0·3	0·8	1·8	22·3	0·7	0·1
Sheep depot fat[24]	5·5	26·2	29·3	*	*	*	34·8	4·2	*
Goat depot fat[25]	7·2‡	27·0	26·8	2·1	*	*	36·9	—	*

* Not estimated.
† Includes traces of lauric acid.
§ Includes 1·4 per cent. of lauric and 0·4 per cent. dodecenoic acids.
‡ Includes 4·7 per cent. of lauric acid.

(ii) *Fully Saturated Glycerides in the Cattle Fats (Molar Percentages)*

	IODINE VALUE OF FAT	TOTAL SATURATED ACID CONTENT	FULLY SATURATED GLYCERIDES			
				COMPONENT ACIDS		
			PER CENT.	MYRIS-TIC	PAL-MITIC	STEARIC
Ox depot fat, South American[20b]	37·1	61·9	25·8	3·9	57·0	39·1
Ox depot fat, South American[20b]	39·3	59·8	26·0	4·5	58·2	37·3
Ox depot fat, South American[20b]	42·1	56·4	22·8	9·3	57·7	33·0
Ox depot fat, North American[20b]	46·6	50·0	13·9	7·2	55·8	37·0
Shorthorn bullock, perinephric[23]	44·7	54·2	15·8	17·1	34·7	48·2
Shorthorn cow, perinephric[23]	43·2	54·9	18·4	12·5	45·4	42·1
Shorthorn heifer, perinephric[23]	40·4	57·7	18·6	9·6	47·6	42·8
Buffalo, Indian[26]	26·4	69·5	32·4	9·2	43·7	47·1
Buffalo, Indian[26]	23·8	73·9	37·2	14·4	52·1	33·5
Sheep depot fat[24]	41·2	61·0	26·6	7·1	52·1	40·8
Goat depot fat[25]	33·5	63·1	29·2	2·9	48·5	45·6§

§ Also 3·0 (mol.) per cent. arachidic acid.

Studies of "Stearic-Rich" Animal Depot Fats by the Crystallisation Procedure

Several pig, ox, and sheep depot fats have been studied from about 1938 onwards by preliminary resolution of the fat into fractions by systematic crystallisation from solvents at various temperatures, followed by determination of the component acids in each fraction and, where necessary, by determination and analysis of the fully saturated glycerides present. The crystallisation procedure was improved in detail as time went on, but the data from all the studies about to be mentioned are considered to present reasonably accurate statements of the chief glycerides present. The following fats have thus been examined by Hilditch and the co-workers named: English heifer perinephric fat (S. Paul,[27a] 1938); external and perinephric tissue fats from a pig (Pedelty,[27b] 1940); two Indian cow depot fats (Murti,[27c] 1940); external and perinephric tissue fats from a ewe (Zaky,[27d] 1941); an Irish neat's foot oil (Shrivastava,[27e] 1948), an Indian sheep body fat (Shrivastava,[27f] 1949), and the perinephric fat from a pig which had been fed on a diet rich in whale oil (Garton and Meara,[27g] 1952). This series as a whole illustrates excellently the manner in which the proportions of the different groups of mixed glycerides in stearic-rich animal body fats vary according to the proportions of oleic, stearic and palmitic acids present in the whole fats. For this purpose they will be mainly discussed together as a series of fats in which the stearic acid content rises progressively from a very low figure until it approaches 30 per cent. (mol.) of the total fatty acids (p. 507, Tables 120A and 120B). A few remarks will, however, first be made with reference to individual fats which have been investigated.

Pig depot fats. It should be noted that the largest proportions of stearic acid generally occur in the fats of ruminant animals, although stearic-rich depot fats are not always confined to these. The pig, for example, produces fats of variable stearic acid content in different sites and under different conditions: although in the instances below in which pig fat glycerides were studied, the highest stearic acid content was 17·6 per cent., in some other cases (*cf.* pp. 117, 121, 123) pig body fats with over 20 per cent. of stearic acid in the total fatty acids have been encountered.

The pig whose perinephric and back fat glycerides were studied by Hilditch and Pedelty,[27b] had been reared on a known diet low in fat. The chief component acids of the perinephric and back fats were, respectively: palmitic, 31·1, 29·0, stearic 17·6, 13·8, oleic 40·6, 43·9, linoleic 5·3, 7·2 per cent. (mol.). The main perinephric glycerides were 34 per cent. of "oleo"-palmitostearins and 40 per cent. of palmitodi-"oleins", whilst the corresponding figures for the back fat were 27 per cent. of "oleo"-palmitostearins and 53 per cent. of palmito-di-"oleins". Palmito-unsaturated C_{18} glycerides thus amounted to 74 and 80 per cent. of the respective fats, the rest being made up of about 5–9 per cent. each of palmitostearins, "oleo"-dipalmitins and stearodi-"oleins" and a very small proportion (3 per cent.) of triunsaturated glycerides containing two oleic groups.

The perinephric fat from a pig which had been fed from weaning on a diet which contained 50 per cent. of whale oil and, in the final stages of fattening, was receiving 4 lb. of whale oil per day, was examined by Garton *et al.*[27g]. Crystallisation from acetone at $-40°$ resolved it into a soluble fraction (26 per cent.) the component acids in which were very similar to those of the whale oil, and an insoluble fraction (74 per cent.) more akin in composition to the perinephric fat of a pig fed on a low fat diet (although it contained more unsaturated C_{16} and C_{20-22} acids than the latter). The high degree of unsaturation of the C_{20} and C_{22} acids of the whale oil was reproduced in the corresponding fatty acids of the pig body fat, and it was evident that the latter consisted of a mixture of typical pig perinephric fat (synthesised by the animal) with substantially unchanged whale oil glycerides. Further investigation of the glycerides in the body fats of pigs fed heavily on specific fatty diets may be expected to throw additional light upon the mode of absorption of ingested fats into the fatty depots of animals.

Riemenschneider et al.[28] (1946) described the resolution of a tallow and a lard into seven fractions by crystallisation from acetone between $-20°$ and $-45°$, and the examination of the component acids in each fraction. Their figures for the general composition of the glycerides present in the whole fats were as follows:

	LARD PER CENT.	TALLOW PER CENT.
Trisaturated	2	15
Disaturated	26	46
Monosaturated	54	37
Triunsaturated	18	2

They noted that the tallow contained much more fully saturated and mono-unsaturated glycerides than lard, and also concluded that the tri-unsaturated glyceride contents of pig fats are greater than hitherto supposed. As pointed out in Chapter V (p. 405), however, the lard in question contained 50 per cent. of oleic acid with 13–14 per cent. of linoleic, linolenic and arachidonic acids, so that the presence in this particular fat of 18 per cent. of tri-unsaturated glycerides in the form of mixed dioleo-mono-polyethenoid glycerides is not unnatural.

Quimby, Wille and Lutton[22b] (1953) carried out extremely thorough separations of commercial specimens of lard, beef tallow and mutton tallow from acetone at temperatures between $21°$ and $-15°C$. In the case of the beef tallow sixty crystallisations in all were performed "representing a maximum of twenty-two stages of fractionation". Their main quantitative data are summarised in Table 119.

TABLE 119, *Lard, Beef and Mutton Tallows (Quimby et al.[22b])*

	LARD PER CENT.	BEEF TALLOW PER CENT.	MUTTON TALLOW PER CENT.
Component acids :			
Myristic	2·6	5	6·6
Palmitic	27·9	30	24·4
Stearic	9·0	25	21·6
Oleic	47·7	37	42·7
Octadecadienoic	11·1	2	1·7
Other polyethenoid C_{18}	1·4	1	2·7
Arachidonic	0·3	Trace	0·3
Component glyceride types :			
Trisaturated	2	18	15
Disaturated	28	41	42
Monosaturated	40	41	38
Triunsaturated	30	Trace	5

These investigators stated that the nature of their evidence was not such as to establish within extremely close limits the glyceride composition of the three fats, but it did indicate that animal fats are "non-random" in their fatty acid distribution and that for a given animal fat there is considerable constancy of palmityl position throughout its constituent glycerides.

Quimby *et al.* studied the configuration of the palmito-glycerides present in two ways: by thermal and X-ray diffraction examination of selected crystallised fractions after their complete hydrogenation, and by comparison of the cooling curves on the completely hydrogenated original fats, and on these fats after they had been "randomised" artificially by traces of sodium methoxide. They state that the latter comparison gave "strong evidence that none of the three fats was originally randomly arranged", but that two types of "non-random" composition were indicated as between lard and the tallows. In the lard the results (p. 499) of earlier work [20c, 22a] were confirmed in that symmetrical or 2-palmito-glycerides were shown to be almost exclusively present, but in both beef and mutton tallow the corresponding glycerides were probably largely in the unsymmetrical form (1-palmitoglycerides): so that, according to this evidence, tallows differ sharply from lard in fatty acid distribution.

Reiser and Reddy[29] (1959) studied the glycerides of a pig depot fat (component acids: saturated 40·1, oleic 55·8, linoleic 4·0 per cent.) by the oxidation and the crystallisation procedures with the following results:

	Trisaturated	Monounsaturated-disaturated	Di-unsaturated-monosaturated	Triunsaturated
By oxidation	2	31	56	11
By crystallisation	2	30	57	10

They also concurred in the view that saturated acyl groups were present in the 2-glyceryl positions, and oleic groups in the 1- and 3-positions.

Proof of the very large proportions of 2-palmito-glycerides in pig fats by study of the component acids in their 2-monoglycerides (isolated by selective enzyme hydrolysis) was given (1958–1963) by different workers,[13a, b, c] and has already been mentioned above (pp. 499, 500, Table 117). Barrett *et al.*[13c] (1963) also estimated the main groups of glycerides in two pig fats by a special form of thin-layer chromatography ("T.L.C.") and from the results of selective enzyme hydrolysis ("S.E.H."):

Pig fat		Trisaturated	2-Oleo-disaturated	1-Oleo-disaturated	Saturated-dioleins	Oleo-linoleo-saturated (and triolein)	Dioleolinoleins (and saturated-dilinoleins)
I	T.L.C.	Trace	1·5	24·5	47	22	5
	S.E.H.	4·5	1	26	48·5	18	2·5
II	T.L.C.	4	1·5	35	42·5	14·5	4
	S.E.H.	12	1·5	39·5	39	7	0·5

These figures not only give further evidence of the presence of 1- (or 3-)oleo-disaturated glycerides, but are in close agreement, for trisaturated and mono-unsaturated-disaturated glycerides, with those for the respective pig fats with similar palmitic, stearic, oleic and linoleic acid contents studied by Pedelty[27b] (p. 502), by Riemenschneider *et al.*[28] (p. 503) and by Quimby *et al.*[22b] (p. 503) by the crystallisation procedure (the same probably holds for the monosaturated and triunsaturated glycerides, but these are not clearly differentiated by the methods used by Barrett *et al.*).

This accordance between different methods of study indicates that the preliminary crystallisation procedure is fully reliable in its application to fats of this general fatty acid composition. It is also evident that the glyceride structure of pig body fats is now defined with considerable certainty.

Ox depot fats. In addition to the perinephric fat of an English heifer examined by Hilditch and Paul,[27a] two body fats of Indian cows from Calicut and Bombay have been studied by Hilditch and Murti.[27c] The Bombay cow fat had an unusually large content of palmitic acid (40·8 per cent.). The proportions of stearic, oleic and polyethenoid C_{18} acids in the English, Calicut, and Bombay cow body fats were respectively as follows: stearic, 21·4, 27·9, 25·5; oleic 35·2, 29·0, 22·9; and polyethenoid C_{18} 3·5, 1·5, 1·1 per cent. (mol.).

The chief constituents of these three fats were as below:

	ENGLISH PER CENT.	CALICUT PER CENT.	BOMBAY PER CENT.
Palmitostearins	14	28	33
"Oleo"-dipalmitins	15	11	18
"Oleo"-palmitostearins	32	38	34
Palmitodi-"oleins"	23	17	11
Stearodi-"oleins"	11	3	1

Triunsaturated glycerides were not detected, but up to 3 per cent. of tripalmitin may have accompanied the palmitostearins and similar small amounts of "oleo"-distearins may have been present.

Oleopalmitostearin is the most abundant glyceride in ox tallows (30–40 per cent. of the whole fat); oleodipalmitin and palmitodiolein each amount to between 10 and 20 per cent., whilst trisaturated glycerides usually form about 15 per cent. or more of the total glycerides, the amount varying according to the proportion of stearic acid in the total fatty acids. This gives a general indication of the composition of ox body fats, whilst the main glycerides in any given case can now be roughly computed (as indicated below, p. 508) from the composition of the fatty acids of a tallow without recourse to the lengthy determination of glyceride composition.

Neat's foot oil. The hooves of oxen and sheep contain a liquid fat of low palmitic and very low stearic acid content. This characteristic cattle fat, although not belonging to the "stearic-rich" type of cattle adipose tissues, is appropriately included at this point.

The glycerides of an Irish neat's foot oil[27e] have been investigated. The component fatty acids of this oil included myristic 1·0, palmitic 18·2, stearic 3·6, hexadecenoic 11·9, oleic 60·5, polyethenoid C_{18} 2·9, and polyethenoid C_{20-22} 1·9 per cent. (mol.). Oleic acid is thus the chief constituent, whilst the proportion of hexadecenoic acid is larger, and that of palmitic acid smaller, than in the main body fats (curiously, however, the total content of C_{16} acids in the neat's foot oil – 30·1 per cent. – is the same as that of palmitic acid in the body fats).

The fat consisted almost wholly of glycerides containing either two or three unsaturated acyl groups, only 7 per cent. of it being oleopalmitostearin. The chief components were palmitodi-"oleins", which comprised about 40 per cent. of the fat. Triunsaturated glycerides also accounted in all for nearly 50 per cent. of the whole fat, but were mainly mixed in character; triolein itself probably amounted to less than 10 per cent. of the oil, and hexadecenodioleins appeared to form somewhat over 20 per cent., the rest being dioleo-glycerides with the third acyl group one of the polyethenoid C_{18} or C_{20-22} acids. The component glycerides "computed" from the fatty acid composition of the oil by the method of Hilditch and Meara[30a] (cf. Chapter V, Appendix, p. 419), gives values (Table 121, p. 509) in fairly close accordance with those found by experiment; this is, of course, an indication of how far the neat's foot oil glycerides conform with the usual "evenly-distributed" pattern.

Sheep depot fats. These include the perinephric and external tissue fats of an English ewe[27d] and an Indian sheep body fat.[27f] The stearic, oleic and poly-ethenoid C_{18} acid contents of the ewe back, ewe perinephric and Indian sheep fats were respectively: stearic 14·5, 25·6, 26·6; oleic 45·8, 37·1, 31·8; poly-ethenoid C_{18} 2·1, 3·3, 3·3 per cent. (mol.). The chief glyceride constituents were:

	ENGLISH EWE		INDIAN SHEEP PER CENT.
	EXTERNAL PER CENT.	PERINEPHRIC PER CENT.	
Palmitostearins	5	14	27
"Oleo"-dipalmitins	13	5	1
"Oleo"-palmitostearins	28	41	28
Palmitodi-"oleins"	46	25	26
Stearodi-"oleins"	7	13	14

In general build the sheep tallows are exactly of the same type as the ox body fats, and what has been said above for the latter also applies to the sheep fats. Oleopalmitostearins and palmitodioleins are the chief glycerides present; the proportion of trisaturated glycerides is determined by the amount of stearic acid in the total fatty acids. The Indian sheep fat, however, differed somewhat from the fats of the English sheep in that it contained more trisaturated glycerides (in relation to its total saturated acid content), and considerably less of the monounsaturated-disaturated glyceride group. The glycerides in sheep, as in ox, body fats may be approximately computed from the fatty acid compositions as described on p. 419 and shown in Table 121.

Progressive alteration in glyceride structure of "stearic-rich" animal fats of varying stearic acid content. The manner in which the proportions of tri-, di-, and mono-saturated glycerides alter in this class of animal fats as the proportions of stearic acid and oleic acid vary can be appreciated by considering as a series the nine fats discussed in the preceding paragraphs. For this purpose the data are arranged in Table 120A with the fats in general decreasing order of total unsaturation. In this Table the minor quantities of octadecadienoic and unsaturated C_{20-22} acids (but *not* unsaturated C_{16} acids) are included with oleic acid in the various categories as "oleo"-glycerides. In neat's foot oil, which contains a fairly high proportion of hexadecenoic acid, mixed glycerides of which this forms a constituent have been excluded from the comparison.

It will be seen that decrease in oleic acid content is accompanied by generally corresponding increases in stearic acid content until the latter reaches about 28 per cent., beyond which further diminution in oleic acid is apparently compensated for by increases beyond the normal (30 per cent.) proportion of palmitic acid. Thus the palmitic acid content of the Bombay cow fat, and also the combined palmitic and myristic acid content of the Calicut cow fat, are abnormally high; this incidentally complicates to some extent comparisons in relation to the development of mixed stearo-glycerides with increasing general saturation in these fats. Nevertheless it is instructive to compare the relative

TABLE 120A.   *Component Glycerides of Pig, Sheep and Ox Depot Fats (per cent. mol.)*

	Neat's[27e] Foot	Ewe[27d] External	Pig[27b] Back	Pig[27b] Peri-nephric	Ewe[27d] Peri-nephric	Heifer[27a] English	Sheep[27f] Indian	Cow[27c] Calicut	Cow[27c] Bombay
Component acids:									
Myristic ($+ C_{12}$)	1·0	3·8	1·3	1·8	3·0	2·6	3·4	5·7	5·9
Palmitic	18·2	31·5	29·0	31·1	27·1	33·4	29·5	33·4	40·8
Stearic	3·6	14·5	13·8	17·6	25·6	21·4	26·6	27·9	25·5
Arachidic	—	0·4	—	—	1·5	1·3	1·3	0·5	0·7
Hexa-($+$tetra-)decenoic	11·9	1·2	2·7	2·4	2·0	2·5	3·5	1·9	2·8
Oleic	60·5	45·8	43·9	40·6	37·1	35·2	31·8	29·0	22·9
Octadecadienoic	2·9	2·1	7·2	5·3	3·3	3·5	3·3	1·5	1·1
Unsaturated C_{20-22}	1·9	0·7	2·1	1·2	0·4	0·1	0·6	0·1	0·3
Component glycerides:									
Fully saturated:									
Tripalmitin	—	Trace	1	—	Trace	3	Trace	—	3
Dipalmitostearin	—	3	2	4	4	8	16	16	23
Palmitodistearin	—	2	2	5	10	6	11	12	10
Tristearin	—	—	—	—	Trace	—	—	—	—
Mono-"oleo"-disaturated:									
"Oleo"-dipalmitin	1	13	5	9	5	15	1	11	18
"Oleo"-palmitostearin	6	28	27	34	41	32	28	38	34
"Oleo"-distearin	—	1	—	—	2	2	—	2	—
Di-"oleo"-monosaturated:									
Palmitodi-"olein"	40	46	53	40	25	23	26	17	11
Stearodi-"olein"	4	7	7	5	13	11	14	3	1
Tri-"oleins"	13	0	3	3	0	0	3	0	0

TABLE 120B.   *Relative Proportions of Palmitodi-"oleins,"*
"Oleo"-palmitostearins and Palmitodistearins

	Neat's Foot	Pig Back	Ewe External	Pig Peri-nephric	Heifer English	Ewe Peri-nephric	Sheep Indian	Cow Calicut	Cow Bombay
C_{18} fatty acids:									
Stearic	3·6	13·8	14·5	17·6	21·4	25·6	26·6	27·9	25·5
Oleic + octadecadienoic	63·4	51·1	47·9	45·9	38·7	40·4	35·1	30·5	24·0
Palmitodi-C_{18} glycerides (increments per cent.):									
Palmitodi-"oleins"	40	53	46	40	23	25	26	17	11
"Oleo"-palmitostearins	6	27	28	34	32	41	28	38	34
Palmitodistearins	—	2	2	5	6	10	11	12	10
	46	82	76	79	61	76	₊ 65	67	55
Palmitodi-C_{18} glycerides (per cent.):									
Palmitodi-"oleins"	87	65	61	51	38	33	40	25	20
"Oleo"-palmitostearins	13	33	37	43	52	54	43	57	62
Palmitodistearins	—	2	2	6	10	13	17	18	18

proportions of palmitodi-"oleins", "oleo"-palmitostearins, and palmito-distearins as the proportion of stearic acid in the whole fat increases (Table 120B).

In the last three lines of Table 120B the amount of each of the respective glycerides is expressed as a percentage of the total monopalmito-glycerides of the fat (the term *monopalmito-* for this purpose including the minor amounts of monomyristo-glycerides present). The progressive changes in the relative proportions of the three types of palmitodi-C_{18} glycerides thus become strikingly evident, and are a strong argument in favour of the hydrogenation hypothesis which has been put forward (*cf.* p. 406) to account for the varying proportions of fully saturated glycerides in these animal fats. It will be observed that, as the proportions of oleic acid decline, the most noticeable change in the glycerides is a steady decrease in the percentage of palmitodi-"oleins", whilst the fully saturated palmitodistearins commence to augment, but do not exceed 18 per cent. in the extreme cases; meantime the percentage of "oleo"-palmitostearin in the monopalmito glycerides rises from 13 per cent. in the most unsaturated fat to over 60 per cent. in the most saturated fat in the series.

Arithmetical computation of component glycerides in "stearic-rich" animal depot fats. In many vegetable fats the experimentally observed results can be simulated, at least so far as the major component glycerides are concerned, by calculations [30a] based upon the proportions of the component acids of the fat, and depending upon arithmetical partition of oleic (or other major unsaturated) acid between the rest of the component acids (see Chapter V, Appendix, p. 419). Such a calculation cannot reproduce the observed proportions of the various individual mixed glycerides in the "stearic-rich" animal depot fats which we are now considering; but, after deducting the palmitic and stearic acids observed to be present in the fully saturated constituents from the total amounts of these acids in the mixed fatty acids of the whole fats, partition of the "oleic" acid between the remaining palmitic and stearic acids gives figures for the various mixed "oleo"-saturated glycerides in fairly close agreement with the observed values. This is illustrated in Table 121 (p. 509) for the nine fats discussed in Table 120A. It will be seen that the values for the mixed "oleo"-glycerides found by analysis (*a*) are in fact closely reproduced by this form of computation (*b*) in four fats which have contents of more than 20 per cent. of stearic acid; the accordance is not so well marked in some cases in those fats which contain less stearic acid.

The agreement between the values (*b*), computed after allowance for the observed fully saturated glycerides, and the observed values (*a*) might be expected if, in the suggested biohydrogenation process, the hydrogen molecules are attached in indiscriminate fashion to some of the double bonds of a preformed mixture of oleo-glycerides assembled on the lines of "even distribution."

In arithmetical computations of the chief mixed glycerides of a "stearic-rich" animal body fat by this method, separate determination of the fully saturated glycerides and their component acids could be avoided by employing the graph in Fig. 10 (p. 407) to give an approximate measure of the proportion of fully saturated glycerides in an animal body fat from the proportion of saturated acids in the total component-acids; for the purposes of approximate calculation, these fully saturated glycerides may be assumed to be made up of 60 per cent. palmitic and 40 per cent. stearic acid (*cf.* pp. 498, 500). The oleic acid present may then be partitioned, as before, between the remaining palmitic and stearic acids. By this means a roughly approximate estimate of the chief

TABLE 121. *Observed and "Computed" Values (per cent. mol.) of Mixed Saturated-Unsaturated Glycerides of "Stearic-Rich" Animal Depot Fats*

	NEAT'S FOOT[27e]		PIG[27b] EXTERNAL		PIG[27b] PERINEPHRIC		SHEEP[27d] EXTERNAL		SHEEP[27d] PERINEPHRIC	
	Found (a)	Calc. (b)	Found (a)	Calc. (b)	Found (a)	Calc. (b)	Found (a)	Calc. (b)	Found (a)	Calc. (b)
Component acids:										
Palmitic*	31·1		33·0		35·3		36·5		32·1	
Stearic†	3·6		13·8		17·6		14·9		27·1	
Oleic‡	65·3		53·2		47·1		48·6		40·8	
Component glycerides:										
"Oleo"-dipalmitin	1	2	5	11	9	14	13	20	5	4
"Oleo"-palmitostearin	6	3	27	26	34	31	28	27	41	47
"Oleo"-distearin	—	—	—	—	—	—	1	—	2	—
Palmitodi-"olein"	40	40	53	43	40	34	46	35	25	23
Stearodi-"olein"	4	7	7	8	5	8	7	11	13	10
Tri-unsaturated	13	10	3	7	3	4	—	2	—	2

COW

	SHEEP[27f] INDIAN		ENGLISH[27a]		CALICUT[27c]		BOMBAY[27c]	
	Found (a)	Calc. (b)	Found (a)	Calc. (b)	Found (a)	Calc. (b)	Found (a)	Calc. (b)
Component acids:								
Palmitic*	37·1		38·5		41·0		49·5	
Stearic†	26·8		22·7		28·4		26·2	
Oleic‡	36·1		38·8		30·6		24·3	
Component glycerides:								
"Oleo"-dipalmitin	1	1	15	11	11	13	18	21
"Oleo"-palmitostearin	28	35	32	40	38	40	34	34
"Oleo"-distearin	—	—	2	—	2	—	—	—
Palmitodi-"olein"	26	18	23	23	17	13	11	7
Stearodi-"olein"	14	18	11	8	3	5	1	2
Tri-unsaturated	3	—	—	—	—	1	—	—

* Including minor component myristic, tetradecenoic and hexadecenoic acids.
† Including minor component arachidic acid.
‡ Including minor component octadecadienoic and unsaturated C_{20-22} acids.

component glycerides of "stearic-rich" animal depot fats can be made directly from their fatty acid compositions alone.

The position as regards our knowledge of the natural glycerides present in animal depot fats is undoubtedly more satisfactory than it was 20–25 years ago; but the foregoing description shows that, apart from a fairly adequate knowledge of the industrially important classes of lards and tallows, there is still room for much investigation into the component glycerides of other classes of animal depot fats. The study in detail, by the modern methods now available, of depot fats from a far wider range of animals and birds is necessary before we can even be certain that such fats are confined to the types which have up to now been indicated. We have endeavoured in the present chapter to give a fair representation of the information already available, but the somewhat fragmentary character of the materials studied, together with the number of animal species of which the depot fats have not yet received attention, should always be borne in mind.

MILK FATS

The first attempts to examine the glyceride structure of a milk fat took, as usual, the form of fractional crystallisation studies, and were made by Amberger,[31] who succeeded in isolating from butter fat small quantities of palmitodistearin (m.p. 62·8°) and stearodipalmitin, also oleodipalmitin and butyropalmito-olein; whilst he indicated that the amount of triolein present was of the order of only 2 per cent. Tristearin and butyrodiolein were also considered possibly to be present. The mixed glycerides isolated evidently amounted only to a comparatively small proportion of the whole of the fat.

In 1928, Arup[32] separated samples of Irish butter fat into a number of fractions by removing solid components which crystallised out from the fat as a whole on standing at various temperatures, and determined the Reichert-Meissl, Kirschner, iodine, etc., values of the separated fractions. The results led him to conclude that the low molecular weight acids, and also the higher saturated acids, are distributed more or less evenly throughout the whole of the fat, and he found no evidence of the presence of simple triglycerides such as tributyrin, triolein, etc.

Somewhat fuller information on the component glycerides of milk fats resulted from the examination of a number of cow milk fats, and of specimens of buffalo, goat, sheep and camel milk fats by the semi-quantitative permanganate-acetone oxidation procedure, which leads to the isolation and determination of the fully saturated components, and the proportions of the saturated fatty acids therein combined.

Cow milk fats. The fully saturated glycerides present in fourteen cow milk fats were examined in this way by Hilditch and co-workers. Eight of these were from animals from England, New Zealand, or India, fed on a natural diet of grass or on ordinary winter stall diet; the remaining six were from animals which had received, in addition to basal stall feed, certain amounts of specific fatty oils or oil cakes. The component acids in these fourteen milk fats were discussed in detail in Chapter III (pp. 146, 147, 155, Tables 51A, 51B, 53), whilst their fully saturated glyceride contents were compared with the proportions of saturated acids in the total fatty acids of each fat in Table 73 of Chapter V (p. 370). The studies of glyceride structure of these cow milk fats included in some cases determination of the component acids of the fully saturated components, but in others were confined to ascertaining the percentage proportions and mean saponification equivalents of the latter group.

The more completely examined fats included two market samples of New Zealand butter,[33a] two English fats and a New Zealand fat from cows fed on normal pasture or winter (stall) diets,[33b] an Indian ghee from cows fed on pasture,[33c] and two English milk fats from cows on a winter stall diet supplemented by either coconut or soya bean cake.[33b] The results obtained are summarised in Table 122 (minor unsaturated component acids were not determined in any

TABLE 122. *Glyceride Structure of Eight Cow Milk Fats*

NO. IN TABLE	COW MILK FAT
E 1929	English, spring pasture, 1929.
E 1928	English, autumn feed, 1928.
NZ (i)	New Zealand, market sample, 1927.
Indian	Indian, pasture feed, 1930.
NZ (ii)	New Zealand, market sample, 1927.
NZ (iii)	New Zealand, spring pasture, 1928.
ES	English, stall feed, 1929 (soya bean cake in diet).
EC	English, stall feed, 1929 (coconut cake in diet).

(i) *Component Fatty Acids of the Whole Fats (Molar Percentages)*

FAT:	E 1929	E 1928	NZ (i)	INDIAN	NZ (ii)	NZ (iii)	ES	EC
Butyric	8·9	8·4	8·4	6·9	9·2	9·2	9·6	9·0
n-Hexanoic	2·7	3·5	3·9	4·0	3·7	3·4	3·0	3·9
n-Octanoic	2·0	2·7	1·3	2·2	1·4	2·2	2·8	1·7
n-Decanoic	3·0	2·9	2·8	4·9	2·7	4·2	5·1	4·3
Lauric	4·7	4·1	4·6	6·7	3·7	4·7	7·5	8·3
Myristic	10·9	7·2	11·0	10·9	10·2	11·5	10·7	17·2
Palmitic	24·3	27·1	26·2	26·8	25·7	25·0	23·7	24·1
Stearic	5·4	6·4	7·1	5·5	10·2	9·5	6·7	3·9
Arachidic	—	0·7	0·8	—	0·5	0·5	0·9	—
Oleic	34·6	33·9	30·8	28·4	28·9	26·1	27·0	25·7
Octadecadienoic	3·5	3·1	3·1	3·7	3·8	3·7	3·0	1·9

(ii) *Fully Saturated Glycerides Present in the Whole Fats*

	E 1929	E 1928	NZ (i)	INDIAN	NZ (ii)	NZ (iii)	ES	EC
Whole Fats:								
Iodine value	41·6	41·3	39·4	36·0	38·0	34·5	34·8	31·6
Total saturated acid content per cent. mol.	61·9	63·0	66·1	67·9	67·3	70·2	70·0	72·4
Fully saturated glycerides:								
per cent. (wt.)	24·3	25·4	29·2	31·7	31·3	37·4	35·0	38·5
per cent. (mol.)	27·2	29·1	31·5	33·7	33·8	39·6	38·2	41·3

(iii) *Component Fatty Acids of the Fully Saturated Glycerides (Molar Percentages)*

	E 1929	E 1928	NZ (i)	INDIAN	NZ (ii)	NZ (iii)	ES	EC
Butyric	11·4	11·7	10·5	11·2	11·0	11·2	9·2	9·2
n-Hexanoic	5·1	5·3	4·9	5·1	6·5	4·6	6·4	5·8
n-Octanoic	2·7	2·2	5·0	0·5	1·8	3·4	3·1	2·8
n-Decanoic	5·3	4·2	3·1	4·4	3·3	5·1	6·3	6·9
Lauric	6·0	5·2	4·7	6·1	4·1	5·3	6·4	11·1
Myristic	15·1	13·2	17·0	15·5	17·9	14·9	19·6	20·1
Palmitic	39·5	43·1	39·3	43·0	39·6	39·9	36·1	35·4
Stearic	14·9	15·1	15·2	14·2	15·8	15·6	12·6	8·7
Arachidic	—	—	0·3	—	—	—	0·3	—

511

of these analyses). Less complete data for six English cow milk fats, two of which were from normally stall-fed animals, whilst the others were for cows which had received in addition eight ounces per day of either linseed, rape, or cod liver oil, have also been recorded[33d] (Table 123).

TABLE 123. *Fully Saturated Glycerides (amounts and mean equivalents) of six Cow Milk Fats*

	WHOLE FAT			FULLY SATURATED GLYCERIDES		
OIL FED TO COW	I.V.	SAP. EQ.	SATURATED ACIDS PER CENT. (MOL.)	PER CENT. (WT.)	PER CENT. (MOL.)	SAP. EQ.
Control	34·5	239·7	71·4	37·1	40·4	221·0
Control	34·9	244·2	69·1	31·1	34·2	224·5
Linseed	46·0	249·0	61·3	22·2	24·8	222·4
Rape	44·5	251·2	59·4	22·4	25·3	225·0
Cod liver	51·7	264·2	53·5	15·3	17·2	235·7
Cod liver	54·1	266·0	50·6	12·8	14·6	235·1

The data for all fourteen fats show consistently that the content of fully saturated glycerides is, within close limits, simply a function of the relative proportions of saturated and unsaturated acids in the whole fat, irrespective of the nature of the saturated acids, or of abnormalities in the component fatty acids caused by ingestion of specific fatty acids (*cf.* Chapter III, p. 155). In this respect butter fats resemble lards and tallows very closely and, indeed, when the relationship between fully saturated glyceride content and total saturated acid content is plotted as a graph, the curve obtained (*cf.* Chapter V, Fig. 10, p. 407) is a prolongation of that given by the corresponding data for the pig and cattle reserve fats. Notably, in spite of the marked differences in the relative amounts of their component acids as compared with normal butters, the milk fats from cows which had received cod liver oil in the diet still conform to this typical relationship. Indeed, their positions on the curve in Fig. 10 emphasise the fact that, from this aspect of glyceride structure, there is complete uniformity in type between cow milk fats and ox, sheep, or pig depot fats.

In the fourteen cow milk fats which were thus examined, the molar proportions of fully saturated components range from 14·6 to 41·3 per cent., so that the non-fully saturated glycerides present in these fats varied in amount from 59 to 85 per cent. There is little or no evidence that triolein is present in any great amount in normal butter fats, and considerable indirect evidence against this possibility (*cf.* Amberger[31] and Arup[32]). Consequently in most of the butters studied the glycerides are probably made up of fully saturated components with mono-"oleo"- and di-"oleo"-glycerides in proportions near to those given in Table 124.

These general characteristics of butter fat glyceride structure have a practical bearing on the variation in the "melting point" or softness of butters. Leaving out of consideration the six fats from animals which had received fatty oils or seed cakes as part of their diets, it will be noticed from Table 124 that the remaining eight milk fats from cows on normal diets differ to a considerable extent in their component glycerides, and therefore in their physical charac-

TABLE 124. *Probable General Composition of Cow Milk Fats*

	FULLY SATURATED PER CENT. (MOL.)	MONO-"OLEO"-DISATURATED PER CENT. (MOL.)	DI-"OLEO"-MONO-SATURATED PER CENT. (MOL.)
English, stall-fed, 1934 (cod liver oil in diet)	15	23	62
English, stall-fed, 1934 (cod liver oil in diet)	17	26	57
English, stall-fed, 1934 (linseed oil in diet)	25	34	41
English, stall-fed, 1934 (rape oil in diet)	25	28	47
English, spring pasture, 1929	27	33	40
English, autumn feed, 1928	29	31	40
New Zealand, market sample, 1927	31	36	33
Indian, pasture fed, 1930	34	36	30
New Zealand, market sample, 1927	34	35	31
English, stall-fed, 1934	34	39	27
English, stall-fed, 1929 (soya bean cake in diet)	38	34	28
New Zealand, spring pasture, 1928	40	33	27
English, stall-fed, 1934	41	33	26
English, stall-fed, 1929 (coconut cake in diet)	41	34	25

teristics of hardness or softness. This difference is not very marked so far as the mono-"oleo"-disaturated glycerides (which melt somewhat above room temperature) are concerned, for these are moderately constant, with a range of about 33–39 per cent. of the total fats. The fully saturated components vary from 27 to 40 per cent., however, with a corresponding variation in the di-"oleo"-monosaturated glycerides of almost the same extent. Consequently, increase in unsaturation (oleic acid content) of a milk fat has a dual effect on the consistency of the butter: not only is the amount of the highest melting (i.e., fully saturated) components reduced, but that of the di-"oleo"-glycerides (which are liquid at the ordinary temperature) is increased to approximately the same extent as the reduction in fully saturated components.

It was pointed out earlier (Chapter III, pp. 148–150) that the amounts of the different component fatty acids present in milk fats vary somewhat according to the general type of diet, the seasonal change from pasture to indoor feeding, the age of the animal, etc. Such variations are, in fact, chiefly connected with differences in the proportions of the unsaturated acids, which are mainly compensated by corresponding alterations in those of the stearic, and of the butyric and other lower saturated acids. The amounts of fully saturated components and of di-"oleo"-monosaturated glycerides are almost the only markedly variable features in the glyceride structure of butter fats, since this depends upon the relative amounts of saturated and unsaturated acids in the whole fat.

The fat (EC) from cows whose diet had included a certain amount of coconut oil cake contained, as a whole, less oleic and linoleic acid than normal, and somewhat more lauric and myristic acids. In its fully saturated components, however, the relative differences are more sharply defined: the lauric acid molar content (Table 122 (iii)) is 11 (instead of about 5–6) and the myristic acid molar content is 20 (against 15–17). Since dilauromyristin is a major component of coconut oil (*cf.* Chapter VI, p. 425), these figures suggest that to some extent this glyceride has passed through directly into the milk fat.

Indian camel, buffalo, sheep, and goat milk fats. The glyceride structure of the milk fats of the Indian camel, sheep, and goat were studied by Dhingra,[34] and that of the Indian buffalo by Bhattacharya and Hilditch,[33c] and by Achaya and Banerjee,[26] on the same lines as those of the cow milk fats which have been considered above. The chief numerical results of the investigations are summarised in Table 125.

TABLE 125. *Glyceride Structure of Indian Camel, Buffalo, Sheep and Goat Milk Fats*

(i) *Component Fatty Acids of the whole Fats (Molar Percentages)*

		BUFFALO				
	CAMEL[34]	I[33c]	II[26]	III[26]	SHEEP[34]	GOAT[34]
Butyric	5·9	10·9	15·4	11·5	8·4	7·6
n-Hexanoic	1·9	2·8	1·1	—	5·4	4·5
n-Octanoic	1·1	1·5	1·4	0·1	5·8	6·2
n-Decanoic	2·1	2·4	1·4	0·5	10·1	11·1
Lauric	5·7	3·3	1·9	0·8	6·0	5·1
Myristic	7·9	10·5	9·2	4·8	11·8	11·2
Palmitic	28·3	28·7	31·9	25·1	20·4	21·5
Stearic	9·7	9·3	12·5	19·0	5·4	7·3
Arachidic	—	0·7	0·1	1·1	1·3	0·1
Oleic	34·1	27·7	23·9*	36·1*	22·2	24·2
Octadecadienoic	3·3	2·2	1·2	1·0	3·2	1·2

* Includes minor amounts of hexadecenoic and unsaturated C_{20} acids.

(ii) *Fully Saturated Glycerides present in the whole Fats*

Whole Fats:						
Iodine value	40·8	33·5	27·4	37·0	32·1	28·8
Total saturated acid content (per cent. mol.)	62·6	70·1	74·9	62·9	74·6	74·6
Fully saturated glycerides:						
per cent. (wt.)	24·2	32·3	40·1	22·1	33·7	36·3
per cent. (mol.)	25·6	34·3	41·7	24·3	36·8	39·3

(iii) *Component Fatty Acids of the Fully Saturated Glycerides (Molar Percentages)*

Butyric	8·9	14·1			9·8	9·4
n-Hexanoic	2·1	5·0			8·2	7·2
n-Octanoic	0·1	0·7			5·4	5·8
n-Decanoic	2·8	1·6			10·8	14·2
Lauric	2·6	4·4			14·1	8·2
Myristic	18·9	9·2			15·9	12·7
Palmitic	50·0	47·1			26·9	31·6
Stearic	14·6	16·8			8·9	10·7
Arachidic	—	1·1			—	0·2

(iv) *Probable General Composition of the Milk Fats (Molar Proportions)*

Fully saturated	25	34	42	24	37	39
Mono-"oleo"-disaturated	37	42	41	40	50	46
Di-"oleo"-monosaturated	38	24	17	36	13	15

Buffalo I, pasture-fed; II, mainly pasture-fed; III, heavy cottonseed diet.

The camel and buffalo milk fat glycerides are, on the whole, very similar to those of the domestic cow. Butyric and n-hexanoic (caproic) acids are low in the whole camel milk fat, but this does not seem to be reflected in any departure from the normal in the general glyceride structure. The fully saturated glyceride content is slightly lower, for the proportion of saturated acids in the whole fat, than in the cow milk fats, as will be seen from Figs. 3 and 10 (pp. 371, 407); but the component acids of the fully saturated glycerides are, on the whole, not very different from those in cow milk fats. The mainly pasture-fed buffalo milk fat II of Achaya and Banerjee[26] was somewhat more saturated in nature than buffalo milk fat I[33c] and contained notably more butyro-glycerides. The fat III, from a buffalo cow fed largely on cottonseed,[26] was quite different and much more unsaturated, although its content of stearo-glycerides was at the same time increased; the effect of dietary fat on the character of the milk fat is evident in this instance (*cf.* Chapter III, p. 161).

Sheep and goat milk fats, on the other hand, seem to stand somewhat apart from cow or buffalo milk fats. Their relatively high contents of caprylic and capric acids received previous mention in Chapter III (p. 161). Their proportions of fully saturated glycerides are definitely lower than in the case of cow milk fats of corresponding mean unsaturation (Figs. 3 and 10, pp. 371, 407), whilst the component acids of the fully saturated portions contain, as is natural, much more caprylic, capric, and also lauric acid than those of the similar parts of cow milk fats, the palmitic and stearic acid contents being correspondingly below those of the latter. In the mixed saturated-unsaturated glycerides, however, the molar contents of myristic, palmitic and stearic acids are very similar to those of the corresponding portions of cow butter fats, and the only difference is that, in the goat and sheep milk fats, there is about 10 per cent. (mol.) less of C_{18} unsaturated acids and 10 per cent. (mol.) more of the butyric-lauric acid group (the increase being mainly in capric and caprylic acids). The excess of capric and caprylic acids, as compared with cow butter fats, therefore appears to be almost wholly at the expense of oleic and, to a less extent, of palmitic acid. Sheep and goat milk fats are also remarkable for their extremely small proportions of di-unsaturated glycerides (*ca.* 15 per cent. of the fats); this, however, has less effect on their melting points than might at first be supposed, doubtless owing to the compensating influences of low contents of palmitic and stearic, with high butyric-lauric (especially caprylic and capric) acids.

More detailed studies of cow (and buffalo) milk fats. The acetone crystallisation procedure was applied in 1940 to a typical English cow milk fat by Hilditch and S. Paul,[35] but crystallisations were only carried out at 0° and room temperature, three fractions being finally obtained which formed 11·4, 24·2, and 64·4 per cent. (mol.) of the whole milk fat and had iodine values respectively of 21·5, 36·8, and 55·2. The results for the component acids in the three fractions, and for those in their fully saturated glycerides (45·3, 24·6, and 11·8 per cent. respectively in the three fractions), with certain data based upon the composition of these fractions after complete hydrogenation, served to indicate the manner in which the unsaturated acids were united in the mixed saturated-unsaturated glycerides. The number of component acids present in the three fractions rendered it difficult to reach precise conclusions as to the component glycerides present; the best that could be done was to consider a number of alternative possibilities (some of which could be rejected as unlikely or impossible on the grounds of comparative solubility, or for other reasons). A number of possibilities remained for each fraction which, when the increments from the latter were assembled, led to the component glyceride estimates shown in Table 126, which must, however, be considered as relative and illustrative rather than absolute. Nevertheless, these figures defined much more completely than had previously been possible, both the nature of the chief mixed glycerides present in cow milk fat and their general proportions.

TABLE 126. *Component Acids and Glycerides of the Cow Milk Fat (per cent. mol.)*

COMPONENT ACIDS		COMPONENT GLYCERIDES	
Butyric	10·2	*Fully saturated* (19 per cent.):	
Hexanoic	2·5	Di-C_4–C_{14}-monopalmitin	6–7
Octanoic	1·3	Di-C_4–C_{14}-monostearin	1
Decanoic	1·5	Mono-C_4–C_{14}-dipalmitin	<1
Lauric	3·3	Mono-C_4–C_{14}-palmitostearin	9
Myristic	8·6	Dipalmitostearin	1–2
Palmitic	21·1	Palmitodistearin	<1
Stearic	9·9		
Arachidic	0·7	*Mono-unsaturated* (56–59 per cent.):	
		"Oleo"-di-C_4–C_{14}	3–9
Decenoic	0·2	"Oleo"-C_4–C_{14}-palmitin	22–30
Dodecenoic	0·2	"Oleo"-C_4–C_{14}-stearin	6–12
Tetradecenoic	0·9	"Oleo"-dipalmitin	1–5
Hexadecenoic	2·8	"Oleo"-palmitostearin	8–17
Oleic	31·4		
Octadecadienoic	4·9	*Di-unsaturated* (15–25 per cent.):	
Unsaturated $C_{20–22}$	0·5	Mono-C_4–C_{14}-di-"olein"	0–10
		Palmitodi-"olein"	4–18
		Stearodi-"olein"	1–8
		Tri-unsaturated (0–7 per cent.):	
		Tri-"olein"	0–7

The figures in Table 126 show that the most abundant glycerides in this butter fat (22–30 per cent. of the fat) contained one of the lower fatty acids (from butyric to myristic) in union with one palmitic and one oleic group as triglycerides. Nearly 40 per cent. of the fat was made up of four other groups of glycerides, these being (in probably decreasing order of magnitude) oleo-palmitostearins, palmitodioleins, oleo-mono-C_4–C_{14}-stearins, mono-C_4–C_{14}-di-oleins; the remaining 30–35 per cent. of the fat included about ten minor component mixed glycerides. The fully saturated glycerides (19 per cent. of the fat) consisted largely of mono-C_4–C_{14}-palmitostearins and di-C_4–C_{14}-mono-palmitins. No indication whatever was obtained of the presence of tributyrin or, indeed, of any other simple triglyceride; tri-unsaturated glycerides, if present at all, did not amount to more than 7 per cent. of the fat and were almost certainly mixed glycerides of oleic with another unsaturated acid (probably mainly octadecadieno-dioleins).

In 1945 Jack and Henderson[36] separated cow butter fat into five fractions by crystallising it from light petroleum (Skellysolve A) successively at 7°, −13°, −23°, and −53° C., and determined the component fatty acids and the amount and fatty acid composition of the fully saturated glycerides in each fraction. They stated that their results, apart from minor differences, confirmed the findings of Hilditch and Paul,[35] and indicated that the fatty acids "tend to be distributed not randomly but as widely as possible" in cow milk fat.

In 1950 Achaya and Hilditch[37] resolved the glycerides of an Indian cow milk fat into eight fractions, and those of an Indian buffalo milk fat into six fractions, by intensive crystallisation from acetone or ether at temperatures between −50° and 0° C. The groups of glycerides so obtained, although still complicated in fatty acid composition, contained much simplified mixtures of mixed glycerides as compared with the original fats. From the component acids of each

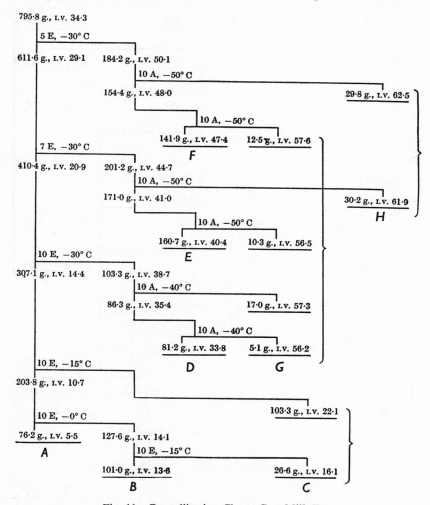

Fig. 11. Crystallisation Chart: Cow Milk Fat

separated glyceride group and of the trisaturated glycerides present in each, it was possible to build up a roughly quantitative statement of the many individual mixed glycerides present in the original fats (Tables 130 and 131, p. 521), and a more closely quantitative statement (Table 132, p. 522) of the various glyceride categories present (trisaturated, mono- or di-unsaturated, mono- or di-palmito-, mono- or di-oleo-, etc.).

The crystallisation schemes employed are illustrated in Figures 11 and 12.

517

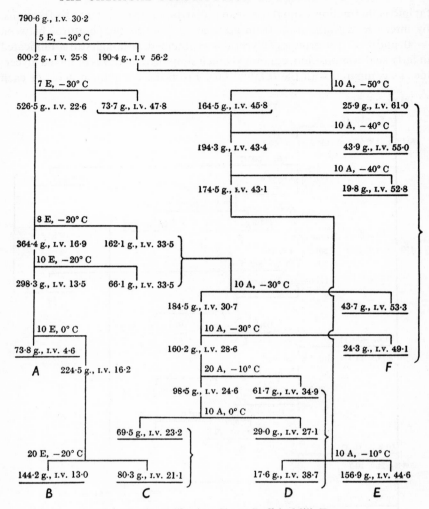

Fig. 12. Crystallisation Chart: Buffalo Milk Fat

TABLE 127. *Crystallisation of Cow and Buffalo Milk Fats*

	ENGLISH COW[35]			INDIAN COW[37]			INDIAN BUFFALO[37]		
	WT. (g.)	PER CENT. (MOL.)	IODINE VALUE	WT. (g.)	PER CENT. (MOL.)	IODINE VALUE	WT. (g.)	PER PER (MOL.)	IODINE VALUE
Original fat	2,450	100	46·9	796	100	34·3	791	100	30·2
Fractions									
A	296	11·4	21·5	76	8·8	5·5	74	8·5	4·6
B	601	24·2	36·8	101	12·7	13·6	144	18·4	13·0
C	1,553	64·4	55·2	130	16·3	20·8	150	18·6	22·0
D	—	—	—	81	10·1	34·2	108	13·7	32·7
E	—	—	—	161	20·2	40·4	157	19·5	43·4
F	—	—	—	142	17·7	47·3	158	21·3	52·8
G	—	—	—	45	6·1	56·8	—	—	—
H	—	—	—	60	8·1	60·5	—	—	—

The solvent employed is indicated in the figures by the letters E (ether) or A (acetone); the number before the letters E or A (e.g. 5E or 10A) refers to the concentration of the solution in cc. of solvent per gram of fat present.

The much greater degree of separation of the milk fat glycerides in the later work as compared with that when temperatures below 0° were not employed is illustrated by the figures in Table 127 (p. 518).

In order to illustrate the analyses undertaken on each fraction of the two Indian milk fats, and the manner in which these were utilised to estimate the amounts of different glyceride fractions present in each group, and therefrom in the original milk fats, the detailed figures for the Indian buffalo milk fat are reproduced in Tables 128 and 129.

By grouping the various related minor component acids together, as in Table 129, the most likely glyceride constitution of the two milk fats can be approximately worked out, with the results shown in Table 130 (p. 521). Whilst, owing to the very large number of acyl components, no great precision may be claimed for the individual proportions suggested for some of the possible mixed glycerides, it is believed that the figures show the relative order of occurrence of the chief types which are present and that they depict milk fat glycerides more fully than has hitherto been possible.

The figures in Table 130, irrespective of the precise degree of numerical

TABLE 128.   *Indian Buffalo Milk Fat : Component Acids (per cent. mol.) in Glyceride Groups A to F and in the corresponding Trisaturated Glycerides*

	A	B	C	D	E	F
Per cent. (mol.) of whole fat	8·5	18·4	18·6	13·7	19·5	21·3
Component acids:						
Butyric	0·3	11·8	11·1	10·5	11·1	20·5
n-Hexanoic	—	3·4	3·6	3·9	3·9	6·1
n-Octanoic	0·2	0·8	0·6	—	1·2	1·5
n-Decanoic	0·3	1·2	1·8	2·6	1·3	2·6
Lauric	—	2·5	1·7	3·3	2·9	3·4
Myristic	14·3	10·7	11·6	13·1	10·6	8·8
Palmitic	46·8	34·4	34·8	24·3	20·9	15·3
Stearic	29·4	19·3	11·6	8·9	5·9	2·5
Arachidic	3·5	2·1	1·6	1·8	1·1	—
Decenoic	—	—	Trace	—	Trace	0·1
Dodecenoic	—	0·1	0·1	0·1	0·3	0·2
Tetradecenoic	0·1	0·4	0·6	0·7	1·4	1·0
Hexadecenoic	1·4	0·5	0·8	1·9	2·8	2·7
Oleic	3·7	12·7	18·2	24·4	33·6	32·7
Octadecadienoic	—	—	0·2	0·8	—	—
Unsaturated C_{20-22}	—	0·1	1·7	3·7	3·0	2·6
Trisaturated glycerides (per cent. (mol.) of group)	84·5	58·8	43·2	44·3	23·6	13·9
Component acids:						
Butyric	0·3	16·4	17·5	16·8	19·3	24·7
n-Hexanoic	—	5·1	5·7	6·3	5·4	9·3
n-Octanoic	—	1·1	0·9	0·8	2·9	4·3
n-Decanoic	—	4·5	4·3	2·3	4·2	8·9
Lauric	0·3	1·5	5·5	7·5	13·4	14·3
Myristic	17·6	10·9	12·9	20·8	15·6	10·8
Palmitic	48·7	38·7	38·5	31·5	27·2	18·5
Stearic	29·3	19·9	12·6	10·6	9·7	6·2
Arachidic	3·8	1·9	2·1	3·4	2·3	3·0

519

accuracy in any given instance, emphasise the extremely large number of individual mixed triglycerides which go to make up a bovine (or, indeed, any ruminant) milk fat. The most abundant glyceride forms can be reduced to the seven classes shown in Table 131 (in which, in addition to the two milk fats immediately under discussion, corresponding data from the less complete analysis of the English cow milk fat[35] are included).

TABLE 129. *Indian Buffalo Milk Fat: Increments of Component Acids and Glyceride Categories Estimated therefrom in Glyceride Groups A to F (per cent. mol.)*

	A	B	C	D	E	F	TOTAL
Per cent. (mol.) of whole fat	8·5	18·4	18·6	13·7	19·5	21·3	100·0
Component acid groups:							
C_4–C_{12}	0·1	3·6	3·5	2·8	4·0	7·2	21·2
Myristic	1·2	2·0	2·2	1·8	2·0	1·9	11·1
Palmitic	4·0	6·3	6·5	3·3	4·1	3·3	27·5
Stearic (+arachidic)	2·8	4·0	2·4	1·5	1·3	0·5	12·5
Monoethenoid C_{10}–C_{16}	0·1	0·2	0·2	0·4	0·9	0·9	2·7
Oleic	0·3	2·3	3·4	3·3	6·6	7·0	22·9
Polyethenoid C_{18}, C_{20}, C_{22}	—	—	0·4	0·6	0·6	0·5	2·1
Trisaturated glycerides:							
Increments (per cent. mol.):	7·2	10·8	8·0	6·1	4·6	3·0	39·7
Component acids:							
C_4–C_{12}	0·1	3·1	2·7	2·0	2·1	1·8	11·8
Myristic	1·2	1·2	1·0	1·3	0·7	0·3	5·7
Palmitic	3·5	4·2	3·1	1·9	1·3	0·6	14·6
Stearic (+arachidic)	2·4	2·3	1·2	0·9	0·5	0·3	7·6
Estd. Glyceride Categories:							
(a) Trisaturated	7·2	10·8	8·0	6·1	4·6	3·0	39·7
Disatd.-mono-unsatd.	1·3	7·6	9·1	2·3	5·7	11·5	37·5
Monosatd.-di-unsatd.	—	—	1·5	5·3	9·2	6·8	22·8
Triunsaturated	—	—	—	—	—	—	—
(d) Di (C_4–C_{12})-mono-*others*	—	—	0·2	0·1	1·6	2·5	4·4
Mono (C_4–C_{12})-di-*others*	0·2	10·8	10·2	8·2	8·7	16·7	54·8
No (C_4–C_{12})-groups	8·3	7·6	8·2	5·4	9·2	2·1	40·8
(c) Dipalmito-mono-*others*	3·5	1·7	1·2	—	—	—	6·4
Monopalmito-di-*others*	5·0	15·6	17·0	10·0	12·2	9·8	69·6
No palmito-groups	—	1·1	0·4	3·7	7·3	11·5	24·0
(d) Di-oleo-mono-*others*	—	—	—	2·4	4·8	2·5	9·7
Mono-oleo-di-*others*	0·9	7·0	10·2	5·2	10·1	15·8	49·2
No oleo-groups	7·6	11·4	8·4	6·1	4·6	3·0	41·1

It will be seen that the two more detailed analyses confirm the earlier conclusion[35] that the fully saturated glycerides of a bovine milk fat consist mainly of mono-C_4–C_{14}-palmitostearins and di-C_4–C_{14}-monopalmitins, and that the other types which are present in significant proportions are C_4-C_{14}-oleopalmitins, oleopalmitostearins, palmitodioleins, C_4–C_{14}-dioleins and C_4–C_{14}-oleostearins; whilst other mixed saturated-unsaturated glycerides not included in the above categories still make up over one-quarter of the fat.

Integration of the individual glycerides suggested in Table 130 into the different classes (di-oleo-, oleopalmito-, dipalmito-, etc. glycerides) shown in Table 132 provides data which are probably accurate to within a few units per cent. These illustrate, in the three milk fats now being discussed, the relative constancy of the palmitic acid content and the variability in the proportions of oleic acid and, inversely, of the lower saturated fatty acids (with consequent variation in the proportions of mono- and di-oleo-glycerides, and of glycerides containing either one or two acyl groups drawn from the saturated C_4–C_{14} group of acids).

TABLE 130.   *Possible Component Glycerides of the Milk Fats*

	COW	BUFFALO
Trisaturated :		
Di-C_4–C_{12}-myristin	1	1
Di-C_4–C_{12}-palmitin	2	3
Di-C_4–C_{12}-stearin	—	1
C_4–C_{12}-myristo-palmitin	12	11
C_4–C_{12}-dipalmitin	2	2
C_4–C_{12}-myristo-stearin	1	1
C_4–C_{12}-palmito-stearin	8	13
Myristopalmitostearin	5	4
Dipalmitostearin	4	4
Disaturated-mono-unsaturated :		
Di-C_4–C_{12}-olein	1	—
C_4–C_{12}-myristo-olein	5	6
C_4–C_{12}-palmito-olein	6	9
C_4–C_{12}-stearo-olein	3	2
Myristopalmito-olein	6	6
Dipalmito-olein	1	—
Myristostearo-olein	1	3
Palmitostearo-olein	10	10
C_4–C_{12}-palmito-monoethenoid*	2	1
Monoethenoid-palmito-stearin ⎫	1	1
C_4–C_{12}-palmito-polyethenoid ⎭		
Monosaturated-di-unsaturated :		
C_4–C_{12}-diolein	6	4
Myristo-diolein	—	1
Palmitodiolein	4	4
C_4–C_{12}-monoethenoid*-olein	7	3
Palmito-monoethenoid*-olein	6	4
C_4–C_{12}-polyethenoid*-olein	4	3
Palmito-polyethenoid*-olein	2	3

* Monoethenoid (C_{10}–C_{16}) acids ; polyethenoid (C_{18}, C_{20}, C_{22}) acids.

TABLE 131.   *Chief Constituent Glycerides of Bovine Milk Fats (per cent. mol.)*

	COW[35] ENGLISH	COW[37] INDIAN	BUFFALO[37] INDIAN
Chief glyceride types :			
1 Palmitic, 2 lower acyl groups	6–7	14	14
1 Palmitic, 1 lower acyl, 1 stearic	9	13	17
1 Palmitic, 1 lower acyl, 1 oleic	30–22	12	16
1 Palmitic, 1 stearic, 1 oleic	8–17	10	10
1 Palmitic, 2 oleic	17–4	4	4
1 Oleic, 1 Stearic, 1 lower acyl	12–6	5	5
2 Oleic, 1 lower acyl	0–10	6	6
Per cent. of total fat:	82–75	64	72

It is evident that in general pattern the glycerides of all three bovine milk fats have much in common. No simple triglycerides have been detected in any of them, and in the more rigorous separation of the Indian milk fats no evidence of the presence of triunsaturated glycerides was obtained. The proportions of

TABLE 132. *Component Acid and Component Glyceride Categories of Bovine Milk Fats (per cent. mol.)*

	COW[35] ENGLISH	COW[37] INDIAN	BUFFALO[37] INDIAN
Component acid categories :			
C_4–C_{12} (saturated)	18·8	21·4	21·2
Myristic	8·6	10·3	11·1
Palmitic	21·1	26·5	27·5
Stearic (+ Arachidic)	10·6	10·7	12·5
Monoethenoid C_{10}–C_{16}	4·1	5·1	2·7
Oleic	31·4	23·9	22·9
Polyethenoid C_{18}, C_{20}, C_{22}	5·4	2·1	2·1
Component glyceride categories :			
(a) Trisaturated	19	35	40
Disaturated mono-unsaturated	56–59	36	38
Monosaturated di-unsaturated	25–15	29	22
Triunsaturated	0–7	0	0
(b) Containing 2 palmitic groups	5	8	6
Containing 1 palmitic group	65	64	70
Containing 0 palmitic group	30	28	24
(c) Containing 2 oleic groups	17	10	10
Containing 1 oleic group	64	52	49
Containing 0 oleic group	19	38	41
(d) Containing 2 C_4–C_{14} (saturated) groups	11–17	21	22
Containing 1 C_4–C_{14} (saturated) group	52–46	52	52
Containing 0 C_4–C_{14} (saturated) group	37	27	26

fully saturated glycerides are typically large in relation to the total contents of saturated acids present in these fats. The similarity in glyceride structure is especially well marked in the distribution of palmitic groups in the glyceride molecules. The circumstance that there is an equally marked parallelism between the proportions and distribution of palmitic acid in the milk and depot fats of a range of mammals is still more interesting. The data (still very fragmentary) available in this respect are shown in Table 133.

TABLE 133. *Distribution of Palmitic Acid in Animal Milk and Depot Fats*

	PALMITIC ACID IN TOTAL ACIDS (PER CENT. MOL.)		DISTRIBUTION IN GLYCERIDES			
			MONOPALMITO-		DIPALMITO-	
ANIMAL	MILK FAT	DEPOT FAT	MILK FAT	DEPOT FAT	MILK FAT	DEPOT FAT
Pig	28	30	—	75–80	—	7–13
Human	23	28	60	—	6	—
Sheep	22	27–30	—	75	—	9–16
Cow (English)	23–24	27–30	65	70	5	13
Cow (Indian)	28	31–33	64	—	8	—
Buffalo (Indian)	27	31	70	—	6	—

The palmitic acid content of the milk fat of any of the animals in Table 133 is very similar to (but a few units per cent. less than) that of the depot fat of the same animal, and it appears that its distribution either as mono-palmito- or as dipalmito-glycerides in both milk and body fats is broadly similar. In this tendency towards constant proportions, palmitic acid (which is one of the two acids present in greatest proportions in milk fats – and is occasionally the major component acid) stands in marked contrast to all the other saturated acids in milk fats. As pointed out in Chapter V (p. 411) and as will be discussed later in Chapter VIII (p. 546–550), the clearly defined and relatively constant palmitic acid pattern in both milk and depot glycerides of the mammals reinforces the view that both classes of fats are produced in the animal from precursor glycerides which are primarily of a mainly unsaturated nature, and in which palmitodioleins or some related palmitodiunsaturated glycerides form the predominating component. In stearic-rich depot fats the glyceride structure is explicable as a result of bio-hydrogenation of some of the oleo- or octadecadieno-groups in the presumed precursor glycerides. In milk fats which contain significant amounts of butyric and other lower saturated fatty acid groups, together with minor amounts of C_{10} to C_{16} monoethenoid acids with unsaturation in the same position (relative to the carboxyl group) as in oleic acid, the related glyceride pattern is similarly explicable[38] as the result of replacement of oleo-groups (and possibly to a less extent of palmito-groups) in the presumed precursor glycerides by lower fatty acids synthesised *in situ* in the mammary gland together with, to a lesser degree, conversion of oleo-groups in the precursor glycerides to shorter chain groups, as indicated by the occurrence of traces of the -9-enoic C_{10} to C_{16} acids in those milk fats in which the short-chain saturated acids also appear in some quantity (i.e., milk fats of the ruminants).

Study of cow milk fat glycerides by selective enzyme hydrolysis has been undertaken by two groups of investigators. Patton, Evans and McCarthy[39a] examined the milk fats from cows before and after 7 days of fasting. At the 2-glyceryl position there was relatively small concentration of palmitic acid in normal milk fat, but considerable concentration in the milk fat of fasted cows. Some concentration of saturated C_{10}, C_{12} and C_{14} acids and of tetra- and hexa-decenoic acids at the 2-position was also observed, stearic and oleic acids being correspondingly lower than in the 1- and 3-positions.

Ast and Vander Wal[39b] made a similar study of two specimens of cow milk fat, and Table 134 gives a general summary of their analytical results, which are, on the whole, similar to those of Patton *et al.*,[39a] but quantitatively the two

TABLE 134. *Acids Combined at 1- and 3-, and at 2-positions in Cow Milk Fats (Ast and Vander Wal[39b])*

	SPECIMEN I			SPECIMEN II		
	Whole fat	At 1- and 3-	At 2-	Whole fat	At 1- and 3-	At 2-
Component acids (per cent wt.):						
Saturated C_4–C_{12}	9·2	10·2	7·1	10·0	9·3	11·2
Myristic*	13·7	11·1	18·9	13·3	10·9	18·2
Palmitic	26·6	25·4	28·9	32·2	28·3	40·0
Stearic	13·1	14·9	9·6	12·5	14·8	7·8
Hexadecenoic	2·6	2·0	3·8	3·9	3·3	5·2
Oleic	29·3	31·9	24·1	25·2	30·1	15·4
Octadecadienoic	2·5	2·1	3·3	1·6	1·6	1·4
Octadecatrienoic	2·3	2·6	1·8	1·0	0·9	1·1
Total saturated	62·6	61·6	64·6	67·8	63·7	77·2
Total unsaturated	36·7	38·6	33·1	32·3	36·3	23·1

* Including fractional amounts of isomeric saturated C_{14} and C_{15}, and tetradecenoic acid.

specimens differ in some instances. Thus predominance of palmitic groups, and converse diminution of stearic and oleic groups in the 2-glyceryl positions is very marked in specimen II. Ast and Vander Wal[39b] point out that, considered in two groups, saturated and unsaturated, the glycerides appear to be patterned on a random basis, whereas consideration of the individual acids shows that they are not distributed at random, but to a large extent selectively at the respective 1,3- and 2-glyceryl positions.

These two attempts to utilise selective enzyme hydrolysis in the study of milk fat glycerides suggest that further investigations with this procedure will give fruitful results.

Beveridge et al.[39c] (1963), employing gas-liquid chromatography on butter fat glycerides, have also concluded that the triglycerides are not assembled on a random basis.

Human milk fat. A study of the component glycerides of human milk fat was published in 1944 by Hilditch and Meara.[30b] The fat was separated into four fractions after systematic crystallisation from acetone at temperatures varying between $-25°$ and $0°$; the proportions and component acids of the four fractions are shown in Table 135, together with the deduced glyceride composition of the human milk fat.

TABLE 135.   *Component Glycerides of Human Milk Fat*

Fractions (from acetone):	A	B	C	D	(Whole fat)
Glycerides (per cent. wt.)	23·7	18·7	21·3	36·3	100·0
Glycerides (per cent. mol.)	24·0	19·0	21·3	35·7	100·0
Iodine value	26·4	36·6	57·4	95·9	60·1
Component acids (per cent. mol.):					
Decanoic	1·7	0·9	1·4	3·4	2·1
Lauric	6·6	7·9	6·7	9·0	7·7
Myristic	11·3	11·5	10·5	5·3	9·0
Palmitic	39·8	34·2	23·6	7·0	23·6
Stearic	14·0	9·5	5·1	0·5	6·5
Arachidic	2·0	0·9	1·0	—	0·9
Decenoic	—	—	Trace	0·1	—
Dodecenoic	0·1	0·1	0·7	0·3	0·3
Tetradecenoic	0·1	0·8	0·7	1·3	0·8
Hexadecenoic	4·0	2·6	4·4	8·3	5·4
Oleic	16·4	26·4	36·2	46·4	33·2
Octadecadienoic	1·1	2·7	7·0	13·8	7·1
Unsaturated C_{20-22}	2·9	2·5	2·7	4·6	3·4

Fully saturated glycerides were absent from fractions C and D, but present as follows in fractions A and B:

A: 32·4 per cent. (mol.); component acids decanoic 1·5, lauric 13·3, myristic 22·8, palmitic 38·0, stearic 20·8, and arachidic 3·6 per cent. (mol.).

B: 7·2 per cent. (mol.); (taken as 50 per cent. palmitic, 25 per cent. each of lauric and myristic acids).

Probable Component Glycerides (Per Cent. Mol.)

Fully saturated (9 per cent.):		Mono-unsaturated (40 per cent.):	
Di-C_{10}–C_{14}-monopalmitin	2	Mono-unsatd.-C_{10}–C_{14}-palmitin	20
Mono-C_{10}–C_{14}-dipalmitin	2	Mono-unsatd.-C_{10}–C_{14}-stearin	2
Mono-C_{10}–C_{14}-palmitostearin	5	Mono-unsatd.-dipalmitin	4
		Mono-unsatd.-palmitostearin	14
Di-unsaturated (43 per cent.):			
Mono-C_{10}–C_{14}-di-unsatd.	24	**Tri-unsaturated (8 per cent.):**	
Palmitodi-unsatd.	19	Probably mainly linoleodioleins	8

Owing to the less complex mixture of component acids in human milk fat, the component glyceride data are more definite in nature than in the bovine milk fats discussed above. About half of the human milk fat consisted of glycerides in which at least two unsaturated acyl groups were present. In the di-unsaturated glycerides, about 24 per cent. (of the whole fat) contained, as saturated acyl group, myristic, lauric or decanoic acid, and about 19 per cent., palmitic acid. In addition, about 8 per cent. of the fat consisted of tri-unsaturated glycerides. Since there was 33 per cent. of oleic and 17 per cent. of minor unsaturated acids in the total fatty acids, it may be significant that there is just sufficient of the latter to account for these di- and tri-unsaturated glycerides being almost wholly constituted as mono-oleo-monosaturated glycerides and dioleo-glycerides respectively (the remaining acyl group in each class being contributed by one of the minor unsaturated acids – preponderantly linoleic). This is supported also by the distribution of linoleic acid in the different glyceride fractions revealed in Table 135. If this be the case, oleic acid is almost the only unsaturated component of the mono-unsaturated-disaturated glycerides. Except for the two di-unsaturated groups already mentioned, the only major component glycerides of the fat are in fact 20 per cent. of mono-C_{10}–C_{14}-oleopalmitins and 14 per cent. of oleopalmito-stearins.

The amount of fully saturated glycerides (9 per cent.), although less than in cow milk fats, is much greater than the negligible amount which is found in fats containing about 50 per cent. each of saturated and unsaturated acids, when these follow the "even distribution" rule.

The above features are fundamentally similar to those subsisting in cow milk fats, where the range of lower saturated acids extends as far as butyric acid. This general similarity between the two milk fats is illustrated in Table 136, which gives a summary of the total component acids of each fat, together with the proportions of glycerides containing (a) one lower saturated group, (b) two lower saturated groups, (c) one palmitic and (d) two palmitic groups (i) in the human milk fat and (ii) in cow milk fats. Table 136 shows close similarity in the values for these respective groups of glycerides, having regard to the varying proportions in the fats as a whole of the acids concerned.

TABLE 136. *Comparative Glyceride Structure of Human and Cow Milk Fats*

	HUMAN[30b]	COW[35] ENGLISH	COW[37] INDIAN
Component acids (per cent mol.):			
C_{14} and lower (saturated)	18·8	27·4	31·7
Palmitic	23·6	21·1	26·5
Stearic (+ arachidic)	7·4	10·6	10·7
C_{16} and lower (monoethenoid)	6·5	4·1	5·1
Oleic	33·2	31·4	23·9
Octadecadienoic	7·1	4·9	1·1
Unsaturated C_{20-22}	3·4	0·5	1·0
Component glyceride groups (per cent. mol.):			
(a) 1 C_{14} (or lower) saturated group	53	*ca.* 50	52
(b) 2 C_{14} (or lower) saturated groups	2	*ca.* 15	21
(c) 1 palmitic group	60	65	64
(d) 2 palmitic groups	6	5	8

The palmitic glycerides are elaborated on similar lines in human and in cow milk fats, about 90 per cent. of the total palmitic acid in each case being present as monopalmito-glycerides. The lower saturated acids also occur predominantly in combination with two acyl groups of different character (palmitic, oleic, etc.), the proportion of glycerides containing two of these lower saturated groups being greater, however, in cow milk fat (in which the lower acids form about 30 per cent. of the total acids, as against 19 per cent. in the human milk fat).

These general resemblances in the glyceride patterns of human and cow milk fats suggest that both are the result of similar biosynthetic processes. The lower saturated acids synthesised in the mammary glands of ruminants are, however, absent from human milk fat, lauric acid (except for very small amounts of decanoic acid) being the saturated acid of lowest molecular weight.

It is also interesting, in this connection, to compare the component acids of human milk fat with those of a female human depot fat as given by Cramer and Brown[40]: lauric 0·1, myristic 2·7, palmitic 24·0, stearic 8·4, tetradecenoic 0·2, hexadecenoic 5·0, oleic 46·9, octadecadienoic (mainly linoleic) 10·2 and unsaturated C_{20-22} acids 2·5 per cent. (wt.). The resemblance to human milk fat in the palmitic acid content of the body fat is evident, and in both, linoleic acid contributes much of the octadecadienoic acids. The difference in the proportions of oleic acid in the two fats is roughly balanced by the increased proportions of C_{14}, C_{12} and C_{10} acids in the milk fat; the quantitatively similar difference in linoleic acid content may arouse speculation as to how far linoleo-glycerides, as well as oleo-glycerides, may be precursors of the characteristic lower acyl-containing glycerides of milk fats (cf. pp. 413–415).

It is not unnatural, in view of the large number of saturated acyl components present in milk fats, that it has so far not been possible to do more than deal with the component glycerides on general, instead of individual, lines. It can nevertheless at least be claimed that their investigation by the methods discussed has served to demonstrate their general composition and their close structural relationships to the corresponding depot fats. It can only be hoped that further research will in time permit at all events some of the more abundant individual components of this important group of natural fats to be more accurately defined.

References to Chapter VII

1. B. Suzuki and Y. Masuda, *Proc. Imp. Acad. Tokyo*, 1927, 3, 531; 1928, **4**, 165; 1931, **7**, 9; B. Suzuki, *ibid.*, 1929, **5**, 265; 1931, **7**, 230.
2. G. Greitemann, *Chem. Umschau*, 1925, **32**, 226.
3. (a) D. A. Harper and T. P. Hilditch, *J. Soc. Chem. Ind.*, 1937, **56**, 322т; (b) T. P. Hilditch and J. T. Terleski, *ibid.*, 1937, **56**, 315т.
4. T. P. Hilditch and L. Maddison, (a) *J. Soc. Chem. Ind.*, 1942, **61**, 169; (b) *ibid.*, 1948, **67**, 253.
5. O. B. Bjarnason and M. L. Meara, *J. Soc. Chem. Ind.*, 1944, **63**, 61.
6. T. P. Hilditch and S. P. Pathak, *J. Soc. Chem. Ind.*, 1947, **66**, 421.
7. A. Cardin, Thesis, University of Liverpool, 1952 (pp. 53–121).
8. W. H. Baldwin and L. E. Parks, *Oil and Soap*, 1943, **20**, 101.
9. T. P. Hilditch and J. A. Lovern, *J. Soc. Chem. Ind.*, 1929, **48**, 359т.

10. J. A. Lovern, *Biochem. J.*, 1934, **28**, 394.
11. T. P. Hilditch and K. S. Murti, *J. Soc. Chem. Ind.*, 1939, **58**, 351.
12. T. G. Green and T. P. Hilditch, *Biochem. J.*, 1938, **32**, 681.
13. (*a*) F. H. Mattson and E. S. Lutton, *J. Biol. Chem.*, 1958, **233**, 868; (*b*) M. H. Coleman, *J. Amer. Oil Chem. Soc.*, 1961, **38**, 685; (*c*) C. B. Barrett, M. S. J. Dallas and F. B. Padley, *ibid.*, 1963, **40**, 580.
14. T. P. Hilditch and W. J. Stainsby, *Biochem. J.*, 1935, **29**, 599.
15. S. S. Gupta and T. P. Hilditch, *Biochem. J.*, 1951, **48**, 137.
16. T. P. Hilditch and I. C. Sime, *Biochem. J.*, 1942, **36**, 98.
17. J. S. Cama, Thesis, University of Liverpool, 1952 (pp. 80–178).
18. S. S. Gupta, T. P. Hilditch and M. L. Meara, *J. Chem. Soc.*, 1950, 3145.
19. S. P. Pathak and C. V. Agarwal, *J. Sci. Food Agric.*, 1952, **3**, 136.
20. A. Banks and T. P. Hilditch, (*a*) *Biochem. J.*, 1932, **26**, 298; (*b*) *ibid.*, 1931, **25**, 1168; (*c*) T. P. Hilditch and W. J. Stainsby, *ibid.*, 1935, **29**, 90; (*d*) R. Bhattacharya and T. P. Hilditch, *ibid.*, 1931, **25**, 1954.
21. (*a*) S. B. Sharples, *Analyst*, 1888, **13**, 70; W. F. K. Stock, *Analyst*, 1894, **19**, 2; (*b*) E. Polenske, *Arb. Kais. Ges.-A.*, 1907, **26**, 445; 1908, **29**, 272; (*c*) A. Börner, *Z. Unters. Nahr. Genussm.*, 1913, **26**, 559; 1914, **27**, 153.
22. (*a*) M. L. Meara, *J. Chem. Soc.*, 1945, 23; (*b*) O. T. Quimby, R. L. Wille and E. S. Lutton, *J. Amer. Oil. Chem. Soc.*, 1953, **30**, 186.
23. T. P. Hilditch and H. E. Longenecker, *Biochem. J.*, 1937, **31**, 1805.
24. G. Collin, T. P. Hilditch and C. H. Lea, *J. Soc. Chem. Ind.*, 1928, **48**, 46т.
25. D. R. Dhingra and D. N. Sharma, *J. Soc. Chem. Ind.*, 1938, **57**, 369.
26. K. T. Achaya and B. N. Banerjee, *Biochem. J.*, 1946, **40**, 664.
27. T. P. Hilditch, (*a*) with S. Paul, *Biochem. J.*, 1938, **32**, 1775; (*b*) with W. H. Pedelty, *ibid.*, 1940, **34**, 971; (*c*) with K. S. Murti, *ibid.*, 1940, **34**, 1301; (*d*) with Y. A. H. Zaky, *ibid.*, 1941, **35**, 940; (*e*) with S. K. Shrivastava, *J. Soc. Chem. Ind.*, 1948, **67**, 139; (*f*) with S. K. Shrivastava, *J. Amer. Oil Chem. Soc.*, 1949, **26**, 1; (*g*) with G. A. Garton and M. L. Meara, *Biochem. J.*, 1952, **50**, 517.
28. R. W. Riemenschneider, F. E. Luddy, M. L. Swain and W. C. Ault, *J. Amer. Oil Chem. Soc.*, 1946, **23**, 276.
29. R. Reiser and H. G. R. Reddy, *J. Amer. Oil Chem. Soc.*, 1959, **36**, 97.
30. T. P. Hilditch and M. L. Meara (*a*) *J. Soc. Chem. Ind.*, 1942, **61**, 117; (*b*) *Biochem. J.*, 1944, **38**, 437.
31. C. Amberger, *Z. Unters. Nahr. Genussm.*, 1913, **26**, 65; 1918, **35**, 313.
32. P. Arup, *Analyst*, 1928, **53**, 641.
33. T. P. Hilditch, (*a*) with (Miss) E. E. Jones, *Analyst*, 1929, **54**, 75; (*b*) with J. J. Sleightholme, *Biochem. J.*, 1930, **24**, 1098; 1931, **25**, 507; (*c*) with R. Bhattacharya, *Analyst*, 1931, **56**, 161; (*d*) with H. M. Thompson, *Biochem. J.*, 1936, **30**, 677.
34. D. R. Dhingra, *Biochem. J.*, 1933, **27**, 851; 1934, **28**, 73.
35. T. P. Hilditch and S. Paul, *J. Soc. Chem. Ind.*, 1940, **59**, 138.
36. E. L. Jack and J. L. Henderson, *J. Dairy Sci.*, 1945, **28**, 65; *J. Biol. Chem.*, 1946, **162**, 119.
37. K. T. Achaya and T. P. Hilditch, *Proc. Roy. Soc.*, 1950, **B**, **137**, 187.
38. S. Hoflund and J. Holmberg, *Nordiska Veterinärmötet*, 1951, **6**, 321; T. P. Hilditch, *Biochem. Soc. Symposia*, 1952, No. **9**, 63.
39. (*a*) S. Patton, L. Evans and R. D. McCarthy, *J. Dairy Sci.*, 1960, **43**, 95, 1196; (*b*) H. J. Ast and R. J. Vander Wal, *J. Amer. Oil Chem. Soc.*, 1961, **38**, 67; (*c*) A. Kuksis, M. J. McCarthy and J. M. R. Beveridge, *Canad. J. Biochem. Physiol.*, 1962, **40**, 1693; *J. Amer. Oil Chem. Soc.*, 1963, **40**, 530.
40. D. L. Cramer and J. B. Brown, *J. Biol. Chem.*, 1943, **151**, 427.

CHAPTER VIII

Some Aspects of the Biosynthesis of Fats

The functions of fats in the living organism, and their importance in animal nutrition, have resulted in much investigation of problems such as their synthesis in the plant or animal, their assimilation and digestion in the animal system, the mechanism by which reserve fats may be utilised, and so on. The biochemistry of fats, indeed, covers a very wide field, the adequate description of which requires a complete volume in itself. Such treatment, developed from the biochemical standpoint, has been given in several well-known monographs, some of which are referred to in the bibliography[1] attached to this chapter. It is thus superfluous (as well as impossible for reasons of space) to attempt to include in the present book a comprehensive survey of the biochemistry of natural fats. Moreover, as stressed at the outset (Chapter I, p. 1) the object of this volume is to present as complete a statement as possible of the existing knowledge of the chemical constitution of natural fatty compounds, especially the glycerides. These materials are the end-products of a number of complex biochemical processes, and it is in general difficult to interpret, from the chemical structure of end-products, the sequence of reactions which may have given rise to them. Nevertheless it seems certain that consideration of a number of the characteristic features concerning the component acids or glycerides found in the various groups of the vegetable and animal kingdoms can on occasion serve as a guide in assessing the soundness of hypotheses based upon more definitely biochemical investigations.

The discussion of fat biosynthesis in this chapter is strictly limited to considerations of the nature suggested. Its object is to indicate how far, in the authors' opinion, the existing data on the composition of glycerides may have a useful bearing upon the study of their synthesis or assimilation by the living organism. It will therefore be restricted to the following general topics:

(i) Biosynthesis of glycerides (*a*) in plants, (*b*) in animals;
(ii) Possible mechanisms of the conversion of carbohydrates into fats;
(iii) Assimilation of preformed (ingested) fats by animals;
(iv) Fatty acids essential to growth or health.

Biochemists will, it is believed, share the view that, in spite of the vast amount of careful experimental work which has been carried out, our knowledge of the development and utilisation of fats *in vivo* is still in many respects scanty, and often very uncertain. The problems are extremely difficult to study experimentally; artificially designed tests, such as specific diets to animals, require the most careful interpretation in order to avoid erroneous conclusions; and the isolation of intermediate metabolic products (which is an enormous aid in such studies) has rarely, if ever, been attained in connection with the synthesis of fats in the living organism. It is perhaps a consequence of the latter fact that several hypotheses have been put forward, attractive in themselves and plausibly accounting for some of the known characteristics of fats, but involving reactions or the production of intermediate products for which there appears to be, in some cases, no valid experimental evidence whatever. Moreover, no theory yet put forward takes any account of those specific features which have been shown by constitutive investigations to be outstanding characteristics of particular groups of natural fats.

The Biosynthesis of Fats in Plants

Any satisfactory explanation of the mechanism of fat-synthesis in the living plant must take into consideration the following, amongst other, definitely known facts:

(a) According to family, genus, or even species, the fatty acids combined in any one plant fat are specific in qualitative, and frequently in quantitative composition.

(b) Speaking generally, there can be no doubt that the most abundant and widely distributed acid in all plant fats is

oleic (octadec-9-enoic) acid, $CH_3 . [CH_2]_7 . CH:CH . [CH_2]_7 . CO_2H$;

with this are closely associated:

linoleic (octadeca-9,12-dienoic) acid,
$$CH_3 . [CH_2]_4 . CH:CH . CH_2 . CH:CH . [CH_2]_7 . CO_2H,$$

and the saturated

palmitic acid, $CH_3 . [CH_2]_{14} . CO_2H$,

all of which are found in practically all fats in amounts varying from very small to comparatively large (e.g. 30 or 40 per cent. or more of the total acids).

Oleic and linoleic acids together probably account for about 80 per cent. or more of the total production of fatty acids in vegetable seed fats, whilst palmitic acid probably amounts to less than 10 per cent. of the total fatty acids produced in the world's seed fats. All other component fatty acids found in seed fats, unsaturated or saturated, together make up, therefore, little more than 10 per cent. of the whole of the seed fats produced annually in the world.

Many of these other unsaturated fatty acids (e.g. linolenic, ricinoleic, erucic, elæostearic, etc.) reproduce in their molecular structure either the one or the other half of the molecule of oleic acid, and thus have close structural resemblance to the latter acid. In the saturated acid series, members other than palmitic (the most abundant) of course belong to the same homologous series $C_nH_{2n}O_2$ where n (in the vegetable kingdom) may be 8, 10, 12, 14, 18, 20, 22, or 24.

Any complete theory of plant fat synthesis must account for the invariable appearance and overall predominance of oleic and linoleic acids, the invariable presence of palmitic acid, and for the occasional development in specific families

529

or species of other acids, saturated or unsaturated, and also for the frequent constitutive resemblances between the rarer unsaturated acids and oleic acid.

(c) The fats in all parts of all plants except the seed (endosperm or embryo) contain, almost always, only palmitic, oleic, and linoleic (linolenic) acids as major components; many seed fats also contain only the same three or four major component acids, but others (according to their families) contain specific major component acids (e.g. lauric, stearic, erucic, etc.) in large proportions.

(d) Except in the Palmæ, and perhaps one or two other families, it is rare, in seed fats, to find more than two or three saturated and two unsaturated acids as major components (cf. Tables 59–69 in Chapter IV). Whilst there are comparatively few families whose seed fats contain unsaturated acids other than those of the C_{18} series, the saturated acids which are sometimes present in quantity range from lauric (C_{12}) to lignoceric (C_{24}), but, as stated, only two or three are usually present in any one instance. The range of molecular magnitude of the seed fat saturated acids is thus very wide, and demands considerable specificity in the synthetic mechanism whereby the seed fats are built up in different families.

(e) Finally, the mode of union of fatty acids into mixed glycerides must be considered, and it must be remembered that in seed fats and also, to a large extent, in fruit-flesh fats the prevailing tendency is markedly in the direction of producing a mixture of triglycerides in which oleic (and sometimes linoleic) acid is selectively attached at the central or 2-position in the triglyceride molecules, whilst all saturated acids and other unsaturated acids, and any excess of oleic and linoleic acids beyond that requisite for combination at the 2-positions, are attached indiscriminately (i.e., at random) at the 1- and 3-positions of the triglycerides.

In the growing parts of plants, especially the leaves, it appears (cf. Chapter IV, p. 177) that glycerides and plant phosphatides are present in the cytoplasm in about equal, but small, proportions.* The origin and functions of the leaf, etc., glycerides are at present uncertain (although if, as discussed below, fruit fats are derived from carbohydrates, it is likely that the same process may take place in the growing plant). It has, however, been believed for many years that the reserve fat stored in seeds or in the flesh of fruits is developed *in situ* and not

---

* Many of the older observations, and unfortunately not a few of the more recent ones, appear to be based merely upon the saponification and iodine values, or even upon the weight alone, of the material extracted by ether from leaves, immature fruit, etc. In all cases but those of fully ripe seeds (and sometimes even there), ether also removes, of course, non-fatty matter, often in considerable amount; the value of the data, in the absence of further purification of the ether-soluble matter or at least of removal of non-fatty matter from the fatty acids obtained after hydrolysis, is therefore doubtful in many cases. To give trustworthy results, phosphatides should first be separated from the crude glycerides, and the fatty acids from the latter should be further purified from "unsaponifiable matter" before their amount and analytical values are recorded.

The employment of chromatographic absorption techniques to segregate glycerides from phosphatides and other materials present in the lipid fractions isolated, together with the use of gas–liquid chromatography for determination of component fatty acids, now makes the accurate study of very small specimens of plant lipids a relatively simple matter.

translocated from the leaf or stem. Thus, de Luca[2a] showed (1861) that olives could make fat after they were separated from the tree, and Pfeffer[2b] (1872) found that pæony seeds, when detached from the plant at an immature stage when they contained no fat, developed a certain amount of fat on being kept.

A more recent contribution to this subject by Burr and Miller[3] (1938), which includes a full review of the earlier literature, describes a study of the respiratory quotients* of the castor bean during seed development and ripening, the results of which show that much fat is synthesised within the castor bean fruit; although a slow translocation of some fat from the leaf or other tissues is not excluded by the experiments of these workers, they clearly show that most of the seed fat is synthesised within the fruit itself.

It will be recalled that detailed figures for component acids, obtained by the modern methods, have demonstrated some similarity between leaf and fruit-coat fats, but have also established in very many instances the presence in seed fats of fatty acids which are absent from either the fruit-coat or leaf fats of the plants concerned.

The important question of the rapid and prominent development of fat in the ripening fruit has been the subject of many investigations, as a result of which it is usually accepted at present that there is adequate ground for believing that the fat is formed from carbohydrate.

We may refer, in the first place, to the morphological studies of Uhlmann[4] (1902) on the development of fat in fruits of various species. He found that in the earliest stages only starch and no fat was present; later the plasma commenced to contain fat in an extremely dispersed condition, no oil droplets being visible in the emulsion under the highest available magnification. As ripening proceeded, the starch granules became smaller and appeared to dissolve in the "oil-plasma"; some evidence of formation of sugar was also observed in most cases. Finally, as maturity approached, the oil commenced to separate from the plasma as a discontinuous phase in minute droplets, which ultimately became of considerable size and occupied the greater part of the cell under observation. This final, relatively rapid development of fatty oil occurred in the later phases of ripening.

On the chemical side, du Sablon[5a] (1896) and Valée[5b] (1903) studied the relative proportions of starch, cane-sugar, glucose, and fat present in almonds

* The "respiratory quotient", or volume ratio of the carbon dioxide produced to the oxygen consumed, is to some extent a guide to the nature of the metabolic action. If carbohydrates are being completely oxidised, e.g.

$$C_6H_{12}O_6 + 6O_2 = 6CO_2 + 6H_2O$$

the respiratory quotient is $1:1$, whereas obviously for the complete oxidation of the long acyl chains of fats a greater proportion of oxygen would be required, so that the ratio of carbon dioxide formed to oxygen used would be less than unity. (For fats, it is about $0.7:1$.)

On the other hand, if a more highly oxygenated substance is being converted into material of lower oxygen content, any oxygen intake will be less than the carbon dioxide output, and a respiratory quotient of more than $1:1$ is observed. Leathes and Raper[1] state that "when satisfactory proof exists that carbohydrates are converted into fat . . . it is reasonable to assume that, when the R.Q. is higher than 1.0, then this reaction is the main one causing the high quotient. The reverse proposition, that when the quotient is lower than 0.7 fat is being converted into carbohydrate, cannot be so easily accepted."

and walnuts at various stages of ripening and found that general decrease in carbohydrate content accompanied the increase in fatty content. It may be pointed out that diminution in percentage content is not sufficient to prove the point, since the very great increase in the total weight of the seed during ripening might counterbalance a fall in percentage; the total amount of carbohydrate present at maturity might remain constant or even increase in spite of a drop in its percentage proportion. This does not appear likely to have occurred in du Sablon's results, however, since the glucose, at least, disappeared completely in both cases. Ivanov[6a] in 1912 obtained similar data for a number of other seeds, and there is thus good reason to associate the production of fats with transformation of carbohydrates. Some of du Sablon's figures are recorded below:

Percentage contents of Carbohydrates and Fat in Almonds during ripening

	JUNE 9	JULY 4	AUGUST 1	SEPTEMBER 1	OCTOBER 4
Glucose per cent.	6·0	4·2	0	0	0
Sucrose per cent.	6·7	4·9	2·8	2·6	2·5
Starch per cent.	21·6	14·1	6·2	5·4	5·3
Fat per cent.	2·0	10·0	37·0	44·0	46·0

Percentage contents of Carbohydrates and Fat in Walnuts during ripening

	JULY 6	AUGUST 1	AUGUST 15	SEPTEMBER 1	OCTOBER 4
Glucose per cent.	7·6	2·4	0	0	0
Sucrose per cent.	0	0·5	0·6	0·8	1·6
Fat per cent.	3·0	16·0	49·0	52·0	62·0

Gerber[7] observed that not only carbohydrate, but also protein, falls in concentration as oil is produced, as will be seen from the following figures:

	OLIVE	
	AUGUST 30	SEPTEMBER 30
Protein per cent.	14·6	4·2
Fat per cent.	29·2	62·3

Seeds usually contain protein as well as fat, and it seems, perhaps, at first sight equally reasonable to postulate proteins or carbohydrates as possible progenitors of fats. Since proteins can, in certain conditions, be converted into carbohydrates, conversion of proteins into fats may take place *via* the intermediate stage of carbohydrate. If so, it becomes rather an academic question as to whether protein or carbohydrate is the fat-precursor.

A number of investigators have at different times studied the respiratory quotient, CO_2/O_2, of ripening oil fruits. Godlewski[8] (1882) observed R.Q. values of 1·18–1·52 during ripening of poppy seeds and castor beans, and Gerber[7] (1897) found the R.Q. of olive fruits to rise to 1·51 in the period in which oil is being rapidly formed, although prior to this stage, and also after maturity, the R.Q. was less than 1·0.

Somewhat more definite knowledge has been gathered as to the later stages of fat-synthesis in the case of certain oil-bearing seeds. In 1912 Ivanov[6a] stated that rape, hemp, poppy, and flax seeds in the early stages of development, contain oils in which considerable amounts of free fatty acids are present and that, in linseed oil (but not in the other three oils), the characteristic high iodine value is only attained in the final stages of ripening.

A very complete examination of linseed oil was carried out by Eyre and Fisher[9a] (1915), reported more fully by Eyre[9b] (1931) and by Barker [9c] (1932). Synthesis of the oil began almost immediately after flowering and proceeded comparatively slowly during the first eleven days. At the end of that time a rapid accumulation of oil set in, amounting to about 3 per cent. per day for some ten days, when, about 21 days from flowering time, the maximum oil content (about 36 per cent.) was reached. Beyond this point no appreciable increase in oil content occurred, but the iodine value of the oil increased, in the following 15–20 days, from about 130 to its normal value of 180–185.

The initial very slow production of seed fat, followed by a briefer period of very rapid fat production, has been observed in a number of other seeds, e.g., cacao beans (Humphries,[10a] 1943), niger seeds (Sahasrabuddhe,[10b] 1932), and tung fruits (Sell et al.,[10c] 1948). Increases of unsaturation (iodine value) during the later stages of ripening were noted in the oils of niger seed,[10b] white lupins[11a] (1941), and soya beans[11b] (1933), but not in sunflower seed (Bauer,[11c] 1934), where the iodine value of the oil was practically constant throughout the ripening period.

The development of the cotton seed has been investigated on similar general lines by American[12a] and Russian[12b] workers (1931), and more thoroughly by Grindley[13] (1950). In Grindley's work, for the first time, attention was paid to the *amounts* of sugar, oil, etc., in a given number (100) of seeds (bolls) at different stages as well as to the *percentages* of the various constituents present and, in addition, the *amounts* and *percentages* of saturated, oleic, and linoleic acids in the oils produced at each stage were determined (instead of mere records of iodine values). The quantities of fatty acids (in the glycerides), carbohydrate, cellulose, protein and lint in 100 cotton bolls at various stages up to 60 days after flowering are illustrated in Fig. 13 (p.535), which shows a general increase in all these components except carbohydrates, which pass through a maximum at about 40 days, and fatty oil, which only commences to appear in quantity after about 30 days and increases rapidly between 40 and 50 days. Numerical data for carbohydrates and fat are reproduced from Grindley's paper in Table 137 (p. 534).

Table 137 shows clearly that, whilst the *percentage* of carbohydrates in the developing cottonseed falls continuously from 31 days onwards, the actual *amount* in the seed continues to increase (albeit more slowly) up to about 40 days, after which it is being consumed more rapidly than it is being formed. Likewise, although the *percentages* of oleic and (to a slight extent) saturated acids tend to fall, and those of linoleic acid increase, during ripening, the *amounts* of the three acids in the seed glycerides all increase to a marked extent. Ivanov[6] and Eyre[9] concluded, from *percentage* data and iodine values of the fatty oils, that the seeming increase of more unsaturated components in the later stages meant that desaturation of less unsaturated acids (saturated or mono-ethenoid) must take place to a considerable extent. Consideration of the

533

TABLE 137. *Fats and Carbohydrates in ripening Cotton Seed*

(i) *Percentage compositions*

AGE OF SEEDS (DAYS)	CARBO-HYDRATE	TOTAL LIPIDS	COMPOSITION OF FATTY ACIDS:		
			SATURATED	OLEIC	LINOLEIC
21	75·7	2·2			
31	75·7	2·4	23·9	29·3	46·8
41	61·5	10·3	22·9	26·4	50·7
51	35·3	21·7	20·5	27·7	51·8
60	30·3	25·3	22·4	25·5	52·1

(ii) *Weights of components in 100 seeds (bolls)*

AGE OF SEEDS (DAYS)	CARBO-HYDRATE (GM.)	TOTAL LIPIDS (GM.)	INDIVIDUAL FATTY ACIDS (GM.):		
			SATURATED	OLEIC	LINOLEIC
21	25·1	0·7			
31	62·8	2·0	0·3	0·4	0·6
41	91·3	15·3	3·3	3·8	7·3
51	84·4	51·8	10·1	13·6	25·5
60	67·9	56·6	12·0	13·7	28·0

(iii) *Free fatty acids and unsaponifiable matter in total lipids*

AGE OF SEEDS (DAYS)	FREE FATTY ACIDS		UNSAPONIFIABLE MATTER	
	PER CENT. OF LIPIDS	WT. (GM.) IN 100 SEEDS	PER CENT. OF LIPIDS	WT. (GM.) IN 100 SEEDS
21	12·9	0·09	41·5	0·30
31	12·9	0·25	26·7	0·52
41	2·5	0·38	2·7	0·41
51	1·3	0·66	1·7	0·86
60	1·1	0·62	1·3	0·74

weights of each acid present in a given weight of seed shows that saturated, oleic, and linoleic acids each augment as ripening goes on; so that, as Chibnall[14] has pointed out, it is merely the interpretation of the data on a *percentage* basis which necessitates a desaturation hypothesis. Considered with reference to the *amounts* of fat per 100 seeds, it is seen that any increase in unsaturation is due to *further synthesis* of unsaturated acids, and there is no need to postulate that fatty acids already formed undergo any further change. In studies of this nature it is important to base conclusions upon a measure of the total amount of fat produced in a plant or animal; the percentage of a component in the dry seed has little significance except in its bearing upon the total weight of that component which has been synthesised.

Again, the proportions of free fatty acid and of unsaponifiable matter in the immature seeds are very high but rapidly diminish as the seeds ripen; but the actual weights present are consistently small in relation to the total weight of the seeds at each stage and in fact, the *amounts* of these minor components tend to augment slightly throughout. This may be thought to render unnecessary the conclusion that there is delay, in the earlier stages of ripening, in the conversion of initially synthesised free fatty acids into glycerides. On the other hand, as Terroine[15] has pointed out, it is not unlikely that the relatively high concentration of water in the seed cells at their earlier stages of development may be too great to permit of complete synthesis of fat at that period.

In 1954 the results of a study of fatty acid formation in soya beans (conducted on similar lines to that of Grindley[13] on cotton seeds) were published by Simmons and Quackenbush.[16] They dealt with soya beans (*var.* Lincoln) grown in Indiana in 1948 and 1949, and examined from 23 to 67 days after flowering. Continuous increases in the *amounts* of saturated, oleic, linoleic, and linolenic acids were observed, although the *percentage* of linolenic acid was highest (about 20 per cent.) at 24 days after flowering (6–7 per cent. in the mature

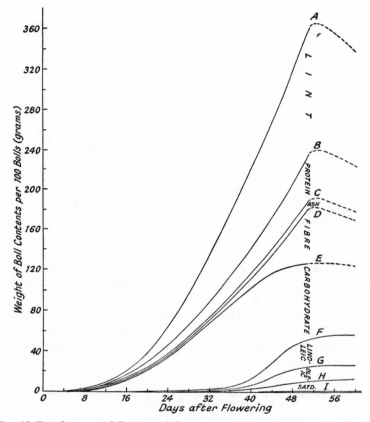

FIG. 13. Development of Cottonseed Components during Ripening (Grindley[13])

seeds). These authors state that they found no evidence for the dehydrogenation of saturated acids during the ripening of the beans.

In 1961 Sims *et al.*[17] examined the development at intervals of ten days of seeds grown at the Plant Breeding Research Institute, Ottawa in the years 1955–1958. Some of their results for linseed (*var.* Raja, grown in 1956) and for Indian safflower seeds (grown in 1957) are shown in Table 138 (p. 536); component fatty acids were determined from the iodine values and U.V. spectrophotometric data after alkali-isomerisation.

In both seeds oil production set in at about the tenth day after flowering and continued rapidly until maxima were reached at about 30 days (linseed) and

TABLE 138. *Development of Fat in ripening Linseed and Safflower Seed*
(Sims et al.[17])

	DAYS AFTER FLOWERING				
	10	20	30	40	50
LINSEED ("RAJA," 1956)					
100 seeds (wt., gm.)	1·00	0·99	0·91	0·79	
Oil content (per cent., dry wt.)	4·9	33·3	39·8	38·5	
Oil, iodine value	122·9	172·8	180·8	181·0	
Component acids (mgm. per 100 seeds):					
Oleic	3·6	31·9	40·9	60·7	
Linoleic	2·1	27·3	46·7	51·8	
Linolenic	2·2	60·9	110·3	118·4	
SAFFLOWER (INDIAN, 1957)					
100 seeds (wt., gm.)		4·80	4·77	4·48	4·42
Oil content (per cent., dry wt.)		15·0	20·2	21·9	22·1
Oil, iodine value		138·3	136·3	144·1	146·2
Component acids (mgm. per 100 seeds):					
Oleic		114·9	151·4	140·5	148·8
Linoleic		297·7	453·8	571·1	602·4
(Ratio linoleic/oleic		2·6	3·0	4·1	4·0)

40 days (safflower). All the unsaturated acids were produced at very similar rates throughout; in the linseed series the relative proportions of linolenic and linoleic acids were almost constant from the twentieth day onwards, but in safflower seeds the ratio of linoleic to oleic acid increased from *ca.* 3 : 1 at the thirtieth day to *ca.* 4 : 1 at the fortieth day, when apparent constancy was reached.

It will be noticed that the marked increase in unsaturation (found by Eyre[9]) after oil production in linseed reached its maximum is not confirmed by the results shown in Table 138.

Hopkins and Chisholm[18a] (1961) observed somewhat similar results to the safflower study (above) in the case of sunflower seeds. Their fatty acid analyses were effected by gas–liquid chromatography, but the results are expressed on a percentage basis only (Table 139).

TABLE 139. *Development of Fat in ripening Sunflower Seeds*
(Hopkins and Chisholm[18a])

	DAYS AFTER FLOWERING					
	10	17	24	31	45	52
Component acids (per cent. wt.):						
Palmitic	10·0	5·8	4·2	4·4	4·3	4·3
Stearic	2·8	1·5	1·3	1·6	1·5	1·2
Oleic	41·5	55·0	57·4	45·3	41·8	41·3
Linoleic	45·7	37·7	37·1	48·7	52·4	53·2
(Ratio linoleic/oleic	1·1	0·7	0·6	1·1	1·3	1·3)

Oil formation commenced about 10 days after flowering and continued steadily for the next six weeks. At first oleic acid was apparently produced more rapidly but after about four weeks linoleic acid became the major component.

The same authors[18b] made a similar study of the ripening seeds of *Asclepias syriaca*, the seed fat of which contains about equal proportions of oleic and octadec-11-enoic acids. Per 1000 seeds the total amount of C_{18} monoene acids increased slightly during the eleven weeks of ripening, but the weight of linoleic acid almost doubled between the 5th and 10th weeks. The *percentages* of the component acids (by G.L.C.) are shown in Table 140.

TABLE 140. *Development of Fat in ripening Seeds of* Asclepias syriaca
(Hopkins and Chisholm[18b])

| | WEEKS AFTER FLOWERING | | | | |
	5	7	8	9	10
Component acids *(per cent. wt.)*:					
Palmitic	6·3	5·1	4·6	4·8	4·7
Hexadecenoic	18·2	12·1	13·4	12·6	10·7
Hexadecadienoic	3·0	2·3	2·1	2·2	2·2
C_{18} monoene	34·6	31·9	31·3	31·5	29·1
Linoleic	36·8	47·6	47·6	47·9	52·3
(Ratio linoleic/C_{18} monoene	1·1	1·5	1·5	1·5	1·8)

This fat also contains hexadecenoic acid as a major component, and the possibility that this acid is the precursor of octadec-11-enoic acid, and oleic acid the precursor of linoleic acid is considered by the authors.

Kartha *et al.*[19a] (1959) made interesting examinations of the development of oil in ripening coconuts and areca nuts, in which the component acids of the mature seed fats consist largely of lauric and myristic acids (*cf.* Chapter IV, Table 69B, p. 341). They record that the iodine values of the immature fats (21·2 coconut and 103·0 areca) fell during ripening to final values of 5·2 (coconut) and 37·0 (areca), and that large amounts of lauric and myristic acids appeared only in the later stages of ripening. Thus the main biosynthetic process appears to be different from that in the very early stages of development of the seed.

In the case of ripening seeds of *Vernonia anthelmintica*, Miwa *et al.*[18c] found (1963) that in the early stages oleic acid was a major component, but diminished later on by about 50 per cent., with the concurrent appearance of 12,13-dihydroxy-oleic acid; the latter increased until full maturity of the seeds was approached, when it declined markedly and epoxy-oleic acid appeared in quantity, thus suggesting that the biosynthetic sequence may be oleic→12,13-dihydroxy-oleic→epoxy-oleic acid.

Another approach to the synthesis of fats in seeds arises from consideration of a number of those seed fats which develop different mixtures of the same component acids when the seed is ripened in different environments. A fairly large number of instances are now known where a plant grown in relatively cool climates produces seed fats of more unsaturated character than when grown in a warmer region. In all such cases the unsaturated acids remain the same (e.g. oleic and linoleic, or oleic, linoleic, linolenic), but the seed fats developed in cooler conditions of growth contain more of the most unsaturated acid present and less oleic acid. Examples of this feature will be found in Chapter IV, where component acids present in the following seed fats grown under different conditions are tabulated in detail: linseed (Table 59A, p. 211; and pp, 210–212), niger seed, tobacco seed, safflower seed (Table 60A, p. 222), sunflower seed (Table 60B, p. 224), cotton seed (Table 62, p. 270), groundnut (Table 67A, p. 306) and soya bean (Table 67B, p. 309). Figures showing the typical variations in ground-nut and sunflower seed oils will, however, be repeated here (Table 141) to facilitate the discussion which follows.

TABLE 141. *Varying Composition of Groundnut and Sunflower Seed Oils*

IODINE VALUE OF OIL	COMPONENT FATTY ACIDS (PER CENT. WT.)		
	SATURATED	OLEIC	LINOLEIC
(a) Groundnut oils			
86·0	18	64	18
86·5	18	63	19
90·2	18	60	22
94·8	17	61	22
90·1	22	53	25
93·6	19	54	26
94·3	23	45	32
96·4	22	45	33
95·5	23	41	36
99·2	23	39	38
(b) Sunflower seed oils			
94·7	10	71	19
106·9	9	58	33
113·4	13	43	44
123·7	12	31	57
125·5	11	31	58
126·7	12	30	58
129·8	14	21	65
131·8	14	18	68
132·3	14	17	69
136·5	14	14	72

It is apparent from data of this kind that, in cooler conditions of growth and slower attainment of maturity in the seeds, the seed fats contain more of the most unsaturated fatty acid (e.g. linoleic) and less oleic acid, but that the change is almost exclusively confined to the relative proportions of the *unsaturated* acids: there is very little alteration in the proportions of saturated acids throughout, and such alteration as there is consists in a very slight *increase* of saturated acids in the most *unsaturated* seed oils.

Ivanov,[66] who was the first to demonstrate that linseed grown in cold climates produces fatty oil richer in linolenic glycerides than when grown in a warmer locality, also put forward the view that the more unsaturated acids were produced by desaturation of less unsaturated (or saturated) acids; but he seems to have overlooked the corollary which necessarily follows from this hypothesis, namely, that the supposed desaturation process must operate most extensively at the lowest temperatures at which a seed develops! This paradox of itself is sufficient to demonstrate the extreme improbability of desaturation playing any part in the biosynthesis of unsaturated acids in seeds.

We shall enlarge further on this matter when discussing the biosynthesis of unsaturated acids in a later section of this chapter ("Possible mechanisms of the conversion of carbohydrate into fats," p. 552).

The present detailed data on seed fat component acids (which were not available at the time of Ivanov's studies) point to the following conclusions in regard to biosynthesis of fats in the ripening seed[20]:

1. *Unsaturated* seed fatty acids are built up by an entirely different mechanism from that which operates in the synthesis of *saturated* acids.

2. Each species of plant elaborates its own specific mixture of acids in its seed fat: but in seeds of the same species the relative amounts of oleic and linoleic (or linolenic) acids may vary considerably, such variation being conditioned mainly by the temperature of the locality where the seed ripens. The most unsaturated member of the group is found most abundantly in seeds grown in cool conditions, i.e., where the rate of synthesis is relatively slow. This suggests that the most unsaturated members (e.g. linolenic or linoleic), or their immediate precursors, are formed before (or, as it were, on the way to) the monoethenoid acid. The order of synthesis of *unsaturated* acids may be presumed, in the light of present knowledge, to be trie-ene (or, more probably, precursor) → diene (or, more probably, precursor) → mono-ene (oleic in the case of C_{18} acids).

3. Seed fat *saturated* acids differ from the unsaturated group in that, whilst one acid (usually palmitic) predominates, it is invariably accompanied by smaller proportions of the next higher, or lower, even-numbered homologue (usually by both). It would appear further that the biosynthesis in seeds of saturated acids is not quite so greatly affected by temperature as that of the unsaturated acids, since slightly higher proportions of *saturated* acids usually appear in the most *unsaturated* seed fats of a given species.

In the majority of seed fatty oils the amount of saturated component acids is small in comparison with the total quantity of unsaturated acids.

4. It should be noted, however, that in no case, where wide variation in the proportions of oleic, linoleic (and linolenic) acid has been observed, is there any indication whatever that the *saturation* process now suggested in connection with the unsaturated series continues to the production of saturated (stearic) acid. On the contrary, there is invariably somewhat less of saturated acids in seed fats of a given species which are highest in oleic acid, and lowest in linoleic (or linolenic) acid content in the seed glycerides.

It will be seen that, up to the present, studies of the development of fat in ripening seeds have nearly all been concerned with the most frequently occurring category of seed fats, i.e., those in which the major component acids are confined to oleic, linoleic, and palmitic, with occasionally linolenic or stearic in addition. It would be extraordinarily interesting to make similar investigations in ripening fruits which give rise to large proportions of one or other of the more "specific" seed fatty acids – for example, rape or mustard seed (erucic as well as oleic and linoleic), seeds of the Palmæ (45–50 per cent. lauric acid) or Umbelliferæ (octadec-6-enoic as well as octadec-9-enoic acid), cacao butter, or other seeds whose fats are rich in stearic as well as oleic and palmitic acids, and many similar instances.

Remarkable features of the final synthesis into glycerides, if the process follows the general course indicated by the studies which have been discussed, are (i) the completeness with which triglycerides are produced, with little or no remaining free fatty acid, or di- or mono-glycerides containing unesterified glycerol hydroxyl groups*; and (ii) the almost exclusive attachment of oleic (and occasionally linoleic) groups to the central (2- or β-) hydroxyl of the glycerol molecule (in so far as the proportions of oleic and/or linoleic acid permit); whilst the (external) 1- and 3- glyceryl positions are occupied by any other fatty acids present, these being apparently assembled in indiscriminate or random fashion.

It may follow that the wide occurrence of this uniform pattern in the glycerides implies that the mixture of fatty acids synthesised in seeds of a given species is much the same at any stage of development of the seed fat.

* Kartha (1964)[19b] studying the fats in coconuts from very early stages of development (with 3–7 per cent. of fat) to full maturity (90 per cent. of fat), found that *no* acetyl value was displayed at any period, either in the earliest stages or at five intermediate periods before the nuts were fully mature; contrary to *in vitro* studies with lipase, the fats at all periods in the ripening nut consisted exclusively of triglycerides. Kartha concludes that this may be "due to the fact that, once a glyceride molecule gets adsorbed on to a lipase molecule, it is not desorbed till all the three hydroxyls are esterified to give a triglyceride, and the fully esterified molecule alone is desorbed".

If further similar studies on other seeds lead to the same findings, these results obviously have a profound bearing on one aspect of seed glyceride biosynthesis.

The Biosynthesis of Fats in Animals

The view originally held in earlier times, that the reserve fat deposited in animal adipose tissue was derived entirely from fat taken as such in their diet, was supplanted about 1850 by Liebig's opinion that animals must synthesise fats to a large extent. He was led to this conclusion by consideration of the large amount of milk fat produced by lactating cows in relation to the fat in their diet, and of the fact, already beginning to be appreciated, that different kinds of animals feeding, for example, on similar pastures, laid down different types of reserve fat. Proof that carbohydrates must be an important source of animal fat was first rigidly given by Lawes and Gilbert[21] in 1860–1866 in connection with the well-known Rothamsted experiments on the feeding of oxen, sheep, and pigs. The results were not always definite in the case of oxen and sheep, but were quite clear with pigs, as the following figures will demonstrate:

	LB.
Protein in food	64·0
Protein in animal	6·5
Protein difference, *possibly* utilised for fat production	57·5
Fat in food	12·4
Fat in animal	71·2
Fat produced from other sources than fat in food	58·8
Carbon in fat produced (58·8 lb.)	45·3
Carbon in available protein (57·5 lb.), less carbon excreted as urea	27·4
Carbon in fat which must have resulted from carbohydrate	17·9

Thus the minimum amount of fat which must have been derived from carbohydrate was about 26 lb., and this, of course, assumes that all unaccounted-for protein had also been transformed into fat — which is clearly improbable.

Similar quantitative evidence for the conversion of carbohydrate into animal fat was provided later by Rubner[22a] for dogs and by Rosenfeld[22b] for geese, whilst Morgulis and Pratt[22c] showed that the formation of fat in the dog is accompanied by the high respiratory quotient necessary for this change.

A full examination was made by Hilditch, Lea and Pedelty[23] of the component acids in the deposited fats of pigs reared on known diets (low in fat) under the direction of Dr. J. Hammond at the Animal Nutrition Station of the School of Agriculture, Cambridge; this investigation demonstrated on the one hand the extent to which fat had been synthesised in the animals, and on the other hand showed which of the fatty acids were produced by synthesis as distinct from assimilation – substantially only palmitic, oleic and stearic. The component acids of the pig depot fats, and the diets given to the animals, in this experiment have been given in Chapter III (p. 116, and Table 39, p. 119). From the data available on (*a*) the constituents of the diets and their fat contents, (*b*) the acids present in the small proportions of different fats in the diets,* and (*c*) the total weights and characteristics of fat present in the various depots, (subcutaneous, perinephric and kidney, intermuscular, mesenteric, caul),

---

* Previously published component acid analyses (by the modern methods) of the fats in question were utilised here.

together with the component acid data for selected fats from each animal, it was possible to construct a rough balance sheet showing (i) the total amount of each fatty acid ingested as fat by the animal, and (ii) the total amount of each fatty acid present as fat in the animals at slaughter. These figures are summarised in Table 142 and illustrated in Fig. 14.

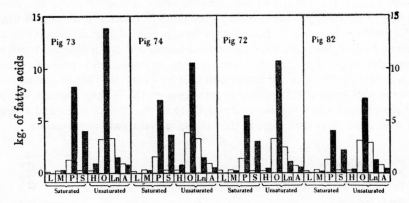

FIG. 14. Ingestion and deposition of fatty acids by pigs. Fatty acids: ingested, *white*; deposited in tissues, *black*. *L*, lauric (and lower saturated) acids; *M*, myristic acid; *P*, palmitic acid; *S*, stearic acid; *H*, hexadecenoic acid; *O*, oleic acid; *Ln*, linoleic acid; *A*, unsaturated C_{20-22} acids.

Irrespective of the particular diet concerned, these figures demonstrate that the amounts of saturated acids below myristic, linoleic, and unsaturated C_{20-22} acids in the deposited fats were less than those ingested as dietary fats, whereas the amounts of palmitic, stearic, and oleic acids in the body fats were greatly in excess of those ingested in the food fats; hexadecenoic acid, although small in quantity in any case, was present in greater quantity in the fats of the animals than in the fats they had ingested, whilst the amount of myristic acid in the depot fats was almost equal to that taken in the food fats.

Clearly, therefore, biosynthesis of fats containing palmitic, oleic, and stearic acid had occurred to a marked extent, whilst it seems certain that hexadecenoic acid and, possibly, a little myristic acid was also synthesised as fat. On the other hand, it is equally clear that fats containing saturated acids of lower molecular weight than myristic acid were neither synthesised nor assimilated by the animal. (This accords with previous observations of workers on the body fats of rats and other animals.)

The amount of linoleic acid in the body fats was not more than, and usually definitely less than, half of that available in the form of ingested fat; this strongly suggests, although it does not form a conclusive proof, that, like the rat,[24] the pig is unable to synthesise linoleic acid and derives glycerides of this acid only by assimilation. The quantity of unsaturated C_{20-22} acids present as glycerides in the depots likewise falls short of that present in the diet (in this instance in the fish meal constituents); but the disparity is less pronounced than in the case of linoleic acid, and the possibility of some slight degree of

TABLE 142. Comparison of Acids in Fat Ingested and Deposited by Pigs[23]

(a) Pigs at different Planes of Nutrition to 200 lb. wt.

PIG: PLANES OF NUTRITION:	73 (HOG) LOW—HIGH			74 (GILT) HIGH—HIGH			72 (HOG) HIGH—LOW			82 (GILT) LOW—LOW		
FATTY ACIDS (KG.)	FED	DEPOSITED	DIFFERENCE	FED	DEPOSITED	DIFFERENCE	FED	DEPOSITED	DIFFERENCE	FED	DEPOSITED	DIFFERENCE
Saturated												
Below C_{14}	0·11	Trace	−0·11	0·11	—	−0·11	0·12	Trace	−0·12	0·16	Trace	−0·16
Myristic	0·24	0·29	+0·05	0·26	0·24	−0·02	0·24	0·21	−0·03	0·27	0·15	−0·12
Palmitic	1·28	8·27	+6·99	1·53	6·92	+5·39	1·36	5·45	+4·09	1·28	4·00	+2·72
Stearic	0·25	3·99	+3·74	0·24	3·58	+3·34	0·20	2·99	+2·79	0·25	2·16	+1·91
Unsaturated												
C_{16} (and C_{14})	0·22	0·89	+0·67	0·22	0·72	+0·50	0·17	0·43	+0·26	0·22	0·31	+0·09
Oleic	3·24	13·87	+10·63	3·80	10·50	+6·70	3·27	10·69	+7·42	3·07	7·09	+4·02
Linoleic	3·30	1·48	−1·82	3·22	1·43	−1·79	2·44	1·07	−1·37	2·85	1·23	−1·62
C_{20-22}	0·87	0·74	−0·13	0·86	0·48	−0·38	0·66	0·53	−0·13	0·74	0·46	−0·28
	9·51	29·53	+20·02	10·24	23·87	+13·63	8·46	21·37	+12·91	8·84	15·40	+6·56

(b) Pigs at Different Planes of Nutrition to 16 Weeks

PIG: PLANES OF NUTRITION:	138 (GILT) HIGH			139 (GILT) LOW		
FATTY ACIDS (KG.)	FED	DEPOSITED	DIFFERENCE	FED	DEPOSITED	DIFFERENCE
Saturated						
Below C_{14}	0·08	Trace	−0·08	0·02	—	−0·02
Myristic	0·14	0·13	−0·01	0·04	0·01	−0·03
Palmitic	0·87	3·81	+2·94	0·32	0·15	−0·17
Stearic	0·07	1·14	+1·07	0·01	0·06	+0·05
Unsaturated						
C_{16} (and C_{14})	0·07	0·51	+0·44	0·01	0·03	+0·02
Oleic	1·97	6·48	+4·51	0·75	0·23	−0·52
Linoleic	0·73	0·38	−0·35	0·08	0·04	−0·04
C_{20-22}	0·21	0·25	+0·04	0·02	0·01	−0·01
	4·14	12·70	+8·56	1·25	0·53	−0·72

synthesis of the acids of this group (e.g., from ingested linoleic acid) in the pig cannot be excluded.

The weight ratios of the increases of palmitic to those of the two C_{18} acids (stearic and oleic) taken together in the five animals considered in the preceding table are $1:2 \cdot 06$, $1:1 \cdot 86$, $1:2 \cdot 50$, $1:2 \cdot 17$, and $1:1 \cdot 90$. The average ratio is 1 part of palmitic to $2 \cdot 08$ parts of C_{18} acids by weight, or $1:1 \cdot 89$ (molar). This is a somewhat striking confirmation, from a fresh angle, of the view[25] that palmitodioleins or their hydrogenated derivatives are the glycerides chiefly produced by synthesis in the pig and other animals for storage in the body tissues.

Similar studies of rat depot fats have been made by Longenecker,[24c] who fed fasted animals on high carbohydrate and high protein diets, and found that the resulting body fat was very similar in each case:

COMPONENT ACIDS (PER CENT. MOL.)

| | SATURATED | | | | UNSATURATED | | | | |
DIET	C_{14}	C_{16}	C_{18}	C_{20}	C_{14}	C_{16}	OLEIC	OCTA-DECA-DIENOIC	ARACHI-DONIC
Carbohydrate	3·1	26·7	3·6	0·4	0·9	15·6	47·2	2·2	0·3
Protein	2·8	29·7	3·8	1·1	1·1	15·6	43·8	2·0	0·2

The total saturated acids amounted respectively to $33 \cdot 8$ and $37 \cdot 4$ per cent., with palmitic acid $26 \cdot 7$ and $29 \cdot 7$ per cent. The unsaturated acids are even more closely similar in proportion, with very low octadecadienoic acid contents; an interesting feature is the proportion of hexadecenoic acid ($15 \cdot 6$ per cent.), which is considerably higher than that observed in other experiments (cf. Chapter III, p. 96) where the rat diets were not wholly devoid of fat.

We may now pass on to the more general question of the different mixtures of fatty acids found in the fats of the various members of the animal kingdom. A complete review of this subject involves, of course, the greater part of the matter in Chapters II, III, V, and VII of this book, and it must be taken for granted that the reader has already made himself familiar with these details. Further, it is naturally most convenient to discuss many features of biochemical interest when specific groups of fats have been considered from the point of view of their component acids or glycerides. This has in fact been done at many points in the chapters mentioned, and there is no need to indulge in extensive repetition in the present discussion. All that will be attempted here is to recapitulate some of the outstanding features of component acids and glyceride composition of fats in the animal kingdom, with the object of stressing some of the ascertained facts which must be satisfactorily accounted for in any complete explanation of the processes whereby fats are synthesised in animals. **Marine animals.** The characteristic and complex mixture of acids present in the glycerides of marine animals has been made abundantly clear by the data collected in Chapter II. The most significant feature, of course, is the high proportion of highly unsaturated C_{20} and C_{22} acids and of hexadecenoic acid — acids which are only present in very small proportions in the depot fats of land animals. Whilst the natural hexa- and tetra-decenoic acids have a close structural resemblance to oleic acid in that all three contain the grouping $=CH.[CH_2]_7.COO—$, it must be borne in mind that the polyethenoid C_{20}, C_{22} (and also C_{18}) acids in these fats contain a quite different type of unsaturation. The chain of seven or more saturated—CH_2—groups adjacent to the carboxyl group is not present; unsaturation usually commences at the 4th or 5th carbon atom of the chain (counting the carboxyl carbon atom as 1), and then consists of a chain of $=CH.CH_2.CH=$ groups in sequence until four, five or six double bonds are present.

The difference in structure connotes difference in biosynthetic processes, or difference in the material which is metabolised into fat. It is frequently supposed that the larger fish or marine mammalia derive their fat entirely by assimilation — ultimately from diatoms or other plankton; if so, the interesting problem remains as to why and how plankton metabolism leads to fat of this particular type, differing from all fats found in the more developed flora and fauna. Some indication that crustacea and fish may synthesise part of their fat has fairly recently appeared (1958) from dietary experiments made by Reiser and co-workers[26a] on mullet, shrimps and crabs. On fat-free diets the animals produced a certain amount of reserve fat in which, however, polyunsaturated acids were present only in low proportions; but when a fish oil was included in the diet the usual type of highly-unsaturated fatty acid mixture appeared in the fat depots. This may suggest that the depot fats of marine animals (as of land animals) may comprise both endogenous and exogenous fat, a conclusion supported by experiments of Bottino and Brenner[26b] (1962), who fed a species of freshwater fish on a fat-free diet for ten weeks, after which radioactive 1-C^{14}-acetate was injected peritoneally a day before the fish were killed. The muscle and liver triglycerides had the usual percentages of palmitic (20), and stearic (7) acids, with very high oleic acid (54 per cent.) and very little polyethenoid acids of either the C_{18}, C_{20} or C_{22} series; the intestinal lipids were similar and included radioactive fatty acids – further evidence that fat synthesis had taken place.

In addition to the general composition of aquatic animal fats, which thus sets them apart from all other natural fats except those of aquatic flora, it must be remembered that, within this generalisation, a number of variations in the proportions (and in some cases the mean unsaturation) of the different homologous groups of component acids are discernible. These typical differences exist, broadly speaking, between the component acids of marine and freshwater fish fats, between the fats of Teleostid and Elasmobranch fish, and apparently between fish and whales of the North Atlantic and of the Southern oceans; these and other instances of general or specific differences in the composition of aquatic animal fats have been discussed fully in Chapter II.

Moreover, a further complication arises in fish fats because in many species the liver acts as a depository of reserve fat in addition to its fat-producing role, whereas in many other species the reserve fat is diffused in the flesh, mesentery, head, etc., of the animal, the liver being relatively low in fat content, resembling in this respect the land animals rather than the first-mentioned type wherein the liver acts also as a fat store. The need for differentiating between the two groups has been stressed by Rapson et al.[27]

Land animals. The lipids of the larger land animals have been dealt with in detail, from the standpoint of their component acids in Chapter III (pp. 98–143), and from that of their component glycerides in Chapters V (pp. 403–409) and VII (pp. 491–510). So far as the depot glycerides of the larger animals are concerned, the salient features are the relative constancy of the palmitic acid content at 30 ($\pm$ 3) per cent., and of the C_{18} acids at 60–65 per cent.; the approximate balance between stearic and oleic acid contents, the sum of which only varies relatively slightly; the appearance of fully saturated glycerides (palmitostearins) in unusual proportions when, but not until, the stearic acid content of the fat rises above about 8–10 per cent. The observed glyceride components of stearic-rich depot fats can be accounted for by the hypothesis that preformed oleo-glycerides (mainly palmitodiolein) are converted to some extent by a hydrogenation process into the corresponding stearo-glycerides (e.g., oleo-palmitostearin and palmitodistearin).

Liver fats. In contrast to most of the adipose tissues, the liver contains important quantities of phosphatides as well as glycerides, and the component acids of each of these groups differ from each other and also from the depot glycerides. The liver is usually regarded as the chief site of the synthesis, and also of the degradation, of fats in the animal organism. Definite evidence that the liver is concerned in fat metabolism was provided by the experiments of Hildesheim and Leathes[28] (1904) on the pig, dog, and rabbit.

The iodine values of liver fats are often (but not always) higher than those of the corresponding reserve fats, and it was long supposed that fatty acids may be desaturated in the liver. Desaturation must clearly operate during the breakdown of fats or during their reconversion into carbohydrate, if this takes place; but it now seems unlikely that this process has any general application in the biosynthesis of unsaturated fats. The essential argument against desaturation as an intermediary stage in fat synthesis in the animal rests on the specifically different nature of the acids concerned, as was stated by Klenk and Schoenbeck[29] (1932) as a result of their determinations of the component acids in ox liver phosphatides, glycerides, and depot glycerides: the highly unsaturated acids of ox liver fat consist of members of the C_{20} and C_{22} series, which clearly cannot result from desaturation of the reserve fat acids, which belong almost entirely to either the C_{16} or C_{18} series.

Reserve (depot) fats. It is probable that the bulk of the fats deposited in the storage depots (adipose tissues) of animals are glycerides preformed elsewhere in the animal (e.g., in the livers) and transported to the adipose tissue cells by the blood stream. It has already been pointed out that the close relationships between the glyceride structure of reserve fats from different animals or from different parts of the same animal appear to point to the production of these bodies by the same mechanism and, in any one animal, probably at one site.

Nevertheless, although it is very unlikely that any major proportion of depot fat is synthesised *in situ* in the adipose tissue itself, there is evidence[30] which in-dicates that adipose tissue cells are able, by virtue of the enzyme systems present, to effect some synthesis of fats from sugars.

At first sight it may not appear likely that the concentration of glycerides normally present in the blood stream should suffice as the source of adipose tissue fat, but a simple calculation will show that it is possible. From the data in such experiments as those quoted in this chapter it appears that the quantity of reserve fat deposited per day in a pig which is being fattened is of the order of 100–200 grams, or about 4–8 grams per hour. The concentration of *glycerides*, as distinct from other fatty compounds, in the blood stream has not yet been given very accurately, but is probably of the order of 0·2–2 per cent. (according to circumstances). As Leathes and Raper (1925) pointed out,[31] in order to carry more fat from one site to another, the blood need not contain more; it is a question of rate of transfer, not of concentration. For the lactating cow, Kay *et al*.[32a] (1936), followed by Maynard *et al*.[32b] and by Shaw and Petersen,[32c] have shown, from the rate of flow of blood through the mammary gland and the glyceride content of the blood, that the amount of glycerides passing into the gland in the blood stream is sufficient to provide all the milk fat formed; whilst, by means of "tracer" experiments with ingested "labelled" stearic acid on a lactating goat, Duncombe and Glascock[32d] (1954) estimated that 70 per cent. of its long-chain milk fatty acids were derived from blood glycerides.

From the comparative studies of the glyceride structure of animal depot fats referred to in Chapter VII (pp. 506–510) it may well be supposed that the prim-ary phase of the glycerides which finally appear as reserve fat is that of a com-paratively unsaturated mixture produced by lipolytic esterification of the mixed fatty acids formed initially by synthesis. These glycerides will usually contain about 25–30 mols. of palmitic (with minor amounts of stearic and myristic) and about 75–70 mols. of oleic (with diethenoid C_{18}) acids, and may be synthesised in the liver and pass thence into the blood stream. In those animals which produce reserve fats with important contents of stearic glycer-ides, however, a partial reduction of some of the initially unsaturated glycerides, whether endogenous (synthesised) or exogenous (ingested), takes place before the fat mixture emerges into the blood stream from the intestines.[33] Such a sequence of processes would be capable of yielding glyceride mixtures having the specific structures observed in lards, tallows, etc. The deposition of related fats differing in degree of saturation (stearo-glyceride contents) would, on this hypothesis, depend upon differentiated or selective absorption of the various glycerides in the blood stream by the cells of different adipose tissues. It is significant that, when stearic-rich fats are thus produced from di- or tri-ethenoid glycerides by rumen bacterial hydrogenation, *trans*-isomeric forms of mono-ene acids are also formed,[34] whereas these are not present in the fats of non-ruminant animals (other than carnivores which feed on ruminant animals).

The nature of depot glycerides in different animals depends, of course, on a number of other factors in addition to the basal diet from which the fat has been synthesised. In the group of body fats which contain little stearic acid (e.g., Chapter III, Tables 27, 29A, 29B, 31–34, pp. 87, 94, 97, 100, 102, 103), the nature of the unsaturated acids appears to vary according to the species, and probably also according to differences in life-habit, etc. Thus the body fats of the domestic fowl seem to contain a fair amount of linoleic acid, although this may be due to some extent to ingested fat. It is an old observation that, judged by average iodine values of the fats, wild animals produce a much more unsaturated reserve fat than those bred in captivity. Thus the iodine value of fat from the wild goose was 99·6 as compared with 67·0 for the fat from domestic geese[35]; and that of fat from rabbits was 101·1 (wild) and 64·4 (tame).[35] These differences might be due to the food, or to external conditions.

Relations between body temperature and the composition of reserve fats. An interesting feature of reserve fat composition is its connection with the site in which it is deposited. In the pig, it will be seen that the intestinal adipose tissue surrounding the kidney is distinctly more saturated than the inner layer of the back tissue fat, and this, in turn, than the outermost layer (due, almost entirely, to the replacement of oleo-glycerides by stearo-glycerides in the more saturated fats). In the hen, on the contrary, the fats from the two external tissues, the neck and the abdominal layer, were found to be practically identical with the layer of fat on the inner surface of the mesenterium.

The usual explanation of these phenomena, and one which seems probable, is that they are mainly conditioned by the temperature of the tissues in which the fat is deposited. In the case of birds, whose skin is well protected from external temperature changes by their feathers, it is not therefore unnatural, on this hypothesis, to find that depot fat from different parts of the body, whether intestinal or outer tissues, is of much the same composition in all cases.

The differences in the composition of fat from the adipose tissues of the pig were first correlated with temperature in 1901 by Henriques and Hansen[36], who compared the setting points and iodine values of fats from various sites with the body temperatures in the case of a pig fed on barley with the following results:

	SOLIDIFYING POINT	IOD. VALUE			BODY TEMPERATURES
Outer back fat					
⎧ outermost	—	60·0		1 cm. deep	33·7°
⎩ inner layer	26·4°	57·1	Back tissue	2 ,, ,,	34·8°
Inner back fat				3 ,, ,,	37·0°
⎧ outer layer	28·0°	51·8		4 ,, ,,	39·0°
⎩ innermost	27·7°	50·6			
Perinephric fat	29·6°	47·7	Rectum		39·9°

They also kept three pigs from the same litter for two months, one at 30–35°, one at 0°, and one at 0° but covered with a sheepskin coat; the iodine values of the outermost layers of the back fats of the animals were, after this treatment, respectively 69·4, 72·3, and 67·0, thus supporting their hypothesis.

The composition of the inner layer of the pig back fats (i.e. beneath the "streak") was apparently more or less homogeneous in Henriques and Hansen's experiments, and this, as well as their general findings, was fully confirmed (1933) in detailed analyses by Dean and Hilditch[37] of the component acids of fat taken from five layers of the adipose tissue from the back of a sow fed on a non-fatty diet (see Chapter III, Table 38 (v), p. 117 and p. 118).

It has been said[38] that "Fat to be of use as a source of energy in the body must be just fluid at the natural body temperature, and as a consequence the fat of cold-blooded animals (fish) is of very low melting point, while the fat of the sheep which has a high body temperature (104° F.) is of higher melting point than that of the bullock with a lower body temperature (101° F.)." Whilst it is clear that fats present in an animal (or plant) must be almost completely, if not wholly, liquid at the natural temperature of the organism, it does not necessarily follow that warm-blooded animals always produce fats of higher melting point and more saturated character than cold-blooded animals or plants which are indigeneous to cool regions.

The instances of fats of fish, sheep, and bullock given in the quotation, for example, should be considered in conjunction with those of such animals as the rabbit (body temperature 103–104° F.) or the hen (104–108° F.). Whilst sheep fat contains only about 40 per cent. of unsaturated acids (mainly oleic), rabbit fat contains nearly 70 per cent., much of which is linoleic acid, with appreciable quantities of still less saturated acids. Again, hen fat contains about 70 per cent. of unsaturated (oleic and linoleic) acids, in spite of the high body temperature of the bird; this fat is, indeed, almost completely liquid at room temperature. Further, the rat, with a body temperature of 100° F. (lower than that of the rabbit) contains about the same high proportion of unsaturated acids, but these consist almost wholly of oleic acid: the more unsaturated linoleic acid, present in quantity in rabbit fat, is almost absent from that of the rat.

It has also been usual to connect the liquid, very highly unsaturated fats of fish with their low body temperature; yet marine mammals such as the whale, dugong (102–104° F.), or porpoise (96–98° F.) have body temperatures of the same order as those of land animals, whereas their fats are very closely similar in composition to the fish oils, and include the same series of highly unsaturated acids.

No wide generalisation can therefore safely be drawn between temperature of the organism and the composition of its fat. Fats which are solid at the normal temperature of plants or animals are obviously incompatible with their conditions of life, but, of animals and plants which exist under relatively warm conditions, some utilise fats of a relatively saturated (solid) character, but others resemble the cold-blooded animals and temperate plants in having fats of a more unsaturated and liquid type. Body temperature clearly plays a part in some instances, but this is often less clearly defined than that conditioned by species or other biological factor.

Milk fats. The component acids and glycerides of milk fats were discussed in Chapters III (pp. 144–164), V (pp. 410–416) and VII (pp. 510–526), and at the same time their relationships to the depot fats were pointed out. It was shown in the earlier chapters that the milk fats of marine mammals and also of many land animals (possibly all land mammals except the ruminants, although detailed evidence for a sufficient range of non-ruminant milk fats has not yet been provided) are qualitatively and often almost quantitatively similar to their respective depot fats. Ruminant milk fats, however, are distinguished by the presence of significant proportions of butyric, hexanoic, octanoic, decanoic and lauric acid (in progressively decreasing amounts) and of small proportions of unsaturated acids of the C_{14}, C_{12}, and C_{10} series (again in progressively decreasing quantities) with unsaturation in the $9:10$ position with respect to the carboxyl group (as in oleic acid). The glyceride pattern of such milk fats exhibits the same departure from the more usual "evenly-distributed" pattern of all other classes of natural glycerides as that of stearic-rich animal depot fats, the proportion of tri-saturated glycerides being much greater than normally observed at corresponding proportions of saturated acids in the total acids of a fat. At the same time the general proportions of mono- and di-palmito-glycerides, and the proportion of palmitic acid (25–30 per cent.) in the total acids of the milk fats, are of the same order as in other and more "evenly-distributed" fats; this is illustrated in Table 91B (Chapter V, p. 412). Just as random hydrogenation of some of the oleo-glycerides in a presynthesised fat consisting largely of palmito-di-unsaturated C_{18} glycerides would account for the characteristic glyceride patterns of stearic-rich animal body fats, so conversion of some of the oleo-groups in blood glycerides (which disappear in the lactating gland in sufficient amount to account for the milk fat produced[32]) into (a) the short-chain saturated glycerides characteristic of ruminant milk fats, and (b) the traces of monoethenoid acids from C_{14} downwards to (but not below) C_{10}, would account for the specific glyceride mixtures encountered in these milk fats.

It has been suggested that such shortening of oleo-groups present in the blood-glycerides might take place by processes of concurrent oxidation and reduction in the lactating gland, and this explanation may well hold so far as the production in decreasing proportions of tetradec-9-enoyl, dodec-9-enoyl, and dec-9-enoyl-glycerides (and also some myristo-, lauro-, and decano-glycerides) is concerned. It is now established, however, by the classical work of Folley, French, Popják and their co-workers[39a] that short-chain *saturated* acids originate by synthesis in the lactating gland itself, butyric acid appearing in greatest amount in bovine milk fats, with progressively lesser proportions of saturated C_6, C_8, etc. acids. It therefore appears probable, and in accordance with the observed distribution of the short-chain groups in the bovine milk fat glycerides, that the short-chain saturated acids synthesised in the lactating gland are converted into glycerides by acyl interchange[40] of oleo- (and to a lesser extent possibly palmito-) glycerides conveyed in the blood stream with the short-chain saturated acids which have been synthesised *in situ*. This explanation suggests that the synthesised short-chain acids are absorbed, as it were, by pre-formed glycerides in the blood during its passage through the udder: random exchange of short-chain acyl groups and oleo-groups in the blood glycerides would result in the specific glyceride patterns observed in ruminant milk fats.

To sum up the present section of this chapter, it may be said that at present there seems to be good reason for the belief that animal fats are mainly manufactured from carbohydrate, etc., in one central site of the body, probably the liver. The fats produced pass into the blood stream and are thence absorbed selectively as required by the cells of the various fat depots. Quite probably, of course, at different stages of the life cycle, modified or different types of blood fat may be produced by the synthetic processes; it is also apparent that, with advancing age, the general character of the reserve fats of an animal alters in some degree. The general structural similarities which have been shown to exist between fats so apparently different in composition as tallows and milk fats may be regarded as confirmatory evidence of a single main centre of fat synthesis in the animal.

Possible Mechanisms of the Conversion of Carbohydrates into Fats

There is abundant evidence in the two preceding sections (pp. 528, 541) that carbohydrates are at all events the main source from which fats are produced by plants and animals. The hypotheses which have been advanced from time to time to account for this transformation will now be considered. The matter will perhaps ultimately prove more difficult to explain in the case of plant fats than of animal fats, for there is less qualitative difference, for example, between the reserve fats of many terrestrial animals (and possibly birds), or between the liver oils of most fishes, than there is between the seed fats of different botanical families. Put in another form, the problem is not merely to give a reasonable explanation of how glucose or fructose or starch can be chemically converted into a general mixture of fatty acids or glycerides; we have also to explain, for example, why the sugars present in the growing endosperm of Palmæ species yield the characteristic Palmæ kernel fatty acids (50 per cent. lauric, 20 per cent. myristic, etc.), while those in the cotton seed lead to a fat with about 25 per cent. each of palmitic and oleic and 50 per cent. of linoleic acid, those in the nutmeg produce 75–80 per cent. of myristic acid, in the castor seed 90 per cent. of ricinoleic acid, in seeds of certain *Aleurites* 80 per cent. of elæostearic acid, in seeds of the Cruciferæ 30–40 per cent. of erucic acid, in those of the Umbelliferæ varying amounts of petroselinic acid, and so on. Together with this, we must remember that, in a great number of other plant families, the main component acids of plant fats are large quantities of oleic and/or linoleic acid with (usually) less palmitic acid.

In the vast majority of natural fats the most abundant component is oleic acid; and, if we include with oleic the structurally closely related linoleic, linolenic, and elæostearic acids, a still larger proportion of the fatty acids present in nature fall into this one group. Indeed, these acids almost certainly account for something like 90 per cent. of the total acids produced in the vegetable seed fats of the world. Logically, therefore, one would have thought that explanations should have been sought for the production from carbohydrates of the most characteristic structure found in all natural fatty acids:

$$CH_3.[CH_2]_7.CH{=}CH.[CH_2]_7.COO{-}$$

In fact, this has never been seriously considered. Instead, attention has been concentrated on another feature of natural fats – the almost exclusive occurrence of straight-chain fatty acids containing an even number of carbon atoms in the molecule. This obviously has an important meaning in connection with the biosynthesis of fats, but it may prove somewhat unfortunate that attention has been diverted so much from the equally fundamental problem of accounting for the synthesis of the most abundant components of all, oleic (*cis*-octadec-9-enoic) and linoleic (*cis-cis*-octadeca-9,12-dienoic) acids. However that may be, much consideration has been given to the possibility that carbohydrates are first broken down to a two-carbon unit (e.g., acetaldehyde), which serves as a basis for re-assemblage into fatty acid chains containing even numbers of carbon atoms.

Before discussing in detail this possibility (now substantially verified as regards the biosynthesis of the higher saturated acids) it may be worth while, from a historical standpoint, to recall briefly other suggestions which have been made at various times.

(a) *Direct condensation of hexoses* (*or pentoses*), first suggested by Emil Fischer,[41] has been occasionally considered by other workers but in the present state of knowledge seems to be a most unlikely course.

(b) *Condensation of aldehyde to polyene aldehydes with reduction of the latter*. It was shown by Reichel and Schmid[42a] that the polyene aldehydes $CH_3.[CH{=}CH]_n.CHO$ synthesised by Kuhn et al.[42b] were converted to some extent into higher fatty acids by the enzymes present in certain moulds. Whilst this gives some experimental backing for the supposition that reduction of ethenoid systems and oxidation of the aldehyde group can be effected by some of the enzymes in living tissues, it is again very unlikely that conjugated polyene aldehydes as such form any part of the biosynthetic sequence.

(c) *Condensation of C_3 units produced from hexose*. The possibility that glucose or fructose was first resolved into C_3 (instead of C_2) units, followed by condensation of C_3 units to C_6, C_9, C_{12}, C_{18}, etc., units of a fatty nature, was suggested by Armstrong and Allan,[43] who pointed out that by such means oleic acid might be one of the ultimate products. This conception harmonised with current views of carbohydrate fermentation (alcoholic), in which triosephosphoric acids play an important part as intermediate products, and was attractive because of the leaning towards C_3, C_6, and C_9 groups which is so clearly observable in the natural unsaturated fatty acids. Examples of this are as follows:

TYPE	GROUPING	EXAMPLES IN WHICH THIS GROUPING OCCURS
C_9	$CH_3.[CH_2]_7.CH{=}$ or $={CH}.[CH_2]_7.COOH$	Oleic, linoleic, linolenic, elæosteric, hexadecenoic, tetradecenoic, ricinoleic, erucic, (also oleyl alcohol).
C_3	$={CH}.CH_2.CH{=}$	Linoleic, linolenic; polyethenoid acids of C_{20}, C_{22}, series.
C_6	$CH_3.[CH_2]_4.CH{=}$ or $={CH}.[CH_2]_4.COOH$	Linoleic, petroselinic.
C_{12}	$CH_3.[CH_2]_{10}.CH{=}$	Petroselinic.

At present, however, this C_3 fragment, if it has intrinsic importance in the biosynthesis of unsaturated fatty acids, seems likely to be produced in the form of "malonyl-Coenzyme A" (p. 555) by carboxylation of acetyl-Coenzyme A than to be the direct scission-product of a hexose.

(d) *Pyruvic acid as an intermediate in fatty acid biosynthesis*. At the period when acetaldehyde was envisaged as the C_2 unit from which fatty acids were built up (*v. infra*) it was alternatively suggested (Smedley et al.[44a,b]) that acetaldehyde or its condensation products condensed with a molecule of pyruvic acid, $CH_3.CO.COOH$, to yield unsaturated keto-acids, with ultimate decarboxylation of a pyruvic acid residue; but in consequence of the more recent work in the enzyme field the question of pyruvic acid as a precursor of acetaldehyde seems to be rather an academic point.

The biosynthesis of higher fatty acids from C_2 units. The idea that acetaldehyde might be a key-intermediate in the conversion of carbohydrate into fatty acids was put forward by Nencki[45a] as long ago as 1878, while at the turn of the century Magnus-Levy,[45b] Leathes[45c] and Raper[45d] suggested that such a change could be effected by simultaneous reduction and oxidation of aldols produced by condensation of aldehydes, e.g.,

$$CH_3.CHO + CH_3.CHO \rightarrow CH_3.CH(OH).CH_2.CHO \rightarrow CH_3.CH_2.CH_2.COOH$$

In 1912–1913 Loeb[46a] and Friedmann[46b] suggested that acetate (rather than aldehyde) might be the key-intermediate, while Smedley-MacLean[46c] showed in 1926 that fatty acids were produced in growing yeast with either acetate or ethyl alcohol as the only nutrient. At about the same period Haehn and Kinttof[47] compared the production of fat in the mould *Endomyces vernalis* when glucose was the nutrient (control experiment) with other experiments in which dilute (1–4 per cent.) aqueous solutions of pyruvic acid, acetaldehyde, aldol, alcohol, or glycerol were used as nutrients, and in each case observed considerably increased formation of fat as compared with the respective control experiments:

Percentage of fat (as fatty acid) in Endomyces

NUTRIENT ADDED	ADDED NUTRIENT	CONTROL	INCREASE
Pyruvic acid	11·2	3·3	7·9
Lactic acid	10·0	2·7	7·3
Acetaldehyde	8·3	2·8	5·5
Aldol	24·3	6·8	17·5
Ethyl alcohol	28·1	3·0	25·1
Glycerol	16·8	3·0	13·8

These results, later confirmed by Reichel and Schmid,[42a] showed that a number of compounds (either containing two carbon atoms or readily transformed *in vivo* into a C_2-derivative) were indeed more effective than glucose, under the experimental conditions employed, in leading to fat synthesis.

As time went on many studies were carried out, mainly on animals or on animal tissues and enzyme systems, in which acetate was proved to be an important intermediate in fat biosynthesis, although not infrequently it was found to be ineffective unless a hexose was also present. Two of the more interesting examples may be quoted.

(*a*) In 1944 Rittenberg and Bloch[48] fed rats and mice on diets containing sodium acetate in which the hydrogen was replaced by deuterium, whilst the carboxyl carbon atom was the carbon isotope of atomic weight 13. The fatty acids produced in the animals contained both deuterium and C^{13}, and the carbon isotope was present in only about half of their total carbon content, indicating that whole acetate molecules were involved in the synthesis by successive condensation of C_2 units.

(*b*) The comprehensive studies of Folley, French, Popják[39a] and their co-workers have shown unequivocally that injection into the lactating gland of an animal of solutions of acetate in which the carboxyl carbon atom was the isotopic C^{14}, is followed by appearance in the milk fats of butyric, hexanoic, etc., acids in which the alternate carbon atoms are isotopic (radioactive). There can therefore be no doubt that synthesis has proceeded by the sequence: $CH_3.C^{14}OOH + CH_3.C^{14}OOH \rightarrow CH_3.C^{14}H_2.CH_2.C^{14}OOH$, and so on.

It should be noted that in ruminant animals (cow, sheep, goat) injection of only acetate into the udder produced fat synthesis, but in non-ruminants (rat, mouse, rabbit) synthesis did not take place unless glucose was also present.

It gradually became clear to the many workers in this field that acetate *per se* does not undergo these condensations unless in some way it becomes "activated". This has been clarified by a very great quantity of investigations since about 1945 into the enzyme systems which are involved in the process. It is not practicable, nor perhaps necessary for the purpose of this chapter, to attempt anything approaching a full account of these numerous researches; for this the reader is referred to recent biochemical reviews and treatises, e.g., Deuel, "The Lipids, Vol. III, Biochemistry" (1957). We propose here merely to present, it is hoped without too much oversimplification, the main outlines of the results at the time of writing, in so far as they indicate the primary mechanism of condensation of C_2 units into long-chain molecules.

Coenzyme A, Acetyl-Coenzyme A, Malonyl-Coenzyme A. In 1945 Lipmann[49a] observed a coenzyme in pigeon and pig liver extracts which promoted the acetylation of choline and other amines, and also the condensation of acetate into long-chain units; this "Coenzyme A" (CoA) was later isolated in a purified state[49b] and its chemical constitution subsequently determined.[50] It contains a mercapto-group $(R.CH_2.CH_2.SH)$ with which acetic acid or acetates unite to form an acetyl derivative, acetyl-Coenzyme A (*Acetyl-CoA*), which is considered to be the "activated" acetate which enters into condensation processes:

$$CH_3.CO.S.CoA + CH_3.CO.S.CoA \rightarrow CH_3.C(OH)(S.CoA).CH_2.CO.S.CoA \rightarrow$$
$$CH_3.CO.CH_2.CO.S.CoA, \text{ etc.}$$

Repetition of this process leads to the successive addition of $-CH_2.CO-$ units. This explains the manner in which acetyl units are combined into polyketonic chains, although the conversion of the latter into saturated alkyl chains has not at present been precisely defined; a possible mechanism is an enzyme reducing system operating in the opposite sense to that by which saturated fatty acids are oxidised in animals to β-ketonic acids ("β-oxidation").

Detailed reviews of work on Coenzyme A and Acetyl-CoA up to 1953 have been given by Lipmann,[50] by Lynen[51] and by Welch and Nichol.[52]

In 1957 Wakil and his co-workers commenced the publication of a series of studies. The results of these, and of concurrent studies by other investigators on the mechanism of fatty acid synthesis, were discussed in a comprehensive review by Wakil in 1961.[53] The general results obtained up to the present may be summed up briefly as below.

Two separate enzyme systems may be involved in fatty acid synthesis[54a]:

(*a*) A mitochondrial system which may involve some enzymes of the β-oxidation type working in reverse, and which may effect further elongation of fatty acids already present by C_2 units at a time (e.g., of palmitic to stearic acid). Synthesis by this mechanism is much less prominent or rapid than that by system (b).

(b) A non-mitochondrial system, located in the cytoplasm of cells, which catalyses conversion of Acetyl-CoA to higher fatty acids in presence of adenosine triphosphate (ATP), manganous ions, bicarbonate ions and reduced triphosphopyridine nucleotide (TPNH). This system, which appears to be the main pathway for synthesis of higher saturated fatty acids, has been found in pigeon and chicken livers, rat livers and kidneys, yeast cells and avocado fruits. It was further resolved into two enzyme systems, in one of which Acetyl-CoA in presence of ATP and manganous ions reacts with bicarbonate ion to produce a second co-enzyme, *malonyl-CoA*[54b]:

$$\text{Acetyl-CoA (CH}_3.\text{CO.CoA)} + \text{HCO}_3^- \rightarrow \text{Malonyl-CoA (COOH.CH}_2.\text{CO.CoA)}.$$

The other enzyme system, in presence of reduced triphosphopyridine nucleotide, effects further condensation of malonyl-CoA with itself and with acetyl-CoA, and leads ultimately (after decarboxylation and reduction) to the production of higher fatty acids, notably palmitic acid[54c]:

$$x\text{Malonyl-CoA} + \text{Acetyl CoA} \rightarrow \text{CH}_3.[\text{CH}_2]_{2x}.\text{COOH} + x\text{CO}_2 + (x+1)\text{CoA}.$$

In the latest communication available[54d] Bressler and Wakil state that malonyl-CoA appears to provide the C_2 units for condensation (possibly in multiple units of four pre-condensed malonyl-CoA groups). Thus, in a particular experiment in which malonyl-CoA was condensed with isotopically labelled 1-C^{14}-acetyl-CoA, Wakil and Ganguly[54c] found that, for each mol. of palmitic acid synthesised, 1 mol. of acetyl-CoA, 7 mols. of malonyl-CoA and 14 mols. of reduced triphosphopyridine nucleotide were consumed, and 7 mols. each of carbon dioxide, Coenzyme A and water were formed. The synthesised palmitic acid contained only one C^{14} atom, this being in the terminal carboxylic group, so that the final condensation must have been:

$$7\ \text{COOH.CH}_2.\text{CO.S.CoA} + \text{CH}_3.\text{C}^{14}\text{O.SCoA} \rightarrow \text{CH}_3.[\text{CH}_2]_{14}.\text{C}^{14}\text{OOH} + 8\ \text{SH.CoA}$$

They state that the enzyme-bound acyl groups undergo a decarboxylation-condensation reaction, followed *either* by reduction (TPNH), dehydration to olefine, and further reduction to an enzyme-bound saturated compound; *or* by repeated condensation and decarboxylation of malonyl groups to form an enzyme-bound keto-acyl compound, the carbonyl groups in which are then successively reduced by TPNH to hydroxyl groups, followed by dehydration and further reduction (TPNH) to the saturated CoA derivative.

In this particular experiment the conditions led to almost exclusive production of palmitic acid, but in other experiments (e.g., Gibson, Porter et al.[54a]) progressively smaller amounts of myristic and lauric acid were produced in addition to the predominating palmitic acid. Stearic acid, in contrast, was usually only observed in small amounts, and is perhaps only produced in quantity by addition under appropriate conditions, of a further acetyl-CoA unit to the C_{16} keto-acyl complex produced by condensation of malonyl-CoA as above.

In the above paragraphs a necessarily abbreviated account has been given of the difficult enzyme studies which appear to have defined, much more precisely than previously but still not completely, the stages by which hexoses are transformed into higher *saturated* fatty acids after resolution into C_2 units which are built up again through the media of acetyl-CoA and malonyl-CoA. It must be stressed, however, that in all this work the products attained belong to the *saturated* series.

It is now appropriate to summarise the known facts concerning the biosynthesis in plants and animals of saturated and unsaturated fatty acids, and of glycerol.

Biosynthesis of saturated fatty acids. From the above general account it would seem that, in the systems studied, palmitic acid is in all instances the predominating product of the biosyntheses. In one case (Wakil and Ganguly[54c]) palmitic acid is the only product mentioned, but in others (Tietz *et al.*[55]) this acid was accompanied by progressively smaller quantities of myristic, lauric and decanoic acids, e.g., a product is mentioned which consisted of palmitic 65, myristic 22 and lauric 12 per cent., with traces of stearic and decanoic acids. Apparently stearic acid is considered to be produced only by a subsidiary process of elongation of some palmitoyl enzyme complexes by further addition of one acetyl-CoA unit.[53, 56a] In this connection it may be mentioned that Popják, French *et al.*[39b] observed that when radioactive acetate ($CH_3.C^{14}OONa$) was injected into a goat, the milk fatty acids up to and including palmitic were radioactive, but radioactivity was almost absent from the stearic and oleic acids also present.

All the studies of the Wakil school involved enzyme systems isolated from animal sources, and the results are consonant with the observed presence of palmitic acid as the predominant saturated acid in animal fats. In the reserve fats of the higher land animals palmitic acid attains approximately 30 per cent. of the total fatty acids,* and is accompanied by only minor amounts of myristic and stearic acids, except in ruminants and quasi-ruminants (Chapter III, pp. 108, 109). The proposed mechanism of biosynthesis of saturated fatty acids is also in harmony with this observation, which has been found to hold for the saturated acids of vegetable as well as animal fats: the predominating saturated acid is accompanied by small proportions of the acids containing two more and two less carbon atoms in their molecules.

It is no disparagement of the advances thus made by enzyme studies in our understanding of the mechanism of biosynthesis of saturated acids to refer in the next place to other aspects which must be taken into account.

(i) Whilst in animal fats and in a very large number of vegetable seed or fruit-coat fats palmitic is the outstanding saturated acid, quite an impressive number of seed fats have another acid as the predominating saturated component (lauric acid in Palmæ and many Lauraceæ seed fats, myristic in Myristicaceæ, decanoic in elm seed fat and some other seed fats of Ulmaceæ, stearic in many Sapotaceæ and Guttiferæ, and arachidic, behenic or lignoceric in some Sapindaceæ and a few Leguminous seed fats). The occurrence of such

* Since, of the remaining 70 per cent. of animal depot fatty acids, 60 per cent. or somewhat more consists of C_{18} acids (mainly oleic and some linoleic), the ratio of palmitic to C_{18} (mainly unsaturated) acids in these fats is very close to $1:2$ (*cf.* pp. 111, 121).

saturated acids is in close alignment with the biological classification of the plants in the seeds of which they occur; it should prove a fascinating, if at present remote, quest to ascertain how, in specific biological groups, the biosynthesis mechanism (or the enzyme systems which control it) is modified in order to produce in different cases different acids as the main saturated components.

(ii) "*Stearic-rich*" *fats of ruminants*. A seeming exception to the general finding that stearic acid is a relatively minor component of animal fats is that in the fats of ruminants, and of somewhat physiologically related types such as marsupials and hippopotamus, stearic acid makes an important contribution (in some cases up to 25 or 30 per cent. of the total fatty acids). It has, however, been conclusively established[33, 34] (*cf.* Chapter III, p. 112) that in these animals linoleic (or other unsaturated) glycerides in their diet are readily hydrogenated to less unsaturated derivatives and finally to stearic glycerides by the specific bacteria and/or protozoa in the rumen or rumen-like digestive tract. The production of these glycerides unusually rich in stearic acid is thus a secondary process carried out on pre-synthesised (unsaturated) fatty acid chains.

(iii) *Short-chain saturated acids of milk fats*. It has already been mentioned (p. 554) that the characteristic short-chain saturated acids of milk fats have been shown to be produced in the lactating glands of ruminants from C_2 units ("acetate" or acetyl-CoA). Popják and Tietz,[57a] however, have observed that this biosynthesis does not require the complex systems requisite for the higher saturated acids,[54a] but proceeds in presence of adenosine triphosphate alone, so that the enzyme system for short-chain saturated acids may be different from that for the acids with long carbon chains. Ganguly[57b] suggests that part only of the milk fat acids are synthesised in the mammary gland, the rest elsewhere (probably in the liver) and transported in the blood to the udders.

Biosynthesis of unsaturated fatty acids. In the reserve fats of most land animals the unsaturated acids (largely oleic, but often with significant proportions of linoleic) amount to at least 60 per cent. of the total fatty acids. In seed fats this proportion is often much exceeded; in liquid seed fatty oils (which are far more abundant than more saturated or solid seed fats) the proportion of saturated fatty acids (mostly palmitic, with a small amount of myristic and/or stearic) is often less than 10 per cent. of the total fatty acids, and the unsaturated acids (oleic, often much linoleic, sometimes linolenic, in relatively few instances epoxyoleic, elæostearic or other unusual acid) will together approach to 90 per cent. of the total fatty acid production in vegetable seeds. Millions of tons of unsaturated C_{18} acids (mainly oleic and linoleic) must therefore be produced annually in the vegetable and animal kingdoms, and adequate explanation of their synthesis is the most pressing aspect of the general problem of fat biosynthesis.

Yet, almost the only approach to it so far has been hypothetical and rather naive: perhaps taking the easiest way out, it is not infrequently taken for granted that all these unsaturated acids arise by "desaturation" (dehydrogenation in a peculiarly selective way) of stearic acid.

Of course in some animals desaturation of stearic or palmitic acid has been shown to occur in some conditions. Thus, "tracer" studies of Schoenheimer and Rittenberg[58] (1936–1940) with rats or mice treated with deuterium in the form of "heavy water" (D_2O) showed the presence of deuterium in the unsaturated acids, but to a less extent than in the stearic or palmitic acids synthesised; but later Bloch[59a] (1948) concluded from similar studies that entirely separate processes are involved in the biosynthesis of saturated and unsaturated fatty acids. Another example is some dietary experiments on eels[60] (1940) which indicated that both hydrogenation and dehydrogenation take place during the elaboration of fish depot fatty acids. Although Bloch et al.[59b] (1961–1962) found evidence that in yeast cells oleic acid is formed directly from stearic acid, Singh and Walker[59c] (1956), observing the *amounts* of saturated, oleic and linoleic acids produced during incubation of *Aspergillus nidulans* at stages up to 21 days, found that the weights of each acid increased or decreased together, and that the results were not in accordance with the hypothesis that, in the biosynthesis of the mould fat, unsaturated acids are provided by dehydrogenation of saturated acids. Similarly, Handwerck and Fouarger[56b] (1959), working with rats, deduced that only a part of the monoethenoid acids was formed directly from the corresponding saturated acids; James[61] (1962), studying the formation of fatty acids by isolated plant (*Ricinus communis*) leaves, found that isotopically labelled palmitic or stearic acid did not produce any labelled unsaturated acids, although isotopically labelled oleic acid gave labelled linoleic acid. Simmons and Quackenbush[16] (1954), in the course of work on the formation of fat in soya beans at different stages of ripening, stated that they found no evidence for dehydrogenation of saturated acids during the ripening.

Evidence on the matter is thus, at least, conflicting; moreover it should be pointed out that in the animal experiments the unsaturated acids presumed to result from desaturation were always small in proportion to the saturated acids from which they arose. These circumstances do not apply in the liquid seed fatty oils in which the bulk of the oleic and linoleic acids in nature are produced. Let us take by way of example a tobacco seed oil with component acids palmitic 7, stearic 3, oleic 15 and linoleic 75 per cent. (wt.): we are asked to believe that in the seed stearic acid is continuously synthesised and concurrently selectively desaturated, first to oleic and then to linoleic, with the final result that 75 per cent. of linoleic acid is produced and 15 per cent. of oleic acid, leaving a minute (3 per cent.) proportion of the stearic intermediate in the finished article.

It seems a remarkably inefficient manner of synthesis for a natural process, especially from the standpoint of the energy changes involved. Indeed, Leathes and Raper[62] expressed the opinion forty years ago that it seems improbable that the saturated acids are the intermediate and the unsaturated acids the final products of biosynthesis, because the saturated acids first formed would be relatively more stable than the unsaturated acids; the saturated acids contain a greater store of potential energy than the unsaturated ones, and it does not seem clear why a substance stored up as a source of energy should be made first with a maximum store and then partially degraded to one with a lower potential energy by an oxidation process. These authors added that it is almost certain that a process of "desaturation" takes place when reserve fat is called upon to yield up its energy, but that it appears unlikely as a process which operates in the synthesis of unsaturated acids previous to their storage as neutral fat. Leathes and Raper also considered the possibility that fats are formed in nature by a series of reactions, the end points of which vary according to the temperature at which they occur: they suggested that at higher temperatures the reactions leading to the formation of higher saturated fatty acids may reach completion, while at lower temperatures the same end point is not reached, the unsaturated fatty acids then forming the final products. It will be seen that, on this view, the unsaturated acids are regarded as the intermediate, and the saturated acids as the ultimate, products of synthesis. As indicated earlier in this chapter (pp. 537–539) there are at least two positive pieces of evidence, based upon the final composition of seed fats, which point exceedingly strongly to the correctness of this view.

(*a*) Some plant species, when grown in different environments, produce seed fats differing in unsaturation, the highest content of linoleic acid (or linolenic acid in the case of linseed oil) and the lowest content of oleic acid being attained when the plant is grown in the coolest climate.

(*b*) Detailed examination of the component acids in oils from the same species grown in different climates has further established the specific nature of these variations as follows:

(i) Each species produces its own characteristic *qualitative* mixture of seed fatty acids, which remains the same irrespective of the environment in which it is grown;

(ii) In any one species, growth in cooler conditions (where chemical transformations will proceed more slowly and less completely than in warmer conditions) leads to seed fats richer in the more unsaturated acids and poorer in oleic acid than the seed fats developed under warmer conditions;

(iii) These variations are confined to the unsaturated C_{18} acids (oleic, linoleic, and, if present, linolenic) in the seed fats: under the conditions which favour maximum production of oleic glycerides, *no additional stearic glycerides are produced*;

(iv) On the contrary, the proportion of *saturated* acids alters very little with differences in climatic temperature. Such small change as there is consists in the production of slightly greater proportions of saturated acids under the (cooler) conditions which lead to maximum unsaturation in the unsaturated acids.

This is the most conclusive evidence which has yet appeared that the biosyntheses of saturated and unsaturated acids follow entirely different routes. It is also notable that whilst, as already pointed out, the characteristic production of a series of saturated acids (with one usually predominating) accords well with the hypothesis of their formation from C_2 units, the unsaturated acids in seed fats, whether mono- or multi-ethenoid, usually possess the same number of carbon atoms, and do not include several members of the homologous series.

The important conclusion to be drawn from the preponderance of the more unsaturated acids in seeds of a given species which have matured at a comparatively low temperature is that the sequence of the final stages of the fatty acid syntheses is from the most unsaturated to the least (mono-ethenoid). If this feature is coupled with the repeated occurrence of groupings of three, or multiples of three, carbon atoms, as in $=CH.CH_2.CH=$, $=CH.[CH_2]_7$. COOH, etc., it is reasonable to conclude that the final stages of unsaturated fatty acid synthesis follow a general pattern somewhat as follows:

$$-C.C.C-..-C.C.C-..-C.C.C-..-C.C.C-..-C.C.C-..-C.C.C-$$
$$\downarrow$$
$$-C.C.C-..-C.C.C-..-C.C.CH:CH.[CH_2]_7.COOH \ (\rightarrow \text{linolenic acid})$$
$$\downarrow$$
$$-C.C.C-..-C.C.CH:CH.CH_2.CH:CH.[CH_2]_7.COOH \ (\rightarrow \text{linoleic acid})$$
$$\downarrow$$
$$CH_3.[CH_2]_7.CH:CH.[CH_2]_7.COOH \ (\text{oleic acid})$$

In this connection the importance which has become attached of late to malonyl-Coenzyme A as a factor in the biosynthesis of saturated acids may well become of further significance in that of unsaturated acids, since the malonyl grouping

$$-OC.CH_2.CO-$$

contains the carbon skeleton

$$=(H)C.CH_2.C(H)=$$

which occurs so repeatedly in the higher unsaturated fatty acids.

Whether these possibilities, based on considerations of the constitution of ultimate products, will inspire further biochemical researches remains to be seen; perhaps it may be permissible to recall that in another instance, the composition of stearic-rich ruminant fats, a similar prediction from the specific nature of the depot fats was substantiated experimentally twenty years after it was made (cf. Chapter III, p. 112). They are, of course, merely general suggestions of what the ultimate course of events may be in the linolenic-linoleic-oleic series. They do not account for other acids such as, for example, the conjugated elæostearic acid or for the petroselinic and tariric group in which unsaturation is in the 6:7 position (which again leaves a C_6 and a C_{12} (multiples of C_3) on each side of the ethenoid linkage). Again, a number of acids (such as erucic) belong to the general series $CH_3.[CH_2]_7.CH:CH.$ $[CH_2]_n.COOH$, in which the non-carboxylic half of the oleic molecule is present; it has been suggested that such acids may arise from a specific lengthening of an oleic precursor, two carbon atoms at a time, at the carboxyl end of the molecule.

No intermediate compounds have ever been detected with any certainty in plant or animal tissues which might indicate earlier stages of the transition from sugar to fat. On any hypothesis it is evident that hydroxylated compounds must intervene in the course of the process. The only pointer here is that hydroxy-fatty acids, in most cases in which they occur in natural fats, have the hydroxyl group attached to a carbon atom which is related to a multiple of 3 carbon atoms in the acid chain[63]: 9-hydroxy-octadec-12-enoic acid in *Strophanthus*, 12-hydroxy-octadec-9-enoic (ricinoleic) acid in *Ricinus*, 18-hydroxy-octadeca-9,11,13-trienoic (kamlolenic) acid in *Mallotus* seed fats.

It will be noticed that, in all this discussion, attention is directed to the synthesis mechanism of *fatty acids*: their assemblage into neutral triglycerides has not been the subject of consideration, except in so far that there is some evidence (not too definite) that in seed fats the acids are first of all synthesised and, subsequently, esterified into glycerides.* It still remains to account for the very characteristic manner in which, in seed fats, oleic and linoleic acids are selectively attached to the central (2-)glyceryl position. Further, in view of the now apparent different routes of synthesis of saturated and unsaturated acids, the marked tendency for animals to synthesise fats containing very large proportions of palmito-di-unsaturated C_{18} glycerides (mainly palmitodiolein, which also occurs frequently in vegetable fats) is a characteristic feature which obviously requires an adequate explanation.

It will be seen that the problem of the synthesis of fats *in vivo* from carbohydrates is extraordinarily complex and difficult. There are so many varieties of fat components that it is not at all easy to make a logical and clear statement of the case, quite apart from the lack of ascertained facts and the uncertain premises of some of the suggested hypotheses. The foregoing arguments may be summed up by saying that there is general and apparently well-founded belief that carbohydrates, and indeed hexoses, are the chief precursors of fats synthesised in plants and animals; that a number of suggestions have been made as to the chemical processes through which the conversion into fat may be effected; but that relatively few of these hypotheses have accorded sufficient weight to consideration of the different characteristic groups of component acids which are known to be representative of various natural biological groups of fats.

If one or other of the sequences of processes suggested above should prove to be a rudimentary approximation (and, with our present knowledge, it can be no more) to the biochemical conversion of carbohydrate into fatty derivatives of the nature of oleic and linoleic acids, there nevertheless still remain a number of difficult problems to solve before the origin of the curiously specific mixtures of components which characterise the fats of different groups in the biological world receives a rational and adequate explanation.

Biosynthesis of glycerol. The glycerol which is requisite for the ready conversion of fatty acids synthesised in plant or animal organs and tissues is produced from hexose, presumably by the same or similar enzyme processes which operate in moulds and yeasts. The course of alcoholic fermentation by yeast is considered to follow the mechanisms suggested by Embden[64a] and by Meyerhof,[64b] which may be summarised as follows:

Glucose is phosphorylated to glucose 1,6-diphosphate, which is broken down into a molecule each of glycerophosphoric acid, $CH_2(OH).CH(OH).CH_2.O(PO_3H_2)$ and phosphoglyceric acid, $(PO_3H_2).O.CH_2.CH(OH).COOH$.

---

* Kartha[19b] has very recently (1964) observed that there are no mono- or di-glycerides produced at any stage in the development of fat in ripening coconuts. This indicates that a glycerol molecule adsorbed on a lipase enzyme is not desorbed until its three hydroxyl groups have all been esterified with fatty acids. If this procedure is subsequently found to hold generally for developing fats in other species of vegetable fruits, it will mark an important advance in our knowledge of the biosynthesis of seed glycerides.

The latter decomposes into phosphoric acid and pyruvic acid, $CH_3.CO.COOH$, which yields acetaldehyde and carbon dioxide. A further molecule of glucose diphosphate interacts with the acetaldehyde to give phosphoglyceric acid and ethyl alcohol. If the presumed acetaldehyde formation is otherwise disposed of (e.g., as the C_2 or "acetate" unit required for fatty acid synthesis) the glycerophosphoric acid produced in the first stage of the sequence represents the source of the glycerol necessary for the conversion of carbohydrate into, ultimately, the natural triglycerides.

According to results obtained by Popják, Hunter and French[65] by the injection of isotopically labelled glucose into rabbits the production of glycerol is much more rapid than that of fatty acids, so that it would appear that excess of glycerol is always available to convert synthesised fatty acids into glycerides.

The remarkable feature is that certain fatty acids (in seed fats, oleic and linoleic) are selectively united with the central (secondary alcoholic) group of the glycerol molecule – possibly, in the first instance, with the 2-hydroxyl group in glycerophosphoric acid, $CH_2OH.CH(O.COR).CH_2.O(PO_3H_2)$.

The Assimilation of Preformed Fats by Animals

When preformed fats form part of the diet of an animal, they are dealt with, not in the liver, but in the epithelial cells (villi) of the small intestine. From these, the fats which are absorbed by the animal pass into the lymph or chyle which flows through the lacteals of the small intestine into the thoracic duct and finally emerges into the blood stream. This peculiarity has rendered the fate of ingested fat more amenable to experimental study than the allied problem of fat synthesis in the animal; and possibly has led to somewhat disproportionate stress being laid at times upon the formation of fat in animals by direct assimilation. At one time it was considered that the fatty acids were entirely absorbed as soaps, but later it was more generally held that the absorption proceeds mainly *via* the fatty acids,[66a] perhaps partially present as soaps, but that it is certainly promoted by the solvent action of the bile acids[66b] and, perhaps, of other substances such as lecithin which may be present. In a later development[67] the view that lipolysis is an essential preliminary to fat absorption supposed that the fat is first completely hydrolysed, and then resynthesised in the intestinal cells with the aid of intermediate phosphorylation (i.e., by the intermediary of phosphatides).

Since about 1940 evidence against the direct chemical intervention of phosphatides in the process of fat absorption has resulted from the studies of several different investigators. Thus G. O. Burr *et al.*,[68a] using maize oil acids which had been isomerised by alkali to conjugated octadecadienoic acids, traced the passage of these into phosphatides and neutral fat in the intestinal mucosa by spectrographic observation, and thereby showed that there was no correlation between the rate of transport of fat and the incorporation of the fatty acids into the mucosal phosphatides; Sinclair and Stewart[68b] found that the hydroxyl values of the phospholipids of the small intestine and the liver in rats fed on a diet containing 48 per cent. of castor oil were the same as those for the control animals; and Chaikoff *et al.*[68c] showed that neither the amount nor the turnover of phosphatides in the mucosa or villi of the small intestine is altered by the ingestion of cream, maize oil, or maize oil fatty acids by dogs or rats.

Later work by Frazer and his school[69] has shown that the concept that fat absorption can only take place after complete hydrolysis of the glycerides should be replaced by a "partition hypothesis", according to which particulate absorption of glycerides as such in an extremely dispersed state occurs through the chyle, whilst fatty acids produced by lipolysis of glycerides in the small intestine pass into the blood stream *via* the portal vein. Frazer utilised a method of tracing the glycerides present in body-fluids (blood) by microscopic observation ("chylomicrography"), employing dark-ground illumination which permitted the particles of unhydrolysed fat (glycerides) to be detected and counted. In this way the sequence of events consequent upon ingestion of fatty meals, or of olive or other fatty oil, was followed. It was found that hydrolysis takes place, but only partially; and that *unhydrolysed fat* passes directly as such by the lacteal-lymphatic system and thence to the fat depots, whilst the fatty acids formed pass by the capillaries and the portal vein to the liver where they may be further metabolised. Frazer's explanation is therefore that ingested fat which is to be deposited as reserve fat by the animal is directly absorbed (without intermediate hydrolysis and resynthesis) *via* the lymphatic system; lipolysis (i.e., resolution into free fatty acids) is not connected with fat deposition, but regulates the fate of absorbed glycerides and thus may also provide fatty acids for soap and phosphatide formation.

Frazer and Sammons[70] (1945) studied the hydrolysis of olive oil with pancreatic lipase over four-hour periods, and demonstrated that the free fatty acid liberated is not accompanied by the equivalent amount of free glycerol; on the contrary, the acetyl value of the unhydrolysed portion rises to a figure equivalent to a content of at least 20–25 per cent. of monoglyceride, indicating that the hydrolysis proceeds in stages and is far from complete in the period of normal digestion of fat. They also showed that bile salt—fatty acid—monoglyceride provides a complex which is an emulsifying system for neutral triglycerides, and which is stable over the pH range of 5·0–9·0. Brown and Shrewsbury[71] had shown earlier (1941) that monostearin or monolinolein can be utilised by rats in the elaboration of triglycerides, and that the ingested monoglycerides appear in the depot fat as triglycerides.

Additional evidence, from a different angle, for Frazer's hypothesis of particulate absorption of ingested glycerides has resulted from Garton's examination[72] of depot fat component glycerides and acids in pigs which had received massive rations of whale oil, or of equal amounts of lard and cod liver oil, in their food. It was found that the body fats in question could be separated, by simple crystallisation from acetone at $-40°$ C., into an insoluble fraction (the component acids of which closely simulated those of typical fat synthesised by the pig[23]), and a soluble fraction, the component acids in which were of much the same nature as those in the ingested marine animal oils (for details see Chapter III, Tables 43A and 43B, pp., 124, 125). The experiment with pigs fed on whale oil proved that the latter had been deposited in the adipose tissues without any interchange of acyl groups with those in glycerides synthesised by the pig, but did not indicate whether the whale oil glycerides had been absorbed directly, or after hydrolysis and resynthesis. Feeding a mixture of lard and cod liver oil, however, led to exactly the same result, whereas in this instance it is inconceivable that, had the ingested lard and cod liver oil been hydrolysed and resynthesised in the small intestine, the resynthesised glycerides would not have displayed an intermingling of the acyl groups of both the ingested lard and the fish oil, so that no straightforward segregation by solvent into largely unchanged marine animal oil and typical synthesised pig fat would have been possible.

Reference may be made here to two more recent studies by Blomstrand *et al.*[73] (1958–1959) in which the carbon atom in the carboxyl groups of palmitic, oleic, or linoleic acids was the C^{14} isotope, and these acids or their glycerides fed to human subjects. When the labelled oleic or palmitic acid was given as free acid, about half was transported in the lymph and incorporated into triglycerides and phospholipids: when fed as triglycerides, about 90 per cent. of the triglycerides in the lymph contained isotopic C^{14} atoms.[73a] The other communication[73b] dealt with the additions to human diet of trilinolein synthesised from isotopically labelled linoleic acid; in this instance the thoracic lymph lipids contained from 20 to 50 per cent. of labelled linoleic acid which must have resulted from hydrolysis of the labelled trilinolein.

Shorland[74a] suggested that animal fats may be divided into two classes, "homolipoid" and "heterolipoid", according to whether or not their composition is readily affected by the incorporation of dietary (exogenous) fats with their own synthetic (endogenous) fat; and subsequently pointed out[74b] that at least four different types of depot fats may be distinguished: (a) mixtures of synthesised and unchanged dietary fat (as in the pigs fed on marine animal oils), (b) mixtures of synthesised fat and of dietary fat (with the same acids as in the latter but in different proportions), e.g., pasture-fed horses, (c) mixtures of synthesised fat and dietary fat (the latter having undergone great modification) and (d) almost wholly synthesised fat. In the present state of very incomplete knowledge of (i) the respective contributions of synthetic and assimilated dietary fats to the depot fats of the majority of animal species and (ii) the variable degrees and the exact manner in which modifications of ingested fats take place prior to being laid down in the fat deposits, it is desirable to accumulate more precise factual data on these subjects rather than to attempt too much, and possibly premature, classification — which is likely to lead to over-simplification and further confusion rather than to be permanently helpful.

The effect on depot fat component acids of fats taken in the diets of animals was dealt with in Chapters II and III, where data were available, following the more normal types of reserve fat in each animal. Many instances are recapitulated in Table 143.

Instances in which acids present in the ingested fats (but not normally in the body fats of the animals concerned) appeared in the depots include the beetle studied by Collin, Miss Cruikshank's hens and their eggs (the latter only in the case of linolenic acid from linseed or hempseed), the crab *Birgus latro*, rats (in the cases of cod liver, cottonseed, coconut, palm, and olive oils), pigs (soya beans, groundnuts, menhaden oil), dog (rape oil), whilst some of the specific acids of rape and cod liver oils appeared in the milk fats of cows receiving these fatty oils.

Examples of interference with the normal composition of animal depot fats as a result of ingestion of dietary fat are perhaps more interesting. Amongst these may be recalled the effects of feeding cottonseed oil to the extent of 8 per cent. or more of the diet of pigs (Ellis, Rothwell and Pool[82b]), and of feeding rats on diets containing 40 per cent. of beef fat or palm oil; in these cases the palmitic acid content of the depot fat fell below both (i) the normal figure for that of the animal on a low-fat diet, and (ii) the palmitic acid content of the ingested fats themselves. This, of course, indicates on the one hand inability to absorb all the palmitic acid contained in the dietary fats and, on the other, interference with the normal composition of the (mainly synthetic) depot fat of the animal.

Similarly, the ingestion of some fatty oils (especially cod liver oil) by cows causes marked alterations in the component acids of their milk fats, although

TABLE 143

FAT	ANIMAL GROUP	SPECIES	INGESTED FATS	INVESTIGATOR	CHAP.	PAGES
Flesh	Fish	Herring	Chiefly copepods	Lovern[75a]	II	45
"	"	Eels	Herring, mussel	Lovern[75b]	II	58
Body	Invertebrate	Hermit crab (Birgus latro)	Coconuts	Hilditch and Murti[77a]	II	33
"	Insects	Pachymerus dactris	Manicaria saccifera nut	Collin[77b]	III	83
Depot	Birds	Domestic hen; also egg (yolk)	Palm kernel oil, hempseed oil, or mutton tallow	Cruikshank[78]	III	88, 91
"	"	Sea-birds	(?) Fish fats	Lovern[75c]	III	89
"	Rodents	Rat	Cod liver oil	Banks et al.[79]	III	95–97
"	"	"	Cottonseed oil	Spadola and Ellis[80]	III	95–97
"	"	"	Cow milk fat	Longenecker and Hilditch[81a]	III	94, 95
"	"	"	Coconut oil, maize oil	Longenecker[81b]	III	96
"	Herbivora	Pig	Soya bean, groundnut	Ellis and Zeller[82a]	III	122
"	"	"	Cottonseed oil	Ellis et al.[82b]	III	123
"	"	"	Menhaden oil	Brown[83]	III	123
"	"	"	Whale oil, cod liver oil	Garton et al.[72]	III	124
"	"	"	Low-fat diet	Hilditch et al.[23]	III	119
"	"	Ox	Soya bean, maize, coconut, menhaden oils	Thomas et al.[84]	III	126
"	Carnivora	Dog	Linseed oil, mutton tallow	Lebedev[85]	III	126
"	"	"	Rape oil	Munk[86]	III	126
Milk	Herbivora	Cow	Coconut, soya bean oils	Hilditch and Sleightholme[87a]	III	155
"	"	"	Linseed, rape, cod liver oils	Hilditch and Thompson[87b]	III	155

in this case the amount of any acid specific to the ingested fat which appears in the milk fat is relatively small.

In the two instances cited of fish fats, Lovern[75a,75b] has shown that modification (usually hydrogenation) of the ingested fat may take place during or after its deposition in the flesh of the eel or herring. Lovern[75d] also fed ethyl palmitate or ethyl myristate to eels: the former caused considerable increase in the palmitic and hexadecenoic acid contents of the depot fat, the latter gave rise to smaller increases in tetradecenoic and palmitic acids (this apparently by compensating hydrogenation of hexadecenoic acid already present in the eel depot fat). K. Bernhard et al.[76] (1958) fed rats with C^{14}-oleic acid or C^{14}-linoleic acid, and found that the unsaturated acids in the liver and the body fats contained 91–98 per cent. of the total radioactivity of the total fatty acids; the radioactivity of palmitic and stearic acids in the rat lipids was very small, suggesting that these had resulted from C_2-unit synthesis rather than by hydrogenation of the unsaturated acids. Also, when C^{14}-stearic acid was fed, the radioactive fatty acids in the rat fats consisted of C^{14}-stearic 57, C^{14}-palmitic 15·5 and C^{14}-oleic 27·5 per cent., suggesting dehydrogenation of C^{14}-stearic to C^{14}-oleic acid, and also, apparently, conversion of some C^{14}-stearic to C^{14}-palmitic acid.

It has been mentioned in earlier parts of this book that saturated acids with fewer than 10 or 12 carbon atoms are not stored in animal reserve fats. Longenecker[81b] showed, by feeding coconut oil to rats, that their depot fatty acids included 27 per cent. lauric and 0·5 per cent. decanoic, compared with 45 per cent. lauric, 8 per cent. decanoic, 5 per cent. octanoic and 0·8 per cent. hexanoic in the fatty acids of the ingested coconut oil. This confirms the findings of Longenecker and Hilditch,[81a] and of other workers who administered butter fat to various animals. Using tributyrin which was "labelled" with deuterium, Morehouse[88] showed that ingested tributyrin appeared transiently in the tissue fats, but disappeared therefrom completely after 36 hours; further, it was not converted into long-chain fatty acids.

Other investigators[89a] have studied the assimilation of fats or fatty acids containing straight chains with an odd number of carbon atoms in the molecule, in the cases of dogs, young goats, and rabbits. The odd-numbered acids, from $C_{11}H_{22}O_2$ onwards, were assimilated and appeared in the fat depots, apparently as readily as the even-numbered acids of similar molecular weight.

The questions of whether reserve fats containing acids of the odd-numbered series can be utilised subsequently as well as those of the natural fatty (even-numbered) series, and whether, over a sufficiently long period, such "odd-numbered" fats may lead to pathological conditions, have also been considered in some of the studies referred to,[89a] but no clear-cut conclusions appear yet to have been reached. Hopkins, Chisholm et al.[89b] (1957) stated that eicosenoic and erucic acids, fed to rats as methyl esters, were laid down in the body fats, but apparently less readily than the linoleic glycerides in similarly ingested maize oil. Carroll and Noble[89c] (1957) found that 10 per cent. of erucic acid in male rat diets did not affect their normal growth rate and state of health, but resulted in the onset of sterility as time went on; although

Thomasson[102b] (1955) advanced evidence which showed that higher contents of erucic glycerides (as in rape or nasturtium seed oils) had a reducing effect on the rate of growth of rats.

Glycerides of specific acids have frequently been deliberately employed as a means of "labelling" or tracing ingested fats in the depots and other tissues of the animal body. Of the natural fats, cod liver oil with its highly unsaturated C_{20} and C_{22} acids, and rape oil with a high content of erucic acid, have often been used in this way, whilst glycerides of the artificially prepared elaidic acid or containing "*iso*oleic" acids of hydrogenation have been utilised. R. G. Sinclair,[90] especially, made systematic use of ingested elaidic glycerides in studying fat metabolism.

The use of deuterium was explored to the same end by Schoenheimer and Rittenberg,[91a] who obtained some remarkable results. Their evidence goes to show that ingested fats are not utilised directly for energy (oxidation), but are first deposited in the depots and subsequently mobilised therefrom. When mice were fed with ethyl (deutero)stearate (produced from linseed oil by hydrogenation with deuterium), their body fats contained (deutero)unsaturated acids, indicating desaturation of stearic to unsaturated acids or glycerides. Also, when the (deutero)unsaturated acids extracted from these animals were fed as esters to another group of mice, (deutero)stearic acid appeared in the body fats of the latter, indicating that hydrogenation of ingested fats may take place. In another experiment it was shown that ingestion of ethyl (deutero)stearate by mice leads to the presence in the depot fats not only of (deutero)stearic and (deutero)-unsaturated acids, as mentioned, but also of (deutero)palmitic acid; this was considered to show that stearic acid is converted in the animal into palmitic acid. The difficulties and the caution necessary in interpreting results obtained by this method have been emphasised by Schoenheimer[91b] and by Bonhoeffer.[91c] There is the possibility that deuterium in an acyl group may be exchanged for ordinary hydrogen in the body, and Schoenheimer et al.[91d] have shown that palmitic acid can acquire deuterium by contact with deutero-sulphuric acid.

Digestibility of ingested fats. Glycerides containing a wide variety of fatty acids (from butyric to arachidic, or from hexadecenoic and oleic to the highly unsaturated C_{22} acids) seem to be equally readily dealt with by animals. So long as the ingested fat is liquid at the temperature of the digestive tract, the specific nature of the natural fatty acids present is largely immaterial, so far as power of assimilation and utilisation is concerned. Fats of higher melting point are, however, absorbed with difficulty and are frequently excreted unchanged. Animals normally excrete a certain proportion of fat, fatty acids (or their salts), and in certain diseased conditions the amount may be much increased. When a normal healthy animal is fed with fats of high melting point, these are, however, excreted for the most part unchanged.

Wesson,[92a] Holmes, [92b] and Langworthy[92c] have determined the "digestive coefficients" of a large number of fats for human beings. Vegetable oils and soft fats (e.g., coconut or palm oils, cacao butter), the softer animal fats (such as butter, chicken fat, lard, beef suet), and cod liver oils all have coefficients of

95 per cent. or over, usually 97–99 per cent. Definitely lower coefficients were observed with mutton tallow (88·0 per cent.), deer fats m.p. 52–53° (81·7 per cent.), and "oleostearin," m.p. 50–56° (80·1 per cent.). It is quite clear that digestibility declines only when the fat approaches a melting point of about 48–50°.

Modern studies of the assimilation of triglycerides in rats by Mattson[93] have yielded interesting results. While tristearin hardly appeared in the lymph glycerides, monounsaturated-distearins and monostearo-diunsaturated glycerides were almost completely absorbed[93a]: the absorption coefficient is influenced by saturated acids only when they are present as trisaturated glycerides.

The assimilation into lymph glycerides of palmitic derivatives in which the palmitoyl carboxyl carbon was the radioactive isotope C^{14} was examined in some detail by Mattson and Volpenhein.[93c] 2-Palmito (1-C^{14})-diolein was absorbed more readily than the isomeric 1-palmito (1-C^{14})-diolein, but either was more freely assimilated than free palmitic (1-C^{14}) acid: with the palmito-dioleins, 85–90 per cent. of the palmitic acid was found in its original position after the processes of digestion and absorption. When mixtures of palmitic (1-C^{14}) acid with oleic or linoleic acid were fed, the palmitic acid was randomly distributed in the lymph triglycerides at all the glyceryl hydroxyl positions; but when free palmitic (1-C^{14}) acid in admixture with triolein or trilinolein was fed, the lymph triglycerides contained 22 per cent. of the palmitic acid attached to the central or 2-position.

A great many studies by a number of workers[94] were devoted at one period to animal-feeding trials (generally with rats) to determine whether natural cow milk fats are superior or not to the different kinds of fat-blends present in modern margarine or butter substitutes. Although in some few instances it appeared that growth was maintained somewhat better when butterfat was given, the great majority of the results go to show unequivocally that there is no significant difference in nutritive value between butter, margarine, or the vegetable oils (such as groundnut, cottonseed, etc., oils) one or more of which is usually present in quantity in margarines. It is interesting also to recall that human milk fat, in its component acids and glycerides, has been shown[95] to resemble the softer varieties of margarine much more closely than it does cow milk fat; in particular, it contains little or no acids with less than 12 carbon atoms in the molecule, and a definite amount (7 to 10 per cent.) of linoleic (octadeca-*cis*-9-*cis*-12-dienoic) acid.

Attention has also been given to the efficiency with which isomeric (*trans-*) forms of oleic glycerides (which are present in some quantity in hydrogenated fatty oils, and also to a smaller extent in butter and other ruminant fats) may be utilised by animals. Melnick and Deuel[96a] found that *trans-* and positional isomers of oleic glycerides are utilised as nutrients as effectively as oleoglycerides, and stated that hydrogenated fats compare favourably with natural fats of similar melting point in serving as sources of "essential fatty acids" (*cf.* below). Allen et al.[96b] fed weanling rats with diets which included *cis-* or *trans-*octadecenoic glycerides, and found that, with glycerides containing octadec-*trans*-9- or -*trans*-8-decenoic acid, 87–89 per cent. of these were metabolised, 10–12 per cent. stored in the fat depots, and not more than 1 per cent. was excreted. In a review of this subject[96c] they stated that the animal (including human) organism appears to be capable of metabolising *trans*-isomers, although there is some evidence which suggests that deposition of *trans*-acids in animal tissues may worsen a pre-existent deficiency of "essential fatty acids"; *trans*-isomers of monoene C_{18} acids, although present (2–7 per cent.) in maternal human depot fat, were not observed in the fœtus nor in the tissues of new-born infants. Mattson[93b] (1960) included methyl *cis-cis-*, *cis-trans-* or *trans-trans-* linoleate, elaidate, or oleate, with and without added *cis-cis-*linoleate, in the diet of weanling rats; only the *cis-cis*-linoleate possessed growth-promoting activity, but presence of the other (*cis-* or *trans-*) esters interfered with growth only if *cis-cis*-linoleate was not also present.

Fatty acids essential to growth or health. Certain unsaturated acids, especially linoleic and arachidonic, appear to be essential to health (or growth in young animals), but are apparently not synthesised by, at all events, certain animals. The most clear-cut instance is the rat, which develops specific diseased conditions if it is unable to obtain linoleic glycerides in its diet (Burr and Burr,[24] 1930). It is also almost certain that linoleic glycerides are not synthesised by the pig, which probably only deposits these in its depot fats as the result of ingestion from cereal, etc., meals.[23,82a]

Nunn and Smedley-MacLean[97a] (1938) observed the absence of tetra- and penta-ethenoid acids in the liver fats of rats fed on diets deficient in linoleic acid, but showed that arachidonic (eicosatetraenoic) acid appeared when methyl linoleate was added to the diet, whilst both eicosatetraenoic ($C_{20}H_{32}O_2$) and docosapentaenoic ($C_{22}H_{34}O_2$) acids were observed when the diet contained methyl linolenate. Smedley-MacLean and Hume[97b] (1940) put forward further evidence which suggested that these multi-ethenoid C_{20} or C_{22} acids promote growth in rats more efficiently than linoleic acid, but may not be essential to the normal metabolism of the cell. Rieckehoff, Holman and Burr[98a] (1949) observed that presence of maize oil in the diet led to formation of tetraenoic acids in the tissue lipids of various organs of the rat, and that the multi-ethenoid fatty acids were produced primarily in the phospholipids of the rat tissues, with very little in the neutral fat (glycerides). In 1950, Widmer and Holman[98b] confirmed that linoleic and linolenic (but not oleic or saturated) glycerides were essential to growth and were precursors of tetra- or hexa-ethenoid acids; they considered that the C_{20} tetraethenoid acid was derived from linoleic but not from linolenic acid, whilst, conversely, the C_{22} hexaethenoid acid resulted from linolenic, but not from linoleic, acid.

Thus the function of linoleic and linolenic acids appeared to be that of "building stones" for the production of multi-ethenoid C_{20} and C_{22} acids, these playing some essential part in enabling the animal to produce new tissues. That it is the presence of a certain amount of polyethenoid glycerides which is necessary to the health of the rat follows from the work of Turpeinen,[99a] who found in 1938 that, whilst small doses of methyl arachidonate or linoleyl alcohol cured the symptoms of fat-deficiency, methyl or ethyl esters of octadec-12-enoic, ricinoleic, erucic, and chaulmoogric acids failed to do so. That only certain polyethenoid derivatives can play the essential role of linoleic acid is seen in the work of Karrer and Koenig,[100] who found that octadeca-9,11-dienoic, nonadeca-10-13-dienoic, and eicosa-11,14-dienoic, acids were all ineffective.

Klenk[101] (1952) drew attention to the fact that the conventional Geneva nomenclature (with the carboxyl carbon atom numbered 1) for polyethenoid fatty acids does not clearly reveal a certain relationship in the arrangement of the double bonds, which however becomes clear if these are numbered from the terminal or methyl end of the molecules:

		POSITION OF DOUBLE BONDS	
	ACID	GENEVA NOMENCLATURE	NUMBERING FROM TERMINAL CH_3-GROUP
C_{18}	Linoleic	9, 12	6, 9
	Linolenic	9, 12, 15	3, 6, 9
	Tetraenoic	6, 9, 12, 15	3, 6, 9, 12
C_{20}	Dienoic	11, 14	6, 9
	Trienoic	5, 8, 11	9, 12, 15
	"	8, 11, 14	6, 9, 12
	Tetraenoic (Arachidonic)	5, 8, 11, 14	6, 9, 12, 15
	"	8, 11, 14, 17	3, 6, 9, 12
	Pentaenoic	5, 8, 11, 14, 17	3, 6, 9, 12, 15
C_{22}	Tetraenoic	4, 7, 10, 13	9, 12, 15, 18
	"	7, 10, 13, 16	6, 9, 12, 15
	Pentaenoic	4, 7, 10, 13, 16	6, 9, 12, 15, 18
	"	7, 10, 13, 16, 19	3, 6, 9, 12, 15
	Hexaenoic	4, 7, 10, 13, 16, 19	3, 6, 9, 12, 15, 18

Thomasson[102a] (1953) pointed out that the polyethenoid acids most active in promoting growth in animals invariably contain the "terminal" ethenoid groupings, 6, 9, etc. (e.g., linoleic and arachidonic acids), so that the terminal structure

$$CH_3 . [CH_2]_4 . CH:CH . CH_2 . CH:CH—$$

seems to be requisite for high "essential fatty acid" activity. Acids with the "terminal" groupings commencing at the 3rd carbon atom (e.g., linolenic, docosahexenoic)

$$CH_3 . CH_2 . CH:CH . CH_2 . CH:CH . CH_2 . CH:CH—$$

are stated to have less biological activity, although the literature is not explicit on this point.

Reinius and Turpeinen[99b] (1954) reported interesting results on the distribution of "essential fatty acid" activity in the organs and fat-depots of normal and of fat-deficient rats fed with radioactive (C^{14}) ethyl linoleate. In the fat-deficient rat a relatively much greater part of the absorbed radioactivity was present in the liver, heart, kidney and mesenterial lipids than in the subcutaneous fat, whereas in the normal rat the subcutaneous fat was relatively high in radioactivity:

Rat: Lipids:	Fat-deficient Relative activity	Normal Relative activity
Organs:		
Liver	26·7	10·3
Kidney	1·4	0·5
Heart	1·0	0·5
Depots:		
Mesentery	5·7	2·6
Subcutaneous	4·9	12·9

These figures are consistent with the existence of a vital need for the "essential" linoleic acid in the liver and some other organs of the rat.

According to Hopkins et al.[103] the proportion of saturated to oleic glycerides in a diet containing linoleic glycerides affects the influence of the latter on the growth of rats. Mixtures of fatty oils all containing 10 per cent. of linoleic glycerides, but in which the saturated contents varied from 10 to 70 per cent., and the oleic contents correspondingly from 80 to 20 per cent., showed that a high content of saturated glycerides was disadvantageous and that the optimum activity resulted from mixtures of about 30 per cent. saturated, 60 per cent. oleic and 10 per cent. linoleic acids in the dietary glycerides.

Klenk and Kremer[101b] (1960) incubated slices of livers of pigeons, turtle, frog, trout and other fish with (1-C^{14}) acetate and found that radioactivity predominated in the dicarboxylic acids produced by oxidative scission of the resultant liver fats, thus indicating that synthesis of the C_{20} and C_{22} polyethenoid acids takes place from exogenous precursors (linoleic and linolenic acids).

Much other investigation of the mechanism of the biosynthesis of C_{20}, C_{22}, etc., polyethenoid acids from short-chain precursors (linoleic, linolenic) has been carried out in the research schools of Reiser[104a] (1950–1951) and of Mead[104b] (1951–1960).

Earlier reviews of the subject of essential fatty acids will be found in the articles[105a] cited in the references to this chapter, and also a recent review[105b] (1958) of digestion and absorption of fats by animals.

References to Chapter VIII

1. J. B. Leathes and H. S. Raper, "The Fats" (Monographs on Biochemistry, London: Longmans, Green and Co. Ltd.), 2nd Ed., 1925. I. Smedley-MacLean, "The Metabolism of Fat", 1943 (London: Methuen and Co. Ltd.). W. R. Bloor, "The Biochemistry of the Fatty Acids", 1943. J. N. McNair, "Plant Fats in Relation to Environment and Evolution", Bot. Rev., 1945, II, 1–59. H. J. Deuel, Jr., "The Lipids, their Chemistry and Biochemistry", vol. I, 1951, vol. II, 1954, vol. III, 1957 (New York: Interscience Publishers Inc.). H. Desnuelle, "Structure and Properties of Phosphatides", and W. Bergmann, "Sterols" (in "The Chemistry of Fats and Other Lipids", vol. I, 1952; London: Pergamon Press). J. A. Lovern, "The Chemistry of Lipids of Biochemical Significance", 1955 (London: Methuen and Co., Ltd.). A. C. Frazer, "Fat Metabolism", Lectures Sci. Basis Med., 1954–5, 4, 31; Brit. Med. Bull., 1959, 14, 212. P. K. Stumpf, "Biosynthetic Pathways of Fatty Acids in Higher Plants", Proc. 4th Int. Cong. Biochem., Vienna, 1958, 13, 354. P. Hele, "Biosynthesis of Fatty Acids", Brit. Med. Bull., 1959, 14, 197. D. M. Gibson, "Fatty Acid Biosynthesis" (in "The Chemistry of Fats and other Lipids," Vol. VI, 1960 (London: Pergamon Press)).

2. (a) S. de Luca, Compt. rend., 1861, 53, 380; (b) W. Pfeffer, Jahrb. Wiss. Bot., 1872, 8, 580.

3. G. O. Burr and E. S. Miller, *Bot. Gaz.*, 1938, **99**, 773.
4. W. Uhlmann, Dissertation, Zurich, 1902.
5. (a) L. du Sablon, *Compt. rend.*, 1896, **123**, 1084; *Rev. gén. Bot.*, 1897, **9**, 313; (b) C. Valée, *Compt. rend.*, 1903, **136**, 114.
6. (a) S. Ivanov, *Beihefte Bot. Zentr.*, 1912, **28**, (I), 159; (b) S. Ivanov, *Ber. Deut. Bot. Ges.*, 1926, **44**, 31; *Z. Angew. Chem.*, 1929, **42**, 292; S. Ivanov and P. Klokov, *Allgem. Oel-Fett-Ztg.*, 1933, **30**, 149.
7. C. Gerber, *Compt. rend.*, 1897, **125**, 658, 732; *Journ. de Bot.*, 1901, **15**, 121.
8. E. Godlewski, *Jahrb. Wiss Bot.*, 1882, **13**, 491.
9. (a) J. V. Eyre and E. A. Fisher, *J. Agric. Sci.*, 1915, **7**, 120; (b) J. V. Eyre, *Biochem. J.*, 1931, **25**, 1902; (c) M. F. Barker, *J. Soc. Chem. Ind.*, 1932, **51**, 218T.
10. (a) E. C. Humphries, *Ann. Bot.*, 1943, **7**, 45; (b) D. L. Sahasrabuddhe, *Indian J. Agric. Sci.*, 1932, **3**, 57; (c) H. M. Sell, A. H. Best, W. Reuther and M. Drosdoff, *Plant Physiol.*, 1948, **23**, 359.
11. (a) P. Neumann, *Biochem. Z.*, 1941, **308**, 141; (b) B. Rewald and W. Riede, *Biochem. Z.*, 1933, **260**, 147; (c) H. K. Bauer, *Fettchem. Umschau*, 1934, **41**, 1.
12. (a) C. Caskey, Jr. and W. D. Gallup, *J. Agric. Res.*, 1931, **42**, 671; (b) E. Lonzinger and R. Raskina, *Maslob. Shir. Delo*, 1931, Nos. 2–3, 57.
13. D. N. Grindley, *J. Sci. Food Agric.*, 1950, **1**, 147.
14. A. C. Chibnall, 1941, privately communicated.
15. E. F. Terroine, *Ann. Sci. Nat. Bot.*, 1920, (X), **2**, 1.
16. R. O. Simmons and F. W. Quackenbush, *J. Amer. Oil Chem. Soc.*, 1954, **31**, 601.
17. R. P. A. Sims, W. G. McGregor, A. G. Plessers and J. C. Mes, *J. Amer. Oil Chem. Soc.*, 1961, **38**, 273, 276; M. E. McKillican and R. P. A. Sims, *ibid.*, 1963, **40**, 108.
18. C. Y. Hopkins and M. J. Chisholm, (a) *Canad. J. Biochem. Physiol.*, 1961, **39**, 1481; (b) *ibid.*, 1961, **39**, 829; (c) T. K. Miwa, F. R. Earle, G. C. Miwa and I. A. Wolff, *J. Amer. Oil Chem. Soc.*, 1963, **40**, 225.
19. (a) A. R. S. Kartha, A. S. Sethi and R. Narayanan, *J. Sci. Indust. Res. (India)*, 1959, **18C**, 172; (b) A. R. S. Kartha, *J. Sci. Food Agric.*, 1964, **15**, 299.
20. T. P. Hilditch, *Nature*, 1951, **167**, 298.
21. J. B. Lawes and J. H. Gilbert, *J. Roy. Agric. Soc.*, 1860, **21**, 433; *Phil. Mag.*, 1866, December; *J. Anat. Physiol.*, 1877, **11**, 577.
22. (a) M. Rubner, *Z. Biol.*, 1886, **22**, 272; (b) G. Rosenfeld, *Berlin Klin. Woch.*, No. 30; (c) S. Morgulis and J. H. Pratt, *Amer. J. Physiol.*, 1913, **32**, 200.
23. T. P. Hilditch, C. H. Lea and W. H. Pedelty, *Biochem. J.*, 1939, **33**, 493.
24. (a) G. O. Burr and M. M. Burr, *J. Biol. Chem.*, 1930, **86**, 587; (b) E. Gregory and J. C. Drummond, *Z. Vitaminsforschung*, 1932, **1**, 257; (c) H. E. Longenecker, *J. Biol. Chem.*, 1939, **128**, 645.
25. A. Banks and T. P. Hilditch, *Biochem. J.*, 1931, **25**, 1168.
26. (a) P. B. Kelly, R. Reiser and D. W. Hood, *J. Amer. Oil Chem. Soc.*, 1958, **35**, 189; 1959, **36**, 104; J. F. Mead, M. Kayama and R. Reiser, *ibid.*, 1960, **37**, 438; (b) N. R. Bottino and R. R. Brenner, *ibid.*, 1962, **39**, 319.
27. W. S. Rapson, H. M. Schwartz and N. J. van Rensberg, *J. Soc. Chem. Ind.*, 1945, **64**, 114.
28. O. Hildesheim and J. B. Leathes, *J. Physiol.*, 1904, **31**, Proc. I.
29. E. Klenk and O. von Schoenebeck, *Z. physiol. Chem.*, 1932, **209**, 112.
30. E. Tuerkischer and E. Wertheimer, *J. Physiol.*, 1941, **100**, 385; E. Mirski, *Biol. J.*, 1942, **36**, 232; J. Teppermann, J. R. Brobeck and C. N. H. Long, *Yale J. Biol. Med.*, 1943, **15**, 855; E. Wertheimer and B. Shapiro, *Physiol. Reviews*, 1948, **28**, 451.
31. J. B. Leathes and H. S. Raper, "The Fats", 2nd Ed., Monographs on Biochemistry, 1925, p. 157 (London: Longmans, Green and Co., Ltd.).
32. (a) W. R. Graham, T. S. G. Jones and H. D. Kay, *Proc. Roy. Soc.*, 1936, **B**, **120**, 330; (b) L. A. Maynard, C. M. McKay, G. H. Ellis, A. Z. Hodson and G. K. Davis, *Cornell University Agric. Expt. Station*, 1938, memoir 211; (c) J. C. Shaw and W. E. Petersen, *J. Dairy Sci.*, 1940, **23**, 1045; (d) W. G. Duncombe and R. F. Glascock, *Biochem. J.*, 1954, **57**, *Proceedings*, xi.

33. R. Reiser *et al.*, *Fed. Proc.*, 1951, **10**, 236; *J. Animal Sci.*, 1952, **11**, 705; *J. Amer. Oil Chem. Soc.*, 1956, **33**, 155; 1959, **36**, 129; G. A. Garton, A. K. Lough, *et al.*, *Nature*, 1958, **182**, 1511; *J. Gen. Microbiol.*, 1961, **25**, 215; D. E. Wright, *Nature*, 1959, **184**, 875; S. B. Tove and G. Matrone, *J. Nutrition*, 1962, **76**, 271.

34. F. B. Shorland, R. O. Weenink and A. T. Johns, *Nature*, 1955, **175**, 1129; (with I. R. C. MacDonald), *Biochem. J.*, 1957, **67**, 328; L. Hartman, F. B. Shorland *et al.*, Nature, 1954, **174**, 185; 1956, **178**, 1057; 1959, **184**, 2024; *Biochem. J.*, 1955, **61**, 603; 1958, **69**, 1.

35. J. Lewkowitsch, "Technology of Oils, Fats and Waxes", 6th Ed., 1922, Vol. II, p. 680.

36. V. Henriques and C. Hansen, *Skand. Arch. Physiol.*, 1901, **11**, 151.

37. H. K. Dean and T. P. Hilditch, *Biochem. J.*, 1933, **27**, 1950.

38. J. Hammond, *Chem. and Ind.*, 1933, **52**, 639.

39. (*a*) S. J. Folley and T. H. French, *Nature*, 1949, **163**, 174; *Biochem. J.*, 1949, **45**, 117; 1950, **46**, 465; S. J. Folley, *Biol. Rev.*, 1949, **24**, 316; *Biochem. Soc. Symposia*, 1952, No. **9**, 52; G. Popják, *ibid.*, 1952, No. **9**, 37; (*b*) G. Popják, T. H. French, G. D. Hunter and A. J. P. Martin, *Biochem. J.*, 1951, **48**, 612.

40. T. P. Hilditch, *Biochem. Soc. Symposia*, 1952, No. **9**, 63.

41. E. Fischer, *Ber.*, 1890, **23**, 2114; "Untersuchungen uber Kohlenhydrate und Fermente" (1909).

42. (*a*) L. Reichel and O. Schmid, *Angew. Chem.*, 1938, **51**, 190; (*b*) R. Kuhn, C. Grundmann and H. Trischmann, *Z. physiol. Chem.*, 1937, **248**, IV; F. G. Fischer, K. Hultzsch and W. Flaig, *Ber.*, 1937, **70** (B), 370; R. Kuhn, *J. Chem. Soc.*, 1938, 605; C. Grundmann, *Ber.*, 1948, **81**, 510.

43. E. F. Armstrong and J. Allan, *J. Soc. Chem. Ind.*, 1924, **43**, 216т.

44. (*a*) I. Smedley, *Zentr. Physiol.*, 1913, **26**, 915; (*b*) E. Lubrzynska and I. Smedley, *Biochem. J.*, 1913, **7**, 375.

45. (*a*) M. Nencki, *J. pr. Chem.*, 1878, **17**, 105; (*b*) A. Magnus-Levy, *Berl. physiol. Ges.*, 1901–2, No. 5; (*c*) J. B. Leathes, "Problems in Animal Metabolism", London, 1906; (*d*) H. S. Raper, *J. Chem. Soc.*, 1907, **91**, 1831.

46. (*a*) A. Loeb, *Biochem. Z.*, 1912, **47**, 118; (*b*) E. Friedmann, *ibid.*, 1913, **55**, 436; (*c*) I. Smedley-MacLean and D. Hoffert, *Biochem. J.*, 1926, **20**, 343.

47. H. Haehn and W. Kintoff, *Ber.*, 1923, **56**, 439; *Chemie der Zelle u. Gewebe*, 1925, **12**, 115.

48. D. Rittenberg and K. Bloch, *J. Biol. Chem.*, 1944, **154**, 311.

49. (*a*) F. Lipmann, *J. Biol. Chem.*, 1945, **160**, 173; (*b*) F. Lipmann *et al.*, *ibid.*, 1947, **167**, 869; 1950, **186**, 235.

50. F. Lipmann, *Advances in Enzymol.*, 1948, **6**, 231; *Harvey Lectures*, (New York, Academic Press), 1948, **44**, 99; *Bacteriol. Revs.*, 1953, **17**, 1.

51. F. Lynen, E. Reichert and L. Rueff, *Annalen*, 1951, **574**, 1; F. Lynen, *Harvey Lectures* (New York: Academic Press), 1954, **48**, 210.

52. A. D. Welch and C. A. Nichol, *Ann. Rev. Biochem.*, 1952, **21**, 633.

53. S. J. Wakil, *J. Lipid Res.*, 1961, **2**, 1.

54. (*a*) D. M. Gibson, J. W. Porter, A. Tietz and S. J. Wakil, *Biochim. Biophys. Acta*, 1957, **23**, 219, 453; (*b*) D. M. Gibson, E. B. Titchener and S. J. Wakil, *ibid.*, 1958, **30**, 376; *J. Amer. Chem. Soc.*, 1958, **80**, 2908; R. O. Brady, *Proc. Nat. Acad. Sci. U.S.*, 1958, **44**, 993; S.J. Wakil, *J. Amer. Chem. Soc.*, 1958, **80**, 6465; (*c*) S. J. Wakil and J. Ganguly, *ibid.*, 1959, **81**, 2597; S. J. Wakil, E. B. Titchener and D. M. Gibson, *Biochem. Biophys. Acta*, 1959, **34**, 227; R. Bressler and S. J. Wakil, *J. Biol. Chem.*, 1961, **236**, 1643; (*d*) *idem, ibid.*, 1962, **237**, 1441.

55. J. W. Porter and A. Tietz, *Biochem. Biophys. Acta*, 1957, **25**, 41; A. Tietz, *ibid.*, 1957, **25**, 303.

56. V. Handwerck and P. Fouarger, (*a*) *Helv. Chim. Acta*, 1959, **42**, 508; (*b*) *ibid.*, 1959, **42**, 501.

57. (*a*) G. Popják and A. Tietz, *Biochem. J.*, 1955, **60**, 147, 155; G. Popják *et al.*, *ibid.*, 1957, **65**, 348; (*b*) J. Ganguly, *Biochim. Biophys. Acta*, 1960, **40**, 110.

58. (*a*) R. Schoenheimer and D. Rittenberg, *J. Biol. Chem.*, 1936, **114**, 381; (*b*) K. Bernhard and R. Schoenheimer, *J. Biol. Chem.*, 1940, **133**, 707, 713.

59. (a) K. Bloch, *Cold Spring Harbor Symp. Quant. Biol.*, 1948, **13**, 29; (b) K. Bloch *et al.*, *J. Biol. Chem.*, 1960, **235**, 337; 1962, **237**, 664; (c) J. Singh and T. K. Walker, *Biochem. J.*, 1956, **62**, 286.

60. J. A. Lovern, *Biochem. J.*, 1940, **34**, 704.

61. A. T. James, *Biochem. J.*, 1962, **82**, 28P.

62. J. B. Leathes and H. S. Raper, "The Fats" (Monographs on Biochemistry), 2nd Ed., 1925, pp. 119, 120.

63. *Cf.* F. D. Gunstone, *J. Chem. Soc.*, 1954, 1613.

64. (a) G. Embden, *et al.*, *Klin. Woch.*, 1933, **12**, 213; (b) O. Meyerhof *et al.*, *Biochem. Z.*, 1933, **260**, 417; 1933, **264**, 40; *Nature*, 1933, **132**, 337, 373.

65. G. Popják, G. D. Hunter and T. H. French, *Biochem. J.*, 1953, **54**, 238.

66. (a) I. Munk, *Arch. Anat. Physiol.*, 1890, **376**, etc.; (b) B. Moore and D. P. Rockwood, *J. Physiol.*, 1897, **21**, 58; B. Moore and W. H. Parker, *Proc. Roy. Soc.*, 1901, **B**, **68**, 64; F. B. Kingsbury, *J. Biol. Chem.*, 1917, **29**, 367.

67. F. Verzár and A. Kuthy, *Biochem. Z.*, 1930, **225**, 267; F. Verzár and E. J. McDougall, "Absorption from the Intestine", London, 1936.

68. (a) R. H. Barnes, E. H. Miller and G. O. Burr, *J. Biol. Chem.*, 1941, **140**, 233; (b) W. C. Stewart and R. G. Sinclair, *Arch. Biochem.*, 1945, **8**, 7; (c) D. B. Zilversmith, I. L. Chaikoff and C. Entenman, *J. Biol. Chem.*, 1948, **172**, 637.

69. A. C. Frazer, *Analyst*, 1938, **63**, 308; *J. Physiol.*, 1939, **95**, *Proceedings*, 21, 23; *Physiol. Revs.*, 1940, **20**, 561; 1946, **26**, 103; *Chem. and Ind.*, 1947, 379; *Biochem. Soc.*, *Symposia*, 1952, No. **9**, 5.

70. A. C. Frazer and H. G. Sammons, *Biochem. J.*, 1945, **39**, 122.

71. W. Q. Brown and C. L. Shrewsbury, *Oil and Soap*, 1941, **18**, 249.

72. G. A. Garton, T. P. Hilditch and M. L. Meara, *Biochem. J.*, 1952, **50**, 517; G. A. Garton and W. R. H. Duncan, *ibid.*, 1954, **57**, 120.

73. R. Blomstrand, (a) (with E. H. Ahrens, Jr.), *J. Biol. Chem.*, 1958, **233**, 321; (b) (with B. Borgström and O. Dahlback), *Proc. Soc. Exptl. Biol. Med.*, 1959, **102**, 204.

74. F. B. Shorland, (a) *Nature*, 1950, **165**, 766; (b) *J. Sci. Food Agric.*, 1953, **4**, 497.

75. J. A. Lovern, (a) *Biochem. J.*, 1938, **32**, 676; (b) *ibid.*, 1214; (c) *ibid.*, 2142; (d) 1940, **34**, 704.

76. K. Bernhard, M. Rothlin and H. Wagner, *Helv. Chim. Acta*, 1958, **41**, 1155.

77. (a) T. P. Hilditch and K. S. Murti, *J. Soc. Chem. Ind.*, 1939, **58**, 351; (b) G. Collin, *Biochem. J.*, 1933, **27**, 1373.

78. (Miss) E. M. Cruickshank, *Biochem. J.*, 1934, **28**, 965.

79. A. Banks, T. P. Hilditch and E. C. Jones, *Biochem. J.*, 1933, **27**, 1375.

80. J. M. Spadola and N. R. Ellis, *J. Biol. Chem.*, 1936, **113**, 205.

81. (a) H. E. Longenecker and T. P. Hilditch, *Biochem. J.*, 1938, **32**, 784; (b) H. E. Longenecker, *J. Biol. Chem.*, 1939, **129**, 13; 1939, **130**, 167.

82. (a) N. R. Ellis and J. H. Zeller, *J. Biol. Chem.*, 1930, **89**, 185; (b) N. R. Ellis, C. S. Rothwell and W. O. Pool, *ibid.*, 1931, **92**, 385.

83. J. B. Brown, *J. Biol. Chem.*, 1931, **90**, 133.

84. B. H. Thomas, C. C. Culbertson and F. Beard, *Amer. Soc. Animal Production Rec. Proc.*, 27th Annual Meeting, 1934, 193.

85. A. Lebedev, *Pflüger's Archiv.*, 1883, **31**, 11.

86. I. Munk, *Arch. Path. Anat. Physiol.*, 1884, **95**, 407.

87. (a) T. P. Hilditch and J. J. Sleightholme, *Biochem. J.*, 1930, **24**, 1098; (b) T. P. Hilditch and H. M. Thompson, *ibid.*, 1936, **30**, 677.

88. M. G. Morehouse, *J. Biol. Chem.*, 1944, **155**, 33.

89. (a) A. Hock, *Ernährung*, 1941, **6**, 278; W. Keil, *Z. physiol. Chem.*, 1942, **274**, 175; 1942, **276**, 26; 1947, **282**, 137; H. Appel. H. Bohm, W. Keil and G. Schiller, *ibid.*, 1940, **266**, 158; 1942, **274**, 186; 1947, **282**, 220; F. E. Visscher, *J. Biol. Chem.*, 1946, **162**, 129; (b) C. Y. Hopkins, M. J. Chisholm, T. K. Murray and J. A. Campbell, *J. Amer. Oil Chem. Soc.*, 1957, **34**, 505; (c) K. K. Carroll and R. L. Noble, *Canad. J. Biochem. Physiol.*, 1957, **35**, 1093.

90. R. G. Sinclair and C. Smith, *J. Biol. Chem.*, 1937, **121**, 361.

91. (*a*) R. Schoenheimer and D. Rittenberg, *J. Biol. Chem.*, 1935, **111**, 163, 169, 175; 1936, **113**, 505; 1936, **114**, 381; 1937, **117**, 485; 1937, **120**, 155, 503; 1937, **121**, 235; (*b*) R. Schoenheimer, *Harvey Lectures*, 1936–1937; (*c*) K. F. Bonhoeffer, *Diskussionstagung Deutsche Bunsengesellschaft*, 1937, 70; (*d*) R. Schoenheimer, D. Rittenberg and A. S. Keston, *J. Amer. Chem. Soc.*, 1937, **59**, 1765.

92. (*a*) D. Wesson, *Trans. Amer. Inst. Chem. Eng.*, 1919, **12**, 20; (*b*) A. D. Holmes, *U.S. Dept. Agric. Bulletins*, 1919, 613, 781; (*c*) C. F. Langworthy, *Ind. Eng. Chem.*, 1923, **15**, 277.

93. (*a*) F. H. Mattson, *J. Nutrition*, 1959, **69**, 338; (*b*) 1960, **71**, 366; (*c*) F. H. Mattson and R. A. Volpenhein, *J. Biol. Chem.*, 1962, **237**, 53.

94. R. K. Boutwell, R. P. Geyer, C. A. Elvehjem and E. B. Hart, *J. Dairy Sci.*, 1940, **23**, 181, 1201, 1205; 1941, **24**, 1827; 1943, **26**, 429; *Science*, 1943, **98**, 499; *J. Nutrition*, 1943, **26**, 601; *Proc. Soc. Exp. Biol. Med.*, 1944, **55**, 153; T. W. Gullickson, F. C. Fountaine and J. B. Fitch, *J. Dairy Sci.*, 1939, **22**, 471; 1942, **25**, 117; R. S. Harris and L. M. Mosher, *Food Res.*, 1940, **5**, 177; J. Boer and Jansen, *Voeding*, 1941, **2**, 204; B. and H. von Euler and I. Saberg, *Ernährung*, 1942, **7**, 65; A. and M. von Besnák and I. Hajdu, *Nutrit. Rev.*, 1943, **1**, 358; *Ernährung*, 1943, **8**, 209; H. J. Deuel, E. Movitt, L. F. Hallman *et al.*, *Science*, 1943, **98**, 139; *J. Nutrition*, 1944, **27**, 107, 335, 339, 509; 1945, **29**, 237, 309; L. P. Zialcita and H. H. Mitchell, *Science*, 1944, **99**, 60; T. P. Hilditch, M. L. Meara, K. M. Henry and S. K. Kon, *J. Dairy Res.*, 1945, **14**, 45; K. F. Mattil and J. W. Higgins, *J. Nutrition*, 1945, **29**, 255; E. F. Brown and J. W. Bloor, *ibid.*, 1945, **29**, 349.

95. T. P. Hilditch and M. L. Meara, *Biochem. J.*, 1944, **38**, 29, 437; A. R. Baldwin and H. E. Longenecker, *J. Biol. Chem.*, 1944, **154**, 255; J. B. Brown and B. M. Orians, *Arch. Biochem.*, 1946, **9**, 201.

96. (*a*) D. Melnick and H. J. Deuel, Jr., *J. Amer. Oil Chem. Soc.*, 1954, **31**, 63; (*b*) R. R. Allen, A. A. Kiess and F. A. Kummerow, *ibid.*, 1958, **35**, 203; (*c*) R. R. Allen and P. V. Johnston, *ibid.*, 1960, **37**, 16.

97. (*a*) L. C. A. Nunn and I. Smedley-MacLean, *Biochem. J.*, 1938, **32**, 2178; (*b*) E. M. Hume, L. C. A. Nunn, I. Smedley-MacLean and H. H. Smith, *ibid.*, 1940, **34**, 879, 884; I. Smedley-MacLean and E. M. Hume, *ibid.*, 1941, **35**, 990.

98. (*a*) I. G. Rieckehoff, R. T. Holman and G. O. Burr, *Arch. Biochem.*, 1949, **20**, 331; (*b*) C. Widmer and R. T. Holman, *ibid.*, 1950, **25**, 1; H. Mohrhauer and R. T. Holman, *J. Lipid Res.*, 1963, **4**, 151.

99. (*a*) O. Turpeinen, *J. Nutrition*, 1938, **15**, 351; (*b*) L. Reinius and O. Turpeinen, *Acta. Chem. Scand.*, 1954, **8**, 1001.

100. P. Karrer and H. Koenig, *Helv. Chim. Acta*, 1943, **26**, 619.

101. (*a*) E. Klenk (with W. Bongard), *Z. physiol. Chem.*, 1952, **291**, 104; (with F. Lindlar), *ibid.*, 1955, **299**, 74; (*b*) (with G. Kremer), *ibid.*, 1960, **320**, 111.

102. (*a*) H. J. Thomasson, *Int. Z. Vitaminf.*, 1953, **25**, 62; *Nature*, 1954, **173**, 452; *ibid.*, 1956, **178**, 1051; (*b*) H. J. Thomasson and J. Boldingh, *J. Nutrition*, 1955, **56**, 469.

103. C. Y. Hopkins, T. K. Murray and J. A. Campbell, *Canad. J. Biochem. Physiol.*, 1955, **33**, 1047.

104. (*a*) R. Reiser and co-workers, *J. Nutrition*, 1950, **40**, 429; 1950, **42**, 325; 1951, **44**, 159; *Arch. Biochem. Biophys.*, 1951, **32**, 113; 1960, **86**, 42; (*b*) J. F. Mead and co-workers, *J. Nutrition*, 1951, **44**, 507; *J. Biol. Chem.*, 1953, **205**, 683; 1956, **218**, 401; 1956, **219**, 705; 1956, **220**, 257; 1957, **224**, 841; 1957, **227**, 1025; 1958, **229**, 575; 1959, **234**, 1411; 1960, **235**, 3385; *J. Amer. Oil Chem. Soc.*, 1961, **38**, 297.

105. (*a*) H. J. Deuel, Jr., "Progress in the Chemistry of Fats and Other Lipids", (London: Pergamon Press), 1954, Vol. II, 99; "The Lipids, Vol. III, Biochemistry", p. 783, 1957 (New York: Interscience Publishers, Inc.); R. T. Holman and S. I. Greenberg, *Arch. Biochem. Biophys.*, 1954, **49**, 49. (*b*) G. Clément, "Recent Advances in the Digestion and Absorption of Fats", *Pathol. Biol. Semaine Hôp.*, 1958, **6**, 931.

CHAPTER IX

Constitution of Individual Natural Fatty Acids

This chapter and the next deal with the constitution and significant properties of the individual fatty acids or alcohols which are the more important acyl units from which the natural triglycerides, phosphatides, or wax esters are elaborated.

The present chapter is devoted to the naturally occurring saturated and unsaturated fatty acids.* Chapter X includes, first, a short section devoted to the synthesis of mixed triglycerides of known configuration – the aspect of synthesised triglycerides which is of growing importance in ascertaining the configuration of the corresponding natural products; and, subsequently, sections dealing with the naturally occurring higher aliphatic alcohols (saturated and unsaturated), and the higher acyl glycerol ethers.

Naturally Occurring Saturated Fatty Acids

The constitution of all the normal saturated aliphatic acids up to and including n-hexacosanoic acid, $C_{26}H_{52}O_2$, and of most of the others up to n-tetratriacontanoic, $C_{34}H_{68}O_2$, and of some even higher members (e.g., n-hexapentacontanoic, $C_{56}H_{112}O_2$), has been formally established by synthesis. The lower members of the series (up to n-heptanoic acid) were synthesised at various times by means of the Frankland-Kolbe sequence of reactions:

$$R.OH \rightarrow R.Cl \rightarrow R.CN \rightarrow R.COOH[1].$$

From n-heptanoic acid to n-octadecanoic acid the proof of the straight-chain structure rested in most cases on the degradation of a higher to a lower acid by the Hofmann[2] sequence of reactions:

$$R.CH_2.COOH \rightarrow R.CH_2.CONH_2 \rightarrow R.CH_2.NH_2 \rightarrow R.CN \rightarrow R.COOH;$$

and also by oxidising the methyl alkyl ketones (prepared from a mixture of the calcium salt of a higher fatty acid and calcium acetate) with chromic acid, when the following changes occur:

$$R.CH_2.COOH \rightarrow R.CH_2.COCH_3 \rightarrow R.COOH.$$

By use of one or both of these processes Krafft[3] and other workers at different times demonstrated the conversion of stearic acid into heptadecanoic acid and the latter into palmitic acid, and so on, progressively down the series

---

* For full accounts of the physical properties and of many specific chemical derivatives of fatty acids the volumes by A. W. Ralston ("Fatty Acids and their Derivatives", 1948: John Wiley & Sons, Inc., New York; Chapman & Hall, Ltd., London) and K. S. Markley ("Fatty Acids", Parts I and II, 1961: Interscience Publishers, New York) may be consulted.

to n-nonanoic (pelargonic) acid. The latter acid was in the meantime prepared synthetically by Jourdan[4] from n-heptyl alcohol.

Thus, many years ago, the structure of the normal saturated fatty acids up to and including n-nonanoic acid, $C_9H_{18}O_2$, was established synthetically, whilst that of each of the higher members from n-decanoic acid to n-octadecanoic (stearic acid) followed from the stepwise degradation of the latter acid, losing one carbon atom at a time, and eventually reaching n-nonanoic acid. The similar proof of the constitution of each of the acids from n-octadecanoic acid to n-hexacosanoic acid was given in 1924 by Levene and Taylor.[5] These workers prepared n-octadecanoic acid by hydrogenation of oleic acid (*cf.* below) and proceeded to build up the higher acids as far as n-docosanoic acid by means of the sequence

$$R.COOEt \rightarrow R.CH_2OH \rightarrow R.CH_2I \rightarrow R.CH_2CN \rightarrow R.CH_2.COOH;$$

the reduction of the esters to corresponding higher aliphatic alcohols was effected by the method of Bouveault and Blanc.[6] Hydrogenation of erucic acid (*cf.* below) furnished behenic acid identical with the synthetic n-docosanoic acid, and this material was the starting point for the similar synthesis of the acids up to and including n-hexacosanoic acid.

Some of the foregoing syntheses of lower saturated acids were confirmed subsequently by others involving an aldol condensation. Thus, condensation of acetaldehyde yields crotonaldehyde, $CH_3.CH:CH.CHO$, which is converted by hydrogenation into n-butyraldehyde, $CH_3.CH_2.CH_2.CHO$, and this yields n-butyric acid on oxidation. n-Hexanoic acid can be produced by a similar sequence of reactions commencing with the condensation of n-butyraldehyde with acetaldehyde. Similar syntheses of the higher saturated acids were carried out in 1936 by reduction of higher polyene aldehydes produced by repeated condensation of crotonaldehyde; and it was not until this date that direct, complete syntheses of the most abundant natural higher members, such as palmitic and stearic acids, were achieved. Kuhn, Grundmann and Trischmann[7a] showed that crotonaldehyde solutions, in presence of weak salts such as piperidine acetate, undergo polymerisation into octatrienal, $CH_3.[CH:CH]_3.CHO$, dodecapentaenal, $CH_3.[CH:CH]_5.CHO$, and hexadecaheptaenal, $CH_3.[CH:CH]_7.CHO$. Reduction of the latter C_{16} polyene aldehyde gave cetyl alcohol, whilst hydrogenation of its condensation product with malonic acid, followed by distillation, yielded stearic acid. F. G. Fischer, Hultzsch and Flaig[7b] also obtained octatrienal and dodecapentaenal by a similar process, and converted the latter into lauraldehyde by reduction, and also, by condensation with malonic acid, into tetradecahexaenoic acid, $CH_3.[CH:CH]_6.COOH$. Later, Schmidt and Obermeit[7c] condensed sorbaldehyde (1 mol.) with crotonaldehyde (2 mols.) in presence of piperidine acetate and obtained tetradecahexaenal, which was converted into palmitic acid by condensation with malonic acid, decarboxylation, and hydrogenation; crotonaldehyde and dodecapentaenal in presence of piperidine acetate gave hexadecaheptaenal with some eicosanonaenal, $CH_3.[CH:CH]_9.CHO$. R. Kuhn[7d] has pointed out that, if polyene aldehyde formation is an integral part of the elaboration of the higher fatty acids in nature, reduction of these substances must set in at an early stage, because no sign of their presence has been observed in, for example, ripening seeds.

SYNTHESIS OF SATURATED ACIDS

Other general methods for synthesis of higher normal saturated aliphatic acids have been devised by means of the following different sequences of reactions:

(a) Cadmium or zinc alkyls have been condensed with carbethoxyacylhalides of n-dicarboxylic acids to give keto-acids, which by Clemmensen reduction give higher saturated acids:[8a]

$$CdR_2 + Cl.CO.[CH_2]_n.COOEt \rightarrow R.CO.[CH_2]_n.COOH \rightarrow R.[CH_2]_{n+1}.COOH.$$

Saturated acids with 33, 34, and 35 carbon atoms have thus been prepared.[8b]

(b) *Condensation reactions employing acetoacetic ester.* The starting-points of these methods are (i) the condensation of acetoacetic ester with an n-alkyl halide, the product being further condensed with a carbethoxy-acyl halide of a n-dicarboxylic acid, or (better), (ii) the condensation of acetoacetic ester with an ω-bromoaliphatic ester, followed by condensation with the chloride of a n-saturated acid:

$$(i) \quad \underset{\underset{CO.CH_3}{|}}{\overset{\overset{COOEt}{|}}{CH_2}} \xrightarrow{CH_3.[CH_2]_m.Br} \underset{\underset{CO.CH_3}{|}}{\overset{\overset{COOEt}{|}}{CH_3.[CH_2]_m.CH}} \xrightarrow{Cl.CO.[CH_2]_n.COOEt}$$

$$CH_3.[CH_2]_m.\underset{\underset{CO.CH_3}{|}}{\overset{\overset{COOEt}{|}}{C}}.CO.[CH_2]_n.COOEt$$

$$(ii) \quad \underset{\underset{CO.CH_3}{|}}{\overset{\overset{COOEt}{|}}{CH_2}} \xrightarrow{COOEt.[CH_2]_m.Br} \underset{\underset{CO.CH_3}{|}}{\overset{\overset{COOEt}{|}}{COOEt.[CH_2]_m.CH}} \xrightarrow{Cl.CO.[CH_2]_n.CH_3}$$

$$COOEt.[CH_2]_m.\underset{\underset{CO.CH_3}{|}}{\overset{\overset{COOEt}{|}}{C}}.CO.[CH_2]_n.CH_3$$

Stepwise hydrolysis of the final adducts in either case gives a long-chain keto-saturated acid, Clemmensen reduction of which gives the n-saturated acid.

This method was first used by G. M. and R. Robinson[9a] who synthesised 10-ketostearic acid in 1925 by procedure (i) from n-heptyl bromide and the carbethoxy-acyl chloride of sebacic acid, COOH.[CH_2]_8.COOH. They later,[9b] (in the course of synthesis of triacontanoic acid, $C_{30}H_{60}O_2$) pointed out the more effective nature of procedure (ii), which was also used by Francis et al.,[9c] and later further improved by Stenhagen et al.,[9d] who recommended the following sequence (iii) of condensations:

(iii) $CH_3.[CH_2]_m.COCl + \overset{\overset{\textstyle CO.CH_3}{|}}{CH_2}.COOEt \rightarrow CH_3.[CH_2]_m.CO.\overset{\overset{\textstyle CO.CH_3}{|}}{CH}.COOEt \xrightarrow{NaOMe}$

$CH_3.[CH_2]_m.CO.CH_2.COOEt + I.[CH_2]_n.COOEt \rightarrow$

$CH_3.[CH_2]_m.CO.CH(COOEt).[CH_2]_n.COOEt \rightarrow$

$CH_3.[CH_2]_m.CO.[CH_2]_{n+1}.COOEt.$

By reduction of synthetic keto-acids obtained by methods (ii) or (iii) numerous *n*-saturated acids (up to $C_{34}H_{68}O_2$)[9d] have been synthesised.

(*c*) *Condensation reactions employing malonic ester.* (i) Addition of two —CH_2— groups to a normal saturated fatty acid may be achieved as follows[10a]:

$CH_3.[CH_2]_m.COOEt \rightarrow CH_3.[CH_2]_m.CH_2(OH) \rightarrow$

$CH_3.[CH_2]_m.CH_2I + CH_2(COOEt)_2 \rightarrow$

$CH_3.[CH_2]_m.CH_2.CH(COOEt)_2 \rightarrow CH_3.[CH_2]_{m+2}.COOH.$

(ii) Bowman[10b] and co-workers have used malonic ester in place of aceto-acetic ester in more general syntheses similar to those described under (*b*) (above), but with the improvement that the condensation products are changed into benzyl esters: the benzyl group can be removed by hydrogenation, and better yields therefore result, since acidic or alkaline hydrolysis is thereby avoided:

$CH_2(COOEt)_2 + Br.[CH_2]_n.COOEt \rightarrow CH(COOEt)_2.[CH_2]_n.COOEt \rightarrow (Na—Ph.CH_2OH)$

$\rightarrow CH(COO.CH_2.Ph)_2.[CH_2]_n.COOCH_2.Ph + CH_3.[CH_2]_m.COCl \rightarrow$

$\rightarrow CH_3.[CH_2]_m.CO.C(COOCH_2.Ph)_2.[CH_2]_n.COOCH_2.Ph \xrightarrow{(Pd—H_2)}$

$\rightarrow CH_3.[CH_2]_m.CO.[CH_2]_{n+1}.COOH.$

By this procedure, keto-saturated acids have been synthesised from appropriate ω-bromo-aliphatic esters and acyl chlorides which, on reduction, gave myristic, stearic, *n*-tricosanoic ($C_{23}H_{46}O_2$), *n*-nonatriacontanoic ($C_{39}H_{78}O_2$), and *n*-hexapentacontanoic ($C_{56}H_{112}O_2$) acids.

(*d*) *Anodic synthesis.* The Kolbe[11] electrolytic preparation of fatty acids has been adapted to the synthesis of higher fatty acids by Linstead[12] and his colleagues. When mixtures of methyl hydrogen esters of *n*-dicarboxylic acids, $COOH.[CH_2]_m.COOMe$, with monocarboxylic acids, $R.COOH$, were electrolysed in methanol solutions, three products resulted: a hydrocarbon $R.R$, a symmetrical dicarboxylic ester $COOMe.[CH_2]_{2m}.COOMe$, and a *n*-saturated ester $R.[CH_2]_m.COOMe$. The latter was readily separated, after hydrolysis, from hydrocarbons and dibasic acids. The following saturated acids were thus synthesised:

ACID	FROM
n-Hexanoic	Methyl hydrogen adipate and acetic acid
n-Octanoic	Methyl hydrogen adipate and butyric acid
n-Decanoic	Methyl hydrogen adipate and *n*-hexanoic acid
n-Decanoic	Methyl hydrogen sebacate and acetic acid
Myristic	Methyl hydrogen adipate and *n*-decanoic acid
Myristic	Methyl hydrogen sebacate and *n*-hexanoic acid
Stearic	Methyl hydrogen adipate and myristic acid
Stearic	Methyl hydrogen sebacate and *n*-decanoic acid
Stearic	$COOMe.[CH_2]_{16}.COOH$ and acetic acid

Properties of Individual Saturated Acids

The melting points of the saturated fatty acids alternate according as the molecule contains an even or odd number of carbon atoms; the melting points of the two series lie on two smooth curves which gradually approach one another with increasing molecular weight. Similar regularities hold in the case of the methyl and ethyl esters of the fatty acids. Owing to the marked tendency of closely related members in the higher fatty acid series to form solid solutions or molecular compounds, great care has to be taken in the interpretation of the observed melting point of any specimen. Thus, it may happen that a specimen possesses an apparent melting point practically identical with that of an individual acid, and may nevertheless be a mixture of two or even three fatty acids. The identification of a saturated fatty acid by means of melting point and mixed melting point determinations is a matter of some difficulty. Indeed, with the higher acids no reliance can be placed on observations of melting point. Thus whilst *n*-eicosanoic acid, $C_{20}H_{40}O_2$, melts at $75 \cdot 4°$ and *n*-docosanoic acid, $C_{22}H_{44}O_2$, at $80 \cdot 0°$, Francis, Piper and Malkin[10a] showed (1930) that certain mixtures of the following acids all melt between the limits $74 \cdot 9°$ and $75 \cdot 2°$:

$$C_{20} + C_{21}, \ C_{21} + C_{22}, \ C_{22} + C_{23}, \text{ and } C_{22} + C_{23} + C_{24}.$$

Considerable attention has been given to the study of the X-ray spectra of solid crystals of the higher saturated fatty acids. Earlier work (1923) on this subject, due to Müller and Shearer[13a], was developed by Piper, Malkin and Austin.[13b] Some of this work had reference to difficulties formerly encountered in assigning chemical structures to natural arachidic and lignoceric acids; at one time branch-chain acids were believed to be present in certain cases, but Francis, Piper and Malkin[10a] showed that the arachidic, lignoceric, cerotic, and montanic acids which they examined from various natural sources were mixtures of *n*-fatty acids and that *iso*-acids were not present. They also emphasised, as a result of examination both of pure acids and a large number of artificial mixtures of the latter, that a normal fatty acid cannot be considered pure unless it has the correct melting point and correct acid value and gives both of two characteristic X-ray spacings.

Chibnall, Piper *et al.*[14] (1934) made a comprehensive investigation of the melting points and X-ray spectrographic data of the alcohols and acids present in a large number of plant and insect waxes. With the aid of the corresponding data for synthetic normal alcohols (and their acetates) and acids (and their ethyl esters) containing from 26 to 36 carbon atoms in the molecule,these workers showed that the natural substances known as ceryl alcohol, cerotic acid, melissyl alcohol, melissic acid, etc., etc., are invariably mixtures of several homologues.* They suggested that names of this kind should be deleted from the literature in so far as they imply a definite molecular species, and that actual compounds (e.g. $n\text{-}C_{26}H_{53}.OH$ or $n\text{-}C_{25}H_{51}.COOH$) should only be

---

* The wax aliphatic acids of high molecular weight, like almost all the glyceride fatty acids somewhat lower in the series, are confined to members which contain an even number of carbon atoms in the molecule.

denoted by their systematic names (e.g. *n*-hexacosanyl alcohol or *n*-hexaco-sanoic acid). The adoption of this sweeping recommendation would certainly effect a helpful clarification in the literature of this part of the subject.

It may be pointed out that, in practice, the need for the employment of X-ray methods of analysis in addition to the ordinary determination of melting point is confined to the comparatively small number of cases in which natural saturated acids containing 20 or more than 20 carbon atoms in the molecule are concerned.

The infra-red spectra of saturated fatty acids and their esters have also, more recently (1952), been studied.[15]

Table 144 gives a summary of the properties of the chief saturated acids encountered in natural fats, together with the X-ray spacings of some of the higher members.

TABLE 144. *Saturated Fatty Acids*

SYSTEMATIC NAME	COMMON NAME	FORMULA	ACID M.P.	ACID B.P.	X-RAY SPECTRA SPACINGS B	X-RAY SPECTRA SPACINGS C
n-Butanoic	Butyric	$CH_3.[CH_2]_2.CO_2H$	− 8°	163°		
3-Methyl-butanoic	*iso*-Valeric	$(CH_3)_2.CH.CH_2.CO_2H$	−51°	177°		
n-Hexanoic	Caproic	$CH_3.[CH_2]_4.CO_2H$	− 4°	205°		
n-Octanoic	Caprylic	$CH_3.[CH_2]_6.CO_2H$	+16°	239°		
n-Decanoic	Capric	$CH_3.[CH_2]_8.CO_2H$	31·3°	269°		
n-Dodecanoic	Lauric	$CH_3.[CH_2]_{10}.CO_2H$	43·5°	102°/1 mm.		
n-Tetradecanoic	Myristic	$CH_3.[CH_2]_{12}.CO_2H$	54·4°	122°/1 mm.		31·6
n-Hexadecanoic	Palmitic	$CH_3.[CH_2]_{14}.CO_2H$	62·9°	139°/1 mm.	39·1	35·6
n-Octadecanoic	Stearic	$CH_3.[CH_2]_{16}.CO_2H$	69·6°	160°/1 mm.	43·8	39·8
n-Eicosanoic	Arachidic	$CH_3.[CH_2]_{18}.CO_2H$	75·4°	205°/1 mm.	48·5	44·2
n-Docosanoic	Behenic	$CH_3.[CH_2]_{20}.CO_2H$	80·0°		53·0	48·3
n-Tetracosanoic	"Lignoceric"	$CH_3.[CH_2]_{22}.CO_2H$	84·2°		57·8	52·6
n-Hexacosanoic	"Cerotic"	$CH_3.[CH_2]_{24}.CO_2H$	87·7°		62·2	56·3
n-Octacosanoic	—	$CH_3.[CH_2]_{26}.CO_2H$	90·9°		67·2	61·1
n-Triacontanoic	—	$CH_3.[CH_2]_{28}.CO_2H$	93·6°		71·4	65·2

NAME	FORMULA	METHYL ESTER M.P.	METHYL ESTER B.P.	ETHYL ESTER M.P.	ETHYL ESTER B.P.	AMIDE M.P.	ANILIDE M.P.
n-Butyric	$C_4H_8O_2$	− 95°	102°	− 93°	120°	115°	96°
iso-Valeric	$C_5H_{10}O_2$	—	127°	—	145°	135°	115°
n-Hexanoic	$C_6H_{12}O_2$	− 71°	151°	− 67°	167°	101°	92°
n-Octanoic	$C_8H_{16}O_2$	− 34°	194°	− 43°	208°	105°	55°
n-Decanoic	$C_{10}H_{20}O_2$	− 18°	224°	− 20°	245°	99°	70°
n-Lauric	$C_{12}H_{24}O_2$	+ 5°	87°/1 mm.	− 10°	269°	100°	78°
n-Myristic	$C_{14}H_{28}O_2$	19°	111°/1 mm.	+ 12°	295°	103°	84°
n-Palmitic	$C_{16}H_{32}O_2$	30°	130°/1 mm.	25°	143°/3 mm.	106°	89°
n-Stearic	$C_{18}H_{36}O_2$	39°	154°/1 mm.	31°	152°/0·2 mm.	109°	94°
n-Eicosanoic	$C_{20}H_{40}O_2$	47°	180°/1 mm.	41°	177°/0·3 mm.	108°	96°
n-Docosanoic	$C_{22}H_{44}O_2$	53°	—	48°	185°/0·2 mm.	111°	102°
n-Tetracosanoic	$C_{24}H_{48}O_2$	58°	—	54°	199°/0·3 mm.	—	—
n-Hexacosanoic	$C_{26}H_{52}O_2$	63°	—	60°	—	109°	—
n-Octacosanoic	$C_{28}H_{56}O_2$	67°	—	65°	—	—	—
n-Triacontanoic	$C_{30}H_{60}O_2$	72°	—	68°	—	—	—

The first references to individual saturated acids, and their general distribution in natural fats, are as follows:

Acid	First mentioned by	General occurrence
Butyric	*ca.* 1820 Chevreul[16] (butter).	Confined to certain milk fats.
iso-Valeric	1817 Chevreul[16] (dolphin jaw).	Dolphin and porpoise depot fats.
Caproic	*ca.* 1820 Chevreul[16] (butter).	Milk fats; traces in Palmæ seed fats.
Caprylic	1844 Lerch[17a] (butter). 1845 Fehling[17b] (coconut).	Milk fats; Palmæ seed fats.

Acid	First mentioned by	General occurrence
Capric	*ca.* 1820 Chevreul[16] (butter).	Milk fats; Palmæ, elm seed fats; sperm head oil.
Lauric	1842 Marsson[18a] (*Laurus nobilis*); 1848 Görgey[18b] (coconut).	Lauraceæ, Palmæ, etc. seed fats; milk fats.
Myristic	1841 Playfair[19] (nutmeg fat).	Myristicaceæ, *Irvingia* seed fats (in quantity); in minor amounts in nearly all natural fats.
Palmitic	1816 Chevreul[16] ("margaric"); 1840 Frémy[20] (palm oil).	In practically all natural fats, either as a minor or major component (palm oil, animal depot and milk fats, cottonseed oil, etc. etc.).
Stearic	1816 Chevreul[16] (tallows).	Minor component of a very large number of natural fats; major component of a few seed fats and of many animal body fats.
Arachidic	1854 Gössman[21] (groundnut oil).	Traces in many seed and animal fats; minor component in Leguminosæ seed fats and in quantity in a very few seed fats.
Behenic	1848 Voelcker[22] (behen oil).	Traces or minor amounts in various seed fats; major component only in *Lophira* seed fats.
Lignoceric	1880 Hell and Hermanns[23a] (beechwood tar); 1888 Kreiling[23b] (groundnut).	Traces or minor amounts in various seed fats; major component only in *Adenanthera* seed fats.
"Cerotic"	1848 Brodie[24] (Chinese insect wax).	In many plant waxes, but very rarely in fats.

A few notes may be added with reference to certain saturated acids:

iso-*Valeric* acid, peculiar to the body oils of porpoise and other marine animals of the Delphinidæ family, and at one time believed to be either *n*-valeric acid or a mixture of butyric and caproic acids, was established as $(CH_3)_2.CH.CH_2.COOH$ by the studies (1930) of Klein and Stigol[25a] and of Gill and Tucker.[25b]

"*Margaric*" *and* "*daturic*" *acids.* It may be recalled here that *n*-heptadecanoic acid, $C_{17}H_{34}O_2$ ("margaric acid"), was once believed to be present in tallows, goose fat, etc., but that this was shown in 1921–22 by Heiduschka and Steinruck[26a] and by Bömer and Merten[26b] to consist of an equimolecular mixture of palmitic and stearic acids. In the meantime, however, Meyer and Beer[27a] had reported that an acid of the formula $C_{17}H_{34}O_2$ was present in the saturated acids of datura oil and gave it the name "daturic acid"; but Verkade and Coops[27b] showed (1929) that this again is a mixture of palmitic and stearic acids. A suggestion that "margaric" or *n*-heptadecanoic acid occurs in alfalfa (*Medicago sativa*) seed fat has been shown by Schuette and Vogel[28] to be without foundation, a mixture of palmitic and stearic acids only being concerned.

Similarly, a *n*-pentadecanoic acid, $C_{15}H_{30}O_2$, formerly reported as a component of yeast fat, is probably a mixture of two or more acids.

Considerable uncertainty formerly existed as to whether the *arachidic* acid of groundnut oil was in reality *n*-eicosanoic acid, because the melting point of the acid isolated from this oil (74–75° C.) was lower than that of the synthetic straight-chain product. For this reason Ehrenstein and Stuewer[29] suggested (1923) that arachidic acid of groundnut oil contained a branched chain of unknown constitution. The examination by X-ray methods of the acid by Morgan and Holmes[30a] also suggested that there was some abnormality about this acid, although arachidic acid prepared by hydrogenation of C_{20} unsaturated acids isolated from whale oil, and also the C_{20} acid present in rambutan tallow (Sapindaceæ) to the extent of 23 per cent., gave the normal X-ray structure for *n*-eicosanoic acid.[30b] However, by means of a specially designed apparatus for fractional distillation in a high vacuum, Jantzen and Tiedcke[31] succeeded (1930) in fractionating a large quantity of the methyl esters of the high molecular weight acids from groundnut oil and obtained definite evidence, from the melting points of the separated methyl esters, and direct comparison of the corresponding acids with synthetic acids, that n-arachidic, n-behenic, and n-lignoceric acids are all present in small quantities in the glycerides of groundnut oil. Uncertainty as to their identification was probably caused by the difficulty in complete separation of the individual acids by crystallisation or by ester-fractionation.

"Cerotic acid" has long been recognised as a constituent of beeswax[24] and of other plant and animal waxes; it is, in fact, the characteristic "acid" of many plant waxes.[14] Since its occurrence is for the most part confined to the waxes rather than to the fats it need not be considered in detail here; but it should also be noted that it has been found in traces in some vegetable fats. Very possibly, even here, it originates from wax esters rather than from true glycerides. As already mentioned, "cerotic acid" of waxes is now recognised to be a mixture of several n-aliphatic acids of the even-numbered series, and is not solely n-hexacosanoic acid.

Although (with the sole exception of iso-valeric acid) the major component acids in natural glycerides contain an even number of carbon atoms, Weitkamp et al.[32] found (1947) that the free fatty acids of human hair contain all the n-saturated acids from $C_7H_{14}O_2$ to $C_{18}H_{36}O_2$ and also arachidic and behenic acids, together with n-unsaturated (monoethenoid) acids from $C_{11}H_{20}O_2$ to $C_{18}H_{34}O_2$ inclusive (cf. p. 623).

Saturated n-dicarboxylic acids. – The saturated normal dicarboxylic acids $C_{21}H_{42}(CO_2H)_2$, etc., present in small quantities in the fruit-coat fat ("Japan wax") of Rhus species, have already been discussed in Chapter IV (p. 198).

NATURAL "ODD-NUMBERED" AND BRANCHED-CHAIN SATURATED ACIDS

Whilst fatty acids containing an even number of carbon atoms make up the overwhelming proportion of those present in natural fats, in a very much smaller number the occurrence of saturated acids with an odd number of carbon atoms is encountered. These fall into two groups:

(i) Acids with a normal alkyl chain (found in very small traces in the depot and milk fats of ruminant and possibly a few other animals[33]);

(ii) Acids with a branched carbon chain. These usually belong to the odd-numbered series, and are mainly of the optically active d-anteiso type $CHMeEt.[CH_2]_n.COOH$ (although iso-acids of the general formula $CHMe_2.[CH_2]_n.COOH$ may contain an even number of carbon atoms). These, like the normal odd-numbered acids, occur in very small amounts in the depot and milk fats of ruminants,[39a, b] but in larger proportions as iso-valeric acid in porpoise and dolphin oils (cf. above, p. 583), and as branched-chain acids of higher molecular weight in certain waxes, notably wool-wax, the waxes of human hair (cf. above) and those of bacilli.

Traces of odd-numbered n-saturated acids in animal depot and milk fats. These have been reported, largely by Shorland and co-workers, as follows: n-heptadecanoic in ox,[33a] sheep[33a] and musk-ox fats,[33b] n-nonadecanoic acid in ox fats[33a]; n-C_{11}, n-C_{13}, n-C_{15}, n-C_{17}, n-C_{19}, n-C_{21} and n-C_{23} acids in cow milk fats.[33c]

Traces of branched-chain acids in animal depot and milk fats. Shorland, Hansen and co-workers[39a] have isolated from ox and sheep depot and milk fats very small traces (of the order of 0·1–0·2 per cent.) of iso-acids. Shorland considers that these are present as glycerides, but on the evidence submitted it is equally possible that they are ester-waxes similar to or identical with the sebaceous waxes of the epidermis. d-14-Methyl-n-hexadecanoic acid (identical with that isolated from wool wax by Weitkamp[35]) was detected in beef fat and the external tissue fat of sheep, and in the latter fat still smaller traces of (+)-12-methyltetradecanoic, 13-methyltetradecanoic, 14-methylpentadecanoic, 15-methylhexadecanoic and 16-methyl-hexadecanoic acids. In cow milk fat, in addition to those just mentioned, traces of (+)-10-methyl- and 11-methyldodecanoic, a methyltridecanoic, and a tri- or tetra-methyl-eicosanoic acid have been noted. Sonnevald, Begemann et al.[39d] detected 3,7,11,15-tetramethylhexa-decanoic acid in butter fat.

The branched-chain methyl-n-aliphatic and methyl-ethyl-n-aliphatic acids melt at con-siderably lower temperatures than straight-chain acids of the same carbon content. Several methyl-n-aliphatic acids in the series C_{12}–C_{20} have been prepared synthetically.[36, 37a,b, 39c]

In contrast to the natural *glycerides* there are certain other groups of lipids (probably all of the class of ester-waxes) in which branched-chain saturated higher fatty acids are present in quantity. The chief of these are as follows:

Wool wax. Sheep's wool contains greasy matter which consists for the most part of ester-waxes in which the alcohols are a mixture of sterols (cholesterol, *iso*cholesterol, lanosterol). The acids with which the latter are combined do not belong to the ordinary normal aliphatic series, but are mainly saturated, with melting points lower than those of the corresponding acids of the n-aliphatic series. Darmstädter and Lifschütz[34a] observed (1895) small amounts of hydroxylated or "lactonic" acids ($C_{15}H_{30}O_3$ or $C_{16}H_{32}O_3$, $C_{30}H_{58}O_3$ or $C_{32}H_{62}O_3$, and $C_{30}H_{60}O_4$ or $C_{32}H_{64}O_4$) and large proportions of a saturated acid ($C_{26}H_{52}O_2$ or $C_{27}H_{54}O_4$, m.p. 72–73°). Abraham and Hilditch (1935)[34b] supported these earlier observations, and also found evidence of the presence of other acids of the formulæ $C_{15}H_{30}O_2$ and $C_{20}H_{40}O_2$. Weitkamp[35] made in 1945 an important contribution as the result of preliminary separation of wool fat methyl esters by adsorption on a column of adsorbent clay followed by elaborate fractional distillation. He reported four groups of acids as follows (per cent. wt.):

n-Acids: C_{10}, C_{12}, C_{18}, C_{20}, C_{22}, traces; C_{14}, C_{16}, 2·8 (each); C_{24}, C_{26}, 1 (each).

iso-Acids, $(CH_3)_2$. CH.$[CH_2]_n$.$COOH$: C_{10}, C_{12}, traces; C_{14} 2·8, C_{16} 5·8, C_{18} 4·0, C_{20} 5·0, C_{22} 4·0, C_{24} 2·8, C_{26} 3·6, C_{28} 0·8.

"*anteiso*"-d-Acids, CHMeEt.$[CH_2]_n$.$COOH$: C_9, C_{11}, C_{29}, C_{31}, traces; C_{13} 1, C_{15} 4·8, C_{17} 3·6, C_{19} 4·8, C_{21} 5·6, C_{23} 3·6, C_{25} 7·0, C_{27} 5·2.

Optically active: 2-hydroxy-n-tetradecanoic traces, and -n-hexadecanoic 4·0.

The *iso*-acids isolated from wool wax by Weitkamp have been, with other members of the series, prepared by synthesis by Stenhagen et al.[36] and by Hougen et al.,[37a] the properties of the synthetic acids agreeing with those of the corresponding *iso*-acids from wool wax. Similarly, the d-"ante-iso"-acid $C_{17}H_{34}O_2$, d-14-methyl-hexadecanoic acid, of wool wax was synthesised, commencing from d-2-methylbutanol-1, CHMeEt.CH_2OH, by Velick and English.[37b] The branched-chain methyl-n-aliphatic acids melt at considerably lower tem-peratures than straight-chain acids of the same carbon content.

Horn et al.[37c] found the free fatty acids of wool wax from merino fleeces to contain nearly 30 per cent. of the optically active 2-hydroxy-n-saturated acids, including 2-hydroxy-n-dodecanoic 0·6, -n-tetradecanoic 3·8, -n-hexadecanoic 18·8, and -n-octadecanoic 4·6 per cent.

The acidic and alcoholic components in (hydrolysed) wool wax have been analysed by gas–liquid chromatography (Murray et al.[37d]).

Comprehensive reviews on the composition of wool wax have been given by Truter[38a] (1951) and by Knol[38b] (1954).

Waxes of certain bacilli. The waxes present in tuberculosis and leprosy bacilli were shown by Anderson[40] and his collaborators to contain, in addition to (usually minor) amounts of palmitic, stearic, or oleic acids, a number of saturated acids with branched chains. Tuberculo-stearic acid, $C_{19}H_{38}O_2$, was isolated (1929) by Anderson and Chargaff[41] from tubercle wax, and was later proved by Spielman[42] to be $d(-)$-10-methylstearic acid. Syntheses of both optical enantiomorphs of 10-methylstearic acid, and of the racemic acid, have been described by Prout et al.,[43a] Ställberg-Stenhagen,[43b] Linstead et al. (anodic syntheses),[43c] Buu-Hoï et al.,[43d] and Hünig.[43e] The natural acid has the d-configuration and possesses a lævo-rotatory power $[\alpha]_D$ −0·08°.

From *Phytomonas tumifaciens* Velick and Anderson[44a] isolated a homologue of tuber-culostearic acid, phytomonic acid, $C_{20}H_{40}O_2$, possibly 10- or 11-methyl-n-nonadecanoic acid (but considered by Hofmann et al.[44b] to be "lactobacillic" acid (p. 612), i.e., 11,12-methylene (cyclopropyl) octadecanoic acid).

Mycoceranic acid, another lævorotatory acid of tubercle bacilli, is a complex mixture of

2,4,6-trimethyl saturated C_{25}, C_{26}, C_{27} and C_{29} acids with 2,4,6,8-tetramethyl saturated C_{30}, C_{31} and C_{32} acids (Polgar[45a,b]). Syntheses of a number of racemic and of optically active members of this group (2,4-dimethyl-substituted, 2,4,6-trimethyl-substituted and 2,4,6,8-tetramethyl-substituted acids of the series C_{25}–C_{28}, etc.) have been effected by Polgar and co-workers,[45c,d] Asselineau, Stenhagen et al.,[45e] and others.

Cason and co-workers (1958)[47a] synthesised 8-, 9- and 11-monomethyltetracosanoic acids for comparison with the physiologically active 10-methyltetracosanoic acid. They have also stated[47b] that the acids of the tubercle bacillus contained all the n-acids from C_{14} to C_{19}, and iso-acids of the same range of molecular weight; 33 per cent. of the total acids was palmitic, with an equal proportion of $C_{18}+C_{19}$ acids, 10-methylstearic acid amounted to 10 per cent., but no other individual acid exceeded one per cent. of the total fatty acids.

A considerable number of mono-, di-, and tri-methyl-n-aliphatic acids have been synthesised, largely in connection with therapeutic or pathological research, in the research schools of Sir R. Robinson, Anderson, Spielman, Cason and Stenhagen. Detailed reference to others than those already mentioned[45c,d,e, 47a] is beyond the scope of the present book; a comprehensive review (up to 1949) was given by Bowman.[50]

(For convenience, reference may be made in this section to some analogous mono-ethenoid acids which accompany the branched-chain saturated acids in the lipids of tubercle bacilli. These include mycolipenic (phthienoic) acid, which was shown by Polgar and Robinson[48c] to be 2,4,6-trimethyltetracos-2-enoic acid, $CH_3.[CH_2]_{17}.CHMe.CH_2.CHMe.CH:CMe.COOH$, a constitution later confirmed by syntheses.[48d, 45f]

Cason and Kalm[47c] have studied the synthesis and structure of similar 2-methyl-alk-2-enoic acids.)

Another constituent acid of tubercle waxes, phthioic acid, $C_{26}H_{52}O_2$, is a branched-chain fatty acid containing three branch methyl groups (Anderson and Spielman, (1936)[46a] Wagner-Jauregg[46b]). Doubt as to the structure of the phthioic acid was later resolved, when the identity of phthioic acid as 3,13,19-trimethyltricosanoic acid (as suggested by Spielman and by Wilson,[46c] and supported by Sir R. Robinson[48a]) was confirmed by syntheses of the racemic form of the latter acid by Polgar and Sir R. Robinson,[48b] and by Linstead et al.[49]

Branched-chain acids of much greater molecular weight are present in certain tubercle and diphtheria bacilli. Lederer et al. have shown (1949 et seq.) that the mycolic acids[51a] which form about 8 per cent. of the waxes in *Mycobacterium tuberculosis* are branched-chain hydroxy-acids derived from n-hexacosanoic acid with the general constitution

$$CH_3.[CH_2]_{23}.CH.COOH$$
$$|$$
$$CH(OH).R,$$

where R is a complex radical of about $C_{60}H_{121}$—, $C_{60}H_{120}(OH)$—, or $C_{60}H_{120}(OCH_3)$—. The lipids of *Corynebacterium diphtheriæ* contain about 6 per cent. of high molecular weight acids,[51b] including coryno-mycolic (I) and the unsaturated corynomycolenic (II) acid:

$$CH_3.[CH_2]_{13}.CH.COOH$$
$$|$$
$$CH(OH).[CH_2]_{14}.CH_3$$
(I)

$$CH_3.[CH_2]_{13}.CH.COOH$$
$$|$$
$$CH(OH).[CH_2]_7.CH:CH.[CH_2]_5.CH_3$$
(II)

Naturally Occurring Unsaturated Fatty Acids

It seems desirable to arrange this important group in a sequence which does not strictly follow the systematic classification with which every student of formal organic chemistry is familiar. If we adhered to the conventional system in the present instance, we should commence with the mono-ethylenic acid of lowest molecular weight found in fats, namely, the decenoic acid, $C_{10}H_{18}O_2$, which occurs in exceedingly small proportions in butter. Next would come the dodecenoic acids, $C_{12}H_{22}O_2$, found in rare instances and in small amounts in a few seed fats and marine animal oils, then the slightly less rare tetradecenoic acids, and so on. After discussing these simple mono-ethylenic higher aliphatic acids we should proceed methodically to consider the corresponding natural di-, tri-, tetra-, and penta-ethylenic acids, and finally have to return to certain mono-ethylenic acids containing a hydroxyl group or a ring-system, and to acetylenic acids. Strict adherence to the formal classification would have, in the case of the natural unsaturated fatty acids, the following disadvantages:

1. It would involve consideration, at the outset, of acids which are exceedingly rare and whose constitutions, in some cases, have not been settled.

2. Oleic acid, which is the most widely distributed of all fatty acids, and also in not a few fats their major component acid, would only be discussed after several of these rarer acids. Yet, by reason of its common occurrence, ordinary oleic acid is the member of the series whose chemical properties have been most thoroughly studied, and is also the acid on which most of the special methods of constitution determination used in this series were worked out in the first instance.

3. The mono-unsaturated acids, as a group, share many characteristic properties which differentiate them sharply from the polyethylenic acids. For example, it may be said that, very broadly speaking, the mono-unsaturated acids are those which determine the general properties of the so-called "non-drying oils", while polyethylenic acids give rise to the characteristic behaviour of the "drying oil" group. This makes it inconvenient to interpose an account of the polyethylenic acids between that of the simple aliphatic mono-ethylenic acids and that of the hydroxy- and cyclic monoethylenic acids or the acetylenic acids.

The following general scheme of treatment of the natural unsaturated acids has therefore been adopted:

1. Ordinary oleic acid, which is present in practically all natural fats and which has received more investigation than any other individual unsaturated fatty acid, is considered separately in the first place. It is not only the most important representative of the fatty acids as a whole, but is also typical of the other mono-ethylenic acids. Its isolation and properties, the methods employed to determine its chemical constitution, its stereo-chemical relationships and its chemical transformations are therefore dealt with at some length. Some of the isomeric forms of this acid which have been produced artificially from ordinary oleic acid are also described.

2. Syntheses of oleic acid, and of other unsaturated higher fatty acids, are considered at this point.

3. Other natural mono-ethylenic fatty acids next receive notice, together with structurally related unsaturated acids (acetylenic, cyclic unsaturated, hydroxy-unsaturated acids). In these cases, and also in the natural poly-ethenoid acids, those acids which possess a structural resemblance to oleic acid are dealt with separately from the rest.

588

4. After completing the survey of the naturally occurring mono-ethylenic and closely related higher fatty acids, we consider the corresponding poly-ethenoid acids, namely, the di-ethylenic linoleic acid, the tri-ethylenic linolenic, elæostearic, and licanic acids, and the poly- (tetra, penta, or hexa-) ethylenic acids of the C_{18}, C_{20}, and C_{22} series.

As a general rule only those naturally-occurring unsaturated acids which have been wholly or comparatively well authenticated are included in this survey.

The order of treatment of the unsaturated acids of the natural fats will therefore be as follows:

Oleic acid (cis-*octadec-9-enoic acid*):
  Isolation and properties, chemical constitution, stereochemical configuration, chemical
    transformations; isomeric forms produced by hydrogenation or other chemical action.
Syntheses of unsaturated higher fatty acids:
  Oleic acid.
  General methods of synthesis of unsaturated higher fatty acids.
Other mono-ethenoid acids:
  Acids of the structure $CH_3.[CH_2]_7.CH:CH.[CH_2]_n.COOH$.
  *cyclo*Propenyl (and *cyclo*Propyl) derivatives of oleic acid.
  Acids of the structure $CH_3.[CH_2]_m.CH:CH.[CH_2]_7.COOH$.
Hydroxy-unsaturated acids:
  (i) Containing the structure —$CH:CH.[CH_2]_7.COOH$.
  (ii) Other hydroxylated fatty acids.
Acids (*including an ethynoid and a tri-ethenoid acid*) $=C(H).[CH_2]_4.COOH$.
Cyclic mono-ethenoid acids.
Mono-ethenoid acids not falling within the above groups.
Poly-ethenoid and poly-ethynoid acids:
  Di-, tri-, tetra-ethenoid and di-ethynoid acids containing the structure $=CH.[CH_2]_7$.
    COOH.
  Tri-, tetra-, penta-, hexa-ethenoid acids (usually containing the structure $=CH.[CH_2]_3$.
    COOH).
  Poly-ethenoid (and poly-ethynoid) acids not falling within the above groups.

OLEIC ACID, *cis*-OCTADEC-9-ENOIC ACID,

$CH_3.[CH_2]_7.CH:CH.[CH_2]_7.CO_2H$.

Oleic acid was first recognised as a constituent of several common fats by Chevreul in his *Recherches sur les corps gras* in 1815, although it was probably not prepared in the pure condition until much later. (The oleic acid or "oleine" of commerce is by no means a pure acid, if it consists of the liquid portions separated by pressing a mixture of fatty acids which has been obtained by distillation in a current of superheated steam under reduced pressure; this liquid oleine will contain, therefore, in addition to oleic acid, any more un-saturated acids (such as linoleic) which may have distilled over without de-composition, varying proportions of palmitic or other saturated acids which have not separated in the solid condition and remained in the residue of "stearines", and isomers of oleic acid formed during processing.)

Isolation of pure oleic acid. For the preparation of pure oleic acid it is usual to select as raw material a fatty oil of comparatively simple composition containing a high percentage of combined oleic acid (for example, olive or almond oil). Since it is more difficult to separate oleic acid quantitatively from linoleic acid than from saturated acids, it may well be preferred to commence from a seed fat such as cacao butter or Allanblackia fat; for, although saturated acids predominate in these materials, the oleic acid present is accompanied by only very small proportions of linoleic or other diethenoid acids.

After removal of most of the saturated acids from the mixed fatty acids of such a fat by crystallising their lead salts from alcohol, the unsaturated acids may be freed from linoleic acid by crystallising the barium salts from benzene containing 5 per cent. of 95 per cent. alcohol[52a] or by crystallising the lithium salts from 80 per cent. alcohol.[52b] The separated barium or lithium salts will be free from linoleates, and yield a mixture of oleic acid with a small amount of palmitic or other saturated acids, from which pure oleic acid (or methyl oleate) may be obtained by ester-fractionation or gas–liquid chromatography (cf. Chapter XI, pp. 688, 697).

Bertram[53] treated mixed fatty acids containing a high percentage of oleic acid with mercuric acetate in methyl alcohol and acetic acid, when the mercury compound of oleic acid remained in solution; after filtering, the oleic acid was regenerated from the filtrates, and further purified by crystallisation from acetone at $-15°$ to $-20°C$.

Brown[54] described methods whereby oleic acid can be obtained practically pure by direct crystallisation from solvents at low temperatures. For example, the acids from olive oil are first separated from saturated acids by crystallising out the latter from acetone at $-20°$, followed by several crystallisations of the oleic acid from about 7 per cent. solution in acetone at $-60°$. The yield of oleic acid, m.p. 13°, so obtained was about 50 per cent. of that present in the olive oil mixed acids.

The low-temperature crystallisation method can be applied equally successfully, of course, to the unsaturated acids from a solid fat such as ox or sheep tallow, cacao butter, etc. The best procedure for the preparation of pure oleic acid or its esters is to commence from a seed-fat (such as cacao butter) which contains very little linoleic acid, and first to remove from its mixed fatty acids as much of the saturated acids as possible, either by separating their lead salts from alcohol[55a] or by crystallising the mixed fatty acids from 95–100 per cent. methanol[55b] at $-20°$. The recovered soluble acids are then further crystallised from acetone several times at temperatures between $-55°$ and $-40°$. The crystallised fraction of oleic acid finally obtained is converted to the methyl ester which is distilled through an efficient fractionating column at low pressure (0·2–1 mm.) in order to remove small amounts of palmitic or other lower acids present in the crystallised oleic acid.

Oleic acid forms a complex with urea which can be usefully employed in the purification of the acid.[56a] For the isolation of pure oleic acid (or its methyl ester) from olive oil, Swern and Parker[56b] recommend crystallisation of 1 part of olive oil acids with 3·6 parts of urea from methanol, when, after cooling at 0°, a urea complex of fatty acids containing 85–90 per cent. of oleic acid is separated. The recovered acid is crystallised from acetone, first at $-20°$, when saturated acids are precipitated, and then at $-50°$, when acids containing about 95 per cent. of oleic acid are deposited. Fractional distillation of the methyl esters of the latter acids yields oleic acid of about 99 per cent. purity.

Properties of oleic acid. Oleic acid crystallises in two forms, one melting at 13°C. and the other at 16°C. It partly decomposes on distillation at atmospheric pressure, but may be distilled at reduced pressure: its boiling point is 285·5–286·0°/100 mm., 232·5°/15 mm., 153·0°/0·1 mm. The methyl and ethyl esters are colourless liquids which distil at about 150°/3 mm. or 130–135°/0·1 mm.

Wheeler and Riemenschneider[57a] state that highly purified methyl oleate melts at $-19·9°$, oleic acid at 13·0–13·2° and 16·0–16·3°, and triolein (prepared by esterification of the latter) crystallises in three polymorphic forms, m.p. $-32°$, $-12°$, and 5°.

On treatment with thionyl chloride or phosphorus chlorides, oleic acid undergoes some decomposition other than the simple formation of its acid chloride, $C_{17}H_{33}.COCl$. Oleic acid chloride, however, is produced smoothly when the acid is heated with oxalyl chloride, and the product purified by distillation in a vacuum. The same method is available for the production of the acid chlorides of elaidic, linoleic, and linolenic acids (Longenecker et al.[58]).

The preparation and properties of the amide, N-methyl-amide, and other N-substituted amides of oleic acid have been described (e.g. by Swern et al.[59]).

Chemical constitution of oleic acid. For a long time after Varrentrapp[60] had shown in 1840 that palmitic acid was produced in large quantities when oleic acid was fused with caustic potash, it was considered that the acid had the constitution $CH_3.[CH_2]_{14}.CH:CH.COOH$; but this reaction undoubtedly involves the migration of a double bond towards the carboxyl group under the influence of the molten potash. The structure at present accepted for oleic acid was first proposed, apparently, by von Meyer and Jacobsen[61a] in 1893 in view of the production, *inter alia*, of nonanoic and azelaic acids in the oxidation of stearolic acid (III, below); Bulatski[61b] however claims that the octadec-9-enoic structure was first established in 1888 by Wagner.[61c] In 1894 Baruch[62] presented evidence in confirmation of von Meyer and Jacobsen's conclusion, based on the following somewhat complicated sequence of changes:

Oleic acid (I) was converted by bromine into dibromostearic acid (II) which, when heated with concentrated alcoholic potash lost two molecules of hydrogen bromide and produced an acetylenic acid, stearolic acid (III). When stearolic acid was treated with concentrated sulphuric acid a molecule of water was added and the ketostearic acids (IV) produced. The oximes of these acids (V) were submitted to the Beckmann rearrangement and amongst the resulting scission products Baruch was able to identify (VIIA) nonanoic acid and 9-amino-nonanoic acid and also (VIIB) *n*-octylamine and *n*-sebacic acid. The respective pairs of products VIIA and VIIB must have been produced by hydrolysis of the corresponding acid amido-derivatives VIA and VIB, which must accordingly have the formulæ assigned to them; consequently, the position of the unsaturated linkage in stearolic acid (and therefore in the original oleic acid) must have been between the ninth and tenth carbon atoms of the chain, counting the carboxylic carbon atom as number one.

$$CH_3.[CH_2]_7.CH{=}CH.[CH_2]_7.COOH \qquad \text{Oleic acid (I)}$$

$$CH_3.[CH_2]_7.CHBr.CHBr.[CH_2]_7.COOH \qquad \text{Dibromostearic acid (II)}$$

$$CH_3.[CH_2]_7.C{\equiv}C.[CH_2]_7.COOH \qquad \text{Stearolic acid (III)}$$

(a) $CH_3.[CH_2]_7.CH_2.CO.[CH_2]_7.COOH$
and
(b) $CH_3.[CH_2]_7.CO.CH_2.[CH_2]_7.COOH$ } Ketostearic acids (IV)

(a) $CH_3.[CH_2]_7.CH_2.C(:N.OH).[CH_2]_7.COOH$
and
(b) $CH_3.[CH_2]_7.C(:N.OH).CH_2.[CH_2]_7.COOH$ } Oximes (V)

$CH_3.[CH_2]_7.CO.NH.CH_2.[CH_2]_7.COOH$ $CH_3.[CH_2]_7.NH.CO.CH_2.[CH_2]_7.COOH$
(VIA)   (VIB)
$CH_3.[CH_2]_7.COOH +$ $CH_3.[CH_2]_6.CH_2.NH_2 +$
$NH_2.CH_2.[CH_2]_7.COOH$ $COOH.[CH_2]_8.COOH$
Nonanoic acid   9-amino-nonanoic acid   *n*-octylamine   *n*-sebacic acid
(VIIA)   (VIIB)

Gunstone[63a] has pointed out that although the four products (VIIA and VIIB) can only come from 10-ketostearic acid, this latter acid could have resulted by hydration of either octadec-9-ynoic or octadec-10-ynoic acid, since either acid yields a mixture of two ketostearic acids on hydration.[63b] Consequently, Baruch's conclusions, although correct, were not on an unequivocal basis.

591

Much simpler proof of the position of the double bond in oleic acid (or other unsaturated acids) has since been given by means of specific oxidation processes. Early attempts to oxidise oleic acid with nitric acid led to the production of a complex mixture of monobasic and dibasic acids; similarly, aqueous acid potassium permanganate gives, in addition to dihydroxystearic acid, a mixture of mono- and di-basic acids. Nevertheless, by oxidising oleic acid with aqueous permanganate at 60° Edmed[64] (1898) was able to obtain in addition to 60 per cent. of dihydroxystearic acid, 16 per cent. of azelaic acid, 16 per cent. of oxalic acid and a small amount of n-nonanoic acid, thus supporting the 9:10 structure already assigned to oleic acid.

The ozonisation process, or addition of ozone to an unsaturated ethylenic linkage, has given much more reliable data on the constitution of ethylenic acids than oxidation with aqueous reagents. Molinari[65a] (1903) appears to have been the first to apply the ozonisation method to the case of oleic acid, although almost concurrently Harries and Thieme[65b] published the results of very exhaustive work on the same method. The ozonisation procedures lead, in the case of ordinary oleic acid, to the production of n-nonanoic and azelaic acids, together with the corresponding n-nonylaldehyde and azelaic acid semi-aldehyde, $COOH.[CH_2]_7.CHO$.* Since about 1959 several workers[65d] have effected improvements in the yields and the methods of isolation (including selective chromatographic adsorption) of the scission products; and very recently (1962) it has been recommended[65e] to hydrogenate the ozonolysis products mildly with Lindlar (poisoned palladium) catalyst, when a mixture of readily identifiable aldehydes is smoothly produced.

Grun and Wittka[66] (1925) obtained good yields of n-nonanoic and azelaic acids by oxidising stearolic acid with chromic acid (*cf.* von Meyer and Jacobsen, 1893[61a]); whilst Armstrong and Hilditch[52b] (1925) showed that direct oxidation of methyl or ethyl oleates with powdered potassium permanganate in hot acetone or acetic acid solution gave a mixture of nonanoic acid and methyl or ethyl hydrogen azelate:

$$CH_3.[CH_2]_7.CH:CH.[CH_2]_7.COOMe \rightarrow$$
$$CH_3.[CH_2]_7.COOH + COOH.[CH_2]_7.COOMe.$$

By hydrolysing the mixed acidic products of oxidation they obtained yields of 80–90 per cent. of azelaic acid and 60–70 per cent. of n-nonanoic acid calculated on the original ester employed. When acetone is used as solvent for the permanganate, some suberic and n-octanoic acids are also concurrently produced; Boekenoogen et al.[52c] have shown that these side-reactions are minimised if acetic acid is used in place of acetone, and also that the dicarboxylic acids resulting from the oxidation can be conveniently separated by partition chromatography.

Later refinements to these methods include:

(a) Oxidation of a dilute aqueous solution of potassium oleate with a mixed solution of potassium periodate and permanganate at pH 6–9 and below

* The semi-aldehyde of azelaic acid is best prepared by the action of periodic acid on the 9,10-dihydroxystearic acids (King[65c]).

40°C., when only the direct acidic scission (and no secondary) products are formed[67a]; these are separated by adsorption on a silicic acid column.[52c]

(b) Treatment of oleic (or other mono- or poly-ene) acid with performic acid in insufficient amount to react with one double bond yields a mixture of dihydroxy acids and unchanged starting material. After complete hydrogenation (Pd on charcoal catalyst) the reaction mixture is oxidised with periodate-permanganate and the acidic degradation fragments examined after separation by gas–liquid chromatography.[67b]

Stereochemical configuration of oleic acid. In common with all symmetrically di-substituted ethylenic compounds, it is possible for the mono-ethylenic higher fatty acids to exist in two geometrically isomeric forms which may be represented as follows:

$$CH_3.[CH_2]_m.\overset{\shortparallel}{C}.H \qquad\qquad CH_3.[CH_2]_m.\overset{\shortparallel}{C}.H$$
$$COOH.[CH_2]_n.\overset{\shortparallel}{C}.H \qquad\qquad H.\overset{\shortparallel}{C}.[CH_2]_n.COOH$$
$$cis\text{-} \qquad\qquad\qquad\qquad trans\text{-}$$

In the case of oleic acid the geometrical isomeride has not so far been found in any natural fat (except in small proportions in the fats of ruminant animals[68]) but it has long been known that on treatment with oxides of nitrogen, or by heating with small quantities of sulphur, oleic acid is partially transformed into an isomeric acid, elaidic acid, which still has the double bond in the 9, 10 position and is thus a geometrical isomeride of oleic acid. For many years, although the reason does not appear by any means clear, it was customary to describe oleic acid as the *trans*-isomeride. It is usual in other cases of geometrical isomerism, in the absence of any definite evidence, to regard the more stable, higher melting form as the *trans*-isomeride (in this case elaidic acid). This reasoning alone would lead us to formulate oleic and elaidic acids as follows:

$$CH_3.[CH_2]_7.\overset{\shortparallel}{C}.H \qquad\qquad CH_3.[CH_2]_7.\overset{\shortparallel}{C}.H$$
$$COOH.[CH_2]_7.\overset{\shortparallel}{C}.H \qquad\qquad H.\overset{\shortparallel}{C}.[CH_2]_7.COOH$$

Oleic, *cis*-octadec-9-enoic acid.   Elaidic, *trans*-octadec-9-enoic acid.

This view is supported by numerous facts which have gradually come to light. In the early years of the present century Italian workers[69] noticed that "elaidic" forms such as elaidic or brassidic acids form solid solutions with the corresponding saturated acids (stearic or behenic), whilst the natural acids (oleic or erucic) do not do so: this suggests that "elaidic" derivatives are sterically related to the saturated acids, i.e. they are the *trans*-isomerides. Later, examination of the X-ray diffraction spectra of oleic and elaidic, and of erucic and brassidic ($C_{22}H_{12}O_2$) acids showed that elaidic and brassidic acids were the *trans*-forms of the respective pairs of acids (Muller and Shearer,[13a] Francis and Willis[70]); and studies of the behaviour of mono-molecular films on water of the same pairs of unsaturated acids (Marsden and Rideal,[71a] Harkins and Florence[71b]) revealed that monolayers of the "elaidic" forms resemble those of the corresponding saturated acids, but differ from those of the "oleic" (natural) forms in being less highly expanded. The presence of a *cis*-ethenoid bond leads to deformation of the chain of carbon atoms, whereas the *trans*-ethenoid bond produces little deformation in the chain, which remains closely similar to that of the saturated acid.

The formation of oleic acid when the 9:10-ethynoid stearolic acid is reduced in presence of titanous chloride is a further indication that oleic acid has the *cis*-configuration (G. M. and R. Robinson[72]), whilst the almost exclusive natural production of *cis*-unsaturated acids follows the usual rule that in natural products the less stable of two possible isomerides is synthesised by the living cell (Armstrong and Allan[73]).

The most conclusive evidence, however, is that afforded by the Raman spectra (Dupont and Yvernault,[74a] van den Hende[74b]) and by the infra-red spectra (McCutcheon *et al.*,[75a] Swern *et al.*,[75b] Sinclair *et al.*,[75c] Ahlers *et al.*,[75d]) of natural unsaturated acids (oleic, petroselinic, ricinoleic, linoleic, and others) and oleyl alcohol, and of their corresponding "elaidic" isomerides. In all cases the natural compound has the *cis*-, and the isomerised "elaidic" form the *trans*-, configuration.

The only exception to the exclusive occurrence of *cis*-oleic acid in natural fats yet observed is in the depot fats of ruminants. In oxen Swern *et al.*[68] found by infra-red analysis up to 5–6 per cent. of *trans*-acids (mainly elaidic, but also positional isomers such as *trans*-octadec-10-(and -11-)enoic acids. Shorland *et al.*[68] showed by infra-red studies that the occurrence of *trans*-acids in animal fats is practically confined to ruminants (ox, sheep, deer), only traces being observed in pig fats, and none in those of the rabbit or horse.

Interconversion of oleic and elaidic acids. The conversion of triolein into trielaidin by means of oxides of nitrogen was apparently first observed by Poutet in 1819,[76] who employed a solution of mercury in nitric acid as the source of the oxides of nitrogen. This test, known as the elaidin test, was formerly much used as a qualitative test for non-drying oils. In 1894 Saytzew[77a] showed that the same change takes place when oleic acid is treated with sulphurous acid or sodium bisulphite under pressure at 180–200°, whilst later Albitski[77b] found that the reverse change of elaidic to oleic acid proceeded under these conditions to the extent of about 20 per cent. Waterman *et al.*[77c] studied extensively the conversion of oleic and other natural unsaturated acids or their glycerides into their *cis-trans*-equilibrium mixtures by means of sulphur dioxide under differing conditions of temperature and pressure. Rankow[77d] (1929) observed that small amounts of sulphur effect the partial transformation of oleic into elaidic acid at about 200°.

The most efficient catalyst, however, for elaidinisation is selenium, which Bertram[78a] showed in 1936 to be effective in concentrations of 0·1–0·3 per cent. at about 180–200°. The *cis-trans*-equilibrium is rapidly attained and, the proportion of selenium being so small, the formation of addition products with the catalyst, or other by-products, is minimised. Indeed, linoleic acid, which yields high proportions of by-products when treated with oxides of nitrogen or elemental sulphur as isomerising agents, can be isomerised with small proportions of selenium at 200° with little loss other than slight polymerisation (*cf.* p. 627).[78b, c]

A quantitative study of the oleic–elaidic acid transformation by means of these various reagents was undertaken in 1932 by Griffiths and Hilditch,[79a] who found that the action is a balanced one, that the same equilibrium is attained commencing from either oleic or elaidic acids, and that the reaction product contained elaidic acid to the extent of about 66 per cent. of the oleic or elaidic acid originally employed. Blekkingh[79b] (1950) contributed a theoretical discussion of elaidinisation equilibria, from which he concluded that the *trans*-: *cis*-equilibrium ratio for a monoethenoid compound is 2:1, whilst for diethenoid compounds the equilibrium would be *trans-trans*-: *cis-trans*-: *trans-cis*-: *cis-cis*- in the ratios of 2:1:1:1.

SOME CHEMICAL TRANSFORMATIONS OF OLEIC ACID

1. Addition of halogens. In common with all the unsaturated higher aliphatic acids, oleic acid reacts additively with halogens. With chlorine dichlorostearic acid is produced, whilst with bromine[80a] oleic acid gives a dibromostearic acid, m.p. 28·5–29°, and elaidic acid an isomeric dibromostearic acid, m.p. 29–30°; mixtures of these dibromostearic acids melt at a much lower temperature,[80b] and the individual acids, on debromination with zinc and alcoholic hydrochloric acid, revert exclusively to the acid from which they were prepared, oleic or elaidic respectively.[78b, 80c] The debromination of bromo-addition products of the higher ethylenic acids is, indeed, a somewhat remarkable change, in that it has been shown not only in the foregoing cases but also in those of linoleic and linolenic acids (see below) that, in the regenerated ethylenic acids, the position of the double bonds is the same as in the original acid from which the bromo-derivative was prepared.

Iodine, or more frequently mixed halogens such as iodine monochloride or iodine monobromide, will also interact additively with ethylenic acids, and this reaction of course forms the basis for the estimation of the iodine value of unsaturated fatty oils and acids by such well-known methods as those of Wijs, Hanus, etc. Derivatives of the halogens, such as hypochlorous acid, also act additively towards oleic acid and in this way, for example, chlorohydroxystearic acids have been obtained from oleic and elaidic acids.

2. The dihydroxystearic acids produced by oxidation of oleic and elaidic acids. Oleic may be transformed by a variety of reagents into one of two 9,10-dihydroxystearic acids, which melt respectively at 95° and 132°. Most of these reactions lead to the exclusive production of one or other of these acids, which are evidently stereoisomerides. Moreover, those reagents which cause the production of the acid, m.p. 95°, from oleic acid result in the formation of the acid, m.p. 132°, from elaidic acid, and conversely. It further follows, then, that the particular dihydroxystearic acid produced in any given case depends upon the geometrical configuration of the original ethylenic acid, and that (since under different conditions each acid results from one and the same geometrical isomeride – e.g., oleic acid) an inversion must take place during some of the chemical processes involved.

In the case of oleic acid, the dihydroxystearic acid m.p. 95° is obtained as a result of the following reactions:

(i) Addition of chlorine or bromine to oleic acid, followed by treatment of the product with aqueous or alcoholic alkali.[81a]

(ii) Addition of hypochlorous acid to oleic acid followed by treatment of the resulting chlorohydroxystearic acid (a) with aqueous or alcoholic potash, or (b) with baryta, when an epoxy-acid is formed which on further treatment with alkali or dilute sulphuric acid yields the dihydroxy acid m.p. 95°.[81a]

(iii) Oxidation of oleic acid by Caro's acid[81a] or by hydrogen peroxide and glacial acetic acid (peracetic acid),[81b] or by perbenzoic acid.[81c] With the latter, or with peracetic or performic acid[81d, 82a] below 25°, a 9,10-epoxystearic acid is first produced which, when its ethylene oxide ring is opened, yields the dihydroxystearic acid of melting point 95°.

The dihydroxystearic acid of m.p. 132° has been obtained from oleic acid in the following ways:

(i) Treatment of the chlorohydroxystearic acid (cf. above) by means of silver oxide.[81a]

(ii) Oxidation of alkaline salts of oleic acid in dilute ice-cold alkaline aqueous solution by potassium permanganate.[72, 83]

(iii) Oxidation of oleic acid by osmium tetroxide in an acidic medium.[84]

In all cases, when elaidic acid has been submitted to the action of the different agents enumerated in the preceding paragraphs, it has been invariably found that the opposite form of dihydroxystearic acid results from that obtained when oleic acid is the starting material. Similar relationships have been observed, by several of the workers mentioned, in the cases of the isomeric petroselinic acids and the isomeric erucic and brassidic acids. Further, it has been observed that, in the oxidation by means of alkaline permanganate, good yields of the dihydroxy-acid are not obtained unless a large excess of alkali is employed[83c] and that the yield of the dihydroxy-acid m.p. 95° produced from the more stable elaidic acid is invariably less than that of the isomeride obtained from oleic acid.[83a]

The stereochemical relationships of oleic and elaidic acids with the two corresponding 9,10-dihydroxystearic acids (and of other cis- and trans-ethenoid long-chain acids with their corresponding dihydroxy-saturated acids) presented a problem which gave rise to much discussion for many years, but which is now satisfactorily cleared up. Lapworth[85a] and Böeseken[85b] remarked in 1926–1927 that oxidation by permanganate does not usually involve any change in stereochemical configuration, so that it might be concluded that the cis- (oleic) acids are directly related to the dihydroxy-saturated acids of higher melting-point, and conversely. A number of specific features in the course of the changes involved respectively in the action of alkali permanganate or of per-acids upon oleic and similar monoethenoid long-chain acids (v. infra) caused different workers to arrive at differing conclusions but finally (1948–1952) studies of corresponding pairs of lower and higher melting forms of isomeric dihydroxy-saturated acids led to an unequivocal decision. The lower melting forms (e.g. 9,10-dihydroxystearic acid, m.p. 95°) readily give cyclic acid complexes with boric acid (Wittcoff *et al.*,[86a] 1948), and also crystalline complexes with urea (Swern *et al.*,[86b] 1952), whereas the higher melting forms (e.g. 9,10-dihydroxystearic acid, m.p. 132°) do not. This indicates that the hydroxyl groups in the lower melting isomers are in closer spatial proximity than those in the higher melting forms, from which it follows that the higher melting dihydroxy-acids are sterically related to the *cis*-ethenoid acids, the lower melting dihydroxy-acids being directly related to the *trans*-ethenoid acids.

$$CH_3 . [CH_2]_7 . \overset{H}{\underset{}{C}} = \overset{H}{\underset{}{C}} . [CH_2]_7 . COOH \quad \rightarrow \quad CH_3 . [CH_2]_7 . \overset{H}{\underset{\overset{|}{\underset{H}{O}}}{C}} - \overset{H}{\underset{\overset{|}{\underset{H}{O}}}{C}} . [CH_2]_7 . COOH$$

Oleic, cis-octadec-9-enoic acid   Erythro-9,10-dihydroxystearic acid, m.p. 132°

$$CH_3 . [CH_2]_7 . \overset{H}{\underset{\underset{H}{}}{C}} = \overset{}{\underset{H}{C}} . [CH_2]_7 . COOH \quad \rightarrow \quad CH_3 . [CH_2]_7 . \overset{H}{\underset{\overset{|}{\underset{H}{O}}}{C}} - \overset{O}{\underset{\overset{|}{}}{\underset{H}{C}}} . [CH_2]_7 . COOH$$

Elaidic, trans-octadec-9-enoic acid   Threo-9,10-dihydroxystearic acid, m.p. 95°

Rotatory powers of the four optically active forms of 9,10,12-trihydroxy-stearic acid (produced by alkaline permanganate oxidation of ricinoleic and ricinelaidic acids, each of which yields two isomeric trihydroxy-acids) conform (Kass and Radlove,[87] 1942) with the view that the higher melting hydroxy-acids produced by hydroxylation are directly related to *cis*-ethenoid acids.

The formation of the high melting *erythro*-dihydroxy acids from oleic and other *cis*-ethenoid acids by direct hydroxylation (e.g., by aqueous alkaline permanganate) being established, it follows that the production of the lower melting *threo*dihydroxy acids from the same (*cis*-) starting materials by other forms of oxidation must involve an "inversion" of the Walden type at some point; this also applies of course to the converse production by the latter means of *erythro*-dihydroxy acids from the *trans*-forms of ethenoid acids (e.g., elaidic). The point (or points) at which a change in configuration takes place have been the subject of much study, especially by G. King[82] and by D. Swern.[81b,d,e, 88] The final conclusions accepted may be summed up briefly as follows:

(i) The procedures which involve an inversion are oxidation of monoethenoid acids by per-acids, or addition of a hydroxy-halide to a monoethenoid acid and subsequent conversion of the halohydrin to a dihydroxy acid.

(ii) With per-acids, although oxidation with perbenzoic acid always gives epoxy-saturated acids,[81c] the latter are not normally isolated when peracetic acid or Caro's acid is the oxidant; but King[82a] showed that under suitable conditions 9,10-epoxystearic acid may be isolated during oxidation of elaidic acid with peracetic acid, and it may reasonably be inferred that oxidation of ethenoid fatty acids with per-acids proceeds by primary formation of epoxides, followed by opening of the epoxide ring.

(iii) King[82b] (1942) also showed that either of the 9,10-dihydroxystearic acids, m.p. 132° or 95° (as also the optically active form, m.p. 141°, of the m.p. 132° acid which occurs in small proportions in castor oil), furnish the opposite isomeride (m.p. 95° or 132° respectively) after conversion by hydrogen chloride at 160° into chlorohydrins, formation of epoxy-stearic acids from the latter, and subsequent opening of the epoxide ring. King concluded, in view of the fact that the optically active acid gave rise to an epoxy-acid which possessed a small, but perceptible, rotatory power, that a Walden inversion takes place during hydration (opening) of the epoxide ring system.

(iv) In 1949 King[82c] published the results of many further experiments on the production of the isomeric 9,10-dihydroxystearic acids by addition to oleic or elaidic acids of hypochlorous, hypobromous, or hypoiodous acids, the conversion of the halo-hydroxy-stearic acids to epoxy-stearic acids, and that of epoxy-stearic to dihydroxy-stearic acids. He found that a change of configuration takes place (*a*) on addition of a hydroxyhalide to a double bond, (*b*) on formation of an epoxide ring from a halo-hydroxy-acid, and (*c*) on opening of an epoxide ring; these conclusions had also been reached by Swern[88] (1948), with the addition that epoxidation of a double bond with a per-acid proceeds directly by "*cis*-addition".

Consequently, production of a dihydroxy-saturated acid from an ethenoid acid and a per-acid involves only *one* configurational change (the opening of the epoxide ring) whilst addition of hypochlorous acid, and its conversion with alkali through an epoxide to the dihydroxy-saturated acid, involves *three* configurational changes. In each instance, however, the final result is that the dihydroxy-saturated acid produced is the form not directly related configurationally to the unsaturated acid which has been submitted to the sequences of operations mentioned.

More intensive oxidation of oleic acid by dilute alkaline permanganate solutions, or further oxidation of the 9,10-dihydroxystearic acid of m.p. 132° by the same reagent, was shown by Lapworth and Mottram[83c] to lead to the production of suberic, oxalic and *n*-octanoic acids (instead of the two C_9 acids, azelaic and *n*-nonanoic). Green and Hilditch[89a] showed that the isomeric 9,10-dihydroxystearic acid of m.p. 95° undergoes the same decomposition, and that the same course is also followed in other dihydroxy-saturated acids, irrespective of the length of the carbon chain, the position of the double-bond, or its *cis*- or *trans*- configuration in the monoethenoid acids from which the dihydroxy-saturated acids originated; they also examined the corresponding behaviour of the polyethenoid linoleic, linolenic, and elæostearic acids under similar conditions of oxidation, and found that in these cases about 80 per cent. was converted by direct scission to azelaic acid, the remaining 20 per cent. leading to suberic acid (as above). Farmer *et al.*,[89b] employing faintly alkaline solutions of permanganate, obtained only azelaic acid in the oxidation of elæostearic and other polyethenoid acids.

3. Ketolstearic acids (9-hydroxy-10-keto- and 10-hydroxy-9-keto-stearic acids).

Holde and Marcusson[90a] showed (1903) that if excess of alkali is avoided in the aqueous permanganate oxidation of oleic acid, the product formed contains for the most part hydroxyketostearic acids. King[90b] (1936) described optimal oxidation conditions which produced the mixed 9-hydroxy-10-keto- and 10-hydroxy-9-keto-acids in 40–50 per cent. yield: the pure isomers were obtained by fractional crystallisation of their semicarbazones (9-hydroxy-10-ketostearic acid, m.p. 74°; 10-hydroxy-9-ketostearic acid, m.p. 75·5°). Swern *et al.*[90d] state that oxidation of alkaline oleates with dilute aqueous permanganate maintained at pH 9·0–9·5 leads to 65–75 per cent. conversion to 9,10-hydroxyketostearic acids, but with excess alkali (pH 12 or above) the ketol yield is much reduced and production of dihydroxystearic acid much increased. Periodic acid oxidises 9-hydroxy-10-ketostearic acid to nonanoic acid and the semi-aldehyde of azelaic acid, and 10-hydroxy-9-ketostearic acid to nonanaldehyde and azelaic acid.[90c]

Morrell and Phillips[91a] stated that passage of gaseous oxygen through dilute alkaline solutions of the potassium salts of the acids at 18° rapidly and quantitatively decomposes them into nonanoic and azelaic acids. Hilditch and Plimmer[91b] showed that this oxidation is dependent upon the concentration of the alkali present, and considered that the ketolstearic acid is resolved into dihydroxystearic and diketostearic acids by the alkali, and that the scission products arise from oxidation of the latter acids, as well as from direct oxidation of hydroxyketostearic acid.

Oxidation of either 9,10-hydroxystearic acid with chromic acid gives 9,10-diketostearic acid, m.p. 85–86°, which is readily reduced by zinc and acetic acid to a mixture (m.p. 66°) of the 9,10- and 10,9-ketolstearic acids (McGhie[92]).

ISOMERIC FORMS OF OLEIC ACID PRODUCED BY HYDROGENATION OR OTHER MEANS

A number of acids of the oleic series which do not occur naturally have been obtained by various chemical reactions from the natural oleic or related acids. The chief instances may be grouped as follows:

(i) **Isomerisation of oleic acid by oxides of nitrogen, sulphur, selenium.** The interconversion of the *cis*- and *trans*- forms of the oleic acids has already been fully discussed (p.594).

(ii) **Isomeric oleic acids ("*iso*oleic acids") produced during catalytic hydrogenation.** It has been known for a long time that hydrogenation of oleic acid or an ester thereof yields not only stearic acid, but also, during the intermediate phases of the process, a certain proportion of solid oleic acids. It was shown by Moore[52b] in 1919 that the chief component of these solid oleic acids is elaidic acid, but that in addition one or more *iso*oleic acids produced by migration of the double bond are present. The amount of *iso*oleic derivatives produced varies according to the conditions of hydrogenation, and is probably at a maximum when the operation is carried out at a high temperature (200° C. or above) and at atmospheric pressure in presence of a moderate concentration of powdered catalyst by the agitation process.[93] Hilditch and Vidyarthi[94] (1929) showed that the isomeric oleic acids, in which migration of the double bond has occurred as a result of hydrogenation, are the *cis*- and *trans*- forms of acids with an ethylene linkage adjacent to the position which it originally occupied; thus, from octadec-9-enoic acid subordinate amounts of the 8:9 and 10:11 ethenoid acids were identified in the products of partial hydrogenation. Waterman *et al.*[95a] (1957) found that, with nickel-kieselguhr catalyst at 180°C., migration took place to an equal extent to the 8:9 and 10:11 positions, but Keppler *et al.*[95b] (1957) considered that double bond migration towards the terminal methyl group predominates. Feuge and Cousins[95c] (1960) found migration as far as the 6:7 and 14:15 positions respectively when methyl oleate was hydrogenated at 200° C., the ratio of *trans*- to *cis*- acids often being about 2:1 (but sometimes greater or less)[95d].

When polyethenoid derivatives such as linoleic or linolenic glycerides are selectively hydrogenated, the monoethenoid compounds formed are naturally not entirely the 9:10 compounds. When, by saturation of the 9:10 or other positions by hydrogen, the remaining double bond occupies a position other than 9:10 in the molecule, the acid so produced is frequently a solid and may be considered as one of the "*iso*oleic acids" of hydrogenation.

(iii) **"*Iso*oleic acids" produced by steam distillation of "sulphonated" oleic acid.** When oleic acid is dissolved in concentrated sulphuric acid and the product subsequently boiled with water, a certain amount of 10-hydroxystearic acid, $CH_3.[CH_2]_7.CH(OH).[CH_2]_8.COOH$, m.p. 83–85°, is produced.[96a] If the products of the action of sulphuric acid on oleic acid are distilled in a vacuum at high temperature in a current of superheated steam the distillate contains, in addition to unchanged oleic acid and a certain amount of hydroxy-stearic acids, a mixture of isomeric forms of oleic acid, which have evidently been produced by elimination of the elements of water from the hydroxy-acids present.[96b] Steger, van Loon et al.[96c] separated the isomeric oleic acids, present in commercial "oleine" produced by the "sulphonation" and distillation process, by the lead salt alcohol method into 66 per cent. of "solid" and 34 per cent. of "liquid" acids. They showed that the former were a mixture of 8:9, 9:10, and 10:11-elaidic acids, whilst the "liquid" acids similarly contained 8:9, 9:10, and 10:11-oleic acids.

SYNTHESES OF UNSATURATED FATTY ACIDS

Methods for the synthetical preparation of long-chain unsaturated acids of the normal series were lacking for many years and it was not until 1925–1934 that isolated syntheses of oleic acid, or its equilibrium mixture with elaidic acid, were published. Since about 1945, however, great activity has developed in this field, and a number of general procedures have been evolved whereby several of the commonly occurring natural monoethenoid acids, and also a few polyethenoid acids, have been synthesised; in addition numerous n-monoethenoid long-chain acids not known to occur naturally have been prepared. The earlier syntheses of oleic acid will be reviewed before dealing with the more recent generalised methods.

Syntheses of oleic acid. The formal synthesis of oleic acid was first attempted in 1925 by G. M. and R. Robinson,[9a] who effected a complete synthesis of 10-ketostearic acid, and also showed that stearolic acid could be converted into oleic acid, but were unable to transform 10-ketostearic acid into stearolic acid. They condensed the sodium derivative of ethyl 2-acetylnonoate (I) (from n-heptyl iodide and acetoacetic ester) with 9-carbethoxynonanoic acid chloride (II) and obtained the ester (III), which, after successive hydrolysis with cold dilute alkali and boiling dilute sulphuric acid, gave 10-ketostearic acid (IV):

$$CH_3.[CH_2]_6.CH.(COCH_3).COOC_2H_5 + Cl.CO.[CH_2]_8.COOC_2H_5$$
$$\text{I} \qquad\qquad\qquad \text{II}$$

$$CH_3.[CH_2]_6.C(COCH_3)(COOC_2H_5).CO.[CH_2]_8.COOC_2H_5$$
$$\text{III}$$

$$CH_3.[CH_2]_7.CO.[CH_2]_8.COOH$$
$$\text{IV}$$

Although stearolic acid (V) can be hydrated to a mixture of 9- and 10-ketostearic acids the reverse change has not yet been accomplished; but its reduction with titanous chloride in acetic acid produced oleic acid (VI) (cf. p. 594):

$$CH_3.[CH_2]_7.C\vdots C.[CH_2]_7.COOH \rightarrow CH_3.[CH_2]_7.CH\colon CH.[CH_2]_7.COOH$$
$$\text{V} \qquad\qquad\qquad\qquad \text{VI}$$

These workers also reduced the synthetic 10-ketostearic acid to 10-hydroxystearic acid and converted the latter into 10-iodostearic acid. Saytzew[97a] and Arnaud and Posternak[97b] had observed much earlier that, on heating with alcoholic potash, 10-iodostearic acid yields a complex mixture of acids in which hydroxystearic, oleic, and isomers of oleic acid are all present. The Robinson synthesis of 10-iodostearic acid thus defines oleic acid as either octadec-9-enoic or octadec-10-enoic acid.

A total synthesis of the equilibrium mixture of *cis*- and *trans*-octadec-9-enoic acids was effected by Noller and Bannerot[98a] in 1934 commencing from 9-chlorononyl aldehyde (I). This aldehyde, on treatment with bromine, hydrogen bromide and methyl alcohol, gave 8,9-dibromo-9-methoxynonyl chloride (II) which, submitted to the Grignard reaction with magnesium *n*-octyl bromide (III), yielded 8-bromo-9-methoxyheptadecyl chloride (IV). Reduction of the latter compound in *n*-butyl alcohol solution with zinc produced heptadec-8-enyl chloride (V), which was converted into the corresponding cyanide (VI) and the latter hydrolysed to the corresponding octadec-9-enoic acid (VII), which proved to be a mixture of 63 per cent. of elaidic acid and 37 per cent. of oleic acid:

$$CHO.[CH_2]_8.Cl \rightarrow CH(OCH_3)Br.CHBr.[CH_2]_7.Cl + Br.Mg.[CH_2]_7.CH_3$$
$$\quad I \qquad\qquad\qquad\qquad II \qquad\qquad\qquad\qquad III$$

$$\downarrow$$
$$CH_3.[CH_2]_7.CH(OCH_3).CHBr.[CH_2]_7.Cl$$
$$IV$$

$$\downarrow$$
$$CH_3.[CH_2]_7.CH:CH.[CH_2]_7.Cl$$
$$V$$

$$\downarrow$$
$$CH_3.[CH_2]_7.CH:CH.[CH_2]_7.CN$$
$$VI$$

$$\downarrow$$
$$CH_3.[CH_2]_7.CH:CH.[CH_2]_7.COOH$$
$$VII$$

A subsequent (1943) synthesis of oleic acid by Baudart[99a] commenced from *n*-decanaldehyde (I), which by bromination in ethyl alcohol gives 1-ethoxy-1,2-dibromo-decane (II). This was submitted to the Grignard reaction with the magnesium derivative of 1-methoxy-6-bromohexane (III), yielding the compound (IV). The latter, by a sequence of steps (V–VIII) somewhat similar to those of the Noller and Bannerot synthesis, finally gave a mixture of 65 per cent. of elaidic and 35 per cent. of oleic acids (IX):

$$CH_3.[CH_2]_8.CHO$$
$$I$$

$$\downarrow$$
$$CH_3.[CH_2]_7.CHBr.CHBr(OC_2H_5) + Br.Mg.CH_2.[CH_2]_4.CH_2(OCH_3)$$
$$\quad II \qquad\qquad\qquad\qquad\qquad\qquad III$$

$$\downarrow$$
$$CH_3.[CH_2]_7.CHBr.CH(OC_2H_5).CH_2.[CH_2]_4.CH_2(OCH_3)$$
$$IV$$

$$\downarrow$$
$$CH_3.[CH_2]_7.CH:CH.[CH_2]_5.CH_2(OCH_3)$$
$$V$$

$$\downarrow$$
$$CH_3.[CH_2]_7.CH:CH.[CH_2]_5.CH_2Br$$
$$VI$$

$$\downarrow$$
$$CH_3.[CH_2]_7.CH:CH.[CH_2]_5.CH_2I + CHNa(COOC_2H_5)_2$$
$$VII$$

$$\downarrow$$
$$CH_3.[CH_2]_7.CH:CH.[CH_2]_6.CH(COOH)_2$$
$$VIII$$

$$\downarrow$$
$$CH_3.[CH_2]_7.CH:CH.[CH_2]_7.COOH$$
$$IX$$

Oleic and/or elaidic acid have since been synthesised by several of the general synthetic methods about to be discussed: by the methoxy-ketone variant of the malonic ester synthesis (Ames and Bowman,[104b] 1951, cf. p. 604), by other methods employing magnesium alkyl halides (Gensler and Thomas,[105] 1952, cf. p. 605), and by syntheses from acetylenic derivatives (Huber,[109b] 1951, cf. p. 606). More recently (1954) an elegant anodic synthesis (cf. anodic syntheses, p. 608) of octadec-9-ynoic (stearolic) acid was effected by Linstead and co-workers.[112e] Electrolysis of n-valeric acid with methyl hydrogen dodec-6-ynedioate (which they had previously synthesised[112d]) gave, after hydrolysis, pentadec-6-ynoic acid, which when electrolysed with methyl hydrogen glutarate yielded the methyl ester of stearolic acid. The acid was readily reduced (as had already been shown by G. M. and R. Robinson[9a]) to oleic acid:

$$CH_3.[CH_2]_3.COOH + COOH.[CH_2]_4.C\vdots C.[CH_2]_4.COOMe \rightarrow$$
$$CH_3.[CH_2]_7.C\vdots C.[CH_2]_4.COOMe \rightarrow$$
$$CH_3.[CH_2]_7.C\vdots C.[CH_2]_4.COOH + COOH.[CH_2]_3.COOMe \rightarrow$$
$$CH_3.[CH_2]_7.C\vdots C.[CH_2]_7.COOMe.$$

General Synthetic Routes to Long-chain n-Unsaturated Acids

(For additional discussion of these methods cf. R. E. Bowman, Ann. Repts. Pure Chem. 1949, **46**, 158–168; F. D. Gunstone, Quart. Reviews, 1953, **7**, 175–197; W. J. Gensler, Chem. Rev., 1957, **57**, 191–280.)

(i) *Chain extension and chain shortening.* Before proceeding to discuss the more complete and generalised methods of long-chain unsaturated acid synthesis which are now available, mention may be made of procedures whereby one or two methylene groups can be added at the carboxyl end of an unsaturated long-chain acid, and of others in which the chain can be shortened by one carbon atom at the carboxyl end of the molecule.

Chain extension. (a) Karrer and Koenig[100] (1943) converted linoleic acid into nonadeca-10,13-dienoic acid by the following method:

$$CH_3.[CH_2]_4.CH\vdots CH.CH_2.CH\vdots CH.[CH_2]_7.COCl \xrightarrow{\text{diazomethane}}$$
$$CH_3.[CH_2]_4.CH\vdots CH.CH_2.CH\vdots CH.[CH_2]_7.CO.CHN_2 \xrightarrow[\text{and hydrolysis}]{\text{Ag}_2\text{O in alcohol}}$$
$$CH_3.[CH_2]_4.CH\vdots CH.CH_2.CH\vdots CH.[CH_2]_7.CH_2.COOH.$$

The resulting nonadeca-10,13-dienoic acid was similarly converted to eicosa-11,14-dienoic acid.

(b) The nitrile of an unsaturated acid may be reduced to an amine, the latter converted successively into an alcohol, an alkyl iodide, and a nitrile which on hydrolysis gives an acid with an extra methylene group:

$$R.CN \rightarrow R.CH_2.NH_2 \rightarrow R.CH_2.OH \rightarrow R.CH_2I \rightarrow R.CH_2.CN \rightarrow R.CH_2.COOH.$$

(c) Two methylene groups can be added in one operation by condensing a long-chain unsaturated alkyl bromide with malonic ester:

$$R.COOEt \rightarrow R.CH_2OH \rightarrow R.CH_2Br + CH_2(COOEt)_2 \rightarrow$$
$$R.CH_2.CH(COOEt)_2 \rightarrow R.CH_2.CH_2.COOH.$$

In this way Adams et al.[101] converted erucyl (docos-13-enyl) bromide into the cis-trans-mixture of tetracos-15-enoic acids.

(d) The anodic syntheses of unsaturated acids by Linstead et al.[112] (p. 608) may be regarded in some instances as further examples of chain extension.

Chain shortening. Mitter and Bagchi[102] converted methyl oleate to methyl heptadec-8-enoate (and the latter to methyl hexadec-7-enoate) by the Barbier-Wieland degradation with phenyl magnesium bromide and subsequent oxidation:

$$CH_3.[CH_2]_7.CH:CH.[CH_2]_7.COOCH_3 \xrightarrow{C_6H_5.MgBr}$$
$$CH_3.[CH_2]_7.CH:CH.[CH_2]_6.CH:CPh_2 \rightarrow$$
$$CH_3.[CH_2]_7.CH:CH.[CH_2]_6.COOH + C_6H_5.CO.C_6H_5.$$

(ii) General methods of synthesis. These group themselves (with some overlapping) under several main headings, namely, malonic ester syntheses (by the acyloin or methoxy-ketone routes), syntheses with the aid of magnesium alkyl halides, syntheses developed from acetylenic hydrocarbons, and anodic syntheses.

Malonic ester (acyloin) syntheses. (i) In its simplest form this procedure was first employed by Baudart[99b] (1946), who adapted the acyloin synthesis of Ruzicka et al.[103] (1942) to the syntheses of hexadec-9-enoic (palmitoleic) and octadec-9-enoic (oleic) acids in their separate cis- and trans-forms. 8-Ethoxy-n-octanoic ester (prepared from ethyl 8-bromo-n-octanoate) was condensed with either ethyl n-heptanoate or ethyl n-nonanoate to yield an acyloin (I) which was reduced to the mixed isomeric 8,9-dihydroxy-derivatives of 1-ethoxy-penta- (or -hepta-) decane:

$$CH_3.[CH_2]_n.COOEt + COOEt.[CH_2]_7.OEt \xrightarrow{Na}$$
$$CH_3.[CH_2]_n.CO.CH(OH).[CH_2]_7.OEt \xrightarrow{Ni, H_2}$$
$$(I)$$
$$CH_3.[CH_2]_n.CH(OH).CH(OH).[CH_2]_7.OEt.$$
$$n = 5 \text{ or } 7$$

The isomeric pairs of glycols, differing in melting-point and solubility, can be separated in the pure condition, and from the individual glycols the corresponding cis- and trans-acids were isolated by the following sequence of reactions:

$$CH_3.[CH_2]_n.CH(OH).CH(OH).[CH_2]_7.OEt \xrightarrow{HBr \text{ and acetic acid}}$$
$$CH_3.[CH_2]_n.CHBr.CHBr.[CH_2]_7.Br \xrightarrow{Zn} CH_3.[CH_2]_n.CH:CH.[CH_2]_7.Br \rightarrow$$
$$CH_3.[CH_2]_n.CH:CH.[CH_2]_7.CN \rightarrow CH_3.[CH_2]_n.CH:CH.[CH_2]_7.COOH.$$

(ii) Bowman and co-workers, from 1949 onwards, have improved the acyloin synthesis in several ways, notably the conversion of ethyl esters of malonic ester condensation products into benzyl* esters, the latter being readily replaced by hydrogen when treated with hydrogen in presence of palladium catalyst ("hydrogenolysis"),[10b] as mentioned earlier in this Chapter (p. 581). Ethyl malonate is condensed with the ethyl ester of an ω-bromo-n-aliphatic

---

* Referred to as —COOBz in reaction schemes which follow.

acid, and the sodium derivative of the product is then treated with benzyl alcohol in benzene solution:

$$CH_2.(COOEt)_2 + Br.[CH_2]_n.COOEt \rightarrow$$
$$(COOEt)_2.CNa.[CH_2]_n.COOEt \rightarrow (COOBz)_2.CNa.[CH_2]_n.COOBz.$$

Interaction of the sodium derivative of the benzyl ester condensation product with the chloride of a 2-hydroxy-n-aliphatic acid yields the benzyl ester product of an acyloin, the latter being converted to the acyloin of a long-chain acid by "hydrogenolysis" and decarboxylation[104a, b, c]. Reduction of the latter yields two stereoisomeric dihydroxy-saturated acids which can be separated by crystallisation and then individually transformed into cis- or trans-ethenoid acids (much as in the Baudart synthesis):

$$CH_3.[CH_2]_m.CH(OH).COCl + Na.C(COOBz)_2.[CH_2]_n.COOBz \rightarrow$$
$$CH_3.[CH_2]_m.CH(OH).CO.C(COOBz)_2.[CH_2]_n.COOBz \rightarrow$$
$$CH_3.[CH_2]_m.CH(OH).CO.CH_2.[CH_2]_n.COOH \rightarrow$$
$$CH_3.[CH_2]_m.CH(OH).CH(OH).[CH_2]_{n+1}.COOH \rightarrow$$
$$CH_3.[CH_2]_m.CHBr.CHBr.[CH_2]_{n+1}.COOH \rightarrow$$
$$CH_3.[CH_2]_m.CH:CH.[CH_2]_{n+1}.COOH.$$

Bowman et al. have synthesised by the acyloin route the cis- and trans-forms of myristoleic (tetradec-9-enoic), palmitoleic (hexadec-9-enoic), and gadoleic (eicos-9-enoic) acids,[104c] and also some monoethenoid long-chain acids not yet observed in natural fats.

Malonic ester (methoxy-ketone) syntheses. Bowman et al.[104a] have also used as starting materials the acid chlorides of 2-methoxy-n-saturated acids (instead of 2-hydroxy-n-saturated acids); this leads to the production of a methoxy-keto-derivative instead of an acyloin:

$$CH_3.[CH_2]_m.CH(OMe).CO.C(COOBz)_2.[CH_2]_n.COOBz \rightarrow$$
$$CH_3.[CH_2]_m.CH(OMe).CO.[CH_2]_{n+1}.COOH.$$

Reduction of the methoxy-ketone by aluminium iso-propoxide (but not by Clemmensen or other methods) gives the corresponding methoxy-hydroxy-acids, which can be converted to methoxy-bromo-acids which on reduction yield cis- and trans- monoethenoid acids. The methoxy-ketone procedure has advantages in that in some instances the final sequence of operations proceeds more readily than when the acyloin route is used;[104b] on the other hand, the latter (when it can be used) permits the separation of the stereo-isomeric dihydroxy-acids, whereas the corresponding methoxy-hydroxy-acids are often not separable by physical methods.

Bowman et al. used the methoxy-ketone route in the synthesis of erucic and brassidic,[104a] oleic and elaidic,[104b] cis- and trans-octadec-4-enoic acids,[104c] and some branched-chain monoethenoid acids.[104d]

Syntheses of chaulmoogric and hydnocarpic acids, based on acetoacetic ester condensations, will be referred to when these cyclic acids are discussed (p. 622).

Syntheses with the aid of magnesium alkyl halides (Grignard reagents). The earlier syntheses of oleic-elaidic acids (p. 601) by Noller and Bannerot[98a] and by Baudart[99a] were based on condensations with magnesium alkyl halides, and similar methods have been used in several later instances (*cf.* below, Baudart,[99c] Gensler and Thomas[105]). The most important application of magnesium alkyl halides, and of some other organo-metallic complexes, is, however, in connection with syntheses of long-chain unsaturated acids from acetylenic compounds, which are dealt with in the next section of this discussion.

Baudart[99c] synthesised the *trans-trans*-form of octadeca-9,12-dienoic acid ("linelaidic" acid) from glutaric aldehyde as follows:

(i) $CHO.CH_2.CH_2.CH_2.CHO \rightarrow CH(OEt)_2.CH_2.CH_2.CH_2.CH(OEt)_2 \rightarrow$
$$Br.CH(OEt).CHBr.CH_2.CHBr.CHBr(OEt).$$

(ii) $CH_3.[CH_2]_4.MgBr + Br.CH(OEt).CHBr.CH_2.CHBr.CHBr(OEt) +$
$$BrMg.[CH_2]_6.OMe \rightarrow$$
$$CH_3.[CH_2]_4.CH(OEt).CHBr.CH_2.CHBr.CH(OEt).[CH_2]_6.OMe \xrightarrow{Zn}$$
$$CH_3.[CH_2]_4.CH:CH.CH_2.CH:CH.[CH_2]_6.OMe \rightarrow$$
$$CH_3.[CH_2]_4.CH:CH.CH_2.CH:CH.[CH_2]_6.Br + CH_2(COOEt)_2 \rightarrow$$
$$CH_3.[CH_2]_4.CH:CH.CH_2.CH:CH.[CH_2]_7.COOH.$$

Gensler and Thomas[105] treated esters of ω-ethenoid acids with N-bromo-succinimide, and condensed the resulting bromo-ethenoid ester with a magnesium alkyl bromide, leading directly to the methyl ester of an unsaturated long-chain acid (together with other side-products):

(i) $CH_2:CH.CH_2.[CH_2]_n.COOMe \rightarrow$
$$CH_2:CH.CHBr.[CH_2]_n.COOMe + CH_2Br.CH:CH.[CH_2]_n.COOMe.$$

(ii) $CH_3.[CH_2]_m.MgBr + CH_2Br.CH:CH.[CH_2]_n.COOMe \rightarrow$
$$CH_3.[CH_2]_m.CH_2.CH:CH.[CH_2]_n.COOMe.$$

Starting from methyl undec-10-enoate ($n = 7$) and magnesium heptyl bromide ($m = 6$), elaidic acid (with some oleic and other by-product acids) was obtained; and similarly *trans*-octadec-11-enoic (vaccenic) acid resulted from methyl tridec-12-enoate ($n = 9$) and magnesium pentyl bromide ($m = 4$).

Syntheses from acetylenic compounds. Since about 1948 alkyl acetylenes have proved a most fruitful starting-point for syntheses of long-chain unsaturated acids. In the form of their sodium derivatives ($R.C:C.Na$) or Grignard complexes ($R.C:C.MgBr$) they have been condensed with appropriate alkyl (polymethylene) dihalides to yield long-chain ethynoid halides which are convertible through the corresponding cyanides to acetylenic acids of known constitution. Mild catalytic hydrogenation of ethynoid acids transforms them into the corresponding *cis*-ethenoid acids, accompanied by relatively little *trans*-ethenoid or saturated acids.

The utility of alkyl acetylenes in fatty acid synthesis was foreshadowed as early as 1903, when Moureu and Delange[106a] showed that metallic derivatives of acetylene react with carbon dioxide or ethyl carbonate to give 2-ethynoid acids:

$$CH_3.[CH_2]_m.C:CNa \text{ or } CH_3.[CH_2]_m.C:C.MgBr \xrightarrow{CO_2} CH_3.[CH_2]_m.C:C.COOH.$$

The first long-chain ethynoid acid to be synthesised from an acetylene was apparently behenolic (docos-13-ynoic) acid, obtained in 1928 by Simonsen *et al.*[106b] by condensing the sodium derivative of *n*-octylacetylene with methyl 12-bromo-dodecanoate:

$$CH_3.[CH_2]_7.C \vdots C.Na + Br.[CH_2]_{11}.COOMe \rightarrow CH_3.[CH_2]_7.C \vdots C.[CH_2]_{11}.COOH.$$

In 1938 Johnson *et al.*[106c] condensed the sodium or bromo-magnesium derivatives of alkylacetylenes with the *p*-toluene sulphonates of *ω*-chloro-*n*-alcohols, as for example:

$$CH_3.[CH_2]_7.C \vdots C.Na + C_6H_4Me.SO_2.O.[CH_2]_3.Cl \xrightarrow{NaNH_2}$$

$$CH_3.[CH_2]_7.C \vdots C.[CH_2]_3.Cl \xrightarrow[\text{hydrolysis}]{KCN} CH_3.[CH_2]_7.C \vdots C.[CH_2]_3.COOH.$$
$$\text{(tetradec-5-ynoic acid)}$$

The general usefulness of this method, together with the conversion of synthesised ethynoid acids into *cis*-ethenoid acids, was, however, established by the comprehensive studies of Strong *et al.*[107] (1948–1950) and subsequent workers. The general procedure described by Ahmad and Strong[107a] in 1948, and exemplified by the synthesis of *cis*-undec-6-enoic acid from *n*-butylacetylene, was as follows:

$$CH_3.[CH_2]_3.C \vdots CH + I.[CH_2]_4.Cl \xrightarrow{NaNH_2} CH_3.[CH_2]_3.C \vdots C.[CH_2]_4.Cl \rightarrow$$

$$CH_3.[CH_2]_3.C \vdots C.[CH_2]_4.CN \rightarrow CH_3.[CH_2]_3.C \vdots C.[CH_2]_4.COOH \xrightarrow[H_2]{\text{Raney Ni}}$$

$$(cis\text{-})CH_3.[CH_2]_3.CH \vdots CH.[CH_2]_4.COOH.$$

Cis-octadec-11-enoic acid was similarly synthesised,[107b] starting from *n*-hexyl acetylene, $CH_3.[CH_2]_5.C \vdots CH$, and 1-chloro-9-iodo-*n*-nonane, $I.[CH_2]_9.Cl$; isomerisation of the synthetic *cis*-acid with selenium gave *trans*-octadec-11-enoic acid, which was apparently identical with natural "vaccenic" acid (*cf.* p. 623). In 1950 Taylor and Strong[107c] synthesised by these methods a range of *cis*-monoethenoid acids from hepta-6-enoic (C_7) to tetradec-7-enoic (C_{14}): they reported that the sodium acetylide condensations proceeded satisfactorily only so long as the alkylacetylene contains not more than 12 carbon atoms (i.e., in $CH_3.[CH_2]_m.C \vdots CH$, *m* must not exceed 9) and the alkyl dihalide $I.[CH_2]_n.Cl$ contains from 3 to 9 atoms. For this reason they were unable to synthesise petroselinic (*cis*-octadec-6-enoic) acid from *n*-undecyl-acetylene (tridec-1-yne, $CH_3.[CH_2]_{10}.C \vdots CH$), but Lumb and Smith[108] effected the synthesis of octadec-6-ynoic acid (identical with the natural tariric acid, p. 620) by condensing the lithium derivative of tridec-1-yne with 1-chloro-4-iodo-*n*-butane; Raney nickel hydrogenation of sodium octadec-6-ynoate in neutral aqueous alcohol solution gave a 50 per cent. yield of petroselinic (*cis*-octadec-6-enoic) acid, from which the *trans*-isomeride was prepared.

Other applications of the original Strong[107] procedure include the synthesis of all the positional isomers of the *n*-octynoic acids $C_8H_{12}O_2$, with ethynoid bonds respectively between the 2:3, 3:4, 4:5, 5:6, 6:7, and 7:8 carbon atoms,[109a] and of the *cis*- and *trans*-members of the octadecenoic series with double bonds in the 7:8, 8:9, 9:10 (oleic-elaidic), 10:11, 11:12 ,and 12:13 positions,[109b] preceded by synthesis of the corresponding octadecynoic acids.

An outstanding achievement of the alkyl acetylene route to long-chain unsaturated acids is the synthesis of linoleic (*cis-cis*-octadeca-9,12-dienoic) acid by Raphael and Sondheimer[110a] in 1950, which commenced by prior synthesis of the following compounds:

$CH \vdots CNa + I.[CH_2]_6.Cl \rightarrow CH \vdots C.[CH_2]_6.Cl$ (8-*Chloro-oct-1-yne*, I);

$CH_3.[CH_2]_4.C \vdots C.MgBr + CH_2O \rightarrow CH_3.[CH_2]_4.C \vdots C.CH_2OH$ (*Oct-2-yn-1-ol*)

$\xrightarrow{\text{MeSO}_2\text{Cl}} CH_3.[CH_2]_4.C \vdots C.CH_2.O.SO_2Me$ (*Oct-2-yn-1-ol methanesulphonate*, II).

Treatment of I with ethyl magnesium bromide in ether and addition of the resulting solution to a solution of II in ether yielded 1-chloro-hexadeca-7,10-diyne:

$$CH_3.[CH_2]_4.C \vdots C.CH_2.C \vdots C.[CH_2]_6.Cl$$

Replacement of the chlorine by iodine, condensation of the 1-iodo-hexadeca-7,10-diyne with malonic ester, and hydrolysis and decarboxylation of the condensation product furnished octadeca-9,12-diynoic acid, m.p. 42–43°:

$$CH_3.[CH_2]_4.C \vdots C.CH_2.C \vdots C.[CH_2]_7.COOH$$

Reduction of the diynoic acid in ethyl acetate solution with palladium gave a product which contained at least 63 per cent. of the naturally occurring *cis-cis*-octadeca-9,12-dienoic (linoleic) acid.

In the following year, two further syntheses of linoleic acid appeared. Wilborsky *et al.*[110b] condensed the bromide of oct-2-yn-1-ol (above) with the bromo-magnesium derivative of the glycol acetal of dec-9-ynoic aldehyde:

$$CH_3.[CH_2]_4.C \vdots C.CH_2Br + BrMg.C \vdots C.[CH_2]_7.CH \underset{\Large O—CH_2}{\overset{\Large O—CH_2}{\Big\langle}} \rightarrow$$

$$CH_3.[CH_2]_4.C \vdots C.CH_2.C \vdots C.[CH_2]_7.CH \underset{\Large O—CH_2}{\overset{\Large O—CH_2}{\Big\langle}}$$

Hydrolysis of the glycol acetal gave octadeca-9,12-diynoic aldehyde, which was oxidised to the diyne acid, and the latter reduced with Raney nickel to give a product which contained 28 per cent. of linoleic acid.

Gensler and Thomas[110c] condensed the magnesium derivative of 1-bromo-oct-2-yne (above) with 8-chloro-oct-1-yne (above) to give the 1-chloro-hexadeca-7,10-diyne obtained in the Raphael synthesis.

Gunstone and Sykes[110d] have by similar methods synthesised hexadeca-8,10-diynoic, octadeca-7,11-diynoic and eicosa-7,13-diynoic acids, and therefrom the corresponding *cis-cis*-dienoic acids by hydrogenation with Lindlar catalyst.

Finally, it should be mentioned that Black and Weedon[111] have synthesised erythrogenic (isanic) acid (*cf.* p. 637) by coupling oct-1-en-7-yne and dec-9-ynoic acid in presence of cuprous ammonium chloride:

$CH_2 \vdots CH.[CH_2]_4.C \vdots CH + CH \vdots C.[CH_2]_7.COOH \rightarrow$
$$CH_2 \vdots CH.[CH_2]_4.C \vdots C.C \vdots C.[CH_2]_7.COOH$$

The preliminary syntheses of the two acetylenic components are described in the original paper; self-coupling of either ethynoid compound can obviously occur in addition to the required cross-coupling, but a yield of 30 per cent. was

607

obtained of octadec-17-en-9,11-diynoic acid, which was found to be identical in most properties with the natural erythrogenic (isanic) acid.

Anodic syntheses. The syntheses (Linstead, Weedon *et al.*,[12] p. 581) of higher saturated acids, by electrolysis of methanol solutions of appropriate mixtures of a monocarboxylic acid with an excess of the methyl hydrogen ester of a dicarboxylic acid, have been extended by these workers to the unsaturated acid series.[112] When oleic (or elaidic) acid and the mono-methyl ester of a dibasic acid are electrolysed under suitable conditions, yields of about 30 per cent. of the methyl ester of a higher monoethenoid acid are produced (together with the other two possible products – a hydrocarbon and a dimethyl ester of a higher dibasic acid – to which the electrolysis also gives rise):

$$CH_3.[CH_2]_7.CH:CH.[CH_2]_7.COOH + COOH.[CH_2]_n.COOMe \rightarrow$$
$$CH_3[CH_2]_7.CH:CH.[CH_2]_{n+7}.COOMe.$$

In this way, Bounds, Linstead and Weedon[112a] obtained erucic acid from methyl hydrogen adipate ($COOH.[CH_2]_4.COOMe$) and oleic acid, and brassidic (the *trans*-form of docosa-13-enoic acid) from the same ester with elaidic acid; further the low and high melting forms of 13,14-dihydroxybehenic acid were obtained respectively when the low (95°) and high (132°) melting forms of 9,10-dihydroxystearic acid were electrolysed with methyl hydrogen adipate. The anodic action does not involve any stereomutation in the ethenoid bonds or in the configuration of the dihydroxy-acids. Similarly, from oleic acid and methyl hydrogen suberate ($COOH.[CH_2]_6.COOMe$) they obtained[112b] *cis*-tetracos-15-enoic acid, $CH_3.[CH_2]_7.CH:CH.[CH_2]_{13}.COOH$, identical with the natural nervonic (selacholeic) acid (p. 610); similar treatment of elaidic acid and methyl hydrogen suberate gave *trans*-tetracos-15-enoic acid.

Strictly speaking, these anodic syntheses of higher unsaturated acids are further instances of "chain extension" (*cf.* p. 602), but on the other hand, in the cases of the monoethenoid acids which have so far been prepared by this method, the starting material (oleic or elaidic acid) had itself been completely synthesised by other methods (*cf.* pp. 600–602) and the anodic syntheses of *cis*- and *trans*-docos-13-enoic acids and *cis*- and *trans*-tetracos-15-enoic acids accordingly also represent complete syntheses of the respective compounds.

cis-Octadec-11-enoic ("vaccenic") acid was synthesised by Linstead *et al.*[112c] by electrolysis of *cis*-hexadec-9-enoic (palmitoleic) acid with methyl hydrogen succinate; 9,10-dihydroxypalmitic acid (m.p. 87°, from *cis*-palmitoleic acid and performic acid) was electrolysed with methyl hydrogen succinate to give 11,12-dihydroxystearic acid, which was converted, *via* the corresponding 11,12-dibromo-acids, into *trans*-octadec-11-enoic ("vaccenic") acid.

Linstead *et al.*[112d] have also obtained octadec-6-ynoic (tariric) and *cis*-octadec-6-enoic (petroselinic acids) by the anodic synthesis procedures. They first prepared dodec-6-ynedioic acid, $COOH.[CH_2]_4.C:C.[CH_2]_4.COOH$, from the sodium derivative of 6-chlorohex-1-yne, $Cl.[CH_2]_4.C:C.Na$, condensed with 4-bromo-1-chloro-*n*-butane, $Br.[CH_2]_4.Cl$, to give the dichloro-dec-6-yne $Cl.[CH_2]_4.C:C.[CH_2]_4.Cl$, which was transformed into the dinitrile and thence to dodec-6-ynedioic acid. Electrolysis of the half ester of the latter with n-octanoic acid gave a 23 per cent. yield of tariric acid, and the latter on mild hydrogenation with palladium gave a 47 per cent. yield of petroselinic acid:

$$CH_3.[CH_2]_6.COOH + COOH.[CH_2]_4.C \vdots C.[CH_2]_4.COOMe \rightarrow$$
$$CH_3.[CH_2]_{10}.C \vdots C.[CH_2]_4.COOMe$$

The anodic synthesis by these workers[112e] of stearolic acid (leading to oleic acid) has been referred to previously (p. 602).

MONOETHENOID ACIDS (OTHER THAN OLEIC)

Acids of the structure $CH_3.[CH_2]_7.CH \vdots CH.[CH_2]_n.COOH$

The following natural *cis*-monoethenoid acids contain the grouping $CH_3.[CH_2]_7.CH =$ which is also present in oleic acid:

$C_{14}H_{26}O_2$	Tetradec-5-enoic	$CH_3.[CH_2]_7.CH \vdots CH.[CH_2]_3.CO_2H$
$C_{18}H_{34}O_2$	Octadec-9-enoic (oleic)	$CH_3.[CH_2]_7.CH \vdots CH.[CH_2]_7.CO_2H$
$C_{20}H_{38}O_2$	Eicos-11-enoic	$CH_3.[CH_2]_7.CH \vdots CH.[CH_2]_9.CO_2H$
$C_{22}H_{42}O_2$	Docos-13-enoic (erucic)	$CH_3.[CH_2]_7.CH \vdots CH.[CH_2]_{11}.CO_2H$
$C_{24}H_{46}O_2$	Tetracos-15-enoic (selacholeic)	$CH_3.[CH_2]_7.CH \vdots CH.[CH_2]_{13}.CO_2H$
$C_{26}H_{50}O_2$	Hexacos-17-enoic (ximenic)	$CH_3.[CH_2]_7.CH \vdots CH.[CH_2]_{15}.CO_2H$
$C_{30}H_{58}O_2$	Triacont-21-enoic (lumequic)	$CH_3.[CH_2]_7.CH \vdots CH.[CH_2]_{19}.CO_2H$

Of these acids, all except tetradec-5-enoic and tetracos-15-enoic occur in the vegetable kingdom, the two exceptions being in animal fats. All these vegetable fatty acids have larger molecules than oleic acid, and this suggests the possibility that they have been produced from that acid in the vegetable organisms by some process of chain extension. Boekenoogen[113a] drew attention to the sequence of increase of four methylene groups at the carboxylic end of the series C_{14}-C_{18}-C_{22}-C_{26}-C_{30}. The implication of this is, however, obscure and no positive evidence for chain extension *in vivo* so far exists in seed fats. On the other hand, it has been shown by Smedley-MacLean[114a] and by others[114b] that linoleic or linolenic acid (C_{18}) is transformed in the livers of animals into multi-ethenoid C_{20} and C_{22} acids (*cf.* Chapter VIII, p. 571). Chain extension of oleic acid has been effected by several chemical methods in the laboratory[100, 101, 112] (pp. 602, 608).

cis-**Tetradec-5-enoic acid**, $C_{14}H_{26}O_2$, has only been observed in the head and possibly the blubber fats of the sperm whale. It forms about 14 per cent. of the component acids of sperm head oil;[115a] its constitution was determined by Tsujimoto[115b] in 1925, and it was synthesised in 1938 from n-dec-1-yne.[106c]

The corresponding *hexadec-7-enoic* acid has not so far been reported in any natural fat.

cis-**Eicos-11-enoic acid**, $C_{20}H_{38}O_2$, has mainly been observed in the vegetable kingdom, where it was first noticed[116] in 1936 in the unusual liquid seed wax of *Simmondsia californica* (*cf.* Chapter IV, p. 296). Here it is the chief component acid and, with minor amounts of erucic acid, is combined with a mixture of eicos-11-enyl and docos-13-enyl alcohols (*cf.* Chapter X, p. 669).

In 1946 Hopkins[117a, b] found that small proportions of the same acid accompanied erucic, linoleic, and oleic acids in the seed oil of *Conringia orientalis* (Cruciferæ), and confirmed its constitution. Subsequently it was shown to be present in rape and mustard seed oils[117c], and in other Cruciferous seed oils,[117d] in several instances forming 10–15 per cent., and in a

20

few from 30 to over 50 per cent. of the total fatty acids;[118a] it has also been found to be present in the seed fats of a few other species, e.g., *Delphinium* (Ranunculaceæ),[118b] milkweed (Asclepidaceæ),[118c] *Pongamia* and *Erythrina* (Papilionatæ),[118d] and to the exceptional extent of 42 per cent. in the component acids of *Cardiospermum* (Sapindaceæ)[118e] and *Marshallia* (Compositæ)[118f] seed fats.

The natural (*cis-*) acid melts at 22° and its *trans*-form at 52–53°; Linstead *et al.*[112c] carried out anodic syntheses of both isomers. The corresponding stereoisomeric 11,12-dihydroxy-arachidic acids melt at 95–96° and 129–130°.

Eicos-11-enoic acid has been reported in two fish oils by Baldwin and Parks[119] (menhaden oil) and by Hopkins[117b] (liver oil of Atlantic cod, *Gadus callarias*); the C_{20} monoethenoid acid present in other marine animal oils is stated to be the eicos-9-enoic acid (*v. infra*, p. 615).

cis-**Docos-13-enoic (erucic) acid,** $C_{22}H_{42}O_2$, first noticed in mustard seed oil in 1849, is an important vegetable fatty acid which, so far as is known at present, is confined to seed fats of the families Cruciferæ and Tropæolaceæ. In these it is widely distributed, forming from 40–50 per cent. of the mixed fatty acids of rape, mustard, wallflower, and some other Cruci-ferous seed oils, but only 20–30 per cent. in the seed oils of other species, whilst in a few instances it is present only in small proportions. The best source of erucic acid for experi-mental purposes is nasturtium (*Tropæolum*) seed, which contains only about 8 per cent. of fat, but the mixed fatty acids of the latter include 80 per cent. of erucic acid.[120] The acid may be readily obtained by fractional distillation of the methyl esters of nasturtium seed mixed fatty acids, or even by simple crystallisation of the latter from 70 per cent. alcohol. This seed fat contains nearly 40 per cent. of trierucin, which, again, may be isolated from it by direct crystallisation. Efficient methods for the isolation of erucic acid from seed oils (such as rape or mustard) in which it forms only 50 per cent. or less of the total fatty acids have been described by Baliga and Hilditch.[117c]

Erucic acid melts at 33·5° and has an iodine value of 74·7. Like other higher mono-ethylenic acids which are solid at the ordinary temperature, erucic acid yields a lead salt which is sparingly soluble in ether and alcohol. On isomerisation with oxides of nitrogen it yields *trans*-docos-13-enoic (brassidic) acid, which melts at 60°. Oxidation of erucic acid by peracetic acid or by Caro's acid yields a 13,14-dihydroxybehenic acid, m.p. 99–100°, whilst alkaline permanganate oxidation produces an isomeric acid, m.p. 130–131°. Both acids with chromic acid give 13,14-diketobehenic acid, m.p. 93–94°, reduced by zinc and acetic acid to mixed 13,14- and 14,13-ketol-behenic acids, m.p. 76–77°.[92]

The constitutional formula of erucic acid follows from the facts that on catalytic hydro-genation it passes completely into behenic acid and that on oxidation it yields a mixture of *n*-nonanoic acid and brassylic acid, $COOH.[CH_2]_{11}.COOH$.[121] The *cis*- and *trans*-docos-13-enoic (erucic and brassidic) acids have been synthesised by chain extension of oleic (elaidic) acids[112a] (p. 608), and also by the malonic ester (methoxy-ketone) synthesis[104a] (p. 604). Docos-13-ynoic (behenolic) acid, $CH_3.[CH_2]_7.C\!:\!C.[CH_2]_{11}.COOH$, which can be prepared from erucic acid in the same manner as stearolic acid is obtained from oleic acid (p. 591), was synthesised by Simonsen *et al.*[106b] from *n*-octyl-acetylene and methyl 12-bromo-dodec-anoate (p. 605).

cis-**Tetracos-15-enoic (selacholeic, nervonic) acid,** $C_{24}H_{46}O_2$, seems to be a characteristic component of the fats of many Elasmobranch fish, but it has not been noticed in Teleostid fish or in marine mammalia; it was first reported in 1927 by Tsujimoto[122] (selacholeic acid), who determined its constitution. In the same year Klenk[123a] isolated the same acid (which he termed nervonic acid) from the cerebrosides of brain tissue, and also established its structure. In 1930 Hale, Lycan and Adams[101] condensed docos-13-enyl bromide (obtained from erucic acid) with ethyl malonate and produced the *cis*- and *trans*-equilibrium mixture of the tetracos-15-enoic acids. In 1954 Linstead *et al.*[112b] obtained the two isomers separately by anodic synthesis from methyl hydrogen suberate and, respectively, oleic or elaidic acids. Since both oleic and erucic acids have been fully synthesised, the syntheses of the tetracos-15-enoic acids are also complete. The synthetic *cis*-acid, identical with the natural nervonic or selacholeic acids, melts[112b] at 40–41°, and the *trans*-acid at 65·5°. The corresponding isomeric 15,16-dihydroxytetracosanoic acids melt at 104–105° and 130·5–131°.

cis-**Hexacos-17-enoic** (**ximenic acid**), $C_{26}H_{50}O_2$, forms a small proportion of the fatty acids in the seed fat of the Indian shrub *Ximenia americana* (Olacaceæ), in which it was discovered in 1939 by Boekenoogen,[113a] who determined its structure. Klenk and Schumann[123b] stated in 1942 that a hexacosenoic acid, m.p. 45°, accompanies nervonic acid in brain cerebrosides.

cis-**Triacont-21-enoic** (**lumequic**) **acid**, $C_{30}H_{58}O_2$, was also found by Boekenoogen[113a] to be present in the seed fatty acids of *Ximenia americana*.

All the above-mentioned monoethenoid acids containing 20, 22, 24, 26, and 30 carbon atoms, together with **octacos-19-enoic** acid (all belonging to the series $CH_3.[CH_2]_7.CH$: $CH.[CH_2]_n.COOH$), were observed in small quantities by Ligthelm *et al.*[113b] in the seed fats of three South African species of *Ximenia* (*cf.* Chapter IV, p. 290). Together these acids amounted to 25–33 per cent. of the total fatty acids, but the content of any one acid rarely exceeded 6–9 per cent., and was frequently only 2–3 per cent. (or less).

Cyclopropenyl (*and cyclopropyl*) *derivatives of oleic acid*

The monoethenoid fatty acids discussed above share in common the structure $CH_3.[CH_2]_7.CH=$, whilst others about to be considered possess the other "half" of the oleic acid molecule, $=CH.[CH_2]_7.COOH$. Between these we find one exceptional unsaturated acid, *sterculic acid* (present in quantity in the seed fats of two species of *Sterculia* (*S. fœtida* and *S. parviflora*), but not in other species of this genus) which contains both halves of the oleic acid structure, the central double bond being linked to a methylene group: in other words, the 9,10 ethenoid bond in oleic acid is replaced by a *cyclo*propenyl group. Sterculic acid has also been found in very small quantities in some seed fats of the Malvaceæ (*Hibiscus*, *Gossypium*, *Lavatera*), where it accompanies somewhat larger, but still minor proportions of a homologous acid, *malvalic acid*.[124]

A corresponding *cyclo*propyl (saturated) acid, *lactobacillic* (*phytomonic*) acid, occurs with other, more conventional acids in the lipids of the bacillus *Lactobacillus arabinosus*, and is conveniently dealt with also at this point.

The constitutions at present accepted for these three acids are:

$$CH_3.[CH_2]_7.C=C.[CH_2]_7.COOH \qquad CH_3.[CH_2]_7.C=C.[CH_2]_6.COOH$$
$$\underset{CH_2}{\vee} \qquad\qquad\qquad\qquad \underset{CH_2}{\vee}$$

Sterculic   Malvalic
ω-(2-*n*-octyl*cyclo*prop-1-enyl)octanoic   ω-(2-*n*-octyl*cyclo*prop-1-enyl)heptanoic
9,10-methylene-octadec-9-enoic   8,9-methylene-octadec-8-enoic

$$CH_3.[CH_2]_5.CH.CH.[CH_2]_9.COOH$$
$$\underset{CH_2}{\vee}$$

Lactobacillic
ω-(2-*n*-hexyl*cyclo*propyl)decanoic
11,12-methylene-octadecanoic

ω-(2-*n*-octyl*cyclo*prop-1-enyl)-octanoic (**sterculic**) **acid**, $C_{19}H_{34}O_2$, forms over 70 per cent. of the acids in the seed fat ("Java olive oil") of *Sterculia fœtida*, and confers on this fatty oil the property of exothermal polymerisation when it is heated to about 250°. Its molecular formula was established in 1941 by Hilditch *et al.*,[125a] and its constitution in 1952 by Nunn.[125b] Sterculic acid melts at 18° and rapidly polymerises even at room temperature; when the acid is reduced with lithium-aluminium-hydride in ether, sterculyl alcohol,

$$CH_3.[CH_2]_7.C=C.[CH_2]_7.CH_2(OH)$$
$$\underset{CH_2}{\vee}$$

m.p. 10·6°, is produced.

Varma *et al.*,[126a] from their interpretation of the infra-red spectrum of sterculic acid, proposed a different structure to that arrived at on chemical grounds by Nunn,[125b] but the latter was supported by Dijkstra and Duin,[126b] and subsequently by Faure,[126c] Brooke and Smith.[126d] The main chemical argument of the latter workers was the formation from sterculic acid by ozonisation at low temperatures of 9,11-diketo-nonadecanoic acid, CH_3. $[CH_2]_7.CO.CH_2.CO.[CH_2]_7.COOH$, which would clearly be produced from an acid of the structure assigned by Nunn. The 9,11-diketo-acid was meantime synthesised by three independent groups of workers,[126e,f,g] and Nunn's structural formula is now generally accepted.

Malvalic acid, $C_{18}H_{32}O_2$, has, as already mentioned, been found in small proportions in the seed fats of cottonseed, okra and a few other Malvaceæ species.[124a,b,c,f] It contains one methylene group less than sterculic acid in the aliphatic acid chain, according to the structure determined by Vickery and Shenstone.[124d]

Seed fats containing malvalic or sterculic acids give the Halphen colour test which is characteristic for cottonseed and other Malvaceæ seed oils. These oils (or seed cakes made from them) when fed to poultry cause a pink discoloration in the whites of the eggs.[124d,e] Both effects are apparently connected with the presence of the *cyclo*propenyl group in malvalic and sterculic acids.

Lactobacillic acid, $C_{19}H_{36}O_2$, was isolated in 1950 by Hofmann and Lucas,[127a] together with *cis*-octadec-11-enoic (*cis*-"vaccenic") acid (p. 624) and other more conventional fatty acids, from the fats present in *Lactobacillus arabinosus* grown on a specific medium. It melts at 28–29°, and was shown by Hofmann and Lucas[127a] to possess a *cyclo*-propane ring-system to which alkyl and carboxy-alkyl side chains were attached. Lactobacillic acid is considered by Hofmann *et al.*[127b] to be identical with phytomonic acid (pp. 173, 586); its structure is shown in the figure (*supra*).

Gentle catalytic hydrogenation of sterculic acid yields *dihydrosterculic* or "9,10-methylene-octadecanoic" acid which, until Hofmann *et al.*[127c] proved that lactobacillic is "11,12-methylene-octadecanoic" acid, was formerly supposed to be identical with the latter. Unequivocal syntheses of both the 9,10- and the 11,12-methylene octadecanoic acids by Hofmann and his colleagues[127d] showed that the latter was identical with natural lactobacillic acid, and the synthetic 9,10- acid to be identical with dihydrosterculic acid produced by hydrogenation of natural sterculic acid.

Acids of the structure $CH_3.[CH_2]_m.CH:CH.[CH_2]_7.COOH$

Numerous natural monoethenoid acids which contain the grouping $=CH.[CH_2]_7.COOH$ will next be described. These include:

$C_{10}H_{18}O_2$	Dec-9-enoic	$CH_2:CH.[CH_2]_7.CO_2H$
$C_{12}H_{22}O_2$	Dodec-9-enoic	$CH_3.CH_2.CH:CH.[CH_2]_7.CO_2H$
$C_{14}H_{26}O_2$	Tetradec-9-enoic (myristoleic)	$CH_3.[CH_2]_3.CH:CH.[CH_2]_7.CO_2H$
$C_{16}H_{30}O_2$	Hexadec-9-enoic (palmitoleic)	$CH_3.[CH_2]_5.CH:CH.[CH_2]_7.CO_2H$
$C_{18}H_{34}O_2$	Octadec-9-enoic (oleic)	$CH_3.[CH_2]_7.CH:CH.[CH_2]_7.CO_2H$
$C_{20}H_{38}O_2$	Eicos-9-enoic (gadoleic)	$CH_3.[CH_2]_9.CH:CH.[CH_2]_7.CO_2H$
$C_{26}H_{50}O_2$	Hexacos-9-enoic	$CH_3.[CH_2]_{15}.CH:CH.[CH_2]_7.CO_2H$

On the whole, acids of exclusively animal origin preponderate in this group, but hexadec-9-enoic acid (although only present in traces in most land vegetable fats) is as ubiquitous in Nature as is oleic acid. Hexadecenoic and gadoleic acids occur in some quantity in fats of aquatic origin, vegetable as well as animal. The production of homologous 9-enoic acids down to dec-9-enoic acid, which is so far restricted to milk fats, could be ascribed to chain-shortening (two carbon atoms at a time) *in vivo* of oleic groups in blood glycerides during their transformation into milk fat. The exclusive production of hexadec-9-enoic acid by degradation of oleic acid seems unlikely in natural fats as a whole, however, since in fats of aquatic animals and of some bacteria and other lower forms of flora hexadec-9-enoic acid is a major component comparable in amount with oleic acid.

Dec-9-enoic acid, $CH_2:CH.[CH_2]_7.COOH$, has so far only been detected in milk fat, especially cow milk fat (in which it only forms about 0·2 per cent. of the total acids). It is unusual, for a natural unsaturated fatty acid, in possessing a terminal methylene group (ω-unsaturation); the double bond, however, occupies the same position, relative to the carboxyl group, as in oleic acid. The probable existence of this acid in butter fat was pointed out by Smedley[128a] in 1912; it was first isolated, and its constitution determined, by Grün and Wirth[128b] in 1922, whilst in 1933 Bosworth and Brown[128c] confirmed its structure and indicated the proportions in which it is present in cow milk fat.

Similar small amounts of **dodec-9-enoic acid,** $CH_3.CH_2.CH:CH.[CH_2]_7.COOH$, were found in butter fat by Hilditch and Longenecker,[129a] who confirmed the observations of Grün and Winkler,[129b] and of Bosworth and Brown,[128c] that this fat also contains over 1 per cent. of *tetradec-9-enoic acid.*

cis-**Tetradec-9-enoic (myristoleic) acid,** $CH_3.[CH_2]_3.CH:CH.[CH_2]_7.COOH$, accompanies hexadec-9-enoic acid (below) in most marine animal liver and body (depot) fats, in which, however, it frequently amounts to not more than 1 per cent. and rarely to more than 4 or 5 per cent. of the total fatty acids. It is also found in very small proportions (usually below 0·5 per cent.) in the depot fats of the ox[130a] and pig[130b] and other land animals, in similar or sometimes slightly larger amounts in their liver glycerides and phosphatides and, as stated above, in cow and other milk fats. The tetradecenoic acid of all animal depot or liver fats yet studied has the above structure. The natural (*cis*-) acid melts at $-4°$, and the *trans*-acid at 18·5°; both forms have been synthesised by the malonic ester (acyloin) procedure.[104c] The isomeric 9,10-dihydroxymyristic acids melt respectively at 80° and 123·4°.

Although tetradec-9-enoic acid has not been detected (in contrast to traces of hexadec-9-enoic acid) as a normal trace component of seed fats, it has been observed in one instance, at present unique, to be a major component of a seed fat from the family Myristicaceæ: Atherton and Meara[131] found that the seed fat of *Pycnanthus kombo* contained nearly 25 per cent. of this acid, in addition to about 60 per cent. of myristic acid, in its component fatty acids.

cis-**Hexadec-9-enoic (palmitoleic, zoomaric) acid,** $CH_3.[CH_2]_5.CH:CH.[CH_2]_7.COOH$, is now known to be a constituent of nearly all natural fats, but it is a very subordinate component except in marine animal oil glycerides and in the glycerides and phosphatides of the livers of land animals. The acid was first noticed as early as 1854 by Hofstädter[132a] among the mixed acids of the head oil of the sperm whale, and was in consequence named physetoleic acid. In 1898 Ljubarsky[132b] isolated it from seal oil, and in 1906 Bull[132c] obtained it in a comparatively pure condition from the mixed acids of cod liver oil, and confirmed its molecular composition as $C_{16}H_{30}O_2$. The name palmitoleic acid, in view of its content of sixteen carbon atoms in the molecule, was proposed by Lewkowitsch in 1906. From about 1924 onwards the acid was observed as a regular component of many marine animal oils, in which it usually forms about 15–20 per cent. of the total fatty acids present. Its structure was established in 1925 as hexadec-9-enoic acid by Armstrong and Hilditch.[133] In 1924 Toyama[134a] stated that an acid of the formula $C_{16}H_{30}O_2$ was present in the blubber of the humpbacked whale, *Megaptera longimana* Rudolphi, to which he gave the name zoomaric acid; he isolated the same acid from a number of other marine animal oils (including some from Elasmobranch fish, such as rays and sharks[134b]) and, in 1927, showed[134c] that the products of disruptive oxidation of zoomaric acid from the oils of the humpback whale, sei-whale (*Balænoptera borealis* Less.), and other whales, and from cod liver oil, were in all cases n-heptanoic and azelaic acids, so that zoomaric and palmitoleic acids are synonymous. Other investigators have shown that the palmitoleic acid present in the head and blubber oils of the sperm whale,[115a, 134d] seal oil,[135a] Scottish cod liver oil,[135b] and porpoise blubber[135c] is also hexadec-9-enoic acid. Meantime it had been demonstrated that palmitoleic acid isolated from various other marine animals yielded palmitic acid on hydrogenation. Since the hexadecenoic acid present in all marine animal oils so far examined has the same constitution, it seems desirable to refer to it by its systematic name, hexadec-9-enoic acid, and to allow the older and empirical terms "palmitoleic" or "zoomaric" acid to lapse.

Hexadec-9-enoic acid is, it is true, most abundant in fats of aquatic origin, but it is not confined to those of aquatic fauna. Lovern[136] has shown that the fats of fresh-water and marine algæ and diatoms contain over 30 per cent. of unsaturated C_{16} acids, in which polyethenoid C_{16} acids are also present in addition to hexadecenoic acid, and that the proportion of the latter in fats of fresh-water fish and zooplankton is greater than in those of marine species.

The depot fats so far examined of amphibia[137a, b, 138a] and reptiles[137b, 138b] contain nearly as much hexadecenoic acid (8–15 per cent.) as the majority of fish fats, whilst depot fats of rats[139a] and birds[139b] contain somewhat less (6–8 per cent.). Similar proportions of hexadec-9-enoic acid are present in the liver glycerides[140] of the larger mammals (ox, sheep, pig), but in the corresponding depot fats[130a, 141a] the amount is smaller (2–3 per cent.). The milk fats of the cow[129a, 141b] and the goat[141c] have also been shown to contain about 3–4 per cent. of hexadec-9-enoic acid.

Hexadecenoic acid is also, probably, a regular component of all phosphatides. In the liver phosphatides of the ox, sheep, and pig it is less abundant than in the corresponding liver glycerides, and forms only about 5 per cent. of the total phosphatide fatty acids.[140] It may also form up to 5 per cent. or so of the fatty acids present in many vegetable seed phosphatides.[142]

Amongst the lower forms of land flora, hexadecenoic acid has been observed in quantity in the fats of diphtheria bacilli,[143a] of yeast,[143b] and of the spores of a cryptogam (*Lycopodium*).[143c] In the storage fats of the more developed land plants it has been proved that the following oils contain up to, but rarely more than, 1 per cent. of hexadecenoic acid: groundnut,[144a] olive,[144b] teaseed,[144b] cottonseed,[144c] soya bean,[144c] and palm oils.[144c] In the case of the acid from soya bean oil, its constitution was shown to be hexadec-9-enoic acid.[144d] It seems very probable that all seed fats and fruit coat fats include very small amounts (not exceeding 0·5–1 per cent.) of hexadec-9-enoic acid in their component fatty acids. So far, in the vegetable kingdom, major proportions of the acid have only been observed in one fruit-coat fat (avocado pear, Cattaneo,[145a] 1949; French,[145b] 1962) and in seed fats of species of the family Proteaceæ. In these, the seed fat of Australian *Macadamia ternifolia* contains 20 per cent. of hexadec-9-enoic acid (Bridge and Hilditch,[145c] 1950), while those of two Argentine species (*Lomatia* and *Embothrium*) contain similar proportions; but, curiously, the seed fat of *Geruina avellana* (in the same family) contains 22 per cent. of the *isomeric* hexadec-11-enoic acid (Cattaneo *et al.*,[145d] 1962).

cis-Hexadec-9-enoic acid has thus been found in fats from all kinds of living organisms; but the most interesting feature of its occurrence is the circumstance that it is a major component acid in fats from the lower forms of life and in those of the more developed forms of aquatic flora and fauna, whilst it is only present in very small amounts in the depot fats of land flora and fauna at the other end of the evolutionary scale. Moreover, in the fats of animals, a progressive diminution occurs in the proportion of hexadec-9-enoic acid corresponding with the evolutionary development of the species. Hexadec-9-enoic acid thus takes a place with oleic, palmitic, and perhaps stearic acid as one of the few fatty acids which appear to be common to all fats.

Natural *cis*-hexadec-9-enoic acid melts at 0·5°, and is converted by selenium or oxides of nitrogen into the equilibrium mixture of *cis*- and *trans*- isomers, the *trans*-acid melting at 31–32°. Both acids have been synthesised by the malonic ester (acyloin) method.[99b, 104c] Oxidation of the *cis*-acid with peracetic acid gives a 9,10-dihydroxypalmitic acid, m.p. 87°, with alkaline permanganate solution an isomeric 9,10-dihydroxypalmitic acid, m.p. 129–130°.

cis-**Eicos-9-enoic (gadoleic) acid,** $CH_3 . [CH_2]_9 . CH : CH . [CH_2]_7 . COOH$, was first noticed by Bull[132c] in cod liver oil in 1906. It has since been found widely distributed in fish and marine mammalian oils, although not so abundantly as hexadecenoic acid (it probably rarely amounts to more than 5–10 per cent. of the total fatty acids). Takano[146a] showed in 1933 that gadoleic acid from sardine oil possesses 9:10 monoethenoid unsaturation, and Toyama and Tsuchiya[146b] subsequently found the same structure in the acid from cod liver, herring, and whale oils. The latter workers observed an isomeric ("gondoic") acid in pilot whale blubber fat, and eicos-11-enoic acid is the C_{20} acid present in menhaden oil[119] and in an Atlantic cod liver oil[117b] (p. 610); the "gadoleic" acid of marine animal oils may therefore consist of either, or both, structural isomers, eicos-9-enoic and eicos-11-enoic acids, but the relative abundance of the two acids is not yet by any means clear.

The *cis*- and *trans*-eicos-9-enoic acids have been synthesised by the malonic ester (acyloin) procedure.[104a] The *cis*-acid melts at 23–23·5°, and the *trans*-acid at 54°. The isomeric 9,10-dihydroxyarachidic acids melt respectively at 97–98° and 130–131°.

Hexacos-9-enoic acid, $CH_3 . [CH_2]_{15} . CH : CH . [CH_2]_7 . COOH$, was observed by Bergmann and Swift[147] amongst the many unsaturated acids of the lipids of the sponge *Spheciospongia vesparia*, and an **octacosenoic acid,** $C_{28}H_{54}O_2$, m.p. 57–58°, of undetermined structure, in the lipid acids of another sponge *Suberites compacta*.

HYDROXY-UNSATURATED ACIDS

The most familiar hydroxy-unsaturated acid, ricinoleic acid, and several other natural hydroxy-unsaturated acids all contain the structure $—CH = CH . [CH_2]_7 . COOH$, and are therefore conveniently dealt with at this point. In order to include the remaining natural hydroxylated fatty acids (saturated or unsaturated) in the same part of this book, they also receive notice below.

(i) *Hydroxy-unsaturated acids with the structure* $—CH : CH . [CH_2]_7 . COOH$
(and some structurally related acids)

$C_{18}H_{34}O_3$ 12-Hydroxy-octadec-9-enoic (ricinoleic)
$$CH_3 . [CH_2]_5 . CH(OH) . CH_2 . CH : CH . [CH_2]_7 . COOH$$
$C_{18}H_{34}O_3$ 9-Hydroxy-octadec-12-enoic
$$CH_3[CH_2]_4 . CH : CH . CH_2 . CH_2 . CH(OH) . [CH_2]_7 . COOH$$

$(C_{18}H_{36}O_4)$ 9,10-Dihydroxyoctadecanoic acid
$$CH_3.[CH_2]_7.CH(OH).CH(OH).[CH_2]_7.COOH)$$

$C_{18}H_{32}O_3$ 12,13-Epoxy-octadec-9-enoic (vernolic)
$$CH_3.[CH_2]_4.\underset{\diagdown O\diagup}{CH.CH}.CH_2.CH:CH.[CH_2]_7.COOH$$

$(C_{18}H_{32}O_3)$ 9,10-Epoxy-octadec-12-enoic
$$CH_3.[CH_2]_4.CH:CH.CH_2.\underset{\diagdown O\diagup}{CH.CH}.[CH_2]_7.COOH)$$

$C_{18}H_{30}O_3$ 15,16-Epoxy-octadeca-9,12-dienoic
$$CH_3.CH_2.\underset{\diagdown O\diagup}{CH.CH}.CH_2.CH:CH.CH_2.CH:CH.[CH_2]_7.COOH$$

$C_{18}H_{30}O_3$ 18-Hydroxy-octadeca-9,11,13-trienoic (kamlolenic)
$$CH_2(OH).[CH_2]_3.CH:CH.CH:CH.CH:CH.[CH_2]_7.COOH$$

$(C_{18}H_{32}O_4)$ 9,14-Dihydroxy-octadeca-10,12-dienoic
$$CH_3.[CH_2]_3.CH(OH).CH:CH.CH:CH.CH(OH).[CH_2]_7.COOH$$

$(C_{18}H_{32}O_3)$ 9-Hydroxy-octadec-*trans*-10-*trans*-12-dienoic
$$CH_3.[CH_2]_4.CH:CH.CH:CH.CH(OH).[CH_2]_7.COOH$$

$(C_{18}H_{26}O_3)$ 8-Hydroxy-octadec-17-en-9,11-diynoic (isanolic)
$$CH_2:CH.[CH_2]_4.C⋮C.C⋮C.CH(OH).[CH_2]_6.COOH$$

$(C_{18}H_{30}O_3)$ 8-Hydroxy-octadec-11-en-9-ynoic
$$CH_3.[CH_2]_5.CH:CH.C⋮C.CH(OH).[CH_2]_6.COOH$$

$(C_{20}H_{38}O_3)$ 14-Hydroxy-eicos-*cis*-11-enoic
$$CH_3.[CH_2]_5.CH(OH).CH_2.CH:CH.[CH_2]_9.COOH$$

12-Hydroxy-*cis*-octadec-9-enoic (ricinoleic) acid. $CH_3.[CH_2]_5.CH(OH).CH_2.$ $CH:CH.[CH_2]_7.COOH$, forms 90 per cent. or somewhat more of the mixed acids of castor seed oil (*Ricinus communis*), in which it was apparently discovered by Saalmüller.[148] It has also been reported from time to time as a very minor component of certain other oils, but it is doubtful whether it occurs frequently in quantity in nature apart from *Ricinus* species. Gurgel and de Amorim[149a] have stated that ricinoleic acid forms about 47 per cent. of the mixed fatty acids of ivory wood oil, the seed fat of *Agonandra brasiliensis*; according to Margaillan,[149b] the oil of *Wrightia annamensis* also contains as its chief component a hydroxyoleic acid probably identical with ricinoleic acid. Experience suggests that the identity of hydroxy-unsaturated acids reported as ricinoleic acid from time to time in a number of seed fats requires additional scrutiny and re-investigation, since in more than one instance an acid originally reported to be ricinoleic acid has turned out to possess a different constitution.

Methods for determining the proportion of ricinoleic acid in a seed fat have been described[150a, b, c] and fatty acid compositions of castor oils from many different localities have been determined. The isolation of ricinoleic acid has also been studied by Hawke,[150d] who has described the chief physical properties of the pure acid, which exists in three polymorphic forms, m.p. 5·0°, 7·7° and 16·0°, and is optically active ($[\alpha]_D + 7·8°$). Treatment with oxides of nitrogen partly transforms it into the *trans*-isomer, ricinelaidic acid, m.p. 52–53°, $[\alpha]_D + 6·7°$.

Goldsobel[151a] showed in 1894, by Baruch's sequence[62] of reactions (*cf.* p. 591), that ricinoleic acid is 12-hydroxy-oleic acid, and in 1899 Maquenne[151b] converted it to azelaic acid by energetic oxidation with potassium permanganate, thus indicating that the ethenoid bond occupies the 9:10 position. More gentle oxidation with dilute alkali permanganate gives two stereoisomeric 9,10,12-trihydroxystearic acids[151c] which melt at 110–111° and 140–142°. Oxidation of ricinoleic and ricinelaidic acids with chromic acid leads respectively to the *cis*- and *trans*- forms of 12-keto-octadec-9-enoic acid.[151d]

Complete syntheses of optically inactive (racemic) ricinoleic acid by different routes have been recorded by Crombie and Jacklin,[152a] Lumb, Smith *et al.*,[152b] and Gensler and Abrahams.[152c] Commencing from optically active methyl $(-)(L)$3-acetoxy-4-carboxybutanoate, Serck-Hanssen[152d] by means of anodic syntheses obtained (L)3-hydroxynonanoic acid and $(-)(L)$12-hydroxyoctadecanoic acid; the latter $([\alpha]_D^{20} + 0.3°)$ is the enantiomorph of the hydroxy-acid produced by catalytic hydrogenation of ricinoleic acid, so that the absolute configuration of the natural acid is $(+)(D)$12-hydroxy-cis-octadec-9-enoic acid.

Destructive distillation of ricinoleic acid, or better of its sodium or calcium salt, produces a mixture of n-heptaldehyde and undec-10-enoic acid (Goldsobel,[151a] 1894; Vernon and Ross,[153a] 1936, Gupta and Aggarwal,[153b] 1954); dry distillation of potassium ricinoleate with excess of potassium hydroxide liberates methyl-n-hexylcarbinol and leaves the potassium salt of sebacic acid (Freund and Schönfeld,[153c] 1891; Hargreaves and Owen,[153d] 1947). On heating, ricinoleic acid readily forms lactone-like compounds known as estolides or poly-ricinoleic acids, a molecule of water being eliminated between the hydroxy-group of one ricinoleic acid molecule and the carboxyl group of another:

$$CH_3 . [CH_2]_5 . CH(OH) . CH_2 . CH:CH . [CH_2]_7 . COOCH([CH_2]_5 . CH_3) . CH_2 .$$
$$CH:CH . [CH_2]_7 . COOH, \text{ etc.}$$

When heated at about 240–250° with a dehydrating catalyst such as sodium pyrosulphate, tungsten oxide, or similar compounds, castor oil, ricinoleic esters or acid undergo dehydration with formation of a second ethenoid bond. The product, which is a mixture of octadeca-9,12-dienoic and (conjugated) octa-9,11-decadienoic glycerides, esters, or acids, has found considerable technical use as a partial substitute ("dehydrated castor oil") for tung oil in paints and varnishes (see also p. 632).

9-Hydroxy-cis-octadec-12-enoic acid, $CH_3 . [CH_2]_4 . CH:CH . [CH_2]_2 . CH(OH) . [CH_2]_7 .$ COOH, is present to the extent of 6–7 per cent. of the acids in the seed fats of *Strophanthus sarmentosus* and other species of this genus (Apocynaceæ).[154a] Its constitution was established in 1952 by Gunstone.[154a] Hydrogenation of the acid leads to 9-hydroxystearic acid (m.p. 81–82.5°), which with chromic acid gives 9-ketostearic acid, m.p. 79.5–81°. With alkaline permanganate the natural acid gives two stereoisomeric 9,12,13-trihydroxystearic acids, m.p. 108–110° and 148–149°. 9-Hydroxy-octadec-12-enoic acid is a close analogue of ricinoleic acid; both are structurally related to linoleic (octadeca-9,12-dienoic) acid but, whereas in ricinoleic acid the 12:13 ethenoid bond appears as 12-hydroxy, in the present instance it is the 9:10-ethenoid bond which is replaced by the $—CH_2—CH(OH)—$ grouping. Raphael et al.[154b] effected the synthesis of 9-hydroxy-cis-octadec-12-enoic acid.

Dihydroxy-saturated acids. The only naturally occurring member of this group is the optically active form of **9,10-dihydroxystearic acid,** m.p. 141°, which occurs in very small proportions (0.5–1 per cent.) in the mixed fatty acids of all castor seed oils.[150a] This acid is one of the optically active enantiomorphs of the racemic 9,10-dihydroxystearic acid of m.p. 132° which can be prepared artificially from oleic or elaidic acids (cf. G. King[82b]).

[Stereo-isomeric dihydroxy-saturated acids have of course been prepared artificially by per-acid or alkaline permanganate oxidation of practically all the natural monoethenoid fatty acids which are mentioned in this Chapter, and the same applies to tetra- or hexa-hydroxy-stearic acids derived from linoleic, linolenic, and other di- or tri-ethenoid acids. The melting-points and similar properties of these acids are recorded under the natural unsaturated fatty acids from which they have been prepared.]

12,13-Epoxy-octadec-cis-9-enoic (vernolic) acid, $C_{18}H_{32}O_3$, forms over 70 per cent. of the component acids in the seed fat of *Vernonia anthelmintica* (Compositæ), in which it was first observed by Vidyarthi,[155a] who believed it to be a positional isomer of ricinoleic acid. Gunstone,[155b] however, showed that it is an epoxy-acid of the assigned structure. It melts at 30–31° and is optically active, $[\alpha]_D - 8°$.

Methods for the detection, isolation and determination of epoxy-oleic acids have been recommended by Bharucha and Gunstone,[156a] Smith, Koch and Wolff[156c] and Holman et al.[156d] Vernolic acid has been synthesised by Osbond[156e] from cis-oct-2-enyl bromide and dec-9-ynoic acid, utilising appropriate Grignard complexes (cf. p. 605).

Opening the epoxide ring in (cis-) vernolic acid, being accompanied by inversion (p. 598), leads to the production of *threo*-12,13-dihydroxy-oleic acids. Bharucha and Gunstone[156b]

617

pointed out that these compounds contain two asymmetric centres, so that the dihydroxy acids should exist in enantiomorphic forms. The *threo*-dihydroxyoleic acid from vernolic acid in the seed fats of *Vernonia anthelmintica*[156b] and *V. colorata* (Chisholm and Hopkins[156f]) is the lævorotatory form (m.p. 61–61·5°, $[\alpha]_D^{24°} - 19°$), but that from *Malope trifida* seed fat was the optical isomer (m.p. 61–61·5°, $[\alpha]_D^{24°} + 18·9°$).[156f] Enzymatic opening of the epoxy ring in vernolic acid yields the dextrorotatory (+)-threo-12,13-dihydroxyoleic acid (Riemenschneider *et al.*[156g]). The racemic mixture of the two dihydroxyoleic acids melts at 52·5–53°, and can be converted[156b] into the geometrically isomeric *trans*-acid, m.p. 67–69°.

Hydrogenation (Adams platinum catalyst) of the optically active forms of *threo*-12,13-epoxyoleic acid gave[156f] the corresponding *threo*-12,13-dihydroxy-stearic acids, m.p. 96·5–97° with respective rotatory powers $[\alpha]_D^{24} + 23·8°$ and $- 23·8°$.

9,10-Epoxyoctadec-*cis*-12-enoic acid, $C_{18}H_{32}O_3$, contains the oxido group in the opposite position to that in which it occurs in vernolic acid. So far this 9,10-epoxy-octadecanoic acid has only been recorded in the seed fat of *Chrysanthemum coronarium* (Smith *et al.*[157a]).

15,16-Epoxy-octadeca-*cis*-9-*cis*-12-dienoic acid. Gunstone and Morris,[157b] by means of urea-complexing, solvent partition, and chromatographic adsorption, isolated from the seed oil of *Camelina sativa* about 1·3 per cent. of this acid, which they showed to be 15,16-epoxy-linoleic acid. Opening of the epoxide ring followed by hydrogenation of the ethenoid bonds yielded (+)-*threo*-15,16-dihydroxystearic acid (m.p. 96–97°, $[\alpha]_D^{20°} + 3·3°$), which on oxidation with periodate gave propionaldehyde and the semi-aldehyde of tridecane dicarboxylic acid; similar oxidation of the dihydroxy-linoleic acid yielded azelaic acid, from which evidence the constitution of the natural epoxy-acid follows.

18-Hydroxy-octadeca-9,11,13-trienoic (kamlolenic) acid, $CH_2(OH).[CH_2]_3.CH:CH. CH:CH.CH:CH.[CH_2]_7.COOH$, was first observed in the seed fat (kamala oil) of *Mallotus philippinensis* (Euphorbiaceæ) by Aggarwal *et al.*,[158a] who considered it to be the ω-hydroxy-derivative of a triene C_{18} acid. Calderwood and Gunstone[158b] later showed that, instead of Puntambekar's view[158c] that the acid is ketonic and not hydroxylic, the acid contains a terminal hydroxyl group and three conjugated groups: it is almost certainly (as indicated above) 18-hydroxy-elæostearic acid. The natural (α-) acid melts at 77–78°, and exhibits the three characteristic "elæostearic" peaks of absorption in the ultra-violet near 270 mμ. In presence of ultra-violet light and a trace of iodine it is converted (like α-elæostearic acid) into a higher-melting β-isomer, m.p. 88–89°. On hydrogenation it yields 18-hydroxy-stearic acid, m.p. 96·5–98·5°.

Ahlers and Gunstone,[158d] confirmed by von Mikusch[158e] and by Crombie and Tayler,[158f] stated that the infra-red spectra of the isomeric kamlolenic acids indicated that the natural acid contained one *cis*- and two *trans*-ethenoid bonds (probably *cis*-9, *trans*-11, *trans*-13), and the β-acid three *trans*-ethenoid bonds (as in the natural (α-) and β-elæostearic acids, *cf.* p. 634).

In the natural kamala oil a considerable portion of the acid appears to be in the form of poly-esters (estolides or lactide-like condensation products of the hydroxy-elæostearic acid), either as such or in concurrent combination with glycerol[158e,g,h] (*cf.* Chapter VI, p. 470).

9,14-Dihydroxy-octadeca-10,12-dienoic acid, $C_{18}H_{32}O_4$, was found to be present in very small amounts in the fatty acids of tung oil by Davis *et al.*[159] It melts at 104–104·5°, and its constitution (which was established by these workers) suggests that it is probably a side-product of autoxidation of the tung oil, rather than an original component of the natural fat.

9-Hydroxy-octadec-*trans*-10-*trans*-12-dienoic (dimorphecolic) acid, $C_{18}H_{32}O_3$, is the chief component acid in the seed-fat of *Dimorphotheca auriantiaca*, a member of the Compositæ family. The natural acid is dextrorotatory; it is at present unique in its constitution and in its presence in the seed fat of a Compositæ species.[160a]

14-Hydroxy-*cis*-eicos-11-enoic (lesquerolic) acid, $C_{20}H_{38}O_3$, is a C_{20} analogue of ricinoleic acid which has been found in its dextrorotatory form in the seed fats of *Lesquerella* species (Cruciferæ).[160b]

8-Hydroxy-octadec-17-en-9,11-dynoic (isanolic) acid, $C_{18}H_{26}O_3$, is the chief component of boleka or isano oil, the seed fat of *Onguekoa gore* (p. 289), of the fatty acids of which it forms over 40 per cent. Riley[161a] showed that the hydroxyl group is attached to the 8th carbon atom from the carboxyl end of the C_{18} chain, and Kaufmann *et al.*,[161b] from the similarity of the ultra-violet absorption spectrum of this acid (termed by them "isanolic" acid) to that of isanic acid (p. 637), have suggested that its probable constitution is 8-hydroxy-octadec-17-en-9,11-diynoic acid, $CH_2:CH.[CH_2]_4.C\dot{:}C.C\dot{:}C.CH(OH).[CH_2]_6.COOH$.

An analogous hydroxy-acid, **8-hydroxy-octadec-11-en-9-ynoic acid,** accompanies the octadec-11-en-9-ynoic(ximenynic) acid present in the seed fat of *Ximenia caffra* (Ligthelm[161c]). Both *cis-* and *trans*-11-*en-* forms of the acid have been synthesised (Crombie and Griffin[161d]).

(ii) *Hydroxy-fatty acids in natural products other than fats*

Higher hydroxy-fatty acids or their derivatives are present in combination in several natural products (waxes, gums, resins, etc.) which are not glyceride in character, or are produced from such natural products by chemical change. It is appropriate here to mention them briefly.

ω-Hydroxy-saturated acids of the *n*-even-numbered series, $CH_2(OH).[CH_2]_n.COOH$, are fairly common in natural waxes. Juniperic (16-hydroxypalmitic) and sabinic (12-hydroxy-lauric) acids were noted many years ago[162a] in some coniferous waxes, and ursolic (30-hydroxytriacontanoic) acid in the cuticle waxes of apples and cranberries.[162b] Murray and Schoenfeld[162c] found ω-hydroxysaturated acids of all the *n*-even-numbered members from C_{18} to C_{30} in carnauba wax.

Jalapa, the purgative principle of the root of *Convolvulus purga* and other *Convolvulus* and *Ipomœa* species, gives rise to two hydroxy-acids, *convolvulinic* and *jalapinolic acids*, which were shown to be respectively 11-hydroxymyristic and 11-hydroxypalmitic acids, $(CH_3.[CH_2]_2.CH(OH).[CH_2]_9.COOH$ and $CH_3.[CH_2]_4.CH(OH).[CH_2]_9.COOH)$ by Kawasaki,[163a] who also prepared them synthetically.

Dihydroxy-saturated acids have also been reported occasionally, e.g., a dihydroxy-myristic (ipurolic) acid in the seeds of *Ipomœa* and some other Convolvulaceæ,[163b] and 9,10-dihydroxystearic acid (p. 617) in *Lycopodium*.[163c]

15,16-*Dihydroxypalmitic* and 2,15,16-*trihydroxypalmitic acids* ("ustilic" acids) are produced by hydrolytic breakdown of ustilagic acid, a constituent of the *Ustilago* fungi which attack barley and other cereal grains in the plant disease known as "smut" (Lemieux[163d]).

Ambrettolide, the component of vegetable musk oils which confers upon them their distinctive odour, is an internal anhydride or lactone of 16-hydroxy-hexadec-7-enoic acid,[164a] $CH_2(OH).[CH_2]_7.CH:CH.[CH_2]_5.COOH$; it has been synthesised by Baudart.[164b] Isomeric forms, some of which possess the musk odour, had previously been obtained synthetically by Collaud[164c] (*iso*-ambrettolide, lactone of 16-hydroxy-hexadec-6-enoic acid) and by Mitter and Bhattacharya[164d] (*epi*-ambrettolide, lactone of 16-hydroxy-hexadec-9-enoic acid). Aleuritic acid has been converted into dihydroambrettolide and iso-ambrettolide.[164e]

Aleuritic acid, 9,10,16-trihydroxypalmitic acid, is an integral part of shellac, in which it is united with shellolic acid and perhaps other constituents to form the lac resin. Its constitution has been determined by Nagel *et al.*[165a] Mitter and Mukherjee[165b] synthesised 16-methoxy-hexadec-9-enoic acid from 6-methoxy-*n*-hexyl bromide and 7-chloroheptaenal by the procedure of Noller and Bannerot,[98] from which 16-methoxy-9,10-dihydroxypalmitic acid and, thence, aleuritic acid should be obtainable. The conversion of aleuritic acid into the equilibrium mixture of *cis-* and *trans*-hexadec-9-enoic acids (and thence, by alkaline permanganate oxidation of the latter, into the isomeric 9,10-dihydroxypalmitic acids, m.p. respectively, 125° and 89–90°) has been effected by Nagel and Mertens.[165c]

One or more hydroxy- and keto-derivatives of short-chain *trans*-2-enoic acids are present in "royal (queen) jelly", the secretion rich in protein of the honey bee on which the larvæ of queen bees feed in their very early stages. These include 10-hydroxy-*trans*-dec-2-enoic acid,[166a] the syntheses of which (and of the *cis*-form) have been effected[166b]: 9-keto-*trans*-dec-2-enoic acid, which has also (with its *cis*-form) been prepared synthetically[166c]; and 7-hydroxy-*trans*-hept-2-enoic acid (also synthesised[166d]).

Hydroxy-fatty acids present in cork. Several long-chain hydroxylated acids have been found to be present, in small proportions, in cork. Amongst these are 9,10,18-*trihydroxy-stearic* (*phloionolic*) *acid*) $CH_2(OH).[CH_2]_7.CH(OH).CH(OH).[CH_2]_7.COOH^{167a}$; 9,10-*dihydroxy-18-carboxy-stearic* (*phloionic*) *acid*, $COOH.[CH_2]_7.CH(OH).CH(OH).[CH_2]_7.COOH^{167a}$; 22-*hydroxy-behenic* (*phellonic*) *acid*, $CH_2(OH).[CH_2]_{20}.COOH^{167b}$; *n-eicosane-*1,20-*dicarboxylic* (*phellagenic*) *acid*, $COOH.[CH_2]_{20}.COOH^{167b}$; and 18-*hydroxy-octadec-9-enoic acid.*[167c] Phloionic acid has been prepared synthetically.[167d]

Acids (*including an ethynoid and a tri-ethenoid acid*) *containing the structure* $=C(H).[CH_2]_4.COOH$

Unsaturation commencing at the *sixth* atom of the C_{18} chain, instead of at the *ninth* atom as in oleic and so many other natural ethenoid fatty acids, is a well-marked characteristic of acids in the seed fats of a few botanical families. In the monoethenoid series it is confined to *petroselinic acid*, which, however, is a prominent component of all Umbelliferous seed fats and of one or two seed fats in other families (Araliaceæ, Simarubaceæ). The mono-ethynoid analogue *tariric acid* occurs in seed fats of some species of *Picramnia* (also a member of the Simarubaceæ), whilst a tri-ethenoid acid of analogous structure is (so far) uniquely represented in the seed fat of *Oenothera*:

$C_{18}H_{34}O_2$	Octadec-6-enoic (petroselinic)	$CH_3.[CH_2]_{10}.CH:CH.[CH_2]_4.CO_2H$
$C_{18}H_{32}O_2$	Octadec-6-ynoic (tariric)	$CH_3.[CH_2]_{10}.C\vdots C.[CH_2]_4.CO_2H$
$C_{18}H_{30}O_2$	Octadec-6,9,12-trienoic	
	$CH_3.[CH_2]_4.CH:CH.CH_2.CH:CH.CH_2.CH:CH.[CH_2]_4.CO_2H$	

The ethynoid and tri-ethenoid compounds structurally akin to octadec-6-enoic acid are conveniently discussed along with the latter acid.

cis-**Octadec-6-enoic** (**petroselinic**) **acid,** $CH_3.[CH_2]_{10}.CH:CH.[CH_2]_4.COOH$, was first noted in 1909 in parsley seed oil by Vongerichten and Köhler,[168a] who described its chief properties and arrived at its structure by Baruch's procedure. In the same year Scherer[168b] observed the acid in the seed fats of two other Umbellates (*Pimpinella anisum* and *Fœniculum capillaceum*), and in 1914 Palazzo and Tamburello[168c] showed that it was present in ivy seed oil (Araliaceæ). Later work by Hilditch with Miss Jones[168d] and Christian[168e] on the seed fats of a large number of other Umbelliferous species showed its presence in amounts varying from 20 to 75 per cent. of all the seed fatty acids. It also forms 77 per cent. of the acids in the seed fat of *Picrasma quassioides*, a tropical plant belonging to the family Simarubaceæ (Tsujimoto[168f]). Modern methods (urea-complexing followed by low-temperature crystallisation) for the isolation of pure petroselinic acid from parsley seed oil are given by Fore *et al.*[168g]

The constitution of the acid (from parsley seed) has been proved by ozonolysis or permanganate-acetone oxidation.[169a, b, c] Petroselinic acid melts at 29° and is transformed, by contact with oxides of nitrogen, into an equilibrium mixture of the geometrical isomerides containing about 60 per cent. of *trans*-octadec-6-enoic acid, which melts at 53°. Oxidation with Caro's acid or peracetic acid yields a *threo*-6,7-dihydroxystearic acid, m.p. 116–117°, whilst oxidation by dilute alkaline permanganate gives the isomeric *erythro*-acid, m.p. 122°.[169b, d] The natural *cis*- acid has been prepared[108, 112d] by partial hydrogenation of tariric acid, which has been completely synthesised by two independent methods (*v. infra*).

Octadec-6-ynoic (**tariric**) **acid,** $CH_3.[CH_2]_{10}.C\vdots C.[CH_2]_4.COOH$, the simplest example of the natural acetylenic acids, has only been observed in seed fats of the Central American genus *Picramnia* (Simarubaceæ). Arnaud[170a] first reported it in 1892 in the seed fat of *P. sow* (tariri fat); he obtained lauric and adipic acids by its oxidation and ascribed the above structure to the acid. In 1910 Grimme[170b] found it in the seeds of *P. carpenteræ*, and, in 1912, to the extent of 20 per cent. of the component acids of the seed fat of *P. linderiana*. In 1933 Steger and van Loon[170c] showed that the fat from *P. sow* contained over 90 per cent. of glycerides of tariric acid, and also confirmed its constitution (by oxidation with ozone).

Tariric acid melts at 50–50·5°, and gives a characteristic di-iodo derivative, 6,7-di-iodo-octadec-6-enoic acid, $CH_3.[CH_2]_{10}.CI:CI.[CH_2]_4.COOH$, m.p. 47–48°. It was synthesised in 1952 by Lumb and Smith[108] (commencing by condensation of the lithium derivative of tridec-1-yne, $CH_3.[CH_2]_{10}.C \vdots CH$ with 1-chloro-4-iodo-*n*-butane, *cf*. p. 606), and in 1954 by Linstead *et al.*[112d] by electrolysis of *n*-octanoic acid and the methyl hydrogen ester of dodec-6-ynedioic acid, $COOH.[CH_2]_4.C:C.[CH_2]_4.COOCH_3$ (*cf*. p. 608).

Octadeca-6,9,12-trienoic acid, $CH_3.[CH_2]_4.CH:CH.CH_2.CH:CH.CH_2.CH:CH.$ $[CH_2]_4.COOH$. This structural isomer of ordinary linolenic acid has so far only been observed in the seed fat of *Oenothera biennis* (evening primrose), in which it was first noticed by Heiduschka and Lüft.[171a] In 1927 Eibner *et al.*[169a] stated that *Oenothera* seed fatty acids include about 10 per cent. of the triene acid, and showed (by ozonolysis) that the latter is octadec-6,9,12-trienoic acid. Their results were fully confirmed by the more modern techniques employed in 1949 by Riley,[171b] who also showed that, like linolenic acid, the isomeric triene acid is rearranged to a conjugated triene acid when heated with alkali at 180°. Riley also proved that the diene C_{18} acid which is the main component (70 per cent.) of *Oenothera* seed fatty acids is ordinary linoleic (*cis-cis*-octadeca-9,12-dienoic) acid, and that the minor amounts of monoethenoid C_{18} acids also present are ordinary oleic acid.

Octadeca-6,9,12-trienoic acid, which has the same structural relation to petroselinic acid that ordinary linolenic acid has to oleic acid, is a liquid which unites with bromine to give a hexabromostearic acid, m.p. 196°, and which with alkaline permanganate yields a hexa-hydroxystearic acid, m.p. 245°. It has been synthesised by Osbond.[191a]

Cyclic Mono- (and Di-) Ethenoid Acids

A small group of acids, characterised by the presence of a *cyclo*pentenyl ring-system at the end of the fatty acid chain, is found in quantity in the seed fats of *Hydnocarpus* and a few other genera of the tropical family Flacourtiaceæ (Chapter IV, p. 292). These fats are specific in their therapeutic value in the treatment of leprosy and some other diseases. The acids in question are hydnocarpic ($C_{16}H_{28}O_2$), chaulmoogric ($C_{18}H_{32}O_2$), and gorlic ($C_{18}H_{30}O_2$); they are all optically active (dextrorotatory). Chaulmoogric acid is probably the most abundant of the three, but hydnocarpic acid is also an important component of these seed fats in some cases; these two acids are mono-ethenoid. Gorlic acid is di-ethenoid, and accompanies chaulmoogric acid in lesser proportions in some of the Flacourtiaceæ seed fats. The structural formulæ of the acids are as follows:

$C_{16}H_{28}O_2$
Hydnocarpic
11-*cyclo*Pent-2-enyl-*n*-undecanoic

$C_{18}H_{32}O_2$
Chaulmoogric
13-*cyclo*Pent-2-enyl-*n*-tridecanoic

$$\begin{array}{c} H_2 \\ H_2C-C\diagdown CH.[CH_2]_{10}.COOH \\ | \qquad | \\ HC\!=\!\!=\!CH \end{array}$$

M.p. 59–60°
$[\alpha]_D + 68°$

$$\begin{array}{c} H_2 \\ H_2C-C\diagdown CH.[CH_2]_{12}.COOH \\ | \qquad | \\ HC\!=\!\!=\!CH \end{array}$$

M.p. 71°
$[\alpha]_D + 56°$

$C_{18}H_{30}O_2$
Gorlic
13-*cyclo*Pent-2-enyl-tridec-6-enoic

$$\begin{array}{c} H_2 \\ H_2C-C\diagdown CH.[CH_2]_6.CH:CH.[CH_2]_4.COOH \\ | \qquad | \\ HC\!=\!\!=\!CH \end{array}$$

liquid
$[\alpha]_D + 60°$

The chemical constitution of chaulmoogric acid (and of the nearly related hydnocarpic acid) was first studied exhaustively in 1904–1907 by Power and Barrowcliff[172a] who, from the products of its oxidation with permanganate and other reagents, concluded that its structure was best represented as a tautomeric mixture of the cyclopentene derivative shown in the above formula with the cyclopropane compound:

$$\begin{array}{cc} \overset{\displaystyle H_2}{C}\!\!-\!\!\overset{\displaystyle H}{C} \\ | \qquad | \\ C\!\!-\!\!C \\ \underset{\displaystyle H_2}{} \quad \underset{\displaystyle H}{} \end{array}\!\!\!>\!\!CH.[CH_2]_{12}.COOH.$$

Later Shriner and Adams,[172b] as a result of further study of the reactions and decomposition products of chaulmoogric acid, showed that it was satisfactorily represented by the cyclopentenoid formula alone, and in 1927 Perkins and Cruz[172c] succeeded in synthesising racemic chaulmoogric acid by condensing the chloride of 11-cyano-undecanoic acid, $CN.[CH_2]_{10}.COOH$, with acetoacetic ester and subsequently condensing the reaction product with sodium and Δ^2-chloro*cyclo*pentene when the compound

$$\begin{array}{cc} \overset{\displaystyle H}{C}\!\!=\!\!\overset{\displaystyle H}{C} \\ | \qquad | \\ C\!\!-\!\!C \\ \underset{\displaystyle H_2}{} \quad \underset{\displaystyle H_2}{} \end{array}\!\!\!>\!\!CH.\overset{\displaystyle CO.CH_3}{\underset{\displaystyle COOC_2H_5}{C}}.CO.[CH_2]_{10}.CN$$

was obtained; on hydrolysis this gave a yield of about 30 per cent. of the keto-acid

$$\begin{array}{cc} \overset{\displaystyle H}{C}\!\!=\!\!\overset{\displaystyle H}{C} \\ | \qquad | \\ C\!\!-\!\!C \\ \underset{\displaystyle H_2}{} \quad \underset{\displaystyle H_2}{} \end{array}\!\!\!>\!\!CH.CH_2.CO.[CH_2]_{10}.COOH$$

which, by reduction with hydrazine and sodium ethylate under pressure, was converted into *dl*-chaulmoogric acid. Anodic syntheses of chaulmoogric and hydnocarpic acids (1955,[172e] 1960[172f]) have also been carried out. Other syntheses of *dl*-hydnocarpic acid were recorded by Bokil and Nargund[173a] and by Diaper and Smith.[173c]

The therapeutic interest of the chaulmoogric-hydnocarpic series has led to the synthetical preparation of a number of analogous acids such as 3-*cyclo*pentenyl-propionic acid and 11-*cyclo*hexylundecanoic acid (Bokil et al.[173b]), chaulmoogric acids substituted in the 2- or α-position of the aliphatic chain (e.g., 2-*cyclo*pentyl and 2-*cyclo*hexyl-dihydrochaulmoogric acids, Buu-Hoï and Cagniant[174a]), and other similar variations.

The optically inactive *dihydrochaulmoogric* (13-*cyclo*pentyl-*n*-tridecanoic) acid, m.p. 71°, which results from hydrogenation of chaulmoogric acid,[172d] has been prepared synthetically by Buu-Hoï et al.[174b] by condensing ethyl *cyclo*-pentanone-2-carboxylate with ethyl 13-bromo-*n*-tridecanoate, leading to 2-ketodihydrochaulmoogric acid which by Clemmensen reduction gives dihydrochaulmoogric acid.

Buu-Hoï[174c] has shown that, by Barbier-Wieland degradation of its ethyl ester with magnesium phenyl bromide, chaulmoogric acid can be converted in two stages into hydnocarpic acid, and the latter similarly into alepric acid (*v. infra*).

The first product of autoxidation of ethyl chaulmoograte is a racemic hydroperoxide formed from the hydrogen atom attached to the asymmetric carbon atom in the *cyclo*pentene ring (Davies and Packer[175]):

$$\begin{array}{cc} H_2C\!\!-\!\!\overset{\displaystyle H_2}{C}\!\!-\!\!C\overset{\displaystyle O.OH}{\underset{\displaystyle [CH_2]_{12}.COOEt}{}} \\ | \qquad \qquad \\ HC\!\!=\!\!=\!\!CH \end{array}$$

Lower analogues of chaulmoogric and hydnocarpic acids have been isolated in small quantities from some of the *Hydnocarpus* seed fats by Cole and Cardoso,[176a] including:

ACID	FORMULA	CONSTITUTION	M.P.
Aleprolic	$C_6H_8O_2$	*cyclo*Pent-2-enyl carboxylic	liq.
Aleprestic	$C_{10}H_{16}O_2$	5-*cyclo*Pent-2-enyl-*n*-pentanoic	liq.
Aleprylic	$C_{12}H_{20}O_2$	7-*cyclo*Pent-2-enyl-*n*-heptanoic	32°
Alepric	$C_{14}H_{24}O_2$	9-*cyclo*Pent-2-enyl-*n*-nonanoic	48°

Wladislaw[176b] has recorded a synthesis of aleprestic acid.

The di-ethenoid *gorlic* acid contains an additional double linking in the aliphatic chain. It was first detected by Wrenshall and Dean[176c] in 1924, whilst in 1928 André and Jouatte[176d] showed that it formed about 10 per cent. of the acids of gorli seed oil. Its structure as 13-*cyclo*pent-2-enyl-tridec-6-enoic acid was proved in 1938 by Cole and Cardoso.[176e]

Mono-ethenoid Acids not falling within the above Groups

There remain other natural mono-ethenoid fatty acids whose constitutions do not reveal features of structural resemblance to any of the well-defined groups which have been described above. These acids, many of which are extremely rare and of restricted occurrence, must now be briefly reviewed.

Unsaturated acids of the odd as well as the even numbered *n*-series from $C_{11}H_{20}O_2$ to $C_{18}H_{34}O_2$ (in addition to *n*-saturated acids from $C_7H_{14}O_2$ to $C_{18}H_{36}O_2$) have been observed by Weitkamp *et al.*[177] in the free fatty acids in human hair fat; C_{16} and C_{18} unsaturated acids are the most abundant, and unsaturation is most frequently in the 5:6 position ($R.CH:CH.[CH_2]_3.COOH$). In contrast to sheep's wool fat and some other skin greases, branched-chain acids are present only in small amounts in human hair fat.

C_{10}, C_{12}, *and* C_{14} *acids of the structure* $CH_3.[CH_2]_m.CH:CH.[CH_2]_2.COOH$. A group of mono-ethenoid C_{10}, C_{12}, and C_{14} acids of this nature (*m* = 4, 6, or 8) has been observed to occur in small quantities in seed fats of certain sub-tropical plants belonging to the Lauraceæ (in which lauric acid is the main component). In 1927 Tsujimoto[178a] noted the presence of small proportions of a do- and a tetra-decenoic acid in the seed fat of *Lindera hypoglauca*, and in 1928 he obtained "tsuzuic" acid from the seeds of *Litsea glauca* and proved its consitution as tetradec-4-enoic acid. Toyama[178b] and others showed in 1937 that dec-4-enoic ("obtusilic"), dodec-4-enoic ("linderic"), and tetradec-4-enoic ("tsuzuic") acids are present in the seed fat of *Lindera obtusiloba*.

Trans-4-decenoic, *trans*-4-dodecenoic, and *trans*-4-tetradecenoic acids have been prepared synthetically[178c]; they differ from the respective natural acids (obtusilic, linderic and tsuzuic), which are presumably the *cis*-isomerides.

Vaccenic acid (*trans*-**Octadec-11- or -10-enoic acid**), $C_{18}H_{34}O_2$, is the *trans*-form of a positional isomer or isomers of *cis*-oleic acid which is present in small proportions in some animal depot and milk fats. It was first observed in 1928 by Bertram,[179a] who stated that it occurred to the extent of 1 per cent. in beef fat and 0·01 per cent. in butter fats, melted at 39°, and gave on oxidation *n*-heptanoic acid and a dicarboxylic acid $COOH.[CH_2]_9.COOH$. Grossfeld and Simmer[179b] reported the presence of vaccenic acid in the following fats: butter (1–4·7 per cent.), beef fat (1·6 per cent.), mutton fat (1–2 per cent.), lard (0·2 per cent.). Böeseken *et al.*[179c] stated that vaccenic esters are present in some quantity amongst the products of partial hydrogenation of elæo-stearic esters (see also p. 635).

Later observations have created some doubt as to whether either Bertram's natural vaccenic acid or the hydrogenated product from elæostearic acid in fact possesses the constitution of an individual octadec-11-enoic acid. In 1948 Ahmad *et al.*[107b] noted that the infra-red spectrum of a specimen of highly-purified natural vaccenic acid (m.p. 42·5°) prepared from beef tallow by Rao and Daubert[179d] was identical with that of the *trans*-octadec-11-enoic acid, which they had prepared synthetically, and whose constitution was later (1950) verified by Strong *et al.*[107d] Benedict and Daubert,[179e] however, observed (1949) that the X-ray diffraction spectrum of the natural vaccenic acid was markedly different from that of the synthetic *trans*-octadec-11-enoic acid or of elaidic (*trans*-octadec-9-enoic) acid (the two latter acids giving identical long and side spacing in the X-ray spectrum). Chemical evidence put forward in 1950 by Gupta, Hilditch, *et al.*[180a] showed that, whilst vaccenic acid from cow milk fat consists largely of *trans*-octadec-11-enoic acid, it is accompanied by an isomer (probably *trans*-octadec-10-enoic acid); and that vaccenic acid from sheep or ox body fats contains considerable proportions of *trans*-octadec-10-enoic acid as well as *trans*-octadec-11-enoic acid. They concluded that "vaccenic" acid is a mixture of *trans*-acids which may well be the result of secondary changes effected in the natural *cis*-glycerides synthesised by ruminants and, perhaps, some other animals, and that the corresponding *cis*-"vaccenic" acids may also be present (although they had not then been detected) in the fats concerned. Subsequently (*v. infra*) Swern *et al.*[180b] pointed out the possibility that the natural *cis*-constituents of these fats might be partly converted, with or without double-bond shift, by unsaturated fatty acid oxidases known to be present in animal tissues, into the observed *trans*-isomers.

Gupta, Hilditch, *et al.*[180a] also re-investigated the products of partial hydrogenation of methyl elæostearate, previously studied by Hilditch and Pathak,[180c] and confirmed that the mono-ethenoid esters so produced are not homogeneous, but contain other mono-ethenoid isomers of the *trans*-octadec-11-enoate (which, however, is the predominant component).

cis-**Octadec-11-enoic** (*cis*-**vaccenic**) **acid** was isolated from the lipids of brain tissue in small quantities by Morton and Todd,[180d] and is also present in the lipids of *Lactobacillus arabinosus*.[127a]

The *cis*- and *trans*-octadec-11-enoic acids have been synthesised by Gensler and Thomas[105] and by Strong *et al.*[107b] by formal methods, by chain extension from hexadec-9-enoic acid through hexadec-9-enyl bromide and malonic ester condensation by van Loon *et al.*,[180e] and by anodic syntheses by Linstead *et al.*[112c]

Other possible natural isomers of oleic (*octadec-9-enoic*) *acid.* In 1944 Millican and Brown[181a] scrutinised the individuality or otherwise of the oleic acid in a number of fats, by careful study of the acids isolated and purified by a combination of fractional distillation and low-temperature crystallisation of the methyl esters. In vegetable fats, these workers found that the octadecenoic acids of olive, cottonseed, maize, and linseed oils are wholly oleic acid, but that those of soya bean and/or rapeseed oil appear to be mixtures predominating in octadec-9-enoic (oleic) acid, but with some other isomeric octadecenoic acid also present. Similarly, they found evidence of other isomeric acids in addition to oleic (the principal component) in the octadecenoic acids of lard, beef tallow, adrenal phosphatides, pig liver lipids, and human depot fat, and considered that in these animal fats the isomer is probably the "vaccenic" acid described by Bertram (cf. above). In 1952 Swern et al.[180b] studied the infra-red spectra of the octadecenoic acids in a number of ox body fats and found greater amounts of trans-acids (elaidic as well as "vaccenic") present than had previously been recognised. As already mentioned (p. 624), these authors suggested the possibility that these isomers were artefacts of the action of tissue oxidases upon naturally synthesised cis-oleic glycerides. Shorland et al.,[181b] from infra-red studies (1954), conclude that trans-acids are only present in ruminant animal fats (ox, sheep, deer), only traces being observed in pig fats, and none in those of the rat, rabbit, or horse.

There is also some reason to believe that the mono-ethenoid C_{18} acids of whale and fish oils may include, in addition to much oleic acid, minor proportions of a structural isomer or isomers of undetermined constitution (C. W. Moore[52b]). The presence of octadec-11-enoic as well as octadec-9-enoic (oleic) has been reported[119] in menhaden oil.

Docos-11-enoic (Cetoleic) acid, $CH_3.[CH_2]_9.CH:CH.[CH_2]_9.COOH,$ accompanies gadoleic acid (usually in smaller proportions than the latter) in many marine animal oils. Formerly believed to be identical with the erucic acid of vegetable fats, it was shown by Toyama[146c] to have the 11:12-ethenoid structure assigned above.

POLYETHENOID ACIDS

Like the monoethenoid acids, the polyethenoid acids may best be considered in several groups: (a) those which contain a terminal group, $=CH.[CH_2]_7.$ COOH, identical with that in oleic acid; (b) acids (mainly in fats of aquatic animals and plants) with three, four, five, or six double bonds, and (most frequently) terminating in the group $=CH.[CH_2]_2.COOH$; and (c) a few polyethenoid acids which do not fall in either of the previous categories (including some shorter-chain (chiefly C_{10}) acids with two conjugated ethenoid groups or several ethenoid and ethynoid groups).

Di-, Tri-, Tetra-ethenoid (and -ethynoid) acids containing the structure $=CH.[CH_2]_7.COOH$

These are found almost entirely in vegetable fats. They include the widely-distributed linoleic and linolenic acids, which are present in small proportions in some fats of animal origin; but the origin of these and the other polyethenoid acids which share the terminal structure of oleic acid is almost certainly exclusively in the vegetable kingdom. The acids in question are:

$C_{18}H_{32}O_2$ Octadec-9:12-dienoic (linoleic)
$$CH_3.[CH_2]_4.CH:CH.CH_2.CH:CH.[CH_2]_7.CO_2H$$

$C_{18}H_{30}O_2$ Octadec-9:12:15-trienoic (linolenic)
$$CH_3.CH_2.CH:CH.CH_2.CH:CH.CH_2.CH:CH.[CH_2]_7.CO_2H$$

$C_{18}H_{30}O_2$ Octadec-9:11:13-trienoic (elæostearic)
$$CH_3.[CH_2]_3.CH:CH.CH:CH.CH:CH.[CH_2]_7.CO_2H$$

$(C_{18}H_{28}O_3$ 4-Keto-octadeca-9:11:13-trienoic (licanic)
$$CH_3.[CH_2]_3.CH:CH.CH:CH.CH:CH.[CH_2]_4.CO.[CH_2]_2.CO_2H)$$

$C_{18}H_{28}O_2$ Octadeca-9:11:13:15-tetraenoic (parinaric)
$$CH_3.CH_2.CH:CH.CH:CH.CH:CH.CH:CH.[CH_2]_7.CO_2H$$

$C_{18}H_{26}O_2$ Octadec-17-en-9,11-diynoic (isanic, erythrogenic)
$$CH_2\!:\!CH\,.\,[CH_2]_4\,.\,C\!:\!C\,.\,C\!:\!C\,.\,[CH_2]_7\,.\,CO_2H$$

$(C_{18}H_{26}O_3$ 8-Hydroxy-octadec-17-en-9,11-diynoic (isanolic)
$$CH_2\!:\!CH\,.\,[CH_2]_4\,.\,C\!:\!C\,.\,C\!:\!C\,.\,CH(OH)\,.\,[CH_2]_6\,.\,CO_2H)$$

$C_{18}H_{30}O_2$ Octadec-*trans*-11-en-9-ynoic (ximenynic, santalbic)
$$CH_3[CH_2]_5\,.\,CH\!:\!CH\,.\,C\!:\!C\,.\,[CH_2]_7\,.\,COOH$$

$(C_{18}H_{30}O_3$ 8-Hydroxy-octadec-11-en-9-ynoic
$$CH_3\,.\,[CH_2]_5\,.\,CH\!:\!CH\,.\,C\!:\!C\,.\,CH(OH)\,.\,[CH_2]_6\,.\,COOH)$$

Linoleic acid has been observed, in small or (often) large proportions, in every vegetable fat so far examined; it is as ubiquitous as oleic acid or palmitic acid, and in this respect stands apart from the rest of the acids tabulated above. Linolenic acid, although a major component in the seed fat glycerides of a fairly large number of species, is more often entirely absent from the majority of seed fats; but it very probably occurs more regularly in the lipids of the leaf tissues of plants, and here may often exceed linoleic acid in relative proportion.

The remaining acids are still more restricted in distribution, and are confined to seed fats of relatively few species, or even to a single species or, at most, the species of a single genus.

Linoleic acid contains the grouping —CH_2. $CH\!:\!CH$. CH_2. $CH\!:\!CH$. CH_2—, and is thus characterised by the presence of a *pentadiene* system —$CH\!:\!CH$. CH_2.$CH\!:\!CH$— or by two allylic residues —CH_2.$CH\!:\!CH$— (Hatt and Szumer[182a] have proposed to term this grouping in long-chain acids "*polyallylic*"). The *pentadiene* system is of course duplicated in linolenic acid (and in the isomeric octadeca-6,9,12-trienoic acid, p. 621), and it is repeated several times in many of the tetra-, penta-, and hexa-enoic acids of aquatic fats (p. 643). The methylene group between two double bonds, —$CH\!:\!CH$.CH_2.$CH\!:\!CH$—, is "activated" by the adjacent ethenoid groups, with the result that one of its hydrogen atoms is specially reactive: it readily unites with oxygen to give a hydroperoxide, and in presence of alkali at about 170° it is detached and the pentadiene system undergoes isomerisation to a conjugated diene system. The ready union of the pentadiene system with oxygen (followed by subsequent conjugation and polymerisation) is the reason why linoleic and linolenic glycerides are of such importance as "drying oils" to the paint and linoleum industries.

cis-cis-**Octadeca-9,12-dienoic** (**Linoleic**) **acid,** CH_3.$[CH_2]_4$.$CH\!:\!CH$.CH_2. $CH\!:\!CH$.$[CH_2]_7$.$COOH$, appears to have first been recognised as an individual acid by Sacc[182b] in 1844. In many vegetable fats its amount is subordinate to that of oleic acid, but, of course, in the "semi-drying" and "drying" classes of seed oils it is a major component of the mixed fatty acids. Linoleic acid is liquid at ordinary temperatures and forms a lead salt comparatively freely soluble in ether and alcohol, and a lithium salt soluble in alcohol and, to a less extent, in acetone. Its isolation in the pure condition is therefore not easy by any simple physical method; but it has been achieved (1937) by repeated crystallisation of suitable seed fatty acids from solvents at very low temperatures (Brown *et al.*[183a]), by adsorption of fatty acid concentrates rich in linoleic acid on a column containing specially prepared silicic acid (1949),[184a] by separating the acid as a complex with urea (1953),[185a, b, c] or by counter-current distribution between two immiscible organic solvents (1959).[185d, e, f]

From pure linoleic acid, Riemenschneider et al.[57b] prepared trilinolein which, after being purified by molecular distillation, yielded dimorphic forms which melted at $-43°$ and $-13°$. Daubert and Baldwin[184b] give these melting points as $-45·6°$ and $-12·9°$.

The only method previously available to obtain pure linoleic acid was to add bromine to the unsaturated acids of a seed fat, when nearly half of the linoleic acid is converted into a crystalline tetra-bromostearic acid, m.p. 115°, which is insoluble in light petroleum. Debromination of this product with zinc yields a so-called "α"-linoleic acid* which, at the hands of several workers, has been shown by ozonisation or permanganate-acetone oxidation to be almost entirely octadeca-9,12-dienoic acid.

This "α"-linoleic acid, when re-brominated, again gives slightly less than half the theoretical yield of crystalline tetrabromostearic acid, the remainder being a liquid form (or forms) of tetrabromostearic acid freely soluble in light petroleum. Debromination of these soluble products furnishes the so-called "β"-linoleic acid,* a mixture of acids in which other geometrical isomerides of octadeca-9,12-dienoic acid are the main constituents (see below).

On oxidising either seed fat or regenerated "α"-linoleic acid with aqueous alkaline permanganate (Hazura[186a]) a mixture of two tetrahydroxystearic (sativic) acids results, one of which melts at 171–173° and the other at 157–159°.†

The constitution of the linoleic acid in linseed, cottonseed, soya bean, poppy seed and groundnut oils has been determined by ozonisation or permanganate-acetone oxidation, whilst that from many other seed fats has been shown to yield the same "α"-tetrabromostearic acid m.p. 115°, and the two sativic acids just mentioned; so that it is reasonably certain that linoleic acid from all these vegetable fats is the same form of octadeca-9,12-dienoic acid.

The stereochemical configuration of natural (seed fat) linoleic acid as cis-cis-octadeca-9,12-dienoic acid was deduced from consideration of the relationship observed between its tetrabromo- and tetrahydroxy-adducts by a number of earlier investigators (v. infra), but it now rests unequivocally upon its infra-red spectrum (McCutcheon et al.,[75a] Ahlers et al.,[75d] 1953).

On isomerisation with selenium or oxides of nitrogen the natural and the "α"-linoleic acid (regenerated from the crystalline tetrabromoadduct, m.p. 115°) were shown in 1939 by Hilditch and Jasperson[78b] and by Kass and Burr[78c] to give about 16 per cent. of a solid acid, m.p. 28–29°, which yields a crystalline tetrabromostearic acid, m.p. 78° (accompanied by an equal amount of a liquid tetrabromo-adduct) and on alkaline permanganate oxidation gives two new tetrahydroxystearic acids, m.p. 122° and 146°. The infra-red spectrum of this isomeric linoleic ("linelaidic") acid, m.p. 28–29°, shows that it is trans-trans-octadeca-9,12-dienoic acid.[75d]

Hopkins and Chisholm (1962)[214g, k] report that the seed fatty acids of Chilopsis linearis (Bignoniaceae) include 15 per cent. of trans-trans-octadeca-9,12-dienoic acid.

* It should be emphasised that the division of natural linoleic and linolenic acids, as frequently practised by investigators in this field, into "α"- and "β"-forms has no structural significance, and only means that the "α"-acid is that which has been isolated in the form of a crystalline, insoluble bromo-adduct, the so-called "β"-acid representing the remainder.

† According to Birosel,[186b] supported by Riemenschneider et al.,[186c] the acid melting at 157–159° is a eutectic mixture of that melting at 173° with an acid of m.p. 163·5°.

Kass and Burr[78c] showed that a liquid isomer of linoleic acid is also produced by selenium isomerisation of the natural acid. In this acid, which gives no crystalline tetrabromo-adduct, but leads to tetrahydroxystearic acids which melt at 126–127° and 156–158°, probably only one of the double bonds has been isomerised, giving one or both of the cis-trans-octadeca-9,12-dienoic acids.

The infra-red and Raman spectra of "α"-linoleic acid prepared from the crystalline tetrabromo-stearic acid, m.p. 115°, shows that this material contains traces of the trans-trans-acid and possibly other (conjugated) isomers of linoleic acid, so that it is somewhat less homogeneous than the natural linoleic acid isolated by wholly physical processes. In 1943 Brown and Frankel[183b] stated that regenerated "α"-linoleic acid may contain up to 1 per cent. of conjugated acids, and that "β"-linoleic acid (regenerated from the soluble tetra-bromo-adducts of the natural acid) consists of some cis-cis-acid, and much isomeric octadecadienoic acids which are probably cis-trans-octadeca-9,12-dienoic acids (the trans-trans-acid being absent), together with small proportions of "much altered" acids.

The amount of solid tetrabromostearic acid precipitated from cold petroleum ether solutions of linoleic acid on addition of bromine was formerly employed to determine linoleic acid in mixtures of fatty acids, but the method is very unreliable unless the results are interpreted in terms of empirical interpolation curves based on results with known mixtures (cf. White and Brown,[183c] 1949).

As already mentioned, natural (seed fat) linoleic acid had been concluded by most in-vestigators, from consideration of the various isomeric tetrabromo- or tetrahydroxy-stearic acids to which it gives rise, to be the cis-cis-form, before the question was finally disposed of when infra-red and Raman spectra became effective means of determining cis- and trans-isomerides. The interpretation of these somewhat involved chemical relationships was, however, complex and difficult, and many studies, some of them now of merely historic interest, have been recorded in this field. It will now suffice to indicate very briefly the chief investigations into the matter, and their main conclusions.

The production of two tetrabromo- and two-tetrahydroxy-stearic acids from linoleic acid led Bedford[187a] in 1906 to conclude that two isomeric ("α" and "β"-) linoleic acids were originally present, but in 1909 Rollett[187b] showed that the "α"-linoleic acid regenerated from the crystalline tetrabromo-acid again yields a mixture of liquid and solid tetrabromostearic acids, and therefore concluded that a single natural isomer was concerned, which, on bromination, gave two tetrabromostearic acids each related to a different geometrical isomeride of the octadecadienoic acid. The correctness of Rollett's view was later (1931–1939) proved by other workers[78b,c, 186c, 187c, d, e], who studied further the inter-relations of linoleic and its isomeric forms with the tetrabromo- (and tetra-hydroxy-) adducts.

Configuration of the possible forms of 9,10,12,13-tetrahydroxystearic acid. The four geo-metrically isomeric forms of octadeca-9,12-dienoic acid (cis-cis-, cis-trans-, trans-cis-, trans-trans-) can each give rise to 9,10,12,13-tetrahydroxy- (or tetrabromo-)-stearic acids existing in sixteen optically active or eight racemic forms. The configuration of the eight possible racemic forms is as follows:

$$(\text{R: } CH_3.[CH_2]_4—; \qquad \text{R': } —[CH_2]_7.COOH)$$

R′	R′	R′	R′
H.Ċ.OH	HO.Ċ.H	H.Ċ.OH	HO.Ċ.H
H.Ċ.OH	HO.Ċ.H	H.Ċ.OH	HO.Ċ.H
H.Ċ.H	H.Ċ.H	H.Ċ.H	H.Ċ.H
H.Ċ.OH	H.Ċ.OH	HO.Ċ.H	HO.Ċ.H
H.Ċ.OH	H.Ċ.OH	H.Ċ.OH	H.Ċ.OH
R	R	R	R
I	II	III	IV

(*Erythro*-9,10-*erythro*-12,13-)   (*Erythro*-9,10-*threo*-12,13-)

R'	R'	R'	R'
H.Ċ.OH	HO.Ċ.H	HO.Ċ.H	H.Ċ.OH
HO.Ċ.H	H.Ċ.OH	H.Ċ.OH	HO.Ċ.H
H.Ċ.H	H.Ċ.H	H.Ċ.H	H.Ċ.H
H.Ċ.OH	H.Ċ.OH	HO.Ċ.H	HO.Ċ.H
H.Ċ.OH	H.Ċ.OH	H.Ċ.OH	H.Ċ.OH
R	R	R	R
V	VI	VII	VIII
(*Threo*-9,10-*erythro*-12,13-)		(*Threo*-9,10-*threo*-12,13-)	

The following pairs of 9,10,12,13-tetrahydroxystearic acids have been reported by various workers:

MELTING-POINTS	FROM	WITH	OBSERVERS
173–4° and 163–4°	Natural linoleic	Alkali permanganate	Hazura,[186a] Birosel,[186b] Riemenschneider *et al.*[186c]
,, ,, ,,	*Erythro*-9,10-dihydroxy-*cis*-12-enoic	,, ,,	McKay and Bader[189a]
144° and 135°	Natural linoleic	Hypochlorous acid, followed by alkali	Nicolet and Cox[188]
,, ,, ,,	Linelaidic (*trans-trans*)	Alkaline permanganate	Hilditch and Jasperson[78b]
148° and 126°	Natural linoleic	Peracetic acid	Green and Hilditch,[187d] McKay *et al.*[189b]
,, ,, ,,	*Threo*-9,10-diacetoxy-*cis*-12-enoic	,, ,,	McKay and Bader[189a]
146° and 122°	Linelaidic	Alkaline permanganate	Kass and Burr[78c]

Of the above investigators, only McKay *et al.*[189] succeeded in allotting specific configurations to all eight racemic 9,10,12,13-tetrahydroxystearic acids.

In 1956 Bharucha and Gunstone[190] took advantage of the large quantities of 12,13-epoxyoleic acid which they had found present in the seed fats of *Vernonia anthelmintica* and *Cephalocroton cordofanus* to prepare from it all eight of the possible 9,10,12,13-tetrahydroxystearic acids shown in the above diagram by the following unequivocal procedures:

(i) The *cis*-epoxy ring was opened by acetylation followed by alkaline hydrolysis, which involves inversion (*cf.* p. 598) and leads to the production of *threo*-12,13-dihydroxyoleic acid; the latter acid yields

(*a*) two *erythro*-9,10-*threo*-12,13-tetrahydroxystearic acids on oxidation with alkaline permanganate and

(*b*) two *threo*-9,10-*threo*-12,13-tetrahydroxystearic acids on oxidation of the acetylated dihydroxyoleic acid with performic acid.

(ii) With hydrogen bromide the *cis*-epoxy ring yields (with inversion) the *threo*-12,13,bromo-hydrin which, when treated with silver acetate in (aqueous) 99 per cent. acetic acid, gives on hydrolysis (again with inversion) *erythro*-12,13-dihydroxyoleic acid; when oxidised the latter acid leads to

(*a*) two *erythro*-9,10-*erythro*-12,13-tetrahydroxystearic acids (alkaline permanganate) and

(*b*) two *threo*-9,10-*erythro*-12,13-tetrahydroxystearic acids (performic acid).

The natural epoxy-oleic acid possesses some optical activity, as did some of the resulting tetrahydroxystearic acids, which doubtless accounts for the different melting points recorded by Bharucha and Gunstone for some of their tetrahydroxystearic acids, as compared with those of the racemic forms. This elegant investigation however appears finally to settle the configurations which should be assigned to the eight racemic acids, as shown in the foregoing table.

Syntheses of linoleic acid. In 1937 Noller and Girvin[98b] effected a synthesis of octadecadienoic acids by similar means to Noller and Bannerot's synthesis of oleic acid,[98a] but the final product was not exclusively composed of octadeca-9,12-dienoic acids; in 1944 Baudart[99c] synthesised *trans-trans*-octadec-9,12-dienoic acid from glutaric aldehyde by means of Grignard condensations (*cf.* p. 605).

9,10,12,13-TETRAHYDROXY-STEARIC ACIDS	CONFIGURATION (pp. 628, 629)	MELTING POINTS		
		BHARUCHA AND GUNSTONE[190]	PREVIOUS WORKERS	
			RACEMIC FORMS	REFERENCES
Erythro-9,10-erythro-12,13-	I	177°	174°	186a, b, c, 189a
"	II	156°	164°	" "
Erythro-9,10-threo-12,13-	III	164°	164°	189a, b
"	IV	113°	126°	"
Threo-9,10-erythro-12,13-	V	157°	164°	189a, b
"	VI	131°	142°	"
Threo-9,10-threo-12,13-	VII	148°	148°	187d, 189b
"	VIII	122°	126°	" "

An unequivocal synthesis of the natural *cis-cis*-linoleic acid was not achieved until 1950, when Raphael and Sondheimer[110a] obtained it by reduction of octadeca-9,12-ynoic acid, which they had synthesised from 8-chloro-oct-1-yne and oct-2-yn-1-ol. In 1951, further syntheses of the natural acid by somewhat similar routes from the same or similar acetylenic starting-points were contributed by Wilborsky *et al.*[110b] and by Gensler and Thomas[110c] (see p. 605 for details). Other syntheses of linoleic acid have subsequently been carried out (Osbond,[191a] Ames and Islip[191b]).

Di-ethenoid (C_{22} *and* C_{26}) *acids of the structure* $CH_3.[CH_2]_4.CH:CH.CH_2.CH:CH.[CH_2]_n.COOH$

It is convenient here to mention two higher diethenoid acids which bear the same structural resemblance to linoleic acid as acids of the general type $CH_3.[CH_2]_7.CH:CH.[CH_2]_n.COOH$ (p. 609) bear to oleic acid; just as the latter series all contain the grouping $CH_3.[CH_2]_7.CH=$, so in these two acids the corresponding grouping $CH_3.[CH_2]_4.CH:CH.CH_2.CH=$ is present:

$C_{22}H_{40}O_2$ Docosa-13,16-dienoic $CH_3.[CH_2]_4.CH:CH.CH_2.CH:CH.[CH_2]_{11}.CO_2H$
$C_{26}H_{48}O_2$ Hexacosa-17,20-dienoic $CH_3.[CH_2]_4.CH:CH.CH_2.CH:CH.[CH_2]_{15}.CO_2H$

cis-cis-**Docosa-13,16-dienoic acid,** $C_{22}H_{40}O_2$, was observed[192a] in 1947 to accompany erucic acid in very small proportions in rape seed oil. It has not been isolated in the pure state, but Baliga and Hilditch[117c] were able to show that it contained the "allylic" or "pentadiene" structure $=CH.CH_2.CH=$, and that unsaturation commenced at the 13th carbon atom from the carboxyl end of the acid chain. On addition of bromine to the acid in light petroleum, a crystalline 13,14,16,17-tetrabromodocosanoic acid, m.p. 106–107°, is produced.

Hexacosa-17,20-dienoic acid, $C_{26}H_{48}O_2$, forms nearly 40 per cent. of the acids in the lipids of the sponge *Spheciospongia vesparia* (Bergmann and Swift,[192b] 1951). It melts at 61°, and yields a tetrabromo-hexacosanoic acid, m.p. 99°.

The **hexadeca-7,10,13-trienoic acid,** $CH_3.CH_2.CH:CH.CH_2.CH:CH.CH_2.CH:CH.[CH_2]_5.COOH$ ($C_{16}H_{26}O_2$), shown by Shorland[192c] to form 11–17 per cent. of the fatty acids in the lipids of rape (*Brassica napus*) leaves also falls in this group, since its triene unsaturation (as in linolenic acid) lies in the end grouping $CH_3.[CH_2.CH:CH]_3-$.

It is of interest to note here that, according to Thomasson,[192e] the fatty acids essential to animal growth and health (*cf.* Chapter III, p. 95, Chapter VIII, p. 572) always contain the grouping $CH_3.[CH_2]_4.CH:CH.CH_2.CH:CH-$ (e.g., linoleic, octadeca-6,9,12-trienoic) or $CH_3.CH_2.CH:CH.CH_2.CH:CH.CH_2.CH:CH-$ (e.g., linolenic, arachidonic).

Other natural octadecadienoic acids (aquatic and animal fats). Although it was more or less tacitly assumed at one time that linoleic (or other octadecadienoic) acid accompanied oleic acid in fair quantity in fish and similar fats, there seems to be no record of the isolation of the characteristic tetrabromo- or tetrahydroxy-adducts of ordinary (seed fat) linoleic acid in these cases. Moreover, Green and Hilditch[187d] showed that the unsaturated C_{18} acids of cod liver oil and whale oil consisted mainly of oleic with polyethenoid C_{18} (probably octa-decatetraenoic) acids, and that octadecadienoic acids did not amount to more than about 10 per cent. of the unsaturated C_{18} group; further, ordinary linoleic acid was not detected.

In cow milk fat, the absence of any but minute amounts of ordinary (seed fat) linoleic acid was pointed out by Hilditch and Jones[193a] (1929), by Bosworth and Brown[128c] (1933) and by Eckstein[193b] (1933). Green and Hilditch,[194a] however, proved that the excess unsaturation over mono-ethenoid in butter fatty acids is due to octadecadienoic acids (probably other geometrical isomeric forms of seed fat linoleic acid) and this was confirmed by selenium isomerisation of butter unsaturated C_{18} acids by Hilditch and Jasperson,[194b] who also showed that conjugated octadecadienoic acids form less than 0·5 per cent. of butter fatty acids (see also Chapter III, p. 151). Much more recently these acids have been reinvestigated by chromatographic and other techniques; thus Scott *et al.*[194c] (1959) concluded that they are a mixture of non-conjugated *cis-cis-* and either *cis-trans-* or *trans-trans*-isomers with some conjugated *cis-cis-* and *trans-trans-* isomers, and J. B. Brown[194d] (1962) estimated that about two-thirds of the non-conjugated C_{18} diene acids is linoleic (*cis-cis-*) with the remainder *cis-trans*-isomers (largely, with double bonds separated by more than one methylene group); *trans-trans*-forms did not seem to be present.

The liver and depot fats of oxen and sheep (and probably other similar animals) contain small quantities of C_{18} acids more unsaturated than oleic, which are for the most part octadecadienoic acids. They are similar to the corresponding cow milk fatty acids in their non-response to the tests for ordinary or seed fat linoleic acid, and are probably similar to the butter octadecadienoic acids in structure[130a, 140] (see also Chapter III, pp. 110, 134). Swern *et al.*,[195] however, isolated crystalline tetrabromostearic acid, m.p. 115°, from the polyethenoid acids of beef tallow.

Other (artificially produced) octadecadienoic acids. (i) *Alkali isomerisation of linoleic acid.* T. Moore[196a] observed that, whilst natural linoleic and linolenic acids show only general absorption in the ultra-violet, the products obtained from these acids after prolonged heating with caustic alkali solutions give well-marked absorption bands owing to shifting of the double bonds and their rearrangement to conjugated di- or tri-ethenoid systems. Kass *et al.*[196b] confirmed this and showed that the conversion is rapid if the acids are heated with excess of alkali hydroxide at 180° or thereabouts in a high-boiling solvent such as ethylene glycol; heating in strongly alkaline aqueous solution under pressure at 180° leads to the same result.[196c] Sreenivasan and Brown[196d] state that the isomerisation can be effected at much lower temperatures (120°) by potassium *tert.* butoxide in 5 per cent. solution in *tert.* butyl alcohol.

The mechanism of the reaction is probably dissociation of a hydrogen atom from the methylene group between two double bonds, leaving a system which by resonance is altered as follows:

$$—CH:CH.CH_2.CH:CH—$$
$$\downarrow$$
$$—CH:CH.\overset{\bullet}{C}H.CH:CH—$$
$$\overset{\wedge}{}$$
$$—\overset{\bullet}{C}H.CH:CH.CH:CH— \text{ and } —CH:CH.CH:CH.\overset{\bullet}{C}H—$$
$$\downarrow \qquad\qquad\qquad\qquad \downarrow$$
$$—CH_2.CH:\overset{\bullet}{C}H.CH:CH— \text{ and } —CH:CH.\overset{\bullet}{C}H:CH.CH_2—$$

The natural (9-*cis*-12-*cis*-) linoleic acid isomerises when heated with alkali at a more rapid rate than the 9-*trans*-12-*trans* acid.[197a] Both acids give a mixture of conjugated octadeca-9,11-dienoic and octadeca-10,12-dienoic acids when alkali-isomerised, and the natural *cis-cis*-linoleic acid is probably converted mainly into a mixture of 9-*cis*-11-*trans*- and

10-*trans*-12-*cis*-linoleic acids.[197b, 75d] Riemenschneider *et al.*[197b] give the melting points of 9-*cis*-11-*trans*- and 10-*trans*-12-*cis*-acids as respectively 22–23° and 3°. According to von Mikusch,[197c] 9-*cis*-11-*cis*- (m.p. 19–20°) and 10-*cis*-12-*cis*- (m.p. 21–22°) acids are also present in alkali-isomerised linoleic acid. Alkali-isomerisation of *trans-trans*-octadeca-9,12-dienoic ("linelaidic") acid gives a *trans-trans*-octadeca-10,12-dienoic acid, (m.p. 42–43°).[75d]

Alkali-isomerisation of natural linoleic acid followed by spectrophotometric measurement of the extinction-coefficient at 234 mμ is by far the best means for quantitative determination of the acid in *natural* fats,[198] (*cf.* Chapter XI, p. 695). In view of the different rates of isomerisation of the various geometrical isomers, however, this method can be applied only when the *natural*, unisomerised fatty acid is present along with other natural unsaturated acids.[184a, 199]

Alkali-isomerisation to conjugated octadecadienoic glycerides is also of technical interest as a means of improving the quality of linoleic-rich oils or alkyd resins for use in paints or varnishes.

(ii) *Dehydration of ricinoleic acid (castor oil).* When ricinoleic acid or its glycerides are heated at about 250° in presence of a suitable dehydrating catalyst, the elements of water are removed and a mixture of octadecadienoic acids is produced:

$$—CH_2.CH(OH).CH_2.CH:CH—$$

$$—CH:CH.CH_2.CH:CH— \text{ and } —CH_2.CH:CH.CH:CH—$$

This process has been of interest to drying oil technologists since it was put forward by Scheiber,[200a] and has given rise to numerous patents. Formerly it was believed that the main product was the conjugated 9,11-linoleic acid,[200b] but later work[200c] showed that 9,12-linoleic acids are usually present in greater proportions than conjugated acids. The following, amongst other, isomeric octadecadienoic acids have been reported in dehydrated castor oil or dehydrated ricinoleic or ricinelaidic acids:

9,12-linoleic (liquid) from castor oil. Apparently a mixture of *cis-trans*-isomers (9-*cis*-12-*trans*- or 9-*trans*-12-*cis*-)[75d];

9,11-linoleic (m.p. 43°) from ricinelaidic acid,[201a] shown by Ahlers *et al.*[75d] to be the *trans-trans*-acid;

9,11-linoleic (liquid) from ricinoleic acid, probably a *cis-trans*-form[75d, 199];

10,12-linoleic (m.p. 57°) from ricinoleic acid,[201b] shown to be the *trans-trans*-form[75d, 201c];

8,10-linoleic (m.p. 56°), obtained by Smit and Böeseken[201d] by debromination of a tetra-bromo-adduct (m.p. 124°) from dehydrated castor oil acids, and shown by von Mikusch[201e] to be *trans-trans*-octadec-8,10-dienoic acid.

Tri-ethenoid acids $C_{18}H_{30}O_2$

cis-cis-cis-**Octadeca-9,12,15-trienoic (Linolenic) acid,** $CH_3.CH_2.CH:CH.$ $CH_2.CH:CH.CH_2.CH:CH.[CH_2]_7.COOH$, is the most usual form of triethenoid C_{18} acid found in seed fats. It is, of course, most familiar from its occurrence in linseed oil, of the mixed fatty acids of which it forms 50 per cent. or more; it also occurs in varying but appreciable proportions in other vegetable drying oils, notably perilla and other Labiate seed oils, hemp, pine seed, walnut seed, rubber seed, and some other seed oils of the Euphorbiaceæ. It does not seem to have been recognised as a separate acid until Hazura isolated it in 1887.[202a] Like linoleic acid, linolenic acid yields a mixture of crystalline and liquid or low melting hexabromostearic acids when treated with bromine.[202b] The crystalline hexabromostearic acid (insoluble in ether) melts at 180–181° and on debromination yields a linolenic acid which again, on bromination, furnishes both crystalline and liquid hexabromo-derivatives.

The behaviour of linolenic acid in this respect is thus exactly parallel with that of linoleic acid, and similar conclusions have been reached as to the implication of these results. Erdmann, Bedford and Raspe[202c] submitted the ethyl linolenate obtained by debrominating the crystalline hexabromo-stearic acid to ozonisation and isolated propionaldehyde, malonic acid, and mono-ethyl azelate from the products of the reaction, which thus afforded proof of the structure of the acid; this has been confirmed on several occasions by later workers.[202d]

Various procedures have been suggested for the preparation of linolenic acid of high purity from the mixed fatty acids of linseed or other linolenic-rich oils. Brown et al.[203a] effected this by a complex series of crystallisations from acetone, and subsequently from hexane, at temperatures down to $-75°$ C., but the yield by this method is comparatively low. Beal et al.[203b] obtained linolenic acid (97 per cent. pure) by liquid–liquid extraction of linseed oil acids with wet furfural and hexane.

A convenient method consists of selective adsorption of the mixed methyl esters of linseed or perilla oil acids on a column of specially prepared silica gel, followed by elution with a mixture of 99 per cent. hexane and 1 per cent. ethyl ether. After repetition of the adsorption process Riemenschneider et al.[184a] obtained methyl linolenate with iodine value 260·2 (theory 260·4) and m.p. $-46°$.

Swern and Parker[185a] obtained concentrates with over 80 per cent. of linolenic acid by stepwise precipitation of the less unsaturated acids by means of their urea complexes, while White and Quackenbush[203c] obtained linolenic acid of 98–99 per cent. purity by countercurrent extraction of the ether solution of the mercuric acetate adduct of linseed oil methyl esters with aqueous methanol (10 methanol : 90 water).

The infra-red spectrum of natural linolenic acid establishes it (McCutcheon,[75a] Ahlers et al.[75d]) as the cis-cis-cis-form of octadeca-9,12,15-trienoic acid. On isomerisation with selenium, it yields a solid isomer, m.p. 29–30° (Kass and Burr[204]), the infra-red spectrum of which shows it to be trans-trans-trans-octadeca-9,12,15-trienoic acid;[75d] its crystalline hexabromo-adduct melts at 169–170°.

The complete synthesis of linolenic acid has been effected, with the aid of general methods already described (pp. 603–609), by Nigam and Weedon,[205] and by Osbond and Wickers.[191a]

Linolenic acid, when oxidised with alkaline permanganate, yields two hexahydroxystearic acids which have been termed respectively linusic (m.p. 203°) and isolinusic (m.p. 173–175°); the latter is more soluble in hot water than linusic acid.[206]

When seed fat linolenic acid is heated with excess of alkali hydroxide for a prolonged time in alcohol (T. Moore[196a]) or for a shorter time in butyl alcohol or ethylene glycol at their boiling points (Kass and Burr[196b]) isomerisation to conjugated acids sets in:

$$—CH:CH.CH_2.CH:CH.CH_2.CH:CH—$$

$$—CH_2.CH:CH.CH:CH.CH_2.CH:CH—and—CH:CH.CH_2.CH:CH.CH:CH.CH_2—$$

$$—CH_2.CH:CH.CH:CH.CH:CH.CH_2—$$

In the products, acids with a conjugated diene system and one isolated ethenoid bond predominate, but about 30 per cent. is completely isomerised to a conjugated triene acid; whereas, however, linoleic acid yields both octadeca-9,11- and -10,12-dienoic acids, the conjugated triene acid formed from linolenic acid appears to be wholly octadeca-10,12,14-trienoic acid, both external double bonds having shifted towards the central one (or, more accurately, a hydrogen atom having migrated from each active methylene group away from the central ethenoid group). The conjugated triene acid melts at 79°, and on disruptive oxidation yields sebacic and butyric acids. It displays the characteristic absorption band in the ultra-violet spectrum at 268 mμ, with $E_{1cm}^{1\%}$ about 1900. Use of the absorption spectrum of isomerised linolenic acid in the quantitative analysis of mixtures of *natural* unsaturated acids is discussed elsewhere (*cf.* Chapter IV, p. 179, Chapter XI, p. 695).[198]

The initial product of catalytic hydrogenation (with nickel or palladium) of linolenic acid (or linoleno-glycerides) is, according to Lemon,[207a] mainly octadeca-9,15-dienoic acid, since it yields but little conjugated diene acid on treatment with alkali hydroxide at 180°. This acid, which may reach 18 per cent. of the total fatty acids in hydrogenated linseed oil, must be produced by preferential hydrogenation of the central (12:13) double bond in the linolenic chain.[207b,c,d,e]

Hydrogenation of methyl linolenate with hydrazine is essentially non-selective, yielding about 5 per cent. of stearate, 25 per cent. of mono-ene, 45 per cent. of dienes and 25 per cent. of unchanged triene. The diene fraction consisted of 30–36 per cent. each of the 9,15-, 9,12-, and 12,15-isomers (Scholfield *et al.*[207f]).

Octadeca-6,9,12-trienoic acid, the non-conjugated triene acid of evening primrose seed fat, and a structural isomer of linolenic acid, has already been discussed with other acids to which the terminal structure $=CH.[CH_2]_4$. COOH is common (p. 621).

Conjugated unsaturated seed fatty acids

The acids remaining to be dealt with in the present group contain conjugated systems of either triene, tetraene, or diyne compounds.

Octadeca-9,11,13,trienoic (Elæostearic) acid, $CH_3.[CH_2]_3.[CH:CH]_3.[CH_2]_7$. COOH, occurs notably in China wood or tung oil, the seed fat of *Aleurites fordii* and *montana*, of the mixed acids of which it forms 70–80 per cent. It has also been found in some other seed fats, sometimes accompanied by 4-keto-elæostearic acid; its distribution, as known at the present time, appears from Tables 61 and 61B (pp. 247, 253–260) in Chapter IV.

The acid present in the natural oil ("α-elæostearic acid", m.p. 48–49°) is transformed by the action of light into a solid crystalline isomeride, m.p. 71° ("β-elæostearic acid"). The change from the "α" to the "β"-geometrical isomeride is much more rapid and complete than the "elaidin" reaction of acids with only one ethenoid bond or with two or more isolated ethenoid bonds. It is promoted not only by light, but also by traces of iodine and other substances, and it also probably occurs when the "α"-acid or its esters are heated above 150–200°. Both forms of the acid show characteristic absorption bands in the ultra-violet at 270 mμ, with $E_{1cm}^{1\%}$ 1800–1900.

The configurations of the natural (α)-acid and of the isomeric β-elæostearic acid have, after much earlier discussion, been settled by studies of the infra-red spectra (*a*) of their maleic anhydride adducts (*v. infra*) by Paschke and Wheeler[208a] and (*b*) of the acids themselves by Ahlers *et al.*[75d] and by Bickford, O'Connor, *et al.*[208b] The natural acid has the 9 *cis*, 11 *trans*, 13 *trans* configuration, whilst β-elæostearic acid is the 9 *trans*, 11 *trans*, 13 *trans* isomer.

Oils containing elæostearic glycerides, and the acid itself or its esters, possess the characteristic of "gelation" (i.e., setting to a solid rubber-like mass) when submitted to the action of heat. With a conjugated system of three double bonds, elæostearic acid does not react normally with solutions such as those of Wijs or Hanus, and for this reason it was for a long time considered to be a di-ethylenic acid; but the work of Böeseken, Steger and van Loon, and others[209] on the molecular refractivity of the acids, the amount of hydrogen absorbed in order to effect complete conversion into stearic acid, and on modified methods of iodine absorption, demonstrated clearly that it contains three ethylenic linkages and that these are almost certainly conjugated. These facts, taken in conjunction with Majima's[210a] study of the products of ozonisation of the acid, in which he isolated n-valeric aldehyde, n-valeric acid, and azelaic acid, fully establish the structural formula of the acid, which was further confirmed by Eibner and Rossmann,[210b] who obtained glyoxal in 60 per cent. yield from the ozonide of the acid, but observed no succinic aldehyde.

Morrell and Marks[211a] studied in great detail the decomposition products of the substances formed when elæostearic acid or its esters combine with atmospheric oxygen, and their work incidentally affords further confirmation of the correctness of the structure assigned to the acid. Morrell and Samuels[211b] showed that, in the α-acid, combination with maleic anhydride occurs at the 11th and 14th carbon atoms, whereas in the β-acid the addition takes place at the 9th and 12th carbon atoms (cf. Rinkes[211c]).

Van Loon et al.[212a] (1944) stated that, in catalytic hydrogenation of elæostearic esters, no conjugated dienes were produced during conversion of elæostearates to mono-ethenoid esters, and no saturated ester was produced until practically all triene esters had been hydrogenated to the monoethenoid state. Woltemate and Daubert[212b] (1950) found that the conjugated triene ester disappeared steadily during hydrogenation with some formation of conjugated diene, but Hilditch and Pathak[180c] (1949) and O'Connor et al.[212c] (1953) supported van Loon et al.[212a] in their findings that, for the most part, two molecules of hydrogen are almost simultaneously added to the elæostearate molecule, giving a mixture of mono-ethenoid compounds in which the cis- and trans-octa-11-decenoates very largely predominate. Until all elæostearate is converted into octadecenoates, practically no stearate is formed. Mills[212d] (1957) stated that hydrogenation of tung oil with nickel-kieselguhr catalyst poisoned with sulphur or selenium pursues a different course, e.g., when the elæostearic content was reduced to ten per cent. there were present conjugated diene 30, non-conjugated diene 25, monoene 20 and saturated glycerides 10 per cent.

Complete syntheses of α- and β- elæostearic acids, and of punicic (trichosanic) acid (v. infra) have been carried out by Crombie and Jacklin.[213a]

Other naturally occurring geometrical isomerides of α-elæostearic acid. Punicic acid, m.p. 44°, was first observed by Toyama and Tsuchiya[214a] in pomegranate seed oil in 1935, and its structure as another stereoisomeric form of α-elæostearic acid was confirmed by Farmer and van den Heuvel.[214b] "Trichosanic acid", m.p. 35–35·5°, was similarly observed by Toyama and Tsuchiya[214a] in the seed fat (snake gourd seed oil) of Trichosanthes cucumeroides. Both punicic and trichosanic acids pass by isomerisation into β-elæostearic acid, and, eventually, as a result of infra-red spectroscopic analysis, Ahlers et al. showed[214c] that punicic acid (which formed 72 per cent. of the fatty acids in the pomegranate seed oil they examined) has a cis-trans-cis-configuration (probably cis-9-trans-11-cis-13), and that trichosanic acid and punicic acid are identical.[214d]

Subsequently a variety of geometrically isomeric forms of other conjugated octadeca-trienoic acids (and one conjugated dienoic acid) have been isolated from seed fats of individual species belonging to a number of plant families, largely owing to the investigations of Hopkins and Chisholm. These (with, where known, the approximate percentage of the conjugated acid in the total fatty acids of the seed fats) include those listed at the top of p. 636.

4-Keto-octadeca-9,11,13-trienoic (α-Licanic) acid, $CH_3.[CH_2]_3.[CH:CH]_3.$ $[CH_2]_4.CO.[CH_2]_2.COOH$, is at present unique amongst natural fatty acids in containing a ketonic group. It is present in large amounts in Brazilian oiticica oil (formerly regarded as the seed oil of Couepia grandiflora, but now known (Holdt[215a]) to be that of Licania rigida). It was first reported by Wilborn[215b] in 1931 who, from the supposed source of the fat, termed it couepic

FAMILY	SPECIES	CONJUGATED ACID	PER CENT. (WT.) OF TOTAL FATTY ACIDS
Valerianaceæ	*Centranthus ruber*[214e]	*cis*-9-*trans*-11-*trans*-13*	*ca.* 43
Rosaceæ	*Cotia chestnut*[214e] *(Parinarium* sp.*)*	*cis*-9-*trans*-11-*trans*-13*	*ca.* 23
	Prunus mahaleb[214e]	,,	*ca.* 29
Cucurbitaceæ	*Momordica balsamina*[214e]	*cis*-9-*trans*-11-*cis*-13†	*ca.* 58
	,, *chorantia*[214e]	*cis*-9-*trans*-11-*trans*-13*	?
Bignoniaceæ	*Catalpa ovata*[214f]	*trans*-9-*trans*-11-*cis*-13	?
	,, *speciosa*[214e]	,,	*ca.* 34
	Chilopsis linearis[214g, k]	,,	25
	,, ,, [214g, k]	*trans*-10-*trans*-12 (diene)	12
	Jacaranda chelonia[214e]	*cis*-8-*trans*-10-*cis*-12	*ca.* 31
	,, *mimosifolia*[214h]	,,	?
Compositæ	*Calendula officinalis*[214i, j]	,,	?

* α-Elæostearic.   † α-Punicic.

acid. Under this name it was also examined by van Loon and Steger,[215c] who stated that it melted at 74–75° and considered that it was a geometrical isomeride of α- and β-elæostearic acid. In 1935, however, Brown and Farmer,[216a] and also Kappelmeier,[216b] showed that the acid contained a keto-group, and re-named it licanic acid. Brown and Farmer found that, although complete hydrogenation of licanic acid leads to the production of stearic acid, the first main product of hydrogenation is 4-ketostearic acid (m.p. 96.5°); they established the constitution of the natural (α-) licanic acid by oxidation. Natural or α-licanic acid melts at 74–75° (semicarbazone, m.p. 110–111°), and passes by the action of light in presence of traces of iodine or sulphur into a β-licanic acid,[216a, b] m.p. 99·5° (semi-carbazone, m.p. 138°). The maleic anhydride adducts formed from the licanic acids and corresponding glycerides were studied by Morrell and Davis.[216c] The natural (α-) licanic acid is probably the *cis*-9-*trans*-11-*trans*-13 form of the ketoelæostearic acid, and β-licanic acid the *trans*-*trans*-*trans* form.[208a] A spectrophotometric method for determining licanic acid in presence of elæostearic acid has been given by Mendelowitz and Riley.[216d]

Octadeca-9,11,13,15-tetraenoic (Parinaric) acid, $CH_3.CH_2.[CH:CH]_4.$ $[CH_2]_7.COOH$, m.p. 85–86°, was discovered by Tsujimoto[217a] in 1933 in "akarittom" fat, the seed fat of *Parinarium laurinum*; he named it parinaric acid, stated that it yielded a "β-parinaric" acid, m.p. 95–96°, by the action of light in presence of traces of iodine, and believed that it was a further stereoisomeride of elæostearic acid. Farmer and Sunderland,[217b] however, showed that it contained a conjugated system of four, and not three, double bonds, and proved that its constitution was that given above. Its absorption spectrum is very similar to that of decatetraene (Kaufmann *et al.*[217c]). Catalytic hydrogenation of methyl parinarate (Riley[217d]) proceeds similarly to that of elæostearates: primarily either two or three molecules of hydrogen are added to give non-conjugated octadecadienoates (containing the grouping —CH:CH. $[CH_2]_2.CH:CH—$) and octadecenoates. Only very small amounts of conjugated diene or triene esters were detected, and very little stearate is formed before all the tetraene and diene esters have passed into the monoethenoid octadecenoates. Infra-red spectra show the natural acid to contain either two *cis*- and two *trans*- or one *cis*- and three *trans*-ethenoid groups, whilst β-parinaric acid has the *trans*-*trans*-*trans*-*trans*-structure (Ahlers *et al.*[75d]).

636

At present parinaric acid is the only known instance of a vegetable fat tetra-ethenoid acid. Other species of *Parinarium*, moreover, yield seed fats with elæostearic and linoleic acids (*P. macrophyllum*), or licanic and elæostearic acids (*P. sherbroense*), but contain none of the C_{18} tetraene acid.

Octadeca-9,11,13,15-tetraenoic acid occurs, however, in the seed fats of members of the Balsaminaceæ, where it was first observed by Tutiya[218a] in *Impatiens balsamina*, and later by Kaufmann[218b] in other species of this genus, in some of which it forms from 30–50 per cent. of the seed fatty acids.

The presence of smaller amounts of parinaric acid (accompanied, as in *Impatiens* seed fats, by some acetic acid) has also been reported by Kaufmann[218c] in the seed fats of some *Iris* and *Nymphæa* species, together with smaller proportions of conjugated triene and diene C_{18} acids.

Octadec-17-en-9,11-ynoic (isanic) acid, $CH_2:CH.[CH_2]_4.C:C.C:C.[CH_2]_7.COOH$, is an acid of quite different nature from the others in this section (which it resembles only in its terminal $C.[CH_2]_7.COOH$ group). It contains a (terminal) vinyl group and two adjacent acetylenic bonds. It was first isolated from the seed fat of *Onguekoa gore* by Hébert (1902), who named it isanic acid, and was studied in detail by Steger and van Loon[219a] in 1937. In the same year Boekenoogen[219b] showed that it possessed a terminal ethenoid group and yielded ethyl hydrogen azelate, oxalic and adipic acids on oxidative scission, results confirmed in 1939 by Castille,[219c] who termed it "erythrogenic" acid. Steger and van Loon (1940), supported by Doucet and Fauve,[219d] considered that the acid (which melts at 39°) has the 17-en-9,11-ynoic structure, a conclusion which was confirmed in 1953 by synthesis of the acid by Black and Weedon.[111]

A **hydroxy-isanic acid,** $C_{18}H_{26}O_3$, which is probably the major component of *Onguekoa* seed fat (and much exceeds the amount of isanic acid present) was shown by Riley[161a] to have the hydroxy-group attached to the 8th carbon atom in the C_{18} chain. Kaufmann *et al.*[161b] termed this acid isanolic acid (*cf.* p. 618). Both the *cis*-11-en- and *trans*-11-en- forms of 8-hydroxy-11-en-9-ynoic (isanolic) acid have been synthesised by Crombie and Griffin.[213c]

Analogues of isanic and isanolic acids, possibly octadec-*cis*-13-en-9,11-diynoic ("bolekic") and the 8-hydroxy-derivative of the latter, are present to a very minor extent in *Onguekoa* seed fat.[213d]

Ximenynic acid, $C_{18}H_{30}O_2$, isolated by Ligthelm and Schwartz[220a] from the seed fat of *Ximenia caffra*, melts at 40–41°, and contains one (*trans*-) ethenoid and one ethynoid group. It is octadec-11-en-9-ynoic acid, as is also "santalbic acid" in the seed fats of *Santalum album* (Gunstone and McGee[220b]) and of other *Santalum* species (Hatt and Szumer[220c]). The acid has been synthesised by Grigor *et al.*,[220d] and also by Crombie and Jacklin.[213b] Its 11-ethenoid bond was shown by infra-red study (Ahlers and Ligthelm[220e]) to have the *trans*-configuration; on oxidation with performic acid it yields 11,12-dihydroxy-octadec-9-ynoic acid, m.p. 88–89°.

An 8-hydroxy-octadec-11-en-9-ynoic acid is also present in *Ximenia caffra* seed fat[220f] (see p. 619).

Tri-, tetra-, penta-, hexa-ethenoid acids
(often containing the structure $=CH.[CH_2]_2.COOH$)

So far as fats from aquatic sources are concerned, a fundamental difference in their polyethenoid acids is that the latter belong to the C_{16}, C_{18}, C_{20}, C_{22}, and C_{24} series and not, as in most vegetable fats, only to the C_{18} series. C_{16}, C_{18}, and C_{24} polyethenoid acids are, however, not very abundant in marine animal fats, whereas those of the C_{20} and C_{22} series frequently form a considerable proportion (e.g. 30–40 per cent.) of the total acids of a marine fatty oil. These highly unsaturated acids were first reported in 1906, under the name of "clupanodonic acid", by Tsujimoto,[221] who at that time believed it to be an acid of the C_{18} series but, in 1920, noted that its formula was $C_{22}H_{34}O_2$ (docosapentaenoic). In the meantime it had become recognised that unsaturated acids of both the C_{20} and the C_{22} series were commonly present in fish oils and that possibly, in each series, acids ranging from tri- to hexaethenoid might be present.

Similar acids, notably arachidonic (eicosatetraenoic), $C_{20}H_{32}O_2$, have also been recognised as present in the liver and other organ fats, and sometimes in traces in the depot fats, of land animals such as the ox and pig. Arachidonic acid is of great interest because of the role which it appears to play as a fatty acid essential to the growth and development of young animals; linoleic acid, which was originally considered to be most essential in this respect, is now believed to possess main importance as a raw material from which arachidonic acid is produced in the animal organism by a process of "chain extension" (cf. Chapter III, p. 95; Chapter VIII, p. 571; Smedley-MacLean et al.,[222a, b] Reiser et al.,[222c] Mead et al.[222d]).

J. B. Brown and co-workers[223a] observed about 0·4 per cent. of arachidonic in pig depot fats (1930) and beef fats (1934), and larger amounts in ox brain lipids (1931) and in ox adrenal phosphatides (1934); from the latter source they obtained methyl arachidonate in 90–95 per cent. purity in 1940 by low-temperature crystallisation from acetone coupled with ester-fractionation.[223b] Mowry, Brode and Brown (1942)[223c] showed by ultra-violet spectrophotometry that conjugated unsaturation was not present in arachidonic acid, but that after alkali-isomerisation it develops the absorption bands characteristic for conjugated polyene acids. These workers, and also Smedley-MacLean et al.[222b] proved from the products of ozonolysis that the acid from adrenal phosphatides is eicosa-5,8,11,14-tetraenoic acid.

Eicosa-5,8,11,14-tetraenoic (arachidonic) acid has been synthesised from acetylenic intermediates by the modern methods (cf. pp. 605–607) by Osbond and Wickers,[191a] Rachlin et al.,[191c] and Gensler et al.[191d]

Brown at first believed that the polyethenoid acids of all land animal fats were confined to this single form; but other workers suggested that both C_{20} and C_{22} acids may be present in these land animal fats (Hilditch, Lea and Pedelty,[130b] pig depot fats; Riemenschneider, Ellis and Titus,[224a] egg yolk fats). Later (1948, 1951) the use of low-temperature crystallisation in the separation of polyethenoid acids from beef adrenal or suprarenal lipids was supplemented by adsorption of appropriate crystallised concentrates of the methyl esters of such acids on silicic acid or alumina columns (White and Brown,[224b] Riemenschneider et al.[224c]), with the result that other acids, such as eicosapentaenoic and dodosapentaenoic, have been shown to be present in addition to eicosatetraenoic (arachidonic) acid.

A list of the sources and constitutions of many of the polyethenoid acids (including arachidonic) which have been isolated from land animals is included in Table 145.

Considerable uncertainty has attached to the structures of polyethenoid acids (especially of the C_{20} and C_{22} series) present in lipids of marine animals, although it has long been known that they are derived from the normal or

straight-chain aliphatic acids. When hydrogenated, they furnish respectively
n-eicosanoic (arachidic) and n-docosanoic (behenic) acids,[133] the straight-
chain structure of these products having been verified by X-ray analysis
(Morgan and Holmes[30b]). The absence of any conjugated double bonds in
polyethenoid C_{20} and C_{22} marine animal fatty acids was indicated in 1936 by
Morrell and Davies,[225a] who found that neither the acids nor their esters gave
adducts with maleic anhydride; this has since of course been fully confirmed
by ultra-violet spectrophotometric evidence.

In many of the earlier studies (usually by ozonolysis) of the constitution of
polyethenoid acids and esters, the latter had usually been isolated or purified
at one stage or another by processes of fractional distillation under reduced
pressure, which involved somewhat lengthy exposure to temperatures of 200°
and above. It has since become evident that isomerisation and/or polymerisation of these highly unsaturated compounds may result by any prolonged
exposure to high temperature (Farmer and van den Heuvel[225b]), and still more
so during hydrolysis of the oils from which they are isolated with hot alcoholic
alkali solution (Edisbury et al.,[225c] Burr et al.[225d]). This probably accounts for
different structures sometimes being assigned by different workers to what is
apparently the same polyethenoid acid. Since about 1945–1950, the use of
methanolysis for conversion of glycerides to methyl esters, the separation of
individual polyenoic acids by adsorption methods or by counter-current
distribution between immiscible solvents and, latterly, the use of gas–liquid
chromatography in the separation of esters by distillation, has eliminated
methods which are suspect of inducing isomeric or other changes in the polyene
systems, and the structures arrived at by oxidation of the compounds so
isolated appear to be more consistent.

In 1928 Tsujimoto[226a] obtained, on ozonisation of a "clupanodonic" acid
($C_{22}H_{34}O_2$) fraction isolated from Japanese sardine oil, succinic acid (COOH .
$[CH_2]_2$. COOH) in amount up to 49 per cent. of the weight of clupanodonic
acid oxidised; this corresponds with nearly two —$CH:CH$. $[CH_2]_2$. $CH:CH$—
groups per molecule of the acid. As shown in Table 145, the structures assigned
by several Japanese workers in the period 1935–1942 to various polyethenoid
acids include one or more of these groups. Farmer and van den Heuvel[225b]
avoided exposure to temperatures higher than 120° for more than two minutes
when they separated the methyl esters of cod liver oil unsaturated acids by
repeated passage through a molecular still. They obtained a series of homologous esters with average numbers of ethenoid linkings per molecule: C_{16} 1·3,
C_{18} 2·7, C_{20} 4·9 and C_{22} 6. From the oxidation products of the docosahexaenoic
acid $C_{22}H_{32}O_2$ they deduced the presence of four : $CH.CH_2.CH$: groups
and one : $CH.[CH_2]_2.CH$: group between the terminal groups $CH_3.CH$: and
: $CH.[CH_2]_2.COOH$. It is significant, however, that in practically all the more
recent studies, in which polyethenoid acids of the C_{16}, C_{18}, C_{20} and C_{22} series
have been isolated by the modern techniques which avoid possible alteration
due to excessive heating with alkali, or to prolonged exposure to high temperatures in distillation, no evidence has been obtained for the presence of any
unsaturated system other than repetition of the "pentadiene", "allylic" or

TABLE 145. Structural formulæ assigned to natural polyethenoid acids of the C_{16}, C_{18}, C_{20}, C_{22} and C_{26} series

ACIDS	ETHENOID STRUCTURE	SOURCE	OBSERVERS	DATE
C_{16} Hexadeca-poly-enoic				
Dienoic	6,9	Menhaden oil	Stoffel and Ahrens[226c]	1958
	,, 7,10	Herring oil	Klenk and Steinbach[228g]	1959
	9,12	Herring oil	Klenk and Steinbach[228g]	1959
	,,	Menhaden oil	Stoffel and Ahrens[226c]	1958
		Herring oil	Klenk and Steinbach[228g]	1959
Trienoic	4,7,10	Herring oil	Klenk and Steinbach[228g]	1959
	6,9,12	Menhaden oil	Stoffel and Ahrens[226c]	1958
	(?) 6,10,14 (Hiragonic)	Herring oil	Klenk and Steinbach[228g]	1959
	7,10,13	Sardine oil	Toyama and Tsuchiya[227a]	1935
	,,	Menhaden oil	Stoffel and Ahrens[226c]	1958
	9,12,15	Rape leaf oil	Shorland[192c]	1945
	,,	Herring oil	Klenk and Steinbach[228g]	1959
Tetraenoic	4,7,10,13	Menhaden oil	Stoffel and Ahrens[226c]	1958
	,,	Herring oil	Klenk and Steinbach[228g]	1959
	(?) 4,8,10,14	*Scenedesmus obliquus* (Alga)	Klenk and Knipprath[228h]	1959
	6,9,12,15	Sardine oil	Tutiya[218a]	1940
	,,	South African pilchard oil	Silk and Hahn[229b]	1954
	,,	Menhaden oil	Stoffel and Ahrens[226c]	1958
		Herring oil	Klenk and Steinbach[228g]	1959
C_{18} Octadeca-poly-enoic				
Dienoic	6,9	Menhaden oil	Stoffel and Ahrens[226c]	1960
	9,12 (Linoleic)	Herring oil	Klenk and Brockerhoff[228e]	1958
	,,	Menhaden oil	Stoffel and Ahrens[226c]	1960
Trienoic	6,9,12	Menhaden oil	Stoffel and Ahrens[226c]	1960
	9,12,15 (Linolenic)	Herring oil	Klenk and Brockerhoff[228e]	1958
	,,	Menhaden oil	Stoffel and Ahrens[226c]	1960
Tetraenoic	(?) 4,8,12,15 (Moroctic)	Sardine oil	Toyama and Tsuchiya[227a]	1935
	6,9,12,15	Herring oil	Klenk and Brockerhoff[228d]	1957
	,,	Menhaden oil	Stoffel and Ahrens[226c]	1960

C₂₀ *Elcosa-poly-enoic*

Dienoic

Position	Source	Author	Year
8,11	Ox liver phosphatides	Klenk and Montag[228k]	1957
" 11,14	Menhaden oil	Stoffel and Ahrens[226c]	1960
"	Carcharodon sp. (shark)	Baudart[230]	1942
"	Ox brain phosphatides	Klenk and Bongard[228a]	1952
"	Herring oil	Klenk and Bricker-Voigt[228j]	1961

Trienoic

Position	Source	Author	Year
5,8,11	Ox brain phosphatides	Klenk and Bongard[228a]	1952
"	Menhaden oil	Stoffel and Ahrens[226c]	1960
8,11,14	Bovine adrenals	Klenk and Eberhagen[228c]	1961
"	Carcharodon sp. (shark)	Baudart[230]	1942
"	Rat tissues	Mead and Slatan[229c]	1956
"	Ox liver phosphatides	Klenk and Montag[228k]	1957
"	Menhaden oil	Stoffel and Ahrens[226c]	1960
"	Bovine adrenals	Klenk and Eberhagen[228i]	1961
11,14,17	Herring oil	Klenk and Bricker-Voigt[228j]	1961
"	Herring oil	Klenk and Bricker-Voigt[228j]	1961

Tetraenoic

Position	Source	Author	Year
(?) 4,8,12,16	Sardine oil	Toyama and Tsuchiya[227a]	1935
5,8,11,14 (Arachidonic)	Sardine oil	Toyama et al.[227b]	1959
"	Ox brain, and adrenal phosphatides	Mowry, Brode and Brown,[223c] Smedley-MacLean et al.[222b]	1941 1940–43
"	Ox brain phosphatides	Klenk and Bongard[228a]	1952
"	Cod liver oil	Klenk and Eberhagen[228c]	1957
"	Menhaden oil	Stoffel and Ahrens[226c]	1960
8,11,14,17	Herring oil	Klenk and Bricker-Voigt[228j]	1961
"	Menhaden oil	Stoffel and Ahrens[226c]	1960
"	Herring oil	Klenk and Bricker-Voigt[228j]	1961

Pentaenoic

Position	Source	Author	Year
(?) 4,8,12,15,18	Sardine, bonito oil	Toyama and Tsuchiya[227a]	1935
5,8,11,14,17	South African pilchard oil	Whitcutt and Sutton[229d]	1956
"	Ox liver phosphatides	Klenk and Montag[228k]	1957
"	Cod liver oil	Klenk and Eberhagen[228c]	1957
"	Heart muscle	Hörhammer et al.[229f]	1959
"	Menhaden oil	Stoffel and Ahrens[226c]	1960
"	Bovine adrenals	Klenk and Eberhagen[228i]	1961
"	Herring oil	Klenk and Bricker-Voigt[228j]	1961

TABLE 145. *Structural formulæ assigned to natural polyethenoid acids of the* C_{16}, C_{18}, C_{20}, C_{22} *and* C_{26} *series—continued*

ACIDS	ETHENOID STRUCTURE	SOURCE	OBSERVERS	DATE
C_{22} Docosa-poly-enoic				
Trienoic	7,10,13	Ox brain phosphatides	Klenk and Bongard[228a]	1952
Tetraenoic	4,7,10,13	Ox brain phosphatides	Klenk and Bongard[228a]	1952
	7,10,13,16	Ox brain phosphatides	Klenk and Bongard[228a]	1952
	,,	Bovine adrenals	Klenk and Eberhagen[228i]	1961
Pentaenoic	(?) 4,8,11,15,19 (Clupanodonic)	Sardine oil	Tsujimoto[226a]	1928
	(?) 4,8,12,15,19 ,,	Sardine oil	Toyama and Tsuchiya[227a]	1935
	(?) 4,7,11,15,19 ,,	Sardine oil	Toyama and Tsuchiya[227a]	1935
	4,7,10,13,16	Mackerel pike oil	Toyama et al.[227a]	1959
	,,	Ox brain phosphatides	Klenk and Bongard[228a]	1952
	7,10,13,16,19	Ox brain phosphatides	Klenk, Bongard[228a], Lindlar[228b]	1952, 1955
	,,	Herring oil	Klenk and Brockerhoff[228e]	1958
	,,	Menhaden oil	Stoffel and Ahrens[226c]	1960
	,,	Bovine adrenals	Klenk and Eberhagen[228i]	1961
Hexaenoic	(?) 4,8,12,15,18,21 (Clupanodonic)	Sardine, bonito oils	Toyama and Tsuchiya[227a]	1935
	or (?) 4,7,11,14,17,20 ,,	Sardine, bonito oils	Toyama et al.[227b]	1959
	4,7,10,13,16,19 ,,	Ox brain phosphatides	Klenk, Bongard[228a], Lindlar[228b]	1952, 1955
	,,	Hog brain lipids	Hammond and Lundberg[229a]	1953
	,,	South African pilchard oil	Whitcutt[229e]	1957
	,,	Ox liver phosphatides	Klenk and Tomuschat[228f]	1957
	,,	Cod liver oil	Klenk and Brockerhoff[228e]	1958
	,,	Herring oil	Klenk and Brockerhoff[228e]	1958
	,,	Menhaden oil	Stoffel and Ahrens[226c]	1960
C_{26} Hexacosadienoic	17,20	Sponges	Bergmann and Swift[192b]	1951

"methylene-interrupted" grouping —CH:CH.CH$_2$.CH:CH— (*cf.* Klenk,[226b] Stoffel and Ahrens[226c]).

The structures assigned to a number of natural polyethenoid acids by various workers are listed in Table 145 (p. 640). The data are probably not exhaustive, but will at all events indicate the present state of knowledge of these compounds. The dates at which the studies were published are included; it will be borne in mind that, for the reasons given above, information given since about 1945–1950 is the more likely to be correct (where there is any discrepancy between this and the results of earlier work).

The data in Table 145 make very clear the fundamental dissimilarity between polyethenoid fatty acids which we have been discussing and polyethenoid acids occurring in the vegetable kingdom (seed fats) or, for that matter, oleic and hexadecenoic acids themselves. The grouping :CH.CH$_2$.CH: (characteristic of linoleic and linolenic acids) indeed occurs also, and repeatedly, in the polyethenoid marine animal fatty acids, but the end-grouping :CH.[CH$_2$]$_7$.COOH is absent; whereas nearly all polyethenoid vegetable acids yet known contain the latter end-group (as also oleic and hexadecenoic acids).

If, for once, we number the double bonds in these acids with the *terminal methyl* group as number 1 instead of the *terminal carboxyl* group (as in the Geneva nomenclature), it is interesting to see that many of the acids have the first ethenoid bond either at the 3rd, 6th, or 9th carbon atom from the terminal methyl group; this was pointed out by Klenk[192d] and by Thomasson,[192e] who further noted that growth-promoting action of a polyethenoid acid appears to be dependent on the presence of the groupings CH$_3$.[CH$_2$]$_4$.CH:CH.CH$_2$.CH:CH—, or CH$_3$.CH$_2$.CH:CH.CH$_2$.CH:CH—.

Polyethenoid (and polyethynoid) acids not falling within the above groups

It will have been seen that the great majority of natural polyethenoid fatty acids conform to one or other of the preceding general types, which are characterised by commencement of unsaturation either (*a*) at the 9th carbon atom of the chain =CH.[CH$_2$]$_7$.COOH, or (*b*) at the 4th (or 5th) carbon atom =CH.[CH$_2$]$_2$.COOH (or =CH.[CH$_2$]$_3$.COOH). The first type (*a*) is found predominantly in vegetable fats, and type (*b*) in animal fats and, especially, fats of aquatic origin (animal or vegetable). There remain a very few conjugated polyethenoid acids which do not fall in either group.

Deca-2,4-dienoic acid, CH$_3$.[CH$_2$]$_4$.[CH:CH]$_2$.COOH, occurs in the seed fats of *Sapium* species (*cf.* Chapter IV, p. 250) to the extent of about 5 per cent. by weight, or about 8 molecules out of every 100 molecules, of their mixed fatty acids. The presence of an acid with a characteristic absorption band at about 260 mμ was first noted in these seed oils by Potts,[231a] and the acid was later isolated and its constitution established by Devine[231b] and by Crossley and Hilditch.[231c] Deca-2,4-dienoic acid is a liquid extremely susceptible to autoxidation in presence of traces of oxygen. On disruptive oxidation (of the methyl ester) it gives *n*-hexanoic acid, and on complete hydrogenation *n*-decanoic acid. Crossley and Hilditch[231c] found that the semi-hydrogenated methyl ester consisted mainly of methyl dec-3-enoate, accompanied by smaller proportions of methyl dec-2-enoate and dec-4-enoate, and of still less methyl decanoate. They[231d] also observed that, on heating with alkali, the conjugated system tends to move away as a whole from the carboxyl group and, concurrently, the ultra-violet absorption shifts towards the usual band-head at 234 mμ characteristic of an isolated conjugated diene system.

The four geometrically isomeric forms have been synthesised (starting from 2-octynal, $CH_3.[CH_2]_4.C\vdots C.CHO$, and bromoacetic ester) by Crombie,[232a] who showed that the natural acid is deca-*trans*-2-*cis*-4-dienoic acid. Subsequently the four geometrically isomeric hexadeca-2,4-dienoic acids were synthesised by Wailes.[232b]

In the seed fat of the related *Sebastiana lingustrina* Hanks and Potts[231e] have found similar proportions of a conjugated diene C_{12} acid, which was shown by Holman and Hanks[231f] to be **dodeca-2,4-dienoic acid, $CH_3.[CH_2]_6.[CH\vdots CH]_2.COOH$.**

Reference should also be made here to the interesting series of **methyl esters of unsaturated C_{10} acids containing conjugated systems of ethylenic and acetylenic groups** which (although not, of course, lipid in nature) have been observed by Sörensen[233] and co-workers in the flowers of several species of the family Compositæ. Esters of the following structures have been discovered (*cf.* Chapter IV, p. 186):

$$C_{11}H_{16}O_2 \quad CH_3.[CH_2]_4.CH:C:C:CH.COOCH_3$$
$$C_{11}H_{12}O_2 \quad CH_3.[CH_2]_2.C\vdots C.C\vdots C.CH:CH.COOCH_3$$
$$C_{11}H_{10}O_2 \quad CH_3.CH:CH.C\vdots C.C\vdots C.CH:CH.COOCH_3$$
$$C_{11}H_8O_2 \quad (?)CH_3.C\vdots C.C\vdots C.C\vdots C.CH:CH.COOCH_3$$

References to Chapter IX

1. E. Linnemann, *Ann.*, 1872, **161**, 175; A. Lieben and A. Rossi, *ibid.*, 1871, **159**, 58, 70; A. Lieben and G. Janecek, *ibid.*, 1877, **187**, 126.

2. A. W. Hofmann, *Ber.*, 1881, **14**, 2725.

3. F. Krafft, *Ber.*, 1879, **12**, 1664.

4. F. Jourdan, *Ann.*, 1879, **200**, 101.

5. P. A. Levene and F. A. Taylor, *J. Biol. Chem.*, 1924, **59**, 905.

6. *Cf.* P. A. Levene and L. H. Cretcher, *J. Biol. Chem.*, 1918, **33**, 505, and P. A. Levene and F. A. Taylor, *ibid.*, 1922, **52**, 227.

7. (*a*) R. Kuhn, C. Grundmann and H. Trischmann, *Z. physiol. Chem.*, 1937, **248**, IV; C. Grundmann, *Ber.*, 1948, **81**, 510; (*b*) F. G. Fischer, K. Hultzsch and W. Flaig, *Ber.*, 1937, **70**, B, 370; (*c*) J. Schmidt and A. Obermeit, *Ann.*, 1941, **547**, 285; (*d*) R. Kuhn, *J. Chem. Soc.*, 1938, 605.

8. (*a*) H. Gilman and J. F. Nelson, *Rec. trav. chim.*, 1936, **55**, 518; J. Cason, *J. Amer. Chem. Soc.*, 1946, **68**, 2078; M. D. Soffer, N. S. Strauss, M. D. Trail and K. W. Sherk, *J. Amer. Chem. Soc.*, 1947, **69**, 1684; R. G. Jones, *J. Amer. Chem. Soc.*, 1947, **69**, 2350; (*b*) H. A. Schuette, A. O. Maylott and D. A. Roth, *J. Amer. Oil Chem. Soc.*, 1948, **25**, 64; N. L. Drake and S. Melamed, *J. Amer. Chem. Soc.*, 1948, **70**, 364.

9. G. M. and R. Robinson, (*a*) *J. Chem. Soc.*, 1925, **127**, 175; 1926, 2204; 1930, 745; (*b*) 1934, 1543; R. Ashton, R. Robinson and J. C. Smith, *J. Chem. Soc.*, 1936, 283; (*c*) F. Francis, A. M. King and J. A. V. Willis, *J. Chem. Soc.*, 1937, 999; (*d*) S. Ställberg-Stenhagen and E. Stenhagen, *Arkiv. Kemi, Min., Geol.*, 1945, **19**, A, No. 1; **20**, A, Nos. 17, 19; and later papers.

10. (*a*) W. Bleyburg and H. Ulrich, *Ber.*, 1931, **64**, 2504; F. Francis, S. H. Piper and T. Malkin, *Proc. Roy. Soc.*, 1930, A, **128**, 214; F. Francis, F. J. E. Collins and S. H. Piper, *ibid.*, 1937, A, **158**, 691; see also ref. 9 (*c*); (*b*) D. E. Ames, R. E. Bowman and R. G. Mason, *J. Chem. Soc.*, 1950, 174; R. E. Bowman and R. G. Mason, *ibid.*, 1951, 2748.

11. H. Kolbe, *Ann.*, 1849, **69**, 257; A. Crum Brown and J. Walker, *ibid.*, 1891, **261**, 107.

12. W. S. Greaves, R. P. Linstead, B. R. Shephard, S. L. S. Thomas and B. C. L. Weedon, *J. Chem. Soc.*, 1950, 3326.

13. (*a*) A. Müller and G. Shearer, *J. Chem. Soc.*, 1923, **123**, 2043, 3156; (*b*) S. H. Piper, T. Malkin and H. E. Austin, *J. Chem. Soc.*, 1926, 2310.

14. A. C. Chibnall, S. H. Piper, A. Pollard, E. F. Williams and P. N. Sahai, *Biochem. J.*, 1934, **28**, 2175, 2189, 2209.

15. R. G. Sinclair, A. F. McKay and R. N. Jones, *J. Amer. Chem. Soc.*, 1952, **74**, 2570.
16. M. E. Chevreul, "Recherches sur les corps gras", 1823, p. 115.
17. (*a*) J. U. Lerch, *Ann.*, 1844, **49**, 212; (*b*) H. Fehling, *Ann.*, 1845, **53**, 399.
18. (*a*) T. Marsson, *Ann.*, 1842, **41**, 329; (*b*) A. Görgey, *Ann.*, 1848, **66**, 290.
19. L. Playfair, *Ann.*, 1841, **37**, 152.
20. E. Frémy, *Ann.*, 1840, **36**, 44.
21. Gössmann, *Ann.*, 1854, **89**, 1.
22. A. Voelcker, *Ann.*, 1848, **64**, 342.
23. (*a*) C. Hell and O. Hermanns, *Ber.*, 1880, **13**, 1713; (*b*) P. Kreiling, *Ber.*, 1888, **21**, 880.
24. B. C. Brodie, *Ann.*, 1848, **67**, 180.
25. (*a*) A. Klein and M. Stigol, *Pharm. Zentr.*, 1930, **71**, 497; (*b*) A. H. Gill and C. M. Tucker, *Oil and Fat Ind.*, 1930, **7**, 101.
26. (*a*) A. Heiduschka and A. Steinrück, *J. pr. Chem.*, 1921, (ii), **102**, 241; (*b*) A. Bömer and H. Merten, *Z. Unters Nahr. Genussm.*, 1922, **43**, 101.
27. (*a*) H. Meyer and R. Beer, *Monatsh.*, 1912, **33**, 311; (*b*) P. E. Verkade and J. Coops, *Biochem. Z.*, 1929, **206**, 468.
28. H. A. Schuette and H. A. Vogel, *Oil and Soap*, 1939, **16**, 16.
29. R. Ehrenstein and H. Stuewer, *J. pr. Chem.*, 1923, (ii), **105**, 199.
30. (*a*) G. T. Morgan and E. Holmes, *J. Soc. Chem. Ind.*, 1928, **47**, 309т; (*b*) *ibid.*, 1925, **44**, 219т.
31. E. Jantzen and C. Tiedcke, *J. pr. Chem.*, 1930, (ii), **127**, 277.
32. A. W. Weitkamp, A. M. Smilianio and S. Rothman, *J. Amer. Chem. Soc.*, 1947, **69**, 1936.
33. (*a*) R. P. Hansen, F. B. Shorland and N. J. Cooke, *J. Sci. Food Agric.*, 1957, **8**, 331; Nature, 1955, **176**, 882; *Biochem. J.*, 1957, **65**, 18; (*b*) M. J. Chisholm and C. Y. Hopkins, *Canad. J. Chem.*, 1957, **35**, 1434; (*c*) R. P. Hansen, F. B. Shorland *et al.*, *Biochem. J.*, 1951, **50**, 207, 358; *ibid.*, 1955, **61**, 702; *Chem. and Ind.*, 1955, 92; *J. Dairy Res.*, 1959, **26**, 190; *Nature*, 1957, **179**, 98.
34. (*a*) L. Darmstädter and J. Lifschütz, *Ber.*, 1895, **28**, 3133; 1896, **29**, 618, 1474, 2890; 1898, **31**, 97, 1122; (*b*) E. E. U. Abraham and T. P. Hilditch, *J. Soc. Chem. Ind.*, 1935, **54**, 398т.
35. A. W. Weitkamp, *J. Amer. Chem. Soc.*, 1945, **67**, 447; *see also*, S. F. Velick, *ibid.*, 1947, **69**, 2317.
36. E. Stenhagen and co-workers, *Ark. Kemi, Min., Geol.*, 1945, **19**, A, Nos. 8, 28; 1948, **26**, A, No. 19.
37. (*a*) F. W. Hougen, D. Ilse, D. A. Sutton and J. P. de Villiers, *J. Chem. Soc.*, 1953, 98; (*b*) S. F. Velick and J. English, *J. Biol. Chem.*, 1945, **160**, 473; (*c*) D. H. S. Horn, F. W. Hougen, E. van Rudloff and D. A. Sutton, *J. Chem. Soc.*, 1954, 177; D. H. S. Horn and (Miss) Y. Y. Pretorius, *ibid.*, 1954, 1460; *Chem. and Ind.*, 1956, R27; (*d*) D. T. Downing, Z. H. Kranz and K. E. Murray, *Austral. J. Chem.*, 1960, **13**, 80. *See also* J. R. Nunn, *J. Chem. Soc.*, 1951, 1740; A. H. Milburn and E. V. Truter, *ibid.*, 1954, 3344.
38. (*a*) E. V. Truter, *Chem. Soc. Quart. Reviews*, 1951, **5**, 390; (*b*) H. W. Knol, *J. Amer. Oil Chem. Soc.*, 1954, **31**, 59.
39. (*a*) R. P. Hansen, F. B. Shorland and N. J. Cooke, *Biochem. J.*, 1951, **50**, 207, 358, 581; 1952, **52**, 203; 1953, **53**, 374; 1953, **55**, 662; 1954, **57**, 297; 1954, **58**, 358; 1955, **59**, 350; *Chem. and Ind.*, 1953, 516; 1954, 1229; *Nature*, 1954, **174**, 39, 603; *Biochem. J.*, 1955, **61**, 141, 547, 702; 1956, **64**, 214; *Chem. and Ind.*, 1956, 1149; *J. Sci. Food Agric.*, 1957, **8**, 331; *Dairy Sci. Absts.*, 1957, **19**, 168; (*b*) S. F. Herb, P. Magidman, F. E. Luddy and R. W. Riemenschneider, *J. Amer. Oil Chem. Soc.*, 1962, **39**, 137, 142; (*c*) *cf.*, e.g., R. Cavanna, *Act. Chem. Scand.*, 1956, **10**, 1527; L. Crombie, M. Manzour-I-Khuda and R. J. D. Smith, *J. Chem. Soc.*, 1957, 479; G. Ställberg, *Arkiv Kemi*, 1958, **12**, 153; G. I. Nikishin, Y. N. Ogibin and A. D. Petrov, *Zhur. Obshchei Khim.*, 1960, **30**, 3543; (*d*) W. Sonnevald, P. H. Begemann *et al.*, *J. Lipid Research*, 1962, **3**, 351.

40. R. J. Anderson, *et al.*, *J. Biol. Chem.*, 1929, **85**, 77; 1933, **101**, 499; 1936, **112**, 759; **113**, 637; **114**, 431; 1937, **121**, 649, 669; etc.

41. R. J. Anderson and E. Chargaff, *J. Biol. Chem.*, 1929, **85**, 77.

42. M. A. Spielman, *J. Biol. Chem.*, 1934, **106**, 87.

43. (*a*) F. S. Prout, J. Cason and A. W. Ingersol, *J. Amer. Chem. Soc.*, 1948, **70**, 298; (*b*) S. Ställberg-Stenhagen, *Ark. Kemi, Min., Geol.*, 1948, **26**, A, No. 12; (*c*) R. P. Linstead, J. C. Lunt and B. C. L. Weedon, *J. Chem. Soc.*, 1950, 3331; 1951, 1130; (*d*) M. Sy, Buu-Hoï and D. Xuong, *Compt. rend.*, 1954, **239**, 1813; (*e*) S. Hünig and M. Salzwedel, *Angew. Chem.*, 1959, **71**, 339.

44. (*a*) S. F. Velick and R. J. Anderson, *J. Biol. Chem.*, 1944, **152**, 523, 533; S. F. Velick, *ibid.*, 1944, **156**, 101; L. G. Ginger, *ibid.*, 1944, **156**, 443; (*b*) K. Hofmann and F. Tausig, *J. Biol. Chem.*, 1955, **213**, 425.

45. (*a*) N. Polgar, *Chem. and Ind.*, 1953, 353; *J. Chem. Soc.*, 1954, 1011; (*b*) N. Polgar and W. Smith, *Chem. and Ind.*, 1961, 1958; (*c*) *idem*, *ibid.*, 1961, 1959; (*d*) N. Polgar *et al.*, *Chem. and Ind.*, 1956, 22; *J. Chem. Soc.*, 1956, 2036; 1956, 1620; 1957, 2931, 2934; 1960, 2802; 1962, 4262; (*e*) C. and J. Asselineau, S. Ställberg-Stenhagen and E. Stenhagen, *Acta. Chem. Scand.*, 1959, **13**, 822; (*f*) *idem*, *ibid.*, 1956, **10**, 478, 1035; *Arkiv Kemi*, 1959, **13**, 543.

46. (*a*) R. J. Anderson and M. A. Spielman, *J. Biol. Chem.*, 1936, **112**, 759; 1944, **156**, 453; 1945, **157**, 203; (*b*) T. Wagner-Jauregg, *Z. physiol. Chem.*, 1937, **247**, 135; (*c*) C. V. Wilson, *J. Amer. Chem. Soc.*, 1945, **67**, 2161.

47. (*a*) J. Cason and D. J. McLeod, *J. Org. Chem.*, 1958, **23**, 1497; (*b*) C. L. Agre and J. Cason, *J. Biol. Chem.*, 1959, **234**, 2555; (*c*) J. Cason and M. J. Kalm, *J. Org. Chem.*, 1954, **19**, 1836, 1947; 1957, **22**, 1284.

48. N. Polgar and (Sir) R. Robinson, (*a*) *J. Chem. Soc.*, 1945, 389; (*b*) with S. David, *ibid.*, 1949, 1541; (*c*) *Chem. and Ind.*, 1951, 685; *J. Chem. Soc.*, 1954, 1008; (*d*) with A. S. Bailey, *ibid.*, 1953, 3031; with D. J. Millin, *ibid.*, 1958, 1902.

49. R. P. Linstead, B. R. Shephard and B. C. L. Weedon, *J. Chem. Soc.*, 1953, 1538.

50. R. E. Bowman, *Ann. Repts. Pure Chem.*, 1949, **46**, pp. 158–168.

51. (*a*) J. Asselineau, *Compt. rend.*, 1949, **229**, 791; 1950, **230**, 1620; J. Asselineau, E. Lederer, *et al.*, *Compt. rend.*, 1949, **228**, 1892; 1950, **230**, 142, 877; 1951, **232**, 2050; *Biochem. Biophys. Acta.*, 1950, **5**, 197; 1951, **7**, 126; 1954, **14**, 246; *Bull. Soc. Chim. Biol.*, 1953, **35**, 661; *Bull. Soc. Chim.*, 1953, [v], **21**, 335, 427; 1954, [v], **22**, 79; 1955, 212, 937, 1232; 1960, 135; (*b*) E. Lederer and J. Pudles, *Bull. Soc. Chim. Biol.*, 1951, **33**, 1003; 1954, **36**, 759; *Biochem. Biophys. Acta.*, 1953, **11**, 163, 602; *Bull. Soc. Chim.*, 1954, 919; M. Gastambide-Odier and E. Lederer, *Nature*, 1959, **184**, 1563; *Biochem. Z.*, 1960, **333**, 285.

52. (*a*) A. Lapworth and (Mrs.) L. Pearson, *Food Investigation Board Report*, (London), 1921, p. 30; 1922, p. 44; A. Lapworth, (Mrs.) L. Pearson and E. N. Mottram, *Biochem. J.*, 1925, **19**, 17; (*b*) C. W. Moore, *J. Soc. Chem. Ind.*, 1919, **38**, 320т; E. F. Armstrong and T. P. Hilditch, *ibid.*, 1925, **44**, 43т; (*c*) P. H. Begemann, J. G. Keppler and H. A. Boekenoogen, *Rec. trav. chim.*, 1950, **69**, 439.

53. S. H. Bertram, *Rec. trav. chim.*, 1927, **46**, 397.

54. J. B. Brown and G. Y. Shinowara, *J. Amer. Chem. Soc.*, 1937, **59**, 6; H. Foreman and J. B. Brown, *Oil and Soap*, 1944, **21**, 183; see also D. Swern, H. B. Knight and T. W. Findley, *Oil and Soap*, 1944, **21**, 133.

55. (*a*) F. D. Gunstone and T. P. Hilditch, *J. Chem. Soc.*, 1945, 836; (*b*) F. D. Gunstone and R. P. Paton, *Biochem. J.*, 1953, **54**, 617.

56. (*a*) H. Schlenk and R. T. Holman, *J. Amer. Chem. Soc.*, 1950, **72**, 5001; J. G. Keppler, S. Sparreboom, J. B. A. Stroink and J. D. von Mikusch, *J. Amer. Oil Chem. Soc.*, 1959, **36**, 308; L. J. Rubin and W. Paisley, *ibid.*, 1960, **37**, 300; (*b*) D. Swern and W. E. Parker, *J. Amer. Oil Chem. Soc.*, 1952, **29**, 431, 614.

57. (*a*) D. H. Wheeler and R. W. Riemenschneider, *Oil and Soap*, 1939, **16**, 207; (*b*) D. H. Wheeler, R. W. Riemenschneider and C. E. Sando, *J. Biol. Chem.*, 1940, **132**, 687.

58. T. R. Wood, F. L. Jackson, A. R. Baldwin and H. E. Longenecker, *J. Amer. Chem. Soc.*, 1944, **66**, 287.

59. E. T. Roe, J. T. Scanlan and D. Swern, *J. Amer. Chem. Soc.*, 1949, **71**, 2215.

60. F. Varrentrapp, *Ann.*, 1840, **35**, 196.

61. (*a*) V. von Meyer and P. Jacobsen, "Lehrbuch der Organischen Chemie", 1893, p. 513; (*b*) N. P. Bulatski, *Trudy Odessk. Univ.*, 1954, **4**, 109; (*c*) E. E. Wagner, *Ber.*, 1888, **21**, 3354.

62. J. Baruch, *Ber.*, 1894, **27**, 172.

63. (*a*) F. D. Gunstone, *Chem. and Ind.*, 1955, 250; (*b*) G. M. and R. Robinson, *J. Chem. Soc.*, 1925, **127**, 175; 1926, 2204; T. F. Greg, J. F. McGhie and W. A. Ross, *J. Chem. Soc.*, 1960, 503; C. C. Cochrane and H. J. Harwood, *J. Org. Chem.*, 1961, **26**, 1278; J. C. Smith and P. D. Thickbroom, *Chem. and Ind.*, 1962, 695.

64. F. G. Edmed, *J. Chem. Soc.*, 1898, **73**, 627.

65. (*a*) E. Molinari, *Annuario della Soc. Chimica di Milano*, 1903, **9**, 507; (*b*) C. Harries and C. Thieme, *Ber.*, 1905, **38**, 1630; *Ann.*, 1905, **343**, 354; *Ber.*, 1906, **39**, 3728; (*c*) G. King, *J. Chem. Soc.*, 1938, 1826; (*d*) F. L. Benton, A. A. Kiess and H. J. Harwood, *J. Amer. Oil Chem. Soc.*, 1959, **36**, 457; E. H. Pryde, D. E. Anders, H. M. Teeter and J. C. Cowan, *J. Org. Chem.*, 1960, **25**, 618; M. Naudet and J. Paseno, *Fette u. Seifen*, 1960, **62**, 1110; R. G. Ackman, M. E. Retson, L. R. Gallay and F. A. Vandenheuvel, *Canad. J. Chem.*, 1961, **39**, 1956; (*e*) O. S. Privett and C. Nickell, *J. Amer. Oil Chem. Soc.*, 1962, **39**, 414; E. H. Pryde, D. E. Anders, H. M. Teeter and J. C. Cowan, *J. Org. Chem.*, 1962, **27**, 3055.

66. A. Grün and F. Wittka, *Chem. Umschau*, 1925, **32**, 257.

67. (*a*) R. U. Lemieux and E. von Rudloff, *Canad. J. Chem.*, 1955, **33**, 1701, 1710; E. von Rudloff, *ibid.*, 1956, **34**, 1413; *J. Amer. Oil Chem. Soc.*, 1956, **33**, 126; E. P. Jones and J. A. Stolp, *ibid.*, 1958, **35**, 71; (*b*) F. D. Gunstone and P. J. Sykes, *Chem. and Ind.*, 1960, 1130; *J. Chem. Soc.*, 1962, 3058, 3063.

68. D. Swern, H. B. Knight and C. R. Eddy, *J. Amer. Oil Chem. Soc.*, 1952, **29**, 44; L. Hartman, F. B. Shorland and I. R. C. McDonald, *Nature*, 1954, **174**, 185.

69. G. Bruni and F. Gorni, *Atti. R. Accad. Lincei*, 1899, [v], **8**, ii, 181; 1900, [v], **9**, ii, 151; L. Mascarelli, *ibid.*, 1914, [v], **23**, ii, 583; L. Mascarelli and B. Toschi, *ibid.*, 1914, [v], **23**, ii, 586; L. Mascarelli and G. Sarna, *ibid.*, 1915, [v], **24**, ii, 30, 91.

70. Private communication from (the late) Professor F. E. Francis.

71. (*a*) J. Marsden and E. K. Rideal, *J. Chem. Soc.*, 1938, 1163; (*b*) W. D. Harkins and R. T. Florence, *Nature*, 1938, **142**, 913.

72. G. M. and R. Robinson, *J. Chem. Soc.*, 1925, **127**, 175.

73. E. F. Armstrong and J. Allan, *J. Soc. Chem. Ind.*, 1924, **43**, 207T.

74. (*a*) G. Dupont and T. Yvernault, *Bull. Soc. Chim.*, 1945, [v], **12**, 84; T. Yvernault, *Oléagineux*, 1946, **1**, 189; (*b*) A. van den Hende, *Bull. Soc. Chim. Belg.*, 1947, **56**, 328.

75. (*a*) J. W. McCutcheon, M. F. Crawford and H. K. Welsh, *Oil and Soap*, 1941, **18**, 9; (*b*) O. D. Shreve, M. R. Heather, H. B. Knight and D. Swern, *Analyt. Chem.*, 1950, **22**, 1498; (*c*) R. G. Sinclair, A. F. McKay and R. N. James, *J. Amer. Chem. Soc.*, 1952, **74**, 2578; (*d*) N. H. Ahlers, R. A. Brett and N. G. McTaggart, *J. Appl. Chem.*, 1953, **3**, 433.

76. J. J. E. Poutet, *Ann. Chim. Phys.*, 1819, (2), **12**, 58; F. Boudet, *Ann.*, 1832, **4**, 1.

77. (*a*) M. C. and A. Saytzew, *J. pr. Chem.*, 1894, **50**, 73; (*b*) A. Albitski, *J. pr. Chem.*, 1900, **61**, (2–3), 65; (*c*) H. I. Waterman and C. van Vlodrop, *J. Soc. Chem. Ind.*, 1936, **55**, 333T; *Verfkroniek*, 1940, **13**, 130; J. H. de Boer, J. P. W. Hautman and H. I. Waterman, *Proc. Kon. Nederl. Akad.*, 1947, **50**, 181; H. I. Waterman, C. van Vlodrop and J. Hannewyk, *Research*, 1948, **1**, 183, 186; (*d*) G. Rankow, *Ber.*, 1929, **62**, 2712.

78. (*a*) S. H. Bertram, *Chem. Weekblad*, 1936, **33**, 3; (*b*) T. P. Hilditch and H. Jasperson, *J. Soc. Chem. Ind.*, 1939, **58**, 233; (*c*) J. P. Kass and G. O. Burr, *J. Amer. Chem. Soc.*, 1939, **61**, 1062.

79. (*a*) H. N. Griffiths and T. P. Hilditch, *J. Chem. Soc.*, 1932, 2315; (*b*) J. J. A. Blekkingh, *Bull. Soc. Chim.*, 1950, (v), **17**, 278.

80. (*a*) D. Holde and A. Gorgas, *Z. angew. Chem.*, 1926, **39**, 1443; (*b*) E. N. Mottram, *Food Investigation Board Report* (*London*), 1922, p. 44; (*c*) B. H. Nicolet, *J. Amer. Chem. Soc.*, 1921, **43**, 2122.

81. (*a*) A. Albitski, *J. Russ. Phys. Chem. Soc.*, 1899, **31**, 76; 1902, **34**, 788; (*b*) T. P. Hilditch, *J. Chem. Soc.*, 1926, 1828; T. P. Hilditch and C. H. Lea, *ibid.*, 1928, 1576; J. T. Scanlan and D. Swern, *J. Amer. Chem. Soc.*, 1940, **62**, 2305; (*c*) J. Böeseken, *Rec. trav. chim.*, 1926, **45**, 838; 1927, **46**, 619; (*d*) T. W. Findley, D. Swern and J. T. Scanlan, *J. Amer. Chem. Soc.*, 1945, **67**, 412; (*e*) D. Swern and E. F. Jordan, *ibid.*, 1945, **67**, 902.

82. G. King, (*a*) *J. Chem. Soc.*, 1943, **37**; (*b*) *ibid.*, 1942, 387; (*c*) *ibid.*, 1949, 1817.

83. (*a*) A. Saytzew, *J. pr. Chem.*, 1883, **33**, 315; (*b*) H. R. Le Sueur, *J. Chem. Soc.*, 1901, **79**, 1313; (*c*) A. Lapworth and E. N. Mottram, *J. Chem. Soc.*, 1925, **127**, 1628.

84. A. R. Bader, *J. Amer. Chem. Soc.*, 1948, **70**, 3938.

85. (*a*) A. Lapworth and E. N. Mottram, *Mem. Manchester Lit. Phil. Soc.*, 1927, **71**, 63; (*b*) J. Böeseken and A. H. Belinfante, *Rec. trav. chim.*, 1926, **45**, 914.

86. (*a*) H. Wittcoff, O. A. Moe and M. H. Iwen, *J. Amer. Chem. Soc.*, 1948, **70**, 742; (*b*) D. Swern, L. P. Witnauer and H. B. Knight, *ibid.*, 1952, **74**, 1655.

87. J. P. Kass and S. B. Radlove, *J. Amer. Chem. Soc.*, 1942, **64**, 2253.

88. D. Swern, *J. Amer. Chem. Soc.*, 1948, **70**, 1235.

89. (*a*) T. G. Green and T. P. Hilditch, *J. Chem. Soc.*, 1937, 764; (*b*) W. B. Brown and E. H. Farmer, *ibid.*, 1935, 761; E. H. Farmer and E. S. Paice, *ibid.*, 1935, 1630.

90. (*a*) D. Holde and J. Marcusson, *Ber.*, 1903, **36**, 2657; (*b*) G. King, *J. Chem. Soc.*, 1936, 1789; (*c*) *ibid.*, 1938, 1826; (*d*) J. E. Coleman, C. Ricciuti and D. Swern, *J. Amer. Chem. Soc.*, 1956, **78**, 5342.

91. (*a*) R. S. Morrell and E. O. Phillips, *J. Soc. Chem. Ind.*, 1938, **57**, 245; (*b*) T. P. Hilditch and H. Plimmer, *J. Chem. Soc.*, 1942, 204.

92. J. F. McGhie, *Chem. and Ind.*, 1954, 131.

93. *Cf.* K. H. Bauer and F. Ermann, *Chem. Umschau*, 1930, **37**, 241; H. I. Waterman and J. A. van Dijk, *Rec. trav. chim.*, 1931, **50**, 279, 679, 793; T. P. Hilditch and A. J. Rhead, *J. Soc. Chem. Ind.*, 1932, **51**, 198т; etc.

94. T. P. Hilditch and N. L. Vidyarthi, *Proc. Roy. Soc.*, 1929, A, **122**, 552; *cf.* also, J. H. Benedict and B. F. Daubert, *J. Amer. Chem. Soc.*, 1950, **72**, 4356; H. I. Waterman *et al.*, *J. Amer. Oil Chem. Soc.*, 1953, **30**, 59.

95. (*a*) J. T. Knegtel, C. Boelhouwer, M. Tels and H. I. Waterman, *J. Amer. Oil Chem. Soc.*, 1957, **34**, 336; (*b*) J. J. A. Blekkingh, H. J. J. Janssen and J. G. Keppler, *Rec. trav. chim.*, 1957, **76**, 35; (*c*) R. O. Feuge and E. R. Cousins, *J. Amer. Oil Chem. Soc.*, 1960, **37**, 267; (*d*) *idem. ibid.*, 1960, **37**, 435.

96. (*a*) A. M. Shukow and P. J. Schestakow, *J. pr. Chem.*, 1903, [ii], **67**, 415; (*b*) M. C. and A. Saytzew, *ibid.*, 1887, [ii], **35**, 386; 1888, [ii], **37**, 269; (*c*) A. Steger and J. van Loon, B. R. N. Vellenga and B. Pennekamp, *Rec. trav. chim.*, 1938, **57**, 25; 1940, **59**, 952.

97. (*a*) A. Saytzew, *J. pr. Chem.*, 1887, [ii], **35**, 387; (*b*) A. Arnaud and S. Posternak, *Compt. rend.*, 1910, **150**, 1525.

98. (*a*) C. R. Noller and R. A. Bannerot, *J. Amer. Chem. Soc.*, 1934, **56**, 1563; (*b*) C. R. Noller and M. D. Girvin, *ibid.*, 1937, **59**, 606.

99. G. Baudart, (*a*) *Compt. rend.*, 1943, **217**, 309; 1945, **220**, 404; (*b*) *Bull. Soc. Chim.*, 1946, [v], **13**, 87; (*c*) *ibid.*, 1944, [v], **11**, 336.

100. P. Karrer and H. Koenig, *Helv. Chim. Acta*, 1943, **26**, 619.

101. J. B. Hale, W. H. Lycan and R. Adams, *J. Amer. Chem. Soc.*, 1930, **52**, 4536.

102. P. C. Mitter and P. N. Bagchi, *J. Indian Chem. Soc.*, 1941, **18**, 461; *see also* Buu-Hoï, *Ann. chim.*, 1944, **19**, 446; *Bull. Soc. Chim.*, 1946, [v], **13**, 147.

103. L. Ruzicka, P. A. Plattner and W. Widmer, *Helv. Chim. Acta*, 1942, **25**, 604, 1086.

104. (*a*) R. E. Bowman, *Nature*, 1949, **163**, 95; *J. Chem. Soc.*, 1950, 177, 325; (*b*) D. E. Ames

and R. E. Bowman, *J. Chem. Soc.*, 1951, 1079; (*c*) B. W. Boughton, R. E. Bowman and D. E. Ames, *ibid.*, 1952, 671, 677; (*d*) D. E. Ames and R. E. Bowman, *ibid.*, 1951, 1087.

105. W. J. Gensler, E. M. Behrmann and G. R. Thomas, *J. Amer. Chem. Soc.*, 1951, **73**, 1071; W. J. Gensler and G. R. Thomas, *ibid.*, 1952, **74**, 3942.

106. (*a*) C. Moureu and R. Delange, *Bull. Soc. Chim.*, 1903, [iii], **29**, 648; *cf.* A. O. Zoss and G. F. Hennion, *J. Amer. Chem. Soc.*, 1941, **63**, 1151; (*b*) R. Bhattacharya, S. R. Saletore and J. L. Simonsen, *J. Chem. Soc.*, 1928, 2678; (*c*) R. Johnson, A. M. Schwartz and T. L. Jacobs, *J. Amer. Chem. Soc.*. 1938, **60**, 1882.

107. (*a*) K. Ahmad and F. M. Strong, *J. Amer. Chem. Soc.*, 1948, **70**, 1699; (*b*) K. Ahmad, F. M. Bumpus and F. M. Strong, *ibid.*, 1948, **70**, 3391; (*c*) W. R. Taylor and F. M. Strong, *ibid.*, 1950, **72**, 4263; (*d*) F. M. Bumpus, W. R. Taylor and F. M. Strong, *ibid.*, 1950, **72**, 2116.

108. P. B. Lumb and J. C. Smith, *J. Chem. Soc.*, 1952, 5032.

109. (*a*) M. S. Newmann and J. H. Notiz, *J. Amer. Chem. Soc.*, 1949, **71**, 1292; (*b*) W. F. Huber, *ibid.*, 1951, **73**, 2730.

110. (*a*) R. A. Raphael and F. Sondheimer, *J. Chem. Soc.*, 1950, 2100; (*b*) H. M. Wilborsky, R. H. Davies and T. R. Howton, *J. Amer. Chem. Soc.*, 1951, **73**, 2590; (*c*) W. J. Gensler and G. R. Thomas, *ibid.*, 1951, **73**, 4601; (*d*) F. D. Gunstone and P. J. Sykes, *J. Chem. Soc.*, 1962, 3055.

111. H. K. Black and B. C. L. Weedon, *J. Chem. Soc.*, 1953, 1785.

112. D. G. Bounds, R. P. Linstead and B. C. L. Weedon, (*a*) *J. Chem. Soc.*, 1953, 2393; (*b*) *ibid.*, 1954, 448; (*c*) *ibid.*, 1954, 4219; 1955, 1097; (*d*) B. W. Baker, R. W. Kierstead, R. P. Linstead and B. C. L. Weedon, *ibid.*, 1954, 1804; (*e*) B. W. Baker, R. P. Linstead and B. C. L. Weedon, *ibid.*, 1955, 2218.

113. (*a*) H. A. Boekenoogen, *Fette u. Seifen*, 1939, **46**, 717; (*b*) S. P. Ligthelm, D. H. S. Horn, H. M. Schwartz and M. M. van Holdt, *J. Sci. Food Agric.*, 1954, **5**, 281.

114. (*a*) L. C. A. Nunn and I. Smedley-MacLean, *Biochem. J.*, 1938, **32**, 2178; E. M. Hume, L. C. A. Nunn, I. Smedley-MacLean and H. H. Smith, *ibid.*, 1940, **34**, 879, 884; I. Smedley-MacLean and E. M. Hume, *ibid.*, 1941, **35**, 990; (*b*) C. Widmer and R. T. Holman, *Arch. Biochem.*, 1950, **25**, 1; R. Reiser and co-workers, *J. Nutrition*, 1950, **40**, 429; 1950, **42**, 325; 1951, **44**, 159; J. F. Mead and co-workers, *J. Nutrition*, 1951, **44**, 507; *J. Biol. Chem.*, 1953, **205**, 683; 1956, **218**, 401; **219**, 705; 1957, **224**, 841; **227**, 1025; 1958, **229**, 575; 1959, **234**, 1411; 1960, **235**, 3385.

115. (*a*) T. P. Hilditch and J. A. Lovern, *J. Soc. Chem. Ind.*, 1928, **47**, 105т; (*b*) M. Tsujimoto, *Chem. Umschau*, 1925, **32**, 202.

116. R. S. McKinney and G. S. Jamieson, *Oil and Soap*, 1936, **13**, 289; T. G. Green, T. P. Hilditch and W. J. Stainsby, *J. Chem. Soc.*, 1936, 1750.

117. (*a*) C. Y. Hopkins, *Canad. J. Res.*, 1946, B, **24**, 211; (*b*) C. Y. Hopkins, M. J. Chisholm and J. Harris, *ibid.*, 1949, B, **27**, 35; C. Y. Hopkins and M. J. Chisholm, *Canad. J. Chem.*, 1954, **32**, 1033; (*c*) M. N. Baliga and T. P. Hilditch, *J. Soc. Chem. Ind.*, 1948, **67**, 258; *J. Chem. Soc.*, 1949, *Suppl. I.*, 91; (*d*) J. Holmberg and G. Sellmann, *Svensk. Kem. Tidskr.*, 1952, **64**, 270.

118. (*a*) F. R. Earle, I. A. Wolff *et al.*, *J. Amer. Oil Chem. Soc.*, 1961, **38**, 678; (*b*) M. J. Chisholm and C. Y. Hopkins, *Canad. J. Chem.*, 1956, **34**, 459; (*c*) idem., *ibid.*, 1960, **38**, 805; *Canad. J. Biochem. Physiol.*, 1961, **39**, 829; (*d*) S. P. Pathak and L. M. Dey, *J. Sci. Food Agric.*, 1956, **7**, 200; *J. Chem. Soc.*, 1957, 1917; (*e*) M. J. Chisholm and C. Y. Hopkins, *Canad. J. Chem.*, 1958, **36**, 1537; (*f*) K. L. Mikolajczak, C. R. Smith, Jr., and I. A. Wolff, *J. Amer. Oil Chem. Soc.*, 1963, **40**, 294.

119. W. H. Baldwin and L. E. Parks, *Oil and Soap*, 1943, **20**, 101.

120. T. P. Hilditch and M. L. Meara, *J. Chem. Soc.*, 1938, 1608.

121. M. Fileti, *J. pr. Chem.*, 1893, **48**, 72.

122. M. Tsujimoto, *J. Soc. Chem. Ind., Japan*, 1927, **30**, 868.

123. (*a*) E. Klenk, *Z. physiol. Chem.*, 1927, **166**, 287; (*b*) E. Klenk and E. Schumann, *ibid.*, 1942, **272**, 177.

124. (a) F. S. Shenstone and J. R. Vickery, *Nature*, 1956, **177**, 94; 1957, **179**, 830; 1961, **190**, 168; (b) C. R. Smith Jr., T. L. Wilson and K. L. Mikolajczak, *Chem. and Ind.*, 1961, 256; (c) *idem.*, *J. Amer. Oil Chem. Soc.*, 1961, **38**, 696; (d) F. S. Shenstone and J. R. Vickery, *Poultry Science*, 1959, **38**, 1055; (e) J. C. Masson, M. G. Vavick, B. W. Heywang and A. R. Kemmerer, *Science*, 1957, **126**, 751; (f) J. A. Cornelius and G. Shone, *Chem. and Ind.*, 1963, 1246.

125. (a) T. P. Hilditch, M. L. Meara and Y. A. H. Zaky, *J. Soc. Chem. Ind.*, 1941, **60**, 198; T. P. Hilditch and M. L. Meara, *ibid.*, 1944, **63**, 112; (b) J. R. Nunn, *J. Chem. Soc.*, 1952, 313.

126. (a) J. P. Varma, B. Nath and J. S. Aggarwal, *Nature*, 1955, **175**, 84; 1955, **176**, 1082; *J. Chem. Soc.*, 1956, 2550; *J. Sci. Indust. Res.* (*India*), 1957, **16**, B, 162; (b) G. Dijkstra and H. J. Duin, *Nature*, 1955, **176**, 71; (c) P. K. Faure, *ibid.*, 1956, **178**, 372; P. K. Faure and J. C. Smith, *J. Chem. Soc.*, 1956, 1818; (d) D. G. Brooke and J. C. Smith, *Chem. and Ind.*, 1957, 1508; (e) *idem*, *ibid.*, 1957, 49; (f) B. A. Lewis and R. A. Raphael, *ibid.*, 1957, 50; (g) V. V. Narayanan and B. C. L. Weedon, *ibid.*, 1957, 394.

127. (a) K. Hofmann and R. A. Lucas, *J. Amer. Chem. Soc.*, 1950, **72**, 4328; K. Hofmann, R. A. Lucas and S. M. Sax, *J. Biol. Chem.*, 1952, **195**, 473; 1953, **205**, 55; K. Hofmann, *Record Chem. Progress*, 1953, **14**, 7; K. Hofmann *et al.*, *J. Amer. Chem. Soc.*, 1954, **76**, 1799; (b) K. Hofmann and F. Tausig, *J. Biol. Chem.*, 1955, **213**, 425; (c) K. Hofmann, G. J. Marco and G. A. Jeffery, *J. Amer. Chem. Soc.*, 1958, **80**, 5717; (d) K. Hofmann, S. F. Orochena and C. W. Yoho, *ibid.*, 1957, **79**, 3608; 1959, **81**, 3356; *cf. also* D. G. Brooke and J. C. Smith, *Chem. and Ind.*, 1958, 103.

128. (a) I. Smedley, *Biochem. J.*, 1912, **6**, 451; (b) A. Grün and T. Wirth, *Ber.*, 1922, **55**, 2206; (c) A. W. Bosworth and J. B. Brown, *J. Biol. Chem.*, 1933, **103**, 115.

129. (a) T. P. Hilditch and H. E. Longenecker, *J. Biol. Chem.*, 1938, **122**, 497; (b) A. Grün and H. Winkler, *Z. angew. Chem.*, 1924, **37**, 228.

130. (a) T. P. Hilditch and H. E. Longenecker, *Biochem. J.*, 1937, **31**, 1805; (b) T. P. Hilditch, C. H. Lea and W. H. Pedelty, *ibid.*, 1939, **33**, 493.

131. D. Atherton and M. L. Meara, *J. Soc. Chem. Ind.*, 1939, **58**, 353.

132. (a) P. G. Hofstädter, *Ann.*, 1854, **91**, 177; (b) E. Ljubarsky, *J. pr. Chem.*, 1898, [ii], **57**, 19; (c) H. Bull, *Ber.*, 1906, **39**, 3570.

133. E. F. Armstrong and T. P. Hilditch, *J. Soc. Chem. Ind.*, 1925, **44**, 180т.

134. Y. Toyama, (a) *Chem. Umschau*, 1924, **31**, 221; (b) *J. Soc. Chem. Ind.*, *Japan*, 1927, **30**, 116, 207; (c) *ibid.*, 1927, **30**, 603; (d) *ibid.*, 1927, **30**, 519.

135. (a) Gansel, *Dissertation*, Stuttgart, 1926; (b) K. D. Guha, *Dissertation*, Liverpool, 1931; (c) J. A. Lovern, *Biochem. J.*, 1934, **28**, 394.

136. J. A. Lovern, *Biochem. J.*, 1936, **30**, 387; 1932, **26**, 1978; 1934, **28**, 1961; 1935, **29**, 1894; 1937, **31**, 755.

137. (a) E. Klenk, *Z. physiol. Chem.*, 1933, **221**, 67, 259, 264; (b) E. Klenk, F. Ditt and W. Diebold, *ibid.*, 1935, **232**, 54.

138. (a) T. G. Green and T. P. Hilditch, *Biochem. J.*, 1938, **32**, 681; (b) T. P. Hilditch and H. Paul, *ibid.*, 1937, **31**, 227.

139. (a) A. Banks, T. P. Hilditch and E. C. Jones, *Biochem. J.*, 1933, **27**, 1375; (b) T. P. Hilditch, E. C. Jones and A. J. Rhead, *ibid.*, 1934, **28**, 786.

140. E. Klenk and O. von Schoenebeck, *Z. physiol. Chem.*, 1932, **209**, 112; T. P. Hilditch and F. B. Shorland, *Biochem. J.*, 1937, **31**, 1499.

141. (a) T. P. Hilditch, C. H. Lea and W. H. Pedelty, *Biochem. J.*, 1939, **33**, 493; (b) T. P. Hilditch and H. Paul, *ibid.*, 1936, **30**, 1905; (c) R. W. Riemenschneider and N. R. Ellis, *J. Biol. Chem.*, 1936, **114**, 441.

142. T. P. Hilditch and W. H. Pedelty, *Biochem. J.*, 1937, **31**, 1964; T. P. Hilditch and Y. A. H. Zaky, *ibid.*, 1942, **36**, 815.

143. (a) E. Chargaff, *Z. physiol. Chem.*, 1933, **218**, 223; (b) M. S. Newman and R. J. Anderson, *J. Biol. Chem.*, 1933, **102**, 219; (c) J. L. Riebsomer and J. R. Johnson, *J. Amer. Chem. Soc.*, 1933, **55**, 3352.

144. (a) H. E. Longenecker, *J. Soc. Chem. Ind.*, 1937, **56**, 199T; (b) T. P. Hilditch and H. M. Thompson, *ibid.*, 1937, **56**, 434T; (c) T. P. Hilditch and H. Jasperson, *ibid.*, 1938, **57**, 84; (d) T. P. Hilditch and H. Jasperson, *ibid.*, 1939, **58**, 187.

145. (a) J. Alvarez, P. Cattaneo, *et al.*, *Anales Asocn. Quim. Argentina*, 1949, **37**, 34; (b) R. B. French, *J. Amer. Oil Chem. Soc.*, 1962, **39**, 176; (c) R. E. Bridge and T. P. Hilditch, *J. Chem. Soc.*, 1950, 2396; (d) P. Cattaneo, G. K. de Sutton *et al.*, *Anales Asocn. Quim. Argentina*, 1962, **50**, 1.

146. (a) M. Takano, *J. Soc. Chem. Ind., Japan*, 1933, **36**, 1317; (b) Y. Toyama and T. Tsuchiya, *ibid.*, 1934, **37**, 14B, 17B; Y. Toyama and T. Ishikawa, *ibid.*, 534B, 536B; (c) Y. Toyama, *ibid.*, 1927, **30**, 597.

147. W. Bergmann and A. N. Swift, *J. Org. Chem.*, 1951, **16**, 1206.

148. L. Saalmüller, *Ann.*, 1848, **64**, 108.

149. (a) L. Gurgel and T. F. de Amorim, *Mem. Inst. Chim. Rio de Janeiro*, 1929, **2**, 31; (b) L. Margaillan, *Compt. rend.*, 1931, **192**, 373.

150. (a) S. S. Gupta, T. P. Hilditch and J. P. Riley, *J. Sci. Food Agric.*, 1951, **2**, 245; (b) K. T. Achaya and S. R. Saletore, *Analyst*, 1952, **77**, 375; (c) B. Sreenivasan, N. R. Kameth and J. G. Kane, *J. Amer. Oil Chem. Soc.*, 1956, **33**, 61; (d) F. Hawke, *J. S. Africa Chem. Inst.*, 1949, **2**, 1, 125.

151. (a) A. G. Goldsobel, *Ber.*, 1894, **27**, 3121; (b) L. Maquenne, *Bull. Soc. Chim.*, 1899, [iii], **21**, 1061; (c) K. Hazura and A. Grüssner, *Monatsh*, 1888, **9**, 948; (d) G. King, *J. Chem. Soc.*, 1950, 9.

152. (a) L. Crombie and A. G. Jacklin, *Chem. and Ind.*, 1954, 1197; *J. Chem. Soc.*, 1955, 1740; (b) P. B. Lumb and J. C. Smith (with V. G. Kendall), *Chem. and Ind.*, 1954, 1228; *idem.* (with A. S. Bailey and C. H. Walker), *J. Chem. Soc.*, 1957, 3027; (c) W. J. Gensler and C. B. Abrahams, *Chem. and Ind.*, 1957, 47; (d) K. Serck-Hanssen, *ibid.*, 1958, 1554.

153. (a) A. Vernon and H. K. Ross, *J. Amer. Chem. Soc.*, 1936, **58**, 2430; (b) S. S. Gupta and J. S. Aggarwal, *J. Sci. Indust. Res., India*, 1954, **13**, B, 277; (c) M. Freund and F. Schönfeld, *Ber.*, 1891, **24**, 3350; (d) G. H. Hargreaves and L. N. Owen, *J. Chem. Soc.*, 1947, 753.

154. (a) F. D. Gunstone, *J. Chem. Soc.*, 1952, 1274; (b) J. Kennedy, A. Lewis, N. J. McCorkindale and R. A. Raphael, *ibid.*, 1961, 4945.

155. (a) N. L. Vidyarthi and M. V. Mallya, *J. Indian Chem. Soc.*, 1939, **16**, 479; N. L. Vidyarthi, *Patna Univ. J.*, 1945, **1**, 51; (b) F. D. Gunstone, *J. Chem. Soc.*, 1954, 1611; *see also* P. S. Raman, *Current Science*, 1954, **23**, 293.

156. (a) K. E. Bharucha and F. D. Gunstone, *J. Sci. Food Agric.*, 1955, **6**, 373; (b) *J. Chem. Soc.*, 1956, 1611; (c) C. R. Smith, K. F. Koch and I. A. Wolff, *J. Amer. Oil Chem. Soc.*, 1959, **36**, 219; (d) L. J. Morris and R. T. Holman, (with H. Hayes) *ibid.*, 1961, **38**, 316; (with K. Fontill) *J. Lipid Res.*, 1961, **2**, 68, 77; *see also* R. A. Barford, S. F. Herb *et al.*, *J. Amer. Oil. Chem. Soc.*, 1963, **40**, 136; (e) J. M. Osbond, *J. Chem. Soc.*, 1961, 5270; (f) M. J. Chisholm and C. Y. Hopkins, *Chem. and Ind.*, 1960, 1134; (g) W. E. Scott, C. F. Krewson and R. W. Riemenschneider, *ibid.*, 1962, 2038; *J. Amer. Oil Chem. Soc.*, 1963, **40**, 587.

157. (a) C. R. Smith, M. O. Bagby, R. L. Lohmar, C. A. Glass and I. A. Wolff, *J. Org. Chem.*, 1960, **25**, 218; (b) F. D. Gunstone and L. J. Morris, *J. Chem. Soc.*, 1959, 2127.

158. (a) J. S. Aggarwal, S. S. Bhatnagar, P. Narain and Karimullah, *J. Sci. Indust. Res., India*, 1948, **7**, B, 136; S. C. Gupta, V. N. Sharma and J. S. Aggarwal, *ibid.*, 1951, **10**, B, 76; S. C. and S. S. Gupta and J. S. Aggarwal, *J. Amer. Oil Chem. Soc.*, 1954, **31**, 287; (b) R. C. Calderwood and F. D. Gunstone, *Chem. and Ind.*, 1953, 436; *J. Sci. Food Agric.*, 1954, **5**, 382; (c) S. V. Puntambekar, *Proc. Indian Acad. Sci.*, 1952, **35**, A, 57; (d) N. H. E. Ahlers and F. D. Gunstone, *Chem. and Ind.*, 1954, 1291; (e) J. D. von Mikusch, *Deutsch. Farb.-Zeitschr.*, 1954, **5**, 166; (f) L. Crombie and J. L. Tayler, *J. Chem. Soc.*, 1954, 2816; (g) L. A. O'Neill, A. C. Dennison and N. H. E. Ahlers, *Chem. and Ind.*, 1954, 756; (h) S. C. and S. S. Gupta and J. S. Aggarwal, *J. Amer. Oil Chem. Soc.*, 1954, **31**, 287; V. H. Kapadia and J. S. Aggarwal,

J. Sci. Indust. Res. (India), 1958, **17**, **B**, 117; K. T. Achaya and J. S. Aggarwal, *Chem. and Ind.*, 1962, 1616.

159. S. B. Davis, E. A. Conroy and N. E. Shakespeare, *J. Amer. Chem. Soc.*, 1950, **72**, 124.
160. C. R. Smith, T. Wilson, I. A. Wolff, *et al.*, (*a*) *J. Amer. Chem. Soc.*, 1960, **82**, 1417; (*b*) *J. Org. Chem.*, 1961, **26**, 2903.
161. (*a*) J. P. Riley, *J. Chem. Soc.*, 1951, 1346; (*b*) H. P. Kaufmann, J. Baltes and H. Herminghaus, *Fette u. Seifen*, 1951, **53**, 537 (*Cf.* A. Seher, *Ann.*, 1954, **589**, 222); (*c*) S. P. Ligthelm, *Chem. and Ind.*, 1954, 249; (*d*) L. Crombie and B. P. Griffin, *J. Chem. Soc.*, 1958, 4435.
162. (*a*) J. Bougault and L. Bourdier, *J. Pharm. Chim.*, 1909, **29**, 561; 1909, **30**, 10; *Compt. rend.*, 1910, **150**, 874; (*b*) A. C. Chibnall, S. H. Piper, J. A. B. Smith and E. F. Williams, *Biochem. J.*, 1931, **25**, 2095; K. S. Markley and C. E. Sando, *J. Biol. Chem.*, 1934, **105**, 643; (*c*) K. E. Murray and R. Schoenfeld, *J. Amer. Oil Chem. Soc.*, 1953, **30**, 25; *Austral. J. Chem.*, 1955, **8**, 432.
163. (*a*) T. Kawasaki, *Proc. Japan Acad.*, 1949, **25**, (10), 15; (*b*) F. B. Power and H. Rogerson, *Amer. J. Pharm.*, 1908, **80**, 251; Y. Asahina (with S. X. Terada), *J. Pharm. Soc. Japan*, 1919, **452**, 821; (with T. Shimidzu), *ibid.*, 1922, **479**, 1; (with S. Nakanishi), *ibid.*, 1925, **520**, 515; (*c*) H. Hirai and Y. Toyama, *J. Chem. Soc. Japan, Indust. Sectn.*, 1949, **52**, 212; (*d*) R. U. Lemieux, *Canad. J. Chem.*, 1953, **31**, 396.
164. (*a*) *cf.* M. Kerschbaum, *Ber.*, 1927, **60**, 902; (*b*) P. Baudart, *Compt. rend.*, 1945, **221**, 205; (*c*) C. Collaud, *Helv. Chim. Acta*, 1942, **25**, 965; (*d*) P. C. Mitter and B. K. Bhattacharya, *J. Indian Chem. Soc.*, 1942, **19**, 69; (*e*) S. C. Bhattacharyya and H. H. Mathur, *Chem. and Ind.*, 1960, 1441.
165. (*a*) *cf.* C. Harries and W. Nagel, *Ber.*, 1922, **55**, 3838; W. Nagel, *ibid.*, 1927, **60**, 605; W. Nagel and W. Mertens, *ibid.*, 1936, **69**, 2050B; (*b*) P. C. Mitter and S. Mukherjee, *J. Indian Chem. Soc.*, 1939, **16**, 673; 1942, **19**, 303; (*c*) W. Nagel and W. Mertens, *Ber.*, 1941, **74**, 976B.
166. (*a*) R. K. Callow, N. C. Johnston and J. Simpson, *Experientia*, 1959, **15**, 421; S. A. Barker, A. B. Foster and D. C. Lamb, *Nature*, 1959, **184**, Suppl. 9, 634; W. H. Brown, E. E. Felauer and R. J. Freure, *Canad. J. Chem.*, 1961, **39**, 1086; (*b*) Sir R. Robinson, *Croat. Chem. Acta.*, 1960, **32**, 119; (with G. I. Fray, E. D. Morgan, *et al.*), *Tetrahedron Letters*, 1960, No. 13, 34; *Tetrahedron*, 1961, **15**, 18; (*c*) M. Barbier and M.-F. Hügel, *Bull. Soc. Chim. France*, 1961, 951, 1324; (*d*) J. Kennedy, N. J. McCorkindale and R. A. Raphael, *J. Chem. Soc.*, 1961, 3813; K. Eiter, *Annalen*, 1962, **658**, 91.
167. (*a*) A. Guillemonat and G. Césaire, *Bull. Soc. Chim.*, 1949, [v], **16**, 792; E. Seoane and I. Ribas, *An. Real. Soc. Esp. Fis. Quim.*, 1951, **47**, **B**, 61; 1959, **55**, **B**, 839; *Chem. and Ind.*, 1957, 490; G. Dupont and R. Dulou (with J. Cohen), *Compt. rend.*, 1955, **240**, 875; *Bull. Soc. Chim. France*, 1956, 819; (*b*) A. Guillemonat and G. Césaire, *Bull. Soc. Chim.*, 1950, [v], **17**, 860; I. Ribas and G. Cil-Curbera, *An. Real. Soc. Esp. Fis. Quim.*, 1951, **47**, **B**, 713; 1953, **49**, **B**, 145; G. Dupont, R. Dulou and A. Chicoisne, *Bull. Soc. Chim. France*, 1956, 1413; (*c*) I. Ribas and E. Seoane, *An. Real. Soc. Esp. Fis. Quim.*, 1954, **50**, **B**, 963, 971; (*d*) W. J. Gensler and H. N. Schlein, *J. Amer. Chem. Soc.*, 1955, **77**, 4846; 1956, **78**, 169.
168. (*a*) E. Vongerichten and A. Köhler, *Ber.*, 1909, **42**, 1638; (*b*) Scherer, *Dissertation*, Strasburg, 1909; (*c*) F. C. Palazzo and A. Tamburello, *Atti. R. Acad. Lincei*, 1914, [v], **23**, (ii), 352; (*d*) T. P. Hilditch and (Miss) E. E. Jones, *Biochem. J.*, 1928, **22**, 326; (*e*) B. C. Christian and T. P. Hilditch, *ibid.*, 1929, **23**, 327; (*f*) M. Tsujimoto and H. Koyangari, *Bull. Chem. Soc. Japan*, 1933, **8**, 161; (*g*) S. P. Fore, R. J. Holmes and W. G. Bickford, *J. Amer. Oil Chem. Soc.*, 1960, **37**, 490.
169. (*a*) A. Eibner, L. Widenmayer and E. Schild, *Chem. Umschau*, 1927, **34**, 312; (*b*) T.P. Hilditch and (Miss) E. E. Jones, *J. Soc. Chem. Ind.*, 1927, **46**, 174T; (*c*) J. van Loon, *Rec. trav. chim.*, 1927, **46**, 492; (*d*) I. Afanasievski, *J. Russ. Phys. Chem. Soc.*, 1915, **47**, 2124.
170. (*a*) A. Arnaud, *Compt. rend.*, 1892, **114**, 79; *Bull. Soc. Chim.*, 1892, [iii], **7**, 233; (*b*) C.

Grimme, *Chem. Rev. Fett-u. Harz-Ind.*, 1910, **17**, 158; 1912, **19**, 51; (c) A. Steger and J. van Loon, *Rec. trav. chim.*, 1933, **52**, 593.

171. (a) A. Heiduschka and K. Lüft, *Arch. Pharm.*, 1919, **257**, 33; (b) J. P. Riley, *J. Chem. Soc.*, 1949, 2728.

172. (a) F. H. Gornall and F. B. Power, *J. Chem. Soc.*, 1904, **85**, 845; F. B. Power and M. Barrowcliff, 1905, **87**, 884; 1907, **91**, 557, 563; (b) R. L. Shriner and R. Adams, *J. Amer. Chem. Soc.*, 1925, **47**, 2727; (c) G. A. Perkins and A. O. Cruz, *ibid.*, 1927, **49**, 1070; (d) A. L. Dean, R. Wrenshall and G. Fujimoto, *Chem. Umschau*, 1927, **34**, 129; (e) K. Mislow and I. V. Steinberg, *J. Amer. Chem. Soc.*, 1955, **77**, 3807; (f) K. Kimura, M. Takahashi and A. Tanaka, *Chem. and Pharm. Bull. (Japan)*, 1960, **8**, 1063.

173. (a) K. V. Bokil and K. S. Nargund, *Proc. Indian Acad. Sci.*, 1941, **13**, A, 233; (b) J. Univ. Bombay, 1942, **10**, A, 118, 114; (c) D. G. M. Diaper and J. C. Smith, *Biochem. J.*, 1948, **42**, 581.

174. (a) Buu-Hoï and P. Cagniant, *Bull. Soc. Chim.*, 1942, [v], **9**, 99; (b) *ibid.*, 1942, [v], **9**, 107; Buu-Hoï, M. Sy and D. Xuong, *Compt. rend.*, 1955, **240**, 785; (c) Buu-Hoï, *Ann. Chim.*, 1944, [xi], **19**, 446.

175. A. G. Davies and J. E. Packer, *Chem. and Ind.*, 1960, 1165.

176. H. I. Cole and H. T. Cardoso, (a) *J. Amer. Chem. Soc.*, 1939, **61**, 2349; (b) B. Wladislaw, *J. Chem. Soc.*, 1955, 4227; (c) R. Wrenshall and A. L. Dean, *U.S. Pub. Health Service Bull.*, 1924, **141**, 12; (d) E. André and D. Jouatte, *Bull. Soc. Chim.*, 1928, [iv], **43**, 347; (e) H. I. Cole and H. J. Cardoso, *J. Amer. Chem. Soc.*, 1938, **60**, 612.

177. A. W. Weitkamp, A. M. Smilianio and S. Rothman, *J. Amer. Chem. Soc.*, 1947, **69**, 1936.

178. (a) M. Tsujimoto, *Chem. Umschau*, 1927, **34**, 9, 91; 1928, **35**, 225; (b) Y. Toyama, *J. Soc. Chem. Ind. Japan*, 1937, **40**, 285в; S. Komori and S. Ueno, *Bull. Chem. Soc. Japan*, 1937, **12**, 433; (c) M. Iwakiri, *J. Chem. Soc. Japan*, 1957, **78**, 1460; 1958, **79**, 816, 910.

179. (a) S. H. Bertram, *Biochem. Z.*, 1928, **197**, 433; (b) J. Grossfeld and A. Simmer, *Z. Unters. Lebensm.*, 1930, **59**, 237; (c) J. Böeseken, J. van Krimpen and P. L. Blanken, *Rec. trav. chim.*, 1930, **49**, 247; (d) P. C. Rao and B. F. Daubert, *J. Amer. Chem. Soc.*, 1948, **70**, 1102; (e) J. H. Benedict and B. F. Daubert, *ibid.*, 1949, **71**, 4113.

180. (a) S. S. Gupta, T. P. Hilditch, S. Paul and R. K. Shrivastava, *J. Chem. Soc.*, 1950, 3484; (b) D. Swern, H. B. Knight and C. R. Eddy, *J. Amer. Oil Chem. Soc.*, 1952, **29**, 44; (c) T. P. Hilditch and S. P. Pathak, *Proc. Roy. Soc.*, 1949, A, **198**, 323; see also R. W. Planck, F. C. Pack, D. C. Heinzelmann, M. F. Stansbury and R. T. O'Connor, *J. Amer. Oil Chem. Soc.*, 1953, **30**, 598; (d) I. D. Morton and A. R. Todd, *Biochem. J.*, 1950, **47**, 327; (e) J. van Loon and D. van der Linden, *Rec. trav. chim.*, 1952, **71**, 292.

181. (a) R. C. Millican and J. B. Brown, *J. Biol. Chem.*, 1944, **154**, 437; (b) L. Hartman, F. B. Shorland and I. R. C. McDonald, *Nature*, 1954, **174**, 185.

182. (a) H. H. Hatt and A. Z. Szumer, *J. Sci. Food Agric.*, 1953, **4**, 273; (b) F. Sacc, *Ann.*, 1844, **51**, 213.

183. (a) J. B. Brown (with G. G. Stoner), *J. Amer. Chem. Soc.*, 1937, **59**, 3; (with J. S. Frankel), *ibid.*, 1938, **60**, 54; 1941, **63**, 1483; (with N. L. Matthews and W. R. Brode), *ibid.*, 1941, **63**, 1064; (with J. S. Frankel and W. Stoneburner), *ibid.*, 1943, **65**, 259; (with B. Sreenavasan *et al.*), *J. Amer. Oil Chem. Soc.*, 1962, **39**, 255; (b) (with J. S. Frankel), *J. Amer. Chem. Soc.*, 1943, **65**, 415; (c) (with M. F. White), *J. Amer. Oil Chem. Soc.*, 1949, **26**, 385.

184. (a) R. W. Riemenschneider, S. F. Herb and P. L. Nichols, *J. Amer. Oil Chem. Soc.*, 1949, **26**, 371; (b) B. F. Daubert and A. R. Baldwin, *J. Amer. Chem. Soc.*, 1944, **66**, 997.

185. (a) D. Swern and W. E. Parker, *J. Amer. Oil Chem. Soc.*, 1953, **30**, 5; 1957, **34**, 43; (b) J. G. Keppler, S. Sparreboom, J. B. A. Stroink and J. D. von Mikusch, *ibid.*, 1959, **36**, 308; (c) A. R. Johnson and G. M. Ali, *ibid.*, 1961, **38**, 453; (d) R. E. Beal and O. L. Brekke, *ibid.*, 1959, **36**, 397; (e) C. R. Scholfield, J. Nowakowska and H. J. Dutton,

ibid., 1960, **37**, 27; (*f*) E. M. Stearns, H. B. White and F. W. Quackenbush, *ibid.*, 1962, **39**, 61.

186. (*a*) K. Hazura, *Monatsh.*, 1887, **8**, 151; (*b*) D. H. Birosel, *Nat. and Appl. Sc. Bull. Univ. Philippines*, 1932, **2**, 193; (*c*) R. W. Riemenschneider, D. H. Wheeler and C. E. Sando, *J. Biol. Chem.*, 1939, **127**, 391.

187. (*a*) F. Bedford, *Dissertation*, Halle, 1906; (*b*) A. Rollett, *Z. physiol. Chem.*, 1909, **62**, 410; (*c*) Y. Inoue and B. Suzuki, *Proc. Imp. Acad. Tokyo*, 1931, **7**, 15; T. Maruyama and B. Suzuki, *ibid.*, 1931, **7**, 379; 1932, **8**, 186, 486; T. Maruyama, *J. Soc. Chem. Ind. Japan*, 1933, **54**, 1082; (*d*) T. G. Green and T. P. Hilditch, *J. Soc. Chem. Ind.*, 1936, **55**, 4т; (*e*) J. B. Brown and J. S. Frankel, *J. Amer. Chem. Soc.*, 1938, **60**, 54.

188. B. H. Nicolet and H. L. Cox, *J. Amer. Chem. Soc.*, 1922, **44**, 144.

189. (*a*) A. F. McKay and A. R. Bader, *J. Org. Chem.*, 1948, **13**, 75; (*b*) (with N. Levitin and R. N. Jones), *J. Amer. Chem. Soc.*, 1954, **76**, 2383.

190. K. E. Bharucha and F. D. Gunstone, *J. Chem. Soc.*, 1956, 1611.

191. (*a*) J. M. Osbond and J. C. Wickers, *Chem. and Ind.*, 1959, 1287; J. M. Osbond, *J. Chem. Soc.*, 1961, 5270; (*b*) D. E. Ames and P. J. Islip, *ibid.*, 1961, 4409; (*c*) A. I. Rachlin, N. Wasyliu and M. W. Goldberg, *J. Org. Chem.*, 1961, **26**, 2688; (*d*) S. N. Ege, R. Wolorsky and W. J. Gensler, *J. Amer. Chem. Soc.*, 1961, **83**, 3080.

192. (*a*) T. P. Hilditch, P. A. Laurent and M. L. Meara, *J. Soc. Chem. Ind.*, 1947, **66**, 19; (*b*) W. Bergmann and A. N. Swift, *J. Org. Chem.*, 1951, **16**, 1206; (*c*) F. B. Shorland, *Nature*, 1945, **156**, 269; (*d*) E. Klenk *et al.*, *Z. physiol. Chem.*, 1952, **291**, 104; 1955, **299**, 74; 1960, **320**, 111; (*e*) H. J. Thomasson, *Int. Z. Vitaminforsch.*, 1953, **25**, 62; *Nature*, 1954, **173**, 452.

193. (*a*) T. P. Hilditch and (Miss) E. E. Jones, *Analyst*, 1929, **54**, 75; (*b*) H. C. Eckstein, *J. Biol. Chem.*, 1933, **103**, 135.

194. (*a*) T. G. Green and T. P. Hilditch, *Biochem. J.*, 1935, **29**, 1564; (*b*) T. P. Hilditch and H. Jasperson, *J. Soc. Chem. Ind.*, 1939, **58**, 241; (*c*) W. E. Scott, S. F. Herb, P. Magidman and R. W. Riemenschneider, *J. Agric. Food Chem.*, 1959, **7**, 125; (*d*) K. Sambasivarao and J. B. Brown, *J. Amer. Oil Chem. Soc.*, 1962, **39**, 340.

195. H. B. Knight, E. F. Jordan and D. Swern, *J. Biol. Chem.*, 1946, **164**, 477.

196. (*a*) T. Moore, *Biochem. J.*, 1937, **31**, 138; 1939, **33**, 1635; (*b*) J. P. Kass, E. S. Miller and G. O. Burr, *J. Amer. Chem. Soc.*, 1939, **61**, 482, 3292; (*c*) B. P. Appln., 5363/1941; (*d*) B. Sreenivasan and J. B. Brown, *J. Amer. Oil Chem. Soc.*, 1956, **33**, 521; 1958, **35**, 89.

197. (*a*) P. Desnuelle and R. Massori, *Compt. rend.*, 1950, **230**, 965; (*b*) P. L. Nichols, S. F. Herb and R. W. Riemenschneider, *J. Amer. Chem. Soc.*, 1951, **73**, 247; (*c*) J. D. von Mikusch, *Industr. Vern.*, 1952, **6**, 15.

198. J. H. Mitchell, H. R. Kraybill and F. P. Zscheile, *Ind. Eng. Chem.* (*Anal.*), 1943, **15**, 1; B. W. Beadle and H. R. Kraybill, *J. Amer. Chem. Soc.*, 1944, **66**, 1232; T. P. Hilditch, R. A. Morton and J. P. Riley, *Analyst*, 1945, **70**, 68; T. P. Hilditch, C. B. Patel and J. P. Riley, *ibid.*, 1951, **76**, 81; *see also* ref. 184*a*.

199. *cf.* R. F. Paschke, D. H. Wheeler, *et al.*, *J. Amer. Oil Chem. Soc.*, 1952, **29**, 229.

200. (*a*) J. Scheiber, *Z. angew. Chem.*, 1933, **46**, 643; (*b*) J. Böeseken and R. Hoevers, *Rec. trav. chim.*, 1930, **49**, 1163; (*c*) T. F. Bradley and D. Richardson, *Ind. Eng. Chem.*, 1940, **32**, 1963; W. C. Forbes and H. A. Neville, *ibid.*, 1940, **32**, 555; G. W. Priest and J. D. von Mikusch, *ibid.*, 1940, **32**, 1314.

201. (*a*) C. Mangold, *Monatsh*, 1894, **15**, 307; (*b*) J. D. von Mikusch, *Lack-u. Farbenchem.*, 1949, **3**, No. 9, 167; (*c*) L. P. Witnauer, P. L. Nichols and F. R. Senti, *J. Amer. Oil. Chem. Soc.*, 1949, **26**, 653; (*d*) W. C. Smit and J. Böeseken, *Rec. trav. chim.*, 1930, **49**, 539, 686; (*e*) J. D. von Mikusch, *J. Amer. Oil Chem. Soc.*, 1952, **29**, 114.

202. (*a*) K. Hazura, *Monatsh.*, 1887, **7**, 158, 268; (*b*) E. Erdmann and F. Bedford, *Ber.*, 1909, **42**, 1334; (*c*) E. Erdmann, F. Bedford and F. Raspe, *Ber.*, 1909, **42**, 1334; (*d*) *Cf.* A. Eckert, *Monatsh.*, 1917, **38**, 1; Y. Inoue and B. Suzuki, *Proc. Imp. Acad. Tokyo*, 1931, **7**, 375; T. P. Hilditch and N. L. Vidyarthi, *Proc. Roy. Soc.*, 1929, **A**, **122**, 563.

203. (a) G. Y. Shinowara and J. B. Brown, *J. Amer. Chem. Soc.*, 1938, **60**, 2734; (b) R. E. Beal, V. E. Sohns, R. A. Eisenhauer and E. L. Griffin, *J. Amer. Oil Chem. Soc.*, 1961, **38**, 524; (c) H. B. White, Jr., and F. W. Quackenbush, *ibid.*, 1962, **39**, 517 (cf. also D. F. Kümmel, *Analyt. Chem.*, 1962, **34**, 1003).

204. J. P. Kass, J. Nichols and G. O. Burr, *J. Amer. Chem. Soc.*, 1941, **63**, 1060.

205. S. S. Nigam and B. C. L. Weedon, *Chem. and Ind.*, 1955, 1555; *J. Chem. Soc.*, 1956, 4049.

206. K. Hazura and A. Friedreich, *Monatsh.*, 1887, **8**, 159, 267; 1888, **9**, 181.

207. (a) H. W. Lemon, *Canad. J. Research*, 1944, **22**, F, 191; (b) K. F. Mattil, *Oil and Soap*, 1945, **22**, 213; (c) A. E. Bailey and G. S. Fisher, *ibid.*, 1946, **23**, 14; (d) C. R. Scholfield, H. J. Dutton, *et al.*, *Analyt. Chem.*, 1961, **33**, 1745; *J. Amer. Oil Chem. Soc.*, 1960, **37**, 579; 1963, **40**, 45; (e) J. G. Willard and M. L. Martinez, *ibid.*, 1961, **38**, 282; (f) C. R. Scholfield, H. J. Dutton *et al.*, *ibid.*, 1961, **38**, 208; 1963, **40**, 175.

208. (a) R. F. Paschke, W. Tolberg and D. H. Wheeler, *J. Amer. Oil Chem. Soc.*, 1953, **30**, 97; (b) W. G. Bickford, E. F. DuPre, C. H. Mack and R. T. O'Connor, *ibid.*, 1953, **30**, 376; *see also* J. S. Hofmann, R. T. O'Connor, D. C. Heinzelman and W. G. Bickford, *ibid.*, 1957, **34**, 338; W. E. Tolberg, R. F. Paschke and D. H. Wheeler, *ibid.*, 1961, **38**, 102.

209. J. Böeseken and H. J. Ravenswaay, *Rec. trav. chim.*, 1925, **44**, 241; J. Böeseken, W. C. Smit, J. J. Hoogland and A. G. van der Broek, *ibid.*, 1927, **46**, 619; J. Böeseken and J. van Krimpen, *Proc. K. Akad. Wetensch. Amsterdam*, 1928, **31**, 238; A. Steger and J. van Loon, *J. Soc. Chem. Ind.*, 1928, **47**, 361T.

210. (a) R. Majima, *Ber.*, 1909, **42**, 674; (b) A. Eibner and E. Rossmann, *Chem. Umschau*, 1928, **35**, 197.

211. (a) R. S. Morrell and S. Marks, *J. Oil Col. Chem. Assoc.*, 1929, **12**, 183; *J. Soc. Chem. Ind.*, 1931, **50**, 33T; (b) R. S. Morrell and H. Samuels, *J. Chem. Soc.*, 1932, 2251; (c) I. J. Rinkes, *Rec. trav. chim.*, 1943, **62**, 557.

212. (a) A. Steger, J. van Loon and P. J. Vlimmeren, *Fette u. Seifen*, 1944, **51**, 49; (b) M. L. Woltemate and B. F. Daubert, *J. Amer. Chem. Soc.*, 1950, **72**, 1233; (c) R. W. Planck, F. C. Pack, D. C. Heinzelmann, M. F. Stansbury and R. T. O'Connor, *J. Amer. Oil Chem. Soc.*, 1953, **30**, 598; (d) M. R. Mills, *J. Oil Col. Chem. Assn.*, 1957, **40**, 10.

213. L. Crombie and A. G. Jacklin, (a) *Chem. and Ind.*, 1955, 1186; *J. Chem. Soc.*, 1957, 1632; (b) *ibid.*, 1957, 1622; (c) L. Crombie and B. P. Griffin, *ibid.*, 1958, 4435; (d) E. M. Meade, "Progress in the Chemistry of Fats and other Lipids", 1957, p. 503: Pergamon Press; F. D. Gunstone (with A. J. Sealy), *J. Chem. Soc.*, 1963, 5772; (with R. C. Badami), *J. Sci. Food Agric.*, 1963, **14**, 863.

214. (a) Y. Toyama and T. Tsuchiya, *J. Soc. Chem. Ind. Japan*, 1935, **38**, 182B, 185B; (b) E. H. Farmer and F. A. van den Heuvel, *J. Chem. Soc.*, 1936, 1809; (c) N. H. E. Ahlers and N. G. McTaggart, *J. Sci. Food Agric.*, 1954, **5**, 75; N. H. E. Ahlers, A. C. Dennison and L. A. O'Neill, *Nature*, 1954, **173**, 1045; (d) N. H. E. Ahlers and A. C. Dennison, *Chem. and Ind.*, 1954, 603; (e) C. Y. Hopkins and M. J. Chisholm, *Canad. J. Chem.*, 1962, **40**, 2078; (f) idem, *J. Chem. Soc.*, 1962, 573; (g) idem, *Chem. and Ind.*, 1962, 2064; (h) idem, *J. Org. Chem.*, 1962, **27**, 3137; (i) J. McLean and A. H. Clark, *J. Chem. Soc.*, 1956, 777; (j) M. J. Chisholm and C. Y. Hopkins, *Canad. J. Chem.*, 1960, **38**, 2500; (k) idem, *ibid.*, 1963, **41**, 1888; *J. Amer. Oil Chem. Soc.*, 1964, **41**, 42.

215. (a) C. Holdt, *Drugs, Oils and Paints*, 1937, **14**, 260; (b) F. Wilborn, *Chem.-Ztg.*, 1931, **55**, 434; (c) J. van Loon and A. Steger, *Rec. trav. chim.*, 1931, **50**, 936.

216. (a) W. B. Brown and E. H. Farmer, *Biochem. J.*, 1935, **29**, 631; *J. Chem. Soc.*, 1935, 1632; (b) C. P. A. Kappelmeier, *Fett. chem. Umschau*, 1935, **42**, 145; (c) R. S. Morrell and W. R. Davis, *J. Chem. Soc.*, 1936, 1481; *J. Oil Col. Chem. Assoc.*, 1936, **19**, 264; (d) A. Mendelowitz and J. P. Riley, *Analyst*, 1953, **78**, 704.

217. (a) M. Tsujimoto and H. Koyanagi, *J. Soc. Chem. Ind. Japan*, 1933, **36**, 110B, 673B; M. Tsujimoto, *ibid.*, 1936, **39**, 116B; (b) E. H. Farmer and E. Sunderland, *J. Chem. Soc.*, 1935, 759; (c) H. P. Kaufmann, J. Baltes and S. Funke, *Fette u. Seifen*, 1938, **45**, 302; (d) J. P. Riley, *J. Chem. Soc.*, 1951, 2579.

218. (a) T. Tutiya, *J. Chem. Soc. Japan*, 1940, **60**, 717, 867, 1188; 1941, **62**, 10, 552; (b) H. P. Kaufmann and M. Keller, *Ber.*, 1948, **81**, 152; (c) H. P. Kaufmann, *ibid.*, 1948, **81**, 159.

219. (a) A. Steger and J. van Loon, *Fette u. Seifen*, 1937, **44**, 243; *Rec. trav. chim.*, 1940, **59**, 1156; 1941, **60**, 342; (b) H. A. Boekenoogen, *Fette u. Seifen*, 1937, **44**, 344; (c) A. Castille, *Annalen*, 1939, **543**, 104; (d) Y. Doucet and M. Fauve, *Compt. rend.*, 1942, **215**, 533.

220. (a) S. P. Ligthelm and H. M. Schwartz, *J. Amer. Chem. Soc.*, 1950, **72**, 1868; *J. Chem. Soc.*, 1952, 1088; (b) F. D. Gunstone and M. A. McGee, *Chem. and Ind.*, 1954, 1112; F. D. Gunstone and W. C. Russell, *J. Chem. Soc.*, 1955, 3782; (c) H. H. Hatt and A. Z. Szumer, *Chem. and Ind.*, 1954, 962; (d) J. Grigor, D. M. MacInnes and J. McLean, *ibid.*, 1954, 1112; *J. Chem. Soc.*, 1955, 1069; (e) N. H. E. Ahlers and S. P. Ligthelm, *J. Chem. Soc.*, 1952, 5039; (f) S. P. Ligthelm, *Chem. and Ind.*, 1954, 249.

221. M. Tsujimoto, *J. Coll. Eng. Tokyo*, 1906, **4**, 1; *J. Soc. Chem. Ind. Japan*, 1920, **23**, 1007.

222. (a) L. C. A. Nunn and I. Smedley-MacLean, *Biochem. J.*, 1938, **32**, 2178; 1940, **34**, 879, 884; I. Smedley-MacLean and E. M. Hume, *ibid.*, 1941, **35**, 990; (b) I. Smedley-MacLean, (with D. E. Dolby and L. C. A. Nunn), *ibid.*, 1940, **34**, 1422; (with C. L. Arcus), *ibid.*, 1943, **37**, 1; (c) R. Reiser *et al.*, *J. Nutrition*, 1950, **40**, 429; 1950, **42**, 325; 1951, **44**, 159; *Arch. Biochem. Biophys.*, 1951, **32**, 113; (d) J. F. Mead *et al.*, *J. Nutrition*, 1951, **44**, 507; *J. Biol. Chem.*, 1953, **205**, 683; 1956, **218**, 401; **219**, 705; 1957, **224**, 841; **227**, 1025; 1958, **229**, 575; 1959, **234**, 1411; 1960, **235**, 3385.

223. (a) J. B. Brown and E. M. Deck, *J. Amer. Chem. Soc.*, 1930, **52**, 1135; J. B. Brown, *J. Biol. Chem.*, 1931, **90**, 133; 1932, **97**, 183; J. B. Brown and C. C. Sheldon, *J. Amer. Chem. Soc.*, 1934, **56**, 2149; W. C. Ault and J. B. Brown, *J. Biol. Chem.*, 1934, **107**, 607, 615; (b) G. Y. Shinowara and J. B. Brown, *ibid.*, 1940, **134**, 331; (c) D. T. Mowry, W. R. Brode and J. B. Brown, *ibid.*, 1941, **142**, 671, 679.

224. (a) R. W. Riemenschneider, N. R. Ellis and H. W. Titus, *J. Biol. Chem.*, 1938, **126**, 255; (b) M. F. White and J. B. Brown, *J. Biol. Chem.*, 1948, **70**, 4269; (c) S. F. Herb, R. W. Riemenschneider and J. Donaldson, *J. Amer. Oil Chem. Soc.*, 1951, **28**, 55; S. F. Herb, L. P. Witnauer and R. W. Riemenschneider, *ibid.*, 1951, **28**, 505.

225. (a) R. S. Morrell and W. R. Davis, *J. Soc. Chem. Ind.*, 1936, **55**, 101T; (b) E. H. Farmer and F. A. van den Heuvel, *J. Soc. Chem. Ind.*, 1938, **57**, 24; *J. Chem. Soc.*, 1938, 427; (c) J. R. Edisbury, A. E. Gillam, I. M. Heilbron and R. A. Morton, *Biochem. J.*, 1932, **26**, 1164; J. R. Edisbury, R. A. Morton and J. A. Lovern, *ibid.*, 1933, **27**, 1451; 1935, **29**, 899; (d) F. A. Norris, I. I. Rusoff, E. S. Miller and G. O. Burr, *J. Biol. Chem.*, 1941, **139**, 199.

226. (a) M. Tsujimoto, *Bull. Chem. Soc. Japan*, 1928, **3**, 299; (b) E. Klenk and co-workers, *cf. Z. physiol. Chem.*, 1952, **291**, 104; 1961, **324**, 1; and elsewhere; (c) W. Stoffel and E. H. Ahrens, Jr, *J. Amer. Chem. Soc.*, 1958, **80**, 6604; *J. Lipid Res.*, 1960, **1**, 139.

227. (a) Y. Toyama and T. Tsuchiya, *Bull. Chem. Soc. Japan*, 1935, **10**, 192, 232, 241, 296, 301, 539, 547; Y. Toyama and T. Yamamoto, *J. Japan Oil Chem. Soc.*, 1953, **2**, 193; (b) Y. Toyama, Y. Iwata and K. Fujimura, *Fette, Seifen, Anstrichm.*, 1959, **61**, 846.

228. W. Klenk (a) with W. Bongard, *Z. Physiol. Chem.*, 1952, **291**, 104; (b) with F. Lindlar, *ibid.*, 1955, **299**, 74; (c) with D. Eberhagen, *ibid.*, 1957, **307**, 42; (d) with H. Brockerhoff, *ibid.*, 1957, **307**, 272; (e) 1958, **310**, 153; (f) with H. J. Tomuschat, *ibid.*, 1957, **308**, 165; (g) with H. Steinbach, *ibid.*, 1959, **316**, 31; (h) with W. Knipprath, *ibid.*, 1959, **317**, 243; (i) with D. Eberhagen, *ibid.*, 1961, **322**, 258; (j) with L. Bricker-Voigt, *ibid.*, 1961, **324**, 1; (k) with W. Mantog, *Annalen*, 1957, **604**, 4.

229. (a) E. G. Hammond and W. O. Lundberg, *J. Amer. Oil Chem. Soc.*, 1953, **30**, 438; (b) M. H. Silk and H. H. Hahn, *Biochem. J.*, 1954, **57**, 582; (c) J. F. Mead and W. H. Slatan, Jr., *J. Biol. Chem.*, 1956, **219**, 705; (d) J. M. Whitcutt and D. A. Sutton, *Biochem. J.*, 1956, **63**, 469; (e) J. M. Whitcutt, *ibid.*, 1957, **67**, 60; (f) L. Hörhammer, F. Wintersberger and H. Wagner, *Arch. Pharm.*, 1959, **292**, 545.

230. G. Baudart, *Bull. Soc. Chim.*, 1942, [v], **9**, 922; 1943, [v], **10**, 440, 443.

231. (a) W. M. Potts, *Paint Oil Chem. Rev.*, 1946, **109**, 16; (b) J. Devine, *J. Sci. Food Agric.*, 1950, **1**, 88; (c) T. P. Hilditch, *J. Oil Col. Chem. Assocn.*, 1949, **32**, 5; A. Crossley and T. P. Hilditch, *J. Chem. Soc.*, 1949, 3353; (d) *idem, ibid.*, 1952, 4613; (e) D. P. Hanks and W. M. Potts, *J. Amer. Oil Chem. Soc.*, 1951, **28**, 292; (f) R. T. Holman and D. P. Hanks, *ibid.*, 1955, **32**, 356.

232. (a) L. Crombie, *J. Chem. Soc.*, 1955, 1007; (b) P. C. Wailes, *Austral. J. Chem.*, 1959, **12**, 173.

233. N. A. Sörensen, with J. Stene, *Annalen*, 1941, **549**, 80; with R. T. Holman, *Acta Chem. Scand.*, 1950, **4**, 416; with K. Stavholt, *ibid.*, 1950, **4**, 1080, 1567, 1575; with T. Bruun and C. M. Haug, *ibid.*, 1950, **4**, 850; 1951, **5**, 1244; with P. K. Christensen, *ibid.*, 1952, **6**, 602, 893; with J. S. Sörensen, T. Bruun and D. Holme, *ibid.*, 1954, **8**, 26, 34, 280; J. S. Sörensen (review), *Chem. and Ind.*, 1953, 240. J. D. Bu'Lock, E. R. H. Jones *et al.*, *J. Chem. Soc.*, 1953, 3719; *Chem. and Ind.*, 1954, 990; 1955, 686.

CHAPTER X

Synthetic Glycerides : Naturally Occurring Fatty Alcohols : Acyl Ethers of Glycerol

The individual acidic components of fats were discussed in Chapter IX, and it remains to give in the present chapter similar information concerning the alcoholic components of the lipids, which fall into four main groups:

(*a*) Glycerol, the trihydric alcohol characteristic of the true fats (triglycerides). This is, of course, by far the most important in relation to the fundamental part which it bears in the fats themselves, but its properties and reactions are so well known that it is unnecessary to deal with the subject here. Its chief interest, as regards the natural fats, lies in the innumerable mixed triglycerides of the fatty acids which can be derived from it, and accordingly the first part of this chapter is occupied by a brief review of the synthesis and characterisation of triglycerides of known configuration, simple or mixed, of the higher fatty acids.

(*b*) Higher alcohols of the normal aliphatic series corresponding with the various natural higher fatty acids, which occur as the alcoholic components of the waxes (wax esters); some of the latter accompany glycerides, others (mainly of higher molecular weight than the previous class) occur alone in the form of plant (cuticle) or insect waxes, etc.

(*c*) Three mono-alkyl ethers of glycerol, known as chimyl, batyl, and selachyl alcohols (ethers of glycerol with one molecule of, respectively, hexadecyl, octadecyl, or octadecenyl alcohols) occur as fatty esters in some marine animal fats, especially the liver oils of some Elasmobranch fish.

(*d*) The sterols or polycyclic alcohols of high molecular weight, and also vitamin A (related to the carotenoid group). These compounds, although they occur in combination with fatty acids as esters to quite a large extent, are of course not aliphatic in nature, and are so complex in structure that their study forms a separate field of organic chemical research in itself. For this reason, the constituents of what is usually termed the "unsaponifiable matter" which may accompany natural fats (sterols and vitamin D, carotenoids and vitamin A, squalene and other hydrocarbons of high molecular weight) are not dealt with in detail in this book.

SYNTHETIC GLYCERIDES*

The problem of the structural configuration of glycerides is of great importance and has attracted many workers in the field of fat chemistry. Difficulties which

* In this section of Chapter X the three hydroxyl groups of glycerol are defined by the numbers 1, 2, 3, to avoid confusion with the polymorphic α-, β', β forms of individual glycerides.

have retarded the work in this field were primarily due (i) to lack of reliable data in the case of naturally occurring glycerides owing to the extreme difficulty of isolating individual glycerides from a mixture, and (ii) to unreliable data recorded in the literature for synthetic glycerides.

In regard to (i) considerable progress has been made in recent years not only by thorough study of the melting and transition points (thermal studies) and the X-ray diffraction characteristics of the various polymorphic forms, but also by fresh techniques, such as enzyme hydrolysis for determining the acyl group in the 2-position of the glyceride molecule, counter-current distribution, thin layer chromatography and infra-red spectroscopy. A great deal of further progress may also be expected in the near future with the application of these and other modern techniques and the greater speed nowadays of ascertaining fatty acid compositions with the aid of gas–liquid chromatography.

The preparative side (ii) has also improved considerably by increased knowledge of the lability of acyl groups in mono- and di-glycerides, of how undesirable isomeric change may be circumvented and by improved methods for producing and checking the purity of the various components (fatty acids, fatty acid chlorides, etc.) in glyceride synthesis.

Other factors which retarded both the synthesis and physical examination of pure glycerides were incomplete knowledge of their various polymorphic forms and failure to appreciate that, although two glycerides may contain the same two or three fatty acids, the relative positions of the acids has a profound effect on physical properties, e.g., 1-oleo-2-palmito-3-stearin and 1-palmito-2-oleo-3-stearin. The first of these two factors was undoubtedly responsible for several melting points being recorded for one and the same glyceride; this has been clarified to some extent by the work of Malkin and of Lutton and their co-workers on melting and transition points and X-ray spectra but, as Chapman (1962) has pointed out in a general review[15b] of this subject, additional information is required before the polymorphism of glycerides can be adequately understood. Use of the enzyme hydrolysis procedure (Chapter XI, p. 706) will assist greatly in determining the nature of acyl groups attached respectively to the 2-, or to the 1- and 3-, hydroxyl groups of the glycerol molecules.

In previous editions this section was chiefly devoted to recording the melting and transition points, and the X-ray diffraction data, of the polymorphic forms of many synthetically prepared triglycerides; in the present edition attention will be concentrated instead upon the methods by which glycerides of unequivocal constitution may be prepared, since this aspect is primarily the most important when it is needful to obtain synthetic mixed glycerides for comparison with individual glycerides isolated from natural fats. The physical data which will be mentioned are confined to those of the polymorphic forms of a selected few synthetic glycerides, namely, those mixed glycerides of most frequent or likely occurrence in natural fats, together with a number of simple triglycerides ("mono-acid triglycerides").

The literature on the properties of polymorphic forms of glycerides is now very large, dealing not only with thermal and with X-ray diffraction data, but also with infra-red spectrum analysis, whilst it would seem that mass spectroscopy and nuclear magnetic resonance may in future attain some importance in this field. The reader is therefore referred to a number of reviews and papers in which these different physical properties of glycerides have received notice:

Thermal and X-ray diffraction data. E. S. Lutton, *J. Amer. Chem. Soc.*, 1951, **73**, 5595; T. Malkin, "Progress in the Chemistry of Fats and other Lipids", Vol. II, p. 1 (Pergamon Press, 1954); F. H. Mattson and R. A. Volpenhein, *J. Lipid Res.*, 1961, **2**, 58; 1962, **3**, 281; H. Lavery, *J. Amer. Oil Chem. Soc.*, 1958, **35**, 418; J. Hannewijk and A. J. Haighton, *ibid.*, 1958, **35**, 457; L. Hartman, *Chem. Revs.*, 1958, **58**, 845; F. D. Gunstone, *Chem. and Ind.*, 1964, 84.

Infra-Red Spectroscopy. D. Chapman, *J. Chem. Soc.*, 1956, **55**, 2522; 1957, 2715; 1958, 3186, 4680; *J. Amer. Oil Chem. Soc.*, 1960, **37**, 73; D. Chapman, A. Crossley and A. C. Davies, *J. Chem. Soc.*, 1957, 1502; H. P. Kaufmann, F. Volbert and G. Mankel, *Fette, Seifen, Anstrichm.*, 1959, **61**, 547; R. T. O'Connor, *J. Amer. Oil Chem. Soc.*, 1961, **38**, 641.

Mass Spectroscopy. H. J. Dutton, *J. Amer. Oil Chem. Soc.*, 1961, **38**, 660.

Nuclear Magnetic Resonance. C. Y. Hopkins, *J. Amer. Oil Chem. Soc.*, 1961, **38**, 664.

Thin Layer Chromatography. O. S. Privett, M. L. Blanck and W. O. Lundberg, *J. Amer. Oil Chem. Soc.*, 1961, **38**, 312; H. K. Mangold, *ibid.*, 1961, **38**, 708; C. B. Barrett, M. S. J. Dallas and F. B. Padley, *ibid.*, 1963, **40**, 580.

General. D. Chapman, *Chem. Revs.*, 1962, **62**, 433.

Although the nature of the natural fats was understood by Chevreul[1] in 1823, there appears to be no record of an attempt to synthesise glycerides until Berthelot[2] prepared tristearin in 1853. Although the possible existence of mixed triglycerides was postulated by Berthelot, it was not until 1889 that Wynter Blyth and Robertson[3] obtained a solid glyceride from butter fat which they identified as an oleo-butyro-palmitin.

In 1902 Guth,[4] who recognised that naturally occurring fats consisted essentially of mixtures of mixed triglycerides, attempted the synthesis of a large number of mono-, di-, and tri-glycerides; but since at that time the existence of several polymorphic forms of each glyceride was not appreciated, the melting point criteria of his synthetic products were uncertain. In 1905 Grün[5] devised new syntheses of di- and tri-glycerides and considerably extended the knowledge existing up to that time; but, although Grün was able to record the isolation of two polymorphs in some instances, he did not realise the ease with which, under certain conditions of synthesis, migration of an acyl group (e.g., from the 2-position to the 1- or 3-position) could take place. Consequently some of his criteria were still indeterminate, if not invalid, and it was not until about 1920 that Emil Fischer[6] (after life-long studies of carbohydrates, polypeptides, and the purines) turned his attention to fats in the closing years of his long career, and established some of the conditions in which shifting of acyl groups takes place during glyceride syntheses in the laboratory. Emil Fischer also indicated some methods by which this migration could be avoided and mixed glycerides of unequivocal configuration could be synthetically produced. A decade later these procedures were used by Fairbourne,[7] C. G. King[8] and their co-workers to prepare a number of symmetrical and unsymmetrical diacid triglycerides and define their physical properties.

We now proceed to brief descriptions of the most certain procedures at present available for the synthetical preparation of glycerides of known configuration. It should be mentioned here that comprehensive reviews on the synthesis of glycerides of all types have been given by Malkin and Bevan,[9a] Hartman,[9b] and Mattson and Volpenhein.[9c]

Although mono- and di-glycerides only occur in nature as a result of hydrolytic splitting of the triglycerides, their preparation in a pure state is of the utmost importance as a stage in the preparation of most pure synthetic triglycerides, especially those containing saturated and unsaturated acyl radicals, an important class in natural oils and fats. Reference will therefore first be made to the synthesis of pure mono- and pure di-glycerides, before proceeding to the tri-glycerides.

Monoglycerides

As mentioned, the first key work that enabled reliable progress in synthesis of glycerides was due to Emil Fischer,[6] who prepared 1-*monoglycerides* by reacting glycerol with acetone to form *iso*-propylidene glycerol, and then treated the residual hydroxyl group with the appropriate acid chloride in the presence of pyridine. The acetone compound was decomposed with hydrochloric acid to yield 1-monoglyceride, which was purified by re-crystallisation. The protection of the two hydroxyl groups during acylation prevented acyl shift.

This still remains the best method for preparing 1-*monoglycerides*, although there have been minor improvements, of which a modern example will be found in the work of H. O. L. Fischer and Baer.[10]

For the synthesis of 2-*monoglycerides* a similar principle is used, namely protection of the 1,3-positions in glycerol[11] by the benzylidene group C_6H_5.CH:, which is introduced by reacting glycerol with benzaldehyde. The trityl (triphenyl methyl) group has also been used to protect 1,3-positions,[12a, b] but in the opinion of some workers[9a] it is not so satisfactory as the benzylidene method. In order to produce the 2-monoglyceride, removal of the protecting group formerly involved catalytic hydrogenation ("hydrogenolysis"), so that the method could not be used for making 2-monoglycerides of unsaturated acids; whilst, if hydrochloric acid is used for removing the benzylidene group, 1-monoglycerides are produced by acyl migration. Martin,[13] however, found that by treating 2-acylated-1,3-benzylidene compounds with boric acid in triethyl borate the 2-acylmonoglyceride was liberated, with the formation of C_6H_5.CH(OEt)$_2$ (leading to benzaldehyde) and without any risk of shift of the acyl group to the 1-(3-) positions – thus enabling the method to be applied to preparing 2-monoglycerides of unsaturated acids.

Other syntheses of monoglycerides have been published and will be found recorded in one or other of the reviews mentioned,[9] but general opinion is clearly that the methods above are those which most readily yield products of conclusive purity.

TABLE 146. *Melting Points of Monoglycerides*
(Highest melting forms, °C.)

	1-MONOGLYCERIDES (UNSYMMETRICAL)	2-MONOGLYCERIDES (SYMMETRICAL)
Laurin	63·0[27a]	51·0[16]
Palmitin	77·0[14a]	68·5[16]
Stearin	81·5[14a]	74·5[16]
Olein	35·5[15a]	23·5[13]
Linolein	12·3[15a]	8·9[13]
Linolenin	15·7[15a]	?
Elaidin	58·5[15a]	54·2[13]

Heating and a variety of other conditions, including the presence of traces of alkali or acid, results in isomerisation of the 1- and 2-monoglycerides, leading to an equilibrium at 88 per cent. of 1-mono- and 12 per cent. of 2-mono-glycerides. Passage of pure mono-glycerides in solvents through silica or other types of adsorbent column is alone sufficient to cause some isomerisation.[17] Pure monoglycerides should be stored at 0°C. or lower, since isomerisation can take place slowly at ordinary temperatures even in the absence of a catalyst.[18] After storing under air-tight conditions for five years, 2-monopalmitin was found by Aylward and Wood[19] to be little changed, but 2-monomyristin had isomerised to give 15 per cent. of 1-monomyristin, whilst 2-monolaurin had been isomerised to the extent of 92 per cent. of 1-monolaurin.

Diglycerides

1,2-Diglycerides. The mono-acid disaturated 1,2-diglycerides are probably best prepared by the method of Howe and Malkin,[20] who blocked the free hydroxyl group in *iso*propylidene glycerol with a benzyl group (i.e., as a benzyl ether), then removed the *iso*propylidene group with dilute acetic acid and acylated the free 1,2-hydroxyl groups with an acyl chloride in presence of pyridine; the benzyl group was lastly removed by "hydrogenolysis". This method does not enable unsaturated or mixed unsaturated-saturated di-glycerides to be prepared.

According to Mattson and Volpenhein[9c] all types of 1,2-diglycerides can be prepared by incomplete acylation of 2-monoglycerides at room temperature, and then separating the mixture of free fatty acid, unchanged 2-monoglyceride, 1,2-diglyceride and triglycerides by silica gel chromatography, with use of Amberlite resin for removing the free fatty acids. Crossley *et al.*[21] have made 1,2-diglycerides by producing from 1,3-diglycerides the equilibrium mixture of 1,2- and 1,3-diglycerides, and separating the latter by crystallisation from light petroleum.

1,3-Diglycerides. A number of methods have been mentioned by Malkin,[9a] but according to Mattson and Volpenhein[9c] there is no ideal method, although they consider that of Baur and Lange,[22] which involved "directed" rearrange-ment, the best available:

The pure mono-acid triglyceride of the desired fatty acid, triacetin and glycerol are mixed in the molar ratio of 0·5:1·0:0·8. A basic catalyst is added and the mixture heated above its melting point for 2 hours. The temperature is then decreased slowly so that preferential crystallisation of the 1,3-diglyceride of the high molecular weight fatty acid results in "direc-ted" interesterification to this product. The catalyst is inactivated with acetic acid and the 1,3-diglyceride recovered by filtration and purified by crystallisation.

This procedure is not applicable to mixed diglycerides or to unsaturated diglycerides. For mixed diglycerides the incomplete acylation procedure as used for 1,2-diglycerides (above) may be employed starting from 1-monoglyceride. Crossley's equilibrium method,[21] commencing from 1,2-diglycerides, can also be applied.

The diunsaturated diglycerides are the most difficult to prepare but, from a mixture of 1,2- and 1,3-diglycerides prepared by incomplete acylation of 1-mono-olein, Mattson and Volpenhein obtained pure 1,3-diolein by crystallisation from hexane at $-20°$C.

TABLE 147. *Melting Points of Diglycerides*
(Highest melting forms, °C.)

	1,2-DIGLYCERIDES (UNSYMMETRICAL)	1,3-DIGLYCERIDES (SYMMETRICAL)
Dipalmitin	63·5[9b]	74·0[14a]
Palmitostearin	*	71·5[14a,26e]
Distearin	71·0[9b]	80·0[14a]
Oleopalmitin	?	44·0[14a], 46·0[26c]
Oleostearin	?	49·0[14a], 52·0,[26e] 54·0[26c]
Diolein	?	21·5,[26e] 25·0[26c]
Dilinolein	?	−2·6[26e]
Dilinolenin	?	−12·3[26e]

* 1-Palmito-2-stearin, 61·0°; 2-Palmito-1-stearin, 69·5°.[9b]

The pure diglycerides are somewhat more stable than the pure monoglycerides, but isomerise under the action of heat (e.g., at 165°C.), also in presence of acid. Equilibrium is reached at 58 per cent. of the 1,3- and 42 per cent. of the 1,2-diglycerides.[21,24]

Isomerisation can occur also by passage through some types of column, but the 1,2-compounds are stable on passage through a silicic acid column.

Triglycerides

Trisaturated mono-acid glycerides occur to a relatively unimportant extent in natural fats and fatty oils; their synthesis is relatively easy by direct esterification of glycerol and fatty acid with an excess of the latter and in the presence of a catalyst such as *p*-toluene sulphonic acid, the crude products being purified by crystallisation.

Mixed saturated triglycerides, such as palmitodistearin, can be prepared by reacting the appropriate acid chloride with either mono- or diglycerides in pyridine-chloroform in the cold for three days; as a rule a 50 per cent. molar excess of fatty acid chloride is employed. Other methods have however been used, such as synthesis with trityl compounds (Verkade[12a]).

Analogous procedures have also been used to prepare mixed saturated-unsaturated triglycerides[9c, 14a] in which either two or three different fatty acids may be present. Mattson and Volpenhein[9c] prefer to start from a monoglyceride, but other workers have proceeded directly from a simple 1,2- or 1,3-diglyceride in order to synthesise a diacid triglyceride.

Tri-unsaturated glycerides are prepared on similar lines, but difficulties arise more readily during their synthesis owing to the greater precautions needful in preparing mono- and di-glycerides of unsaturated acids, especially those of linoleic and linolenic acids.

Triglycerides are far less prone than mono- or di-glycerides to undergo interchange of acyl groups, but this takes place (readily at 80°C., and slowly at still lower temperatures) in the presence of catalysts such as sodium methoxide in strictly anhydrous conditions. In the absence of any catalyst there is probably little or no change likely below 250°C., but beyond that (e.g., at 300°C. or above) fairly rapid acyl interchange sets in (with concurrent pyrolytic changes), leading eventually to the production of triglycerides in which the acyl groups are distributed at random, in close accordance with the theory of probability.[25a]

Pyrolytic changes undergone by tricaprin and 2-oleopalmitin under aerobic and anaerobic conditions at 190°, 250° and 300°C. have been described.[25b]

In Table 148 will be found the transition and melting points and, where available, the X-ray "long spacings" of the polymorphic forms (α, β', β) of a number of synthetic triglycerides. These include some of the simple (mono-acid) triglycerides, and some mixed glycerides which are among those most frequently found in natural fats, and are quoted in order to assist the reader in the identification of individual natural glycerides. For a full discussion of the theoretical basis of X-ray diffraction data reference must be made to one of the monographs mentioned on p. 660. Here it need only be said that the X-ray pattern consists of two distinct series, the "long spacings" and the "short" or "side spacings". The long spacings, which in some degree reflect the length of the glyceride molecule, increase with increasing length of the acyl chains, but as a rule there is no very clear difference between the long spacings

TABLE 148. *Transition Points, Melting Points and X-Ray Spacings of Some Typical Triglycerides*

	TRANSITION AND MELTING POINTS (°C.)			LONG SPACINGS (A)		
	α	β'	β	α	β'	β
Simple triglycerides:						
Trilaurin[26a]	35·0	?	46·4	35·6	32·9	31·2
Trimyristin[26a]	46·5	54·5	57·0	41·2	37·6	35·8
Tripalmitin[26a]	56·0	63·5	65·5	45·6	42·6	40·6
Tristearin[26a]	65·0	70·0	72·0	50·6	47·2	45·0
Triolein[26b]	−32	−13	5–5·5	45·2	45·8	43·3
Trielaidin[26c]	37	?	42	?	?	44·1
Trilinolein[26b, d]	−45	−13	−13	?	?	?
Trilinolenin[26d]	−44·6	?	−24	?	?	?
Trierucin[26c]	17	25	30	?	54·7	51·1
Mixed triglycerides:						
1-Laurodimyristin[27f]	37	42	46·5	?	35·3	36·5
2-Laurodimyristin[27g]	35	45	50	39·6	36·7	34·7
1-Myristodilaurin[27f]	33·5	39	43·5	?	34·5	33·0
2-Myristodilaurin[27g]	37	44	48	?	34·5	33·6
1-Stearodipalmitin[27f]	55	59·5	62·5	47·8	43·9	42·5
2-Stearodipalmitin[27g]	59	65	68	50·2	44·7	43·2
1-Palmitodistearin[27f]	57	61	65	48·8	44·7	46·5
2-Palmitodistearin[27g]	56	64	68	50·5	47·5	44·2
1-Oleodipalmitin[15a, 27b, d, e]	18·5	27–30	34·5	79	65	67·5
2-Oleodipalmitin[14a, 15a, 27c, d, e]	18–21	32–35	36–38	47	42	61
1-Palmito-2-oleo-stearin[14a, b, 15a, 23, 27d, e]	18–21	31–33	37–38	48	67–69	63–64
2-Palmito-1-oleo-stearin[14a, 15a, 23, 27d, e]	24–25	37–40	40–41	40	68–69	67–68
2-Stearo-1-palmito-olein[14a, 15a, 23, 27d, e]	25–26	37–40	40–41·5	41	43–44	67–69
1-Oleodistearin[14b, 15a, 27b, d, e]	27(?)	30–31	42–43·5	80	83–85	71
2-Oleodistearin[14a, b, 15a, 27c, d, e]	22–23	37–38	42–43·5	50	45	65–66
1-Palmitodiolein[27b]	−13	2·5	19	No record		
1-Stearodiolein[27b]	−1·5	8·5	23	" "		

of triglycerides containing the same acids, but attached to different positions in the glycerol molecules. The short or side spacings (which are not included in Table 148) similarly represent the width of the molecules, and usually form a quaternary system which is practically the same irrespective of the length of the fatty acid chain; at the same time, isomeric glycerides of different configuration may exhibit detectable differences between their short spacings.

It should be noted that the nomenclature applied to the polymorphic forms of triglycerides, and their correlation with X-ray spectra, is somewhat confused — as will be gathered from perusal of the literature cited on p. 660, and of the references given in Table 148.

Synthesis of optically active mono-, di-, and tri-glycerides, and of other optically active glycerol derivatives. A wide range of optically active derivatives of glycerol has been synthesised by E. Baer, H. O. L. Fischer and co-workers from 1939 onwards. In the first instance d- and l-acetonylglycerols were prepared[28a] by oxidising 1,2,5,6-diacetonyl d- (or l-) mannitol with lead tetra-acetate, and hydrogenating the acetonyl-d- (or l-) glyceraldehyde so obtained to d- (or l-) acetonyl-glycerol ($[\alpha]_D \pm 12\cdot6°$). From these they prepared various acylated derivatives, which on removal of the acetone complex yielded optically active monoglycerides*; for example:

l-α-Monoglycerides[28b]

	M.P.	$[\alpha]_D$
Lauroyl	54–55°	− 4·9°
Palmitoyl	71–72	− 4·4
Stearoyl	76–77	− 3·6
p-Nitrobenzoyl	88–89	− 17·1

Conversion of these optically active monoglycerides into unsymmetrical mixed triglycerides, however, led to the surprising result that when all three acyl substitutes were long-chain aliphatic acids, the optical rotatory power disappeared, although with aromatic derivatives it persisted:

Mixed Triglycerides from l-α-Monoglycerides[28b]

	M.P.	$[\alpha]_D$
l-α-Lauro-β,α′-distearin	48·5°	0·0°
l-α-Palmito-β,α′-dilaurin	44	0·0
l-α-Stearo-β,α′-dipalmitin	62·5	0·0
l-α-(p-Nitrobenzoyl)-β,α′-distearin	67·5	− 1·4
l-α-(p-Nitrobenzoyl)-β,α′-dibenzoin	88	− 19·9

It thus became clear that, in the mixed triglycerides of higher aliphatic acids, lack of observable rotatory power may occur in an enantiomorphic form of a molecule which possesses asymmetry. This leads to the probability (already discussed in Chapter V, p. 403) that natural asymmetric triglycerides, although optically inactive, are not racemic.

---

* Steric considerations cause the production of l-monoglycerides from d-acetonylglycerol, and conversely; this apparent change of configuration is due only to the peculiar asymmetry, centred around the 2-carbon atom, of the glyceraldehyde-glycerol series, and does not involve a "Walden" inversion.

By other reactions, Baer and Fischer also produced optically active 1,2-dipalmitin and 1,2-distearin,[28c] and, in a different group of compounds, synthesised the optically active α-glycerol ethers of n-hexadecyl, n-octadecyl, and n-octadec-9-enyl (oleyl) alcohols,[28d] which were found to be identical respectively with the naturally occurring chimyl, batyl, and selachyl alcohols (cf. this chapter, p. 670). The rotatory power of the diacetyl derivative of the synthetic α-glycerol n-octadecyl ether was $[\alpha]_D - 7\cdot6°$ (in chloroform).

Commencing from d- or l-acetonylglycerol, the corresponding l- and d-α-glycerophosphoric acids were prepared[28e]; the l-acid was shown to be identical with the glycerophosphoric acid produced during alcoholic fermentation or glycolysis, and also present in phosphatides. From l-α-monobenzoylglycerol ($[\alpha]_D - 16\cdot8°$) Baer, Cushing and Fischer[28e] succeeded in preparing a typical mono-phosphatidic acid (although not of the aliphatic series), l-α-benzoyl-β-glycerophosphate, $[\alpha]_D + 9°$. Later Baer et al.[28f] (1948), and also Verkade et al.[29] (1952), synthesised several optically active di-aliphatic α-phosphatidic acids, and converted them into their choline and ethanolamine salts: amongst these were the dimyristoyl-, dipalmitoyl-, distearoyl-, 1-stearoyl-2-palmitoyl-, and 1-palmitoyl-2-stearoyl-α-glycerophosphoric acids.

Baer and Kates[28g] (1950) deduced that only α-glycerophosphoric acids occur in natural phosphatides. Long and Maguire[30] showed (1954), by studies of the action of a phospholipase, that egg-"lecithin" is entirely derived from l-α-glycerophosphoric acid.

General reviews of synthetical work on optically active glycerides have been published by Baer and Fischer (1941[31a]), on optically active phosphatides by Baer (1956[31b]), and on the latter and optically active glycerol ethers by Malkin (1957, 1961[31c]).

NATURALLY OCCURRING HIGHER ALIPHATIC ALCOHOLS

The chief higher fatty alcohols present in lipids dealt with in this book are cetyl (n-hexadecyl), n-octadecyl, and n-tetradecyl alcohols in the saturated series and oleyl (n-octadec-9-enyl) alcohol in the unsaturated series; these correspond respectively in carbon content and in chemical constitution with palmitic, stearic, myristic, and oleic acids. Other alcohols, saturated and unsaturated, of the C_{12}, C_{20}, C_{22} and C_{24} series are also occasionally encountered, whilst in the true (ester-) waxes of plants and insects the characteristic alcohols are members of the saturated series of still higher (e.g. C_{26} to C_{36}) carbon content ("ceryl", "melissyl", etc., alcohols).

It may be pointed out that, artificially, any of these natural alcohols can be prepared from the corresponding acids, or the esters of the latter, by several methods:

(i) Reduction of fatty acid esters in solution in absolute alcohol or butyl alcohol with sodium (Bouveault and Blanc[32]):

$$R.COOC_2H_5 + 2H_2 = R.CH_2OH + C_2H_5OH.$$

In this way all the alcohols from octadecyl, $C_{18}H_{37}(OH)$, to pentacosyl, $C_{25}H_{51}(OH)$, were prepared from the corresponding acids by Levene and

Taylor[33a] in the course of their syntheses of the normal saturated fatty acids containing from 19 to 26 carbon atoms; whilst cetyl, tetradecyl, dodecyl, oleyl, and probably other alcohols of this group have been obtained from the corresponding fatty acid esters by the same means at various times by different workers.[33b]

(ii) Hydrogenation of glycerides, simple esters, or the free fatty acids themselves at 200 atmospheres pressure and about 200° in presence of reduced basic copper chromate ("copper chromite" catalyst).[34] This process is now used extensively for the technical production of various higher fatty alcohols.

(iii) Reduction of fatty acids, their esters or glycerides by excess of lithium aluminium hydride.[35a] Yields of 85–90 per cent. of the corresponding alcohols are obtained by this method, which can be applied to saturated, mono-ethenoid, poly-ethenoid acids or esters, little or no reduction of ethenoid unsaturation taking place (even with linolenic or elæostearic acids).

Direct syntheses of "even-number" higher alcohols up to $C_{18}H_{37}(OH)$ have also been effected by the hydrogenation of polyene aldehydes prepared by condensation of crotonaldehyde (Kuhn[36]).

Saturated Higher n-Aliphatic Alcohols

The group of alcohols of intermediate molecular weight occurring in natural lipids (mainly in certain marine animal oils) includes *n*-dodecanol (*n*-dodecyl, lauryl alcohol), m.p. 24–26°; *n*-tetradecanol (*n*-tetradecyl, myristyl alcohol), m.p. 39°; *n*-hexadecanol (*n*-hexadecyl, cetyl alcohol), m.p. 50°; *n*-octadecanol (*n*-octadecyl, stearyl alcohol), m.p. 59°; and *n*-eicosanol, m.p. 71°. The alcohols of higher molecular weight, which occur as esters of acids of similar molecular size in plant cuticle waxes, bees and other insect waxes, etc., are mixtures of alcohols with even numbers of carbon atoms from C_{24} to C_{36}. Usually a somewhat complex mixture of these compounds, inseparable by methods at present available, is present; but occasionally in some leaf waxes one particular alcohol is present to the virtual exclusion of all others. Very comprehensive studies of the alcohols of plant and insect waxes have been carried out by Chibnall *et al.*,[37] who reached the conclusions given in the preceding sentences. These investigators deprecate the use in the literature of such terms, for example, as ceryl or melissyl alcohol for, respectively, the alcohols $C_{26}H_{53}(OH)$ and $C_{30}H_{61}(OH)$, since the natural products referred to under these names are almost invariably mixtures of the even-numbered homologues. They propose that a large number of names of this nature should be abandoned, and that the mixtures which they represent should be referred to as such (e.g. $C_{26}+C_{28}+C_{30}$ alcohols, etc.).

The following notes may be added with reference to the distribution in nature of some of the higher *n*-aliphatic alcohols:

n-**Dodecanol,** $CH_3.[CH_2]_{10}.CH_2(OH)$, was reported in porpoise (*Tursiops truncatus*) head and jaw oils by Gill and Tucker,[38a] but Lovern[38b] was unable to confirm this observation. Ueno and Koyama[38c] have stated that traces of this alcohol, and also of *n*-decanol and *n*-octanol, occur in the alcohols of sperm blubber oil.

n-**Tetradecanol,** $CH_3.[CH_2]_{12}.CH_2(OH)$, occurs as a minor component (about 8 per cent.)

in the wax esters of sperm head oil (André and Francois,[39a] Hilditch and Lovern[39b]), and also in the head oil of the porpoise (Lovern[38b]).

n-**Hexadecanol,** cetyl alcohol, $CH_3.[CH_2]_{14}.CH_2(OH)$, was observed by Chevreul[40] about 1817 in sperm head oil, in which it forms about 45 per cent. of the total higher alcohols (André and Francois,[39a] Hilditch and Lovern[39b]). Tsujimoto,[39c] and also Toyama,[39d] stated in 1925 that it was a constituent of the alcohols of Arctic sperm blubber oil. Hilditch and Lovern[39b] found about 25 per cent. of cetyl alcohol in sperm blubber alcohols, and Lovern[38b] observed 60 per cent. of cetyl alcohol in the alcohols of porpoise (*Phocæna communis*) head oil. The occurrence of much cetyl alcohol in the body fat of a tropical deep-sea fish, the castor-oil fish (*Ruvettus pretiosus*), has been recorded by Cox and Reid,[39e] and in the body fat of *Ruvettus tydemani* and the ovary fat of the grey mullet, *Mugil japonicus*, by Tsujimoto and Koyanagi.[39f]

n-**Octadecanol,** $CH_3.[CH_2]_{16}.CH_2(OH)$, is present in small quantities in sperm head[39a, b] and blubber oils[39b, d] and probably also in porpoise and dolphin blubber oils,[38b] but in any of these it probably does not amount to more than 5 per cent. of the total alcohols present.

n-**Eicosanol,** $CH_3.[CH_2]_{18}.CH_2(OH)$, is possibly present in minute amounts in the oils mentioned in the preceding cases, but has not been definitely isolated therefrom. It has been found in waxes present in certain dermoid cysts.[41a]

"**Even-number**" normal alcohols from $C_{26}H_{53}(OH)$ to $C_{36}H_{73}(OH)$. The following details are included in the papers by Chibnall *et al.*[37] referred to previously:

n-**Hexacosanol,** $C_{26}H_{53}(OH)$, m.p. 79·5°, is almost the only higher alcohol constituent in the wax from blades of cocksfoot grass, and the same statement holds for n-**Octacosanol,** $C_{28}H_{57}(OH)$, m.p. 83·4°, in the wax of wheat blades, and for n-**Triacontanol,** $C_{30}H_{61}(OH)$, m.p. 86·5°, in lucerne leaf wax. Of other plant cuticle waxes, apple cuticle wax alcohols are a mixture of C_{26}, C_{28}, and C_{30}, carnauba wax alcohols include all the "even-number" alcohols from C_{26} to C_{34} (especially the higher members), while candelilla, and also cotton wax alcohols range from C_{28} to C_{34}; Japanese workers have reported "ceryl" alcohol in the outer skin of onions[41b] and in the leaf wax of *Michelia compressa*.[41c]

Murray and Schoenfeld[42a] (1951) gave the composition of carnauba wax n-monohydric alcohols as: below C_{24} 1, C_{24} and C_{26} 4, C_{28} 5, C_{30} 14, C_{32} 51, and C_{34} 22 per cent. (wt.), with three dihydric alcohols (glycols) amounting to 2 per cent. of the total wax alcohols.[42c]

In the insect waxes the mixture of "even-number" alcohols appears frequently to be still more complex. Beeswax alcohols range from C_{24} to C_{34}, those of lac wax from C_{26} to C_{36}. Cochineal wax appears to be unusual in containing 15-keto-n-tetratriacontanol, CH_3. $[CH_2]_{18}.CO.[CH_2]_{13}.CH_2(OH)$, as its chief component alcohol.*

Aliphatic long-chain alcohols in wool wax have been reported by several workers, in addition to the cyclic cholesterol and *iso*-cholesterol which form the bulk of the alcoholic components. Tiedt and Truter[43a] (1951), and Murray and Schoenfeld[42d] (1955), mention the presence of n-monohydric alcohols of even carbon content from C_{18} to C_{26}, while Murray and Schoenfeld[42b] (1952) state that "*iso*-" and "*ante-iso*" alcohols form over 20 per cent. of the total wool wax alcohols, including "*iso*-" even numbered members ($Me_2CH.[CH_2]_n.CH_2.OH$) with 18, 20, 22, and 24 carbon atoms, and dextro-rotatory "*ante-iso*" odd-numbered members ($MeEt.CH.[CH_2]_n.CH_2.OH$) with 17, 19, 21, 23, 25, and 27 carbon atoms. Milburn and Truter[43c] synthesised several of the wool wax alcohols of the *iso*- and the *anteiso*-series by lithium aluminium hydride reduction of the corresponding *iso*- and *anteiso*-acids, which they had prepared by anodic syntheses from appropriate methyl-substituted aliphatic acids with methyl hydrogen esters of appropriate dicarboxylic acids.

n-Aliphatic dihydric alcohols are present to the extent of 1·5 per cent. in wool wax alcohols (Murray and Schoenfeld[42b] (1952), Tiedt and Truter[43b] (1951)); Horn and Hougen[43d] (1953)

* It may be mentioned that these plant and insect waxes usually also include, in addition to the wax esters of higher "even-number" normal aliphatic alcohols and acids, hydrocarbons (n-paraffins) containing an *odd number* of carbon atoms[37] and including, in different cases, paraffins of the odd-number series from C_{25} to C_{37}. n-Nonacosane, $C_{29}H_{60}$, and n-hentriacontane, $C_{31}H_{64}$, are frequently major constituents of the hydrocarbon fractions of some of these waxes.

state that these include alkane-1,2-diols (3 per cent., probably branched-chain) with 16, 18, 20, 22, and 24 carbon atoms, together with 15 per cent. of n-aliphatic monohydric alcohols.[43e]

Unsaturated Higher Aliphatic Alcohols

In the group of marine animal oils (notably those of the sperm whales and the porpoise family) in which wax esters accompany glycerides, unsaturated as well as saturated alcohols are present; the unsaturated members recorded range from C_{10} to C_{22}. In the unusual seed wax of *Simmondsia californica* the alcohols present are mono-ethenoid C_{20} and C_{22} compounds.

cis-n-**Octadec-9-enol** (**Oleyl alcohol**), $CH_3 . [CH_2]_7 . CH : CH . [CH_2]_7 . CH_2$ (OH), is the most important of the unsaturated group, and is the most abundant higher alcohol component of sperm head and blubber oils and porpoise blubber oils. It was apparently first definitely recognised by Tsujimoto[39c, 44a] and by Toyama[39d, 44b] in certain shark oils and also in sperm oils. Both authors state that the greater part of the alcohols present in the body oils of the ordinary sperm and Arctic sperm whale consist of oleyl alcohol, whilst Hilditch and Lovern[39b] give the percentage of the alcohol in sperm body oil as 66–70 per cent. and that in the head oil as about 27–30 per cent. of the total higher alcohols present. According to Lovern[38b] oleyl alcohol also forms about 30 per cent. of the mixed alcohols present in porpoise head oil.

It is probable, according to Hilditch and Lovern, that small amounts of diethylenic alcohols, $C_{18}H_{33}(OH)$, also occur together with oleyl alcohol in sperm oil.

Oleyl alcohol was prepared synthetically many years ago by the Bouveault-Blanc reduction of ethyl oleate with sodium and amyl alcohol.[32] It is a colourless syrupy liquid which solidifies at about 2° and boils at 208–210°/15 mm., 150–152°/1 mm. The acetate (b.p. 208°/16 mm.) yields nonanoic and acetoxy-nonanoic acids when oxidised with potassium permanganate, thus establishing the position of the double bond.

Oleyl alcohol is converted into an equilibrium mixture of oleyl and elaidyl alcohols by the action of oxides of nitrogen, but it has not been found possible to separate the geometrical isomerides by crystallisation. Elaidyl alcohol (m.p. 35–35·5°) has, however, been prepared by Toyama[45a] by sodium reduction of ethyl elaidate, and also by André and Francois[45b] by a similar procedure. Oleyl alcohol when oxidised by perhydrol in acetic acid yields a 9,10-dihydroxy-octadecyl alcohol (m.p. 82°), whilst elaidyl alcohol gives with the same reagent an isomeric alcohol, m.p. 125–126°; when oleyl or elaidyl hydrogen phthalates are oxidised in dilute alkaline solution with potassium permanganate, the product from oleyl hydrogen phthalate is the hydrogen phthalate of the 9,10-dihydroxy-octadecyl alcohol which melts at 125–126°, and that from elaidyl hydrogen phthalate is the corresponding ester of the isomeric alcohol, m.p. 82°.[45c] These relationships are parallel in all respects with those of oleic and elaidic acids when submitted to oxidation by the respective reagents (*cf.* Chapter IX, p. 596).

Octadeca-9,12-dienol (*Linoleyl alcohol*), $CH_3 . [CH_2]_4 . CH:CH . CH_2 . CH:CH . [CH_2]_7 .$ $CH_2(OH)$, which may or may not be amongst the small amounts of diethenoid C_{18} alcohols present in sperm whale oils, has been prepared artificially by Turpeinen[46] by Bouveault-Blanc reduction of methyl linoleate. It melts at −5° to −2°, and boils at 148–150°/1 mm.; it furnishes a *p*-nitrophenyl-urethane, m.p. 91–92°, and unites additively with bromine to give small yields of a tetrabromo-octadecanol, m.p. 87°.

The following unsaturated alcohols have been prepared from the corresponding natural fatty acids by reducing the latter with lithium aluminium hydride (Ligthelm *et al.*,[35a] 1950):

cis-*Octadeca*-9,12-*dien*-1-*ol* (*Linoleyl alcohol*), liquid (tetrabromo-adduct m.p. 93°).

cis-*Octadeca*-9,12,15-*trien*-1-*ol* (*Linolenyl alcohol*), liquid (hexabromo-adduct m.p. 170°).

cis-*Octadec*-9-*en*-1,12-*diol* (*Ricinoleyl alcohol*), liquid, (hydrogenated to octadecane-1,12-diol, m.p. 79·5–80°).

Octadeca-9,11,13-*triene*-1-*ols*. α-Elæostearyl alcohol, liquid, and β-Elæostearyl alcohol, m.p. 58·5–59·5°.

Ximenynyl alcohol, $C_{18}H_{31}(OH)$, m.p. 30–31°.

The unsaturated alcohols corresponding with the unsaturated fatty acids of South African pilchard oil have been prepared by the same method by Silk, Sephton and Hahn[35b] (1954). **Other natural unsaturated higher aliphatic alcohols.** Japanese investigators have reported the occurrence of the following (in each case in minor proportions):

	ALCOHOL	STRUCTURE	SOURCE	INVESTIGATORS
$C_{10}H_{19}(OH)$	Decenol	Undetermined	Sperm blubber	Ueno and Koyama[38c]
$C_{12}H_{23}(OH)$	Dodecenol	Undetermined	Sperm blubber	Ueno and Koyama[38c]
$C_{14}H_{27}(OH)$	Tetradec-5-enol (physeteryl)	$CH_3.[CH_2]_7.CH:CH.[CH_2]_3.$ $CH_2(OH)$	Sperm head	Toyama and Tsuchiya[47a]
$C_{16}H_{31}(OH)$	Hexadec-9-enol (zoomaryl)	$CH_3.[CH_2]_5.CH:CH.[CH_2]_7.$ $CH_2(OH)$	Sperm head / Sperm blubber	Toyama and Tsuchiya[47a] / Toyama and Akiyama[47b]
$C_{20}H_{33}(OH)$	Eicosatetraenol (catadonyl)	Undetermined	Sperm blubber	Toyama and Akiyama[47b]
$C_{22}H_{35}(OH)$	Docosapentaenol (clupanodonyl)	Undetermined	Sperm blubber	Toyama and Akiyama[47b]

Komori and Agawa[48] reported that, of the oil (87 per cent.) in the livers of the Japanese deep sea fish *Læmonema morosun*, about one-third is fatty alcohols; 60 per cent. of these consists of cis-docos-11-enol, m.p. 32°. From the latter the isomeric *trans*-docos-11-enol (m.p. 52–53°) is produced by elaidinisation, and *n*-docosanol (m.p. 71°) by hydrogenation.

Hilditch and Lovern[39b] estimated that sperm head oil contains about 4 per cent. of hexadecenyl alcohol, and about 10 per cent. of an eicosenyl alcohol, $C_{20}H_{39}(OH)$, smaller amounts of the latter also occurring in sperm blubber oil.

It may also be added here (although it cannot yet be asserted that there is necessarily any connection between the alcohols about to be mentioned and those of the lipid waxes) that Takei *et al.*[49] have detected the presence of the mono-ethenoid aliphatic alcohols hexenol, $C_6H_{11}(OH)$, and nonenol, $C_9H_{17}(OH)$, in the growing leaves of a number of plants (including tea, ivy, clover, oak, wheat, cypress and violet).

GLYCERYL ETHERS
(CHIMYL, BATYL, AND SELACHYL ALCOHOLS)

These three compounds are found, usually in small quantities, in the non-fatty or unsaponifiable matter left after hydrolysis of various marine animal oils, especially those of the Elasmobranch group. In a few liver oils of Elasmobranch fish the quantity of these substances present forms a relatively large proportion of the total "unsaponifiable" matter. The formulæ, chemical structure, and melting points of the three compounds are as follows:

ALCOHOL	M.P.	FORMULA	STRUCTURE
Chimyl	60·5–61·5°	$C_{19}H_{40}O_3$	$CH_3.[CH_2]_{15}.O.CH_2.CH(OH).CH_2(OH)$
Batyl	70–71°	$C_{21}H_{44}O_3$	$CH_3.[CH_2]_{17}.O.CH_2.CH(OH).CH_2(OH)$
Selachyl	liquid	$C_{21}H_{42}O_3$	$CH_3.[CH_2]_7.CH:CH.[CH_2]_8.O.CH_2.CH(OH).CH_2(OH)$

Of the three compounds selachyl alcohol is probably most, and chimyl alcohol least, abundant. Their occurrence was first demonstrated in 1922 by

Tsujimoto and Toyama,[50a] and the latter worker ascertained that each contained two free hydroxyl groups capable of acetylation. Subsequently (1932) André and Bloch[50b] brought forward evidence to show that in the original fish oils these compounds are present in the form of fatty acid esters, each of the free hydroxyl groups being combined with a higher fatty acid.

Swain[51a] (1948) showed that the unsaponifiable matter in marine animal oils can be separated by adsorption on a column of activated alumina, from which light petroleum removes squalene (or other hydrocarbons), benzene or methylene dichloride then elutes monohydric alcohols (cholesterol, vitamin A), and final elution with ethyl ether removes dihydric alcohols (the glycerol-ethers). The latter can be determined quantitatively by oxidation with periodic acid, which converts the glycol groups into formaldehyde and a long-chain aldehyde (Karnovsky and Rapson[51b]).

Although at first there was some uncertainty as to whether the molecular formula of batyl alcohol was $C_{20}H_{42}O_3$ or $C_{21}H_{44}O_3$, Toyama[50c] definitely established the latter as being correct in 1924, while at the same time he announced the isolation of the lower saturated homologue, chimyl alcohol, of formula $C_{19}H_{40}O_3$; Tsujimoto and Toyama[50a] had previously shown that selachyl alcohol, $C_{21}H_{42}O_3$, passed into batyl alcohol by hydrogenation. Having shown that dry distillation of selachyl acetate gave rise to oleyl alcohol, and that its oxidation with potassium permanganate yielded nonanoic acid, Toyama expressed its constitution as $CH_3 \cdot [CH_2]_7 \cdot CH:CH \cdot [C_{11}H_{21}O](O \cdot CO \cdot CH_3)_2$.

From 1928 onwards a detailed investigation into the structure and synthesis of batyl and chimyl alcohols was carried out by Heilbron and co-workers[52] who, in the first place, showed that n-octadecyl iodide (not methyl iodide as reported by Weidemann[53]) was produced by the action of hydriodic acid on batyl alcohol,[52a] which must, therefore, be a monoglyceryl ether of octadecyl alcohol, having the structure (i) or (ii).

(i) $C_{18}H_{37} \cdot O \cdot CH_2 \cdot CH(OH) \cdot CH_2(OH)$
(ii) $C_{18}H_{37} \cdot O \cdot CH(CH_2OH)_2$

The next step was to synthesise one or other of these mono-ethers of glycerol. Condensation of octadecyl chloride with sodium allyl oxide, followed by oxidation of the resultant octadecyl allyl ether with perhydrol, led to the production of α-octadecylglyceryl ether, and this had the same melting point (70–71°) as pure batyl alcohol,[52b] but a mixed melting point determination of the two substances showed, however, a small but definite depression, which was emphasised in the case of the respective diphenylurethanes. It was therefore concluded that either (a) batyl alcohol is actually the β-octadecyl glyceryl ether or (b) the natural alcohol is an optically active stereoisomeride of the racemic synthetic α-ether. That the unsymmetrical α-glyceryl ether structure is correct was finally proved by Davies, Heilbron and Jones[52c] who oxidised batyl alcohol with lead tetraacetate (a reagent specific for αβ-glycols), and identified formaldehyde and glycollic aldehyde octadecyl ether (m.p. 51°) in the fission products. In view of this, the optical properties of batyl alcohol were examined, when it was ascertained that, contrary to the finding of Toyama,[50c] the alcohol exhibits small but definite optical activity, its specific rotation in chloroform being $[\alpha]_{5461}^{20°} +2 \cdot 6°$. The activity is more readily demonstrated in the case of batyl acetate, the specific rotation of which is $[\alpha]_{5461}^{20°} -8 \cdot 5°$ in chloroform.

As the batyl alcohol employed[52c] was prepared from selachyl alcohol it follows that the latter must be α-oleyl glycerol ether.

The synthesis of α-cetyl glyceryl ether (m.p. 61–62°) was effected by the same method as that described for the synthesis of the α-octadecyl homologue, and, although no direct comparison with the naturally occurring chimyl alcohol (m.p. 60·5–61·5°) was possible, there is little doubt that this also is α-cetyl glyceryl ether.

The synthesis of β-cetyl glyceryl ether (m.p. 61–62°) and β-octadecyl glyceryl ether (m.p.

62–63°) was subsequently achieved by condensing the sodium salt of $\alpha\alpha'$-benzylidene glycerol with cetyl or octadecyl iodide, followed by hydrolysis of the resultant product.[52d] Each product gave several degrees depression in melting point when mixed with the natural chimyl or batyl alcohols.

An alternative synthesis of batyl alcohol by Kornblum and Holmes[54] starts from the condensation of n-octadecyl iodide with sodium allyl oxide, $CH_2:CH.CH_2(ONa)$, which affords n-octadecyl-allyl ether in good yield. The ether, when treated with peracetic acid in acetic acid solution at 80–85°, yields batyl alcohol, m.p. 70–71°.

The synthesis of the optically active forms of chimyl and batyl alcohols from d- and l-acetonyl glycerols and the corresponding alkyl iodides by Baer and Fischer[28d] has already been mentioned earlier in this chapter (p. 666). Melting point data for both positional isomers (glycerol-1-alkyl ethers and glycerol-2-alkyl ethers) have been given by Bevan and Malkin[55a] in the cases of the pairs of isomeric batyl and chimyl alcohols, and of some of their derivatives, including an analogue of kephalin from the symmetrical "β"-batyl alcohol. Batyl distearate (m.p. 62–63°), chimyl dipalmitate (m.p. 52–53°) and selachyl dioleate (liq.) have been synthesised by Lawson and Getz.[55b]

The occurrence of these glyceryl ethers in nature is a matter of considerable biological interest. The pure alcohols have neither growth-promoting nor antirachitic properties (Weidemann[53]) and their function, if any, in the animal organism is at present obscure. From the standpoint of chemical structure, they represent in some measure an intermediate link between glycerides (true fats) and waxes as shown below.

GLYCERIDE	GLYCERYL ETHERS	WAXES
$(R.CO.O)_3.C_3H_5$	$(R.CO.O)_2.C_3H_5(OR')$	$R.CO.O.R'$

$(R = CH_3.[CH_2]_7.CH:CH.[CH_2]_7—, CH_3.[CH_2]_{16}—, \text{ or } CH_3.[CH_2]_{14}—;$
$R' = CH_3.[CH_2]_7.CH:CH.[CH_2]_8—, CH_3.[CH_2]_{17}—, \text{ or } CH_3.[CH_2]_{15}—)$

Lovern[56] has indeed suggested that, since appearance of these alcohol-ethers in fish oils is invariably accompanied by sub-normal unsaturation in the fatty acids of the oil, their production may be regarded as evidence of an unusual tendency towards saturation or hydrogenation in the fish oils in question; so that the alcohol-ethers represent a hydrogenation of the glyceride molecule which has involved the reduction of an ester-carbonyl group. This is well illustrated by the liver oil of the ratfish,[56] which contains nearly 37 per cent. of these compounds (mainly selachyl, with a little chimyl and batyl, alcohol), the fatty acids of the oil including 50 per cent. C_{18} unsaturated (mean unsaturation only $-2\cdot2H$), 20 per cent. C_{20} unsaturated (mean unsaturation only $-2\cdot9H$) and 8 per cent. C_{22} unsaturated (mean unsaturation only $-3\cdot5H$). Incidentally it may be noted that ratfish liver oil consists substantially of di-acyl esters of selachyl and the related alcohol-ethers, with practically no glycerides.

References to Chapter X

Synthetic glycerides:

1. M. E. Chevreul, Récherches chimiques sur les corps gras, 1823.
2. M. Berthelot, *Ann. Chim. Phys.*, 1854, [iii], **41**, 216.
3. A. Wynter Blyth and G. H. Robertson, *Proc. Chem. Soc.*, 1889, **5**, 5.
4. F. Guth, *Z. biol. Chem.*, 1902, **44**, 78.
5. A. Grün, *Ber.*, 1905, **38**, 2284; A. Grün and P. Schacht, *ibid.*, 1907, **40**, 1778; A. Grün and E. Theimer, *ibid.*, 1792.

6. E. Fischer, M. Bergmann and H. Bärwind, *Ber.*, 1920, **53**, 1589; E. Fischer, *Ber.*, 1920, **53**, 1621.
7. A. Fairbourne, *et al.*, *J. Chem. Soc.*, 1926, 3148; 1929, 129; 1930, 369.
8. C. G. King (with H. P. Averill and J. N. Roche), *J. Amer. Chem. Soc.*, 1929, **51**, 866; (with H. E. Robinson and J. N. Roche), *ibid.*, 1932, **54**, 705; (with O. E. McElroy), *ibid.*, 1934, **56**, 1191.
9. (*a*) T. Malkin and T. H. Bevan, "Progress in the Chemistry of Fats and other Lipids", Vol. IV, p. 63 (Pergamon Press, London, 1957); (*b*) L. Hartman, *Chem. Revs.*, 1958, **58**, 845; (*c*) F. H. Mattson and R. A. Volpenhein, *J. Lipid Res.*, 1962, **3**, 281.
10. H. O. L. Fischer and E. Baer, *J. Amer. Chem. Soc.*, 1945, **67**, 2031.
11. M. Bergmann and N. M. Carter, *Z. physiol. Chem.*, 1930, **191**, 211.
12. (*a*) P. E. Verkade, *Fette und Seifen*, 1938, **45**, 457; *Chem. Weekblad*, 1949, **45**, 449; P. E. Verkade *et al.*, *Rec. Trav. Chim.*, 1935, **54**, 716; 1936, **55**, 267; 1937, **56**, 365; 1940, **59**, 1123; 1942, **61**, 831; 1943, **62**, 393; (*b*) B. F. Daubert, *J. Amer. Chem. Soc.*, 1940, **62**, 1713.
13. J. B. Martin, *J. Amer. Chem. Soc.*, 1953, **75**, 5482.
14. (*a*) D. Chapman, A. Crossley and A. C. Davies, *J. Chem. Soc.*, 1957, 1502; (*b*) W. Landmann, R. O. Feuge and N. V. Lovegren, *J. Amer. Oil Chem. Soc.*, 1960, **37**, 638; 1961, **38**, 681.
15. (*a*) L. Hartman, *Chem. Rev.*, 1958, **58**, 845; (*b*) D. Chapman, *ibid.*, 1962, **62**, 433.
16. L. J. Filer Jr., S. S. Sidhu, B. F. Daubert and H. E. Longenecker, *J. Amer. Chem. Soc.*, 1946, **68**, 167.
17. E. Handschumacher and L. Linteris, *J. Amer. Oil Chem. Soc.*, 1947, **24**, 143; J. B. Martin, *J. Amer. Chem. Soc.*, 1953, **75**, 5483; G. Y. Brokaw, E. S. Perry and W. C. Lyman, *J. Amer. Oil Chem. Soc.*, 1955, **32**, 194.
18. E. Becker and L. Krull, *Fette, Seifen, Anstrichm.*, 1958, **60**, 449; J. D. Brandner and R. L. Birkmeir, *J. Amer. Oil Chem. Soc.*, 1960, **37**, 390.
19. F. Aylward and P. D. S. Wood, *Chem. and Ind.*, 1960, 1442.
20. R. J. Howe and T. Malkin, *J. Chem. Soc.*, 1951, 2663.
21. A. Crossley, I. P. Freeman, B. J. F. Hudson and J. H. Pierce, *J. Chem. Soc.*, 1959, 760.
22. F. J. Baur and W. Lange, *J. Amer. Chem. Soc.*, 1951, **73**, 3926.
23. B. M. Craig, W. O. Lundberg and W. F. Geddes, *J. Amer. Oil Chem. Soc.*, 1952, **29**, 169.
24. F. H. Mattson and R. A. Volpenhein, *J. Lipid Res.*, 1961, **2**, 58; (*b*) 1962, **3**, 281.
25. (*a*) C. Barker, R. V. Crawford and T. P. Hilditch, *J. Chem. Soc.*, 1951, 1194; (*b*) A. Crossley, T. D. Heyes and B. J. F. Hudson, *J. Amer. Oil Chem. Soc.*, 1962, **39**, 9.
26. (*a*) C. E. Clarkson and T. Malkin, *J. Chem. Soc.*, 1934, 666; 1948, 985; (*b*) D. H. Wheeler, R. W. Riemenschneider and C. E. Sando, *J. Biol. Chem.*, 1940, **132**, 687; R. H. Ferguson and E. S. Lutton, *J. Amer. Chem. Soc.*, 1947, **69**, 1445; (*c*) M. G. R. Carter and T. Malkin, *J. Chem. Soc.*, 1947, 554; (*d*) A. R. Baldwin and B. F. Daubert, *J. Amer. Chem. Soc.*, 1944, **66**, 997; (*e*) B. F. Daubert and E. S. Lutton, *ibid.*, 1947, **69**, 1449.
27. T. Malkin (*a*) (with M. R. el Shurbagy), *J. Chem. Soc.*, 1936, 1628; (with M. R. el Shurbagy and M. L. Meara), *ibid.*, 1937, 1409; (*b*) B. F. Daubert *et al.*, *J. Amer. Chem. Soc.*, 1943, **65**, 2144; *Oil and Soap*, 1945, **22**, 113; (*c*) T. Malkin and B. R. Wilson, *J. Chem. Soc.*, 1949, 369; (*d*) E. S. Lutton, *J. Amer. Chem. Soc.*, 1951, **73**, 5595; (*e*) H. Lavery, *J. Amer. Oil Chem. Soc.*, 1958, **35**, 418; (*f*) M. G. R. Carter and T. Malkin, *J. Chem. Soc.*, 1939, 577; (*g*) T. Malkin and M. L. Meara, *ibid.*, 1939, 103.
28. E. Baer and H. O. L. Fischer, (*a*) *J. Amer. Chem. Soc.*, 1939, **61**, 761; 1945, **67**, 944; *J. Biol. Chem.*, 1939, **128**, 463; (*b*) *ibid.*, 1939, **128**, 475, 480; *J. Amer. Chem. Soc.*, 1945, **67**, 2031; (*c*) J. C. Sowden and H. O. L. Fischer, *J. Amer. Chem. Soc.*, 1941, **63**, 3244; (*d*) E. Baer and H. O. L. Fischer, *J. Biol. Chem.*, 1941, **140**, 397; 1944, **155**, 147; 1947, **170**, 337; (*e*) E. Baer and H. O. L. Fischer, *ibid.*, 1939, **128**, 491; 1940, **135**, 321; E. Baer, I. B. Cushing and H. O. L. Fischer, *Canad. J. Research*, 1943, **21**, B, 119; (*f*) E. Baer and M. Kates, *J. Amer. Chem. Soc.*, 1948, **70**, 1394; 1950, **72**, 942; E. Baer, *J. Biol. Chem.*, 1951, **189**, 235; *J. Amer. Chem. Soc.*, 1953, **75**, 5533; E. Baer and J. Maurukas, *ibid.*, 1952, **74**, 152; *J. Biol. Chem.*, 1955, **212**, 25; E. Baer, D.

22   673

Buchnea *et al.*, *J. Amer. Chem. Soc.*, 1956, **78**, 232; 1959, **81**, 1758, 2166; *Canad. J. Biochem. Physiol.*, 1958, **36**, 243; 1959, **37**, 953; E. Baer *et al.*, *J. Biol. Chem.*, 1961, **236**, 1269, 1273; (*g*) E. Baer and M. Kates, *ibid.*, 1950, **185**, 615.

29. P. E. Verkade and J. H. Uhlenbroek, *Proc. K. Ned. Akad. Wet.*, 1952, **55**, B, 110; *Rec. trav. chim.*, 1953, **72**, 395; with J. H. van der Neut, *ibid.*, 1953, **72**, 365; L. W. Hessel, I. D. Morton, A. R. Todd and P. E. Verkade, *Rec. trav. chim.*, 1954, **73**, 150; P. E. Verkade and L. J. Stegerhoek, *Proc. K. Ned. Akad. Wet.*, 1954, **57**, B, 444; 1958, **61**, B, 155; P. E. Verkade, *ibid.*, 1962, **65**, B, 164.

30. C. Long and M. F. Maguire, *Biochem. J.*, 1954, **57**, 223.

31. (*a*) E. Baer and H. O. L. Fischer, *Chem. Rev.*, 1941, **29**, 287; (*b*) E. Baer, *Canad. J. Biochem. Physiol.*, 1956, **34**, 288; (*c*) T. Malkin and T. H. Bevan, "Progress in the Chemistry of Fats and other Lipids", Vol. IV, p. 97 (Pergamon Press, London, 1957); T. Malkin, *Chem. and Ind.*, 1961, 605.

Naturally occurring fatty alcohols:

32. L. Bouveault and G. Blanc, *Bull. Soc. Chim.*, 1904, **31**, 1210; *cf.* L. Palfray and P. Anglaret, *Compt. rend.*, 1947, **224**, 404.

33. (*a*) P. A. Levene and F. A. Taylor, *J. Biol. Chem.*, 1924, **59**, 905; (*b*) *cf.* R. G. Jones, *J. Amer. Chem. Soc.*, 1947, **69**, 2350.

34. H. T. Böhme, E. P. 346237/1930, 351359/1930, 356606/1930, 358869/1931; W. Schrauth, O. Schenck and K. Stickdorn, *Ber.*, 1931, **64**, B, 1314; W. Schrauth, *Angew. Chem.*, 1933, **46**, 459; H. Adkins and R. Connor, *J. Amer. Chem. Soc.*, 1931, **53**, 1091; H. Adkins and K. Folkers, *ibid.*, 1931, **53**, 1095; H. Adkins, B. Wojcik and L. W. Covert, *ibid.*, 1933, **55**, 1293, 1669.

35. (*a*) V. M. Micovic and M. L. Mihailovic, *Bull. Soc. Chim. Belgrade*, 1949, **14**, 256; S. P. Ligthelm, E. von Rudloff and D. A. Sutton, *J. Chem. Soc.*, 1950, 3178; (*b*) M. H. Silk, H. H. Sephton and H. H. Hahn, *Biochem. J.*, 1954, **57**, 574.

36. *Cf.* R. Kuhn, *J. Chem. Soc.*, 1938, 605.

37. A. C. Chibnall, S. H. Piper, A. Pollard, E. F. Williams and P. N. Sahai, *Biochem. J.*, 1934, **28**, 2189; 1961, **78**, 435. For carnauba wax alcohols, see also S. D. Koonce and J. B. Brown, *Oil and Soap*, 1944, **21**, 167, 231.

38. (*a*) A. H. Gill and C. M. Tucker, *J. Oil and Fat Ind.*, 1930, **7**, 101; (*b*) J. A. Lovern, *Biochem. J.*, 1934, **28**, 394; (*c*) S. Ueno and R. Koyama, *J. Chem. Soc. Japan*, 1936, **57**, 1; *Bull. Chem. Soc. Japan*, 1936, **11**, 394.

39. (*a*) E. André and T. François, *Compt. rend.*, 1926, **183**, 663; (*b*) T. P. Hilditch and J. A. Lovern, *J. Soc. Chem. Ind.*, 1929, **48**, 365т; (*c*) M. Tsujimoto, *Chem. Umschau*, 1925, **32**, 127; (*d*) Y. Toyama, *J. Soc. Chem. Ind. Japan*, 1927, **30**, 527; (*e*) W. M. Cox and E. E. Reid, *J. Amer. Chem. Soc.*, 1932, **54**, 220; (*f*) M. Tsujimoto and H. Koyanagi, *J. Soc. Chem. Ind. Japan*, 1937, **40**, 403в.

40. M. E. Chevreul, *Ann. Chim. Phys.*, 1817, [ii], **7**, 155.

41. (*a*) F. Ameseder, *Z. physiol. Chem.*, 1907, **52**, 121; (*b*) M. Okajima, *J. Sci. Res. Inst. Tokyo*, 1954, **48**, 281; (*c*) T. Koyama and T. Morikita, *Kumamoto Pharm. Bull.*, 1955, No. 2, 69.

42. K. E. Murray and R. Schoenfeld, (*a*) *J. Amer. Oil Chem. Soc.*, 1951, **28**, 235, 461; (*b*) *ibid.*. 1952, **29**, 416; (*c*) *Austral. J. Chem.*, 1955, **8**, 432; (*d*) *ibid.*, 1955, **8**, 424; also D. T. Downing, Z. H. Kranz and K. E. Murray, *ibid.*, 1960, **13**, 80.

43. J. Tiedt and E. V. Truter, (*a*) *Chem. and Ind.*, 1951, 911; (*b*) *Quart. Rev.*, 1951, **5**, 395; *J. Chem. Soc.*, 1952, 4628; (*c*) A. H. Milburn and E. V. Truter, *J. Chem. Soc.*, 1954, 3344; (*d*) D. H. S. Horn and F. W. Hougen, *Chem. and Ind.*, 1951, 670; *J. Chem. Soc.*, 1953, 3353; (*e*) D. H. S. Horn, *J. Sci. Food Agric.*, 1958, **9**, 632.

44. (*a*) M. Tsujimoto, *J. Soc. Chem. Ind. Japan*, 1921, **24**, 275; (*b*) Y. Toyama, *Chem. Umschau*, 1922, **29**, 237.

45. (*a*) Y. Toyama, *Chem. Umschau*, 1924, **31**, 13; (*b*) E. André and T. François, *Compt. rend.*, 1927, **185**, 279, 387; (*c*) G. Collin and T. P. Hilditch, *J. Chem. Soc.*, 1933, 246.

46. O. Turpeinen, *J. Amer. Chem. Soc.*, 1938, **60**, 56.

47. (a) Y. Toyama and T. Tsuchiya, *Bull. Chem. Soc. Japan*, 1935, **10**, 572; (b) Y. Toyama and G. Akiyama, *ibid.*, 1935, **10**, 579; 1936, **11**, 29.
48. S. Komori and T. Agawa, *J. Amer. Oil Chem. Soc.*, 1955, **32**, 525.
49. S. Takei, M. Ono, Y. Kuraiva, *et al.*, *J. Agric. Chem. Soc. Japan*, 1938, **14**, 709, 717.

Naturally occurring glyceryl ethers (chimyl, batyl, and selachyl alcohols):

50. (a) M. Tsujimoto and Y. Toyama, *Chem. Umschau*, 1922, **29**, 27, 35, 43, 237, 245; (b) E. André and A. Bloch, *Compt. rend.*, 1932, **195**, 627; (c) Y. Toyama, *Chem. Umschau*, 1924, **31**, 61.
51. (a) L. A. Swain, *Canad. Chem.*, 1948, **32**, 553; *J. Fish. Res. Bd. Canada*, 1948, **7**, 389; (b) M. L. Karnovsky and W. S. Rapson, *J. Soc. Chem. Ind.*, 1946, **65**, 138, 425.
52. (a) I. M. Heilbron and W. M. Owens, *J. Chem. Soc.*, 1928, 942; (b) G. G. Davies, I. M. Heilbron and W. M. Owens, *ibid.*, 1930, 2542; (c) W. H. Davies, I. M. Heilbron and W. E. Jones, *ibid.*, 1933, 165; (d) *ibid.*, 1934, 1232.
53. G. Weidemann, *Biochem. J.*, 1926, **20**, 685.
54. N. Kornblum and H. N. Holmes, *J. Amer. Chem. Soc.*, 1942, **64**, 3045.
55. (a) T. H. Bevan and T. Malkin, *J. Chem. Soc.*, 1960, 350; (b) D. D. Lawson and H. R. Getz, *Chem. and Ind.*, 1961, 1404.
56. J. A. Lovern, *Biochem. J.*, 1937, **31**, 755.

CHAPTER XI

Notes on Experimental Techniques Employed in the Quantitative Investigation of Fats

Since the last edition of this book there have been considerable advances in the experimental methods used in the quantitative study of the compositions of natural fats, notably in the use of gas–liquid chromatography for determining fatty acid compositions, developments in thin layer chromatography, and the use of enzyme hydrolysis for ascertaining the fatty acid in the 2-position in triglycerides. This concluding chapter will be found to be considerably altered in its form from that in earlier editions; the very full description of certain procedures (notably ester fractionation, the use of which is now likely to diminish very largely) has been replaced by more brief notices of the chief techniques employed (or likely to be employed) at present, supplemented by bibliographical references at the end of the chapter to appropriate mono-graphs and articles in which a procedure has been dealt with exhaustively.

The more or less standard methods for the determination of characteristics such as iodine and saponification values are not here given in detail; workers in this field will be, for the most part, already familiar with the procedure to be followed in determinations of the latter kind, and, in any case, full details are available in a number of publications[1] cited in the bibliography (p. 707).

It may be pointed out here that the determinations ultimately required in quantitative study of component acids or glycerides of natural fats are, almost wholly, those of molecular or equivalent size, and of unsaturation. The determination of the former (i.e., saponification value or saponification equivalent, the latter form being on the whole more useful in work of this kind) is a standard operation of fat analysis; it need only be added that, since much depends on the accuracy of each determined equivalent in the subsequent calculations, extreme care should be taken to maintain the greatest possible exactitude in all determinations of saponification equivalents. Unsaturation is usually evaluated by iodine values, determined preferably by the Wijs or Hanus methods. Special cases however arise here. Thus, in mixtures of oleic, linoleic, and linolenic compounds it may be desirable to determine each separately, either by alkali isomerisation followed by spectrographic analysis, or thiocyanometrically (*cf.* p. 695). Also, if conjugated unsaturation is present, determination of the total unsaturation by the Wijs or Hanus procedures is not possible. Although some of these determinations are not essential when some of the newer methods of ascertaining fatty acid composition are used, it is very desirable that, even with these, agreement should be found between the saponification equivalent and unsaturation measurements made on the original material and those calculated from the determined composition.

The procedures with which we are about to deal fall into two separate categories, those employed in determining the proportions of the components in the mixture of *fatty acids* present in a natural fat, and those used in the estimation of the chief component *glycerides* of a natural fat.

I. Quantitative Investigation of Component Fatty Acids

In the previous (3rd) edition of this book reference was made (p. 581) to the use of adsorption methods for the determination of fatty acid compositions and the hope expressed that the quantitative value of some of them would be confirmed, since they would be particularly valuable when only very small quantities of material are available, as often happens in biological investigations. This hope has been fully realised, particularly with gas–liquid chromatography (G.L.C.), which has almost supplanted the older methods mainly dependent on fractional distillation of the fatty esters and analysis of the fractions. G.L.C. is also speedier and is therefore attractive to use even when large quantities of material are available. Its accuracy has been amply proved by the analysis of known mixtures of fatty acids under appropriate conditions and also, in a number of instances, by comparison of the ascertained fatty acid compositions of natural fats with those previously obtained on the same fats by the older methods. Strange to say according to James[2] there has been no comparison of G.L.C. with the ester-fractionation method applied to identical samples of the same natural fat.

In the first place, however, we will outline the older method of fractional distillation in a vacuum of the methyl (or ethyl) esters of the fatty acids from a natural fat and also, since it is rarely advisable to attempt to distil fractionally the esters from a mixture of fatty acids as a whole, we shall refer to certain preliminary separations which lead to the production of two or more groups of esters, the fractional distillation of which is considerably simplified by comparison with that of the total fatty acids from a fat.

PRELIMINARY SEPARATIONS OF MIXED FATTY ACIDS

In the majority of cases (when acids of lower molecular weight than octanoic, $C_8H_{16}O_2$, are absent) the only preliminary separation needful is to segregate, as far as possible, the saturated from the unsaturated members. This was formerly almost always effected by taking advantage of the differing solubility in alcohol of the lead salts of these two types of fatty acids; but, where facilities for low temperature work are available, crystallisation of the mixed fatty acids from appropriate solvents over a range of temperatures down to $-60°C$. or lower is to be preferred to separations by means of their lead or other salts.

When, however, the fats contain appreciable amounts of acids of lower molecular weight than octanoic (caprylic), it is necessary to remove the more volatile acids of lowest molecular weight before proceeding to separate the higher saturated and unsaturated acids. This only applies in the cases of the acids of milk fats, dolphin, and porpoise oils and a few others, but for the sake of completeness it is preferable to deal with this contingency before discussing the more general separation procedures.

Preparation of the mixed fatty acids from a fat. It is clearly desirable that complete hydrolysis of the original fat be ensured, and therefore it is well, in most cases, to saponify 100 parts by weight of fat with a solution of 30 parts by weight of potassium hydroxide in about 500 parts of alcohol (95–100 per cent.); the solution is boiled freely under reflux condenser for 3 hours, and most of the alcohol then removed by distillation. The soaps are dissolved in water and, after removal where necessary of unsaponifiable matter (*vide infra*), converted into the free fatty acids by warming with dilute sulphuric acid.* When the acids are completely liberated, they may be removed by extraction with ether and are eventually dried under vacuum at 100°.†

When highly unsaturated acids are known to be present in quantity, as in fish and some other oils, it is not desirable to employ any large excess of alkali or to prolong the saponification process unduly, because of the readiness of such acids to undergo isomeric rearrangement under these conditions. It then becomes preferable to risk the chance of slightly incomplete conversion of the whole fat into fatty acids rather than to incur rearrangement of some of the highly unsaturated components, and in these cases the use of only a slight excess of alkali over that theoretically required, with heating under reflux for only one to two hours, is advised.

A useful alternative to hydrolysis with alcoholic alkali is to convert the glycerides of a fatty oil into methyl esters directly by "ester interchange". The fat (1 mol.) is placed with methanol (5 mols.) and sodium or potassium methoxide (0·5 per cent. on the fat) in a flask, and the contents of the flask heated so that the solvent refluxes for 5 or 6 hours (it is of course imperative to take care that the "methanolysis" has proceeded to completion). After cooling overnight, the methyl esters are recovered and may be segregated into more and less unsaturated fractions by direct crystallisation from solvents at low temperatures, in the same way as the corresponding mixed fatty acids (but usually at somewhat lower working temperatures).

Removal of unsaponifiable matter from the mixed fatty acids. Normally speaking, all the unsaponifiable matter present in a fat tends to pass with the alcohol-soluble lead salts, or with the most soluble fraction of low-temperature solvent-crystallised acids, into the esters of the "liquid" or mainly unsaturated acids (*vide infra*), and finally to appear in the small residue of these esters left un-distilled. It is very desirable, before the acids are converted into esters, to remove unsaponifiable matter by extracting with ether the aqueous-alcoholic solution of the soaps (before converting these into the free fatty acids). Details of the extraction of unsaponifiable matter will be found in monographs on the analysis of fats and fatty oils, but where a large quantity of soap solution has to be extracted a continuous procedure, such as that described in the 3rd edition of this book (p. 573), will be found useful.

Separation of volatile from non-volatile acids. In the case of the acids of milk fats and a few other fats which contain butyric, *iso*valeric, or hexanoic acids,

---

* When unsaturated acids are present in quantity, it is advisable to liberate the free acids under an atmosphere of carbon dioxide.

† See, however, the special case of mixed fatty acids in which volatile acids of low molecular weight are present (below).

the latter may first be removed from the mixed fatty acids by distillation in a current of steam. A convenient procedure is as follows:

After hydrolysis of the fat with alcoholic* alkali, it is essential to remove alcohol completely from the soaps before acidifying, owing to the readiness with which butyric acid esterifies. After distilling off as much alcohol as possible, the remaining traces are removed by heating the soaps in a steam bath under the vacuum of a water pump, water being added, when necessary, to keep the soaps in solution as far as possible. The fatty acids are liberated from the soaps by the addition of 10 per cent. excess of sulphuric acid (40 per cent. solution), the acid being preferably added to the cold soap solution, and the mixture being cooled to prevent loss of butyric acid by volatilisation. Steam distillation is then commenced, using a double spray trap, and after about half an hour, the soaps become completely decomposed, giving a clear layer of fatty acids floating on the surface of the aqueous solution. Distillation is continued for 4 or 5 hours, in order to remove all the butyric and hexanoic acids. Small quantities of octanoic and decanoic acids also pass over into the steam distillate, together with traces of oleic and/or decenoic acid.

The fatty acids in the steam distillate are extracted by means of pure ether and fractionated directly, using a short fractionating column, mainly at atmospheric pressure; the residue from the fractionation is tested for iodine value as well as equivalent, and the iodine value calculated to oleic (or, if preferred, to decenoic) acid. The extracted aqueous liquors and the recovered distilled ether must both be titrated with alkali, the small amounts of acid being calculated as butyric acid.

The residual, non-steam-volatile fatty acids, after cooling in an atmosphere of carbon dioxide to prevent oxidation, are recovered and then submitted to further segregation by one of the usual methods (cf. below).

Separation of mixed fatty acids by crystallisation from solvents at low temperatures. In earlier editions of this book full accounts were given of (a) the separation of fatty acids into "saturated" and "unsaturated" portions by means of the lead salt-alcohol process, and (b) the segregation of highly unsaturated acids (e.g., from marine oils) by the lithium salt-acetone procedure. These have not been repeated in this edition since, now that production and maintenance of low temperatures are available in most laboratories, fractional crystallisation from solvents is a far more direct method (Brown,[3a] 1941) for separation (a), and this or some other solvent separation such as counter-current distribution for separation (b).

Foreman and Brown[3b] gave a comprehensive survey of the solubilities of the saturated acids from lauric to behenic, and of oleic, linoleic, linolenic, eicosenoic and erucic acids, in acetone, methyl alcohol, and petroleum (b.p. 57–63°) at temperatures down to −50°C. and lower. Further data on low temperature solubilities of fatty acids in organic solvents have since been published.[3c] In their report Foreman and Brown (1944) pointed out two factors which are of great importance in the practical application of this technique:

(a) Cooled solutions of fatty acids come to equilibrium exceedingly slowly at low temperatures, and it is therefore desirable to afford as long as possible for the crystallisation.

* The alcohol used in the saponification must first be thoroughly refluxed with caustic soda and then distilled from the caustic alkali, in order to remove any traces of aldehyde, acetic or other lower acids, the presence of which would interfere with the determination of the volatile acids from the fat.

(b) Although the higher saturated acids are only very slightly soluble in many of the pure solvents (e.g., palmitic acid in acetone at $-30°$, 0.38 gm. per litre, in ether at $-40°$, less than 0.1 gm. per litre), the presence of other acids (e.g., oleic or linoleic) of greater solubility introduces mutual solubility effects which may cause the retention in solution of considerably more of the saturated acid than would be expected from the data for pure solvents.

The low-temperature crystallisation procedure is an extremely useful means of preliminary resolution of natural mixtures of fatty acids, but the factors just mentioned must be carefully borne in mind. Moreover, each case must be considered, in selecting the solvents and the most suitable temperatures for crystallisation, from the standpoint of the specific mixture of acids present in the fat under examination, or in portions of the acids already partly segregated and to be submitted to further crystallisation. The following general points may however be noted:

(i) To minimise to the greatest degree the effects of "mutual solubility" it is best to commence crystallisation at the *lowest* temperature to be used. This leaves in the most soluble fraction a minimum quantity of the less unsaturated acids, but of course carries down with the deposited acids a certain amount of the most unsaturated components. Most of these are removable, however, by recrystallisation of the deposited acids at the same (lowest) temperature.

The same principle applies, of course, if the methyl esters instead of the free fatty acids are segregated; indeed, the only difference when esters are employed is in the somewhat lower temperatures which may be requisite to effect similar separation to that obtained when fatty acids are used.

(ii) The most unsaturated (polyethenoid) acids remain mainly in solution in acetone at or below about $-50°$; diethenoid (linoleic) acids, if present in high proportions, may however require a somewhat higher temperature, but usually are left in solution in acetone at $-40°$ (accompanied by more significant proportions of mono-ethenoid (oleic) acid than at $-50°$).

(iii) The acids finally separated at $-40°$ or $-50°$ from acetone consist largely of mono-ethenoid and saturated members. These may usually be further resolved by crystallisation from ether at $-30°$ or $-40°$ into an insoluble fraction of iodine value 10–20, and a soluble fraction of iodine value in the region of 80–100.

(iv) An exception to the otherwise advisable practice of commencing segregation of fatty acids (or esters) at the lowest temperature of crystallisation is desirable when 40 per cent. or more of the mixed fatty acids (as in "stearic-rich" animal fats) consists of palmitic and stearic acids. In such mixtures, owing to the "mutual solubility effect", significant proportions of these saturated acids are held in solution with the unsaturated acids when the primary crystallisation at low temperatures is conducted on the total mixture of fatty acids, and it is best to remove as much palmitic and stearic acids as possible before the crystallisation procedure is applied (as indicated above) to the rest of the acids. This may be done by a lead salt separation on the mixed fatty acids, or by crystallising the latter (Gunstone and Paton,[4] 1953) from methanol at $-20°$.

The best procedure in preliminary resolution of fatty acid or ester mixtures varies somewhat widely according to the nature of the acids present in the fat under investigation. Details of a fatty acid mixture from an animal depot fat (horse mesenteric fat, S. S. Gupta[5a]) are given in Fig. 15. The mixed fatty acids were crystallised from 10 per cent. solutions in acetone or ether according to the scheme outlined. Examples of a "linoleic-rich" seed oil, a whale oil, and a milk fat will be found in papers by R. V. Crawford,[5b] L. Maddison[5c] and K. T. Achaya[5d] (and in the 3rd Edition of this book, pp. 578–579).

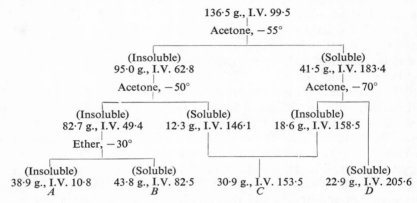

FIG. 15. Crystallisation of mixed fatty acids of horse mesenteric fat.

The following groups of acids were thus finally obtained:

	WT. (g.)	PER CENT.	IOD. VAL.
A	38·9	28·5	10·8
B	43·8	32·1	82·5
C	30·9	22·6	153·5
D	22·9	16·8	205·6

(For the ester-fractionation data for each group, and the final determined composition of the horse mesenteric fat component acids, see Table 149, p. 690).

Fats containing conjugated unsaturated acids. These are not so readily separable by low temperature crystallisation as the more common linoleic and oleic acid mixtures. The elæostearic acid of tung oils, for example, can be concentrated by crystallisation from acetone or, better, light petroleum at −60° to −40°, but the fractions from which it has thus been separated tend to retain appreciable proportions of the conjugated acid.[5e]

For details of segregation of *methyl esters of mixed fatty acids* by low temperature crystallisation the studies of Cramer and Brown[6a] on human depot fats, de la Mare and Shorland[6b] on pig fats, and Winter et al.[6c] on seal blubber fats may be consulted.

Details of crystallisation technique. The operations are facilitated, of course, if low temperature chambers (at all events down to −20° or −30°C.) are available. Where these are not available the following remarks may be of some help.

The solution to be cooled is placed, preferably, in a round-bottomed flask immersed in a bath containing alcohol, this bath being surrounded by several inches of sawdust or other non-conducting material in a wooden or stout cardboard box. The alcohol bath is cooled to the desired temperature by the addition of solid carbon dioxide.

It seems desirable to cool slowly at first until a nucleus of crystals has separated, after which cooling can be rapidly effected; this aids in the formation of a deposit of crystals which filter readily. If desired, mechanical stirring may be maintained throughout, but it is perhaps simpler, and almost as efficacious, to rely on intermittent stirring by a rod manipulated by hand.

It is important, for reasons already stated, to allow the mixture to remain for as long as possible at the crystallisation temperature. At least 4–5 hours should be given, whilst even more would be an advantage.

The solution may eventually be filtered either by insertion of a cooled sintered-glass filter plate fused to a glass delivery tube, or by transference to a Buchner funnel enclosed in a wooden box, the space between funnel and box being packed with crushed solid carbon dioxide so that the funnel temperature is the same as that to which the solution has been cooled.

Separation of mixed fatty acids as complexes with urea. The property of urea to form complexes with many types of organic compounds in a more or less selective manner extends to its behaviour with the higher fatty acids. When a natural fatty acid mixture is treated in methanol or aqueous methanol solution with urea (preferably in stages), the least soluble complexes of urea and saturated acids tend to separate first, followed by those with oleic and other mono-ethenoid acids, whilst the urea complexes of the polyethenoid acids are more soluble. This procedure can therefore be employed, in much the same way as low temperature crystallisation from solvents and with apparently similar degrees of concentration of the various groups of acids, in the preliminary resolution of mixtures of natural fatty acids.

It appears to give, on the whole, similar results to the direct crystallisation methods, but involves the consumption of urea in amounts equal to about three times that of the weight of fatty acids treated. Recovery of fatty acids from separated urea complexes is very simple, since they are decomposed merely by warming with excess of water. Moreover, the complexes of unsaturated fatty acids with urea are remarkably stable to autoxidation,[7a] so that this procedure is as well suited as low temperature crystallisation to effect fatty acid segregation with little chance of damage to the unsaturated components. On the other hand, since the degree of segregation is at all events no better as urea complexes than by low temperature crystallisation, the latter process would seem to be more simple to carry out when facilities for low temperature work are available. The use of urea complexes in the segregation of mixtures of higher fatty acids has been reviewed by Schlenk and Holman,[7a] Schlenk[7b] and Newey et al.[7c] Swern and Parker[7d] have described its application to the isolation of pure or concentrated preparations of oleic, linoleic, linolenic, erucic and petroselinic acids.

In a number of instances the urea adduct has been used in determining the fatty acid composition of oils. Thus, Mehta and co-workers used elution with ethanol of fractions from the adducts of safflower and sesame oil fatty acids or methyl esters and determined their saponification and iodine values[8a]; or a solid–liquid counter-current distribution process with the urea adduct to obtain fractions from kenaf seed oil fatty acids[8b] and a similar procedure with karanja oil.[8c]

There have been numerous other publications on the use of urea adducts for effecting fractionation of fatty compounds, based mainly on difference in unsaturation.[9]

Separation of mixed fatty acids by chromatographic (adsorption) methods. Some of the methods which will be described are not strictly "chromatographic" but are dependent on partition of a solute between two solvents.

683

However, it has become the custom to describe all these methods as "chromatographic". They are:

(i) Column chromatography – adsorption.
(ii) Column chromatography – partition.
(iii) Paper chromatography.
(iv) Column chromatography – gas-liquid (G.L.C.) – strictly a form of partition chromatography.

All four methods have been used for quantitative estimation of fatty acid compositions, but the general view at present is that (i), (ii) and (iii) are best reserved for separation of classes of fatty acids or identification (and possibly isolation) of individual components, rather than for determining the complete fatty acid composition of a natural fat. On the other hand, although (iv), G.L.C., can be used for preparative purposes it is mainly used for ascertaining complete fatty acid compositions and indeed has to a large extent replaced the old-established ester-fractionation method for this purpose. A description of (iv), G.L.C., will therefore be given after that of the ester-fractionation procedure, whereas short accounts of (i), (ii) and (iii) will be given at this point. Obviously it is not possible to deal here *in extenso* with all the basic theory and the experimental work published in connection with the application of chromatographic procedures in this field; readers are referred to a number of general publications.[10]

(i) **Column Chromatography – Adsorption.** The selective adsorption and elution of fatty acids or their esters on columns of various adsorbents has been used for the separation of different types of acid and the isolation of pure fractions. Originally fatty acid mixtures were used as it was convenient to determine them quantitatively by titrating the eluant fractions, but methyl esters are preferred because the application to them of other analytical procedures, such as G.L.C., is easier. Glass columns of various diameters are used, with the height five to ten times the diameter. Various materials have been used for packing, e.g., alumina, carbon, magnesia and silica; the preparation of these is an important factor in obtaining success. The fatty acid mixture in solvent solution, usually a non-polar solvent, is carefully applied to the top of the column and then followed by the pure solvent until the bands or zones have developed. These are then eluted by a succession of solvents or solvent mixtures to elute the different acids or esters in succession. It is convenient to use fraction collectors and, apart from titration for fatty acid fractions, immediate and continuous monitoring of columns has been accomplished interferometrically by comparing the refractivity of the outflowing solution with a standard solvent.

Dutton and Reinbold[11a] separated binary mixtures of ethyl stearate, oleate, linoleate, and linolenate by fractional adsorption on an alumina column, and Kurtz[11b] similarly separated methyl stearate-oleate, oleate-linoleate, or linoleate-linolenate mixtures on a column packed with alternate layers of silica gel and anhydrous sodium sulphate. Riemenschneider *et al.*[11c] prepared methyl linoleate and methyl linolenate in an almost pure condition by adsorption of the methyl esters of, respectively, tobacco seed oil and perilla oil mixed esters on a column of silica gel* mixed with Supercel (kieselguhr), and Hammond and Lundberg,[11d] and Abu-Nasr and Holman,[11e] similarly isolated methyl or ethyl docosapenta- and hexa-enoates from fish oils. Morris et al.,[12a] using a silicic acid column, isolated cis-12,13-epoxyoleate from the methyl esters of Vernonia anthelmintica oil.

Column chromatography in which the adsorbent (silica[12b] or a cation exchange resin[12c]) contains a silver ion (impregnation with silver nitrate) has been shown (1963) to give effective separations of methyl oleate, linoleate and linolenate, and of the cis- and trans-forms of esters (e.g., methyl oleate and elaidate).

The passage of almost pure methyl esters or glycerides in petrol solution through a column of activated alumina is often a very efficient method of removing the last traces of impurities.

One of the most useful applications of column chromatography to lipids is for their separation[12d] into various classes – hydrocarbons, free sterols, sterol esters, triglycerides, fatty acids, etc.

As Schlenk and Gellerman[13] point out in a review of "Column chromatography of fatty acids", this technique is now used mainly for preparative purposes, but Holman et al.[14] have used it quantitatively with charcoal or charcoal and Supercel columns and both frontal and displacement analysis. Other reviews on this subject are quoted in the references[15] at the end of this chapter.

(ii) **Column Chromatography – Partition.** This depends on the distribution of fatty acids or their esters between two immiscible solvents according to their several partition coefficients. It is carried out by allowing a mobile phase to flow through an immobile phase held on an inert support in a column. The stationary phase should be the solvent in which the compounds to be separated have the greater solubility; they are eluted in turn by a large volume of the mobile phase in which they are less soluble. With fatty acids of shorter chain length (C_1–C_{10}) the stationary phase is the more polar solvent, whereas the reverse is the case with the higher fatty acids and the procedure is known as reversed-phase partition chromatography. This procedure is the most frequently used in fatty acid investigations and is based on the work of Martin and Howard (1950),[16a] although reversed-phase chromatography had been used with fatty acids earlier by Boldingh,[16b] who used filter paper treated with dilute vulcanised rubber and methanol alone or with an equal volume of acetone as the solvent; later he used powdered rubber saturated with benzene and methyl alcohol-acetone-water. Howard and Martin[16a] on the other hand used a column of Hyflo Supercel treated with dichloromethylsilane vapour to make

---

* Silica gel, however carefully "activated" by heating in a vacuum, is liable to retain traces of firmly adsorbed oxygen, and a small portion of highly-unsaturated esters adsorbed upon it may become oxidised to brown-coloured polymerised materials. To avoid this it has been found useful first to pass through the Riemenschneider adsorption column a dilute light petroleum solution of highly-unsaturated esters; after standing for some time the column is eluted with ethyl ether until no further organic matter is removed. The ether is then completely displaced by light petroleum, and the adsorbent (which has not at any time been allowed to come in contact with air) may then be efficiently used for the separation of highly-unsaturated fatty esters without any production of polymerised by-products from the latter compounds.

it hydrophobic and aqueous methanol-octane and/or aqueous acetone-medicinal paraffin as the solvents.

As originally applied the method only separated mixtures of C_{12}–C_{24} saturated acids, but various modifications have been used to get over the difficulty that each double bond in an unsaturated acid causes it to be eluted with the saturated acid containing 2 carbon atoms less, e.g., oleic with palmitic, and linoleic with myristic acid.

Boldingh[16b] overcame this difficulty by chromatographing the mixed acids after complete hydrogenation or after oxidation with alkaline permanganate. Crombie *et al.*[17a] also used oxidation with alkaline permanganate. Popják and Tietz,[17b] and Lough and Garton,[17c] combined appropriate fractions, hydrogenated and then chromatographed them, and obtained additional values by alkali isomerisation and U.V. spectrophotometry. Savary and Desnuelle[17d] hydroxylated the unsaturated acids with potassium permanganate. Brenner and Mercuri[17e] also used a modified Martin and Howard procedure, which they claim is speedier, gives more compact elution and satisfactory results with C_{12}–C_{24} acids; they titrate eluant fractions with KOH. Another modification is that of Green,[17f] who used powdered polythene as the stationary phase and aqueous acetone as the mobile phase.

Finally reference must be made to Gunstone's work,[18a] in which he obtained chromatograms *per se*, after hydrogenation, and after ozonolysis. He used a stationary column of Hyflo Supercel impregnated with acetylated castor oil, as well as one treated with medicinal paraffin in order to estimate the oxygenated acids. His technique represents one which has apparently been applied with success to separating and determining the fatty acid composition of four oils containing a wide range of acids and it is therefore given in some detail as an example of a satisfactory procedure.

The columns used are 35 cm. long and 1·3 cm. diameter and contain 25 g. of a mixture of kieselguhr (Hyflo Supercel) with neutral medicinal paraffin (1:1·4) or neutral acetylated castor oil (1:1·3). The paraffin columns are run at 35° and are jacketed with iso-propyl chloride vapour; the acetylated castor oil columns are run at 20°. Development is carried out with a range of aqueous acetone solutions containing 0·001 per cent. bromothymol blue and saturated with the appropriate stationary phase, each of which elutes a particular acid or group of acids. Paraffin columns are used for the usual range of saturated and unsaturated acids and give some information about oxygenated acids, which are however, more adequately separated on acetylated castor oil columns. The eluate is collected in a 2 ml. siphon which empties into a specially constructed titration cell where it is titrated with 0·01 N methanolic alkali.

The mixed acids alone, after hydrogenation, and after ozonolysis are chromatographed on paraffin columns using 20–30 mg. of acid. In the presence of epoxy acids the mixed acids must be acetylated before hydrogenation; if oxygenated acids are present it may also be necessary to chromatograph the mixed acids, before and after acetylation, on an acetylated castor oil column.

Reversed phase partition chromatography has been used by a number of other investigators to determine the fatty acid composition of natural oils, e.g., palm oil, mafura oil, tallow and palm kernel oil (Kapitel[18b]); fatty acids of plasma triglycerides (Lough and Garton[18c]); fatty acids of cholesterol esters from serum and plasma (Riley and Nunn[18d]); palm kernel and palm oils (Crombie and Boatman[18e]); higher fatty acids from blood, chyle and fæces (van de Kaemer *et al.*[18f]).

(iii) **Paper Chromatography.** There are a considerable number of variations in the application of this procedure and for a full account of these and the underlying theory the reader should consult one of the standard works on chromatography.[10] Simply, the procedure consists in placing a spot of the material on a vertical piece of filter paper and allowing the paper to dip into a solvent for several hours. The solutions of the individual components advance at different rates so that they form on the papers discrete spots or areas, which can be identified by staining in various ways.

The application of paper chromatography to lipids has recently been reviewed by Rouser et al.,[19] who state that "Paper chromatography has set new, high standards for the purity of lipids and allied substances and has been used extensively in the development of new column procedures and for monitoring column fractions." This is probably a fair assessment, but paper chromatography has also been used successfully for the quantitative examination of fatty acid mixtures by Kaufmann[20] and others, although with the development of gas–liquid chromatography it may not be used extensively for this purpose in the future. Further information on the application of paper chromatography, particularly to fatty acids, will be found in the reviews by Schlenk et al.[21a,b]

A good description of the application of paper chromatography to the quantitative estimation of fatty acids in a natural mixture has been given by Ballance and Crombie[22] in the course of their examination of the fat from the fungus *Trichoderma viride*. Their procedure may be summarised as follows:

Preparation of paper. Whatman No. 1 chromatography papers (13 cm. × 45 cm.) are immersed in a solution of liquid paraffin (Nujol) (35 ml.) in benzene (65 ml.), blotted for 10 minutes under an evenly distributed 18 lb. weight and dried by hanging in air at room temperature. After removal of the top (11 cm.) and bottom (4 cm.) portions, each paper is cut into standard 30 cm. × 2 cm. lengths ("top" and "bottom" refer to a paper hung vertically with the direction of machining pointing upwards).

Application of fatty acids to the paper. The mixture, dissolved in chloroform (approximately 6 mg./ml.), is delivered (1–5 μl, at a time, total volume 10–20 μl) on the starting line (5 cm. from the upper edge of the paper) by means of an Agla micrometer syringe. After evaporation of the solvent the papers are equilibrated (4 hours) in contact with vapour from the eluting solvent prior to downward development.

Elution system – paraffin-acetic acid. The fatty acids are eluted at 21° for 16 hours with 90 per cent. (v/v) acetic acid (or if lower M.W. acids (C_8–C_{10}) are present 70 per cent. acetic acid). After the position of the solvent front has been marked the papers are dried by hanging in air.

Detection of fatty acid spots. The papers are dried in air at room temperature and copper salts of the fatty acids formed by immersing the papers in cupric acetate solution (20 ml. of a saturated solution in 1 l. of water for 20 minutes). Excess of copper is removed by washing for 15 minutes in dilute acid (0·2 ml. of acetic acid/l.). After drying the copper is detected by immersing the papers (30 seconds) in 0·03 per cent. (w/v) dithio-oxamide in ethanol, and estimating photometrically.

Paper chromatography has been employed in quantitative estimation of fatty acids in a number of natural fats and fatty oils by several other workers besides Ballance and Crombie (*loc. cit.*), including Inoue and Noda,[23a] Kaufmann[23b] and Seher.[23c]

References to a few of the many publications on the application of paper chromatography to the examination, both qualitative and quantitative, of fatty acids and fats are given[24] in the bibliography on p. 709.

QUANTITATIVE DETERMINATIONS OF COMPONENT FATTY ACIDS
FRACTIONAL DISTILLATION OF HIGHER FATTY ACID ESTERS IN A VACUUM

Those portions of the mixed fatty acids which are to be further resolved by ester-fractionation are converted into methyl esters by boiling with about four times their weight of methyl alcohol containing about 1 per cent. of concentrated sulphuric acid, and subsequently removing unesterified acid by washing the ether solution of the esters with dilute potassium carbonate solution. The conversion into methyl esters is usually 97–98 per cent., but if by accident it falls below this figure, the unesterified acid should be recovered and re-esterified.

Alternatively, it is often convenient to convert a fat directly into methyl esters (if acids below C_8 are not present) by gently heating it in methanol containing a small proportion (0·1–0·5 per cent.) of sodium methoxide, when the glycerides are quantitatively transformed into the methyl esters of their component acids (methanolysis).

Another useful procedure, notably for small samples (for G.L.C.), is to treat a solution of the mixed fatty acids in ether with diazomethane.[41]

It originally became the custom to use methyl esters because of their slightly lower boiling points as compared with those of ethyl esters. This point is of less significance than formerly, but it is convenient to continue with the (methyl) esters with which so much data have already been obtained, owing to the possible confusion in calculation of results which might ensue from the use, in different cases, of methyl and of ethyl esters.

The esters (20 to 150 gm., as may be requisite) are fractionally distilled from a flask fitted with an electrically-heated and packed (E.H.P.) column (Longenecker[25a]). Full details of the "Willstatter" flask originally used for the distillation and of the various types of electrically-heated and packed columns will be found in earlier editions of this book. Many efficient columns can now be constructed or purchased from laboratory suppliers. Norris and Terry[25b] have recorded boiling point data for different pressures when using a Podbielniak column[25c] as follows:

PRESSURE (mm.):	1	2	5	10	20
Methyl myristate	114°	125°	143·5°	157·5°	172·5°
Methyl palmitate	136	149	166·5	180·5	196·5
Methyl stearate	155·5	170	189·5	204·5	222
Methyl oleate	152·5	166·6	186	201	218·5
Methyl linoleate	149·5	163	182·5	198	215

The Podbielniak column has been widely used, as described by Weitkamp and Brunstrum.[25d]

Since the final temperature attained by the remaining undistilled esters at the base of the column may be relatively high (e.g., ca. 250°), its possible effect on polyethenoid fatty esters must be taken into consideration. Norris et al.,[25e] and also Holman,[11e] have concluded that with non-conjugated esters containing five or six double bonds there is little risk of more than very slight

688

dimerisation in the course of a fairly prolonged fractional distillation, and that the action of alkalies during hydrolysis of fats and their treatment prior to fractionation is a much more important potential source of structural alteration (to conjugated isomers). On the other hand, of course, esters of conjugated acids (e.g., methyl elæostearates) cannot be distilled without substantial alteration (polymerisation) at the temperature at which they distil in heated columns of the above types.

Several workers[25f] have published details of specially constructed small fractionating columns suitable for dealing with smaller quantities (1–5 gm. or 5–20 gm.) of mixed fatty esters.

The saponification equivalents and iodine values of the fractions are determined and, where necessary, the type of unsaturation by the U.V. spectrophotometric method. Complete fractionation data of the component acids of a horse mesenteric fat[5a] are set out in Table 149. Other detailed data of the component acids of cow milk fat, whale blubber oil, tobacco seed, rubber seed and tung oils, and of procedures used in the calculation of individual ester fractions will be found in the previous (3rd) edition of this book.

TABLE 149. Complete Fractionation Data for the Component Acids of a Horse Mesenteric Fat (S. S. Gupta[5a])

The fatty acid mixture present in this fat is broadly typical of those in many land animal fats and also of those in vegetable fats which contain fairly high proportions of palmitic and/or stearic acid. The crystallisation and ester-fractionation procedures employed in the analysis of the horse mesenteric fatty acids are, in general, suitable for component acids of animal and vegetable fats.

In this analysis the mixed acids (136.5 g.) of the fat were resolved by preliminary crystallisation from acetone and ether (cf. p. 628 and Fig. 15) at low temperatures into the following groups:

	WT. (g.)	PER CENT.	IODINE VALUE
A	38.9	28.5	10.8
B	43.8	32.1	82.5
C	30.9	22.6	153.5
D	22.9	16.8	205.6

The methyl esters of each group of acids were fractionally distilled (E.H.P. column) at ca. 0.5 mm. pressure with the result given below.

(a) Fractional Distillation of Methyl Esters of Acids "A"

No.	G.	COLUMN HEAD °C.	S.E.	I.V.	SATURATED C_{14}	C_{16}	C_{18}	C_{20}	OLEIC	N–S
A1	1.03	95–110	247.0	0.9	0.83	0.19	—	—	0.01	—
A2	2.62	110–120	265.0	1.3	0.46	2.12	—	—	0.04	—
A3	3.57	120–126	269.4	1.4	0.11	3.40	—	—	0.06	—
A4	4.10	126	269.5	1.1	0.10	3.95	—	—	0.05	—
A5	4.40	126	270.3	1.7	0.03	4.28	—	—	0.09	—
A6	3.00	126	271.4	1.7	—	2.85	0.09	—	0.06	—
A7	4.19	126–138	287.3	31.1	—	1.40	1.27	—	1.52	—
A8	3.16	Residue	303.9*	33.4*	—	—	1.71	0.21	1.19	0.05
	26.07									
Weights					1.53	18.19	3.07	0.21	3.02	0.05
Per cent. Esters					5.9	69.7	11.8	0.8	11.6	0.2
Per cent. Acids					5.8	69.7	11.9	0.8	11.6	0.2

* A8, Esters, freed from unsaponifiable matter, S.E. 298.8, I.V. 32.8.

CALCULATED COMPOSITION OF ESTER-FRACTIONS

No.	G.	COLUMN HEAD °C.	S.E.	I.V.	SATURATED			UNSATURATED				
					C₁₄	C₁₆	C₁₈	C₁₆	OL.	LIN.	LEN.	N-S

No.	G.	COLUMN HEAD °C.	S.E.	I.V.	C_{14}	C_{16}	C_{18}	C_{16}	OL.	LIN.	LEN.	N-S
B1	1·49	90–100	245·1	5·8	1·29	0·11	—	0·09	—	—	—	—
B2	1·95	100–120	270·4	32·1	—	1·29	—	0·58	—	0·08	—	—
B3	3·18	120–135	280·9	61·1	—	1·13	—	0·58	—	1·47	—	—
B4	3·80	135–140	294·4	84·7	—	0·23	0·18	—	—	3·39	—	—
B5	3·63	140	294·1	90·4	—	0·10	0·08	—	—	3·45	—	—
B6	5·86	140	296·2	91·0	—	—	0·25	—	—	5·61	—	—
B7	4·33	140	296·2	90·4	—	—	0·21	—	—	4·12	—	—
B8	2·04	140	296·1	86·8	—	—	0·18	—	—	1·86	—	—
B9	1·70	Residue	310·5*	84·3*	—	—	0·20	—	—	1·43	—	0·07
27·98												
Weights					1·29	2·86	1·10	1·25	20·15	0·30	0·96	0·07
Per cent. Esters					4·6	10·2	3·9	4·5	72·0	1·1	3·4	0·3
Per cent. Acids					4·6	10·2	3·9	4·4	72·1	1·1	3·4	0·3

* B9, Esters, freed from unsaponifiable matter, S.E. 297·6, I.V. 83·0.

(c) Fractional Distillation of Methyl Esters of Acids "C"

CALCULATED COMPOSITION OF ESTER-FRACTIONS

No.	G.	COLUMN HEAD °C.	S.E.	I.V.	SATURATED			UNSATURATED							
					C_{12}	C_{14}	C_{16}	MONO-	C_{16} DI-	TRI-	OL.	C_{18} LIN.	LEN.	C_{20-22}	N-S
C1	0·97	100–110	240·0	38·2	0·23	0·49	—	—	0·25	—	—	—	—	—	—
C2	2·98	110–120	262·0	89·4	—	0·63	0·54	—	1·81	—	—	—	—	—	—
C3	2·97	120–130	276·5	133·2	—	—	0·48	—	1·43	—	—	1·06	—	—	—
C4	2·79	130–132	286·1	160·5	—	—	0·24	—	—	—	—	2·55	—	—	—
C5	3·25	132	294·2	162·8	—	—	0·24	—	—	—	—	3·01	—	—	—
C6	3·25	132	294·3	167·5	—	—	0·15	—	—	—	—	3·10	—	—	—
C7	2·29	132	294·6	165·8	—	—	0·13	—	—	—	—	2·16	—	—	—
C8	2·31	132	294·1	168·8	—	—	0·09	—	—	—	—	2·22	—	—	—
C9	2·39	132	294·9	167·3	—	—	0·12	—	—	—	—	2·27	—	—	—
C10	2·30	Residue	326·8*	146·3*	—	—	—	—	—	—	—	0·84	—	1·38	0·08
25·50															
Weights					0·23	1·12	1·99	2·38	0·32	0·79	7·09	2·53	7·59	1·38	0·08
Per cent. Esters					0·9	4·4	7·8	9·3	1·3	3·1	27·8	9·9	29·8	5·4	0·3
Per cent. Acids					0·9	4·4	7·8	9·3	1·2	3·1	27·9	9·9	29·8	5·4	0·3

* C10, Esters, freed from unsaponifiable matter, S.E. 315·4, I.V. 148·7.

691

TABLE 149. Complete Fractionation Data for the Component Acids of a Horse Mesenteric Fat (S. S. Gupta) – continued

(d) Fractional Distillation of Methyl Esters of Acids "D"

CALCULATED COMPOSITION OF ESTER-FRACTIONS

No.	G.	COLUMN HEAD °C.	S.E.	I.V.	SATURATED			UNSATURATED							
								C16			C18			C20–22	N–S
					C12	C14	C16	MONO-	DI-	TRI-	OL.	LIN.	LEN.		
D1	1·27	80–100	250·5	84·4	0·21	0·33	—	—	—	—	—	—	—	—	—
D2	1·04	100–110	266·6	131·7	—	0·03	0·08	—	0·73	—	—	1·88	—	—	—
D3	2·52	110–120	286·1	190·4	—	—	0·31	—	0·93	—	—	2·02	—	—	—
D4	2·36	120–125	288·9	209·5	—	—	0·13	—	0·33	—	—	2·80	—	—	—
D5	3·02	125–130	291·7	212·4	—	—	0·22	—	0·21	—	—	3·21	—	—	—
D6	3·39	125–130	293·0	217·0	—	—	0·18	—	—	—	—	1·51	—	—	—
D7	2·57	Residue	317·1*	202·7*	—	—	—	—	—	—	—	—	—	0·97	0·09
	16·17														
Weights					0·21	0·36	0·92	1·50	0·20	0·50	0·81	2·49	8·12	0·97	0·09
Per cent. Esters					1·3	2·2	5·7	9·3	1·2	3·1	5·0	15·4	50·2	6·0	0·6
Per cent. Acids					1·3	2·2	5·7	9·2	1·2	3·1	5·0	15·4	50·3	6·0	0·6

Weights, freed from unsaponifiable matter, S.E. 306·3, I.V. 207·1.

* D7, Esters, freed from unsaponifiable matter, S.E. 306·3, I.V. 207·1.

(e) Spectrophotometric Analyses of Acids from unsaturated-C16 or unsaturated-C18 Ester-fractions

	B6 (C18)	C8 (C18)	D6 (C18)	D2 (C16)
Ester-Fraction:				
Alkali-isomerised:				
at 170°/15 mins. $E^{1\%}_{1cm.}$ at 268 mμ	23	225	358	119
at 180°/60 mins. $E^{1\%}_{1cm.}$ at 234 mμ	37	369	570	211
Acids (per cent. wt.):				
Saturated	4·3	4·1	5·4	10·7
Mono-ethenoid	90·1	39·5	6·7	60·9
Di-ethenoid	1·3	14·1	20·6	8·3
Tri-ethenoid	4·3	42·3	67·3	20·1
Whence unsaturated esters (per cent. wt.):				
Hexadecenoic	—	—	—	68·2
Hexadecadienoic	—	—	—	9·3
Hexadecatrienoic	—	—	—	22·5
Oleic	94·1	41·2	7·1	—
Linoleic	1·4	14·7	21·8	—
Linolenic	4·5	44·1	71·1	—

(f) Calculated Composition of Total Horse Mesenteric Fatty Acids

ACID	PER CENT. A 28·5	B 32·1	C 22·6	D 16·8	TOTAL 100·0	FATTY ACIDS (EXCLUDING UNSAPONIFIABLE) PER CENT. (WT.)	PER CENT. (MOL.)
Lauric	—	—	0·20	0·21	0·41	0·4	0·6
Myristic	1·66	1·46	0·98	0·37	4·47	4·5	5·3
Palmitic	19·87	3·27	1·76	0·95	25·85	25·9	27·3
Stearic	3·37	1·26	—	—	4·63	4·7	4·4
Arachidic	0·23	—	—	—	0·23	0·2	0·2
Hexadecenoic	—	1·43	2·10	1·55	5·08	5·1	5·4
Hexadecadienoic	—	—	0·28	0·21	0·49	0·5	0·5
Hexadecatrienoic	—	—	0·70	0·52	1·22	1·2	1·3
Oleic	3·31	23·15	6·30	0·84	33·60	33·7	32·2
Linoleic	—	0·35	2·25	2·59	5·19	5·2	5·0
Linolenic	—	1·10	6·72	8·44	16·26	16·3	15·8
Unsaturated C_{20-22}	—	—	1·23	1·02	2·25	2·3	2·0
Unsaponifiable	0·06	0·08	0·08	0·10	0·32	—	—

Analytical Characteristics of Original Horse Fat
(including Unsaponifiable Matter)

	CALC. FROM DATA IN (f) ABOVE	DETERMINED ON ORIGINAL FAT
Saponification Equivalent	282·9	283·1
Iodine value	94·2	95·6

693

Calculation of the Composition of Individual Ester-Fractions (General Principles). The ideal, in the ester-fractionation procedure for the analysis of a mixture of fatty acids, is to produce a series of ester-fractions, each of which shall contain not more than two saturated esters, accompanied by not more than one unsaturated ester (or, at least, esters of unsaturated acids with the same number of carbon atoms). The composition of such fractions can be directly calculated from their saponification equivalents and iodine values. This holds for many fats in which the only unsaturated components belong to the C_{18} series of acids (oleic, or, oleic with linoleic and/or linolenic, etc.). When, as is usually the case, both oleic and linoleic (and/or linolenic) acids are present, the mean iodine value of the C_{18} unsaturated esters can be determined and the assumption made that these esters distil throughout in the same proportions; this is not absolutely correct, but the error thereby introduced is usually negligible.

When linolenic acid accompanies linoleic and oleic acid, as is the case in many liquid seed fats, it is necessary (having arrived at the total amount of unsaturated C_{18} acids) to determine the amount of each of the three unsaturated acids present. This may be best carried out from spectrographic measurement of the conjugated di- and tri-ethenoid acids produced by controlled alkali-isomerisation of the linoleic and linolenic acids present[26]; or, thiocyanometric analysis may be resorted to, the empirically agreed values (cf. Chapter IV, p. 179) for the thiocyanogen values of linoleic and linolenic acids being employed.

In some other fats, especially those from aquatic sources, the mixture of unsaturated acids (especially in the C_{20} and C_{22} series) is complex, the constitution of many of the polyethenoid acids is still uncertain, and neither of the methods mentioned can yet be applied in these instances. In cases of this kind, where unsaturated acids of the C_{14}, C_{16}, C_{20}, C_{22}, and even C_{24} series accompany those of the C_{18} group, it becomes necessary to adopt a different method of evaluation of the ester-fractions, some of which then contain two saturated esters with esters of unsaturated acids belonging to two series (e.g., C_{16} and C_{18}, or C_{18} and C_{20}, etc.); or it may happen that mixtures of *three* groups of the homologous series are present (e.g., myristic, palmitic, hexadecenoic and unsaturated C_{18} esters). Here it is necessary to know the amount and/or equivalent of the saturated esters present in the ester-fractions concerned. In very many instances (usually where the proportion of unsaturated esters is low in comparison with that of the saturated esters, or *vice versa*) it has been found safe to assume that the equivalent of both saturated and unsaturated parts of the ester-fraction are the same, and the evaluation can then be effected on the basis only of the iodine value and saponification equivalent of the ester-fraction.

If a fraction of weight w, equivalent E_w and iodine value I_w contains a weight u of unsaturated esters (of the same carbon content, e.g., C_{18}) with iodine value I_u and equivalent E_u,

$$u = w.I_w/I_u$$

and the mean equivalent E, of the saturated esters $(w-u)$ present follows from the equation

$$E_s = \frac{w-u}{w/E_w - u/E_u}$$

From E_s the weights of saturated esters are calculated as binary mixtures of the homologues (e.g. C_{16} and C_{18}) between the equivalents of which E_s lies.

Again, ester-fractions which include only (unsaturated) derivatives of acids of two groups in the homologous series (e.g. C_{18} and C_{20}, or C_{20} and C_{22}) can be evaluated directly from their saponification equivalents. In other cases, however, the computation becomes somewhat more complicated, since the weights of more than three independent components are involved.

If x, y, z be the respective weights of saturated and two unsaturated esters in a fraction of weight w, and E_x, E_y, E_z, E_w be the corresponding equivalents and I_y, I_z, I_w be the corresponding iodine values, we have:

(i) $x+y+z = w$
(ii) $x/E_x + y/E_y + z/E_z = w/E_w$
(iii) $y.I_y + z.I_z = w.I_w$

694

(Obviously, in equation (ii), saponification values V_x, V_y, V_z, V_w can be alternatively used if desired, the equation becoming: $x.V_x + y.V_y + z.V_z = w.V_w$.)

The values of y and z, the unsaturated components, are thus determined whilst, from that of x, the binary mixture of saturated esters is evaluated directly from its equivalent (E_x).

It may be pointed out that, in use, the equations (i), (ii), (iii) can be conveniently simplified by employing in equation (ii), the reciprocal of the equivalents $\times 10^6$.

The mode of evaluation of ester-fractionation data in any given instance must be considered in relation to the particular circumstances, and choice made accordingly. Illustrations of modes of calculation recommended for ester-fractions of (a) mainly saturated nature with small amounts of corresponding unsaturated acids, (b) the more or mainly unsaturated types, (c) wholly unsaturated C_{18} esters, and (d) fractions with equivalents above those of unsaturated C_{18} esters, were given in some detail in the previous (3rd) edition of this book (pp. 612–615).

DETERMINATION OF LINOLEIC, LINOLENIC, CONJUGATED POLYENE AND SOME OTHER ACIDS BY SPECTROPHOTOMETRIC METHODS

Conjugated polyethenoid long-chain fatty acids exhibit characteristic and well-marked absorption bands in the ultra-violet spectrum. Polyethenoid acids containing the "pentadiene" or "allylic" system —$CH_2.CH:CH.CH_2.CH:CH.CH_2$—, when heated with alkali at 170–180°, are isomerised to conjugated systems —$CH_2.CH_2.CH:CH.CH:CH.CH_2$—. From the extinction coefficients and the wave-lengths of the respective band heads, observed either directly on the fatty acids (for conjugated acids originally present) or on the acids after isomerisation with alkali under standardised conditions (for acids such as linoleic or linolenic), the proportions of linoleic, linolenic, elæostearic, and some other similar acids can be determined. The spectrophotometric method has been considered for some years the best means for accurate determination of *natural* linoleic, linolenic, and elæostearic acids, providing that the analysis is carried out by strictly standardised procedure and that other geometrical (*trans-*) isomers of the natural acids are not present.

The method was originally proposed in 1943 by Mitchell, Kraybill and Zscheile,[26a] who isomerised fatty oils containing linoleic and/or linolenic glycerides at 180° for 25 minutes with a solution of potassium hydroxide in ethylene glycol, and gave reference values for the specific extinction-coefficients of linoleic and linolenic acids after treatment under the conditions mentioned. In 1945, Hilditch, Morton and Riley[26b] recommended that, for the determination of linolenic acid, alkali isomerisation (in glycol) should be conducted at 170° for 15 minutes, but that for linoleic acid it should be effected at 180° for 60 minutes; the reference values given by these authors for the extinction-coefficients (E^1_{1cm}.) of pure linoleic and linolenic acids were later checked by Hilditch, Patel and Riley,[26b] who confirmed the value for linoleic acid but gave revised values for linolenic acid. Hilditch *et al.*[26b] further recommended that the isomerisation should be carried out with fatty acids as such, rather than as esters or glycerides.

The method has also received much study by American workers,[26c] who on the whole prefer to conduct a single alkali-isomerisation for both linoleic and linolenic acids. Various minor modifications have been suggested, notably by Brice, Swain et al.[26d]; these workers give reference data for alkali-isomerisation at 180° in glycerol for 30 and 45 minutes, and in glycol for 25 and 45 minutes, the latter time being preferred. The slower rate of alkali-isomerisation of *trans-trans* or *cis-trans* forms of linoleic acid has been pointed out,[26e] and it is important to note that when these are present with the natural *cis-cis*-acid this method of analysis is accordingly inapplicable.

Sreenivasan and Brown (1956)[26g] found that the isomerisation reaches equilibrium rapidly, and at a lower temperature (120° C)., in presence of a 5 per cent. solution of potassium *tert*.-butoxide in *tert*.-butanol.

The direct spectrophotometric determination of elæostearic acid has been described by several workers,[27] including the concurrent determination of linoleic acid when this accompanies elæostearic acid in natural glycerides.

Comprehensive reviews of the subject have been given by Pitt and Morton[28a] and by Holman.[28b]

Full descriptions of the methods of alkali-isomerisation and of the subsequent spectrophotometric examinations are given in the papers by Hilditch et al.,[26b] in the reports of the A.O.C.S. Spectroscopy Committee in 1949 and subsequent years,[26c] by Brice et al.,[26d] by Herb and Riemenschneider,[26e] and by Mehlenbacher.[26h] Alternative types of constant temperature baths for the isomerisation of fatty oils and acids have been described.[26f] All these workers emphasise that exact attention is necessary in regard to the concentration of potassium hydroxide in the glycol or glycerol (and the purity of the latter), the proportion of glycol or glycerol alkali solution to the fatty acid mixture analysed, the constancy of the isomerisation temperature, and the exact timing of the actual isomerisation. It is also most desirable, if not imperative, to carry out the isomerisation in an atmosphere of nitrogen.

The reference values for the extinction-coefficients of the pure unsaturated acids differ

TABLE 150. *Reference Values for Spectrophotometric Determination of Polyethenoid Acids*

(a) *Values of* $E_{1cm.}^{1\%}$ *(Hilditch et al.[26b])*

	UNISOMERISED		AFTER ALKALI-ISOMERISATION (KOH/GLYCOL)	
			AT 170° FOR 15 MINS.	AT 180° FOR 60 MINS.
	234 mμ	268 mμ	268 mμ	234 mμ
α-Elæostearic	—	1780	1690	197
Conjugated diene	1200	—	—	1140
Linolenic	—	—	555	575
Octadeca-6,9,12-trienoic	—	—	522	603
Linoleic	—	—	—	906
Hexadecatrienoic	—	—	617	639
Hexadecadienoic	—	—	—	1006

(b) *Values of "specific extinction-coefficients"* * *(U.S.A. workers)*

ACID	WAVE-LENGTH mμ	BEADLE AND KRAYBILL[26a] KOH/GLYCOL AT 180° 25 MINS.	BRICE, SWAIN, et al.[26d]			
			KOH/GLYCOL AT 180°		KOH/GLYCEROL AT 180°	
			25 MINS.	45 MINS.	30 MINS.	45 MINS.
Linoleic	234	86·0	91·5	93·4	90·2	93·3
Linolenic	234	60·9	62·2	59·8	60·9	59·2
Linolenic	268	53·2	50·7	49·3	49·3	48·6
Arachidonic	234	59·3	57·8	55·5	57·6	55·8
Arachidonic	268	53·4	52·8	44·8	53·4	46·8
Arachidonic	316	22·6	20·6	22·0	18·2	19·6

* $E_{1cm.}^{1\%}$ = 10 × "specific extinction-coefficient".

somewhat according to the precise method of isomerisation used, and of course the values appropriate to the conditions followed should be used in calculating the results of analyses by this procedure. Typical reference values given by different workers are illustrated in Table 150.

COLUMN CHROMATOGRAPHY: GAS–LIQUID CHROMATOGRAPHY AS A MEANS OF ASCERTAINING FATTY ACID COMPOSITION

As mentioned previously it would appear likely that G.L.C. will almost entirely replace ester-fractionation and other methods as a procedure for the determination of fatty acids. Its advantages are (a) it can deal with very small quantities, such as are often the only amounts available in biological investigations, (b) it is far more speedy – at the worst it takes hours instead of days, and (c) there exist good records of its use with a range of synthetic mixtures of pure acids, which serve as guides to the optimum conditions for its application in any particular instance. Moreover, suitable equipment for analyses by gas–liquid chromatography is supplied by a number of firms.

It should however be emphasised that, as in the case of analyses of most natural products, results are far more certain, if they are checked by carrying out analyses by at least two methods. For example, the spectrophotometric method for unsaturated acids can be a relatively quick check on results obtained by G.L.C.

The method was first applied to fatty oils by James and Martin[29a] and has been developed by James and his co-workers and many others to its present highly successful condition.

The essential features of the technique* are: (a) a source of permanent gas at constant pressure; (b) a column containing a mixture of a stationary phase (a substance liquid at the column temperature, but having a vapour pressure 10^{-3} mm. or less) on an inert microporous support for the stationary phase; (c) a heating jacket for both column and detector; (d) the detector, to measure concentration of vapour in each zone leaving the column; (e) a recorder to present the information supplied by the detector.

The procedure consists in introducing a small quantity, usually a fraction of a millilitre, of mixed fatty acid esters into the top of a packed heated column so that the vapours are carried in an inert gas phase (nitrogen, helium, argon or hydrogen have been used) through the column. The column is packed with an inert substance such as Celite, Chromosorb, crushed fire brick, etc. on which is distributed the stationary liquid phase. Originally this consisted of silicone or silicone grease, but other liquids of negligible vapour pressure at the temperature of operations, have since been found useful, e.g., dioctyl phthalate, Apiezon greases, Reoplex plasticiser or dibasic acid esters (e.g., adipate or succinate) of diethylene glycol.

When the individual fractions arrive at the exit of the column, they are

---

* A very thorough account of the technique, with fuller details of its different parts than can be given here, will be found in an article by A. T. James in Glick's "Methods of Biochemical Analysis", vol. viii, pp. 1–58, (Interscience Publ., New York, 1961).

detected and measured by suitable means – originally by titration, but nowa-days detectors and recording devices are used. The following properties of the exit vapours which can be turned into an electric signal by a detector have been used: thermal conductivity, dielectric constant, heat of combustion, degree of ionisation of a resulting flame, and induced ionisation. The electrical output from the detector is amplified and fed into a suitable recording device. The latter is usually a pen recorder and merely records a straight line ("base line") when no component is emerging, but registers a peak as each single component emerges. With certain detectors and operating conditions the ratios of the areas of the peaks above the base line are equal to the ratios of the concentrations of the components in the mixture analysed.

In the opinion of many workers the argon ionisation detector is one of the most satisfactory: it is highly sensitive, very robust and requires a minimum of electronics for its operation. The detector consists of two essential parts: an electrode system with a beta ray source (usually Lead 210 – Radium D) together within a housing and a stream of argon gas, which is also used as the carrier gas in the instrument.

The following factors determine the partition coefficient and therefore the velocity of movement along the gas–liquid interface for a given component in a mixture: volatility, temperature of the gas/liquid system, relative polarity of the liquid phase and component, and the gas pressure within the system. In order to obtain separation in a reasonably short time it is necessary with fatty acid mixtures to use temperatures in the region of 200°C. Higher temperatures are undesirable since they may lead to reduction of efficiency and instability in some detectors, owing to the production of artefacts, even from saturated acids. In order to minimise decomposition it is preferable to use the methyl esters rather than the fatty acids themselves, because the polarity of the acids is a disadvantage, and moreover the esters have a somewhat lower boiling point than the corresponding acids.

The equipment may initially possess, or may develop faults, or its handling can be incorrect: it is therefore essential if unequivocal results are to be obtained that (a) the saponification equivalents, iodine values and any other charac-teristics available of the total fatty acids as calculated from those of the amounts of individual fatty acids obtained (as methyl esters) in the G.L.C. analysis should be in agreement with those determined on the original starting material, and (b) the equipment should have been tested with a synthetic mixture of esters or acids of known composition, and preferably with a somewhat similar range and quantity of fatty acids. This type of test should be repeated at regular intervals and particularly when the equipment is left unused for any length of time.

The retention times or Rf values are dependent not only on any given component, but also on the design and method of operating the column. It is therefore advisable to identify the components responsible for the peaks in the chromatogram, either:

(a) after a first analysis, by adding a known percentage (say 20–30 per cent.) of a pure methyl ester of a significant acid (such as palmitic) and checking that the corresponding peak in the original chromatogram is enlarged and that the requisite increase in that peak is obtained; or

(b) by preparing a chromatogram, immediately after that of the actual analysis, from a mixture of methyl esters of pure fatty acids of known composition. This latter method is preferable, particularly if one is studying a natural fat the composition of which has not previously been examined.

In order to make even more certain of the accuracy of the determination, a repeat test may be made with a mixture of pure esters containing all the major components (5 per cent. or over) of the sample as ascertained in the first determination. The saponification equivalents and iodine values calculated from the determined composition should accord with those of the mixture itself.

A variety of types of column and packing have been used, all of which probably can give satisfactory results under the best conditions of operation, but we will only briefly outline one:

Support. Celite 60–100 mesh (acid washed), Chromosorb W or kieselguhr 60–150 mesh specially treated with boiling 18–20 per cent. HCl, washed with water, 2 per cent. methanolic KOH, methanol, and dried at 100–110° C. and sieved to separate 60–100 and 100–150 mesh fractions.

Stationary phase. Apiezon L grease, silicone elastomer E301 and ethylene glycol adipate ester.

Column. Glass, approximately 4 mm. internal diameter and $4\frac{1}{2}$ feet long (stainless steel has been used).

The silicone elastomer is used as 5 per cent. with 95 per cent. 60–100 mesh B.S. kieselguhr support by mixing an ethereal solution of the elastomer with the requisite quantity of support and gently mixing while the ether is evaporated; finally drying the powder at 100–110° C. for 1 hour.

The Apiezon L high vacuum grease is prepared similarly, but the volatiles are stripped out by passing nitrogen through the packing at 200° C. for 15 hours.

The ethylene glycol adipate ester packing is prepared similarly to the Apiezon one, except that acetone is used as solvent and the volatile removal is at 150–160° C.

A small, pea size, bundle of Fibreglass yarn is gently rammed into the constriction at the bottom of the column and then the column is completely filled with the stationary phase (which is packed by gently holding it against a vibrator). Further stationary phase is added and packed until all but the top 6 inches of the column is compactly filled. A second wad of Fibreglass yarn is placed on the top of the filling.

The sample of methyl esters, usually prepared by the diazomethane procedure, is introduced into the column by means of a standard micro-pipette and the column operated at an appropriate temperature; when a wide range of acids is present it is advisable to carry out determinations at two column temperatures.

A few of the many publications on the design, filling and manipulation of G.L.C. columns are noted[29b, 30] in the bibliography which concludes this chapter. Details of the method of measuring peak areas of the chromatogram will be found in many of the references quoted (e.g., A. T. James[2]) and in "The Analysis of Fatty acids and Fatty Alcohols", (Prices' (Bromborough) Ltd., 1960) to which publication we are indebted for some of the information included in this section of the chapter.

II. Quantitative Investigation of Component Glycerides

The first quantitative studies (1927) of component glycerides in natural fats depended upon the (chemical) isolation and determination of their fully-saturated glycerides, and of the component acids in these; from about 1935 onwards preliminary resolution of fats into simpler mixtures of mixed glycerides by systematic crystallisation from solvents (usually at low temperatures) became increasingly useful in the study of glyceride structure. These two general techniques were the only approach available until about 1955, when counter-current distribution of fats between two immiscible solvents was introduced as an alternative to low-temperature crystallisation; at about the same time pancreatic lipase commenced to be used for the selective hydrolysis of acyl groups attached at the 1- and 3-positions of the glyceride molecules, leaving the 2-(mono)glycerides intact.

These four procedures (with a brief reference to a fifth, thin-layer chromatography, which at the time of writing is at an early stage of development) will now be further discussed, but since each has received considerable notice in earlier chapters, the information given here will be mainly supplementary to these previous references (page references to which are included).

QUANTITATIVE DETERMINATION OF FULLY-SATURATED GLYCERIDES IN A NATURAL FAT

The following notes may be added to the general description already given in Chapter V (p. 364).

The fat is dissolved in anhydrous acetone (10 vols.), to which may usefully be added sufficient glacial acetic acid to combine with alkali liberated during reduction of the permanganate (Kartha[31]), and finely powdered potassium permanganate (passing a 50-mesh sieve) is added at such a rate that the mixture is kept in gentle ebullition. When the amount of permanganate present is four times that of the esters taken, the mixture is refluxed for some hours. The bulk of the acetone is then removed by distillation, and the residual solid matter powdered with about its own weight of powdered sodium bisulphite, after which it is dropped into dilute sulphuric acid solution, and decolorisation of manganic oxides present is completed by heating. The organic compounds present are extracted with ether, and the ether solution washed repeatedly with potassium carbonate solution, or with aqueous ammonia, and then with water, in order to remove all acidic products of oxidation.

In place of the tedious removal of acidic scission products by washing the ether solution with aqueous alkali carbonates (in which great difficulty is experienced with emulsions) the ether solution of the reaction-products may be given a preliminary washing with a solution of ammonia or of potassium bicarbonate, and then dried and passed over a column of aluminium oxide (tinted with bromothymol blue). All acidic matter is adsorbed on the column, which should be so adjusted that the acidic compounds are wholly adsorbed in the upper half of the column. The column is washed several times with ether or chloroform, and the combined eluates distilled to remove solvent and leave the completely neutral (fully-saturated) esters or glycerides (Sylvester et al.,[32a] Schuette and Nagore[32b]).

An alternative method of oxidation (Youngs[33a]) is to adopt the von Rudloff procedure.[33b] The aqueous oxidant solution (21 gm. of sodium periodate and 25 ml. of 0·1 M potassium permanganate per litre) is mixed with potassium carbonate and tertiary butanol, and the mixture refluxed for an hour with a one per cent. solution of the fat in tertiary butanol. The relative proportions of fat and oxidant depend on the iodine value of the fat; for fats with iodine values up to 100, 1 gm. of fat requires about 250 ml. of oxidant solution mixed with about 330 gm. of potassium carbonate in 300 ml. of the butanol. After destroying excess of oxidant and removing the butanol the remaining aqueous phase is acidified and the oxidised fat extracted with ether. The fully-saturated glycerides are separated from the azaleo-glycerides by adsorption on a silicic acid column and elution with light petroleum.

When the amount of fully-saturated glycerides in a fat is very small, it is preferable to apply the oxidation procedure not to the whole fat, but to the least soluble fractions isolated from it by the crystallisation procedure (below). The fully-saturated glycerides present are concentrated in these, and frequently constitute major proportions of the least soluble glyceride fraction obtained by systematic crystallisation of a natural fat.

PRELIMINARY RESOLUTION OF FATS BY SYSTEMATIC CRYSTALLISATION FROM SOLVENTS

In its most general form this procedure concerns the crystallisation of a natural fat or fatty oil from an appropriate solvent (usually acetone, but ether or light petroleum is useful in some instances) at successively higher temperatures from $-60°$ or $-70°$ upwards. The technique is of course the same as in the similar separation of the mixed saturated and unsaturated acids of a fat (this Chapter pp. 680–682) and requires little additional description. It should however be noted that, owing to the complex mixture of mixed glycerides which usually has to be resolved and to the similarity in solubility of some of the components, the effect of "mutual solubility" is even more pronounced than in the case of free acid mixtures, and the time taken to reach equilibrium between deposited glycerides and those left in solution is similarly greater than in the case of the fatty acids themselves.

As with the fatty acids, it is best to commence the crystallisation at the lowest temperature to be employed, and to recrystallise the separated solids at progressively higher temperatures. Often, especially with the more unsaturated (liquid) fats, it is well to recrystallise deposited glycerides at the same tempera-ture as in the previous crystallisation, before proceeding to a higher tempera-ture. Each fat must be dealt with as its particular composition demands: comparison with a fat of similar composition from the fairly wide range of fats which has now been studied by this method will often indicate the most likely solvents and temperatures to be selected, but otherwise an exploratory series of crystallisations on a smaller proportion of fat than that to be used in the final glyceride study is a useful pointer to the most suitable procedure.

The primary crystallisation of a solid fat such as tallow or cacao butter from acetone is best carried out for some days at $0°$, when most of the mono-unsaturated and trisaturated glycerides (accompanied by some diunsaturated glycerides) will be deposited and should be recrystallised under the same conditions. The second crop of deposited solids may then be recrystallised at higher temperatures from acetone, or from ether at $0°$ or room temperature;

whilst the combined glycerides left in solution should be crystallised from acetone at a lower temperature (e.g., $-60°$ or $-40°$, according to circumstances) and then progressively at higher temperatures, as above.

Of solvents, *acetone* has been found on the whole most generally useful. Care should be taken to use *anhydrous* acetone, since the presence of very little moisture in acetone has a marked effect on the solubility therein, especially at low temperatures, of di- and tri-unsaturated glycerides. *Ether* is occasionally preferred to acetone, notably for the final segregation of trisaturated, accompanied by as little as possible of mono-unsaturated-disaturated, glycerides at $0°$ or at room temperature. *Light petroleum (b.p.* 40–$60°$ C.) has sometimes been found useful at some stages of the resolution of oils rich in elæostearic (or other conjugated) glycerides.

The use of low-temperature crystallisation of fats from solvents has already been discussed in some detail in Chapter V (pp. 372–382), where it was pointed out that the procedure was later found to be ineffective in defining the proportions of unsaturated glycerides such as trilinolein and oleodilinoleins, or trilinolenin and linoleolinolenins, in the more highly unsaturated fatty acids. Even in these cases, however, it has given fairly accurate accounts of the relative proportions of mono-unsaturated-disaturated, di-unsaturated-monosaturated, and tri-unsaturated glycerides in such oils (*cf.* Chapter VI, Tables 107, 108, 109, pp. 456, 458, 463). In other instances, in which glycerides of highly unsaturated conjugated acids are present (with relatively high melting points and concurrent low solubilities) the crystallisation method has appeared to give results of approximate accuracy, as in makita oil (Chapter VI, p. 470), kamala oil (p. 470) and tung oils (p. 469).

The preliminary segregation of natural glycerides by systematic crystallisation from solvents is, however, undoubtedly entirely reliable for the more saturated (solid and semi-solid) fats, and is indeed the best procedure for this class of fats and for others in which unsaturated acids do not predominate. As stated in Chapter V (p. 373), the exact point at which the crystallisation method ceases to be wholly effective is not at present clear, but it seems at the moment that it gives satisfactory results so long as a fat does not contain more than 50 per cent. of linoleic (or total polyethenoid) acids. Thus it appears that the method is quite valid for fatty oils with unsaturated components akin to those of, for example, cottonseed and similar oils.

The application of this technique has been illustrated in detail earlier in this volume for the mesenteric fat of a horse (Chapter V, Table 75, Fig. 4, p. 375) and the milk fats of cow and buffalo (Chapter VII, Table 127, Figs. 11, 12, pp. 517–519). A few further examples are added here, viz., groundnut oil[34a] (Table 151, Fig. 16), badger fat[34b] (Table 152, Fig. 17) and an Antarctic whale oil[34c] (Table 153).

TABLE 151. *Low-Temperature Crystallisation of West African Groundnut Oil[34a]*
(R. V. Crawford)

The neutral oil (252·7 g., iodine value 86·8) was crystallised according to the scheme shown diagrammatically in Fig. 16.

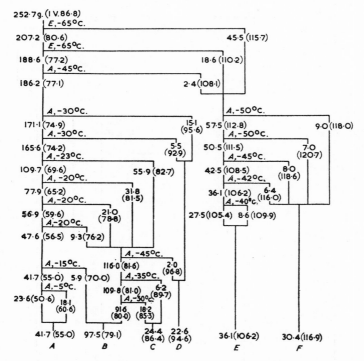

FIG. 16. Crystallisation of West African Groundnut Oil Glycerides.

The component acids in each of the six glyceride fractions, and therefrom in the whole fat, were as below.

	A	B	C	D	E	F	WHOLE FAT
Weight (g.)	41·7	97·5	24·4	22·6	36·1	30·4	252·7
Iodine value	55·0	79·1	86·4	94·6	106·2	116·9	86·8
Glycerides (per cent. mol.)	15·9	39·1	9·8	9·1	14·4	11·7	100·0
Component acids (per cent. mol.):							
Palmitic	12·9	11·3	8·1	7·1	6·4	2·9	9·2
Stearic	8·6	3·3	8·4	7·4	6·7	3·1	5·5
Saturated C_{20}, C_{22}, and C_{24}	26·1	3·8	—	—	—	—	5·6
Oleic	38·2	71·9	67·1	61·3	50·1	47·4	59·1
Linoleic	14·2	9·7	16·4	24·2	36·8	46·6	20·6

TABLE 152. *Low-Temperature Crystallisation of Badger Fat*[34b]
(S. S. Gupta and M. L. Meara)

The neutral fat (225·5 g., iodine value 90·9) was crystallised according to the scheme shown in Fig. 17.

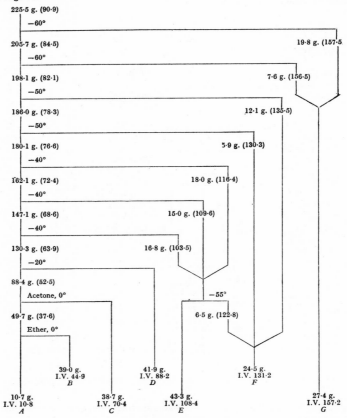

FIG. 17. Crystallisation of badger fat glycerides.

The component acids in each of the seven glyceride fractions, and therefrom in the whole fat, were as below.

	A	B	C	D	E	F	G	WHOLE FAT
Weight (g.)	10·7	39·0	38·7	41·9	43·3	24·5	27·4	225·5
Iodine value	10·8	44·9	70·4	88·2	108·4	131·2	157·2	90·9
Glycerides (per cent. mol.)	4·9	17·7	17·3	18·6	19·1	10·7	11·7	100·0
Component acids (per cent. mol.):								
Myristic	13·3	10·8	9·2	6·8	5·2	6·2	3·9	7·5
Palmitic	50·0	36·2	26·1	18·4	10·3	7·8	4·5	20·2
Stearic	25·1	15·2	8·6	7·5	2·1	1·9	0·5	7·5
Hexadecenoic	—	3·6	7·8	8·4	11·1	14·1	12·0	8·6
Oleic	11·6	24·6	29·4	35·7	42·2	32·4	25·5	31·1
Octadecadienoic	—	4·1	5·4	9·5	12·4	14·3	12·0	8·7
Octadecatrienoic	—	1·5	2·5	4·2	4·8	7·4	8·0	4·1
Unsaturated C_{20}	—	4·0	11·0	9·5	11·9	15·9	33·6	12·3
(mean unsaturation):		(−4·3H)	(−4·3H)	(−4·8H)	(−5·1H)	(−6·2H)	(−6·2H)	(−5·4H)

704

TABLE 153. *Low-Temperature Crystallisation of Antarctic Whale Oil*[34c]
(L. Maddison)

The neutral oil (504 g., iodine value 115·2) was crystallised as follows:

	FRACTIONS		
	SEPARATED		ANALYSED
	g.	I.V.	
Soluble in acetone at:			
$-60°$	89·9	215·2	F
$-60°$ (recrystallisation)	31·2	192·9	E
$-40°$	95·8	120·1 ⎫	
$-40°$ (1st recrystallisation)	44·3	117·1 ⎬	D
$-40°$ (2nd recrystallisation)	12·4	109·5 ⎭	
$-20°$	109·7	82·7	C
$-10°$	29·5	67·6 ⎫	
$-10°$ (1st recrystallisation)	11·5	63·8 ⎬	B
$-10°$ (2nd recrystallisation)	7·2	51·6 ⎭	
Insoluble in acetone at $-10°$	72·5	29·1	A

The component acids in the six glyceride fractions, and therefrom in the whole fat, were as below:

	A	B	C	D	E	F	WHOLE FAT
Weight (g.)	72·5	48·2	109·7	152·5	31·2	89·9	504·0
Iodine value	29·1	63·2	82·7	118·3	192·9	215·2	115·5
Glycerides (per cent. wt.)	14·4	9·6	21·8	30·2	6·2	17·8	100·0
Glycerides (per cent. mol.)	15·2	9·8	21·8	30·2	6·0	17·0	100·0

Component acids (per cent. mol.):

	A	B	C	D	E	F	WHOLE FAT
Lauric	0·1	0·2	Trace	1·2	—	—	0·4
Myristic	24·5	18·1	11·4	6·8	5·1	4·1	11·0
Palmitic	41·9	24·8	18·0	9·5	5·8	3·1	16·5
Stearic	4·7	4·2	2·8	1·5	—	—	2·2
Arachidic	1·0	—	—	—	—	—	0·1
Unsaturated:							
C_{14}	1·3	2·1	2·4	4·2	4·3	4·2	3·2
C_{16}	4·4	11·6	15·2	19·0	17·4	16·8	14·8
C_{18}	17·5	30·6	40·6	44·4	36·0	31·7	35·4
C_{20}	4·0	6·4	8·1	9·1	17·7	23·3	10·8
C_{22}	0·6	2·0	1·5	4·3	13·7	16·8	5·6

Mean unsaturation:

Unsaturated:	A	B	C	D	E	F	WHOLE FAT
C_{14}	$-2\cdot0H$	$-2\cdot0H$	$-2\cdot0H$	$-2\cdot0H$	$-2\cdot0H$	$-2\cdot0H$	$-2\cdot0H$
C_{16}	$-2\cdot0H$	$-2\cdot0H$	$-2\cdot1H$	$-2\cdot1H$	$-2\cdot3H$	$-2\cdot3H$	$-2\cdot1H$
C_{18}	$-2\cdot1H$	$-2\cdot2H$	$-2\cdot2H$	$-2\cdot4H$	$-2\cdot7H$	$-2\cdot7H$	$-2\cdot4H$
C_{20}	$-2\cdot7H$	$-4\cdot9H$	$-7\cdot4H$	$-7\cdot0H$	$-8\cdot4H$	$-8\cdot3H$	$-7\cdot0H$
C_{22}	$-4\cdot0H$	$-6\cdot2H$	$-9\cdot7H$	$-9\cdot2H$	$-10\cdot3H$	$-10\cdot3H$	$-9\cdot8H$

PRELIMINARY RESOLUTION OF FATS BY PARTITION BETWEEN TWO IMMISCIBLE SOLVENTS (COUNTER-CURRENT DISTRIBUTION)

This method has been applied to the study of the glycerides of several unsaturated fatty oils and of cacao butter, as already described in Chapter V (pp. 383–385), to which reference may be made for details. It consists in continuous counter-current circulation of an oil dissolved in two immiscible solvents in a semi-automatic apparatus of the kind described by Craig.[35a] Full accounts of the principles and technique of the method have been given by Dutton[35b] and by Scholfield.[35c]

23 705

The procedure was applied to the glycerides of linseed,[36a] soya bean,[36b] safflower seed,[36c] and maize[36d] oils, and to cacao butter,[36e] by Dutton, Scholfield and their co-workers. Their results showed the presence in the more unsaturated oils of much more trilinolenin or trilinolein (as the case might be) than had been revealed by the crystallisation-segregation procedure, but confirmed in general the results obtained by the latter process in the case of the comparatively saturated cacao butter fat. It is perhaps to be regretted that the studies of the four unsaturated seed fats were made on a partial basis, i.e., the results were mainly confined to determination of only the most unsaturated components (e.g., trilinolenin and linoleolinolenins, or trilinolein and oleodilinoleins, etc.); but so far as they go they are of great importance and have thrown much new light on the constitution of seed oils of this type.

The solvent systems used in these glyceride studies were either a pentanehexane fraction with furfural, or a mixture of 2 vols. pentane-hexane with 1 vol. furfural and 1 vol. nitroethane.

Counter-current distribution has been similarly employed with fatty acids or their methyl esters; indeed an early application in this field was in the separation of the fatty acids of a pig fat by Ahrens and Craig[37a] in 1952, with systems of heptane/methyl alcohol, and formamide/acetic acid. Subsequently it has been preferred to use methyl esters rather than the free acids, which are less effective owing to their tendency to molecular association.

Counter-current distribution of methyl esters (or the free acids) has been of use chiefly in preliminary separation of fatty ester mixtures prior to analysis by gas–liquid chromatography, and in the preparation of pure or highly concentrated individual esters such as linoleate or linolenate. Thus esters of the C_{10}–C_{18} fatty acid series have been separated by counter-current distribution between hexane and 80 per cent. ethanol *or* nitromethane *or* nitroethane,[37b] or between hexane and a mixture of *n*-octanol and dimethyl sulphoxide[37c]; methyl oleate can be separated from methyl elaidate, using *iso*octane with a 0·2 M solution of silver nitrate in 90 per cent. methanol[37d]; pure methyl linoleate, and methyl linolenate of 97 per cent. purity, were obtained from methyl esters from soya bean oil,[37e] and counter-current distribution has also proved useful in separating mono-ene, di-ene and tri-ene esters produced in the partial hydrogenation of methyl linoleate or linolenate.[37f]

SELECTIVE HYDROLYSIS OF TRIGLYCERIDES BY PANCREATIC LIPASE

Since the important discovery was made[38a,b] that pancreatic lipase can remove the acyl groups from the 1- and 3-positions of triglycerides, leaving the 2-acylglycerides unattacked (*cf.* Chapter V, pp. 385–388), increasing use has been made of this process in order to ascertain the distribution of fatty acids between the respective 2-positions and 1- or 3-positions in the glycerides of natural fats. The application of this method may be illustrated from the directions given by Mattson and Volpenhein[39]:

0·5 gm. of the triglyceride is suspended in 9·0 ml. of a buffered solution made up with 1·0 M tris(hydroxymethyl)aminomethane adjusted to pH 8·0, and 0·5 ml. of a 45 per cent. aqueous solution of calcium chloride, and 0·2 ml. of a 1 per cent. aqueous solution of bile salts. To this suspension, maintained at 40°C. with continuous agitation, a suspension of pancreatic lipase (80 mgm. pancreatin in 1 ml. of the buffer solution, prepared immediately before use) is added, and digestion at 40°C. continued until approximately 60 per cent. of glyceridic fatty acids have been hydrolysed (usually 15–30 minutes). The requisite time to reach this degree of hydrolysis must be determined for each batch of pancreatin employed.

At this point 5 ml. of dilute hydrochloric acid (1:1 v/v) and 15 ml. of ethanol are added, and the lipids extracted with ethyl ether. The ethereal extract is washed three times with water, dried with sodium sulphate, and the ether removed under vacuum. The recovered lipids are chromatographed in benzene solution on a column of silica gel, from which tri-glycerides are removed by elution with benzene, diglycerides with a 10 per cent. solution of ether in benzene, and monoglycerides with ethyl ether. The resultant monoglycerides are accompanied by free fatty acids (about 5 per cent.), which are removed by treating the ether solution with a slurry of an anion-exchange resin in ether and filtering, when the purified monoglycerides are recovered from the solvent.

The fatty acid compositions of the isolated monoglycerides and of the original triglycerides are determined by conventional means, usually gas–liquid chromatography. The per cent. (wt.) of any individual acid (F) attached to the 2-glyceryl position is given by:

$$\frac{\text{Per cent. of F in the monoglyceride acids} \times 100}{\text{Per cent. of F in the original triglycerides} \times 3}$$

DETERMINATION OF GLYCERIDE CONSTITUTION BY THIN-LAYER CHROMATOGRAPHY

The use of "thin-layer" chromatography as a means of segregating the glycerides of natural fats into more simple mixtures was mentioned in Chapter V (p. 385), at the end of which references were given to some of the communications which have appeared on this subject (p. 421, refs. 32). At the moment of writing, the only application of this procedure to the quantitative determination of component glycerides in fats has been made by Barrett et al.,[40] who have obtained very promising results by employing silica gel impregnated with silver nitrate as a markedly selective adsorbent. Some account of their results with cacao butter, shea fat and palm oil will be found in Chapter VI, pp. 427, 433, 475, and with pig fat in Chapter VII (p. 504).

References to Chapter XI

1. J. Lewkowitsch, "Chemical Technology and Analysis of Oils, Fats and Waxes", 6th Ed. (Macmillan, London, 1922); A. Grün, "Analyse der Fette und Wachse", Vol. I (Springer, Berlin, 1925); K. A. Williams, "Oils, Fats and Fatty Foods", 3rd Ed. (Churchill, London, 1950); V. C. Mehlenbacher, "Official and Tentative Methods of the American Oil Chemists' Society", 2nd Ed. (Chicago, 1946) (with annual additions from 1947–1962); "Deutsche Einheitsmethoden", (Wissenschaft Verlag, Stuttgart, 1950–1957); British Standard Specification No. 684 (1958); H. P. Kaufmann, "Analyse der Fette und Fett Produkte" (Springer, Berlin, 1958); V. C. Mehlenbacher, "Analysis of Oils and Fats" (Illinois, 1960).
2. A. T. James, in "Methods of Biochemical Analysis" (D. Glick), vol. 8, pp. 1–58, (Interscience Publ., New York, 1961).
3. (a) J. B. Brown, Chem. Reviews, 1941, 29, 333; (b) H. D. Foreman and J. B. Brown, Oil and Soap, 1944, 21, 183; (c) D. K. Kolb and J. B. Brown, J. Amer. Oil Chem. Soc., 1955, 32, 357; O. S. Privett, W. O. Lundberg, et al., ibid., 1958, 35, 366.
4. F. D. Gunstone and R. P. Paton, Biochem. J., 1953, 54, 617.
5. (a) S. S. Gupta and T. P. Hilditch, Biochem. J., 1951, 48, 137; (b) R. V. Crawford and T. P. Hilditch, J. Sci. Food Agric., 1950, I, 230; (c) T. P. Hilditch and L. Maddison, J. Soc. Chem. Ind., 1948, 67, 253; (d) K. T. Achaya and T. P. Hilditch, Proc. Roy. Soc., 1950, B, 137, 187; (e) T. P. Hilditch with J. P. Riley, J. Soc. Chem. Ind., 1946, 65, 74; with A. Mendelowitz, J. Sci. Food Agric., 1951, 2, 548.

6. (a) D. L. Cramer and J. B. Brown, *J. Biol. Chem.*, 1943, **151**, 427; (b) P. B. D. de la Mare and F. B. Shorland, *Analyst*, 1944, **69**, 337; (c) G. Winter and W. J. Nunn, *J. Sci. Food Agric.*, 1951, **2**, 18, 311, 314; 1953, **4**, 439, 442.

7. (a) H. Schlenk and R. T. Holman, *Science*, 1950, **112**, 19; *J. Amer. Chem. Soc.*, 1950, **72**, 5001; A. M. Abu-Nasr, W. M. Potts and R. T. Holman, *J. Amer. Oil Chem. Soc.*, 1954, **31**, 16; (b) H. Schlenk "Progress in the Chemistry of Fats and other Lipids", Vol. II, p. 243 (Pergamon Press, London, 1954); (c) H. A. Newey, T. F. Bradley *et al.*, *Ind. Eng. Chem.*, 1950, **42**, 2538; (d) D. Swern and W. E. Parker, *J. Amer. Oil Chem. Soc.*, 1952, **29**, 431, 614; 1953, **30**, 5. See also M. H. Silk and H. H. Hahn, *Biochem. J.*, 1954, **57**, 574, 577.

8. T. N. Mehta, (a) (with S. B. Dabhade), *J. Amer. Oil Chem. Soc.*, 1958, **35**, 501; (b) (with S. S. Lokras), *Indian J. Appl. Chem.*, 1960, **23**, 18; (c) (with P. M. Meshramkar), *ibid.*, 1960, **23**, 23.

9. See, e.g., T. N. Mehta *et al.*, *J. Indian Chem. Soc.* (*News Ed.*), 1954, **17**, 177, 182; 1955, **18**, 1, 220; 1956, **19**, 1, 32; *Indian J. Appl. Chem.*, 1960, **22**, 218; K. T. Achaya *et al.*, *J. Sci. Indust. Res., India*, 1955, **14**, B, 348; J. S. Aggarwal *et al.*, *ibid.*, 1955, **14**, B, 229; *J. Indian Chem. Soc.*, 1956, **33**, 197; V. S. Patil and N. G. Magar, *J. Sci. Indust. Res., India*, 1956, **15**, B, 650; M. Sakurai and M. Fujiwara, *J. Chem. Soc.* (*Japan*), *Indust. Sect.*, 1956, **59**, 33; J. S. Shenolikar and M. R. Subbaram, *J. Sci. Indust. Res., India*, 1959, **18**, B, 439; G. Rankoff *et al.*, *Compt. Rend. Acad. Bulg. Sci.*, 1960, **13**, 71.

10. See, e.g., R. C. Brimley and F. C. Barrett, "Practical Chromatography" (Chapman and Hall, London, 1954); E. and M. Lederer, "Chromatography" (Elsevier, Amsterdam, 1957); H. G. Cassidy, "Fundamentals of Chromatography" (Interscience Publ., New York, 1957); A. J. Keulemans, "Gas Chromatography" (Reinhold, New York, 1957); D. and B. A. Ambrose, "Gas Chromatography" (Newnes, London, 1961); E. Heftmann, "Chromatography", (Chapman and Hall, London, 1962); H. P. Burchfield and E. E. Storrs, "Biochemical Applications of Gas Chromatography" (Academic Press, London, 1962); G. E. Howard, "Introduction to Principles and Technique of Gas Chromatography", *Chem. and Ind.*, 1963, 622; A. T. James, "(Chromatographic) Separation of Long-Chain Unsaturated Fatty Acids", *Analyst*, 1963, **88**, 572; *also* H. P. Kaufmann (ref. 1 above) and V. C. Mehlenbacher (ref. 1 above).

11. (a) H. J. Dutton and C. L. Reinbold, *J. Amer. Oil Chem. Soc.*, 1948, **25**, 120; (b) K. E. Kurtz, *J. Amer. Chem. Soc.*, 1952, **74**, 1902; (c) R. W. Riemenschneider, S. F. Herb and P. L. Nichols, *J. Amer. Oil Chem. Soc.*, 1949, **26**, 371; (d) E. G. Hammond and W. O. Lundberg, *ibid.*, 1953, **30**, 438; (e) A. M. Abu-Nasr and R. T. Holman, *ibid.*, 1954, **31**, 41; *see also, inter alia*, W. M. L. Crombie, R. Comber and S. G. Boatman, *Nature*, 1954, **174**, 181; C. H. Lea and D. N. Rhodes, *Biochem. J.*, 1954, **57**, xxiii; 1955, **59**, v; P. Savary and P. Desnuelle, *Bull. Soc. Chim.*, 1954, 939.

12. (a) L. J. Morris, H. Hayes and R. T. Holman, *J. Amer. Oil Chem. Soc.*, 1961, **38**, 316; (b) B. de Vries, *Chem. and Ind.*, 1962, 1049; *J. Amer. Oil Chem. Soc.*, 1963, **40**, 184; (c) C. F. Wurster, Jr., J. H. Copenhaver, Jr. and P. R. Shafer, *J. Amer. Oil Chem. Soc.*, 1963, **40**, 513; (d) J. Hirsch and E. H. Ahrens, Jr., *J. Biol. Chem.*, 1958, **233**, 311.

13. H. Schlenk and J. L. Gellerman, *J. Amer. Oil Chem. Soc.*, 1961, **38**, 555.

14. R. T. Holman and L. Hagdahl, *Arch. Biochem.*, 1948, **17**, 301; *J. Amer. Chem. Soc.*, 1950, **72**, 701; *J. Biol. Chem.*, 1950, **182**, 421; R. T. Holman, *J. Amer. Chem. Soc.*, 1951, **73**, 1261; R. T. Holman and W. T. Williams, *ibid.*, 1951, **73**, 5285, 5289; N. A. Khan, W. O. Lundberg and R. T. Holman, *ibid.*, 1954, **76**, 1779; J. G. Hamilton and R. T. Holman, *ibid.*, 1954, **76**, 4107.

15. R. T. Holman, "Progress in the Chemistry of Fats and Other Lipids", vol. I, p. 104 (Pergamon Press, London, 1952); J. J. Wren, *J. Chromatog.*, 1960, **4**, 173; B. G. Creech, *J. Amer. Oil Chem. Soc.*, 1961, **38**, 538.

16. (a) A. J. P. Martin and G. A. Howard, *Biochem. J.*, 1950, **46**, 532; (b) J. Boldingh, *Experientia*, 1948, **4**, 270; *Rec. trav. chim.*, 1950, **69**, 247; *see also* J. Hirsch, *Fed. Proc.*, 1959, **18**, 246.

17. (a) W. M. L. Crombie, R. Comber and S. G. Boatman, *Biochem. J.*, 1955, **59**, 309; (b) G. Popják and A. Tietz, *ibid.*, 1954, **56**, 406; (c) A. K. Lough and G. A. Garton, *ibid.*, 1957, **67**, 345; (d) P. Savary and P. Desnuelle, *Bull. Soc. Chim.*, 1953, 939; (e) R. R. Brenner and O. Mercuri, *An. Asoc. Quim. Argentina*, 1959, **47**, 318; (f) T. Green, *Chem. and Ind.*, 1955, 59.

18. (a) F. D. Gunstone and P. J. Sykes, *J. Chem. Soc.*, 1960, 5050; *J. Sci. Food Agric.*, 1961, **12**, 115; (b) W. Kapitel, *Fette, Seifen, Anstrichm.*, 1956, **58**, 91; (c) A. K. Lough and G. A. Garton, *Biochem. J.*, 1957, **67**, 345; (d) C. Riley and R. F. Nunn, *ibid.*, 1960, **74**, 56; (e) W. M. L. Crombie and S. G. Boatman, *J. W. African Inst. Palm Oil Res.*, 1955, **3**, 64; (f) J. H. van de Kaemer *et al.*, *Biochem. J.*, 1955, **58**, 180.

19. G. Rouser, A. J. Bauman, N. Nicolaides and D. Heller, *J. Amer. Oil Chem. Soc.*, 1961, **38**, 565.

20. H. P. Kaufmann *et al.*, *Fette, Seifen, Anstrichm.*, 1954, **56**, 154; 1956, **58**, 234, 492; 1960, **62**, 1.

21. A. Schlenk and H. K. Mangold (a) (with A. G. Camp), *J. Amer. Chem. Soc.*, 1955, **77**, 6070; (b) (with J. L. Gellerman and J. A. Tillotson), *J. Amer. Oil Chem. Soc.*, 1957, **34**, 377.

22. P. E. Ballance and W. M. L. Crombie, *Biochem. J.*, 1958, **60**, 632.

23. (a) Y. Inoue and M. Noda, *J. Agr. Chem. Soc., Japan*, 1951, **24**, 291; 1952, **25**, 161; (b) H. P. Kaufmann, *Fette, Seifen, Anstrichm.*, 1956, **58**, 492; 1961, **63**, 614; (c) A. Seher, *ibid.*, 1956, **58**, 498.

24. J. Boldingh, *Rec. Trav. Chim.*, 1950, **69**, 247; H. P. Kaufmann, *Fette u. Seifen*, 1950, **52**, 331, 713; (with J. Budwig), *ibid.*, 1950, **52**, 555; 1951, **53**, 69; (with W. H. Nitsch), *Fette, Seifen, Anstrichm.*, 1955, **57**, 473; (with Mohr) *ibid.*, 1957, **59**, 920; Y. Inoue and M. Noda, *J. Agric. Chem. Soc. Japan*, 1950, **23**, 368; 1952, **25**, 91; 1952, **26**, 634; 1953, **27**, 50; (with O. Hirayama), *J. Amer. Oil Chem. Soc.*, 1955, **32**, 132; *Bull. Agric. Chem. Soc. Japan*, 1956, **20**, 197, 200; *J. Agric. Chem. Soc. Japan*, 1961, **35**, 135, 138; P. Savary, *Bull. Soc. Chim. Biol.*, 1954, **36**, 927; L. Crombie, *Chem. Soc. (London) Ann. Repts.*, 1955, **52**, 300; H. Wagner, L. Abisch and K. Bernhard, *Helv. Chim. Acta*, 1955, **38**, 1536; F. Franks, *Analyst*, 1956, **81**, 384; R. Chayen and E. M. Lindsay, *J. Chromatog.*, 1960, **3**, 503; R. L. Ory, *ibid.*, 1961, **5**, 153.

25. (a) H. E. Longenecker, *J. Soc. Chem. Ind.*, 1937, **56**, 199T; (b) F. A. Norris and D. E. Terry, *Oil and Soap*, 1945, **22**, 41; (c) W. J. Podbielniak, *Ind. Eng. Chem.*, [*Anal. Ed.*], 1933, **5**, 119, 135; 1941, **13**, 639; (d) A. W. Weitkamp and L. C. Brunstrum, *Oil and Soap*, 1941, **18**, 47; (e) F. A. Norris, I. I. Rusoff, E. S. Miller and G. O. Burr, *J. Biol. Chem.*, 1941, **139**, 199; 1943, **147**, 273; (f) Cf. e.g., J. A. Lovern, *Biochem. J.*, 1934, **28**, 394; W. Diemair and W. Schmidt, *Biochem. Z.*, 1937, **294**, 348; R. Schoenheimer and D. Rittenberg, *J. Biol. Chem.*, 1937, **120**, 155; A. Klem, *Nature*, 1938, **142**, 616; D. H. S. Horn and F. W. Hougen, *J. Chem. Soc.*, 1953, 3533.

26. (a) J. H. Mitchell, H. R. Kraybill and F. P. Zscheile, *Ind. Eng. Chem.* [*Anal. Ed.*], 1943, **15**, 1; B. W. Beadle and H. R. Kraybill, *J. Amer. Chem. Soc.*, 1944, **66**, 1232; B. W. Beadle, *Oil and Soap*, 1946, **23**, 140; (b) T. P. Hilditch, R. A. Morton and J. P. Riley, *Analyst*, 1945, **70**, 68; T. P. Hilditch, C. B. Patel and J. P. Riley, *ibid.*, 1951, **76**, 81; (c) A. R. Baldwin and B. F. Daubert, *Oil and Soap*, 1945, **22**, 180; R. T. O'Connor and D. C. Heinzelmann, *J. Amer. Oil Chem. Soc.*, 1947, **24**, 212; 1955, **32**, 616; *Amer. Oil Chem. Soc.*, Spectroscopy Committee Repts., *ibid.*, 1949, **26**, 399; 1951, **28**, 331; *et seq.*; S. F. Herb and R. W. Riemenschneider, *Analyt. Chem.*, 1953, **25**, 853; (d) B. A. Brice, M. L. Swain *et al.*, *J. Opt. Soc. Amer.*, 1945, **35**, 532; *Oil and Soap*, 1945, **22**, 219; *J. Amer. Oil Chem. Soc.*, 1949, **26**, 272; 1956, **33**, 149; (e) R. W. Riemenschneider, S. F. Herb and P. L. Nichols, *ibid.*, 1949, **26**, 371; 1950, **27**, 329; 1951, **28**, 55; 1952, **29**, 279; R. F. Paschke, D. H. Wheeler *et al.*, *ibid.*, 1952, **29**, 229; (f) H. J. Lips and H. Tessier, *ibid.*, 1949, **26**, 659; F. A. van den Heuvel and G. H. Richardson, *ibid.*, 1953, **30**, 104; E. G. Hammond and W. O. Lundberg, *ibid.*, 1953, **30**, 433; (g) B. Sreenivasan and J. B. Brown, *ibid.*, 1956, **33**, 521; 1958, **35**, 89; (h) V. C. Mehlenbacher, "Analysis of Oils and Fats" (Illinois, 1960).

27. T. P. Hilditch, with J. P. Riley, *J. Soc. Chem. Ind.*, 1946, **65**, 74; with A. Mendelowitz, *J. Sci. Food Agric.*, 1951, **2**, 548; R. T. O'Connor, D. C. Heinzelmann, F. C. Pack and R. W. Planck, *J. Amer. Oil Chem. Soc.*, 1953, **30**, 182.

28. (*a*) G. A. J. Pitt and R. A. Morton, "Progress in the Chemistry of Fats and other Lipids", vol. IV, p. 227 (Pergamon Press, London, 1957); (*b*) R. T. Holman, "Methods of Biochemical Analysis", Vol. IV (Interscience, New York, 1957).

29. (*a*) A. T. James with A. J. P. Martin, *Biochem. J.*, 1950, **50**, 679; (*b*) idem, ibid., 1956, **63**, 138, 144; A. T. James (with V. R. Wheatley) ibid., 1956, **63**, 269; (with J. Webb), ibid., 1957, **66**, 515; A. T. James et al., *Lancet*, 1958, **i**, 502; *Amer. J. Clin. Nutrn.*, 1958, **6**, 595.

30. See, inter alia: F. R. Cropper and A. Heywood, *Nature*, 1953, **172**, 1101; J. G. Keppler, (with G. Dijkstra and J. S. Schols), *Rev. Trav. Chim.*, 1955, **74**, 805; (with R. K. Berthuis), *Nature*, 1957, **179**, 731; (with R. K. Berthuis and G. Dijkstra), *Ann. N.Y. Acad. Sci.*, 1959, **72**, 616; B. M. Craig and N. L. Murty, *Canad. J. Chem.*, 1958, **36**, 1297; *J. Amer. Oil Chem. Soc.*, 1959, **36**, 549; M. A. Khan and B. T. Whitham, *J. Appl. Chem.*, 1958, **8**, 549; W. Insull, Jr. and E. H. Ahrens, Jr., *Biochem. J.*, 1959, **72**, 27; *Analyt. Chem.*, 1959, **31**, 307; *Lancet*, 1959, **i**, 115; S. R. Lipsky, R. A. Landowne and J. E. Lovelock, *J. Amer. Chem. Soc.*, 1959, **81**, 1010; *Biochim. Biophys. Acta*, 1959, **31**, 336; *Analyt. Chem.*, 1959, **31**, 852; S. R. Lipsky and R. A. Landowne, *Ann. N.Y. Acad. Sci.*, 1959, **72**, 559; *Ann. Rev. Biochem.*, 1960, **29**, 649; R. W. Riemenschneider (with S. F. Herb and P. Magidman), *J. Amer. Oil Chem. Soc.*, 1960, **37**, 127; F. E. Luddy, R. A. Barford and R. W. Riemenschneider, ibid., 1960, **37**, 447; V. C. Mehlenbacher, ibid., 1960, **37**, 613; L. J. Moores, R. T. Holman and K. Fontell, *J. Lipid Res.*, 1960, **1**, 412; J. J. Wren, *J. Chromatog.*, 1960, **4**, 173; L. A. Horrocks, P. G. Cornwell and J. B. Brown, *J. Lipid Res.*, 1961, **2**, 92; H. K. Mangold and R. Kammereck, *Chem. and Ind.*, 1961, 1032; V. R. Huebner, *J. Amer. Oil Chem. Soc.*, 1961, **38**, 628; T. D. Heyes, *Chem. and Ind.*, 1963, 660; C. Litchfield, R. Reiser and A. F. Isbell, *J. Amer. Oil Chem. Soc.*, 1963, **40**, 302; T. K. Miwa, ibid., 1963, **40**, 309; A. Kuksis, M. J. McCarthy and J. M. R. Beveridge, ibid., 1963, **40**, 530; R. G. Ashman, *Nature*, 1962, **194**, 970; *J. Amer. Oil Chem. Soc.*, 1963, **40**, 558, 564.

31. A. R. S. Kartha, "Studies in the Natural Fats", Thesis, University of Madras, 1951.

32. (*a*) N. D. Sylvester, A. N. Ainsworth and E. B. Hughes, *Analyst*, 1945, **70**, 295; (*b*) H. A. Schuette and S. Dal Nagore, *J. Amer. Oil Chem. Soc.*, 1951, **28**, 229.

33. (*a*) C. G. Youngs, *J. Amer. Oil Chem. Soc.*, 1961, **38**, 62; (*b*) E. von Rudloff, *Canad. J. Chem.*, 1956, **34**, 1413.

34. T. P. Hilditch (*a*) with R. V. Crawford, *J. Sci. Food Agric.*, 1950, **1**, 372; (*b*) with S. S. Gupta and M. L. Meara, *J. Chem. Soc.*, 1950, 3145; (*c*) with L. Maddison, *J. Soc. Chem. Ind.*, 1948, **67**, 253.

35. (*a*) L. C. Craig, et al., *Analyt. Chem.*, 1949, **21**, 500; 1951, **23**, 1236; (*b*) H. J. Dutton, "Progress in the Chemistry of Fats and Lipids", vol. II, p. 292 (Pergamon Press, London, 1954); (*c*) C. R. Scholfield, *J. Amer. Oil Chem. Soc.*, 1961, **38**, 562; see also D. G. Therriault, ibid., 1963, **40**, 395.

36. (*a*) H. J. Dutton and J. A. Cannon, *J. Amer. Oil Chem. Soc.*, 1956, **33**, 46; (*b*) C. R. Scholfield and M. A. Wicks, ibid., 1957, **34**, 77; (*c*) C. R. Scholfield and H. J. Dutton, ibid., 1958, **35**, 493; (*d*) idem, ibid., 1961, **38**, 175; (*e*) idem, ibid., 1959, **36**, 325; 1961, **38**, 96.

37. (*a*) E. H. Ahrens, Jr., and L. C. Craig, *J. Biol. Chem.*, 1952, **195**, 299; (*b*) J. A. Cannon, K. I. Zilch and H. J. Dutton, *Analyt. Chem.*, 1952, **24**, 1530; (*c*) F. Will, ibid., 1961, **33**, 647; (*d*) H. J. Dutton, C. R. Scholfield and E. P. Jones, *Chem. and Ind.*, 1961, 1874; (*e*) H. J. Dutton, *J. Lipid Res.*, 1961, **2**, 63; (*f*) C. R. Scholfield et al., *J. Amer. Oil Chem. Soc.*, 1960, **37**, 579; 1961, **38**, 208; K. Schilling, *Fette, Seifen, Anstrichm.*, 1961, **63**, 421.

38. (*a*) P. Desnuelle, P. Savary et al., *Compt. Rend.*, 1955, **240**, 2571; *Biochim. Biophys. Acta.* 1956, **21**, 349; 1957, **24**, 414; 1959, **31**, 26; 1961, **50**, 319; *Rev Français Corps Gras*, 1958, **5**, 493; (*b*) F· H. Mattson et al., *J. Nutrition*, 1952, **48**, 335; *J. Biol. Chem.*, 1955,

214, 115; 1956, **219**, 735; 1958, **233**, 868; 1961, **236**, 1891; *see also* M. H. Coleman, *J. Amer. Oil Chem. Soc.*, 1963, **40**, 568.
39. F. H. Mattson and R. A. Volpenhein, *J. Lipid Res.*, 1961, **2**, 58; 1962, **3**, 281.
40. C. B. Barrett, M. S. J. Dallas and F. B. Padley, *J. Amer. Oil Chem. Soc.*, 1963, **40**, 580; *see also* F. D. Gunstone, F. B. Podley and M. I. Quveshi, *Chem. and Ind.*, 1964, 483.
41. A. T. James (ref. 2, above); H. Schlenck and J. L. Gellermann, *Analyt. Chem.*, 1960, **32**, 1412; W. Stoffel, F. Chu and E. H. Ahrens, Jr., *ibid.*, 1959, **31**, 307; W. R. Morrison, T. D. V. Lawrie and J. Blades, *Chem. and Ind.*, 1961, 1534.

Indexes

The more important references are indicated by page numbers in **Heavy Type**.

Pages in which the *components acids* of fats are dealt with are distinguished by an asterisk * after the page number. Those in which the *component glycerides* are dealt with are similarly distinguished by a dagger †.

For convenience, the numerous individual fats (with plant families), individual fatty acids, and glycerides are dealt with in separate indexes, which follow the general subject index as below:

General Index of Subjects   715

Index of Individual Fats and Waxes   723

Index of Plant Families   737

Index of Individual Fatty Acids   739

Index of Individual Glycerides (Natural and Synthetic)   743

General Index of Subjects

Acetate, conversion (biosynthetic) into fatty acids, 51, **413**, **414**, 550, **553–558**, 560, 563, 573

Acetonyl glycerols, 666

Acetyl co-enzyme A, 553, **555–558**

Acyl groups, migration of, in glycerides (*see also* "Inter-esterification"), **659–664**

Adenosine tri-phosphate, 556, 558

Adrenals, **137***, 625, 641

Adsorption, selective (chromatographic) of fatty acids, fats or other lipids, *see* "Chromatography"

Alcohols, higher aliphatic, 11, 12, 31, **35–37**, 40, 49, **73**, **74**, 180, 182, 184, 186, 187, **297**, 403, **488**, 553, 571, 579, **582**, **583**, 594, 609, 611, 658, **666–672**

Aldehydes, 552, **553**, 554, 563, **579**, 592, 601, 617, 644, 667

Aleuritic acid, **619**

Ambrettolide, **619**

Amphibia, fats of, *see* "Fats, amphibia"

Assimilation of preformed fats by animals, 13, **33**, **51**, **58**, **83**, **88**, **95–97***, **123–126***, 135–136, **155–157***, 165, 412, 414, **489–491***, 502, **510–513***, **564–573**

Azelaic acid, 151, 591, 592, 598, 599, 616, 635 semi-aldehyde, **592**, 598

Azelao-glycerides, 363–365, **417**, 431, **432**, 434, **437**, 442, **701**

Bacteria, fats of, *see* "Fats, bacilli"

Bark fats, *see* "Fats, bark and stem"

Batyl alcohol, 11, **35–37**, 403, 658, **666**, **670–672**

Belfield test, 499

Benzylidene glycerol, 661, 672

Bio-hydrogenation, 22, 23, 37, 58, 59, 110, **112**, **113**, 139, **406–408**†, 414, **508**†, **509**†, **523**, 539, 547, 550, **553–558**, 561, 568, 569

Bio-oxidation, 23, 58, 414, 533, 546, 550, 553–555, 558–560, 569

Biosynthesis of fats, animals, 51, 81–83, **93–95***, 101, 109, 110, **112***, **113***, 117–122, **126**, 149, 150, 165, 404, **406–409**†, **412–415**†, **506–510**†, **523**†, 528, **541–551**, 573, 638
    by enzymes, 404, 547, **553–558**
    by moulds, **554**, **559**

Biosynthesis of fats plants, 186, 210–212, 226–228, 246–250, 308–310, 319–321, 402, **529–540**, 580

Biosynthesis of saturated fatty acids, *see* "Fatty acids, biosynthesis of, saturated"

Biosynthesis of unsaturated fatty acids, *see* "Fatty acids, biosynthesis of, unsaturated"

Birds, fats of, *see* "Fats, bird"

Blood glycerides, 80, **138–143***, 412, 546, 547, 550, 551, 612, 686

Blood phosphatides, 80, **138–143***, 686

Bromo-additive compounds of fatty acids, 26, 27, 69, 84, 89, 118, 120, 134, 151, 156, 161, **179**, **206**, 344, 345, 347, **595**, 596, 603, 621, **627**, **628**, 630, 631, **632**, **633**

Bromo-additive compounds of glycerides, 23, **361**, **362**, 446, 459, 466, **482**

Butter fats, *see* "Fats, land animals, milk"

Carbohydrates, conversion into fats, 82, 83, **93–95***, 102, 111, **120**, 126, 165, **413**, **528–537**, 541–544, 547, **550–562**

Carnivora, fats of, *see* "Fats, carnivora"

Cerebrosides, 2, 3, 33, 34, 157, 610, 624, 638, **641**, **642**

Ceryl alcohol, 582, 666–668

Cetyl alcohol, 49, **73**, **74**, **488**, 579, **666–668**

Cetyl glyceryl ether, 11, **35–37**, 658, 666, **670–672**

Cetyl laurate, **488**

Cetyl myristate, **488**

Cetyl palmitate, **488**

Chimyl alcohol, 11, **35–37**, 658, 666, **670–672**

Chorohydroxystearic acids, 596–598

Cholesterol, 35, 36, 41, 50, 73, 74, 81, 92, 133, **138–143***, 586, 658, 668, 671, 686

Choline, 3, **344**, **345**, 666

Chromatography, gas-liquid, 26, **41***, **48***, 51, 80, **91***, **106***, **107***, **129***, 138, **139–143***, **152***, **153***, **164***, **165***, 178, **179**, **181***, 206, **250***, **281***, 295, **296***, **309***, **524**, 530, **536***, 586, 590, 593, 639, 659, 676, **678**, 684, **697–699** (*See also* Tables 57, 59, 60, 60B, 62, 63, 63B, 66, 67, 67A, 67B, 68, 69A, 69B)

715

Chromatography
paper, 136, **157**, **158***, 162, 244, **253***, 363, 385, 433, 684, **686**, **687**
partition, reversed-phase, etc., 26, 80, 136, **138–143***, 152, 162, 178, **179**, **195***, **206**, 210*, 220*, 230*, 233*, 253*, 256*, 258*, 271*, 290*, 313*, 328*, 342*, 363, **385**, **466**, 530, 586, 592, 618, **626**, 631, **633**, 638, 639, 662, 663, 671, 678, **683–686**, 700, 701, 707 (*See also* Tables 57A, 60, 61, 62, 67, 68, 69B)
thin layer, 136, 363, 385, **402**, **433**†, **434**†, **439**†, **448**, **449**†, **454**†, **475**†, **476**†, 481, **504**†, 659, **660**, 676, 700, **707**
Clupanodonyl alcohol, 670
Cork, 619, 620
Counter-current distribution (C.C.D.), 18, 363, 373, **383–385**†, **433**†, **456**†, **457**†, **459**†, **461**†, **464**†, 639, 659, 680, 700, **705**, **706**
Crustacea, 11, **31–33***, **489**†, **490**†, 545, 567
Cryptogam fats, *see* "Fats, cryptogam"

Debromination of bromo-fatty acids, 595, **627–629**, 632, 633
n-Decanol, 667
n-Decenol, 670
Depot fats, animals, *see* "Fats, land animals, depot"
Desaturation, 58, 95, 157, 533, 534, 546, **558–560**, 569
Deuterium-containing fats, **554**, **558**, **559**, **569**
Di-basic acid glycerides, 198
Dibromostearic acids, 591, **595**
Dichlorostearic acids, 595
Digestibility of ingested fats, 125, 157, **569–571**
Diglycerides, 562, 659–661, **662**, **663**, **665**, **666**
isomeric forms, **662**, **663**
Dihydroxyarachidic acids, 610, 615
Dihydroxybehenic acids, 608, 610
Dihydroxymyristic acids, 613, 619
Dihydroxypalmitic acids, 608, 615, 619
Dihydroxystearic acid (naturally occurring), **248–250***, **257***, 449, **597**, 616, 617
Dihydroxystearic acids, 248–250*, 257, 449, 595–598
Diketobehenic acids, 610
Diketononadecanoic acid, 612
Diketostearic acids, 599
Directed esterification, 622
n-Docosanol, 666, 670
n-Docosenol, **297**, 609, 666, 670
n-Dodecanol, 666, **667**
n-Dodecapentaenal, 579
n-Dodecenol, 670

"Drying" oils, 200, 203, 204, **206–248***, **381–385**†, **395**†, 396, **401**†, **455–471**†, 532, 533, **535–538**, 567, 571–573, 588, 618, 625–627, **632–637**, 682, **684**, 689, 694, **695–697**, 702, **705**, **706**

Egg fats, *see* "Fats, egg"
Egg phosphatides, **90–93***, 638, 666
n-Eicosadienol, 73
n-Eicosanol, 73, 666, 667, **668**
n-Eicosenol, 73, **297**, 609, 666, 670
Elaeostearyl alcohol, **670**
Elaidic glycerides, ingested, 570, 571
Elaidyl alcohol, **669**
Embryo (seed), 188, 189, **280**, 296, 390, 530
Endosperm (seed), 188, 189, **280**, 296, **339**, **340***, 345, 346, 389, 390, 530, 552
Environment, influence of, on seed fats, **16**, 200–202, 207, **208**, 210–212*, 226–228*, 246–251*, 264, 265, **280**, **281***, **305–311***, **456–458**†, 461†, 462†, **537–539***, **560**
Enzyme hydrolysis, selective, *see* "Glyceride configuration, use of pancreatic lipase"
Enzyme synthesis of fatty acids and fats, 404, **553–558**
Epoxy-fatty acids, 8, 15, 205, 209, **219**, **220**, 238*, 239*, 245, 255*, 266, 276*, 296, 329*, **395**†, **451**†, 537, 558, 596–598, **616–618**, 629, 685, 686
Ester-fractionation, 25, 26, 73, 117, 179, 585, 590, 638, 639, 676, 678, **688–695**
data, typical detailed, 688, **690–695**
Estolides, 617, 618
Essential fatty acids, **94**, 95, **571–573**, 630, 638, **643**
Ethanolamine, 3, 345, 666
"Even" or "Widest" distribution, *see* "Fatty acids, 'even' or 'widest' distribution amongst glycerides"

Fasting, effect on animal body fats, 51, **54–56***, 95, **96***, **105**, **106***, 112, **121–122***, 126
effect on animal milk fats, **153–154***, 156, 414, 523
Fats§
amphibia, 12, **62–68***, **84–86***, **131***, **133***, **135***, 404, **490**, **491**†, 573, 614
animal, biosynthesis, 51, 81–83, **93–95***, 101, 109, 110, **112**, **113***, **117–122**, **126**, 149, 150, **165**, 404, **406–409***, **412–415**†, **506–510**†, **523**†, 528, **541–551**, 573, 638
bacilli, 14, 111, **172–174***, **586**, **587**, 611–614, 624
bark and stem, 177, 178, **183–185***, 348, 531
bird, 13*, 22, **86–90***, **131***, 359, 369†, 396, 404, 405, 409, 417, 418, **491**, 492†, 548, 549, 566, 567, 573, 614
§ For individual fats, *see* pp. 723–736.

Fats

brominated, separation by crystallisation, 23, **361, 362**, 446, **457–459**†, 466, 482

carnivora, 13*, 98, **126–132***

copepod, **30***, **31**, 48, 68, 567

crustacea, 11, **31–33***, **489, 490**†, 545

cryptogam, 14, **172–177***, 614, 640

egg, birds, **90–93***, 386, 566, 567, 638
   fish, 36, **55***, **56**, 60, 135

fish, 11, 12, 13*, 23, 24, 26, **34–62***, 121, 362, **409**, **410**†, **481–483**†, **486, 487**†, 545, 549, 559, 566–569, 573, 610, 613–615, 631, **637–643**, 658, 669, 671, 672, 680, 694

influence of food, salinity etc., 44, 45, 58, 545, 549, 567, 568

formal classification, **2, 3**

fruit coat, 14, 19, 20, **187–202***, 304*, **348**, 359, 361, **365–367**†, **378**†, **380**†, **393**, 417, **471–477**†, 566, 584, 614, 686, 707

herbivora, **99–116***, 125, 126, **131–140***, **143–161***, 365, **369**†, **370**†, 374, 375, **379**†, 409, **493–495**†, 567, 594, 625, 682, 689, **690–693***

human, blood lipids, 80, **140–143***
   body, 13*, **128–131***, **370**†, 409, **412**†, **497**†, **526**†, 565, 566, 625, 682
   bone, **130***
   internal organs, **141***, **142***, 641
   milk, 144, **162–165***, **411**, **412**†, **524–526**†, 570

hydrogenated, separation by crystallisation from solvents **361**, 429, 450, 454, 455, 473, 477, 515

insect, **81–84***, 566, 567

invertebrates, **27–34***, **81–84***, **489**, **490**†, 566, 567, 642

land animal, bone or hoof, **113–116***, **379**†, 405, **505**†, **506**†

   depot, 12, 13, 21, 22, 23, 40, **81–132***, 359, 360, **368–370**†, 371, **374–376**†, **379**†, 396, **403–409**†, **412**†, 415, 417, 419, **491–510**†, **522**†, **525**†, **541–544**, **546–551**, 552–562, **564–573**, 584, 613, 614, 625, 638, 681, **682**, 686, **689–693***, 701, 702, 704*, 706

   depot, "stearic rich" (mainly ruminants and marsupials), 13, **22**, **99–116***, 125, 126, **131***, 359, 360, **368–370**†, 371, 372, **379**†, **403–409**†, 410, **412**†, 419, 492, 495, **497–510**†, 541, 546, 547, 549–551, 555, 557, **558**, 584, 585, 594

   liver, 90, 95, **133–137***, **546**, 547, 573, 613, 614, 625, 631, **638**, 641

   milk, 12, **13, 14, 22, 23, 143–165***, 360†, **370**†, **371**†, **410–412**†, **510–526**† 549–**551, 558**, 583–585, 613, **680**

   organs, other than liver, **104***, **106***, 108, **116, 117***, 131, 135, 136, **137**, **138***, 541, 548, 573, 641, 642

leaf, 177, 178, **180–183***, 186, **348**, 530, 531

Fats

marine mammalian, **11, 12, 23–25**, 27, **62–76***, 362, **409**†, **410**†, **415**†, **416**†, **481–489**†, 545, 549, 565, 567, 583, 584, 609, 610, **613–615**, 631, **637–643**, 667, 669, 678–680, 682, **689**, 694

milk, **13, 67***, **71***, 144

moulds and fungi, **174–177***, 554, 619

natural, biological relationships, **10–16**, 28, 31, 42–44, **50–76***, 80–99, 115, 118, **131***, 132–137, 141, 144, 147, 148, 151–153, 158–163, 182, 183, 186, **189, 198**, 200–205, 243–245, **264, 265**, 280, **285, 304, 305**, 308, **320–323, 332, 333**, 340, **346–348, 528–552**, 557–562

component acids of (see also "Fatty acids, component, quantitative determination"), **5–16, 26–76***, **82–165***, **172–354***, 368–415*, 425–477*, 484–525*

component glycerides of (see also "Glycerides, component, quantitative determination of"), 4–6, **16–24**, **358–420**†, **424–477**†, **481–526**†, 677, **700–707**

separation by crystallisation, see "Glycerides, separation by crystallisation"

of aquatic origin, fresh water, **11, 12**, **26–31***, **50–58***, 76, 545, 573, 614, 626, 637, 694

   marine, **11, 12, 26–50***, **58–76***, 89, 135, 362, **409**†, **410**†, **415**†, **416**†, **481–489**†, 544–546, 549, 565–568, 583, 584, 588, 609, 610, 612–615, 626, 631, **637–643**, 658, 667, 669, **670–672**, 678–680, 682, **689**, 694

omnivora, 13, 22, **126–132***, **370**†, 387, 409, **412**†, **495–497**†

optically active, 292, 293*, 403, 665

petals and stamens, **186***, 644

plant, biosynthesis of, 186, 210–212, 226–228, 246–250, 308–310, 319–321, 402, **529–540**, 580

reptile, 12, **84–86***, **131, 133–135**, 404, 614

rodent, 22, **93–98***, **131***, **369***, 396, 409, **491**†, **492**, 548, 549, 566–573, 614, 641

root, 178, **185*, 186***, 348

sea bird, **89*, 90**, 567

seed, 10, **14–16, 19–21**, 188, 189, **199***, **202–342***, 359–362, **365–368**†, 371–373, **377–378**†, **380–404**†, 417–420, **424–471**†, **529–540**, 552, 557, **558–562**, 564–574, 583–585, 588, 590, 609–633, 637, 682–686, 689, 694, 701, 702, **703***, 705–707

linoleic-rich ("semi-drying" or "drying" oils), 203, **204, 206–242***, 264–318*, **381–385**†, 387–390, **394**†, **401**†, **451–462**†, 529–540, 564, **571–573**, 625–627, **682–686**, 689, **695–697**, 702, **705, 706**

Fats
seed
linolenic-rich ("drying" oils), 203, 204, **206–248***, **381–385†**, **395†**, 396, **401†**, **455–471†**, 532, 533, **535–538**, 567, 571–573, 588, 625, 626, **632–634**, 682, **684**, 689, 694, **695–697**, 702, 705, 706
oleic-rich ("non-drying" oils), 203, **206–208**, 304–309, 319, **377–378†**, **380–382†**, 387, 392†, 394†, 399†, 400†, **446–451†**
testa, 188, 189, **339**, **340***
yeast, 14, **174***, 614
Fatty acids
acetylenic, 8, 9, **16**, 183–185, 187, **204**, 218, 221, 230*, 285, 286, **289–291***, 334, 337*, 561, 588, 589, 591, 594, 600, 602, 605–609, 618–620, 630, 637
bio-synthesis of, 51, 82, 83, **93–95***, 101, 110, **112**, **113**, **117–122**, 125, 126, 148–153, **165**, **186**, 210–212, 226–228, 246–250, 308–310, 319–321, 406, **412–415**, 523, **529–562**, 573, 612, 638
from acetate, 51, **413**, **414**, 550, **553–558**, 560, 563, 573
saturated, 51, 82, 83, 93–95*, 101, **112**, **113**, **117–122**, 125, 126, 148–153, **165**, 210–212, 226–228, 246–250, 308–310, 319–321, 406, **412–415**, 523, **557**, 612
unsaturated, 51, 82, 83, **93–95***, 101, 110, **112**, **113**, **117–122**, 125, 126, 148–153, 165, **186**, 210–212, 226–228, 246–250, 308–310, 319–321, **412–415**, **558–562**, **573**, 612, 638
"branched chain", 7, 8, 12, 40, 48, 51, **74***, **75***, 110, 111, 129*, **152**, **153**, 164, **172**, **173**, 175*, 184, 316, **585–587**, 623
bromo-additive compounds of (*See* "Bromo-additive compounds of fatty acids")
component, quantitative determination (*See also* "Natural fats, component acids of"), **178**, **179**, **206**, **678–700***
quantitative separation of volatile and lower molecular weight acids, **678–680**
separation of unsaponifiable matter, 530, 534, **679**
containing fluorine, *see* "Fluoro-fatty acids"
cyclic, 8, 9, 15, 173, 174, 203–205, 218, **266**, 285, **292–293***, 323, 325*, 571, 588, 589, 604, **611**, **612**, **621**, **623**
epoxy-, *see* "Epoxy-fatty acids"
"even" or "widest" distribution among glycerides, **17**, 22, **365–368**, **371**, **389–402**, **417**, **418**, **424–477†**, 485, **492–496**, 506, 508, 510, 516, 525, 550
ethynoid or polyethynoid, *see* "Fatty acids, acetylenic"

Fatty Acids
fractional distillation of esters, *see* "Fractional distillation of esters of higher fatty acids"
hydroxy, *see* "Hydroxy-fatty acids"
individual, *see* SEPARATE INDEX, pp. 739–742
constitution of, 578–644
isolation or separation of, as urea inclusion compounds, **590**, 597, 618, 620, 627, 633, **683**
by chromatographic adsorption, (*See also* "Chromatography, gas–liquid", "Chromatography, paper," and "Chromatography, partition"), 26, 136, **138–143***, 152, 162, 179, 195*, 206, 586, 618, 626, 631, 633, 638, **683–686**
by low temperature crystallisation, 66, 69, **179**, **206**, **590**, 610, 620, 624, 626, 633, 638, 678, 679, **680–683**, **690**
infra-red and Raman absorption spectra, 109, 290, 583, **594**, 612, 618, 624, 625, **627**, **628**, **633–636**, 637
lead salts, *see* "Lead salts of fatty acids, separation of"
lithium salts, *see* "Lithium salts of fatty acids, separation of"
methyl esters of, boiling points, **583**, **688**
mobility of acyl groups in glycerides, **659–664**
names and formulae, **6–9**, 572, 583, **584–587**
"odd-numbered", 7, 8, 12, 40, 41, 48, **74–75***, 98, 110, 111, 129*, 150, **152**, **153**, 164, **172**, **173***, 175*, **176***, 184, 205, 266, 285, 316, **323**, 339, 342, 488, 489, 568, 578, 579, 592, 598, 602, **611**, **612**, 623, 635, 679
optically active, 173, 248–250, 585–587, 597, 616–618
physical properties, *see* under individual acids in SEPARATE INDEX, pp. 739–742
preparation of, for analysis of component acids, **678–680**
saturated, melting points and X-ray spectrum analysis of, **583**
syntheses of, **578–581**
(or methyl esters), separation by gas–liquid chromatography, *see* "Chromatography, gas–liquid"
separation of saturated and unsaturated (*See also* "Lead salts of fatty acids, separation of", "Fatty acids, isolation or separation of as urea inclusion compounds" and "Fatty acids, isolation or separation by low temperature crystallisation") 179, 206, **590**, 678, **680–683**
solubility in organic solvents, **680–681**

Fatty Acids
  unsaturated, conjugated, 9, 15, **16**, 110,
    151, **179**, **180**, 185, **203–205**, 208,
    239, **243**, **244**, **247***, **248***, **250–260***,
    267*, 273, 285, 316, 395, **468–471**†,
    529, 552, 553, 558, 561, 598, 617, 618,
    624, **625**, **626**, 631–633, **634–637**, 643,
    644, 667, 682, **695**, **696**, 702
  geometrical isomerism of (*cis-* and
    trans-), **109**, **110**, 113, 130, **150**, **151**,
    220, 252, 267, 273*, 290, 547, 569,
    570, **571**, **593–598**, 599–610, 613,
    615–620, **623–625**, **627–629**, 631,
    632, **633–637**, 644
  hydrogenation of (double-bond migra-
    tion), **599**
  positions in glyceride molecules, 6,
    18–20, 22, **91***, 363, **385–388**, **396–**
    402, 415, 430, **432–437**†, **439**†, **449**†,
    450†, **454**†, **473**†, **476**†, **491**†, **492**†,
    497, **499**†, **500**†, **504**†, **523**†, 530, 562,
    570, 659, 676, **706**, **707**
  shorter chain (C_{10}) in flowers and
    leaves, 186, 187, 644
  spectrophotometric determination of,
    93, 110, 140, 141, 151, 152, **158***,
    164*, **179**, **180**, 185, **206**, 250, 295,
    535, 564, **631–634**, 636, 638, 676,
    686, 692, 694, **695–697**
  syntheses of, **600–609**, 610, 612, 615–
    617, 619–624, **629–630**, **633**, 635–638,
    644
Films, monomolecular, 593
Fish, life cycle of, and composition of fats,
  41–47*, **54–57***
Fluoro-fatty acids, 16, **205**
Fractional distillation of esters of higher
  fatty acids, 25, 26, 73, 117, 179, 585,
  590, 638, 639, 676, 678, **688–695**
Fruit coat fats, *see* "Fats, fruit coat"
Fruits, structure of, **188**, **189**

Galactosyl glycerides, **181**
Gas–liquid chromatography, *see* "Chromatography, gas–liquid"
Geometrical isomerism in fatty acids, fatty
  alcohols and glycerides, **109**, **110**, 113,
  130, **150**, **151**, 187, 220, **252**, 267, 273*,
  290, 547, 569, **570**, **571**, **593–598**, 599–
  610, 613, 615–620, **623–625**, **627–629**,
  631, 632, **633–637**, 644, 664, 670
Glycerides
  blood, 80, **138–143***, 412–415, 546, 547,
    550, 551
  bromo-additive compounds of, 23, **361**,
    362, 446, **457–459**†, 466, 482
  component, quantitative determination
    of, 6, **18**, **358–420**†, **424–477**†,
    481–526†, 677, **700–707**

Glycerides
  component
    computation from component acids,
      390, **396–402**, **417–420**, 434, 436–439,
      443, 448, 451–453, 456–459, 463, 472,
      473, **508**, **509**
    configuration, use of pancreatic lipase, 18,
      20, 22, **91**, 158, 363, **385–388**, **396**, **397**,
      415, 418, 435, **439**†, **449**†, **450**†, **454**,
      476†, 481, 483, 491, 492, 500, **504**†, **523**,
      659, 676, **706**, **707**
    fully saturated, component acids of,
      368–370, 393, **403**†, **404**†, **425–427**†,
      473†, **489**†, **490**†, **498**†, **511**†, **512**†,
      514†, **519**†, **520**†, **524**†
    determination of, 360, 361, **363–365**,
      372–377, 417, **429**†, 438, **700**, **701**
    in natural fats, **18–22**, 112, 358, 360,
      361, **363–379**†, **389–393**†, **396–398**,
      403–408†, 410, **411**, **412**†, **417–420**,
      424–430†, **432**†, **438–445**†, **473–**
      477†, 481, **489–508**†, **510–525**†, 546,
      700
    hydrogenated, separation by crystallisa-
      tion, **361**, 429, 450, 454, 455, 473, 477,
      515
    individual, *see* SEPARATE INDEX, pp.743–745
    infra-red spectroscopy, **402**, **403**, **434**, **659**,
      660
    mass spectroscopy, 660
    melting points, 434, 439, 475, 476, 498,
      512, 590, 659, 660, **662–665**
    migration of acyl groups, **659–664**
    natural mixed, configuration of, 4, 5,
      16–24, 91, 158, 363, **385–388**, **396–403**,
      415, **430**†, **432–437**†, **439**†, **449**†, **450**†,
      454†, **463**†, **468**†, **470**†, **471**†, **475**†,
      476†, **491**†, **492**†, **497**†, **499**†, **500**†,
      504†, **523**†, **524**†, 530, 562, 570
    nuclear magnetic resonance of, **660**
    of dibasic acids, 198
    optically active, **293**, **403**, **665**, **666**
    polymorphism, 17, 19, **402**, 432–434,
      437, 454, 475, 476, 627, **658–665**
    separation by chromatographic adsorp-
      tion, 136, **138–143***, 363, 385, **433**†,
      434†, **439**†, **448**†, **449**†, **454**†, **466**, **467**†,
      475†, **476**†, **504**†, 530, 662, 663, 676,
      685, **687**, **707**
    separation by counter-current (C.C.D.)
      distribution, 18, 363, 373, **383–385**†,
      433†, **456**†, **457**†, **459**†, **461**†, **464**†, 639,
      659, 680, 700, **705**, **706**
    separation by crystallisation from acetone
      (or other solvent), 18, **123**, **124***, **359–**
      363, **372–382**†, **389–395**†, **408–410**†,
      417, 419, **425–429**†, **432**†, **433**†, **435–**
      465†, **467–470**†, **472–477**†, 481, **483–**
      488†, **490**†, **493**†, **494**†, **497**†, **499**†,
      501†, **503**†, **504**†, **515–521**†, **524**†, **700–**
      705

Glycerides
  separation by crystallisation in a thermal gradient, 433†
  separation by fractional distillation, 360, 361
  separation by thin layer chromatography, 136, 363, 385, **402**, **433**†, **434**†, **439**†, **448**, **449**†, **454**†, **475**†, **476**†, 481, **504**†, 659, **660**, 676, 700, **707**
  simple, **17–19**, 23, 286, 296, 359–361, 373, 376, 377, **380–384**, **393**, 408, **425–430**, 442, 449, 450, 472, 476, 477, 659, **664**, 702, 706
  synthetic, 578, **658–666**
  theories of fatty acid distribution in, **17–24**, **365–372**, **383**, **389–402**, **412**†, **417**, **418**, **424–477**†, 485, **492–496**, 516, 525, 550
  thermal studies of, 408, 504, 659, **660**
  transition points of, 434, 439, 454, 475, 476, 659, **664**
  tri-unsaturated, 122, 286, 296, 358–364, 373–377, **380–385**†, 389, 392, **394–403**†, 405, 410, 417, 420, **435**†, **438**†, **440**†, **442**†, **446–472**†, **474–477**†, 482, 485–488†, **491**†, 493–496†, 502–505†, **507**†, **509**†, **516**†, **524**†, **525**†, **663**, **664**, 702, 706
  X-ray diffraction studies, 296, 311, **402**, 403, **408**, **659**, **660**, **664**, **665**
Glycerol, 554, **562**, **563**, 565, **658**
  higher aliphatic ethers of, 11, **35–37**, 40, 403, 658, **666**, **670–672**
Glycerophosphoric acid, 2, 3, **345**, **403**, 562, 563, **666**
Glycol, fatty acid esters of, 406
Grasses, **180***, 345, 668

Halphen colour reaction, **323**, 612
n-Hentriacontane, 668
n-Heptaldehyde, 617
Herbivora, fats of, see "Fats, herbivora"
Hexabromostearic acids, 151, 161, 179, 206, 621, **632**, 633
n-Hexacosanol, 180, 583, **668**
n-Hexadecaheptaenal, 579
n-Hexadecanol (cetyl alcohol), 49, **73**, **488**, 579, **666–668**
n-Hexadecenol, **73**, **670**
n-Hexadecyl glyceryl ether, 11, **35–37**, 658, 666, **670–672**
Hexahydroxystearic acids, 621, 633
n-Hexenol, 187, 670
Human fats, see "Fats, human, depot and milk"
Human waxes, see "Wax, human hair"
Hydrazine, hydrogenation of methyl linoleate with, 634
Hydrogenation of unsaturated acyl groups, double bond migration during, **599**

Hydroxy-fatty acids, 16, 172, 175, **176***, 184, 203, 220, 221, 238, 239, 243, **248–250***, 256, 257, **267***, **273***, 275, 276, 285, 289*, **290***, 296, **316***, 329*, 395, **449**†, **450**†, **470**†, 552, 553, 564, 571, 586, 588, 589, 594, **595–599**, 604, 608–610, **615–620**, **627–630**, 637
Hydroxyketostearic acids, see "Ketolstearic acids"
2-Hydroxy-n-saturated acids, 586
Hydroxystearic acid, 599, 600, 617, 618

Infra-red absorption spectra, fatty acids, 109, 290, 583, **594**, 612, 618, 624, 625, **627**, **628**, **633–636**, 637
  glycerides, **402**, **403**, **434**, 659, **660**
Ingested fats, digestibility of, 125, **569–571**
  effect on animal depot fats, 13, **33**, **51**, **58**, **83**, **88**, **91***, **95–97***, **122–126***, 136, 370, **412–415**, **489–491**†, 502, 503, 510–513†, 528, **541–543**, 545, **564–573**
  effect on animal milk fats, **155–157***, 161, 165, 370, 412, **414**, **510–513**†, **566**, **567**
  effect on human fat, 565, 566
  fatty acids essential to health, **94**, **95**, **571–573**, 638, **643**
Ingested foods (other than fats), effect on animal fats, 82, 83, 88, 93, 94, 97, 101, 102, 117, 125, 126, **145–149***, 370†, **511–513**†
Inositol, 2, 50, 136, 344
Insect, fats of, see "Fats, insect"
  waxes of, see "Waxes, insect"
Interesterification, 23, **384**, **406**, 413, 415, 504, 550, 662, 664
Invertebrates, fats of, see "Fats, invertebrates"
Iodine value, relation to fatty acid composition of depot fats, **88**, 98, **132**, 154, 310
Isopropylidene glycerol, 661, 662

Kephalins, 3, 91, 92, 136, **158**, 174, **281**, **344–346**
Ketolstearic (hydroxyketo) acids, **598**, **599**
Ketosis, effect on cow milk fats, 153, 154, 156, 414
Ketostearic acids, 591, 600, 617
Keto-n-tetratriacontanol, 668

"Labelled" fats, 51, 95, **412–415**, 545, **547**, 550, **554–559**, 565, 566, **568–570**, **572**, **573**
Layers, monomolecular, 593
Lead salts of fatty acids, separation of, 26, 66, 69, **179**, **206**, 310, 345, 590, 600, 610, 626, **678**, **679–681**
Leaf fats, see "Fats, leaf"
Leaf waxes, see "Waxes, leaf"

Lecithins, 3, **90–93**, 136, 158, 174, **281**, **344–346**, 386, 564, **666**
Linolenyl alcohol, **670**
Linoleyl alcohol, 571, **669**
Lipase, 18, 20–22, 91, 158, **385–388†**, **396**, 565, 666, **706**, **707**
   pancreatic, *see* "Glyceride configuration, use of pancreatic lipase"
Lipids, blood, 80, **138–143***, 412–415, 686
   coronary deposits, 129, **141–143***
   formal classification of, **2, 3**
   galactoso-, **181**
Lipoproteins, **50, 92**
Lithium salts of unsaturated acids, separation of, 26, 66, 69, 590, 626, **680**
Liver fats, *see* "Fats, land animal, liver"
Liver phosphatides, **60***, 68, 81, **134–137**, 141, 142, 152, 613, 614
Lymphatic system, 564, 565

Maleic anhydride, adducts with unsaturated acids, 634–636, 639
Malonyl co-enzyme A, 553, **555–557**, 561
Marine mammals, fats of, *see* "Fats, marine mammalian"
Mass spectroscopy, 660
Melissyl alcohol, 184, 582, 666, 667
Methanolysis, **679**
Methyl esters of fatty acids, boiling points, **583, 688**
Milk fats, *see* "Fats, land animals, milk"
   mode of production of, 22, 23, 149, 165, **412–415**, 523, **549–551, 558**
Milk phosphatides, **157, 158***
Mobilisation of reserve fats, 44, 45, **51, 54**, 93–97, **111*, 112, 121*, 122**, 153, **154***, 165, 414, 568, 569
Monoglycerides, 562, **565**, 659, 660, **661, 662**
   isomeric forms, **662**
Musk, vegetable, 619

n-Nonacosane, 668
"Non-drying" oils, 203, **206–208**, 304–309, 319, **377†, 378†, 380–382†**, 387, 392†, 394†, 399†, 400†, **446–451†, 476, 477†**, 590
n-Nonenol, 670
Nuclear magnetic resonance, **660**

n-Octacosanol, **668**
n-Octadecadienol, 571, **669**
n-Octadecanol, 49, 73, **488, 666–668**
n-Octadecenol (oleyl alcohol), 37, 49, **73, 488**, 553, 594, 666, 667, **669**, 671
n-Octadecenyl (oleyl) glyceryl ether, 11, **35, 36**, 40, 658, 666, **670–672**

n-Octadecyl glyceryl ether, 11, **35, 36**, 403, 658, 666, **670–672**
n-Octatrienal, 579
Omnivora, fats of, *see* "Fats, omnivora"
Optically active fats, 293, **403**
Optically active glycerides, 293, **403, 665, 666**
Optically active glyceryl ethers, 403, **666**, 671
Optically active phosphatides, 403, **666**
Oxidation of fats, permanganate-acetone, 361, **363–372**, 405, 406, 417–420, 424, 427, 429, 432, 442, 488, 504, **700, 701**
   permanganate-periodate, 593, 700
Oxidation of fatty acids, alkaline permanganate, 118, **179, 206**, 592, **596–598**, 610, 615–617, 619–621, **627**, 629, 633, 686
   Caro's acid, 596
   osmium tetroxide, 596
   per-acids, 593, 596–598, 610, 615, 617, 620, 629, 637
   periodate, 618
Oxidostearic acids, *see* "Epoxy-fatty acids"
Ozonisation, **592**, 612, 620, 621, 627, 633, 635, 638, 639, 686

Pancreatic lipase, hydrolysis of fats by, *see* "Glyceride configuration, use of pancreatic lipase"
Paper chromatography, *see* "Chromatography, paper"
n-Pentacosanol, 666
Phosphatides, Phospholipids, **2, 3**, 31, **32***, 33, **50*, 60*, 66***, 68, 81, **90–93***, **132–143***, 152, **158***, 172, 174, 175, **176***, 177, **178**, 180, 182, **186, 344–347***, **386**, 403, 530, 546, 564, 565, 578, 613, 614, 625, 638, 641, 642, **666**
   blood, **138–143***
   egg, **90–93***, 386, 638, **666**
   seed, **344–347***
Phosphatidic acids, **3, 177, 178**, 180, 345, 403, **666**
Phosphatidyl choline, 3, 91, 92, 136, **158, 344**, 386, **666**
Phosphatidyl ethanolamine, 3, 50, 91, 92, 136, **158, 344, 666**
Phosphatidyl inositides, 3, 50, 136, **344**
Phosphatidyl sevine, **3, 158, 344**
Physeteryl alcohol, 670
Plasmalogens, **3, 50, 136**
Polenske value, **144**, 154, 162, 411, 499
Polyene aldehydes, 553, **579**, 667
Polymorphism of glycerides, *see* "Glycerides, polymorphism"
Pristane, 36
Proteins, conversion into fats, 93, 95, 111, 532, 541, 544
Pyruvic acid, **553**, 554, 563

Reichert value, **144**, 154, 159, 162, 411, 510
Reptile, fats of, *see* "Fats, reptile"
Resin (Rosin) acids, **184**, **185**, 260, 287, 329
Resin (Amberlite), 662
Respiratory quotient, 531, 532, 541
Ricinoleyl alcohol, **670**
Rodents, fats of, *see* "Fats, rodent"
Root fats, *see* "Fats, root"
Royal jelly, 619

Saturated acids, determination of by lead
    salt separation, *see* "Lead salts of fatty
    acids, separation of"
  determination of by oxidation (Bertram),
    see "Oxidation of fatty acids, alkaline
    permanganate"
Sebum lipids, **98***
Seed fats, *see* "Fats, seed"
Selachyl alcohol, 11, **35–37**, 40, 658, 666,
    670–672
Selenium (elaidinisation), **447†**, **594**, 599,
    606, 615, 628, 631, 633
"Semi-drying" oils, 203, **204**, **206–242***,
    264–318*, **381–385†**, 387–390, **394†**,
    401†, **451–462†**, 529–540, 564, **571–573**,
    625–627, **682–686**, 689, **695–697**, 702,
    705, 706
Shellac, 619
Spectrophotometric (UV) analysis of unsat-
    urated fatty acids, 93, 110, 140, 141, 151,
    152, **158***, **164***, **179**, **180**, 185, **206**, 250,
    295, 535, 564, **631–634**, 636, 638, 676,
    686, 692, 694, **695–697**
Spectroscopy, *see* "Infra-red-", "Spectro-
    photometric ovalysis," "X-ray-"
Spermaceti, 72, 73, 488, 489
Sphingolipids, 2, 3, 91, 157, **158**
Sphingomyelin, 2, 3, 91, 157, **158**
Sphingosine, **2, 3**
Squalene, 11, **36**, 658, 671
Sterols, 35, 36, 41, 50, 73, 74, 80, 81, 92, 133,
    136, **138–143***, 177, 180, 182, 184, 586,
    658, 668, 671, 685, 686
Synthetic triglycerides, *see* "Triglycerides,
    synthetic"

Talloel, Tall oil, **184, 185***
Temperature, climatic, influence on plant
    fats, **16**, 200–202, 207, 208, **210–212***,
    226–228*, **246–251***, 264, 265, **280**,
    281*, **305–311***, **456–458†**, 461, 462†,
    475, **537–539***, 560
  influence on animal fats, 51, 56, 59, **60***,
    108, **118, 548, 549**, 560
Testa, 188, 189, **339–340***
Tetrabromostearic acids, 118, 134, 151, 161,
    179, 206, 345, 347, **627, 628**, 631

n-Tetracosanol, 666
n-Tetradecahexaenal, 579
n-Tetradecanol, **73**, **488**, 666, **667**
n-Tetradecenol, **73**, 670
Tetrahydroxystearic acids, 118, 134, 151,
    627–630
Thermal studies of glycerides, 408, 504, 659,
    660, 662–664
Thin-layer chromatography, *see* "Chroma-
    tography, thin-layer"
Thiocyanogen value, 87, 91, **179**, **180***, **206**,
    346, 676, 694
n-Triacontanol, **668**
Triglycerides, isomeric forms, **659**, **664**
  synthetic, **663–666**
Trihydroxypalmitic acid, 619
Trihydroxystearic acids, 597, 616, 617, 620
Triphosphopyridine nucleotide, **556**
Trisaturated glycerides, *see* "Glycerides,
    fully saturated"
Trityl (triphenylmethyl), 661, 663
Triunsaturated glycerides, *see* "Glycerides,
    triunsaturated"

Unsaponifiable matter, removal of, from
    natural fats, **679**
Urea inclusion complexes of fatty acids, **590**,
    597, 618, 620, 627, 633, **683**
Ustilago fungus, 619

Volatile fatty acids, separation for analysis,
    679, 680

Wax, human hair, **585**, 623
  wool, 111, 138, 585, **586**, 623, **668**
Waxes, 2, 3, 11, 12, 32, **49**, 50, **72***, **73**, 74,
    84, **98***, 111, 138, 157, 172, 173, **180–
    183***, **198**, 294, **296**, **297***, **488†**, 578, 582,
    584, **585–587**, 623, 658, **666–672**
  insect, 84, 582, 584, **585**, **666–668**
  leaf, 172, **180–183***, 582, 584, 585, **666–
    668**
Wood pulp, 184

Ximenynyl alcohol, 670
X-ray spectrum analysis of fatty acids and
    glycerides, 109, 296, 311, 402, 403, 408,
    504†, **582–584**, 593, 624, 639, **659–660**,
    664, 665

Zamene, 36
Zoomaryl alcohol, 670

Index of Individual Fats and Waxes

The references are to seed fats, unless otherwise specifically indicated.

Except in a few special cases, systematic zoological and botanical names are not indexed unless there is no common synonym for an animal or plant, or unless it is rare or unfamiliar. (Both common and systemic names of each species are given throughout the tables of component fatty acids in Chapters II–IV.)

Abies balsamea, 213*
Abrus precatorius, 313*
Abutilon sp., 266, 270*, 275*
Acacia sp., 304*, 305*, 312*
Acentrocneme hesperiaris (larva), 82*
Acharas sapota, 327*, 378†, 380†, 399†, 440†
Acrocomia sp., 339*, 341*, 366†
Acrodiclidium sp., 333
Actinidia sp., 216*
Actinodaphne hookeri (fruit coat), 191*, 192
Actinodaphne sp., 335*, 425†
Adansonia sp., 271*
Adenanthera pavonina, 304*, 312*
Aegle marmelos, 268*
Agave sp., 218, 237*
Ageratum sp., 231*
Agonandra brasiliensis, 221, 230*, 250, 616
Ailanthus sp., 334*, 336*
Akebia lobata, 268*
Albizzia sp., 304*, 312*
Aleurites cordata, 245, 247, 248, 255*
Aleurites fordii, 15, 16, 203, 208, 243, 245, 247*, 248, 255*, 468, 469, 552, 634
Aleurites moluccana, 208, 245, 246*, 247*, 255*
Aleurites montana, 15, 16, 203, 208, 243, 245, 247*, 248, 255*, 468, 469, 552, 634
Aleurites triloba, see "A. moluccana"
Aleurites trisperma, 208, 243, 245, 247, 248, 255*, 552
Alfalfa (leaf), 182*
   (seed), 305*, 314*, 584
Algae, 27–29*, 31, 172, 614
Allanblackia sp., 20, 320*, 325*, 359†, 366†, 368†, 378†, 380†, 392†, 400†, 402, 404, 436†, 437†, 459, 590
Allium sp., 237*
Almond, 202, 207, 243, 254*, 400†, 447†, 531, 590
Althaea sp., 266, 270*

Alyssum sp., 295*, 298*, 300*
Amanita muscaria (toadstool), 177*
Amaranthus sp., 273*
Amburana, 313*
Ammi visnaga, 287*
Amoora, 324*
Anacardium sp., 269*
Anacharis alsinastrum (Canadian pond-weed), 28, 29*
Anamirta cocculus, 324*
Anchusa sp., 216*
Anda-assu, 256*
Andiroba, 324*, 399†, 443†
Anemone sp., 236*
Angelica, 287*
Angel fish (liver), 36, 38*
Angler fish (liver), 42–43*
Anise, star, 268*
Aniseed, 287*
Anogeissus schimperi, 14, 219, 272*, 276*
Anona sp., 268*
Antelope (abdominal), 100*, 101*
Anthemis sp., 231*, 232*
Antidesma sp., 245, 255*
Antirrhinum sp., 234*
Apocynum sp., 272*
Apple cuticle (wax), 619, 668
Apricot, 202, 243, 254*
Arabis sp., 295, 298*, 300*
Arachis hypogaea, see "Groundnut"
Arctium sp., 232*
Arctostaphylos sp., 216*
Arctotis sp., 219, 232*
Areca catechu (fruit coat), 198
   (seed), 198, 202, 341*, 342*, 424†, 425†, 537
Argemone sp., 206, 231*, 250
Argyria sp., 328*
Armado (fish) (mesentery), 53*

* Component acid data.   † Component glyceride data.

723

Arnica montana (petals), **186**
Arrow wood, **274***
Artemisia sp., **219, 220, 232***
  (petals), **186***, **187**
Asclepias sp., **221, 235***, 537
Asimina triloba, **268***
Asparagus sp., 221, **237***
Aspergillus sp. (mould), **175***, **176**, 559
Asphodelus sp., **237***
Aspidium dilatatum (fern), **177***
Ass (milk), 144
Aster sp., **232***
Astrocaryum sp. (fruit coat), 198
Astrocaryum sp. (seed), 198, **339***, **341***
  366*
Attalea sp. (fruit coat), 198
Attalea sp. (seed), 198, **339–341***
Autranella congolensis, **327***
Avens, 243, **253***
Avocado pear (fruit coat), 14, **191***, **198**, 556,
  614
Azadirachta indica (petals), **186***
  (seed), **320***, **324***, **366**†, **378**†, **443**†

Babassu nut, **341***, 360†, **424**†, **425**†
Baboon, sacred (depot), 13, **127***, **128***, **493**†,
  494†
Bacury (*see also* "*Platonia insignis*"), 320,
  321*, **326***, **438**†
Badger (depot), **127***, **128***, **131***, **379**†,
  409†, 495†, **496**†, 702, **704**
Bael, **268***
Bagilumbang, 248, **255***
Bagre (fish) (mesenteric), 53*
Baku butter, **327***, 378†, 380†, 399†, **440**†
Balanites aegyptica, **269***
Baobab, **271***
Barley, **280–283***, 619
  (phosphatides), 345
Basil, sweet, 208, **214***
Bassia, see "*Madhuca*"
Basswood (bark), **183***
Batava palm (seed), 339
Bauhinia sp., **312***
Bay, **335***
Bayberry (fruit coat), **191***
Bean, **314***
Bear, brown, 12, **101***
  Ceylon sloth (depot), 12, 13, **100***, **101***,
    131*, **493**†, **494**†
  Indian (depot), 12, **100***, **101***
Bee (wax), 84, 585, 668
Beech, 218, 219, **229***, 584
Beef tallow, *see* "Ox (depot)"
Beet (root) (phosphatides), 344
Belgagra (fish) (body), **53***
Belladonna, **234***
Ben, **311, 315***, 584

Benincasa sp., **258***
Bertholletia sp., **272***
Betel nut, see *Areca*
Bhakur (fish), **52***
Bidens frondosa, **232***
Bischofia sp., **245, 255***
Bittersweet vine, **214***
Blackberry, 208, 243, **254***
Blepharis edulis, **273***
Boar, wild (thigh), **125***
Boga (fish) (mesentery), **53***
Boleka nut, *see* Isano nut
Boltonia sp., **232***
Bombax sp., 266, **271***
Bonducella nut, **305***, **313***
Bonito (fish), 641, 642
Borage, **216***
Borneo tallow, 20, **320***, **326***, 359†, **366**†,
  368†, 378†, 380†, 387†, **400**†, 402, 404†,
  431†, 435†, 436†, 459
Brachychiton sp., **321–323***, **325***, **329***
Brachycome sp., **232***
Brassica sp., 295, 296, **298***, **300***, **301***,
  366†, 450, 630
Brazil nut, **272***
Broussonetia sp., **213***
Buchanania latifolia, **269***, **444**†
Buckthorn, **215***
  sea (bark), **183***
  (fruit coat), **192***, 200
  (seed), 200, **216***
Buckwheat (leaf), **182***
Buddleia sp., **274***
Buffalo (depot), 22, **104***, **106***, 369†, 409†,
  501†
  (milk), 22, 144, **159–161***, 365†, **370**†,
  379, **410–412**†, 510†, **514–522**†, 702
Burdock, **232***
  (root), **185***
Burnet, 243, **254***
Butea frondosa, **313***
Butia palm, **342***
Butter, *see* "Cow (milk)"
Butterfly, Brazilian (*Myelobia smerintha*), **82**
Buttonweed, **270***
Butyrospermum parkii, see "Shea nut"

Cabbage, **298***, **301***, 387†
  (leaf), 182*
  Kerguelen, **300***, **302***
Cacao bean (shell), **191***, **199***, 200, 232
Cacao butter, 20, **199***, 200, 264, **320***, **322***,
  325*, 359†, **361**†, 366†, 368†, 378†,
  380†, 383†, **384**† 387†, **388**†, 392†,
  396†, **400**†, 402–404, 419, **431–435**†,
  459, 533, 539, 569, 590, 701, 705–707
Caesalpinia sp., **313***
Cajanus cajans, **313***

* Component acid data.   † Component glyceride data.

Cakile sp., **299***, **301***
Calabash, **273***
Caloncoba sp., 292, **293***
Calanus cristatus (copepod), **30***
Calanus finmarchicus (copepod), **30***, 48
Calendula sp., **220**, 636
Calocarpum mammosum, see "Mammy apple"
Calophyllum inophyllum, see "Dilo"
Calycanthus sp., **236***
Camel (depot), 98, **99***, **100***, **131***
    (milk), 144, **159–161***, 370†, 410†, 411†, 510†, **514**†, **515**†
Camelina sativa, 295, 296, **299***, **301***, 450†, 618
Camellia sp., **235***
Camomile, **231***, **232***
Canarium commune (Java almond), (fruit coat), 192
    (seed), **321***, **326***, 327
Candelilla (wax), 668
Candlenut, 202, 207, **246***, **247***, **255***, 380†, 382†, 389, 463†, 465†, 466†
Candytuft, **299***, **301***
Cantaloup melon, **258***
Cantharides beetle (body), **83***
Caper spurge, 208, **244**, **255***
Capparis sp., **269***
Capsella bursa-pastoris, 295, **299***, **301***
Caragana arborescens, 313
Carapa sp., **321***, **324***, 443†
Caraway, **287***
Carcharias sp. (fish) (liver), **39***, 40
Carcharodon carcharias (fish), 641
Cardiospermum sp., 15, **311***, **315***, **316***, 610
Cardoon, **232***
Carica papaya, **272***
Carnauba (wax), 619, 668
Carp, (fish), (body), **52***
    Chinese (body and mesentery), **52***
Carpotroche brasiliensis, **293***
Carrot, **287***
Carthamus sp., *see* "Safflower"
Caryocar villosum (fruit coat), **190***, **199***, 200, **366–368**†, 393†, 403, 471†, 476†
    (seed), **199***, 200, 265, **272***, 366†, 441†
Cashew, **269***
Cassia sp., **313***
Castor oil fish (*Ruvettus pretiosus*) (body), **49***, 668
Castor (seed) (*Ricinus communis*), **248–250***, **257***, 395†, 449†, 531, 532, 552, 564, **616**, **617**, **632**, 686
Cat (depot), 12, 13, **126**, **127***, **131***
    (kidney), **137**
    (milk), 144, 411
Catalpa sp., 267, **273***, 636
Catfish (liver), **42–43***, 45
Catmint, **214***

Catnip, **214***
Cat-tail, **231***
Cay-Cay nut, **336***
Cedar nut, **213***
Ceiba sp., **271***
Celastrus paniculatus (fruit coat), **192***, **199***
    (seed), **199***, 208, **209**, **214***
Celastrus scandens, 208, **209**, **214***
Celery, **287***
Celosia argentea, **273***
Celtis sp., **230***
Centaurea sp., **232***
Cephalocroton sp., **219**, 245, **255***, 629
Cerbera odollam, **272***
Cercidium floridum, **313***, **316***
Chaetacme sp., **230***
Charlock, **298***, **301***
Chaulmoogra, 292, **293***, 361†, **621**, **622**
Cheiranthus sp., 295, **299***, **301***
Chelone barbata, **234***
Cherry, 243, **254***
Chervil, 286, **287***
    fern-leaved, 286
Chestnut, horse, 219, **230***
Chia seed, 206, 208, **215***, **245***
Chicken (bird), **87***, **387**†, **396**†, 409†, 417, 492†, 556, 569
Chicory, **232***
Chilopsis sp., 267, **273***, 627, 636
Chimonanthus sp., **236***
Chimpanzee (depot), **127***, **128***
China wood, *see* "Tung"
Chinese insect wax, 584
Chinese vegetable tallow, *see* "Stillingia tallow"
Chironomids (*Tanytarsus lewisi*) (insect), **83***
Chlorella pyrenoidosa (freshwater alga), **28**, **29***
Choanephora sp. (fungus), **175***, **176***
Chorizia insignis, **271***
Chrozophora plicata, 245, **255***, 380†, 381†, 392†, 394†, 399†, 451†, 453†
Chrysanthemum sp., **219**, **232***, 618
Chufa (sedge) (root), **185***
Cicely, sweet, 286
Cicer arietinum, **313***
Cinchona sp., **274***
Cinnamon, **335***, 378†, 426†, 427†
    wild (fruit coat), **191***
    (seed), **336***, 427†
Cirsium sp., **232***
Citromyces sp. (mould), **175***
Citron, green, **259***
Citrus sp., 266, **268***, 378†, 380†, 384, 451†, 453†, 455†
Cladophora sauteri (*alga*), **29***
Clarkia elegans, 209, **215***
Cleome sp., **269***, **276***

Clitoria sp., **313***
Clover (leaf), 112, **180***, **181***, **182**, 670
  (seed), **305***, **315***
Clubmoss (spores), **177***, 614
Clupeidae (fish) (body), **45–48***
Cnicus sp., **232***
Cnidoscolus sp., **255***
Coalfish (liver), **42–43***
Cobaea scandens, **236***
Cocculus trilobus, **324***
Cochineal (insect) (wax), 84, 668
Cockle burr (seed), **233***
Cocksfoot grass (leaf), **180***, **181***, 668
  (phosphatides), **180**, 345
  (wax), 668
Coconut, 21, 86, 95, 96, 125, 126, 155, 198,
  202, 320, **339–342***, 360†, 365†, 366†,
  378†, **424–426**†, 537, 540, 562, 567–569,
  583, 584
Cocos nucifera, see "Coconut"
Cocos pulposa, **342***
Cod (body), 50
  (liver), 23, 34, **41–43***, 92, 95, 96, 124, 125,
  155, 156, 361†, 362†, **409**†, 414, **482**†,
  565, 567, 569, 610, 613–615, 631, **639**,
  641, 642
  S. Georgia, (body), **46–47***, 48
Codlin moth (larva), **82***
Coffee, **274***
  (wild), **313***
Cohune palm (seed), **341***
Coix lacrymae, **282***
Colewort, **299***, **301***
Colliguaya sp., **245**, **255***
Colza, **298***, **300***, **301***
Comandra pallida, **291***
Conger eel (liver and body), **56–58***, 59
Conophor, **245***, **257***, **463–465**†, **467**†
Conringia orientalis, **299***, **301***, 609
Convolvulus purga (root), 619
Coral tree nut, **312***
Cordyline sp., **237***
Coreopsis sp., **232***
Coriander, **287***
Corn salad (fruit coat), **192***
  (seed), 209
Cornflower, **232***
Cosmos sp., **232***
Cotton (wax), 668
Cottonseed, 14, 95, 96, 112, 113, 123, 207,
  265, 266, **270***, 361†, 365†, 366†, 380†,
  382†, 384, **387**†, 392†, 394†, 399†,
  400†, 417, 451†, 452†, 454†, 455, 459,
  533–535, 552, 566, 567, 570, 584, 611,
  614, 624, 627, 702
  (hydrogenated), 95, 96, 361†
  (phosphatides), **345–347***
Couepia grandiflora, see "*Licania rigida*"
Coula, **221**, **230***

Courbonia virgata (fruit coat), **191***
  (root), **185***
  (seed), **269***
Cow (colostrum), **147***
  (milk), 13, 21, 22, 94, 95, 109, 120, 126,
  129, **144–157***, 360†, **365**†, **370**†, **379**†,
  410–412†, 414, 481, **510–526**†, 541, 547,
  555, 564, 566–570, 583–585, 613, 614,
  623, 624, 631, 678, 679, 682, 689, 702
Cow (milk) (phosphatides), **157***, **158***
Crab (*Birgus latro*) (body), 32, **33***, **489**†,
  566
Crabs, **32***, 545
Crambe sp., 295, **299***, **301***
Cranberry, Highbush, **274***
Crataegus sp., 243, **253***
Crescentia alata, **273***
Cress, 295, **299***, **302***
Cricket (Japanese) (body), **82***
Crocodile (body), **85***, **86***, **131***
Croton, sp., **255***
Cucumber (leaf), 187
  wild (seed), **259***
Cucumis sp., **258***
Cucurbita (*Citrullus*) sp., **251**, **258***, **259***
Cucusta reflexa, **328***
Cuphea llavea, 15, **332***, **335***, **337***
Cuttle fish (visceral), **32***, 362†
Cyamopsis sp., **313***
Cyclops strenuus (copepod), **30***, 567
Cydonia sp., 243, **253***
Cylindrocarpon sp. (fungus), **176***
Cynara sp., 219, **232***
Cynoglossum sp., **216***
Cypress (leaf), 187, 670
Cystophyllum hakodantense (alga), **31***
Cysts, dermoid (wax), 668

Dacryodes rostrata (Java almond) (fruit
  coat), **191***, **199***, 366†, **393**†, **471**†, **476**†
Dacryodes rostrata (Java almond) (seed),
  199*, **327***, 366†, **368**†, 404†, **436**†
Daffodil (petals), **186**
Dandelion (petals), **186**
Daphnia galatea (zooplankton), **30***
Daphniphyllum sp., **255***
Dasyatis akijei (fish liver), **39***
Dasylirion sp., **237***
Date, 339
Datura, **234***, 584
Deer (depot), **99***, **100***, 110, **131***, 570, 594,
  625
Delphinium sp., 15, **221**, **236***, 294, 610
Descurainia sp., **299***, **301***
Dhupa, **326***, 378†, **380**†, 400†, **435**†, **436**†
Diaptomus gracilis (zooplankton), **30***, 31
Diatoms, **28***, 29, 545, 614
Dicentra sp., **231***

Dichapetalum toxicarium, 16, **205***
Digitalis sp., **234***
Dika, **336***, **366**†, 368†, 378†, 403, **429**†, **430**†
Dilo (Dombo), **320***, **325***, **400**†, **438**†
Dimorphotheca aurantiaca, 16, **220**, **232***, **618**
Diptheria bacillus, 13, **172**, **173***, **587**, 614
Dipsacus sp., **235***
Dipteryx sp., **313***
Dodder, 295, 296, **299***, **301***, **450**†
Dodonea viscosa, **315***
Dog (depot), 22, 126, **387**†, **409**†, 541, 564, 566, 568
  (liver), 546
  (milk), 144, 411
Dogfish, (liver), 36, **38***, **40***
Dog's mercury, **245***, **256***, **468**
Dolphin, 23, 62, **74–75***, 583, 585, 678
  (body), **74–75***, 668
  (head), 62, **74–75***
  Ganges, **75***
Doronicum sp., **232***
Doum palm, **342***
Duck (egg), 90, 359†
Dugong (marine mammal), 549
Dumori butter, **327***, **440**†

Earthworm, **81***
Echinacea sp., **232***
Echinocystis sp., **259***
Echinops sp., **232***
Eels (body), **56–58***, 559, 567, 568
  sand, 362†
Elaeagnus sp., **216***
Elaeis guineensis, see "Palm"
Elaeis melanococca (fruit coat), **190***, 192, **195***, 200
Eland (milk), **160***, **162***
Elderberry (fruit coat), 189, **192***, **199***, 200
  (seed), **199***, 200, **274***
Elephant (body), **100–102***, **131***, **379**†, **493**†, **495**†
  (liver), **133–136***
Elettaria sp., **328***
Elm, **219**, **332***, **335***, **337***, 557, 584
Emblica officinalis, **255***
Embothrium sp., **219**, **237***, **239***, 614
Emu (body), **87***, **88***, **131***
Encelea sp., **232***
Endomyces vernalis (mould), 554
Entada phaeseolides, **312***
Ergot (mould), **176***
Erigeron sp. (petals), **187**
Eriodendron sp., **271***
Erisma sp., 337
Eruca sp., 295, **299***, 301*
Erysimum sp., 295, **299***, **301***
Erythrina sp., **294**, **313***, **316***, 610
Erythrophleon sp., **313***

Essang, 243, 245, 247, **248***, **256***
Etmopterus spinax (shark) (eggs), 36
Euchlaena mexicana, **282***
Euonymus sp., **214***
Eupatory, **232***
Euphausia superba (copepod), 48, 68
Euphorbia sp., **244**, **245***, **255***, **468**†
Evening Primrose, 15, **209**, **215***, 286, 620, 621, 634
Exocarpus sp., **290***
  (root), **185**, **186**, **291**

Fagara coco, **268***, **275***
Fan-fish (liver), **39***, **40**
Fanweed, **300***, **302***
Fennel, **287***
Fenugreek, **315***, **400**†
Ferret (body), **127***
Fig, **213***
Filbert, **229***
Firmiana simplex, **323***, **325***, **329***
Flamingo (bird), **87***, **88***
Flax, *see* "Linseed"
Fleabane, purple, 15, 19, 205, **219**, **220***, **233***, **238***, **239***, **245**, 266, **395**†, **451**†, 537, **617**
Foeniculum capillaceum, 620
Foeniculum officinale, **287***
Foxglove, **234***
Foxtail millet, **282***
Frangula sp., **215***
Frog (body), 12, 13, 84, **85***, **131***
  (liver), **133–135***, 573
Fucus vesiculosus (alga), **29***, 30

Gadidae (fish) (livers), **41–44**
Gaillardia sp., **232***
Galega sp., **314***
Galeocerdas sp. (fish livers), **39***, **40**
Gama grass (seed), **282***
Gamboge butter, **366**†
Gannet (bird), **89***
Garcia nutans, 245, 247, **248***, **255***
Garcinia sp., 20, **325***, **366**†, **378**†, **380**†, **392**†, **400**†, 402, 404†, **437**†, **438**†, 459
Gardenia sp., **274***
Geelbek (fish), **61**
Geruina sp., **219**, **237***, **239***, 614
Geum sp., 243, **253***
Ginger (leaf), **182**
Gmelina asiatica, **322***, **328***, **329***
Gnetum scandens, 208, **320***, **324***
Goat (depot), **99***, **100***, 110, **112***, **369**†, 409†, **501**†, 568
  (milk), 13, 144, **159–161***, 365†, **370**†, **410**†, **411**†, **510**†, **514**†, **515**†, 547, 555, 557, 614

* Component acid data.   † Component glyceride data.

Godetia sp., **215***
Gonyo almond, **269***
Goose, 86, 359†, 360†, 541, 548, 584
  (egg), 90
  grey, **87***, **88***
Gooseberry, Cape, **234***
Gorli seed, **293***, **623**
Gossypium sp., 15, **266**, 270*, 366†, 611
Gourd, **258***
Granadilla, **231***, **456**†
Grape, 207, 228, **230***, 250
  Muscadine, **230***
  wild, **230***
Grapefruit, **266**, **268***
Grindelia sp., **233***
Groper (fish), (head), 54, **59–60***
  (liver), **42–43***, 54, **59–60***, 62, 135
Groundnut, 14, 92, 122, 123, 125, 155, 156,
  202, 207, 208, **305–309***, **313***, 361†,
  366†, **378**†, **380**†, **382**†, **387**†, **394**†,
  399†, **400**†, **447–449**†, 459, 538, 566, 567,
  570, 584, 585, 614, 627, 702, **703**
  (hydrogenated), 155, 156, 361†
  (phosphatides), **344–347***
Grouper (fish) (viscera), **46–47***
Gru-gru palm (seed), **341***, **366**†
Guava, **235***
Guinea pig (rodent), **97***, 98
Guinea fowl (egg), **91***
Gull, Herring, **89***
  Skua, **89***
Gurgi nut, **325***
Gurnard (fish), 48, **61**
Guyova, **235***
Gynandropsis sp., **269***
Gynocardia, **293***

Hackberry, 218, **230***
Haddock (flesh lipids), **50**
  (liver), **42–43***
Hake (liver), **42–43***
  (New Zealand), **42–43***, 44
Halibut (body), **46–47***, 54, 59
  (liver), **42–43***, 44, 45, 54, 59
Hare, 98
Hawthorn (bark), **183***
  (seed), 208, 243, **253***
Hazelnut, 202, **229***
Hazina kernel, 320
Helianthus sp., *see* "Sunflower"
Heliopsis sp., **219**, **233***
Hemerocallis sp., **237***
Hempseed, 88, 91, 92, 207, 208, **213***, 381†,
  463†, 465†, 466†, 532, 566, 567, 632
Hen (domestic), 12, 13, 86, **87***, **88***, 93,
  131*, 369†, 405, 491†, 548, 549, 566,
  567
  (egg fats), **90–92***, 566, 567, **638**

Henbane, 218, **234***
Hernandia sp., **270***
Herrania sp., **322***, **325***
Herring (body), 23, **45**, **46–47***, **48**, **50**, **58**,
  362†, **409**†, **410**†, **482**†, **486**†, **487**†,
  567, 568, 615, **640–642**
  (visceral), **46–47***, **48**
Hesperis matronalis, **295**, **299***, **301***
Hevea brasiliensis, 16, 208, **245**, **246***, **256***,
  382†, **463**†, **465**†, **466**†, 632, 689
Hibiscus sp., 15, **266**, **271***, 380†, 611
Hickory nut, 218, **228***, **229***
Hilsa (fish) (body), **53***
Hippopotamus (depot), **99–101***, **131***, 558
Hodgsonia sp., **259***, 366†, 380†, 382†, 404†,
  445†, **446**†
Hogweed, **287***
Holaptelea integrifolia, **230***
Holarrhena antidysenterica, **272***, **275***
Honesty, **295**, **299***, **302***
Honeysuckle, **274***
Hongay seed, **314***
Hop, **213***
Horse (bone and hoof), 102, **103***, 116,
  130*
  (depot), 12, 22, 98, 99, **102***, **103***, 110,
  131*, **374–376**†, **379**†, **387**†, 409†, **493**†,
  494†, 566, 594, 625, **682**, **690–693**, 702
  (liver), 104, **133–136***
  (milk), 102, 129, 144, **160***, **161***, 410†,
  411†
Horsebean, **315***
Horse mackerel (fish) (body), **46–47***
Houndstongue, **216***
Human (abdominal), **128***, **129***
  (aorta), **140–143***, 686
  (blood), **140–143***, 686
  (bone), **130***
  (brain), 610, 611, 624
  (colostrum), **164***
  (depot), 12, 13, 22, **128–131***, 387†, 497†,
  571, 625
  (hair), **585***, **623***
  (milk), 144, **162–165***, 370†, 379†, **410–
  412**†, **522–526**†, 570, 571
Hulsea sp., **233***
Hura polyandra, **245**, **256***
Hydnocarpus sp., 292, **293***, **621**
Hygrophyla spinosa, **273***
Hyoscyamus niger, *see* "Henbane"
Hyphaene sp., **342***
Hyptis spicigera, 209, **214***, **245***, **468**†

Iberis sp., **295***, **299***, **301***
Ilex sp., **214***
Illicium sp., **268***
Illipé butter, **327***, **441**†
Impatiens balsamina, **244***, **637**

* Component acid data.   † Component glyceride data.

Impatiens sp., **244***, 637
Ipomaea sp., **328***, 619
Iris sp., **244**, 637
Iriya, **336***
Ironwood, **326***, **328***
Iron wood nut, **328***
Irvingia sp., **333***, **336***, 366†, 429†, 430†, 584
Isabghol, **235***
Isano nut, 16, **230***, **289***, **290***, **618**, **619**, 637
Isatis tinctoria, **299***, **302***
Isomeris arborea, **269***
Iva sp., **233***
Ivory wood (seed), **221**, **230***, 250, 616
Ivy (leaf), 670
  (seed), 15, 286, **287***, **620**

Jaboty kernel, **334***, **337***
Jacaranda sp., 636
Jacopever (fish), (body), **46–47***, 48, 61, **62***
  (head), **61**, **62***
  (liver), **42–43***, 44, **61**, **62***
  (viscera), **61**, **62***
Jamba, **299***, **301***
Japan wax (fruit coat), 189, **190***, **198**, **199***, 472†, 585
Jatropha sp., **245**, **256***
Java almond (fruit coat), **191***, **199***, 366†, 393†, 471†, 476†
  (seed), **199***, **327***, 366†, 368†, 404†, 436†
Java olive (fruit coat), **191***
  (seed), **325***, 611
Jessenia batava (fruit coat), **190***, **195***, 201
Joannesia princeps, **245**, **256***
Job's tears (grass), **282***
John Dory (fish), (body), **46–47***, 48, 61
  (liver), **42–43***, 61
Jute, 266, **270***, 381†, 399†, 456†, 461†

Kabeljou (fish), 61
Kadam, **260***
Kamala, **248**, **256***, **468**, 470†, **618**, 702
Kangaroo (depot), 12, 13, **99–101***, **131***, 493†, 494†
Kansive nut, 320
Kanya butter, **326***, 437†
Kapok, **271***
Karanja, 683
Katio, **327***
Kenaph, 265, **271***, **276***, 683
Kepayang, **259***
Khakan kernel, **337***
Kingklip (fish), 61
Kirondro seed, **336***
Kiwi, New Zealand (bird), **88***
Kochia sp., **236***

Koelreuteria sp., **315***
Koeme, **259***
Kokum butter, 366†, 437†, 438†
Kombo, *see "Pycnanthus kombo"*
Kon, **316***
Krill, 48, 68
Kuhnia sp., **233***
Kusum, **316***, 366†, 378†, 442†

Lac (insect wax), 668
Lactobacillus sp., **173***, 611, 612, 624
Lactuca sp., *see "Lettuce"*
Laemonema morosum (fish) (body), **49**, 670
Lagenaria sp., **259***
Lagwort, **314***
Lallemantia iberica, **214***
Lallemantia royleana, 209, **214***
Lalob, **269***
Laminaria digitata (alga), **29***
Lampern (fish) (body), **46–47***, **49**, 54
Lantana sp., **328***
Lard, *see "Pig (depot)"*
Larkspur, **236***
Laurel, cherry, 243, **254***
  Indian, **325***, 399†, 438†
  Portuguese, 243, **254***
Laurus nobilis (laurel), (fruit coat), **191***, 192, **199***, 366†, 367†, 471†, 476†
  (seed), 19, **199***, 333, **335***, 360†, 366†, 393†, 429†, 584
Lavatera trimestris, 266, **271***, 611
Leek, **237***
Lens esculenta, **314***
Leonatis sp., 209, **214***
Leonorus sibiricus (leaf), **182***
Leonurus sp., **214***
Lepidadenia sp., **335***
Lepidium sp., 295, **299***, **302***
Lepidorhinus iguanosus (shark) (liver), 36
Leprosy bacillus, **172**, 586
Leptomeria sp. (stem), **183***, 291
  (root), **186***, 291
Lespedeza sp., **305***, **314***
Lesquerella sp., 295, 296, **299***, **302***, 618
Lettuce, **233***
Leucaena sp., **312***
Liatris sp., **233***
Licania arborea, 243, **244**, **253***
Licania crassifolia, 243, **244**, **253***
Licania rigida, 16, 208, 243, **244**, **253***, **468**, 469†, 635
Licania venosa, 243, **244**, **253***
Lima bean, **314***
Lime, 266, **268***, **270***, **275***, 378†, 382†, 399†, 451†, 453†, 455†
Limnanthes douglassii, 15, **205***
Linaria sp., **234***
Lindackenia dentata, 292

* Component acid data.   † Component glyceride data.

Lindera sp., 205, 333, **426†**, **623**
Ling (fish) (liver), **42–43***
  Cape (fish) (liver), **61**
  New Zealand (fish) (liver), **42–43***, **60**, 62, 135
Linseed, 19, 91, 92, 112, 113, 126, 155, 156, 206, 207, **209–212***, **215***, 308, 361†, 362†, **373†**, **383†**, **395†**, **396†**, **401†**, **463–466†**, 532, 533, 535–538, 560, 566, 567, 569, 624, 627, **632**, **633**, 634, 706
  (phosphatides), 345–347*
Lion (depot), 12, 13, **126**, **127***, **131***
Liquidambar sp., **236***
Listris sp., **233***
Litsea sp., 205, **335***, **426†**, **623**
Lizard (body), 12, 13, 84, **85***, **131***
Lobelia sp., **236***
Lobularia sp., 295, **299***, **302***
Locust (body), **82***
Lomatia sp., **219***, **237***, **239***, **614**
Lonicera sp., **274***
Loofah (*Luffa* sp.), **259***
Lophira alata, **311***, **315***, 378†, 382†, 445†
Lophira procera, **311***, **315***, 378†, 382†, 400†, 445†
Love-in-a-mist, **236***
Lucerne (leaf), **182***, 668
  (leaf) (wax), 668
  (seed), **305***, 584
Luffa sp., **259***
Lukrabo, **293***
Lumbang, *see* "Candlenut"
Lunaria sp., 295, **299***, **302***
Lupin (phosphatides), 346
  (white), 533
Lupinus termis, **314***
Lycogala epidendrum (mould), **174***
Lycopodium clavatum (Clubmoss spores), 14, **177***, 614, 619
Lycopus asper, 209, **214***
Lytta vesicatoria (insect), **83***

Macassar, *see* "Kusum"
Macadamia ternifolia, **219**, **237***, **239***, **614**
Macleaya sp., **231***
Maclura sp., **213***
Madhuca sp., **321***, **327***, 366†, 378†, 380†, 393†, 400†, 441†
Mafura, *see* "*Trichilia*"
Mahogany, **324***
Maize, 19, 95–97, 126, 207, **280**, **281***, **283***, 380†, **381†**, **383†**, **384†**, **395†**, **400†**, 419, 456†, 459, 461†, 564, 567, 568, 571, 624, 706
  blight (mould), **177***
Majorana sp., **214***
Makita, *see* "*Parinarium* sp."
Malabar tallow, *see* "*Vateria indica*"

Malcolmia sp., **300***, **302***
Mallotus sp., 16, 245, **248**, **256***, **468**, **470†**, 561, 618
Mallow sp., **265**, **270***, **271***
Malva sp., 266, **271***
Mammy apple, **320***, **327***
Mangel (root), **185***
Mango, **269***, **443†**
Mani nut, 320
Manicaria saccifera, 83, **339***, **342***, **366†**, 567
Mappia foetida, 221, **230***
Marah sp., **259***
Maratti, **293***
Margosa, *see* "Neem"
Marigold, 220
Marjoram, **214***
Marmot, 98
Marsdenia sp., **235***
Marshallia sp., 294, 610
Martynia diandra, **273***
Maté, Yerba, **214***
Matricaria sp., **233***
  (petals), 187
Matthiola sp., **300***, **302***
Maytenus disticha (fruit coat), **192***
  (seed), **214***
Meadowsweet, 243, **254***
Medicago sp., **305***, **314***, 584
Mee, **327***, **441†**
Melia azedarach, **324***
Melon, cantaloupe, **258***
  water, **258***, **259***
Melontree, **272***
Menhaden (fish) (body), **46–47***, **48***, 123, 126, **487†**, 566, 567, 615, **640–642**
Mentha sp., **214***
Mentzelia sp., **237***
Meratia sp., **235***
Mercurialis sp., **245***, **256***, 468†
Mesua ferrea, **326***
Michelia champaca, **268***
Michelia compressa (leaf) (wax), 668
Milkweed, 218, **235***, 294, 610
Millet, **280**, **282***, **283***
Milletia sp., **314***
Mimosa sp., **312***
Mimusops sp., **327***, 378†, 380†, 399†, 440†
Mink (depot), **127***, **128***
Mint, **214***
Mirabilis jalapa, 209, **216***
Mkanyi, *see* "*Allanblackia*"
Molinillo, 209, **214***
Momordica sp., 252, **259***, 636
Monarda sp., **214***
Monilia albicans (fungus), **177***
Monodora myristica, **268***
Monkfish (liver), **42–43***

---

* Component acid data.   † Component glyceride data.

Moringa sp., **315***
Mouse (rodent), (depot), **97***, 98, 554, 555, 559, 569
(milk), 144, 411
Mowrah, **327***, 366†, 368†, 378†, 380†, 392†, 399†, **400†**, 404†, **441†**
Mulberry, 208, **213***
Mullein, **235***
Mullet, grey (fish) (ovary), **73**, 668
Mungo bean, **305***, **314***
Murumuru, **341***
Musk-ox (depot), 110, 111
Musk rat (rodent) (scent gland), **98***
Mussel (*Mytilus edulis*), **31***, **32***, 33, 58, 567
Mustard, **298–302***, **387†**, 539, 609, 610
hare's ear, 294, **299***, **301***
tumbling, **300***, **302***
Mutton tallow, *see* Sheep (depot)
Myelobia smerintha (insect), **82***
Myristica fragrans syn. *officinalis* (fruit coat), **199***
Myristica fragrans syn. *officinalis* (seed), **199***, 333, **336***, 360†, 366†, 427†
Myristica malabarica (seed), 333, **336***, 366†, **393†**, **428†**
Myristica sp., 320, 333, **336***, 378†, 427†, **428†**
Myrobalan, **272***
Myrrhis odorata, 286
Myrtle wax (fruit coat), 189, **191***
Mystus sp. (fish) (viscera), **53***

Nain (fish), **53***
Nasturtium, **296**, 569, 610
Nasturtium officinale, **295**, **300***, **302***
Neat's foot (hoof), 104, **114–116***, 379†, 405, **505–509†**
Nectandra sp., 333
Neem (petals), **186***
(seed), **324***, 366†, 378†, 380†, 392†, 399†, 400†, 404†, **443†**
Nemesia sp., **234***
Neolitsea involucrata (fruit coat), **191***, **199***
Neolitsea sp. (seed), **199***, **336***, 378†, **425–427†**
Neou, *see* "*Parinarium* sp."
Nepeta sp., **214***
Nephelium sp., **311***, **315***, 366†, 368†, **442†**
Nerisyrenia sp., **300***, **302***
Nerium thevetifolium, **272***
Neurospora crassa (mould), **175***
Nettle, stinging (leaf), **182***
(seed), **235***
Niam, *see* "*Lophira alata*"
Nigella sp., **236***
Niger seed, **221**, **222***, **226**, 228, **233***, 381†, 399†, **457†**, **458†**, **460–462†**, 533, 538
Night-scented stock, **300***, **302***

Nitella opaca (alga), **29***
Nitzschia closterium (diatom), **28**, **29***
Njatuo tallow, **327***, 366†, 368†, 402, 404†, **439†**
Njave, **327***, **440†**
Noli palm (fruit coat), **195***, **201**
Nutmeg, **199***, **336***, 360†, 366†, 368†, 403, 552, 584
Nymphaea alba, 244, 637

Oak (leaf), 670
(seed), 208, **229***
Indian, **229***
pin, swamp, **229***
Oats, **280–283***
(phosphatides), 345
Ocimum basilicum, 209, **214***, **468**
Ocimum kilimandscharicum, 209, **214***, **245***, **468†**
Oedogonium sp. (alga), **29***
Oenocarpus sp. (fruit coat), **190***, **195***, 201
Oenothera biennis, 15, **209**, **215***, 286, 620, 621, 634
Oidium lactis (mould), **175***
Oiticica, *see* "*Licania rigida*"
Okari nut, **272***
Okra, **265**, **271***, **276***, 380†, 382†, 392†, 394†, 399†, **451†**, **452†**, **454†**, 459, 612
Olive (fruit coat), 14, 20, 96, 189, 192, **196***, **197***, **199–202***, 207, 359†, 361†, 366†, 367†, 380†, 384, **387†**, **471†**, **477†**, 531, 532, 564–566, 590, 614, 624
(seed), **199***, 200, 219, **236***
Omphalea sp., **256***
Omphalocarpum sp., **327***
Oncoba sp., **293***
Onguekoa Gore, 16, 204, 221, **230***, **289***, **290***, 637
Onion (skin) (wax), 668
Onopordon sp., **233***
Opossum (body), 110
Orange, **266**, **268***, 380†, 382†, 399†, **451†**
Ostrich (body), **87***, **88***
Osyris alba, **291***
Otobo, **336***
Ouricoury nut, **341***
Owala nut, **312***, **444†**
Ox (adrenals), **137***, 625, **638**, **641**, **642**
(blood), **138–140***, 686
(bone), **114***, **115***
(brain), 137, 610, 611, 624, **638**, **641**, **642**
(depot), 12, 13, 21, 22, 98, 99, **104–112***, 120, **126**, **131***, 369†, 379†, **387†**, **406–409†**, 481, 492, **497–499†**, **500–509†**, 541, 549, 566, 567, 569, 584, 585, 590, 594, 613, 614, 623–625, 631, **638**, 686, 701
(heart-muscle), **137***, 641

* Component acid data.   † Component glyceride data.

Ox (hoof), 104, **114–116***, **505–507**†
  (liver), **133–136***, 546, 613, 614, 631, **641**,
  642
  (spleen), **137**
Oyster nut, *see "Lophira alata"*

Pachira sp., **266**, **271***
Pachymerus dactris (beetle) (body), **83***, 566,
  567
Pachypleurum sp. (root), **185***
Pachyrrhizus angulatus, **314***
Pachyrrhizus erosus, **314***
Paeony, **236***, 531
  (root), **185***
Pahuna (fish) (liver), **52***
Pala (fish) (body), **49***
Palaquium sp., **327***, **366**†, **368**†, 402, **404**†,
  439†
Palm (*Elaeis guineensis*) (fruit coat), 14, 91,
  96, 189, **190***, **194***, **195***, **199–201***,
  361†, **366**†, **367**†, **378**†, **380**†, 384,
  387†, **388**†, **393**†, 403, 417, **471**†,
  473–476†, 566, 569, 584, 614, 686
Palm (*Elaeis guineensis*) (kernel), 88, 91,
  155, 156, **199***, 200, 320, **339–342***,
  360†, **365**†, **366**†, **378**†, **424–426**†, 567,
  686, 707
Palma sp., **342***
Palmiche nut, Cuban, **342***
Panda, giant (depot), **100***, **101***, **131***
Pangium edule, **293***
Panther (depot), **126**, **127***
Papaver sp., **231***
Papaw, **268***
Papaya, **272***
Parinarium sp., 16, 19, 208, 243, **244**, **253***,
  254*, **394**†, **395**†, **469**†, **470**†, **636**, 637,
  702
Parkia sp., **304***, **312***
Parkinsonia sp., **313***
Paroacaxy nut, **312***
Parsley, **286**, **287***, **620**
Parsnip, **287***
Passion fruit, 218, 228, **231***, **456**†
Pasture grasses (leaf), 110, 112, **180***, **181***
  (phosphatides), 180, **345***
Patua palm (fruit coat), **190***, **195***, 201
Paulownia sp., **234***
Payena sp., 320, **327***
Pea (leaf), **181**
Peanut, *see* "Groundnut"
Pecan nut, 218, **228***, **229***
Pemphigus sp. (insect) (body), **83***
Penguin, **89***
Penicillium javanicum (mould), **175***
Penicillium sp. (moulds), **175***, 176
Pentaclethra sp., **304***, **312***, **378**†, 380–
  382†, **399**†, **444**†

Pentadesma sp., 320, **326***, **366**†, **368**†,
  404†, **437**†
Pentstemon sp., **235***
Peppermint (leaf), **182***
Perch (fish) (body), **52***
Perilla ocimoides, 16, 206, 208, **215***, **245***,
  465, **468**, 632, 633
Perriera madagascariensis, **334***, **336***
Persea gratissima (fruit coat), 14, **191***, 192,
  198, 205
Petrel, Fulmar, **89***
Phaseolus sp., **305***, **314***
Pheasant (depot), 110, **387**†, **492**†
Phormium sp., **237***
Phulwara butter, **327***, **366**†, **368**†, **431**†,
  441†
Phycomyces sp. (mould), **175***
Phyllanthus sp., **256***
Physalis sp. *see* "Cape gooseberry"
Physic nut, **256***
Phytomonas tumefaciens (bacillus), **172***,
  173*, **586**
Phytoplankton, 27, 30, 545
Picramnia sp., 16, 204, **289***, 334, **337***, **620**
Picrasma sp., 286, **334**, **337***, **620**
Pig (bone), **114***, **115***
  (brain), 642
  (blood), 547
  (depot), 12, 13, 22, 98, 99, 110, **116–125***,
  131*, **360**†, **361**†, **369**†, **379**†, **387**†,
  388†, **396**†, 405, **406–409**†, 417, 481,
  492, **497–500**†, **502–504**†, **507–509**†,
  541–544, 548, 565–567, 571, 594, 613,
  614, 625, 638, 707
  (liver), **133–136***, 555, 571, 613, 614, 625
  (milk), 144, **160***, **161***, **410–412**†, **522**†
Pigeon (bird), **387**†, **492**†, 555, 556, 573
  (egg), 90
Pigweed, **273***
Pike (body), **52***, 642
  (mesenteric), **52***
Pilchard (body), **46–47***, **640–642**, 670
Pili, **327***
Pimelodus sp. (fish), 51
Pimpinella anisum, **287***, **620**
Pine, black (leaf), **182***
  digger, **213***
  nut, **213***
  red, **213***
  seed, **213***, 632
Pinto bean, **314***
Pinus sp., 209, **213***
  (trunk), **184**, **185***
Piqui-a (fruit coat), **190***, **199***, 200,
  366–368†, **393**†, 403, **471**†, **476**†
  (seed), **199***, 200, 265, **272***, **366**†, **441**†
Pistachio, 202, **269***
Pisum sativum (leaf), **181***
Pithomyces sp. (fungus), **175***, **176***

* Component acid data.   † Component glyceride data.

Pitjoeng, 293*
Plantago ovata, 218, 235*
Platonia sp., 19, 320, 321*, 326*, 378†, 380†, 393†, 400†, 438†
Platypus, duck-billed, 75, 76*
Plum, 243, 254*
Poke (root), 185*
Polanisia sp., 269*
Pollack (fish) (liver), 42–43*
    (tissues), 50
Pollan (fish) (body), 52*
Pomegranate, 16, 252, 635
Pomfret (fish) (body), 49*
Pongamia sp., 294, 305*, 314*, 316*, 400†, 610
Poppy (petals), 186
    (seed), 206, 218, 228, 231*, 381†, 456†, 460–462†, 532, 627
Porcupine (rodent), 97*
Porpoise, 23, 62, 74–75*, 583, 585, 614, 678
    (body), 12, 62, 74–75*, 489†, 549, 614, 668, 669
    (head), 12, 62, 74–75*, 667, 669
    (jaw), 12, 62, 74–75*, 667
Portulaca sp., 237*
Po-Yoak, *see "Parinarium* sp."
Prawn (lipids), 32*
Pringlea antiscorbutica, 300*, 302*
Princepia utilis, 254*
Pristis cuspidatus (fish), 39*
Proboscidea sp., 273*
Prunus sp., 208, 243, 254*, 447†, 636
Psidium sp., 235*
Psoralea sp., 314*
Ptelea sp., 269*, 276*
Pterocarpus marsupium (tree, bark), 183*
Pulasan tallow, 315*, 366†, 404†, 442†
Pulses, 305*, 313–315*
Puma (depot), 126, 127*
Pumpkin, 258*
Punica sp., 16, 252
Putranjiva sp., 245, 256*
Pycnanthemum sp., 215*
Pycnanthus kombo, 14, 19, 333, 336*, 337*, 378†, 393†, 427†, 428†
Python (snake), 85*, 86*, 131*

Quince, 243, 253*
Quisqualis indica, 272*
Quokka (marsupial), 101, 110

Rabbit (rodent) (depot), 12, 97*, 98*, 110, 131*, 359†, 369†, 387†, 409†, 491†, 548, 549, 555, 563, 568, 594, 625
    (liver), 135
    (milk), 144
Radish, 295, 300*, 302*, 387†

Ragweed, 231*
Rambutan tallow, 315*, 366†, 404†, 442†, 584
Rape (leaf), 181*, 182*, 640
    (seed), 126, 155, 156, 294*, 298*, 300*, 301*, 361†, 366†, 387†, 403, 450†, 532, 539, 566, 567, 569, 609, 610, 624, 630
    (hydrogenated), 361†
    Jamba, 299*, 301*
    (phosphatides), 346, 347
Rat (depot), 12, 13, 93–97*, 98, 110, 131*, 369†, 387†, 396†, 405, 409†, 491†, 544, 549, 554, 555, 559, 564–568, 570–573, 614, 625, 641
    (liver), 95, 135, 136, 556, 571–573, 641
    (milk), 411
Ratfish (liver), 36, 37, 38*, 672
Ratibida sp., 233*
Ratsbane, 205*
Ravison, 298*, 301*
Ray (fish) (liver), 613
Rayan, 327*
Red cod (liver) (New Zealand), 42–43*, 44
Reindeer (bone), 114*, 115*
    (depot), 12, 98, 100*
Reticularia lycoperdon (mould), 174*
Rhamnus sp., 209, 215*
Rhodotorula sp. (yeasts), 174*
Rhodymenia palmata (alga), 29*
Rhus (fruit coat), 189, 190*, 198, 199*, 472†, 585
    (seed), 199*, 269*
Rice, 280, 282*, 283*
Ricinodendron sp., 243, 245, 247, 248*, 256*
Ricinus sp., 16, 203, 243, 245, 248–250*, 257*, 449†, 559, 561, 616
Rock lobster (hepatopancreas), 33*
Rocket, 299*, 301*
Rohu (fish), 53*
Rosa sp., 254*
Rose (petals), 186
    wild, 208, 243, 254*
Rosewood tree (bark), 183*
Roystonia sp., 342*
Rubber seed, 207, 245, 246*, 256*, 382†, 463†, 465†, 466†, 632, 689
Rubus sp., 243, 254*
Rudbeckia sp., 233*
Ruvettus pretiosus (fish) (body), 49, 668
Ruvettus tydemani (fish) (body), 668
Rye, 280–283*
Ryegrass (leaf), perennial, 180*, 181*

Sabalo (fish) (muscle), 53*
Safflower, 19, 207, 208, 218, 221, 223*, 226, 228, 373†, 381†, 383†, 384†, 395†, 401†, 451†, 453†, 457†, 459–462†, 535, 536, 538, 683, 706

* Component acid data.   † Component glyceride data.

Saith (fish) (liver), 42–43*
Salmon (body), 12, 46–47*, 49, 52, 54, 55*, 56, 362†
 (liver), 55*, 56
 (mesentery), 55*, 56
 ova, 54, 55*, 56
 parr, 54, 55*
 smolt, 54, 55*
 Alaskan (ova), 55*
Salsola sp., 236*
Salvadora sp., 334*, 337*
Salvia sp., 215*, 245*
Samadera sp., 334*, 337*
Sambucus sp., 274*
Sanguisorba sp., 243, 254*
Santalum album, 16, 285, 290*, 637
Santalum sp. (stem), 183, 291
 (root), 186, 291
Sapium sp. (fruit coat), 189, 190*, 192, 199*, 200, 359†, 366†, 367†, 378†, 380†, 393†, 400†, 471†, 472†
 (seed), 199*, 200, 205, 245, 250*, 251*, 257*, 382†, 468†, 643
Sapindus sp., 315*
Sapocainha, 293*
Sapota, 327*, 378†, 380†, 399†, 440†
Sardine (Japanese) (body), 46–47*, 362†, 482†, 615, 639–642
Sassafras albidum, 332, 336*
Satureja sp., 215*
Sawfish (Indian) (liver), 39*, 40*
Scabiosa sp., 235*
Scabious, 235*
Schizandra chinensis, 268*
Scenedesmus sp. (alga), 640
Schleichera sp., 311*, 316*, 366†, 380†, 442†
Scymnorhinus lichia (shark) (liver), 36, 38*
Sea anemone, 32*
Sea-bass (fish) (viscera), 46–47*
Seal (blubber), 23, 62, 63–64*, 67–68, 409†, 410†, 481, 486–488†, 613, 614
 (liver), 66*, 68
 (milk), 13, 66*, 68, 416†
Sea-lion (blubber), 65*, 68, 409†, 410†, 486†, 488†
Sea urchin (semen), 33*
Sebastiana sp., 245, 251*, 257*, 643
Secale cornutum (ergot) (mould), 176*
Sedge (root), 185*
Selenia grandis, 300*, 302*
Senega (root), 185*
Seringe, 259*
Sesame, 207, 208, 218, 234*, 361†, 366†, 380†, 382†, 392†, 451†, 453†, 455†, 683
 (phosphatides), 345
Sesbania sp., 314*

Setaria italica, 282*, 283*
Shad (fish) (body), 53*
Shark sp. (liver), 34, 36, 37–40*, 362†, 482†, 613, 669
Shea nut, 322*, 327*, 366†, 368†, 378†, 387†, 388†, 399†, 404†, 431†, 439†, 707
Sheep (bone), 114*, 115*
 (depot), 12, 13, 21, 22, 88, 91, 92, 98, 99, 104–113*, 131*, 360†, 365*, 369†, 379†, 387†, 406–409†, 481, 492, 497–499†, 500–509†, 541, 549, 555, 567, 570, 584, 585, 590, 594, 614, 623, 625, 631, 686, 701
 (liver), 133–136*, 614
 (milk), 13, 21, 22, 109, 144, 159–161*, 365†, 370†, 410–412†, 510†, 514†, 515†, 522†, 585, 631
 Somali (depot), 107*
Shepherd's purse, 299*, 301*
Shinia nut, 269*
Shorea sp., 320*, 326*, 366†, 378†, 380†, 400†, 431†, 435†, 436†
Sideroxylon sp., 328†
Silkworm (*Bombyx mori*) (cocoon), 81*, 82*
Simaruba sp., 334*, 337*
Simmondsia californica (seed wax), 204, 294, 296, 297*, 609
Sisymbrium sp., 295, 300*, 302*
Skate (liver), 36, 38*
Skimmia japonica, 269*, 276*
Sloe, 254*
Snake, Moccasin, 85*, 86*
Snapdragon, 234*
Snoek (fish), 61
Soapberry, 315*
Soap nut, 315*
Solanum sp., 234*, 451†, 453†
Solidago sp., 233*
Sophia sp., 300*, 302*
Sophora sp., 315*
Sorghum, 282*, 283*
Soya bean, 14, 19, 122, 123, 125, 126, 155, 156, 207, 305*, 308, 309–311*, 314*, 361†, 362†, 380–383†, 387†, 391, 395†, 401†, 463–466†, 533, 535, 538, 559, 566, 567, 614, 624, 627, 706
 (phosphatides), 344, 346, 347*
Speedwell, 235*
Sperm whale (blubber), 12, 62, 72–73*, 488†, 609, 614, 667–670
 (head), 12, 34, 50, 62, 72–73*, 488†, 584, 609, 613, 614, 668–670
 (liver), 73*
Spermophile (rodent), 97*
Sphenarium purpurascens (insect) (body), 82*
Spinach (leaf), 182*
Spinax niger (shark) (liver), 36

* Component acid data.   † Component glyceride data.

Spiraea sp., **254***
Sponges (lipids), **33***, **615**, 630, 642
Sporidesmium sp. (fungus), **175***
Sprat (body), **46–47***
Spruce (stem), 184
Squalidae (fish) (livers), **36**, **38***
Squash, Hubbard, **258***
Squid (cuttlefish) (visceral), **32***
Stachys sp., **215***
Stag (depot), **100***
Stanleyella texana, **300***, **302***
Staphylea pinnata, **235***
Stemphylium sp. (fungus), **176***
Stephania tetrandra, **324***
Sterculia foetida (fruit coat), **191***, 476
  (seed), 15, 205, **266**, 285, **322***, **323***,
  325*, 327, 436, 611
Sterculia parviflora (fruit coat), **191***, 192
  (seed), **322***, **325***, 611
Sterculia platonifolia (seed), **322***, **325***
Sterculia tomentosa (fruit coat), **191***
  (seed), **322***, **325***
Sterculia urens (seed), **321***, **322***, **325***
Stillingia oil (seed), **199***, 200, 205, **245**,
  250*, **251***, **257***, **382**†, **468**†
  tallow (fruit coat), 189, **190***, **199***, 200,
  359†, **366**†, **367**†, **378**†, **380**†, **393**†,
  400†, 403, **471**†, **472**†
Stoat (body), **127***
Stockfish (liver), **42–43***, **44**, **61**, 62
Stonebass (fish), **61**
Strophanthus sp., 16, **267**, **272***, **273***, **275***,
  561, 617
Strychnus nux vomica, **274***
Sturgeon, 12, 54, **58***
Stylosanthes sp., **315***
Styrax sp., **236***
Sugar cane (phosphatides), **344**
  (wax), **184***
Sumach (fruit coat), 189, **190***, **198**, **199***,
  472†, 585
  (seed), **199***, **269***
Sunflower (seed), 92, 97, 207, 208, **221**, **224**–
  228*, **233***, 247, 308, **373**†, **380–382**†,
  389, 456, **457**†, **458**†, **460–462**†, 533,
  536, **538**
  (phosphatides), **345–347***
Surin kernel, **327***
Swietenia sp., **324***
Symphonia sp., 320
Symplocos sp., **236***

Taban merah, **327***, **366**†, **368**†, 402, 404†,
  439†
Tabibenia sp., **273***
Taeniopoda auricornis (insect) (body), **82***
Talisay, **272***

Tall oil, **184**, **185***
Tallow, *see* "Ox and Sheep (depot)"
Tamarindus indica, **313***
Tangkallak kernel, **335***
Tapeworm, **81***
Taraktogenos kurzii, **293***
Tea (leaf), 670
Teak, **328***
Teaseed, 14, 219, **235***, 361†, **366**†, **447**†, 614
Teazle, 219
Teazlewort, **235***
Tectona grandis, **328***
Teosinte, **282***
Telfairia occidentalis, **251**, **259***
Telfairia pedata, **251**, **259***
Tent moth (*Malacosoma americana*)
  (chrysalis), **82***
Tephrosia sp., **315***
Terminalia sp., **272***, **399**†, **400**†, **451**†, **453**†
Tetracarpidium conophorum, *see* Conophor
Tetradenia sp., **333**, **426**†
Theobroma cacao, *see* Cacao butter
Thevetia sp., **273***, **400**†
Thistle, **232***
  cotton, **233***
  globe, **232***
  plumed, **232***
  saffron, **232***
Thlaspe arvense, **295**, **300***, **302***
Thorn apple, *see* Datura
Thyme, 209, **215***
Tiger (depot), **126**, **127***, **131***, **379**†, **495**†,
  497†
Tilia cordata (bark), **183***
Tithonia sp., **233***
Toad, 84, **85***
Toadflax, **234***
Tobacco, 221, **222***, **226***, 228, **234***, **381**†,
  456†, **458**†, **460–462**†, 538, 559, 689
Tomato, **234***
Tonka bean, **305***, **313***
Torresia cearensis, **313***, **316***
Tortoise, 12, 13, **131***
  Greek (body), 84, **85***, **131***
  (liver), **133–136***
Torulopsis utilis (yeast), **174***
Tragopogon sp., 220
Treculia africana, 208, 209, **213***
Trema guineensis, **230***
Trewia sp., **257***
Trichilia emetica (fruit coat), **191***
  (seed), **324***, 686
Trichoderma (fungus), 687
Trichosanthes sp., (fruit coat), **190***, 192,
  199*
  (seed), 16, **199***, **251***, **260***, 635
Trifolium sp., **315***
Trigonella sp., **315***
Tripsacum dactyloides, **282***

* Component acid data.   † Component glyceride data.

Tropaeolum, sp., 294, **296***, 569, 610
Trout, brown (fresh-water), **52***, 54, 573
   sea (body), **46–47***, **49**, 54, 573
Tuberculosis bacillus (wax), **172***, **173***,
   586, 587
Tucuma kernel, **341***, **366**†
Tulip (petals), **186**
Tung, Chinese, **247***, **248**, **255***, **382**†, **395**†,
   468, **469**†, 533, 618, **634**, 689, 702
   Florida, **247***
   Japanese, **248***, **255***
Tunny (fish), (body), **46–47***, 54, **59***
   (liver), **42–43***, 44, 54, **59***
Turbot (body), **46–47***, 54, 59
   (liver), **42–43***, 44, 54, 59
Turkey (bird), **87***
Turluru kernel, **342***
Turtle, Chinese, **85***, 86, 573
   Dark Sea, **85***, 86
   Dull Sea, **85***, 86
   Green, **85***, 86, **490**†
   Indian sea, **85***
   Mexican, 84, **85***
Typha latifolia, **231***

Ucuhuba, **336***
Ulmus sp., *see* Elm
Urtica dioica, **235***
Ustilago Zeae (maize blight), **177***, **619**

Valerian, 209
Vateria indica, **326***, **378**†, **380**†, **400**†, **435**†,
   436†
Vanguera spinosa, **274***
Verbascum sp., **235***
Vernonia anthelmintica, 15, 19, 205, **219**,
   220* **233***, **238***, **239***, 245, **266**, **395**†,
   451†, 537, **617**, 629, 685
Vernonia sp., 15, **233***, 618
Veronica sp., **235***
Vetch, **305***
Viburnum sp., **274***
Vicia sp., **305***, **315***
Vigna sp., **315***
Violet (leaf), 187, 670
Viquiera sp., **233***
Virginia stock, 295, **300***, **302***
Virola, sp., 333, **336***, **378**†, **427**†, **428**†

Wallaby (marsupial), 110
Wallflower, 295, **298***, **301***, 610
Walnut, 207, 218, **229***, 532, 632
Watercress, 295, **300***, **302***
Weasel (body), **127***
Weta (*Hemideina thoracica*) (insect) (body),
   82*
Whale (Balaenidae), (blubber), 13, 23, 34,
   48, 62, **68–71***, 123, 124, **361**†, **362**†,
   384, **409**†, **410**†, 481, **482–486**†, 549,
   565, 567, 584, 613–615, 631, 682, 689,
   702, **705**
   (bone), **70***
   (liver), **71***
   (milk), 13, **71***, **415**†
   (tongue), **70***
   beaked (Ziphiidae), **73***
   white (Delphinapteridae), **75***
Wheat (leaf), 187, 668, 670
   (leaf) (wax), 668
   (seed), **280**, **282***
   (phosphatides), **345**
Whitefish (*Coregonus* sp.) (body), **51***
Woad, 295, **299***, **302***
Wool (sheep) (wax), 111, **585, 586, 668**
Wrightia annamensis, 616
Wrightia tinctoria, **273***
Wyethia sp., **233***

Xanthium strummarium, **233***
Xanthium sp., **233***
Ximenesia sp., **233***
Ximenia americana, **221***, **230***, **290***, 611
   (bark, stem), **183, 291**
   (root), **186, 291**
Ximenia sp., 16, 204, **221***, **285**, **290***,
   294, 619, 637
Xylia xylocarpa, **304***, **312***
Xylopia aethiopica, **268***

Yam bean, **314***
Yeast, 14, **174***, 554, 556, 559, 562, 614
Yellowtails (fish) (viscera), **44***
Yucca sp., **237***

Zelkova serrata, 15, **219**, **332***, **335***, **337***
Zizyphus sp., **215***
Zooplankton, 27, **30**, 545

Index of Plant Families

Acanthaceae, **204, 273**
Agavaceae, **204, 237**
Amarantaceae, **204, 273**
Anacardiaceae, **190**, 199, **204**, 265, 269, **443, 444**
Anonaceae, **204**, 265, **268**
Apocynaceae, 16, **204**, 265, 266, **272, 273**, 617
Aquifoliaceae, **204, 214**
Araliaceae, **204, 286, 287**, 620
Asclepiadaceae, **204, 235, 294**, 610

Balsaminaceae, **224**
Berberidaceae, **204, 268**
Betulaceae, **204, 229**
Bignoniaceae, **204, 267, 273**
Bombacaceae, 15, **204**, 264, **271**
Boraginaceae, **204, 216**
Burseraceae, **191**, 199, **204**, 265, 304, 321, **326**
Buxaceae, **204, 296**

Calycanthaceae, **204, 236**
Campanulaceae, **204, 236**
Capparidaceae, 185, **191, 204, 269**
Caprifoliaceae, **192**, 199, **204**, 265, **274**
Caricaceae, **204, 272**
Caryocaraceae, **190**, 199, **204**, 265, **272, 441**
Celastraceae, **192**, 199, **204**, 208, 209, **214**
Chailletaceae, **205**
Chenopodiaceae, 182, 185, **204, 236**
Combretaceae, 14, **204**, 265, **272**
Compositae, 15, 16, **204**, 205, 206, 208, 218–221, **231–233, 294**, 451, 461, 610, 617, 618, 644
Coniferae, 188, **204**, 207, **213**
Convolvulaceae, **204**, 304, 321, **322, 328**
Cruciferae, 15, 182, **204, 294–296, 298–302**, 319, 450, 609, 610, 618
Cucurbitaceae, 16, **190**, 199, 203, **204**, 218, 243, **251, 252, 258–260**, 445
Cyperaceae, 185

Dichapetalaceae, **205**
Dilleneaceae, **204, 216**
Dipsacaceae, **204, 235**
Dipterocarpaceae, **204**, 304, 321, **326, 435, 436**

Elaeagnaceae, 183, **192**, 199, **204**, 209, **216**
Ericaceae, **204, 216**
Euphorbiaceae, 15, 16, **190**, 199, 203, **204**, 205, 208, 218, 219, 221, 243, **244–251**, **255–257**, 296, 449, 468, 618

Fagaceae, **204**, 208, **229**
Flacourtiaceae, 15, **204, 292, 293, 621**

Gnetaceae, **204**, 304, **324**
Graminae, 15, **204**, 264, **280–283**, 460
Guttiferae, **204**, 209, 304, **320, 321, 325, 326**, 402, **436–438**, 557

Hamamelidaceae, **204, 236**
Hernandiaceae, **204, 270**
Hippocastanaceae, **204, 230**

Juglandaceae, 204, 229

Labiatae, 15, 182, **204**, 206, 209, **214, 245**, 468, 632
Lauraceae, 14, 189, **191**, 198, 199, 200, **204**, 205, 304, **332, 335**, 336, **425–429**, 557, 584, 623
Lecythidaceae, **204**, 265, **270**
Leguminosae, 15, 181, 182, 183, 203, **204**, 208, 220, 294, **304–310, 312–315, 444**, **447–449**, 557, 610
Liliaceae, **204**, 221, **237**
Limnanthaceae, 15, **205**
Linaceae, 15, **204**, 209, **215**
Loasaceae, **204, 237**
Loganiaceae, **204, 274**
Lythrarieae, 15, 16, **204, 252, 335**

Magnoliaceae, **204**, 265, **268**
Malvaceae, 15, **204**, 205, 264, 266, **270, 271**, 285, 323, 452, 454, 611
Martyniaceae, **204**, 265, **273**
Meliaceae, **191, 204**, 304, 321, **324, 443**
Menispermaceae, **204**, 265, 304, 321, **324**
Moraceae, **204**, 208, 209, **213**
Moringaceae, **204**, 304, **311, 315**
Myricaceae, **191**

737

Myristicaceae, 14, 198, 199, 200, **204**, 304, **333**, **336**, **425–429**, 557, 584, 613
Myrtaceae, **204**, 219, **235**

Nyctaginaceae, **204**, 209, **216**

Ochnaceae, **204**, 304, **311**, **315**, **444**
Olacaceae, 16, 183, 185, 203, **204**, 218, **221**, **230**, **289**, **290**, **291**, 294, 611
Oleaceae, **192**, 199, **204**, **236**
Onagraceae, 15, **204**, 209, **215**, 220

Palmae, 15, **190**, **194**, **195**, **198**, 199, 200, **204**, 304, 319, **339–342**, 403, **424**, **425**, 530, 539, 552, 557, 584
Papaveraceae, **204**, 208, 221, **231**, 461
Passifloraceae, **204**, **231**
Pedaliaceae, **204**, 208, **234**, 455
Phytolaccaceae, 185
Pinaceae, **213**
Plantaginaceae, **204**, **235**
Polemoniaceae, **204**, **236**
Polygalaceae, 185
Polypodiaceae, 177
Portulacaceae, **204**, **237**
Proteaceae, 14, 198, **204**, 205, **219**, **237**, **614**
Punicaceae, **252**

Ranunculaceae, 15, **204**, 221, **236**, 294, 610
Rhamnaceae, **204**, 209, **215**
Rosaceae, 15, 16, 183, 203, **204**, 208, 218, 221, **243**, **244**, 250, **253**, **254**, 447, 468, 469
Rubiaceae, **204**, 265, **274**
Rutaceae, **204**, 265, **268**, 455

Salvadoraceae, **204**, 304, **334**, **337**
Santalaceae, 16, 183, 185, **204**, **290**, **291**
Sapindaceae, 15, **204**, **294**, 304, **311**, **315**, **316**, **442**, 557, 610
Sapotaceae, **204**, 209, 304, **320**, **321**, **327**, **328**, 402, **439–441**, 557
Scrophulariaceae, **204**, 221, **234**, **235**
Simarubaceae, 16, 203, **204**, 218, 221, **286**, **289**, 304, **333**, **336**, **337**, **429**, 620
Solanaceae, **204**, 218, 221, **234**, 461
Staphyleaceae, **204**, **235**
Sterculiaceae, 15, **191**, 199, **204**, 205, 264, 266, 304, 321, **322**, **323**, **325**, **432–435**
Symplocaceae, **204**, **236**

Theaceae, **204**, **235**, 447
Tiliaceae, 183, **204**, 264, **270**, 461
Tropaeolaceae, **204**, **294**, **296**, 610
Typhaceae, **204**, **231**

Ulmaceae, 15, **204**, **219**, **230**, 304, **332**, **335**, 557
Umbelliferae, 15, **204**, 220, **286**, **287**, 319, 539, 552, **620**
Urticaceae, **204**, **235**

Valerianaceae, **192**, **204**, 209, **215**
Verbenaceae, **204**, 304, 321, **322**, **328**
Vitaceae, **204**, **230**
Vochysiaceae, **204**, 304, **334**, **337**

Zingiberaceae, **204**, **328**
Zygophyllaceae, **204**, **269**

Index of Individual Fatty Acids

Main references only: incidental references to fatty acids (e.g., in the Tables of component acids of fats) are not indexed.

Other organic acids, including some substituted (e.g., bromo- or hydroxy-) fatty acids, will be found in the General Index.

Aleprestic, **292, 623**
Alepric, **292, 623**
Aleprolic, **292, 623**
Aleprylic, **292, 623**
Aleuritic, **619**
Arachidic (*n*-eicosanoic), 7, **8**, 15, 98, 110, 152, **158**, 204, 285, **304–309, 311–316,** 319, 324–328, 347, **442,** 444, 557, 569, 582, **583–585,** 639
Arachidonic, **9, 35,** 90, 95, 136, 484–488, 544, **571, 572, 630, 638, 641, 696**

Behenic (*n*-docosanoic), **8,** 152, **204, 304, 309, 311–316,** 444, 445, 557, 579, 582, **583–585,** 593, 639, 680
Behenolic, **605, 610**
Bolekic, 290, 637
Brassidic, 593, 596, **604, 608, 610**
Butyric, 4, **8,** 14, 22, 23, 144, **149, 152–157,** 160–162, **411,** 413, 414, 511, 514, 516, 519, 550, 554, 569, 579, **583,** 679

Capric (*n*-decanoic), **8,** 14, **15,** 33, 48, 72, 110, 144, **152–157,** 160–162, **204, 219,** 304, **332, 335, 339–342, 411,** 490, 511, 514–516, 519, 524, 526, 550, 557, 568, 579, **581, 583, 584**
Caproic (*n*-hexanoic), **8,** 14, 144, **152–157,** 160–162, 339, 342, **411,** 413, 414, 511, 514, 516, 519, 550, 554, 568, 579, **581, 583,** 679
Caprylic (*n*-octanoic), **8,** 14, 33, 48, 144, **152–157,** 160–162, 337, 339–342, **411,** 413, 490, 511, 514–516, 519, 550, 568, **581, 583,** 598
Cerotic, **8,** 582, **583–585**
Cetoleic, **8, 34, 625**
Chaulmoogric, **9, 204,** 218, **285, 292, 293,** 571, 604, 621, 622
Clupanodonic, **9, 35,** 89, 90, **642**
Convolvulinic, **619**

Corynomycolenic, **587**
Corynomycolic, **173, 587**
Couepic, *see* "Licanic"

"Daturic", **584**
n-Decadiendiynoic, **187, 644**
n-Decadienoic, **205, 245, 250, 251, 257, 643, 644**
n-Decanoic, *see* Capric
n-Decatrienoic, **187, 644**
n-Decendiynoic, **187, 644**
n-Decenoic, **8, 145,** 153, 163, 205, 414, 550, **612, 613, 623**
n-Decen-triynoic, **187, 644**
Dihydrochaulmoogric, **622**
Dihydrosterculic, **612**
Dihydroxy-myristic, **613**
Dihydroxy-octadecadienoic, 248, **618**
Dihydroxy-octadecenoic, **220,** 257, 537, **616, 629**
Dihydroxystearic, **248–250,** 257, **595–599, 608, 617,** 619
Dimorphecolic, **16, 220, 239,** 616, **618**
n-Docosadienoic, **205, 294,** 295, **298–302,** 468, **630**
n-Docosahexaenoic, **9,** 136, 484–488, **572, 639, 642**
n-Docosanoic, *see* "Behenic"
n-Docosapentaenoic, **9, 35,** 91, 95, 136, 484–488, **571–573, 642**
n-Docosatetraenoic, **9,** 484–488, **572, 642**
n-Docosatrienoic, **642**
n-Docosenoic (*see also* "Cetoleic and Erucic"), **8, 34, 205,** 294
n-Docosynoic, **605**
n-Dodecadienoic, **245, 251, 257, 644**
n-Dodecanoic, *see* "Lauric"
n-Dodecenoic, **8, 145,** 153, 163, 205, 333, 414, 550, 585, **612, 613, 623**

n-Eicosadienoic, 239, 322, **572,** 602, **641**
n-Eicosadiynoic, 607

n-Eicosanoic, *see* "Arachidic"
n-Eicosapentaenoic, **9**, 136, 484–488, **572**, **641**
n-Eicosatetraenoic, *see* "Arachidonic"
n-Eicosatrienoic, 136, **572**, **641**
n-Eicosenoic, **8**, **15**, **34**, 152, **204**, **205**, **219**, **221**, **239**, 285, **294–300**, 316, 322, 347, 449, 568, 604, **609**, **610**, **612**, **615**, 680
Elaeostearic, **9**, **15**, 180, 203, **204**, 208, 218, **243–245**, **247**, **248**, **251**, **253–257**, **259**, 260, **267**, 285, 319, 395, 468–471, 529, 551, 553, 558, 561, 598, 624, 625, **634** –**636**, 637, 682, **695**, 696
Elaidic, **109**, **110**, **113**, **150**, 569, **593–598**, **604**, **605**
Epoxy-octadecadienoic, **296**, **616**, **618**
Epoxy-octadecenoic, **8**, **15**, **205**, **219**, **220**, **238**, **239**, **245**, **255**, **266**, **276**, 395, 451, 537, 558, **616–618**
Erucic, 7, **8**, **15**, 185, **204**, 205, 218, 219, 285, **294–300**, 319, 322, 347, 449, 529, 530, 539, 551, 553, 561, 568, 569, 571, 579, 593, 596, **604**, **608–610**, 680, 683
Erythrogenic, **9**, **289**, 607, 626, **637**

ω-Fluoro-oleic, **16**, **205**

Gadoleic, **8**, **34**, **612**, **615**
Gondoic, **615**
Gorlic, **9**, **204**, **292**, **293**, **604**, **621**, **623**

n-Heneicosanoic, **585**
n-Heneicosenoic, 152, 153
n-Heptadecanoic, 40, 41, 48, 110, 152, 153, **584**, **585**
n-Heptadecenoic, 111, 150, 153, 585, 623
n-Heptanoic, 153, 578, 585
n-Heptenoic, 606
n-Hexacosadienoic, 33, **630**, **642**
n-Hexacosahexaenoic, **9**, **35**, 98
n-Hexacosanoic, 152, 153, **158**, 221, 578, 579, 583, 585, 587
n-Hexacosapentaenoic, **9**, **35**, 98
n-Hexacosenoic, **8**, 33, 221, **238**, 285, **290**, 294, **609**, **611**, 612, **615**
n-Hexadecadienoic, 537, **640**, **696**
n-Hexadecadiynoic, 607
n-Hexadecatetraenoic, **9**, **640**
n-Hexadecatrienoic, **9**, **35**, 484, **630**, **640**, **696**
n-Hexadecenoic (palmitoleic, zoomaric), **8**, 10, 12, **13**, **14**, **34**, 72, 84–89, 94, 96, 109, 125, **131**, **145**, 150, 153, 163, **198**, **205**, **219**, **239**, 294, 339, 347, 414, 484– 488, 537, 542–545, 553, 568, 569, 585, **603**, **604**, 609, **612–615**, 623
n-Hexanoic, *see* "Caproic"
Hexapentacontanoic, 578, 581
Hiragonic, **9**, **35**, **640**

Hydnocarpic, **9**, **204**, 218, **285**, **292**, **293**, 604, **621**, **622**
Hydroxy-decenoic, **8**, **619**
Hydroxy-eicosenoic, **296**, **299**, **616**, **618**
Hydroxy-elaeostearic, **16**, **245**, **248**, **256**, 561, **616**, **618**
Hydroxy-heptenoic, **619**
Hydroxy-ketostearic, **598**
Hydroxy-octadecadienoic, **16**, **220**, **239**, **296**, **616**, **618**
Hydroxy-octadecenoic, **8**, **16**, **176**, **204**, **248**– **250**, **257**, **267**, 273, 275, 285, 296, 299, 561, **615–617**
Hydroxy-octadecen-ynoic, **289**, **290**, **616**, **618**, **619**, 626, 637

Ipurolic, **619**
Isanic, **9**, **16**, **289**, **290**, 607, 626, **637**
Isanolic, **16**, **289**, **290**, **616**, **618**, 626, **637**

Jalapinolic, **619**
Japanic, **198**
Juniperic, **619**

Kamlolenic, **16**, **245**, **248**, **256**, 469, 561, **616**, **618**
Keto-elaeostearic, *see* "Licanic"
Ketostearic, **580**, **591**

Lactobacillic, **173**, **586**, **611**, **612**
Lauric (*n*-dodecanoic), 7, **8**, **15**, 32, 33, 48, 72, 75, 85, 86, 110, 120, 152, 162, 200, **204**, 205, 285, 304, 319, **332–342**, 393, **411**, 425–429, 490, 511, 514, 516, 519, 524, 526, 530, 537, 539, 542, 550, 551, 556, 557, 568, **583**, **584**, 680
Lesquerolic, **296**, **299**, **616**, **618**
Licanic, **9**, **16**, **204**, 218, **243**, **244**, **253**, **254**, 285, 625, **635**, **636**, 637
Lignoceric, 8, 15, 152, **204**, 285, **304**, **309**, **311–316**, 444, 445, 530, 557, 582, **583–585**
Linderic, **623**
Linelaidic, **605**, **627**, **629**
Linoleic, 6, 7, **9**, **14**, **15**, 23, **94**, **95**, 110, **112**, 134, 139, 151, 179, 203, **204**, **206–243**, **248**, 253–260, 264–274, 280–283, 286, 287, 295–300, **304–316**, 319–322, 324– 328, 339–342, 345–347, **381**, **382**, **386**– **388**, 395, 396, 451–458, 463, 474, 477, 493, **526**, **529**, **530**, 533–539, 541–544, 547–549, 551, 553, 558–563, 565, 566, 568, **570–573**, 594, 598, 602, **625**– **631**, **640**, 680, 681, 683, **695**, 696
Linoleic (syntheses), **607**, **629**, **630**

Linolenic, 7, 9, 23, **102, 103, 112**, 131, 134, 151, 162, 179, 203, **204, 206–217**, 221, **243, 244, 245–247, 251, 253–259**, 266, 273, 275, 276, 280, 281, 283, **296–300**, 304, 305, **309–315**, 319, **322, 329**, 345–347, 395, 462–467, 493, 529, 536, 539, 553, 558, 561, 566, **571–573**, 598, 625, 630, 631, **632–634, 640**, 680, 683, **695, 696**

Lumequic, **8**, 285, **290, 609, 611**

"Lycopodic", 177

Malvalic, 7, **15**, 205, **266**, 271, 285, **323, 611, 612**

"Margaric", **584**

Melissic, 582

Methyl-*n*-aliphatic (synthetic), **586, 587**

Methyl-*n*-dodecanoic, 152, 153, **585**

Methyl-*n*-heptadecanoic, 153

Methyl-*n*-hexadecanoic, **111**, 152, 153, 184, **585, 586**

Methyl-*n*-nonadecanoic, 153, 586

Methyl-*n*-pentadecanoic, 111, 152, 153, **585**

10-Methylstearic, **173, 586, 587**

Methyl-*n*-tetracosanoic, **587**

Methyl-*n*-tetradecanoic, 110, 111, 152, 153, **585**

Methyl-*n*-tridecanoic, 152, 153, 585

Montanic, 582

Moroctic, **640**

Mycoceranic, **173, 586**

Mycolic, **172, 587**

Mycolipenic, **173, 587**

Myristic, 7, **8, 15**, 22, 109, 131, 189, **204**, 285, 304, 321, **332–342**, 393, **411**, 425–429, 537, 542–544, 547, 550, 551, 556, 558, **581, 583, 584**

Myristoleic, *see* "Tetradecenoic"

Nervonic, **8, 34, 608–610**

Nisinic, **9, 35**

n-Nonadecanoic, 48, 110, 152, 153, **585**

n-Nonadecadienoic, 572, 602

n-Nonanoic, 153, 339, 578, 585, 591, 592, 598

n-Nonatriacontanoic, 581

Obtusilic, **623**

n-Octacosanoic, **583**

n-Octacosenoic, 33, 294, **611, 615**

n-Octadecadienoic, (*see also* Linoleic), 9, 110, 131, 134, **151**, 161, **267, 273**, 564, 571, 572, **627, 631, 632, 636, 640**

n-Octadecanoic, *see* "Stearic"

n-Octadecatetraenoic (*see also* "Parinaric, Stearidonic"), **9, 16, 35**, 484–488, **572, 640**

n-Octadecatrienoic (*see also* "Elaeostearic, Linolenic"), **9, 15, 16**, 209, 216, **220, 251, 252, 259, 267, 273**, 286, **469, 620, 621, 633, 636, 640, 696**

n-Octadecen-di-ynoic, **9, 16**, 183, 185, **221**, 285, **289, 290**, 626, **637**

n-Octadecenoic (*see also* "Oleic, Petroselinic, Vaccenic"), **8**, 150, **173, 221, 239**, 537, 547, **604, 606**, 635

n-Octadecen-ynoic, **16**, 183, 185, **204, 221**, 285, **290, 291**, 626, **637**

n-Octadecynoic, **8, 16, 204**, 285, 286, **289**, 334, 337, 561, **606, 608, 620**

n-Octanoic, *see* "Caprylic"

n-Octynoic, 606

Oleic, **6, 7, 8**, 10, **13, 15**, 22, 23, **131, 148, 149**, 152–157, 179, 189–197, 200, 201, **204**, 209, **221**, 253–260, 268–274, 280–283, 286, 287, 295–300, 304–316, 319–328, 332–342, 345–347, **380, 381, 386–388**, 396, **411**, 414, 419, 447–449, 451–455, 472–477, 484–488, **500**, 507, 509, **529, 530**, 533–539, 541–547, 551, 553, 557–563, 565, 568–570, 585, **589–602, 609, 612**, 680, 681, 683

Oleic (syntheses), **600–604**

*iso*Oleic, **109, 110, 113, 150**, 547, 569–571, **594, 599, 624, 625**

Palmitic, **6, 7, 8**, 10, 12, **13, 15**, 21, 22, 101, **107, 108, 131, 148**, 189–195, 200, **204**, 208, 218, **264, 265, 268–274, 280–283**, 304–316, 319–329, 332–342, 345–347, 393, **405, 411, 431–436, 441**, 452, 453, 472–477, **500**, 507, 509, **522, 526, 529, 530**, 541–547, 551, 556–559, 565, 566, 568–570, 578, 579, **583, 584**, 680, 681

Palmitoleic, *see* "*n*-Hexadecenoic"

Parinaric, **9, 16, 244, 253, 254**, 285, 395, **470, 471**, 625, **636**

n-Pentadecanoic, 40, 41, 48, 152, 153, **584, 585**

*cyclo*Pent-2-enyl-*n*-tridecanoic, *see* "Chaulmoogric"

*cyclo*Pent-2-enyl-*n*-tridecenoic, *see* "Gorlic"

*cyclo*Pent-2-enyl-*n*-undecanoic, *see* "Hydnocarpic"

Petroselinic, **8, 15, 204**, 205, 218, 285, **286, 287**, 319, 334, 337, 539, 551, 553, 561, 594, 596, **606, 608, 620**, 683

Phellagenic, **620**

Phellonic, **620**

Phloionic, **620**

Phloionolic, **620**

Phthienoic, **587**

Phthioic, **587**

Physetoleic, *see* "*n*-Hexadecenoic"

Phytomonic, **586**, 611, 612

Punicic, **16, 252, 635, 636**

Ricinelaidic, 597, **616**, 632
Ricinoleic, **8**, **16**, **176**, 203, **204**, 218, 221, **238**, **243**, 245, **248–250**, **257**, 285, 395, 449, 529, 551, 553, 561, 571, 594, 597, **615–617**, **632**

Sabinic, **619**
Santalbic, **16**, 285, **290**, **291**, 626, 637
Selacholeic, **8**, 12, **34**, 37, **608–610**
Shibic, **9**, **35**
Stearic, 7, **8**, 10, 13, **15**, 21, 22, 23, 99–101, **108**, **112**, **131**, **204**, 205, 208, 219, 265, 268–274, 285, 304, **319–322**, **324–328**, 347, **405–408**, 411, **431–440**, **497–510**, 530, 539, 541–547, 556–560, 568–570, 578, 579, **581**, **583**, **584**, 593, 681
Stearidonic, **9**, **35**
Stearolic, **591**, **592**, **594**, **600**, **602**, 609, 610
Sterculic, 7, **8**, **15**, 205, **266**, 271, 285, **323**, **611**

Tariric, **8**, **16**, **204**, 285, 286, **289**, 334, 337, 561, **606**, **608**, **620**
n-Tetracosahexaenoic, **9**, **35**, 98
n-Tetracosanoic, *see* "Lignoceric"
n-Tetracosenoic, **8**, **34**, 294, **295**, **299**, 603, **608–610**
n-Tetradecahexaenoic, 579
n-Tetradecenoic, **8**, **14**, 72, 120, **145**, 153, 163, 205, **333**, 337, 414, 545, 550, 553, 568, 585, **604**, 606, **609**, **612**, **613**, **623**
Tetrahydroxystearic, **628**, **629**
Tetramethylhexadecanoic, 152, **586**
n-Tetratriacontanoic, 578, 581

Thynnic, **9**, **35**
n-Triacontanoic, 580, **583**
n-Triacontenoic, **8**, 285, **290**, **609**, **611**
Trichosanic, **16**, **251**, **252**, **258**, **260**, 635
n-Tricosanoic, 152, 153, 581, **585**
n-Tridecanoic, 48, 152, 153, 339, **585**
Trihydroxystearic acids, 597
Trimethyl-*n*-tetracosenoic, **587**
Trimethyl-*n*-tricosanoic, **587**
Tsuzuic, **623**
Tuberculostearic, **586**

n-Undecanoic, 152, 153, 339, **585**
n-Undecenoic, 585, 606, 623
Unsaturated C$_{20-22}$ **9**, 12, **13**, 27, 84, 85, 88, 89, 95, 111, 124, 125, 128, 131, 135–137, 151, 153, 484–488, 542–546, 569, **571–573**
Ursolic, **619**
Ustilic, **619**

Vaccenic, **109**, **150**, 173, **605**, 606, **608**, **623–625**
*iso*Valeric, 7, **8**, 12, 23, **74**, **75**, **489**, **583**, **584**, 585, 679
Vernolic, **8**, **15**, 205, **219**, **220**, **238**, **239**, **245**, **255**, **266**, 395, 451, 537, **616–618**, 629

Ximenic, **8**, 285, **290**, **609**, **611**
Ximenynic, **16**, 184, **221**, 285, **290**, 626, **637**

Zoomaric, *see* "*n*-Hexadecenoic"

Index of Individual Glycerides (Natural and Synthetic)

(Saturated acyl groups placed in ascending order of molecular weight.)

Arachidodibehenin, 482
Arachidodiolein, 435, 440, 442, 443
Arachidonodiclupanodonin, 482

Butyrodiolein, 360, 510, 516, 520, 521
Butyrodipalmitin, 516, 521
Butyromyristo-olein, 521
Butyro-myristo-palmitin, 521
Butyro-myristo-stearin, 521
Butyropalmito-olein, 360, 510, 516, 521
Butyropalmitostearin, 516, 520, 521
Butyrostearo-olein, 516, 520, 521

Caprodilaurin, **426**, 427
Caprodiolein, 516, 520, 521, 524
Caprodipalmitin, 516, 521, 524
Caprodistearin, 468, 521
Caprolauromyristin, **426**, 429, 430
Caprolauro-olein, **426**, 427, 521, 524
Caprolauro-palmitin, 426
Capromyristo-olein, 426, 521, 524
Capromyristopalmitin, 426, 516, 521, 524
Capromyristostearin, 521
Capropalmito-olein, 426, 516, 520, 521, 524
Capropalmitostearin, 516, 520, 521, 524
Capro-oleo-linolein, 427
Capro-stearo-olein, 521, 524
Caproyldiolein, 516, 521
Caprylodiolein, 516, 521

Diarachidobehenin, 482
Diarachidonoclupanodonin, 482
Dibutyromyristin, 516, 521
Dibutyro-olein, 516, 521
Diburyropalmitin, 516, 520, 521
Dibutyrostearin, 516, 521
Dicaprolaurin, 426
Dicapro-olein, 426, 516, 521
Dicapropalmitin, 516, 520, 521, 524
Dicaprostearin, 516, 521
Dicetoleo-arachidonin, 482
Dicetoleogadolein, 482
Dicetoleo-olein, 482

Dihexadecenolinolein, 482
Dihexadecenolinolenin, 482
Dihexadeceno-olein, 482
Dihydrochaulmoogro-didihydrohydno-
    carpin, 361
Dihydrohydnocarpo-didihydrochaul-
    moogrin, 361
Dilaurolinolein, 427
Dilauromyristin, **360**, **425–430**, 513, 521,
    664
Dilauro-olein, 426, 427, 521
Dilauropalmitin, **426**, 427, 521, 524, **665**
Dilaurostearin, 521
Dilinolein, **663**
Dilinolenin, **663**
Dilinoleo-linolenin, 362, **383**, **453**, 455
Dimyristo-olein, 428, 516, 520, 521
Dimyristopalmitin, 32, 360, **428**, 429, 516,
    520, 521, 524
Dimyristostearin, 516, 521
Dimyristotetradecenoin, **428**
Diolein, **663**
Dipalmitin, **663**, **666**
Dipalmitostearin, 359, 360, **403**, 432, 444,
    472, 473–475, 498, **507**, 510, 516, 521,
    664, **665**
Distearin, **663**, **666**
Distearo-arachidin, 482

Elaeostearo-diparinarin, **470**
Erucodi-olein (-linolein), **450**

Gadoleodiarachidonin, 482

Hexadeceno-arachidono-clupanodonin, 482
Hexadecenodiarachidonin, 482
Hexadecenodiolein, 115, 477, 494, **505**
Hexadeceno-oleo-myristin, 485
Hexadeceno-oleo-palmitin, 115, 485, **491**,
    494, 497
Hexadeceno-palmitostearin, 497
Hexadeceno-stearidono-clupanodonin, 482

Laurodimyristin, 360, **428–430, 664**
Laurodiolein, 426, 427, 429, 516, 521, 524
Laurodipalmitin, 521, 524
Laurodistearin, **403, 665**
Lauromyristo-olein, 426–430, 521
Lauromyristopalmitin, **426, 428**, 429, 430, 521
Lauromyristotetradecenoin, 428
Lauro-oleo-linolein, 427
Lauro-oleopalmitin, 516, 521, 524
Lauro-oleostearin, 516, 521, 524
Lauropalmito-olein, **426**, 516, 521
Lauropalmitostearin, 516, 521, 524
Linoleno-arachidono-clupanodonin, 482
Linolenodiclupanodonin, 482
Linolenodierucin, 361
Linolenodigadolein, 482
Linolenodilinolein, 18, **464, 465**, 466, 702, 706
Linolenodiolein, 466
Linoleno-gadoleo-clupanodonin, 482
Linoleodierucin, 361, 403, **450**
Linoleodigadolein, 482
Linoleodihexadecenoin, 482
Linoleodilinolenin, 18, 361, 362, **383, 464, 465**, 466, 467, 702, 706
Linoleodiolein, 362, 373, 439, 440, **443, 447, 448, 452–458**, 464, 466, **474, 477**, 494, 516, 521, 524
Linoleopalmitostearin, **439**

Mono-elaidin, **662**
Monolaurin, **662, 665**
Monolinolein, 565, **662**
Monolinolenin, **662**
Monomyristin, **662**
Mono-*p*-nitrobenzoin, **665**
Mono-olein, **662**
Monopalmitin, **662, 665**
Monostearin, 565, **662, 665**
Myristodiolein, 429, **440**, 516, 520, 521, 524
Myristodipalmitin, 360, 516, 521, 524
Myristoditetradecenoin, 428
Myristo-oleo-linolein, 427
Myristo-palmito-arachidin, 482
Myristo-palmito-olein, 428, 516, 521
Myristopalmitostearin, 498, 516, 520, 521, 524
Myristopalmitotetradecenoin, 428
Myristo-stearo-olein, 516, 521
Myristo-tetradeceno-olein, 428

p-Nitrobenzoyldibenzoin, **403, 665**
p-Nitrobenzoyldistearin, **665**

Oleo-arachidono-clupanodonin, 482
Oleodiarachidin, **435**
Oleodiarachidonin, **442**, 482

Oleodicaprin, 516
Oleodiclupanodonin, 482
Oleodierucin, 361, 403, **450**
Oleodilaurin, 516, 521
Oleodilinolein, 362, 373, 377, **383**, 439, **448, 452–458, 461, 464**, 466, 702, 706
Oleodilinolenin, 361, **383, 464**, 466
Oleodimyristin, 516
Oleodipalmitin, 359, 360, 362, **384, 403**, 419, **433–435**, 438, **441**, 446, 447, **472, 474–476**, 494, 502, **505–509**, 510, 516, 521, 524, **664**
Oleodistearin, 20, **359**, 360, 377, **384, 402**, 419, **432–442**, 443, 507, 509, **664**
Oleo-elaeostearo-parinarin, 470
Oleolauromyristin, 426–429
Oleolinoleolinolenin, 18, **453**, 455, **464, 465**, 466
Oleolinolenostearin, 362
Oleolinoleostearin, 362
Oleomyristohexadecenoin, 485
Oleomyristopalmitin, 472, 474, 485, 494, 516, 521
Oleopalmitin, **663**
Oleopalmito-arachidin, 443, 496
Oleopalmito-hexadecenoin, 485
Oleopalmitolinolenin, **494**
Oleopalmitostearin, 20, **359**, 360, 361, 377, **384, 403, 408**, 419, **432–439**, 440, **441, 443**, 446, 472–475, 491, 494, 497, **502, 505–509**, 516, 520, 521, 524, 659, **664**
Oleostearoarachidin, **440, 442**
Oleostearin, 570, **663**

Palmitodilinolein, **383**, 439, 452, 453, **456–458**
Palmitodiolein, 112, 113, 115, 360, 361, 377, **408**, 419, **432–441, 443**, 446, **447, 472, 474–476**, 482, 485, 494, 497, **502, 505–509**, 516, 520, 521, 524, 570, **664**
Palmitodistearin, 360, 361, **408**, 434, 440, **443**, 454, 498, 499, **507, 508**, 510, 516, 663, **664**
Palmito-hexadeceno-oleins, 115, 491, 494
Palmito-oleolinolein, **439, 443**, 494
Palmito-oleo-stearin, *see* Oleopalmito-stearin
Palmitostearins, 22, 112, 360, **408**, 433, 435, 437–439, 443, 476, 491, 502, **506–509**, 663
Palmitostearo-arachidin, 482
Parinaro-dielaeostearin, 470

Stearodono-diclupanodonin, 482
Stearo-arachidobehenin, 482
Stearodibehenin, 361
Stearodilinolein, 439
Stearodiolein, 377, 419, **433–443**, 474, 491, 494, 497, 502, **506–509**, 516, **664**
Stearo-oleolinolein, 439

Triarachidonin, 482
Tributyrin, 510, 516, 568
Tri-elaeostearin, **395, 469**
Trielaidin, **664**
Trierucin, **296**, 450, 610, **664**
Tri-*iso*-valerin, 23, 74
Tri-"kamlolenin", **470**
Tri-keto-elaeostearin, **469**
Trilaurin, 19, **360**, **393**, **425–427**, **429**, 476, **664**
Trilinolein, 18, 19, 373, 376, 377, **383**, 384, 394, **395**, 420, 444, 450, 452, 453, **456–458**, **461–464**, 570, **627**, **664**, 702, 706
Trilinolenin, 18, 19, 373, **383**, 394, **395**, **463–467**, **664**, 702, 706

Trimyristin, 19, **360**, **393**, **427**, **428**, 429, **664**
Triolein, 115, 359, 360, 376, 435, 438–440, 442, **443**, 444, 446, **447**, 450, 452, 453, 456–458, 472–475, **477**, 482, **505**, 507, 510, 512, 516, 570, **664**
Tripalmitin, 19, 21, 359, 367, **393**, **438**, **441**, 444, 471, **472**, 473–477, 491, 495, 497, 507, **664**
Triparinarin, 19, 394, **395**, **470**, **471**
Tripetroselinin, **286**
Triricinolein, **395**, **449**, **450**
Tristearin, 360, 361, 434, 443, 466, 476, 507, 510, 570, 660, **664**
Trivernolin, 19, **395**, **451**